NELSON

Advanced Functions & Introductory Calculus

Authors

Chris Kirkpatrick

Rob McLeish

Ralph Montesanto

Christine Suurtamm

Susanne Trew

David Zimmer

THOMSON

NELSON

Australia   Canada   Mexico   Singapore   Spain   United Kingdom   United States

THOMSON

NELSON

Advanced Functions & Introductory Calculus,

Chris Kirkpatrick, Ralph Montesanto,
Susanne Trew, Christine Suurtamm,
Robert McLeish, David Zimmer

Director of Publishing
David Steele

Publisher, Mathematics
Cheryl Turner

Program Manager
Colin Garnham

Project Manager
Robert Templeton,
First Folio Resource Group, Inc.

Senior Production Editor
Linh Vu

Content Editors
Don Rowsell, Mike Waters

Copy Editor
Susan Marshall

Senior Designer
Suzanne Peden

Creative Director
Angela Cluer

Production Coordinator
Sharon Latta Paterson

Cover Design
Peter Papayanakis

Composition
Nelson Gonzalez

Photographs and Permissions
Maria DeCambra

Performance Task Authors
Mary Bourassa, Donna Del Re,
Don Rowsell, Susan Smith

Creative Art/Technical Art
Irma Ikonen, David McKay,
Deborah Crowle, Steven Corrigan,
Marie Price, Peter Papayanakis

Printer
Transcontinental Printing Inc.

The authors thank the following
for their assistance in the
development of this book: David
Wright; Andrew Dmytriw;
Susan Smith; Jan and Barry Scully;
Vanessa Davison; First Folio
Resource Group Inc.: Matthew
Calder, Susan Cartier, Katrina Koh,
Jane Lee, Alan Leung, Khai Quoc
Ngo, and Linda Nigro.

**National Library of Canada
Cataloguing in
Publication Data**

Main entry under title:
Nelson advanced functions and
introductory calculus
Includes index.
ISBN 0-17-615778-6

1. Functions. 2. Calculus. I.
Kirkpatrick, Chris.
QA37.2.N44 2002   515
C2002-900988-X

Advisory Panel

Reviewers

Contents

Introduction

Part 1
Advanced Functions

Chapter 1
Polynomial Function Models   1

The Chapter Problem   3
Chapter Challenges   4
Getting Ready   4

1.1 Polynomial Functions   6
1.2 Investigating the Characteristics of Polynomial Functions   19
1.3 Creating New Polynomial Functions: An Introduction to Composition   28
1.4 Dividing Polynomials   39
1.5 Factoring Polynomials   45
1.6 Solving Polynomial Equations   54
1.7 Solving Polynomial Inequalities   65

Chapter 1 Review   75
Chapter 1 Performance Task   79
Chapter 1 Review Test   80

Chapter 2
Exponential and Logarithmic Function Models   81

The Chapter Problem   82
Chapter Challenges   83
Getting Ready   84

2.1 Investigating Exponential Models   86
2.2 Graphs of Exponential Functions   96
2.3 Various Forms of Exponential Functions   107
2.4 The Logarithmic Function   114
2.5 Laws of Logarithms   121
2.6 Solving Exponential Equations   128
2.7 Creating Logarithmic Models   135
2.8 Solving Logarithmic Equations   143
2.9 Creating and Applying Exponential and Logarithmic Models   149

Chapter 2 Review   157
Chapter 2 Performance Task   163
Chapter 2 Review Test   164

Cumulative Review Test 1   **165**

Part 2
Differential Calculus: Polynomial and Rational Functions

Chapter 3
Rates of Change in Polynomial Function Models   167

The Chapter Problem   168
Chapter Challenges   169
Getting Ready   170

3.1 Examining Rates of Change in Polynomial Models   172
3.2 A Closer Look at Rates of Change: The Tangent Problem   183
3.3 Limits of Polynomial Functions   194
3.4 Using Limits to Find Instantaneous Rates of Change –
        The Derivative   206
3.5 Finding Some Shortcuts – The Constant and Power Rules   217
3.6 Finding Some Shortcuts – The Sum and Difference Rules   225
3.7 Polynomial Function Models and the First Derivative   233
3.8 Polynomial Function Models and the Second Derivative   247

Chapter 3 Review   256
Chapter 3 Performance Task   261
Chapter 3 Review Test   262

Chapter 4
Using the Derivative to Analyze Polynomial
Function Models   263

The Chapter Problem   264
Chapter Challenges   265
Getting Ready   266

4.1 Analyzing a Polynomial Function: Intervals of Increase
        and Decrease   268
4.2 Maximum and Minimum Values of a Polynomial Function   277
4.3 The First Derivative Test   286
4.4 Finding Some Shortcuts – The Product Rule   296
4.5 Finding Optimal Values for Polynomial Function Models   303
4.6 Rates of Change in Business and Economics   313
4.7 Sketching Graphs of Polynomial Functions: Concavity   322

Chapter 4 Review   334
Chapter 4 Performance Task   339
Chapter 4 Review Test   340

Chapter 5
Rates of Change in Rational Function Models   341

The Chapter Problem	342
Chapter Challenges	343
Getting Ready	344
5.1 Graphs of Rational Functions	346
5.2 Limits and End Behaviour of Rational Functions	360
5.3 Continuity of Rational Functions	371
5.4 Rate of Change of a Rational Function – The Quotient Rule	378
5.5 Differentiability of Rational and Other Functions	387
5.6 Finding Optimal Values for Rational Function Models	395
5.7 Sketching Graphs of Rational Functions	405
Chapter 5 Review	419
Chapter 5 Performance Task	425
Chapter 5 Review Test	426
Cumulative Review Test 2	**427**

Part 3
Differential Calculus: Composite, Exponential, and Logarithmic Functions

Chapter 6
Rates of Change in Composite Function Models   429

The Chapter Problem	430
Chapter Challenges	431
Getting Ready	432
6.1 Composition of Functions	434
6.2 Rates of Change for Composite Functions – The Chain Rule	446
6.3 Differentiation Techniques: Combining the Differentiation Rules	458
6.4 Finding Optimal Values for Composite Function Models	465
6.5 Sketching Graphs of Composite Functions	473
6.6 Implicit Differentiation	479
6.7 Related Rate Models	486
Chapter 6 Review	497
Chapter 6 Performance Task	501
Chapter 6 Review Test	502

Chapter 7
Rates of Change in Exponential and Logarithmic Function Models   503

The Chapter Problem   504
Chapter Challenges   505
Getting Ready   506

7.1 Introducing a Special Number, e 508
7.2 The Derivative of $y = e^x$ 515
7.3 The Natural Logarithm and its Derivative   522
7.4 Differentiating Other Logarithmic and Exponential Functions   530
7.5 Sketching Graphs of Exponential and Logarithmic Functions   537
7.6 Models of Exponential Growth   544

Chapter 7 Review   551
Chapter 7 Performance Task   555
Chapter 7 Review Test   556

Cumulative Review Test 3   **557**

Explorations Appendix   **559**

Technology Appendix   **590**

Trigonometry Appendix   **596**

Glossary   **615**

Answers   **617**

Index   **674**

Photo Credits   **676**

Summary of Mathematical Terms and Formulas

Introduction to *Nelson Advanced Functions and Introductory Calculus*

Nelson Advanced Functions and Introductory Calculus is designed to help you develop skill at creating and analyzing mathematical models to solve real-world problems involving rates of change. In some cases, you will have the chance to practise familiar mathematical skills like solving equations, graphing data, and modelling. You will also have the opportunity to develop your own strategy for solving new types of problems. Throughout this book, you will be encouraged to communicate what you have learned to others.

Varied Instructional Approaches

The different instructional approaches in this book allow you to explore concepts on your own or by working with others. Some lessons may be led by your teacher, while others may be done through the use of hands-on activities. For some lessons, you may be asked to read solved examples on your own to build an understanding of a concept.

There are two kinds of lessons in *Nelson Advanced Functions and Introductory Calculus*, Concept Lessons and *Explorations*:

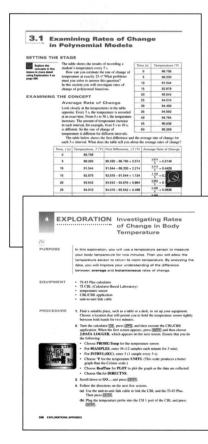

Concept Lessons

Concept Lessons present concepts and ideas in real-life contexts. In some cases, your teacher may guide your class through a Concept Lesson to build your understanding of new concepts and skills, while in other cases you may be asked to read through the lesson on your own. Each Concept Lesson has solved examples, which will help to clarify your understanding. Following the solved examples are the *Check, Consolidate, Communicate* questions and the *Key Ideas*. The *Key Ideas* summarize the important ideas in the lesson. Concept Lessons also have *Exercise* sections to help consolidate your understanding.

Explorations

The *Explorations* in the **Explorations Appendix** introduce and explore new concepts that will be studied in more detail in the Concept Lessons. Some Explorations require the use of technology, while others do not. Explorations provide a hands-on learning experience that can be done in class or on your own at home. An *Exploration* icon appears in the margin of a Concept Lesson that has an associated *Exploration*.

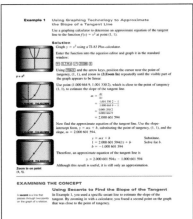

The Role of Technology

The use of graphing technology is integrated throughout this book. For instance, where it is appropriate, some examples are solved with a graphing calculator, in order to develop your skill with this tool. In such cases, step-by-step instructions and screen shots are provided. A calculator is useful because it allows you to determine approximate solutions to real-world problems. The mathematics developed in the course is useful because it provides algebraic techniques that will give exact solutions to these problems. An icon of a calculator graph in the margin denotes that a graphing calculator is needed to complete an activity. The **Technology Appendix** summarizes the key calculator skills of this course.

Features of *Nelson Advanced Functions and Introductory Calculus*

Connections

Mathematics is not just something you do in mathematics class. You use it in other classes and your daily life. It will also be important as you make a career choice. Mathematicians and teachers are not the only people who use mathematics in their careers. At the start of each chapter is a *Chapter Problem* that illustrates how math is used in different careers and situations. There are also two *Challenge* questions that will require you to use the problem solving skills you learn in the chapter.

Assessment Features

Performance Tasks

At the end of each **Chapter Review** is a *Performance Task*, which might be a short problem-solving question or a longer experiment or investigation. These *Performance Tasks* may be done at school or at home. Your teacher may assign some of these tasks so that both of you can see how well you understand the concepts of the chapters. You may also decide to do these tasks on your own, for extra practice and review. Some tasks may be done on your own, while for others you will likely work in a group. These tasks, along with quizzes, tests, and exams, allow you to demonstrate your understanding of the important ideas in this course.

Achievement Chart Questions

Within each set of Concept Lesson exercises are four questions, labelled *Knowledge and Understanding; Application; Thinking, Inquiry, Problem Solving;* and *Communication*. You can use these four questions to determine your strengths and weaknesses and, with the help of your teacher, develop a plan for improving your achievement level. There is an additional set of such questions at the end of each section.

Also in each set of exercises is a *Check Your Understanding* question. This question will help you determine whether you understand the main ideas of the section.

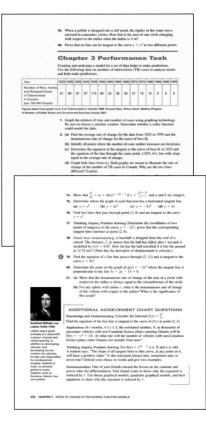

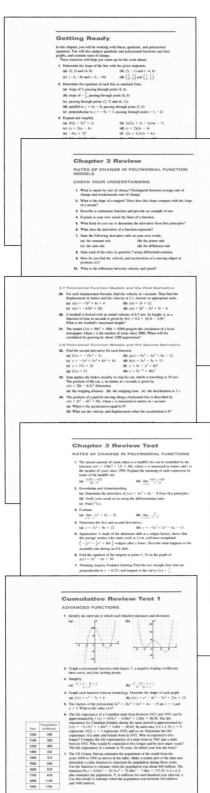

Preparation Features

Getting Ready

The *Getting Ready* exercises in each chapter review important ideas from previous grades and chapters that will be starting points for new learning within the chapter. You can use these exercises to determine whether you are ready for the new work to come. If you cannot do some exercises, be sure to ask your teacher or another student for help.

Review Features

Chapter Review At the end of each chapter is a **Chapter Review**, which consists of three types of questions, *Check Your Understanding questions, Additional Review Questions by Section*, and *Review Questions by Achievement Chart Categories*.

The *Check Your Understanding* questions will help you decide, on your own, whether you understand the important ideas of a chapter. Think about each question and write the answer in your notebook. As you do, you will be creating your own summary of the chapter. You can use your answers to these questions, along with the other **Chapter Review** exercises, to prepare for quizzes, tests, and exams.

The *Review Questions by Section* are grouped according to the individual sections within a chapter. They will help you to reinforce your understanding of the concepts and skills developed in each section. Refer to the appropriate *Key Ideas* and solved examples when answering these questions.

The *Review Questions by Achievement Chart Categories* are grouped according to the four Achievement Chart categories (*Knowledge and Understanding; Application; Thinking, Inquiry, Problem Solving;* and *Communication*). They will help you to reinforce your understanding of the important ideas of the entire chapter. You can use these questions to review your work and prepare for tests.

Chapter Review Test Each chapter concludes with a chapter review test that you can use to find out whether you are ready for a class test or exam.

Cumulative Review Test There is a cumulative review test after Chapters 2, 5, and 7. Each test incorporates concepts and ideas from the previous chapters. You can use these tests as another source of review and extra practice when preparing for tests and exams.

Additional Features

Icons

This icon indicates there is an *Exploration* in the **Explorations Appendix** that can be used to introduce the concepts of the Concept Lesson.

This icon indicates graphing technology (software or calculator) is needed to complete the question or *Exploration*.

People of Mathematics

These brief biographies tell you about women and men who have contributed to the world of mathematics, especially in the field of calculus. You may wish to do further research on these mathematicians.

Appendixes

Explorations Appendix The **Explorations Appendix** consists of 15 hands-on activities that introduce and investigate fundamental concepts of this course. Each *Exploration* is associated with a Concept Lesson. An *Exploration* icon in the margin of the Concept Lesson will direct you to the appropriate *Exploration*.

Technology Appendix The **Technology Appendix** summarizes the important skills you may have acquired with the TI-83 Plus graphing calculator from previous math courses. New skills, specific to calculus, are also summarized. Where appropriate, *Technology Help* reminders in the margin of lessons will direct you to the appropriate set of instructions in the **Technology Appendix**.

Trigonometry Appendix The **Trigonometry Appendix** allows you to extend your calculus skills to this additional branch of functions. Explanations and solved examples are used to introduce differentiation of trigonometric functions and applications of this concept. The **Trigonometry Appendix** also contains exercises that enable you to practise your analytical skill with trigonometric functions.

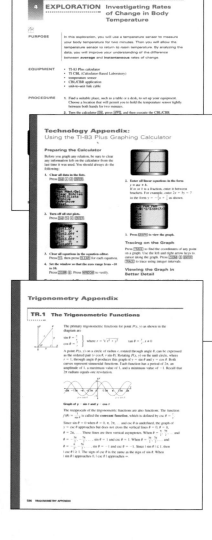

1 Polynomial Function Models

One goal of mathematics is to find functions to model data. If the model is a good fit, you can use it to analyze present behaviour as well as to predict past and future behaviour. In previous courses, you studied linear and quadratic functions. Both these functions are part of a much larger group of functions called polynomials. This chapter will extend your earlier studies beyond degree-2 functions.

In this chapter, you will

- investigate polynomial functions and study their properties

- examine the nature of change in polynomial functions

- sketch the graphs of polynomial functions

- model data using graphs of polynomial functions

- extend the notion of polynomial functions beyond linear and quadratic functions

- develop the algebra and technology skills for solving problems modelled by polynomial functions

- extend your factoring and division skills with polynomials

- solve polynomial equations with and without technology

- solve polynomial inequalities with and without technology

The Chapter Problem

Developing a Model for Canada's Population

The population of Canada is measured on a regular basis through the taking of a census. The table shows the population of Canada at the end of each period. From 1851 to 1951, each period is a ten-year interval. From 1951 to 2001, each period is a five-year interval.

Period	Census Population at the End of a Period (in thousands)	Period	Census Population at the End of a Period (in thousands)
1851–1861	3 230	1951–1956	16 081
1861–1871	3 689	1956–1961	18 238
1871–1881	4 325	1961–1966	20 015
1881–1891	4 833	1966–1971	21 568
1891–1901	5 371	1971–1976	23 450
1901–1911	7 207	1976–1981	24 820
1911–1921	8 788	1981–1986	26 101
1921–1931	10 377	1986–1991	28 031
1931–1941	11 507	1991–1996	29 672
1941–1951	13 648	1996–2001	30 755

Source: Statistics Canada, Demography Division

How can you use this data to predict the population of Canada over the next five years? To answer this question, you could organize the data using models called **polynomials**. There are several types of polynomial functions. You can use any polynomial to make predictions, but each type has its own strengths and weaknesses.

You will investigate these questions throughout this chapter: What are the various polynomial models, and how can you use them to predict the population of Canada over the next five to fifty years? Which model is the most accurate predictor? What things could happen that could alter the model? What are the limitations of a polynomial model?

For help with this problem, see pages 18, 27, 38, 53, 64, and 74.

Chapter Challenges

Challenge 1

tetrahedron

The numbers 1, 4, 10, 20, and 35 are called tetrahedral numbers because they are related to a four-sided shape called a tetrahedron.

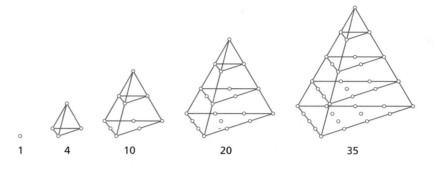

1   4   10   20   35

(a) Determine the next three tetrahedral numbers.

(b) You could use a polynomial to generate more tetrahedral numbers. Use finite differences to determine the degree of this polynomial.

(c) Determine the polynomial model that you can use to generate tetrahedral numbers.

(d) What is the 50th tetrahedral number?

(e) Is 47 850 a tetrahedral number? Justify your answer.

Challenge 2

Let $S(n)$ be the sum of the cubes of the integers from 1 to n such that

$$S(n) = 1^3 + 2^3 + 3^3 + \ldots + n^3$$

(a) Determine the polynomial model that you can use to calculate the sum of the cubes of the first n integers.

(b) Determine $S(1000)$.

(c) Prove that $S(n)$ is always a perfect square.

GETTING READY

In this chapter, you will be working with algebraic expressions and functions that require many of the same skills used for linear and quadratic functions. These exercises will help you warm up for the work ahead.

1. Evaluate for $x = -2$.
   (a) $f(x) = -3x + 5$
   (b) $f(x) = (4x - 2)(3x - 6)$
   (c) $f(x) = -3x^2 + 2x - 1$
   (d) $f(x) = (5x + 2)^2$

2. State the conjugate of each number.
   (a) $3 + 2i$
   (b) $-1 - 3i$
   (c) 4
   (d) $16i$

3. Expand, simplify, and express in standard form.
   (a) $(x - 6)(x + 2)$
   (b) $(5 - 2x)(3 + 4x)$
   (c) $x(5x - 3) + 2x(3x + 2)$
   (d) $(x - 1)(x + 3) - (2x + 5)(x - 2)$

4. Factor.
   (a) $x^2 - 8x + 12$
   (b) $2x^2 + 5x - 3$
   (c) $6x^2 + 17x + 5$
   (d) $6x^2 + 11x + 4$
   (e) $4x^2 - 25$
   (f) $2x(x + 1) - 5(x + 1)$

5. Solve.
   (a) $(x + 4)(x - 2) = 0$
   (b) $(2x - 5)(3x + 8) = 0$
   (c) $x^2 - 5x - 6 = 0$
   (d) $6x^2 + 7x - 5 = 0$
   (e) $3x^2 = 13x + 10$
   (f) $10x^2 - 4x - 8 = 2x^2 - 2x + 7$

6. Solve using the quadratic formula. Round your answers to two decimal places.
   (a) $9x^2 - x - 7 = 0$
   (b) $41x^2 + x = 31$
   (c) $-18x^2 + 9x = -23$

7. Expand and simplify.
   (a) $(x - i)(x + i)$
   (b) $(2x - 3i)(2x + 3i)$
   (c) $[x - (2 + i)][x - (2 - i)]$
   (d) $(2i - 5)^2$

8. Determine the roots of each equation.
   (a) $x^2 + 4 = 0$
   (b) $x^2 - 2x + 13 = 0$
   (c) $x^2 - 6x + 14 = 0$

9. Solve and graph the solution set for each inequality.
   (a) $6 - 2x > x - 6$
   (b) $1 \leq x + 3 < 5$
   (c) $x^2 \leq 36$

10. Let $f(x) = 3x - 2$.

    (a) Graph $f(x)$.

    (b) Describe $f(x)$ when $x > 3$.

    (c) State the restriction on x when $4 \leq f(x) \leq 10$.

11. Graph $f(x) = -2x^2 - 4x + 16$ by hand. Explain the properties of quadratic functions you used to draw the graph.

12. A T-ball player hits a baseball from a tee that is 0.5 m tall. The flight of the ball is modelled by $h(t) = -4.9t^2 + 6t + 0.5$, where h is the height in metres at t seconds.

    (a) Once the ball is hit, how long is it in the air?

    (b) When does the ball reach its maximum height?

    (c) What is the maximum height?

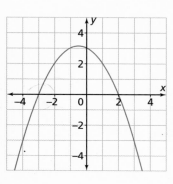

13. Determine the equation of the function from its graph on the left.

14. The graph of a quadratic function passes through points $(-4, 0)$ and $(3, 0)$.

    (a) Determine an equation that represents all such curves.

    (b) Determine the equation of the graph that also passes through $(5, -36)$.

15. The population of Canada from 1971 to 1996 is shown.

Period	1971–1976	1976–1981	1981–1986	1986–1991	1991–1996
Population × 1000	23 450	24 820	26 101	28 031	29 672

Source: Statistics Canada

    (a) Use a graphing calculator to draw a scatter plot of the data. What pattern does the scatter plot appear to follow?

    (b) Determine a quadratic equation that models the data.

    (c) Graph the equation.

    (d) Predict the population for 1998.

16. A model rocket is shot straight up from the roof of a building 21 m high. The table shows the height of the rocket during the first two seconds.

Time (s)	0.00	0.25	0.50	0.75	1.00	1.25	1.50	1.75	2.00
Height (m)	21.00	24.44	27.28	29.49	31.10	32.09	32.48	32.24	31.40

    (a) Use a graphing calculator to draw a scatter plot of the data.

    (b) Determine a quadratic equation that models the data.

    (c) Graph the equation.

    (d) When will the rocket hit the ground?

1.1 Polynomial Functions

SETTING THE STAGE

In earlier math courses, you used linear functions, quadratic functions, and trigonometric functions to model real-world problems. Are there any other types of functions that you can use to model real-world relations?

A toy manufacturer has created a new card game. Each game is packaged in an open-top cardboard box, which is then wrapped with clear plastic. The box for the game is made from a 20-cm by 30-cm piece of cardboard. Four equal squares are cut from the corners, one from each corner, of the cardboard piece. Then the sides are folded and the edges that touch are glued. What must be the dimensions of each square so that the resulting box has maximum volume?

You will need a mathematical model to represent the situation. In this section, you will examine a new class of functions called **polynomials**.

EXAMINING THE CONCEPT

Defining a Polynomial

To develop a model for this problem, begin by defining the variables.
Let x represent the side length of each square cut from the cardboard.
Let V represent the volume of the box. Then draw and label diagrams.

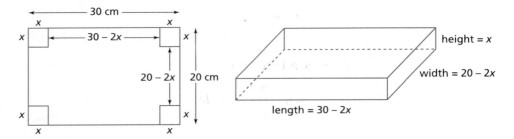

Two-dimensional and three-dimensional sketches of the cardboard box

$$\text{Volume} = \text{length} \times \text{width} \times \text{height}$$

$V(x) = (30 - 2x)(20 - 2x)(x)$	Expand by multiplying the binomials.
$\quad = (600 - 60x - 40x + 4x^2)(x)$	Expand by multiplying by the monomial.
$\quad = 600x - 60x^2 - 40x^2 + 4x^3$	Collect like terms.
$\quad = 600x - 100x^2 + 4x^3$	Rearrange powers of x in descending order.
$\quad = 4x^3 - 100x^2 + 600x$	

The resulting algebraic model $V(x) = 4x^3 - 100x^2 + 600x$ is an example of an equation that contains a **polynomial**.

Definition of a Polynomial in One Variable

A polynomial is an expression of the form
$a_n x^n + a_{n-1} x^{n-1} + \ldots + a_2 x^2 + a_1 x + a_0,$ where $a_0, a_1, \ldots, a_n$ are real numbers and n is a whole number. The coefficient of the term of highest degree in a polynomial is called the leading coefficient.

Any polynomial that is written with descending powers of the variable is in **standard form**.

Degree of a Polynomial

The degree of a polynomial is the value of the highest exponent of the variable.

A **linear function** has the form $f(x) = mx + b$. The functions $f(x) = 3x - 5$, $g(x) = \left(-\frac{2}{3}\right)x + 4$, and $h(x) = 9x$ are all linear. In each of these functions, the right side is a polynomial of degree 1.

Linear functions belong to the larger class of functions called **polynomial functions**.

Polynomial Function

A polynomial function is a function whose equation is defined by a polynomial in one variable.

Polynomials of degree 5 or greater do not have special names. They are simply called polynomials.

A **quadratic function** in the form $f(x) = ax^2 + bx + c$, $a \neq 0$, is a polynomial function of degree 2.

The model for the volume of the cardboard box, $V(x) = 4x^3 - 100x^2 + 600x$, is a degree-3 polynomial function, called a **cubic function**. This function is in the form $f(x) = ax^3 + bx^2 + cx + d$, $a \neq 0$. The polynomial function $f(x) = ax^4 + bx^3 + cx^2 + dx + e$, $a \neq 0$, is a **quartic function** and has degree 4.

Example 1   **Standard Form and the Degree of a Polynomial Function**

Express $f(x) = 2x + 5 - 3x^3 - 9x^2$ in standard form and state its degree.

Solution
Rearrange the terms in descending order: $f(x) = -3x^3 - 9x^2 + 2x + 5$.
The largest exponent in $f(x)$ is 3. The function has degree 3, so it is a cubic function.

• • • • • • • •

You can use polynomial functions to model many real-life situations. For example, the function $h(t) = -4.9t^2 + 20t + 1.6$ models the height, h, in metres of a ball above the ground t seconds after the ball has been thrown into the air.

Example 2   **Evaluating Polynomial Functions**

A 2-cm by 2-cm square is cut from each corner of a 20-cm by 30-cm piece of cardboard. What is the volume of the corresponding cardboard box? The polynomial function $V(x) = 4x^3 - 100x^2 + 600x$ models the volume, V, in cubic centimetres and x represents the side length of each square that is cut from each corner.

Solution
To determine the volume, substitute $x = 2$ and evaluate.

$$V(x) = 4x^3 - 100x^2 + 600x$$
$$V(2) = 4(2)^3 - 100(2)^2 + 600(2)$$
$$= 4(8) - 100(4) + 1200$$
$$= 832$$

The volume of the box will be 832 cm^3 if a 2-cm by 2-cm square is cut from each corner of the piece of cardboard.

EXAMINING THE CONCEPT

Describing Polynomial Functions

You can describe any function in terms of the values of $f(x)$ for a specific interval of the domain. The symbol $f(x)$ in this case means the value of the function at a number x. The symbol $f(x)$ is also the name of the function, which may be called just f. The function is **increasing** if the graph of the function *rises* from left to right along the x-axis. The function is **decreasing** if the graph of the function *falls* from left to right along the x-axis.

Increasing and Decreasing Functions

A function f is **increasing** on an interval I if $f(x_1) < f(x_2)$, $x_1 < x_2$, and x_1 and x_2 are in I. A function f is **decreasing** on an interval I if $f(x_1) > f(x_2)$, $x_1 > x_2$, and x_1 and x_2 are in I.

Intuitively, a function is increasing if the graph rises from left to right and decreasing if the graph falls from left to right.

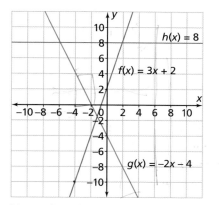

Linear functions with degrees 0 and 1.

The graph of the linear function $f(x) = 3x + 2$ has a positive slope, so the function *increases* on the set of real numbers. The graph of $g(x) = -2x - 4$ has a negative slope, so the function *decreases* on the same domain. The horizontal line that represents $h(x) = 8$ has slope 0, so the function is neither increasing nor decreasing.

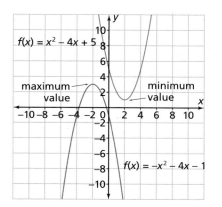

Quadratic functions with degree 2.

The top parabola opens up, and the bottom parabola opens down. The quadratic function of the parabola that opens up decreases to a minimum value (at the vertex) and then increases. The quadratic function of the parabola that opens down increases to a maximum value (at the vertex) and then decreases.

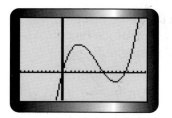

$V(x) = 4x^3 - 100x^2 + 600x$

To quickly graph a cubic function use graphing technology. Enter the model for the volume of the cardboard box, $V(x) = 4x^3 - 100x^2 + 600x$, into the equation editor of a graphing calculator. Set the window to **Xmin=−10**, **Xmax=20**, **Ymin=−1000**, **Ymax=2000** to produce this graph.

The graph of $V(x)$ is a continuous curve that rises, falls, and then rises again. $V(x)$ is increasing on the intervals $x < 3.92$ and $x > 12.74$. $V(x)$ is decreasing on the interval $3.92 < x < 12.74$. As a result, the graph turns at two different points.

Turning Point

A turning point is a point on a curve that is higher or lower than all nearby points. A turning point occurs where a function changes from increasing to decreasing or vice versa. When the function $y = f(x)$ changes from increasing to decreasing at (x, y), then (x, y) is called a **local maximum point** and $f(x) = y$ is the **local maximum value**. When the function $y = f(x)$ changes from decreasing to increasing at (x, y), then (x, y) is called a **local minimum point** and $f(x) = y$ is the **local minimum value**.

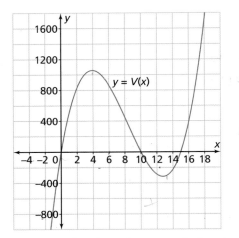

The graph of $V(x)$ has two turning points at about $(3.92, 1056.3)$ and $(12.74, -315.6)$. The local maximum is $(4, 1056)$ and the local minimum is $(12.74, -315.6)$. The maximum and minimum values are 1056.3 and -315.6, respectively. The graph also has three x-intercepts, $x = 0$, $x = 10$, and $x = 15$. These values correspond to the real zeros of the function.

The zeros of a function occur when $f(x) = 0$. To find the zeros, factor $V(x)$ and set each factor to 0.

$$V(x) = (30 - 2x)(20 - 2x)(x)$$

$$\begin{array}{lcl} 30 - 2x = 0 & \text{or} \quad 20 - 2x = 0 & \text{or} \quad x = 0 \\ 30 = 2x & 20 = 2x & \\ 15 = x & 10 = x & \end{array}$$

$V(x)$ has a local maximum and a local minimum.

The terms zeros and *x*-intercepts can be used interchangably.

The zeros define intervals where $V(x)$ is positive or negative. The graph lies *below* the x-axis for $x < 0$ and $10 < x < 15$, and $V(x)$, or the volume of the box, is negative. The graph lies *above* the x-axis for $0 < x < 10$ and $x > 15$, and $V(x)$, or the volume of the box, is positive.

The values of $V(x)$ must be positive because the model describes volume, which can have only positive values. If $x > 10$, a box cannot be created at all! The only realistic interval is $0 \le x \le 10$.

Then the appropriate model for the volume of the cardboard box is $V(x) = (30 - 2x)(20 - 2x)(x)$, where $0 \le x < 10$. The model is a polynomial function with a **restricted domain**. In this case, the unrestricted domain of $V(x)$ is the set of real numbers.

Simplify $V(x)$ further by factoring.

$$\begin{aligned} V(x) &= (30 - 2x)(20 - 2x)(x) \\ &= -2(-15 + x)(-2)(-10 + x)(x) \quad \text{Simplify.} \\ &= 4x(x - 15)(x - 10) \end{aligned}$$

In factored form, the zeros of the function are clearly visible.

Zeros of Polynomial Functions in Factored Form

The zero of a **linear** function $f(x)$ is s in $f(x) = k(x - s)$.
The zeros of a **quadratic** function $f(x)$ are s and t in $f(x) = k(x - s)(x - t)$.
The zeros of a **cubic** function $f(x)$ are s, t, and u in
$f(x) = k(x - s)(x - t)(x - u)$.

Example 3 **Sketching the Graphs of Polynomial Functions in Factored Form**

For the polynomial function $h(x) = -(x + 1)(x - 3)(x - 5)$,

i. determine the zeros   **ii.** sketch the graph   **iii.** describe the shape

Solution

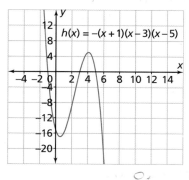

$h(x) = -(x + 1)(x - 3)(x - 5)$ is in factored form. The function is cubic and has zeros -1, 3, and 5. The turning points do not necessarily occur at the midpoint between each pair of x-intercepts, as they do for a quadratic function. To complete the graph, determine more points. Create a table with x-values to the left of the smallest zero, between the zeros, and to the right of the largest zero. The more points used, the better the sketch.

x	-3	-2	0	1	2	4	6	7
$h(x)$	96	35	-15	-16	-9	5	-21	-64

This function decreases when $x < 0.57$ and $x > 4.1$. It increases when $0.57 < x < 4.1$. The local minimum is $(0.57, -16.9)$ and the local maximum is $(4.10, 5.05)$.

EXAMINING THE CONCEPT

Families of Polynomial Functions and the Role of *k*

Any linear function $f(x) = k(x - s)$ has a zero at s and slope k.
When $k > 0$, f increases and when $k < 0$, f decreases.
When $k = 0$, the graph of the function (a line) is horizontal.
   A family of linear functions is created if s is constant and k varies.
The graphs of the family of functions pass through the same x-intercept point.

$f(x) = k(x - 2)$

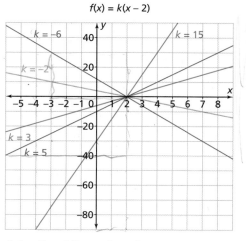

A family of linear functions

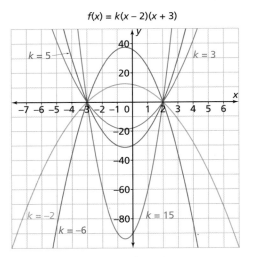

$$f(x) = k(x - 2)(x + 3)$$

A family of quadratic functions

Any quadratic function $f(x) = k(x - s)(x - t)$ has zeros s and t. When $k > 0$, the parabola opens up. The function decreases and then increases from left to right. When $k < 0$, the parabola opens down. The function increases and then decreases from left to right. A family of quadratic functions is created if s and t are constant and k varies. The graphs of the family of functions pass through the same x-intercept points.

The volume function $V(x) = 4x(x - 15)(x - 10)$ is in factored form. Look at similar cubic functions with the general factor k, where $k \in \mathbf{R}$, that is, $f(x) = kx(x - 15)(x - 10)$.

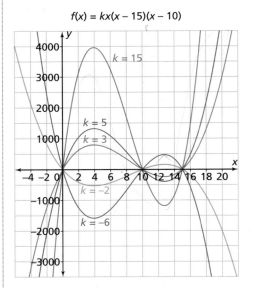

$$f(x) = kx(x - 15)(x - 10)$$

A family of cubic functions

The cubic function $f(x) = k(x - s)(x - t)(x - u)$ has zeros s, t, and u. When $k > 0$, the function increases, decreases, and increases again, from left to right. When $k < 0$, the function decreases, increases, and decreases again, from left to right.

Since a family of polynomial functions is possible for a set of given zeros, knowing the coordinates of an additional point on the graph allows you to determine the equation of a specific function.

Example 4   **Determining the Equation of a Polynomial Function from Its Graph**

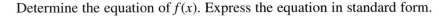

Determine the equation of $f(x)$. Express the equation in standard form.

Solution

The function has three zeros, -3, -1, and 1, and the corresponding factors are $x + 3$, $x + 1$, and $x - 1$. Because the function decreases, increases, and decreases again, the function is cubic and the value of k is negative. The function is of the form $f(x) = k(x + 3)(x + 1)(x - 1)$. Substitute the coordinates of a point on the curve, for example, $(2, -45)$, and solve for k.

$$-45 = k(2 + 3)(2 + 1)(2 - 1) \quad \text{Solve for } k.$$
$$-45 = 15k$$
$$-3 = k$$

$$\begin{aligned} f(x) &= -3(x + 3)(x + 1)(x - 1) \\ &= -3(x + 3)(x^2 - 1) \quad\quad \text{Expand.} \\ &= -3(x^3 - x + 3x^2 - 3) \\ &= -3x^3 - 9x^2 + 3x + 9 \end{aligned}$$

The equation of the function in standard form is
$f(x) = -3x^3 - 9x^2 + 3x + 9.$

EXAMINING THE CONCEPT

A Closer Look at Zeros of Polynomial Functions

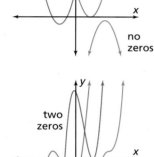

A quadratic function can have no zeros, one zero, or two zeros.

The vertex or turning point in the graph of a quadratic function with only one zero lies on the x-axis.

$$f(x) = k(x - s)(x - t)$$

In this case, s and t are equal, so

$$f(x) = k(x - s)(x - s) \text{ or } f(x) = k(x - s)^2$$

A cubic function will always have at least one zero.

The function with three zeros is $f(x) = k(x - s)(x - t)(x - u)$.

The function with two zeros is $f(x) = k(x - s)(x - t)^2$, where t is the zero that is also a turning point of the function.

A function with only one zero is $f(x) = k(x - s)^3$ or $f(x) = k(x - s)(x^2 + ax + b)$ where $(x^2 + ax + b)$ has no real roots.

CHECK, CONSOLIDATE, COMMUNICATE

1. A cubic polynomial function is $g(x) = 3(x - 2)(x + 4)(x + 6)$.
   State the zeros and describe the shape of the curve.
2. Explain how to describe the graph of a polynomial function.
3. Sketch a possible polynomial function for each case.
   Label the x-intercepts and any turning points.
   (a) f is a quadratic function where $f(x) = k(x - s)(x - t)$ and $k < 0$
   (b) f is a cubic function where $f(x) = k(x - s)(x - t)(x - u)$ and $k > 0$
   (c) f is a cubic function where $f(x) = k(x - s)(x - t)^2$ and $k < 0$
   (d) f is a quadratic function where $f(x) = k(x - s)^2$ and $k > 0$

KEY IDEAS

- The function f is a polynomial function if
  $f(x) = a_n x^n + a_{n-1} x^{n-1} + \ldots + a_2 x^2 + a_1 x + a_0$, $a_1, \ldots, a_n$ are real
  numbers and n is a natural number. The degree of the function is n if
  the leading coefficient, $a_n \neq 0$.
- The graph of a polynomial function of degree 1 is a straight line.
  The graph of a degree-2 polynomial is a U-shaped parabola.
  The graphs of many degree-3 polynomials are S-shaped curves.
- The zeros of a polynomial function $f(x)$ correspond to the x-intercepts in
  the graph of $f(x)$. Use the x-intercepts and several other points to graph
  $f(x)$.

Function	Type	Zeros	Description of Graph
$f(x) = k$	linear, degree 0	None, $k \neq 0$	horizontal line
$f(x) = k(x - s)$	linear, degree 1	$x = s$	$k > 0$, $f(x)$ is increasing $k < 0$, $f(x)$ is decreasing
$f(x) = k(x - s)(x - t)$	quadratic, degree 2	$x = s$ $x = t$	$k > 0$, $f(x)$ is decreasing and then increasing $k < 0$, $f(x)$ is increasing and then decreasing
$f(x) = k(x - s)(x - t)(x - u)$, ($s$, t, and u not all equal)	cubic, degree 3	$x = s$ $x = t$ $x = u$	$k > 0$, $f(x)$ is increasing, decreasing, and then increasing $k < 0$, $f(x)$ is decreasing, increasing, and then decreasing

- Use the zeros of a polynomial function to find the equation of the function
  if one point that satisfies the function is known.

1.1 Exercises

1. Expand and simplify. Express each equation in standard form.

(a) $f(x) = (x - 1)(x + 3)(x - 5)$ **(b)** $f(x) = (2x + 3)(x + 1)(3x - 1)$

(c) $f(x) = -3(x - 2)(x + 3)(1 - x)$ **(d)** $f(x) = 5(4x + 3)(x - 5)$

(e) $f(x) = (2x - 1)(x + 2)(3x + 1)(x - 3)$

(f) $f(x) = -6(2x - 3)^2(x + 2)$

2. For each function in question 1, state the degree of the polynomial and
identify the type of function.

3. Determine the zeros of each function.

   (a) $f(x) = (x + 2)(x - 3)$

   (b) $f(x) = (3x - 5)(2x + 7)$

   (c) $f(x) = (x - 4)(x + 3)(x - 5)$

   (d) $f(x) = (2x - 9)(3x + 4)(4x - 1)$

   (e) $f(x) = (6 - 5x)(4 + 3x)(5 - 2x)$

   (f) $f(x) = (x + 3)(x - 3)(2x - 5)(4 - 3x)$

4. The volume, V, of a particular box is a function of its height, h, in centimetres. If $V(h) = 4h^3 - 6h^2 + 80$, what is the volume, in cubic centimetres, when $h = 3$ cm?

5. The volume, V, of a spherical cell is a function of the radius, r, $V(r) = \frac{4}{3}\pi r^3$. What is the volume when the radius is 6.0×10^{-6} m?

6. Graph each function using its zeros and a table of values.

   (a) $f(x) = 3(x - 3)(x + 5)$

   (b) $f(x) = -2(x + 1)(x + 7)$

   (c) $f(x) = 0.4(x - 1)(x + 1)(x + 2)$

   (d) $f(x) = -0.2(3x - 4)(2x + 5)(2x - 3)$

   (e) $f(x) = 0.5(x + 2)(x - 3)^2$

   (f) $f(x) = -0.1(x - 2)^2 (x + 3)^2$

7. Without graphing, indicate whether the graph of each function is a straight line, a U-shaped parabola, or an S-shaped curve.

   (a) $f(x) = 6 - 2x$

   (b) $f(x) = 3x^2 - 2x + 1$

   (c) $f(x) = -3x^3 + 6x^2 - x + 1$

   (d) $f(x) = -2(x - 4)(x + 5)(x - 2)$

   (e) $f(x) = -2(3x - 4)(2x + 5)$

   (f) $f(x) = -5(x + 7)$

8. Confirm your answers for question 7 using graphing technology.

9. For each graph, estimate the interval on which the function is increasing, the interval on which the function is decreasing, the coordinates of all turning points, and the local maximum and minimum values.

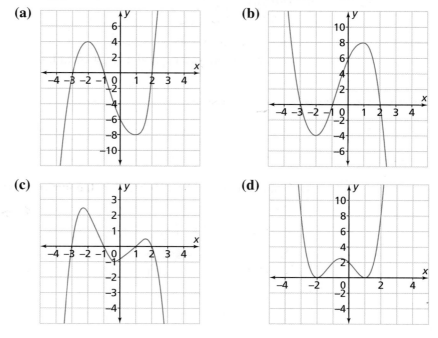

(a)

(b)

(c)

(d)

10. For each function, use graphing technology to estimate the intervals of increase and decrease and the local maximum and minimum.

(a) $f(x) = -2(x + 3)(x - 4)$ (b) $f(x) = 3(2x - 1)(4x + 5)$

(c) $f(x) = 2(x + 4)(x - 3)(x + 5)$ (d) $f(x) = -0.5(x - 1)(x + 1)(x - 2)$

(e) $f(x) = -3(x - 5)^2$ (f) $f(x) = 1.5(x + 2)(x - 3)^2$

11. **Knowledge and Understanding:** Determine the equation of each function and sketch its graph.

(a) $f(x) = k(x + 4)(x - 6)$, and passes through $(1, -50)$

(b) $f(x) = k(x - 3)(x + 4)(x - 5)$, and passes through $(2, 18)$

(c) $f(x) = k(2x - 3)(x + 4)(3x - 5)(x - 10)$, and passes through $(1, 180)$

12. **Communication:** A cubic function of degree 3 can have three zeros.

(a) Explain how to use this fact to graph the function.

(b) Graph $f(x) = k(x - 2)(x - 1)(x + 1)$ for $k = 2$ and $k = -2$.

13. Verify your sketches for question 12 using a graphing calculator and comment on their closeness of fit to the actual curves.

14. Determine the equation of each cubic polynomial function from its graph.

(a) (b)

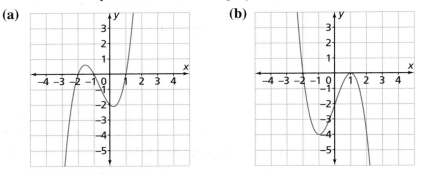

15. Determine the equation of each polynomial function.

(a) (b)

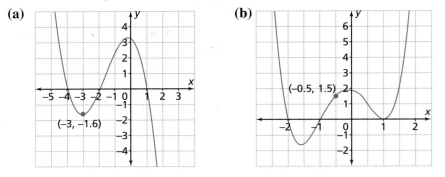

16. Determine the quadratic function with zeros -3 and -5 and $f(7) = -720$.

17. Determine the cubic function with zeros -2, 3, and 4, and $f(5) = 28$.

18. Application: The function $y = 26.55x^3 - 170.56x^2 + 249.62x + 1257.80$, $0 \leq x \leq 4$, approximates the number of petajoules of energy used in Canada for residential purposes from 1995 to 1999.

(a) State the restricted domain of this model and describe what x represents in this case.

(b) Use graphing technology to graph the function. Describe its shape and identify the coordinates of any turning points. Use $\boxed{\text{CALC}}$ and the minimum/maximum feature to help determine the intervals on which the function is increasing and decreasing.

(c) Determine the amount of residential energy Canadians used in 1998.

(d) Suppose no restrictions were placed on the domain of the function. How much residential energy would be used in 2010?

19. Let $f(x) = x^3 - 2x^2 - 5x + 6$.

(a) Use graphing technology to graph $f(x)$.

(b) Describe the behaviour of the graph in terms of the intervals when $f(x)$ is increasing and decreasing.

(c) State the value of the independent variable for all turning points.

(d) State the coordinates of all local maximum and minimum points.

20. Sure Grip Athletic Shoes tracks the relation between total sales and the number of dollars spent on a new advertising campaign. The function $S(x) = -0.000\,025x^3 + 0.015x^2$, $50 < x < 350$, represents the sales, S, in hundreds of thousands of dollars. The budget, x, for the advertising campaign is measured in tens of thousands of dollars.

(a) What advertising budget was used to generate the model? What does that mean for sales outside this domain?

(b) Use graphing technology to graph the function.

(c) What are the maximum sales this advertising campaign might generate under this model? When does this occur? What happens to sales after this point?

(d) What happens to sales when $6\,000\,000$ is spent on the new advertising campaign?

21. Thinking, Inquiry, Problem Solving: The function $f(x) = kx^3 - 8x^2 - x + 3k + 1$ has a zero, 2. Determine the value of k. Graph $f(x)$ and determine all zeros. Rewrite $f(x)$ in factored form.

22. Check Your Understanding: Give an example of a polynomial function in factored form for each case.

(a) degree 2; two zeros, the function decreases then increases

(b) degree 3; three zeros, the function increases, decreases, then increases

(c) degree 3; two zeros, the function decreases, increases, then decreases

(d) degree 1; one zero, the function increases

(C) **23. (a)** The graph of a quadratic function that neither crosses nor touches the x-axis has no real zeros. Determine the equation of the quadratic function with roots $2 + i$ and $2 - i$.

(b) Complex roots are always expressed as conjugate pairs. Determine the equation of a quartic function with complex roots $3 + 2i$ and $2 - 3i$.

24. Let $f(x)$ be any polynomial function. Prove that the slope of the line joining points $(x_1, f(x_1))$ to $(x_2, f(x_2))$ will be positive if $f(x)$ is increasing and negative if $f(x)$ is decreasing.

ADDITIONAL ACHIEVEMENT CHART QUESTIONS

Knowledge and Understanding: Determine the zeros of $p(x) = (x^2 - x - 2)(x^2 + 2x - 15)$ and find sufficient points on $p(x)$ to sketch the graph. Use your graph to estimate the maximum and minimum values.

Application: The price of equipment, in thousands of dollars, is fixed. The number of weeks of labour is w, and the production, p, in thousands of dollars is $p(w) = 6w^5 - 15w^4 - 10w^3 + 30w^2 + 10$, where $0 \le w \le 3$. Use graphing technology to graph the function. Use [TRACE] to determine the interval, in weeks, during which production is increasing and decreasing. Use [TRACE] to determine the coordinates of the turning points and end points. For what number of weeks is production at a maximum? a minimum?

Thinking, Inquiry, Problem Solving: Graph each equation on the same set of axes: $y = x^3$, $y = x^3 + x^2$, $y = x^3 + x^2 + x$. How are the graphs similar? different? Use the above results to describe the similarities and differences of $y = x^4$, $y = x^4 + x^3$, $y = x^4 + x^3 + x^2$, and $y = x^4 + x^3 + x^2 + x$, without drawing their respective graphs.

Communication: Graph a polynomial function that decreases twice and increases once.

René Descartes (1596–1650)

René Descartes gave his name to an important creation in mathematics, the Cartesian plane. He is also famous for saying "I think, therefore I am." Do some research—why was this saying important in philosophy?

The Chapter Problem

Developing a Model for Canada's Population

CP1. Create a scatter plot. Draw a degree-1 polynomial to represent the curve of best fit for the data. On the same graph, draw a nonlinear polynomial curve of best fit. What degree do you think the function of the curve could be? Explain.

CP2. What is the restricted domain of each model? Within this domain are the models increasing or decreasing?

CP3. Use each model to determine the population in 2001. Which model is better, based on actual data?

CP4. Use each model to determine the population in 2006 and 2016. Which model might be better? Explain.

1.2 Investigating the Characteristics of Polynomial Functions

SETTING THE STAGE

Knowing the zeros of a polynomial function can help you sketch the function's graph. You also know that the degree of the function plays a role in defining the shape of the graph. The graph of the linear function $f(x) = 4x - 6$ is a line. The graph of the quadratic function $g(x) = x^2 + 3x - 5$ is a parabola. In most cases, the higher the degree of the polynomial function, the more complex the graph. In this section, you will examine the graphs of more complex polynomial functions.

EXAMINING THE CONCEPT

Characteristics of Polynomial Functions

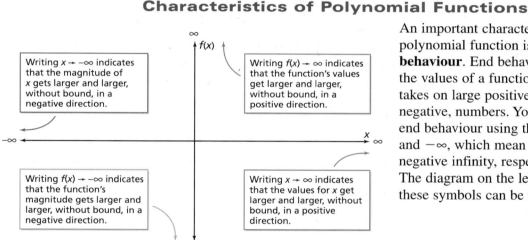

Writing $x \to -\infty$ indicates that the magnitude of x gets larger and larger, without bound, in a negative direction.

Writing $f(x) \to \infty$ indicates that the function's values get larger and larger, without bound, in a positive direction.

Writing $f(x) \to -\infty$ indicates that the function's magnitude gets larger and larger, without bound, in a negative direction.

Writing $x \to \infty$ indicates that the values for x get larger and larger, without bound, in a positive direction.

An important characteristic of any polynomial function is its **end behaviour**. End behaviour describes the values of a function, $f(x)$, as x takes on large positive, or large negative, numbers. You can describe end behaviour using the symbols ∞ and $-\infty$, which mean positive and negative infinity, respectively. The diagram on the left shows how these symbols can be used.

Example 1 **Describing the End Behaviour of a Polynomial Function from Its Graph**

Describe the end behaviour of $f(x)$ as $x \to -\infty$ and $x \to \infty$.

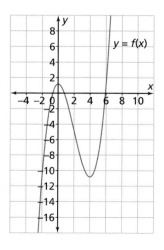

Solution

As $x \to \infty$, the values of $f(x)$ get larger in magnitude in the positive direction. In symbols, $f(x) \to \infty$.

As $x \to -\infty$, the values of $f(x)$ get larger in magnitude in the negative direction. In symbols, $f(x) \to -\infty$.

Investigating the End Behaviour and Turning Points

1. Using graphing technology, adjust the window settings so that the intervals $-5 \leq x \leq 5$ and $-40 \leq y \leq 20$ are on the axes.

2. Graph each function, and then copy and complete the table.
   (a) $f(x) = 9x^2 - 8x - 2$
   (b) $f(x) = -x^4 - 3x^3 + 3x^2 + 8x + 5$
   (c) $f(x) = 2x^6 - 13x^4 + 15x^2 + x - 17$
   (d) $f(x) = -2x^4 - 4x^3 + 3x^2 + 6x + 9$
   (e) $f(x) = x^3 - 5x^2 + 3x + 4$
   (f) $f(x) = 2x^5 + 7x^4 - 3x^3 - 18x^2 - 20$
   (g) $f(x) = -x^7 + 8x^5 - 16x^3 + 8x$
   (h) $f(x) = -2x^3 + 8x^2 - 5x + 3$

Function	Degree	Number of Turning Points	Leading Coefficient: Positive or Negative?	Degree: Even or Odd?	End Behaviour as $x \to -\infty$	End Behaviour as $x \to \infty$
(a)						
(b)						
...	...	...	...	...	...	...
(h)						

3. Make a conjecture about the maximum number of turning points in the graph of a polynomial function with degree 8, 9, or n.

4. Make a conjecture about the end behaviour of a function with a degree that is (a) even and (b) odd.

5. Make a conjecture about the end behaviour of a function with a degree that is
   (a) even and has a positive leading coefficient
   (b) even and has a negative leading coefficient
   (c) odd and has a positive leading coefficient
   (d) odd and has a negative leading coefficient

Example 2   **Describing the End Behaviour of a Polynomial Function from Its Equation**

Describe the end behaviour of $f(x) = -2x^5 - 3x^3 + 4x^2 - 4$ as $x \to -\infty$ and $x \to \infty$.

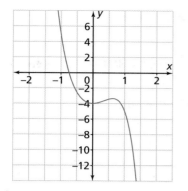

$f(x) = -2x^5 - 3x^3 + 4x^2 - 4$

Solution

The degree of the function is an odd number, 5. Therefore, the end behaviours are opposite. The leading coefficient is a negative number, -2, and as $x \to \infty$, the values of $f(x)$ get larger in the negative direction. As $x \to -\infty$, the values of $f(x)$ get larger in the positive direction. In other words,

$$\text{as } x \to \infty, f(x) \to -\infty, \text{ and}$$
$$\text{as } x \to -\infty, f(x) \to \infty$$

The graph of the function verifies the analysis.

· · · · · · · · ·

Investigating the Number of Zeros

1. Using graphing technology, adjust the window settings so that the intervals $-10 \le x \le 10$ and $-10 \le y \le 10$ are on the axes.

2. State the degree of each polynomial and then graph it. Determine the number of zeros.

   (a) $f(x) = x^3 - 2x^2 - 4x + 8$ **(b)** $f(x) = x^3 + x^2 - 2x - 7$
   (c) $f(x) = x^3 + 2x^2 - 3x - 5$

3. Before graphing, clear all previous functions. State the degree of each polynomial and then graph it. Determine the number of zeros.

   (a) $f(x) = x^4 + 2x^3 - x^2 - 2x$ **(b)** $f(x) = -x^4 + 2x^3 + x^2 + 2x$
   (c) $f(x) = 2x^4 - 6x^3 + x^2 + 4x + 5$ **(d)** $f(x) = -x^4 - x^3 + 3x^2 + x - 2$
   (e) $f(x) = x^4 + x^3 + x + 1$

4. Make a conjecture about the minimum and maximum number of zeros possible for a polynomial function with degree

   (a) 5   **(b)** 6   **(c)** 7   **(d)** 8   **(e)** n

Investigating Finite Differences in Polynomial Functions

Recall that for a linear function, the rate of change is constant, so the first differences are constant. The rate of change for a quadratic function is variable, but the second differences are constant.

Does the degree of a polynomial function influence the value of the finite differences?

1. Make a conjecture about the finite differences of a cubic polynomial.

2. To verify your conjecture, create a table with the first, second, and third differences for $f(x) = 2x^3 - 3x^2 + 4x - 1$, where $-2 \le x \le 5$.

Use either pencil and paper or a graphing calculator. If you are using a TI-83 Plus, follow these steps:

(a) Press [STAT] [1] and enter the *x*-values into **L1**.

(b) Scroll right and up to select **L2**. Enter the function, using **L1** as the variable *x*. Press [ALPHA] [+] [2] [2nd] [1] [^] [3] [−] [3] [2nd] [1] [^] [2] [+] [4] [2nd] [1] [−] [1] [ALPHA] [+].

(c) Press [ENTER] to display the values of the function in **L2**.

(d) Find the first differences. Scroll right and up to select **L3**. Then press [ALPHA] [+] [2nd] [STAT]. Scroll right to **OPS** and press [7] to choose ΔList(. Enter **L2** by pressing [2nd] [2] [)] [ALPHA] [+]. Press [ENTER] to see the first differences displayed in **L3**.

(e) Repeat step (d) to find the second differences. In **L4**, apply ΔList(to **L3**. To find the third differences in **L5**, apply ΔList(to **L4**. **L1** contains the values of *x*, **L2** the values of $f(x)$, **L3** the first differences, **L4** the second differences, and **L5** the third differences.

3. Choose another cubic polynomial function and create the differences table. If you are using the TI-83 Plus, simply scroll right and up to highlight **L2** and then press [ENTER]. Then edit the original function. Enter the new coefficients and press [ENTER] to view the new table.

4. Choose a polynomial function of degree 4 and create a differences table.

5. Choose a polynomial function of degree 5 and create a differences table.

6. What conclusion can you make about the finite differences of a polynomial function with degree *n*?

7. What relation exists between the leading coefficient of a polynomial of degree *n* and its common difference?

CHECK, CONSOLIDATE, COMMUNICATE

1. What is the maximum number of turning points in the graph of a polynomial of degree 1? degree 2? degree 3? degree 20? degree *n*?

2. Describe the end behaviour of an even-degree polynomial with a positive leading coefficient and with a negative leading coefficient.

3. Describe the end behaviour of an odd-degree polynomial with a positive leading coefficient and with a negative leading coefficient.

4. Explain why there is at least one *x*-intercept in the graph of an odd-degree polynomial.

5. A degree-4 polynomial has a leading coefficient of −2. What is the value of the fourth finite difference?

KEY IDEAS

• Polynomial functions behave differently, depending on the degree. If the degree is even, the end behaviours are the same. If the degree is odd, the end behaviours are opposite.

- The degree and the leading coefficient determine the end behaviours of a polynomial function.

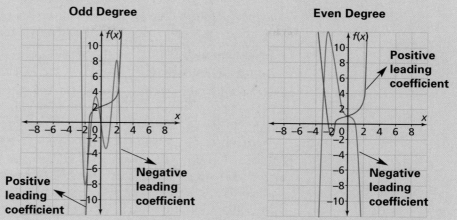

Odd Degree

Even Degree

Positive leading coefficient

Negative leading coefficient

Positive leading coefficient

Negative leading coefficient

- The graphs of polynomial functions of degree n may have
  0 to n x-intercepts when n is even.
  1 to n x-intercepts when n is odd.
- The graphs of polynomial functions of degree 4 can be W-shaped curves.
- The graphs of polynomial functions of degree n have at most $n - 1$ turning points.
- The nth finite differences of polynomial functions of degree n are constant.
- The third finite difference of a degree-3 polynomial is related to the leading coefficient by a factor of $3 \times 2 \times 1$.
- The fourth finite difference of a degree-4 polynomial is related to the leading coefficient by a factor of $4 \times 3 \times 2 \times 1$.

1.2 Exercises

A **1.** Use the graph of each polynomial function to identify the polynomial as cubic or quartic, state the sign of the leading coefficient of its function, describe the end behaviour, and say whether the graph has a turning point.

(a)   **(b)**   **(c)**   **(d)**

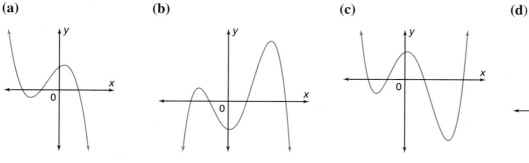

2. **Communication:** Explain why odd-degree polynomial functions can have only local maximums and local minimums, but even-degree polynomial functions can have maximums and minimums.

3. Explain how to use finite differences to see if a set of data can be modelled using linear, quadratic, cubic, or quartic polynomial functions.

4. Use finite differences to determine what type of polynomial function could model each relationship.

   (a) Michelle earns $200/week, plus 5% of sales.

Sales ($)	0	500	1000	1500	2000
Earnings ($)	200	225	250	275	300

   (b) A model rocket is launched from the roof of the school.

Time (s)	0	1	2	3	4
Height Above Ground (m)	10	25	30	25	10

   (c) The volume of a box varies at different widths.

Width (cm)	1	2	3	4	5	6
Volume (cm³)	0	6	24	60	120	210

   (d) The input for a function gives a certain output.

Input	0	1	2	3	4	5	6
Output	0	1	16	81	256	625	1296

5. Describe the end behaviour of each polynomial function using the degree and the leading coefficient.

   (a) $f(x) = 2x^2 - 3x + 5$ (b) $f(x) = -3x^3 + 2x^2 + 5x + 1$

   (c) $f(x) = 5x^3 - 2x^2 - 2x + 6$ (d) $f(x) = -2x^4 + 5x^3 - 2x^2 + 3x - 1$

   (e) $f(x) = 0.5x^4 + 2x^2 - 6$ (f) $f(x) = -3x^5 + 2x^3 - 4x$

6. Confirm your descriptions for question 5 using a graphing calculator.

7. **Knowledge and Understanding**

   Let $f(x) = -3(x + 2)(x - 4)(x - 2)(x + 6)$.

   (a) Determine the end behaviour of f as $x \to \infty$ and $x \to -\infty$.

   (b) Determine the zeros of f.

   (c) Express f in standard form, and state the maximum number of possible turning points.

   (d) Sketch a possible graph of $f(x)$.

8. Confirm your sketch for question 7 using a graphing calculator.

9. Repeat question 7 for each polynomial.
   (a) $f(x) = 2(x + 3)(x - 2)^2(x + 5)$
   (b) $f(x) = -0.2(x + 3)^2(x + 1)(x - 2)^2$
   (c) $f(x) = (x + 4)(x + 3)^2(x - 1)(x - 2)^2(x - 3)$

B 10. **Application:** The total revenue for Atlantic Fish Distributors is related to the company's advertising budget as shown.

Advertising Budget × $10 000	50	100	150	200	250	300	350	400	450	500
Revenue × $100 000	34.375	125.000	253.125	400.000	546.875	675.000	765.625	800.000	759.375	625.000

   (a) Create a scatter plot showing revenue versus advertising budget.

   (b) Use finite differences to determine what type of polynomial function could best model the data.

   (c) For every $50 000 spent on advertising, there is a corresponding change in revenue. At what point does the increase in revenue change to a decrease in revenue? Why is this point important to the shape of the graph?

11. Match each graph with the appropriate polynomial function.

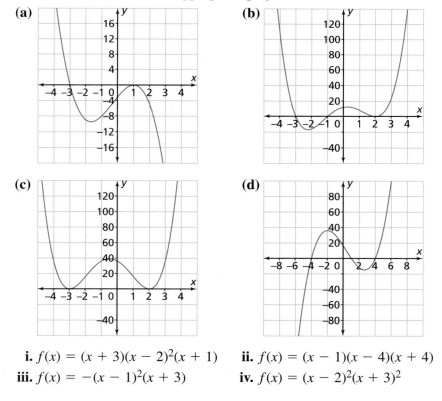

(a)

(b)

(c)

(d)

   i. $f(x) = (x + 3)(x - 2)^2(x + 1)$ **ii.** $f(x) = (x - 1)(x - 4)(x + 4)$
   iii. $f(x) = -(x - 1)^2(x + 3)$ **iv.** $f(x) = (x - 2)^2(x + 3)^2$

12. Sketch the graph of a polynomial function that satisfies each set of conditions.

(a) degree 4, positive leading coefficient, 3 zeros, 3 turning points

(b) degree 4, negative leading coefficient, 2 zeros, 1 turning point

(c) degree 4, positive leading coefficient, 1 zero, 3 turning points

(d) degree 3, negative leading coefficient, 1 zero, no turning point

(e) degree 3, positive leading coefficient, 2 zeros, 2 turning points

13. Let $f(x) = 2(x - 3)^2 (x + 1)$.

(a) Sketch a possible graph.

(b) Confirm your sketch using a graphing calculator.

(c) Sketch another, similar type of graph that uses the other zero as a turning point. How will the original equation change?

14. State the third finite difference for each polynomial. Verify the value with a difference table.

(a) $f(x) = -2x^3 + 4x^2 - 3x - 2$ (b) $f(x) = 3(x - 1)(x + 2)(x - 6)$

15. State the fourth finite difference for each polynomial. Verify the value with a difference table.

(a) $f(x) = 0.25x^4 - 0.15x^3 + 1.5x^2 - 0.5x + 3$

(b) $f(x) = -0.15(x + 2)(x + 3)(2x - 1)(3x - 2)$

16. Check Your Understanding: Copy and complete the table.

Degree of $f(x)$	Sign of Leading Coefficient of $f(x)$	End Behaviour of $f(x)$ as $x \to \infty$	End Behaviour of $f(x)$ as $x \to -\infty$
odd	positive		
even	negative		
odd	negative		
even	positive		

17. Thinking, Inquiry, Problem Solving: You can use finite differences to determine the leading coefficient of any polynomial function. Determine the relation that exists between the nth finite difference and the leading coefficient, a, for the general polynomial function $f(x) = a_n x^n + a_{n-1} x^{n-1} + \ldots + a_2 x^2 + a_1 x + a_0$.

18. The polynomial $f(x) = ax^5 + 3x^4 - 2x^3 - 3x^2 + x - 1$ has a common difference of -120. What is the value of a?

19. Write a polynomial function of degree 5 such that $f(x) \to \infty$ as $x \to -\infty$. Graph $f(x)$ using graphing technology. Determine the coordinates of all turning points. Identify the intervals in which $f(x)$ is increasing and decreasing.

ADDITIONAL ACHIEVEMENT CHART QUESTIONS

Knowledge and Understanding: Let $f(x) = x^4 - 5x^2 + 4$.

(a) Determine the end behaviour as $x \to \infty$ and $x \to -\infty$, the maximum number of zeros, and the maximum number of turning points.

(b) Use graphing technology to graph f and confirm your answers for (a).

Application: The Adanac Clothing Company makes scarves and sells them wholesale. A distributor pays $15 per scarf to buy 10 scarves. The price decreases by $1 per scarf if the distributor buys 5 more scarves. The price continues to drop by $1 per scarf for every additional 5 scarves bought. Determine a polynomial function to represent the revenue. Use the function to find the number of scarves that Adanac should sell to maximize revenue.

Number of Scarves Sold	Revenue ($)
10	150
15	210
20	260
25	300
⋮	⋮

Thinking, Inquiry, Problem Solving

The function $g(x) = x^4 - 2x^3 - 5x^2 - 4x + 4$ has two zeros. The intervals in which the zeros lie can be determined without graphing the function. Identify the intervals with the zeros from the choices below. Defend your choices using mathematical reasoning.

(a) $-1 \le x \le 0$ **(b)** $0 \le x \le 1$ **(c)** $1 \le x \le 2$

(d) $2 \le x \le 3$ **(e)** $3 \le x \le 4$ **(f)** $4 \le x \le 5$

Communication: A classmate was absent when this section was covered. Describe to her or him at least five pieces of information you can obtain about the graph of a polynomial function by examining the function. Be sure to describe where you are looking, what you are doing, and why you are doing it to find the information. Use $h(x) = 2x - 4 - 5x^4 + 3x^3$ to guide your description.

The Chapter Problem

Developing a Model for Canada's Population

CP5. Using graphing technology, create a scatter plot. Enter the years since 1851 into **L1** and the population into **L2**. Use linear regression and quadratic regression to find two different polynomial models.

CP6. What is the end behaviour of each model? Which model has a turning point?

CP7. Use each model to determine the population in 2001. Which model is the better predictor based on the actual population of Canada in 2001?

CP8. Use each model to determine the population in 2006 and 2016. Which model might be the better predictor? Explain.

1.3 Creating New Polynomial Functions: An Introduction to Composition

SETTING THE STAGE

Can you combine polynomial functions using the basic mathematical operations? If so, what is the result?

Rhona is a licensed plumber and Bill is an apprentice training for his licence. Rhona earns \$28/h and receives \$22/day to travel to the job site. Bill earns \$12/h and receives a \$10/day travel allowance. The polynomial model for Rhona's daily earnings, R, in dollars is $R(h) = 28h + 22$, where h is the number of hours worked. Similarly, Bill's earnings are modelled by $B(h) = 12h + 10$.

In this section, you will examine what happens when polynomial functions are combined using familiar operations to form new polynomial functions.

EXAMINING THE CONCEPT

Adding and Subtracting Functions

When Rhona and Bill are working together on a job, the contractor for the job site needs a single function to determine the costs for plumbing work.

The total daily cost, $T(h)$, is a function of the number of hours worked, h, by Rhona and Bill.

Time (h)	Rhona's Earnings, $R(h)$ ($)	Bill's Earnings, $B(h)$ ($)	Total Earnings, $T(h) = R(h) + B(h)$ ($)
0	22	10	22 + 10 = 32
1	50	22	50 + 22 = 72
2	78	34	78 + 34 = 112
3	106	46	106 + 46 = 152

So
$$\begin{aligned} T(h) &= R(h) + B(h) \\ &= (28h + 22) + (12h + 10) \\ &= 28h + 22 + 12h + 10 \\ &= 40h + 32 \end{aligned}$$

In both the table and the graph, the values of the functions are added together to obtain the value of the new function.

Adding or subtracting two functions means adding or subtracting the corresponding outputs, or, in terms of the graph, adding or subtracting the y-coordinates.

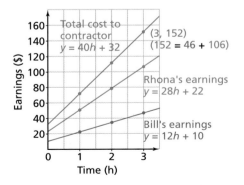

Example 1 Subtracting Two Polynomial Functions

Let $f(x) = -2(x + 1)(x - 2)(x - 4)$ and $g(x) = (x + 1)(x - 2)(x - 4)$.

(a) On the same axes, sketch the graph of each function. Use intercepts, the degree of the function, and the leading coefficient to develop the sketch.

(b) Graph $h(x) = f(x) - g(x)$.

(c) Identify the domain of each function.

Solution

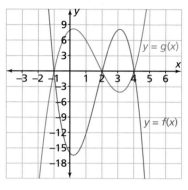

(a) The zeros for both $f(x)$ and $g(x)$ are -1, 2, and 4.

By inspection, both functions are degree-3 polynomials. The leading coefficient of $f(x)$ is negative. Therefore, as $x \to -\infty$, $f(x) \to \infty$ and as $x \to \infty$, $f(x) \to -\infty$. For $g(x)$, the leading coefficient is positive. Therefore, as $x \to -\infty$, $g(x) \to -\infty$ and as $x \to \infty$, $g(x) \to \infty$.

The y-intercept of $g(x)$ is 8 and the y-intercept of $f(x)$ is -16. Using this information results in the sketch to the left.

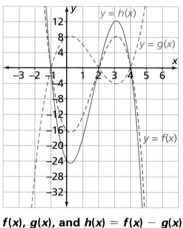

$f(x)$, $g(x)$, and $h(x) = f(x) - g(x)$

(b) $h(x) = f(x) - g(x)$

To find points that lie on $h(x)$, subtract the y-coordinates of points that have the same x-coordinate. The **difference function** has the same zeros as the two original functions, that is, -1, 2, and 4. Subtracting the y-intercepts results in point $(0, -24)$. Create a table to record some additional key points on f and g, and use these to find more points on h.

x	$f(x)$	$g(x)$	$h(x) = f(x) - g(x)$
1	-12	6	$-12 - 6 = -18$
3	8	-4	$8 - (-4) = 12$
5	-36	18	$-36 - 18 = -54$

(c) Since $f(x)$ and $g(x)$ are polynomial functions, their domains are the same, that is, the set of real numbers. The difference function $h(x)$ is also a polynomial function, and its domain is also the set of real numbers.

For any two functions, the y-values can only be added or subtracted when the x-values are common. For any polynomial function, the domain is the set of real numbers, so the difference, or sum, function will have the same domain, the set of real numbers. However, the range of $f(x) \pm g(x)$ must be determined each time.

EXAMINING THE CONCEPT

Multiplying Two Polynomial Functions

What is the result when two polynomial functions are multiplied?

Example 2 **Multiplying Two Polynomial Functions**

Let $f(x) = x + 3$ and $g(x) = -x^2 + 5$, $x \in \mathbf{R}$.

(a) Sketch each graph on the same axes.

(b) Make a table for $-3 \leq x \leq 3$, and determine the corresponding values of $h(x) = f(x) \times g(x)$.

(c) Use the table to sketch $h(x)$ on the same axes. Describe the shape of the graph.

(d) Determine the algebraic model for $h(x)$. What is its degree?

(e) What is the domain of $h(x)$? How does this domain compare with the domains of $f(x)$ and $g(x)$?

Solution

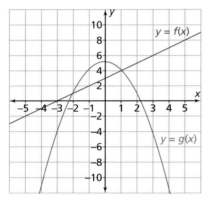

(a) Use intercepts to sketch the graphs.

The graph of function $f(x)$ is linear with slope 1 and y-intercept 3.

The graph of function $g(x)$ is quadratic with vertex $(0, 5)$. The parabola opens down.

(b)

	$f(x) = x + 3$	$g(x) = -x^2 + 5$	$h(x) = f(x) \times g(x)$
-3	0	-4	$0 \times (-4) = 0$
-2	1	1	$1 \times 1 = 1$
-1	2	4	$2 \times 4 = 8$
0	3	5	$3 \times 5 = 15$
1	4	4	$4 \times 4 = 16$
2	5	1	$5 \times 1 = 5$
3	6	-4	$6 \times (-4) = -24$

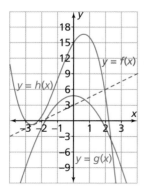

(c) The graph of $h(x)$ is a cubic polynomial.

(d) $h(x) = f(x) \times g(x)$
$$= (x + 3)(-x^2 + 5)$$
$$= -x^3 - 3x^2 + 5x + 15$$

This polynomial function has degree 3.

(e) The domain of $h(x)$ is the set of real numbers, which is the same as the domains of $f(x)$ and $g(x)$.

• • • • • • • •

> ## Adding, Subtracting, and Multiplying Polynomial Functions
>
> For the polynomial functions f and g,
> - the sum is $(f + g)(x) = f(x) + g(x)$
> - the difference is $(f - g)(x) = f(x) - g(x)$
> - the product is $(fg)(x) = f(x) \times g(x)$
>
> The domain of $f \pm g$ and fg is the set of all x, for which both f and g are defined. Any x belonging to the domain of f *and* to the domain of g belongs to the domain of $f(x) \pm g(x)$ or $f(x) \times g(x)$.

EXAMINING THE CONCEPT

The Composition of Functions

input → output
$x \quad \to \quad g(x) \to f(g(x))$
$\quad g \qquad \quad f$
$\quad\quad$ input → output

What happens when the output of one function is the input of another?

You can think of a function as an input-output machine. The input set is the domain of the function, and the output set is the range of the function. In the first step of the diagram, the x is an input and $g(x)$ is an output. In the second step, $g(x)$ is an input and $f(g(x))$ is an output.

Combining two functions in this way is called **composition.** Composition is the result of substituting the output of one function into another. The new function is called the **composite** of f and g and is written $f \circ g$.

Example 3   Determining the Equation of a Composite Function

Recall the situation in Setting the Stage. Rhona earns a daily wage according to $R(h) = 28h + 22$. The job site where Rhona works requires all employees to become members of a union. Rhona then pays 1.5% of her daily earnings as union dues. Determine the function that represents her daily union dues.

Solution

This situation involves two functions,

Daily Earnings: $R(h) = 28h + 22$
Daily Union Dues: $U(R(h)) = 0.015 \times R(h)$

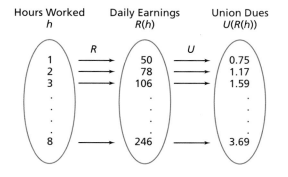

Examine the mapping that shows how the number of hours worked per day is related to the daily union dues. The domain for Rhona's daily earnings is the number of hours worked. But the domain for the daily union dues are her daily earnings, not the number of hours worked. In other words, the domain of the substitution function is the range of the substituted function.

Find the composite of the two functions.

$$U(R(h)) = 0.015(R(h))$$
$$= 0.015(28h + 22)$$
$$= 0.42h + 0.33$$

The function $U(R(h)) = 0.42h + 0.33$ represents Rhona's daily union dues.

· · · · · · · ·

Composite Functions

For two functions f and g, the composite function $f(g(x))$ is formed by evaluating f at $g(x)$. This new function is defined as $f \circ g$. The domain of $f \circ g$ is a subset of the domain of g and is found by examining $f \circ g$ and comparing the domain of f with the range of g.

Example 4   **Determining the Value of a Composite Function**

For the functions $f = \{(4, 1), (3, 2), (2, 3)\}$ and $g = \{(1, 5), (2, 4), (4, 2)\}$, determine each value.

(a) $f(g(4))$ **(b)** $g(f(4))$

Solution

(a) First find the value of g where $x = 4$. In the ordered pair (4, 2), $x = 4$.
Therefore, $g(4) = 2$.

Then $f(g(4)) = f(2)$. Now find the value of f where $x = 2$.
In the ordered pair (2, 3), $x = 2$.

So $f(g(4)) = f(2)$
$$= 3$$

(b) Find the value of f where $x = 4$. In the ordered pair (4, 1), $x = 4$.
Therefore, $f(4) = 1$.

Then $g(f(4)) = g(1)$. Now find the value of g where $x = 1$.
In the ordered pair (1, 5), $x = 1$.

So $g(f(4)) = g(1)$
$$= 5$$

· · · · · · · ·

Example 5   **Applying a Composite Function**

Ali buys a pair of shoes and has a coupon for $15 off. The day he buys the shoes, the store has a sale offering 20% off the price of all shoes.

(a) Write a function to represent the cost, C, of a pair of shoes at price, p, if just the coupon reduction is applied to the cost of the shoes. Write a function that represents the cost, D, if just the discount is applied to the cost.

(b) What does the function $D(C(p))$ represent if a pair of shoes has a regular price of \$80? Determine $D(C(80))$.

(c) What does the function $C \circ D$ represent for a pair of shoes with a regular price of \$80? Determine $C \circ D$ for the same pair of shoes.

(d) Does $C \circ D = D \circ C$? Justify your answer.

Solution

(a) $C(p) = p - 15$ and $D(p) = 0.8p$

(b) $D(C(p))$ means the coupon is applied first and then the discount is applied to the cost of the shoes. So, when $p = 80$,

$$
\begin{aligned}
D(C(80)) &= D(80 - 15) \\
&= D(65) \\
&= 0.8(65) \\
&= 52
\end{aligned}
$$

(c) $C \circ D$ means the discount is taken first and then the coupon reduction is applied. When $p = 80$,

$$
\begin{aligned}
(C \circ D)(x) &= C(D(80)) \\
&= C(0.8(80)) \\
&= C(64) \\
&= 64 - 15 \\
&= 49
\end{aligned}
$$

(d) In this case, $C \circ D \neq D \circ C$. The order of composition makes a difference. When $p = 80$, $D(C(80)) = 52$ and $C(D(80)) = 49$. In fact, these two functions are different.

$$
\begin{aligned}
(C \circ D)(p) &= C(0.8p) \\
&= 0.8p - 15
\end{aligned}
\qquad\qquad
\begin{aligned}
(D \circ C)(p) &= D(p - 15) \\
&= 0.8(p - 15) \\
&= 0.8p - 12
\end{aligned}
$$

CHECK, CONSOLIDATE, COMMUNICATE

1. Explain how a new polynomial function can be made from two polynomial functions by addition, by subtraction, and by multiplication.

2. State $(f + g)(x)$, $(f - g)(x)$, $(f \times g)(x)$, and $f(g(x))$ for $f = \{(-1, 4), (0, 5), (6, 3)\}$ and $g = \{(-1, 6), (0, 9), (4, 2)\}$.

3. Determine $(f + g)(x)$, $(f - g)(x)$, $(f \times g)(x)$, and $f(g(x))$ for $f(x) = x^2 + 3x - 2$ and $g(x) = x - 3$.

1.3 Exercises

A

1. **Knowledge and Understanding:** Let $f = \{(-4, 4), (-2, 4), (1, 3), (3, 5), (4, 6)\}$ and $g = \{(-4, 2), (-2, 1), (0, 2), (1, 2), (2, 2), (4, 4)\}$. Determine

   (a) $f + g$ **(b)** $f - g$ **(c)** $g - f$ **(d)** fg

2. Use the graph of f and g to sketch the graph of $f + g$.

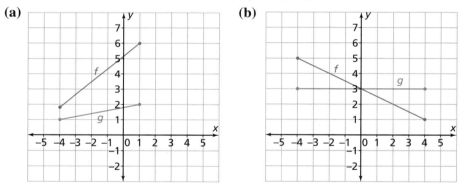

   (a)   **(b)**

3. Use the graph of f and g to sketch the graph of $f - g$.

   (a) 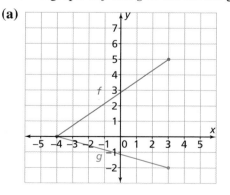   **(b)**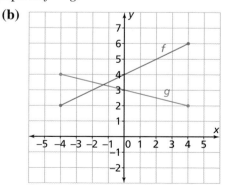

4. Use the graph of f and g to sketch the graph of fg.

(a)

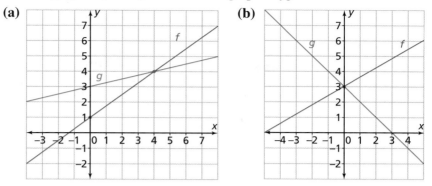

(b)

5. Let $f = \{(3, 2), (5, 1), (7, 4), (9, 3), (11, 5)\}$ and
$g = \{(1, 3), (2, 5), (3, 7), (4, 9), (5, 11)\}$. Determine

(a) $f(g(3))$ (b) $g(f(9))$

6. Let $f = \{(-1, 3), (0, 2), (1, 3), (2, 6)\}$ and
$g = \{(-1, 0), (0, 1), (1, 2), (2, 3)\}$. Determine

(a) $f(g(x))$ (b) $g(f(x))$

7. Let $f(x) = 3x - 2$ and $g(x) = 2x - 4$, $x \in \mathbf{R}$. Determine an expression for each case, and state the domain of the expression.

(a) $(f + g)(x)$ (b) $(g - f)(x)$ (c) $(f - g)(x)$ (d) $(fg)(x)$

8. Let $f(x) = 3x - 1$, $0 \le x \le 6$, and $g(x) = x^2 - 6x$, $-1 \le x \le 4$.
Determine an expression for each case, and state the domain of the expression.

(a) $(f + g)(x)$ (b) $(f - g)(x)$ (c) $(g - f)(x)$ (d) $(fg)(x)$

9. Let $f(x) = x^2 - 4$ and $g(x) = 3x$. Determine

(a) $f(g(1))$ (b) $g(f(2))$ (c) $g(g(1))$ (d) $f(f(-2))$

B **10.** **Communication:** Consider two functions f and g.

(a) Explain why the domains of f and g must be the same in order to add, subtract, or multiply the functions.

(b) Explain why the domain of f is the range of g for $f(g(x))$.

11. Let $f = \{(-1, 4), (0, 2), (1, 0), (2, -2)\}$.

(a) Give an example of g if $f + g = \{(-1, 6), (0, 4), (1, 2), (2, 0)\}$.

(b) Give an example of g if $fg = \{(-1, 12), (0, 6), (1, 0), (2, -6)\}$.

12. Let $f(x) = 3x + 2$, $-2 \le x \le 4$, and $g(x) = -4x + 1$, $-3 \le x \le 5$.

(a) Graph f and g on the same axes.

(b) Use appropriate ordered pairs to sketch the graph of $f - g$. What is the domain of $f - g$?

13. In each case, determine $f(x) \times g(x)$ and draw its graph.
    (a) $f(x) = -2x + 3$, $x \in \mathbf{R}$, and $g(x) = 3x + 4$, $x \in \mathbf{R}$
    (b) $f(x) = 3x - 2$, $x \in \mathbf{R}$, and $g(x) = x^2 + 3$, $x \in \mathbf{R}$
    (c) $f(x) = -x^2 + 2$, $x \in \mathbf{R}$, and $g(x) = 2x^2 - 1$, $x \in \mathbf{R}$

14. In each case, functions f and g are defined for $x \in \mathbf{R}$. For each pair of functions, determine the expression and the domain for $f(g(x))$ and $g(f(x))$. Graph each result.
    (a) $f(x) = 3x^2$, $g(x) = x - 1$
    (b) $f(x) = 2x^2 + x$, $g(x) = x^2 + 1$
    (c) $f(x) = 2x^3 - 3x^2 + x - 1$, $g(x) = 2x - 1$
    (d) $f(x) = x^4 - x^2$, $g(x) = x + 1$

15. In each case, $x \in \mathbf{R}$ for $f(x)$ and $g(x)$. Graph $f(x)$ and $g(x)$ on the same axes and use this graph to graph $h(x) = f(x) + g(x)$.
    (a) $f(x) = -x^2 + 1$ and $g(x) = 3$
    (b) $f(x) = -2x^2 + 2$ and $g(x) = 2x^2 - 1$
    (c) $f(x) = (x - 1)(x + 2)(x + 4)$ and $g(x) = (x - 1)(x + 4)(x + 6)$

16. Verify your work in question 15 using a graphing calculator.

17. Repeat question 15 for $h(x) = f(x) - g(x)$.

18. A company produces a product for $9.45 per unit, plus a fixed operating cost of $52 000. The company sells the product for $15.80 per unit.
    (a) Determine a function, $C(x)$, to represent the cost of producing x units.
    (b) Determine a function, $S(x)$, to represent sales of x units.
    (c) Determine a function that represents profit.

19. Steve earns $24.39/h operating an industrial plasma torch at a rail car manufacturing plant. He receives $0.58/h more for working the night shift, as well as $0.39/h for working weekends.
    (a) Write a function that describes Steve's regular pay.
    (b) What function shows his night shift premium?
    (c) What function shows his weekend premium?
    (d) What function represents his earnings for the night shift on Saturday?
    (e) How much does Steve earn for working 11 h on Saturday night, if he earns time and a half on that day's rate for more than 8 h of work?

20. A circle has radius r.
    (a) Write a function for the circle's area in terms of r.
    (b) Write a function for the radius in terms of the circumference, C.
    (c) Determine $A(r(C))$.
    (d) A tree's circumference is 3.6 m. What is the area of the cross section?

**Johann Peter Gustav
Lejeune Dirichlet
(1805–1859)**

Originally, the
definition of a function
was much less precise
than it is today.
Dirichlet was
responsible for the
definition of a function
that we use today.

21. **Application:** A solar panel is used to power an overhead sign on a highway. Each square metre of solar panel receives about 200 W of solar power. This solar panel converts about 15% of the solar energy to electrical power.

(a) Write a function for the solar power, $S(A)$, measured in watts (W) for any given area, A, in square metres.

(b) Write a function for the total electrical power, $P(S)$, in watts (W) this solar panel can generate.

(c) How large must the solar panel be if the sign uses 6 W of electrical energy?

22. Refrigeration slows down the growth of bacteria in food. The number of bacteria in a certain food is approximated by $B(T) = 15T^2 - 70T + 600$, where T represents the temperature in degrees Celsius and $3 \leq T \leq 12$. Once the food is removed from refrigeration, the temperature, $T(t)$, is given by $T(t) = 3.5t + 3$, where t is the time in hours and $0 \leq t \leq 3$.

(a) Write the expression for the number of bacteria in the food, t hours after it is removed from refrigeration.

(b) At 1.5 h, about how many bacteria are in the food?

(c) When will the bacteria count reach about 1200?

23. A franchise owner operates two coffee shops. The sales, S_1, in thousands of dollars, for shop one are represented by $S_1(t) = 700 - 1.4t^2$, where $t = 0$ corresponds to the year 2000. Similarly, the sales for shop two are represented by $S_2(t) = t^3 + 3t^2 + 500$.

(a) Which shop is showing an increase in sales after the year 2000?

(b) Determine a function that represents the total sales for the two coffee shops.

(c) What are the expected total sales for the year 2006?

(d) If sales continue according to the individual functions, what would you recommend that the owner do? Explain.

C 24. **Thinking, Inquiry, Problem Solving:** Let $f(x) = mx^2 + 2x + 5$ and $g(x) = 2x^2 - nx - 2$. The functions are combined to form the new function $h(x) = f(x) \times g(x)$. Points $(1, -40)$ and $(-1, 24)$ satisfy the new function. Determine $f(x)$ and $g(x)$.

25. Let $h(k) = 3k - 2$, $g(t) = 3t + 2$, and $f(x) = 3x - 2$.

(a) Determine $C(k) = f(g(h(k)))$.

(b) Show in a diagram how $k = 4$ carries through to its final value.

ADDITIONAL ACHIEVEMENT CHART QUESTIONS

Knowledge and Understanding: Let $f(x) = x^2 + 3x - 1$ and $g(x) = -2x + 5$. Determine

(a) $f(x) + g(x)$ **(b)** $f(x) - g(x)$ **(c)** $f(x) \times g(x)$ **(d)** $f(g(x))$

Application: The temperature of the Earth's crust is a linear function of the depth below the surface. The function $T(d) = 0.01d + 20$ gives the temperature, $T(d)$, in degrees Celsius d metres below the Earth's surface. An elevator goes down a mine shaft at 7.5 m/s. Express the temperature as a function of the time travelled.

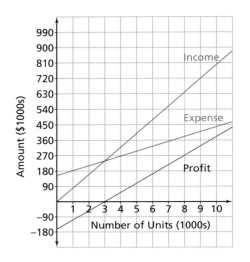

Thinking, Inquiry, Problem Solving: If $f(x) = ax + b$, $g(x) = cx + d$, and $f \circ g(x) = g \circ f(x)$, determine the relation among a, b, c, and d.

Communication: The graph on the left shows two functions and the function that represents the difference between the two functions. Identify and describe the two original functions and the difference function.

The Chapter Problem

Developing a Model for Canada's Population

In this section, you learned about creating new polynomial functions. Apply what you learned to answer these questions about The Chapter Problem on page 2.

CP9. Refer to the two different polynomial models that you created for question CP5 (section 1.2). Write the linear and quadratic functions to model the population of Canada.

CP10. Graph both functions on the same axes.

CP11. Determine the polynomial function that represents the average of the previous models, and graph the new function.

CP12. Use the new function to estimate the population of Canada in 2001, 2006, and 2016. Compare your results with other data on the Internet. How do they compare?

1.4 Dividing Polynomials

SETTING THE STAGE

You can use the zeros of a polynomial function to sketch the graph of the function or to determine the restricted domain. In both cases, you can easily find the zeros if the function is in factored form. So you must be able to factor polynomial functions, which involves dividing one polynomial by another. In this section, you will examine techniques for dividing polynomials.

EXAMINING THE CONCEPT

Long Division with Polynomials

Dividing polynomials is similar to dividing numbers using long division. Evaluate $17 \div 4$.

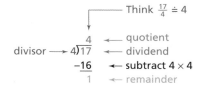

Therefore, $17 \div 4 = 4\frac{1}{4}$.   Check: $4 \times 4 + 1 = 17$

Division Statement

In any division, divisor $\times$ quotient + remainder = dividend.

Keep the division statement in mind when dividing polynomials.

Example 1   **Long Division with Polynomials**

Divide $x^2 + 3x - 28$ by $x + 5$.

Solution

Think $\frac{x^2}{x} = x$.

Think $-\frac{2x}{x} = -2$.

$$
\begin{array}{r}
x - 2 \\
x + 5 \overline{\smash{\big)}\ x^2 + 3x - 28} \\
\underline{x^2 + 5x} \\
-2x - 28 \\
\underline{-2x - 10} \\
-18
\end{array}
$$

Subtract $(x)(x + 5)$ and bring down -28.

Subtract $(-2)(x + 5)$.

Check: $(x + 5)(x - 2) - 18 = x^2 + 3x - 10 - 18$
$$= x^2 + 3x - 28$$

In this example, the divisor does not divide evenly into the dividend, and the remainder is -18. A polynomial divides evenly when the remainder is 0. The process of division ends when the remainder is 0, or if the degree of the remainder is lower than the degree of the divisor.

• • • • • • • •

Example 2 **Long Division and Factors**

Divide $x^3 - 7x - 6$ by $x + 1$.

Solution
Rewrite the question as a long division. Ensure that the powers are in descending order in both the divisor and the dividend. Include any missing powers by using a coefficient of 0. In this example, there is no x^2-term in the dividend, so add $0x^2$ to the dividend.

$$
\require{enclose}
\begin{array}{r}
x^2 - x - 6 \\
x+1 \enclose{longdiv}{x^3 + 0x^2 - 7x - 6} \\
\underline{x^3 + x^2} \quad\quad\quad\quad\quad \\
-x^2 - 7x \quad\quad \\
\underline{-x^2 - x} \quad\quad \\
-6x - 6 \\
\underline{-6x - 6} \\
0
\end{array}
$$

⟵ Subtract $(x^2)(x + 1)$ and bring down $-7x$.

⟵ Subtract $(-x)(x + 1)$ and bring down -6.

⟵ Subtract $(-6)(x + 1)$.

Check: $(x + 1)(x^2 - x - 6) + 0 = x^3 - x^2 - 6x + x^2 - x - 6$
$$= x^3 - 7x - 6$$

The last subtraction results in 0. When the remainder is 0, the divisor divides evenly into the dividend. Both the divisor and quotient are factors of the dividend. In this case, $x + 1$ and $x^2 - x - 6$ are factors of $x^3 - 7x - 6$.

Therefore, $x^3 - 7x - 6 = (x + 1)(x^2 - x - 6)$.

EXAMINING THE CONCEPT

Synthetic Division

Synthetic division is an efficient way to divide a polynomial by a binomial of the form $x - k$, where k is the value that makes the binomial in the divisor equal to 0.

Divide $4x^3 - 5x^2 + 3x - 7$ by $x - 2$. In this case, $k = 2$.

List the coefficients of the dividend, 4, -5, 3, and -7. Bring down the first coefficient of the quotient, which is 4. Multiply by the k-value, which is 2. Add the product to the next coefficient of the dividend: $8 + (-5) = 3$. This result, 3, is the next coefficient of the quotient. Repeat these steps until there are no more coefficients in the dividend.

The process of synthetic division is simpler to use than long division, because it only uses the coefficients of the polynomials involved.

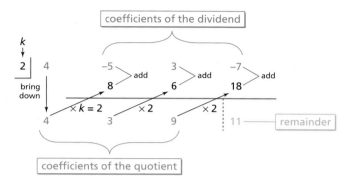

Therefore, $(x - 2)(4x^2 + 3x + 9) + 11 = 4x^3 - 5x^2 + 3x - 7$.

Another way to write this is $\dfrac{4x^3 - 5x^2 + 3x - 7}{x - 2} = 4x^2 + 3x + 9 + \dfrac{11}{x - 2}$.

Example 3   **Synthetic Division and Higher Degree Polynomials**

Use synthetic division to divide $13x - 2x^3 + x^4 - 6$ by $x + 2$.

Solution
Rearrange the terms of the dividend in descending order, $x^4 - 2x^3 + 0x^2 + 13x - 6$. Notice that a third term, with a coefficient of 0, has been added to the dividend.

In this case, $k = -2$.

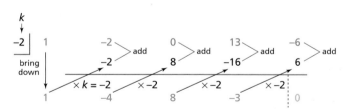

The quotient is $x^3 - 4x^2 + 8x - 3$, and the remainder is 0. Therefore, $(x + 2)(x^3 - 4x^2 + 8x - 3) = x^4 - 2x^3 + 13x - 6$.

• • • • • • • •

You can also use synthetic division when the coefficient of the variable in the divisor is a number other than 1. First determine the number that makes the divisor equal to 0.

Example 4 More on Synthetic Division

Use synthetic division to divide $12x^3 + 2x^2 + 11x + 16$ by $3x + 2$.

Solution

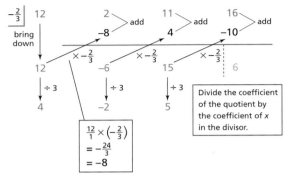

The coefficient of x in $3x + 2$ is 3. To find k, let the divisor equal 0 and solve for x.

$$3x + 2 = 0$$
$$3x = -2$$
$$x = -\frac{2}{3}$$

Therefore, $k = -\frac{2}{3}$.

The quotient is $4x^2 - 2x + 5$ and the remainder is 6.

$$(3x + 2)(4x^2 - 2x + 5) + 6 = 12x^3 + 2x^2 + 11x + 16$$

CHECK, CONSOLIDATE, COMMUNICATE

1. How must the divisor and dividend be arranged for either long division or synthetic division?
2. How can you determine whether the divisor and quotient are factors of the dividend?
3. Write the division statement that shows the relations among the divisor, dividend, quotient, and remainder.

KEY IDEAS

- A polynomial in the form $a_n x^n + a_{n-1} x^{n-1} + \ldots + a_1 x^1 + a_0$ can be divided by another polynomial of degree n or less using long division.
- If the remainder is 0, the divisor and the quotient are factors of the dividend.
- **Synthetic division** is a shortcut for dividing a polynomial in one variable by a binomial. This division yields the same results as long division.

1.4 Exercises

(A) 1. Rearrange in descending order.

(a) $2x^5 + 3x - 5x^3 + x^2 - x^4 + 5$ (b) $3x^2 - 2x^4 + 5x - 3 - 2x^3$

(c) $3x^3 - 5x^4 + 2$ (d) $-3 + 4x^6 + 3x^2 - 2x$

(e) $-4 + 3x^7 - 4x^2$ (f) $x^4 + 1$

2. Divide using long division.

(a) $x^3 - 3x^2 - 3x + 5$ by $x - 1$　　(b) $x^3 - x^2 - 16x - 12$ by $x + 3$

(c) $x^4 - 8x^3 + 2x^2 + 24x + 9$ by $x^2 - 2x - 1$

(d) $x^4 - 10x^2 + 9$ by $x - 1$　　(e) $x^4 - 1$ by $x + 1$

(f) $x^5 - x^3 - x^2 + 1$ by $x^2 - 1$

3. Determine the remainder, r, so that the division statement is true.

(a) $(2x - 3)(3x + 5) + r = 6x^2 + x + 5$

(b) $(x + 3)(x + 5) + r = x^2 + 9x - 7$

(c) $(x + 3)(x^2 - 1) + r = x^3 + 3x^2 - x - 3$

(d) $(x^2 + 1)(2x^3 - 1) + r = 2x^5 + 2x^3 + x^2 + 1$

4. Use synthetic division to simplify. State any remainder as a fraction.

(a) $(x^3 - 7x - 6) \div (x - 3)$

(b) $(2x^3 - 7x^2 - 7x + 19) \div (x - 1)$

(c) $(6x^4 + 13x^3 - 34x^2 - 47x + 28) \div (x + 3)$

(d) $(2x^3 + x^2 - 22x + 20) \div (2x - 3)$

(e) $(12x^4 - 56x^3 + 59x^2 + 9x - 18) \div (2x + 1)$

(f) $(6x^3 - 2x - 15x^2 + 5) \div (2x - 5)$

5. **Knowledge and Understanding**

(a) Divide $x^5 + 1$ by $x + 1$ using long division.

(b) Verify your results using synthetic division.

B 6. **Communication:** Create a cubic polynomial division question where the divisor is $x + 3$. Show how each step in synthetic division relates to a step in long division.

7. Create a quartic polynomial question where the divisor is $2x - 3$. Show how each step in synthetic division relates to a step in long division.

8. Determine whether each binomial is a factor of the given polynomial.

(a) $x + 5, x^3 + 6x^2 - x - 30$

(b) $x + 2, x^4 - 5x^2 + 4$

(c) $x - 2, x^4 - 5x^2 + 6$

(d) $2x - 1, 2x^4 - x^3 - 4x^2 + 2x + 1$

(e) $3x + 5, 3x^6 + 5x^5 + 9x^2 + 17x - 1$

(f) $5x - 1, 5x^4 - x^3 + 10x - 10$

9. Use long division to determine the remainder.

(a) $\dfrac{x^3 + 3x^2 - x + 1}{x^2 - 1}$　　(b) $\dfrac{4x^4 - 37x^2 - 2}{x^2 - 9}$

(c) $\dfrac{5x^5 - 3x^2 - 2x + 1}{x^3 - x}$　　(d) $\dfrac{6x^4 + 31x^3 + 39x^2 - 4x - 2}{x^2 + 5x + 6}$

(e) $\dfrac{x^3 - 3x^2 - x + 3}{x^2 - 2x - 3}$　　(f) $\dfrac{x^3 + 8x^2 + 4x - 8}{x^2 + 2x - 3}$

10. When $8x^3 + 4x^2 - px + 6$, $p \in \mathbf{R}$, is divided by $2x - 1$, the remainder is 3. Determine the value of p.

11. The polynomial $x^3 + px^2 - x - 2$, $p \in \mathbf{R}$, has $x - 1$ as a factor. What is the value of p?

12. **Application:** The volume of a rectangular box is $(x^3 + 6x^2 + 11x + 6)$ cubic centimetres. The box is $(x + 3)$ cm long and $(x + 2)$ cm wide. How high is the box?

13. A tent has the shape of a triangular prism. The volume of the tent is $(x^3 + 7x^2 + 11x + 5)$ cubic units. The triangular face of the tent is $(2x + 2)$ units wide by $(x + 1)$ units high. How long is the tent?

14. **Check Your Understanding:** In a polynomial division question, the divisor is $2x + 3$, the quotient is $2x^2 + 3x - 4$, and the remainder is -11.

   (a) What is the dividend?

   (b) Verify your answer for (a). Use either long division or synthetic division.

C 15. The volume of a cylindrical can is $(4\pi x^3 + 28\pi x^2 + 65\pi x + 50\pi)$ cm³. The can is $(x + 2)$ cm high. What is the radius?

16. **Thinking, Inquiry, Problem Solving:** Let $f(x) = x^n - 1$, where n is an integer and $n \geq 1$. Is $f(x)$ always divisible by $x - 1$? Justify your decision.

ADDITIONAL ACHIEVEMENT CHART QUESTIONS

Knowledge and Understanding: Use long division to determine whether each binomial is a factor of $-3x^2 + 2x + x^3 - 24$. Check your answers using synthetic division.

(a) $x - 3$ (b) $x + 4$ (c) $x - 4$ (d) $x - 2$

Application: The formula for the volume of a sphere is $V = \frac{4}{3}\pi r^3$. A given sphere has a volume of $\left[\frac{4}{3}\pi(x^3 - 3x^2 + 3x - k)\right]$ cubic units and a radius of $(x - 1)$ units. Find the value of k.

Thinking, Inquiry, Problem Solving: The bottom line in this synthetic division gives the coefficients of the quotient. The number at the far right of the bottom line is the remainder.

$$
\begin{array}{r|rrrrr}
k = -2 & 1 & -3 & 12 & 4 & -11 \\
& & -2 & 10 & -44 & 80 \\
\hline
& 1 & -5 & 22 & -40 & \mathbf{69}
\end{array}
$$

To obtain a remainder of 0, would it be better to try lesser values or greater values of k? Defend your choice.

Communication: Create a table to show the advantages and disadvantages of both synthetic division and long division. Which division method do you prefer, and why?

1.5 Factoring Polynomials

SETTING THE STAGE

To explore the concepts in this lesson in more detail, see Exploration 1 on page 559.

To sketch the graph of a polynomial function you need to know how the function behaves for large and small values of x. You have seen that this behaviour is influenced by the degree of the function as well as by the leading coefficient. The zeros of the function also define the shape of the curve. To determine the zeros of a polynomial function, convert the function from standard form to factored form. In this section, you will factor polynomials with a degree of 3 and higher.

EXAMINING THE CONCEPT

Developing the Remainder Theorem

To evaluate the polynomial function $P(x) = 4x^3 - 2x^2 - 6x - 1$ for $x = 2$, substitute 2 for x.

$$P(2) = 4(2)^3 - 2(2)^2 - 6(2) - 1$$
$$= 32 - 8 - 12 - 1$$
$$= 11$$

To find the remainder when $P(x)$ is divided by $x - 2$, you can use synthetic division:

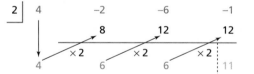

When $P(x)$ is divided by $x - 2$, the remainder is equal to $P(2)$. This result is not coincidental. Use the division statement to verify why this result occurs.

$$\text{dividend} = \text{quotient} \times \text{divisor} + \text{remainder}$$
$$P(x) = (4x^2 + 6x + 6)(x - 2) + 11$$
$$P(2) = [4(2)^2 + 6(2) + 6](2 - 2) + 11$$
$$= (34)(0) + 11$$
$$= 0 + 11$$
$$= 11$$

When the dividend is evaluated at the value that makes the binomial divisor equal to 0, the remainder is the end result.

Case 1: $P(x) \div (x - k)$

$P(k) = r$, if $Q(x)$ is the quotient and r is the remainder when the polynomial $P(x)$ is divided by $x - k$.

$$P(x) = Q(x) \times (x - k) + r$$
$$\begin{aligned} P(k) &= Q(k) \times (k - k) + r \\ &= Q(k) \times 0 + r \\ &= 0 + r \\ &= r \end{aligned}$$

Case 2: $P(x) \div (jx - k)$

$P\left(\dfrac{k}{j}\right) = r$, if $Q(x)$ is the quotient and r is the remainder when the polynomial $P(x)$ is divided by $jx - k$.

$$P(x) = Q(x) \times (jx - k) + r$$
$$\begin{aligned} P\left(\frac{k}{j}\right) &= Q\left(\frac{k}{j}\right) \times \left[j\left(\frac{k}{j}\right) - k\right] + r \\ &= Q\left(\frac{k}{j}\right) \times (k - k) + r \\ &= Q\left(\frac{k}{j}\right) \times 0 + r \\ &= 0 + r \\ &= r \end{aligned}$$

The Remainder Theorem

When a polynomial function $P(x)$ is divided by $x - k$, the remainder, r, is $P(k)$.

When a polynomial function $P(x)$ is divided by $jx - k$, the remainder, r, is $P\left(\dfrac{k}{j}\right)$.

Example 1 **Using the Remainder Theorem**

What is the remainder when $x^3 + 6x^2 - x - 30$ is divided by $x + 5$?

Solution
Use the **remainder theorem**. When $x + 5 = 0$, $x = -5$. The remainder is $P(-5)$.

$$\begin{aligned} P(x) &= x^3 + 6x^2 - x - 30 \\ P(-5) &= (-5)^3 + 6(-5)^2 - (-5) - 30 \\ &= -125 + 150 + 5 - 30 \\ &= 0 \end{aligned}$$

• • • • • • • •

In the previous example, the remainder is 0, which means that $x + 5$ divides evenly into the polynomial $P(x)$. In general, when $P(k) = 0$, then $x - k$ is a factor of $P(x)$. Use this relation to determine the factors of any polynomial.

The Factor Theorem

A polynomial function $P(x)$ has a factor $x - k$ if and only if $P(k) = 0$.
Therefore, if $P(k) = 0$, then $x - k$ is a factor.
If $x - k$ is a factor, then $P(k) = 0$.
Similarly, $jx - k$ is a factor of $P(x)$ if and only if $P\left(\dfrac{k}{j}\right) = 0$.

Example 2   **Using the Factor Theorem**

Which binomials are factors of $P(x) = 2x^3 - x^2 - 7x + 6$?

(a) $x + 3$ **(b)** $2x - 3$

Solution

(a) Evaluate $P(x)$ when $x + 3 = 0$ or $x = -3$.

$$P(-3) = 2(-3)^3 - (-3)^2 - 7(-3) + 6$$
$$= -54 - 9 + 21 + 6$$
$$= -36$$

Because $P(-3) \neq 0$, $x + 3$ is not a factor of $P(x)$.

(b) Evaluate $P(x)$ when $2x - 3 = 0$ or $x = \dfrac{3}{2}$.

$$P\left(\frac{3}{2}\right) = 2\left(\frac{3}{2}\right)^3 - \left(\frac{3}{2}\right)^2 - 7\left(\frac{3}{2}\right) + 6$$
$$= 2\left(\frac{27}{8}\right) - \frac{9}{4} - \frac{21}{2} + 6$$
$$= \frac{27}{4} - \frac{9}{4} - \frac{42}{4} + \frac{24}{4}$$
$$= \frac{0}{4}$$
$$= 0$$

Because $P\left(\dfrac{3}{2}\right) = 0$, $2x - 3$ is a factor of $P(x)$.

Example 3   **Factoring a Polynomial Using the Factor Theorem**

Factor $x^3 + 2x^2 - 11x - 12$.

Solution

Use the factor theorem to find a binomial factor of the form $x - k$. Systematically substitute various values of k into the polynomial until a substitution results in 0. Use values for k that are factors of the constant term, -12. In this case, the factors of -12 are ± 1, ± 2, ± 3, ± 4, ± 6, and ± 12.

When $k = 1$,

$$f(1) = (1)^3 + 2(1)^2 - 11(1) - 12$$
$$= 1 + 2 - 11 - 12$$
$$= -20$$

$\therefore x - 1$ is not a factor.

When $k = -1$,

$$f(-1) = (-1)^3 + 2(-1)^2 - 11(-1) - 12$$
$$= -1 + 2 + 11 - 12$$
$$= 0$$

$\therefore x + 1$ is a factor.

Use synthetic division to divide $x^3 + 2x^2 - 11x - 12$ by $x + 1$ to determine another factor.

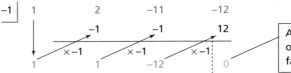

Therefore,

$$x^3 + 2x^2 - 11x - 12 = (x + 1)(x^2 + x - 12) \quad \text{Factor the remaining trinomial.}$$
$$= (x + 1)(x + 4)(x - 3)$$

· · · · · · · ·

In any polynomial that can be factored, the linear factors are of the form $(x - k)$ or $(jx - k)$. As a result, only a rational number of the form $\frac{p}{q}$, where p is a factor of the constant term and q is a factor of the leading coefficient, is a zero of the polynomial.

The Rational Zero Test

In the polynomial $P(x) = a_n x^n + a_{n-1} x^{n-1} + \ldots + a_1 x + a_0$, all coefficients are integers. Every rational zero of $P(x)$ is of the form $\frac{p}{q}$, where p is a factor of the constant term a_0 and q is a factor of the leading coefficient a_n.

Example 4 **Sketching the Graph of a Polynomial Function in Standard Form**

(a) Graph $f(x) = 3x^3 + x^2 - 22x - 24$.

(b) Describe the shape of the graph.

Solution

(a) Begin by determining the zeros of $f(x)$. Express the function in factored form. Numbers that could make $f(x) = 0$ are of the form $\frac{p}{q}$, where p is a factor of -24 and q is a factor of 3.

$p \in \{\pm 1, \pm 2, \pm 3, \pm 4, \pm 6, \pm 8, \pm 12, \pm 24\}$, $q \in \{\pm 1, \pm 3\}$, and

$\frac{p}{q} \in \left\{ \pm 1, \pm 2, \pm 3, \pm 4, \pm 6, \pm 8, \pm 12, \pm 24, \pm \frac{1}{3}, \pm \frac{2}{3}, \pm \frac{4}{3}, \pm \frac{8}{3} \right\}$

Systematically substitute the numbers for $\frac{p}{q}$ into $f(x)$ until one number produces a value of 0.

$f(1) = 3(1)^3 + (1)^2 - 22(1) - 24 \qquad f(-1) = 3(-1)^3 + (-1)^2 - 22(-1) - 24$
$\qquad = -42 \qquad\qquad\qquad\qquad\qquad\qquad = -4$

$\therefore x - 1$ is not a factor. $\qquad\qquad \therefore x + 1$ is not a factor.

$f(2) = 3(2)^3 + (2)^2 - 22(2) - 24 \qquad f(-2) = 3(-2)^3 + (-2)^2 - 22(-2) - 24$
$\qquad = -40 \qquad\qquad\qquad\qquad\qquad\qquad = 0$

$\therefore x - 2$ is not a factor. $\qquad\qquad \therefore x + 2$ is a factor.

Use synthetic division to determine a second factor.

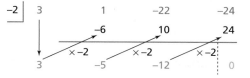

$$f(x) = 3x^3 + x^2 - 22x - 24$$
$$= (x + 2)(3x^2 - 5x - 12) \qquad \text{Factor the trinomial.}$$
$$= (x + 2)(3x + 4)(x - 3)$$

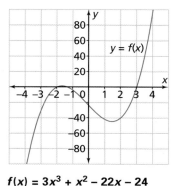

$f(x) = 3x^3 + x^2 - 22x - 24$

Therefore, $f(x)$ has zeros -2, $-\dfrac{4}{3}$, and 3. Find additional points using a table, and determine the end behaviour of the function.

x	-3	-1	0	1	2	4
$f(x)$	-30	-4	-24	-42	-40	96

$f(x)$ has an odd degree and a positive leading coefficient.

As $x \to \infty$, $f(x) \to \infty$.

As $x \to -\infty$, $f(x) \to -\infty$.

(b) From this graph, $f(x)$ increases to a local maximum at about $(-1.7, 1.5)$. $f(x)$ then decreases to a local minimum at about $(1.5, -45)$. $f(x)$ then increases indefinitely.

· · · · · · · ·

Example 5   **Factoring Polynomials by Grouping**

Factor $x^4 - 6x^3 + 2x^2 - 12x$.

Solution

You can usually use the factor theorem to factor a polynomial. But first check that the terms can be grouped and whether any common factors can be removed.

$$x^4 - 6x^3 + 2x^2 - 12x = (x^4 - 6x^3) + (2x^2 - 12x) \qquad \text{Group first two and last two}$$
$$\text{terms. Factor out } x^3 \text{ and } 2x.$$
$$= x^3(x - 6) + 2x(x - 6) \qquad \text{Factor out } (x - 6).$$
$$= (x - 6)(x^3 + 2x) \qquad \text{Factor out } x.$$
$$= x(x - 6)(x^2 + 2)$$

CHECK, CONSOLIDATE, COMMUNICATE

1. Explain how to determine, without actually dividing, the remainder when $3x^4 - 2x^3 + 4x^2 - x + 7$ is divided by $x - 3$.
2. Explain the two different methods for determining whether $x + 6$ is a factor of $6x^3 + 47x^2 + 59x - 42$.
3. Let $f(x) = 2x^3 + 13x^2 + 5x - 6$. List all rational numbers that could be substituted into $f(x)$ when determining whether $f(x) = 0$.

KEY IDEAS

- Remainder Theorem: When polynomial function $P(x)$ is divided by $x - k$, the remainder, r, is $P(k)$. When polynomial function $P(x)$ is divided by $jx - k$, the remainder, r, is $P\left(\dfrac{k}{j}\right)$.
- Factor Theorem: Polynomial function $f(x)$ has a factor $x - k$ if and only if $f(k) = 0$. So, if $f(k) = 0$, $x - k$ is a factor, and if $x - k$ is a factor, $f(k) = 0$. Similarly, polynomial function $f(x)$ has a factor $jx - k$ if and only if $f\left(\dfrac{k}{j}\right) = 0$.
- To factor a polynomial of degree 3 or higher:
  1. Try to factor the polynomial by grouping.
  2. If grouping fails, find one factor by substituting numbers (according to the rational zero test) into the polynomial until one number produces a value of 0.
  3. Use either long or synthetic division to find another factor.
  4. If the resulting factor is greater than degree 2, repeat steps 1 and 2. Otherwise, go to step 4.
  5. If one factor is a quadratic polynomial, factor it, if possible.

1.5 Exercises

(A) 1. Divide to show that $x - 3$ is a factor of each polynomial. Confirm your answers using the factor theorem.
- **(a)** $x^2 + x - 12$
- **(b)** $x^3 - 13x + 12$
- **(c)** $-2x^4 - 7x^3 + 22x^2 + 63x - 36$
- **(d)** $x^4 - 12x^3 + 54x^2 - 108x + 81$
- **(e)** $6x^4 + 13x^3 - 89x^2 - 17x + 15$
- **(f)** $x^5 + 2x^4 - 18x^3 - 36x^2 + 81x + 162$

2. State the remainder when $x + 2$ is divided into each polynomial.
- **(a)** $x^2 + 7x + 9$
- **(b)** $6x^3 + 19x^2 + 11x - 11$
- **(c)** $x^4 - 5x^2 + 4$
- **(d)** $x^4 - 2x^3 - 11x^2 + 10x - 2$
- **(e)** $x^3 + 3x^2 - 10x + 6$
- **(f)** $4x^4 + 12x^3 - 13x^2 - 33x + 18$

3. Determine whether $2x - 5$ is a factor of each polynomial.
- **(a)** $2x^3 - 5x^2 - 2x + 5$
- **(b)** $3x^3 + 2x^2 - 3x - 2$
- **(c)** $2x^4 - 7x^3 - 13x^2 + 63x - 45$
- **(d)** $6x^4 + x^3 - 7x^2 - x + 1$

4. **Knowledge and Understanding:** Which expression is a factor of $8x^3 - 125$: $(3x + 2)$, $(x - 5)$, or $(2x - 5)$? Justify your decision.

5. Factor using the factor theorem.
   (a) $x^3 - 3x^2 - 10x + 24$ (b) $4x^3 + 12x^2 - x - 15$
   (c) $x^4 + 8x^3 + 4x^2 - 48x$ (d) $4x^4 + 7x^3 - 80x^2 - 21x + 270$
   (e) $x^5 - 5x^4 - 7x^3 + 29x^2 + 30x$ (f) $x^4 + 2x^3 - 23x^2 - 24x + 144$

6. Factor fully.
   (a) $x^3 + 9x^2 + 8x - 60$ (b) $x^3 - 7x - 6$
   (c) $x^4 - 5x^2 + 4$ (d) $x^4 + 3x^3 - 38x^2 + 24x + 64$
   (e) $x^3 - x^2 + x - 1$ (f) $x^5 - x^4 + 2x^3 - 2x^2 + x - 1$

B 7. **Communication:** Suppose that $f(x)$ is a cubic polynomial function with integral coefficients. Describe how you could find a zero and use it to find any other zeros that $f(x)$ might have.

8. Determine whether or not the given value is a zero of $f(x)$. If the value is a zero, determine any other zeros the function might have.
   (a) $f(x) = 2x^3 + x^2 - 13x + 6$, $x = 0.5$
   (b) $f(x) = 6x^3 + 17x^2 - 4x - 3$, $x = -2.25$
   (c) $f(x) = x^3 - 2x^2 - 21x - 18$, $x = 6$
   (d) $f(x) = 2x^4 - x^3 - 26x^2 - 11x + 12$, $x = 4$
   (e) $f(x) = x^4 - 3x^3 + 3x^2 - 3x + 2$, $x = 2$
   (f) $f(x) = 3x^4 - 2x^3 + 5x^2 - 2x + 7$, $x = -3$

9. Factor using the factor theorem.
   (a) $6x^3 + 5x^2 - 21x + 10$ (b) $9x^3 - 3x^2 - 41x + 35$
   (c) $6x^4 - 19x^3 - 2x^2 + 44x - 24$ (d) $10x^4 + 13x^3 - 43x^2 - 52x + 12$
   (e) $8x^3 + 12x^2 - 2x - 3$ (f) $30x^3 - x^2 - 6x + 1$

10. (a) Use the factor theorem to factor.
    i. $x^3 - 1$ **ii.** $x^3 - 27$ **iii.** $x^3 - 125$ **iv.** $8x^3 - 27$
    (b) A polynomial in the form $a^3 - b^3$ is called a **difference of cubes**. Use the pattern of factoring in (a) to factor $a^3 - b^3$.
    (c) Use the result of (b) to factor $64x^3 - 27$. Check by multiplying the factors.

11. (a) Use the factor theorem to factor.
    i. $x^3 + 1$ **ii.** $x^3 + 8$ **iii.** $x^3 + 64$ **iv.** $8x^3 + 125$
    (b) A polynomial in the form $a^3 + b^3$ is called a **sum of cubes**. Use the pattern of factoring in (a) to factor $a^3 + b^3$.
    (c) Use the result of (b) to factor $125x^3 + 64$. Check by multiplying the factors.

12. Factor fully.
    (a) $x^3 - 64$ (b) $y^3 + 27$
    (c) $64x^3 + 1$ (d) $125x^6 - 27$
    (e) $8x^9 + 216$ (f) $512 - 27x^{12}$
    (g) $x^6 + 1331$ (h) $343x^{15} - 8$

13. Factor by grouping.
    (a) $2x^3 + 2x^2 + x + 1$ (b) $3x^3 + 6x^2 - x - 2$
    (c) $8x^3 + 12x^2 + 2x + 3$ (d) $10x^3 + 5x^2 - 4x - 2$
    (e) $6x^5 - 2x^4 - 9x^2 + 3x$ (f) $6x^6 + 9x^5 - 4x - 6$

14. Graph $f(x) = 2x^3 - 3x^2 - 3x + 2$ using x-intercepts, the end behaviour of $f(x)$, and selected points on the graph.

15. Verify your answer to question 14 using graphing technology.

16. Graph $f(x) = -6x^4 - 23x^3 - 23x^2 + 2x + 8$ using x-intercepts, the end behaviour of $f(x)$, and selected points on the graph.

17. Verify your answer to question 16 using graphing technology.

18. The polynomial $12x^3 + kx^2 - x - 6$ has factors $2x - 1$ and $2x + 3$. Determine the value of k.

19. **Application:** When $ax^3 - x^2 + 2x + b$ is divided by $x - 1$, the remainder is 10. When it is divided by $x - 2$, the remainder is 51. Find a and b.

20. The volume of a box is $V(x) = x^3 - 15x^2 + 66x - 80$.
    (a) Determine expressions for the dimensions of the box in terms of x.
    (b) Graph the volume function and indicate any restrictions on x.
    (c) Explain why $x = 7$ is inadmissible in the context of the question.

21. **Thinking, Inquiry, Problem Solving:** Determine a general rule to help decide whether $(x - a)$ and $(x + a)$ are factors of $x^n - a^n$ and $x^n + a^n$.

22. **Check Your Understanding:** Determine the factors of $f(x) = 2x^4 - x^3 - 14x^2 - 5x + 6$.

23. Verify your answer to question 22 using graphing technology.

24. The graph of $f(x) = ax^4 + bx^2 + cx - 24$ crosses the x-axis at 1, -2, and 3.
    (a) Determine all zeros of $f(x)$.
    (b) Graph $f(x)$ and comment on its end behaviour.
    (c) State the coordinates of all turning points and indicate whether each turning point is a local maximum or local minimum for $f(x)$.

ADDITIONAL ACHIEVEMENT CHART QUESTIONS

Knowledge and Understanding: For $f(x) = x^3 + 16 - 4x - 4x^2$, find the zeros and end behaviour of f. Use this and any other information to graph f by hand.

Application: The volume of a rectangular-based prism is
$V(x) = -8x + x^3 - 5x^2 + 12$.

(a) Express the height, width, and depth of the prism in terms of x.

(b) Indicate any restrictions for x. Justify your restrictions.

Thinking, Inquiry, Problem Solving: Show in more than one way that
$f(x) = x^6 + x^4 + x^2 + 4$ has no factors in the form $x - k$, where k is any real number.

Communication: Let $f(x) = x^3 + 8x^2 - 11x - 15$ and
$g(x) = 4x^3 + 8x^2 - 11x - 15$. Send an e-mail to a classmate listing possible binomial factors for $f(x)$, and explain how you determined them. Explain why the possible binomial factors for $g(x)$ would be different. List four possible binomial factors for $g(x)$ that are not in the list of $f(x)$.

The Chapter Problem
Developing a Model for Canada's Population

In this section, you learned that $P(k) = 0$ if $x = k$ is a zero of a polynomial function, $P(x)$, and $x - k$ is a factor of $P(x)$. Apply what you learned to answer these questions about The Chapter Problem on page 2.

CP13. Using graphing technology, create a scatter plot. Enter the years since 1851 in **L1** and the population in **L2**. Using regression, determine a degree-3 polynomial model and a degree-4 polynomial model. Which model fits the data better?

CP14. What are the end behaviours of each model? Which function's end behaviour, as $x \to \infty$, better reflects the trend in the actual data?

CP15. Verify that $x - 40$ and $x - 110$ are not factors of the quartic regression equation.

1.6 Solving Polynomial Equations

SETTING THE STAGE

Explore the concepts in this lesson in more detail using Exploration 2 on page 561.

Recall the model for the volume of a cardboard box. The box is created by cutting a square from each corner of a piece of cardboard and folding up the sides.

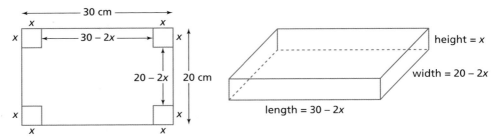

Let x represent the side length of each square cut from the cardboard and V represent the volume of the box. Then $V(x) = 4x^3 - 100x^2 + 600x$, $0 \leq x \leq 10$.

What are the dimensions of the square that must be cut from each corner so the resulting box has a volume of 1008 cm³?

You will need to find a value for x so that $V(x) = 1008$. Substituting $V(x) = 1008$ in the model yields $1008 = 4x^3 - 100x^2 + 600x$. This equation is an example of a **polynomial equation**.

In this section, you will solve polynomial equations.

EXAMINING THE CONCEPT

Solving a Polynomial Equation by Factoring

Factoring is one way to solve polynomial equations. Rearrange the terms so that one side of the equation equals 0. Start by subtracting 1008 from both sides.

$$1008 - 1008 = 4x^3 - 100x^2 + 600x - 1008$$
$$0 = 4x^3 - 100x^2 + 600x - 1008 \qquad \text{Factor the right side.}$$
$$0 = 4(x^3 - 25x^2 + 150x - 252) \qquad \text{Divide both sides by 4.}$$
$$0 = x^3 - 25x^2 + 150x - 252$$

Solving this equation is like finding the zeros of $f(x) = x^3 - 25x^2 + 150x - 252$. Possible numbers that could make the polynomial equal to 0 are factors of -252.

Use the factor theorem and systematically substitute the factors of -252 until you find the first factor.

$$f(1) = (1)^3 - 25(1)^2 + 150(1) - 252 = -126$$
$$f(-1) = (-1)^3 - 25(-1)^2 + 150(-1) - 252 = -428$$
$$f(2) = (2)^3 - 25(2)^2 + 150(2) - 252 = -44$$
$$f(-2) = (-2)^3 - 25(-2)^2 + 150(-2) - 252 = -660$$
$$f(3) = (3)^3 - 25(3)^2 + 150(3) - 252 = 0$$

Then $x = 3$ is a zero and $(x - 3)$ is a factor.

Use synthetic division to determine a second factor.

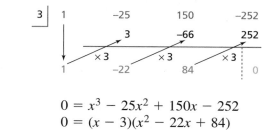

$$0 = x^3 - 25x^2 + 150x - 252$$
$$0 = (x - 3)(x^2 - 22x + 84)$$

Set each factor equal to 0 and solve each equation separately.

$$x - 3 = 0 \quad \text{or} \quad x^2 - 22x + 84 = 0$$
$$x = 3$$

$x^2 - 22x + 84$ is not factorable. Use the quadratic formula.

$$x = \frac{-b \pm \sqrt{b^2 - 4ac}}{2a}$$
$$= \frac{22 \pm \sqrt{(-22)^2 - 4(1)(84)}}{2(1)}$$
$$= \frac{22 \pm \sqrt{148}}{2}$$
$$\doteq \frac{22 \pm 12.1655}{2}$$
$$x \doteq 17.08 \text{ and } x \doteq 4.92$$

This equation has three solutions, $x = 3$, $x \doteq 17.08$, and $x \doteq 4.92$. Two solutions are valid for the restricted domain $0 \le x \le 10$, but the solution $x \doteq 17.08$ is not. This solution is called **inadmissible**.

Cutting four 3-cm by 3-cm squares, or four 4.92-cm by 4.92-cm squares, from a piece of cardboard will result in a box with a volume of 1008 cm³.

In this example, a degree-3 polynomial equation was solved, and it had three solutions or roots. Since finding the roots of a polynomial equation is like finding the zeros of the corresponding function, you can conclude the following:

Roots of a Polynomial Equation

A polynomial equation of degree n can have
   0 to n real solutions or roots when n is even
   1 to n real solutions or roots when n is odd

Example 1　Determining the Roots of a Polynomial Equation

Find the roots of $6x + 4 = 2x^4 - 3x^3 + 2x^2$.

Solution

Rearrange the equation so that 0 is on one side.

$$0 = 2x^4 - 3x^3 + 2x^2 - 6x - 4$$

Determine a factor of $2x^4 - 3x^3 + 2x^2 - 6x - 4$.

The factors of the leading coefficient, 2, are ± 1 and ± 2. The factors of the constant term, -4, are ± 1, ± 2, and ± 4. Therefore, the possible rational zeros of the polynomial are ± 1, ± 2, ± 4, and $\pm \frac{1}{2}$. Find one factor.

$$2(1)^4 - 3(1)^3 + 2(1)^2 - 6(1) - 4 = -9 \qquad \text{no}$$
$$2(-1)^4 - 3(-1)^3 + 2(-1)^2 - 6(-1) - 4 = 9 \qquad \text{no}$$
$$2(2)^4 - 3(2)^3 + 2(2)^2 - 6(2) - 4 = 0 \qquad \checkmark$$

Therefore, $x = 2$ is a root and $x - 2$ is a factor. Use synthetic division to find a second factor.

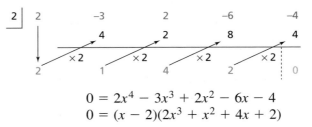

$$0 = 2x^4 - 3x^3 + 2x^2 - 6x - 4$$
$$0 = (x - 2)(2x^3 + x^2 + 4x + 2)$$

The second factor, $2x^3 + x^2 + 4x + 2$, has a leading coefficient of 2 and factors of ± 1 and ± 2. The constant term, 2, has factors of ± 1 and ± 2. Possible rational zeros of this polynomial are ± 1, ± 2, and $\pm \frac{1}{2}$. Substitute each factor into $2x^3 + x^2 + 4x + 2$ until the result is 0.

$$2(1)^3 + (1)^2 + 4(1) + 2 = 9 \qquad \text{no}$$
$$2(-1)^3 + (-1)^2 + 4(-1) + 2 = -3 \qquad \text{no}$$
$$2(2)^3 + (2)^2 + 4(2) + 2 = 30 \qquad \text{no}$$
$$2(-2)^3 + (-2)^2 + 4(-2) + 2 = -18 \qquad \text{no}$$
$$2\left(\frac{1}{2}\right)^3 + \left(\frac{1}{2}\right)^2 + 4\left(\frac{1}{2}\right) + 2 = 4\frac{1}{2} \qquad \text{no}$$
$$2\left(-\frac{1}{2}\right)^3 + \left(-\frac{1}{2}\right)^2 + 4\left(-\frac{1}{2}\right) + 2 = 0 \qquad \checkmark$$

Therefore, $x = -\frac{1}{2}$ is a root and $2x + 1$ is a factor. Use synthetic division to continue factoring.

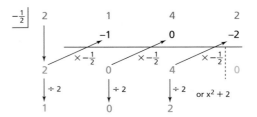

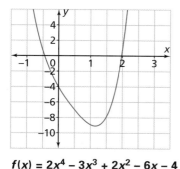

$f(x) = 2x^4 - 3x^3 + 2x^2 - 6x - 4$

$$0 = 2x^4 - 3x^3 + 2x^2 - 6x - 4$$
$$0 = (x - 2)(2x^3 + x^2 + 4x + 2)$$
$$0 = (x - 2)(2x + 1)(x^2 + 2)$$

Solve the equation by setting each factor equal to 0.

$$x - 2 = 0 \quad \text{or} \quad 2x + 1 = 0 \quad \text{or} \quad x^2 + 2 = 0$$
$$x = 2 \qquad\qquad 2x = -1 \qquad\qquad x^2 = -2$$
$$x = -\frac{1}{2} \qquad\qquad x = \pm\sqrt{-2}$$
$$x = \pm\sqrt{2}\sqrt{-1}$$
$$x = \pm\sqrt{2}\,i$$

The equation has four roots. Two of the roots are the real numbers 2 and $-\frac{1}{2}$. The other two roots are the imaginary numbers $\sqrt{2}\,i$ and $-\sqrt{2}\,i$, which are complex conjugates. Only the real roots correspond to the zeros of the corresponding function, as the graph shows. Recall that a complex number is a real number, an imaginary number, or a combination of real and imaginary numbers. A polynomial equation of degree n has n complex roots. Some of these complex roots may also be real roots.

EXAMINING THE CONCEPT

Solving Polynomial Equations That Cannot Be Factored

Many polynomial equations cannot be factored. In these cases, use graphing technology to approximate the solutions to the equation.

Example 2   **Using Graphing Technology to Solve a Polynomial Equation**

The table shows the population of Thunder Bay, Ontario. The function $p(x) = 0.28x^4 - 21.21x^3 + 578.35x^2 - 6382.66x + 143\,673$ represents the population of Thunder Bay from 1966 to 1998, where x is the number of years since 1966.

Year	Population
1966	143 673
1976	119 253
1986	122 217
1996	125 562
1998	128 607

Source: Statistics Canada

(a) What is the restricted domain for this model?

(b) Determine when the population was 122 775.

Solution

(a) The model is valid only for the years from 1966 to 1998. Since x is defined as the number of years since 1966, the restricted domain is $0 \le x \le 32$.

(b) To determine when the population was 122 775, find a number for x such that $p(x) = 122\,775$.

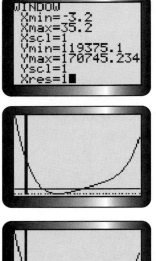

First graph the quartic function $p(x) = 0.28x^4 - 21.21x^3 + 578.35x^2 - 6382.66x + 143\,673$ and the horizontal line $p(x) = 122\,775$. Then determine the points of intersection. Enter the quartic model into **Y1** and the horizontal line into **Y2** of the equation editor of the graphing calculator. To graph, use **ZoomFit** (press $\boxed{\text{ZOOM}}$ $\boxed{0}$).

There are two points of intersection and thus two solutions to the equation. To find the left point of intersection, press $\boxed{\text{2nd}}$ $\boxed{\text{TRACE}}$ and choose **5:intersect.** Position the cursor on the graph of the quartic model near the point of intersection. Then press $\boxed{\text{ENTER}}$ three times to display the coordinates. Repeat this process for the right point of intersection.

The two solutions are $x \doteq 5.5$ and $x \doteq 21.3$. These values represent the years since 1966. Convert the decimal numbers into months. So, according to the model, the population of Thunder Bay was about $122\,775$ in 1971, during the sixth month, and in 1987, during the third month.

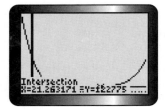

Another way to solve $122\,775 = 0.28x^4 - 21.21x^3 + 578.35x^2 - 6382.66x + 143\,673$ is to rearrange the equation so one side is 0.

Solving $0 = 0.28x^4 - 21.21x^3 + 578.35x^2 - 6382.66x + 20\,898$ can be done with the calculator's **zero** operation. Refer to page 592 of the Technology Appendix for instructions.

• • • • • • • •

Example 3   Determining the Equation of a Polynomial Function from Its Roots

The complex zeros of a polynomial function are 2, -3, and $3 - 2i$. The graph of the function passes through point $(1, -64)$. Determine the equation of the function and graph the function.

Solution

Non-real zeros of polynomial functions always appear as complex conjugates. The complex conjugate of $3 + 2i$ is $3 - 2i$. Write the function as a product of its factors.

$$f(x) = k \times (x - 2) \times [x - (-3)] \times [x - (3 - 2i)] \times [x - (3 + 2i)]$$
$$f(x) = k(x - 2)(x + 3)(x - 3 + 2i)(x - 3 - 2i) \qquad \text{Multiply.}$$
$$f(x) = k(x^2 + x - 6)(x^2 - 3x - 2ix - 3x + 9 + 6i + 2ix - 6i - 4i^2)$$
$$f(x) = k(x^2 + x - 6)(x^2 - 6x + 9 - 4i^2)$$
$$f(x) = k(x^2 + x - 6)[x^2 - 6x + 9 - 4(-1)] \qquad \text{Simplify.}$$
$$f(x) = k(x^2 + x - 6)(x^2 - 6x + 13) \qquad \text{Expand and simplify.}$$
$$f(x) = k(x^4 - 5x^3 + x^2 + 49x - 78) \qquad \text{Substitute } (1, -64)$$
$$-64 = k(1^4 - 5(1^3) + 1^2 + 49(1) - 78) \qquad \text{Solve for } k.$$
$$-64 = k(-32)$$
$$2 = k$$

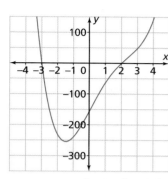

$$f(x) = 2x^4 - 10x^3 + 2x^2 + 98x - 156$$

The equation of the function is $f(x) = 2(x^4 - 5x^3 + x^2 + 49x - 78)$ or $f(x) = 2x^4 - 10x^3 + 2x^2 + 98x - 156$.

• • • • • • • •

Example 4 Solving a Problem Using the Roots of a Polynomial Equation

The equation $3x^3 + 25x^2 - 48x + 20 = 0$ has roots 1, h, and k. Determine a quadratic equation whose roots are $h + k$ and hk.

Solution

One root of the equation is 1. Therefore, $x - 1$ is a factor. Determine another factor by synthetic division.

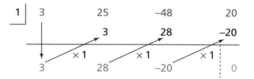

Then
$$3x^2 + 28x - 20 = 0$$
$$(3x - 2)(x + 10) = 0$$
$$3x - 2 = 0 \text{ or } x + 10 = 0$$
$$x = \frac{2}{3} \quad \text{and} \quad x = -10 \text{ are the other roots.}$$

Therefore, $h = \frac{2}{3}$ and $k = -10$. A quadratic equation with roots $h + k$ and hk is

$$\left\{ x - \left[\frac{2}{3} + (-10) \right] \right\} \times \left[x - \left(\frac{2}{3} \right)(-10) \right] = 0$$
$$\left(x + \frac{28}{3} \right)\left(x + \frac{20}{3} \right) = 0$$
$$(3x + 28)(3x + 20) = 0$$
$$9x^2 + 144x + 560 = 0$$

1. Explain how to determine, graphically, the real roots of any polynomial equation.
2. Why will a graphical solution not give all roots to a polynomial equation?
3. Explain how to algebraically solve factorable cubic and quartic equations to determine all roots.

KEY IDEAS

- Some polynomial equations can be solved algebraically by determining all the factors. Setting each factor equal to 0 and solving gives the roots of the equation.
- Polynomial equations have complex roots. Some of the complex roots are real numbers; these correspond to the zeros of the polynomial. Other complex roots are imaginary numbers or combinations of real and imaginary numbers.
- Non-real roots are always complex conjugates.
- The real roots of a polynomial equation correspond to the real zeros of the corresponding polynomial function. As a result, a polynomial equation of degree n can have
  - 0 to n real solutions or roots when n is even
  - 1 to n real solutions or roots when n is odd
- Use graphing technology to approximate the real roots of non-factorable polynomial equations.

1.6 Exercises

A　**1.** Solve.

(a) $(x + 2)(x^2 - 5x + 6) = 0$

(b) $(x + 3)(x - 2)(2x - 5) = 0$

(c) $x^3 + 4x^2 - 2x - 18 = x^3 + 3x^2 - x + 2$

(d) $2x^4 = 48x^2$

(e) $6x^3 - 9x = 0$

(f) $(9x^2 + 1)(3x - 1)(3x + 1) = 0$

2. Determine the roots algebraically by factoring.

(a) $x^3 - 8x^2 - 3x + 90 = 0$　　(b) $x^4 + 9x^3 + 21x^2 - x - 30 = 0$

(c) $2x^3 - 5x^2 - 4x + 3 = 0$　　(d) $2x^3 + 3x^2 = 5x + 6$

(e) $4x^4 - 4x^3 - 51x^2 + 106x = 40$　(f) $12x^3 - 44x^2 = -49x + 15$

3. Use graphing technology to find the real roots to two decimal places.

(a) $x^3 - 7x + 6 = 0$

(b) $x^4 - 5x^3 - 17x^2 + 3x + 18 = 0$

(c) $3x^3 - 2x^2 + 16 = x^4 + 16x$

(d) $x^5 + x^4 = 5x^3 - x^2 + 6x$

(e) $105x^3 = 344x^2 - 69x - 378$

(f) $21x^3 - 58x^2 + 10 = -18x^4 - 51x$

4. **Knowledge and Understanding:** Find the real roots of $9x^4 = 106x^2 - 225$ algebraically.

5. Verify your answer to question 4 using graphing technology.

6. One non-real root of a polynomial is given. State the other non-real root.

(a) $-4i$

(b) $6i$

(c) $2 - 3i$

(d) $5 + 7i$

(e) $-3 + 2i$

(f) $-5 - 4i$

7. A box has dimensions that are linear factors of $(x^3 - 7x^2 + 14x - 8)$ cubic centimetres. What dimensions give a volume of 12 cm³?

B 8. Determine all roots, where $x \in \mathbf{C}$.

(a) $x^3 - x^2 + 16x - 16 = 0$

(b) $x^3 - 3x^2 + x + 5 = 0$

(c) $x^4 - x^3 - 3x^2 - 9x = 108$

(d) $4x^3 - 4x^2 = 1 - x$

(e) $x^4 - 2x^3 + x^2 + 2x - 2 = 0$

(f) $x^4 + 4x^3 + 14x^2 = -4x - 13$

9. Determine the real roots.

(a) $y = (x - 3)(x + 5)(x - 2)$

(b) $y = (x - 7)^2(3x + 5)(2x - 1)$

(c) $y = x^3 - 8x^2 + 15x$

(d) $y = -x^3 + 2x^2 + 5x - 6$

(e) $y = x^4 - 4x^2 - 9x + 36$

(f) $y = 2x^3 + 3x^2 - 2x$

10. Solve $1.00x^4 + 2.32x^3 + 3.19x^2 - 3.30x - 12.25 = 0$ for all real values of x, to two decimal places.

11. **Communication:** Between 1985 through 1995, the number of home computers, in millions, sold in the United States is estimated by $C(t) = 0.0092(t^3 + 8t^2 + 40t + 400)$, where t is in years and $t = 0$ for 1985.

(a) Explain why you can use this model to predict the number of home computers sold in 1993, but not to predict sales in 2005.

(b) Explain how to find when the number of home computer sales in the United States reached 15 million, using this model.

(c) In what year did home computer sales reach 15 million?

12. Two roots of a degree-4 polynomial equation are $1 - i$ and $3 + 2i$. Determine the general equation of the family of quartic functions with these roots.

13. All of the roots of a polynomial equation are 1, -2, -4, and 6.

(a) Determine the general equation of the family of functions with these roots and identify its degree.

(b) The graph of a polynomial function with the corresponding zeros passes through $(-1, -84)$. What is the function?

14. Determine the equation of a cubic function with zeros 2, 4, and -5. The graph of the function has a y-intercept of 20.

15. The graph of a cubic function with zeros 2, $1 - 2i$, and $1 + 2i$ passes through $(5, -180)$. Determine the function, comment on its end behaviour, state the y-intercept, and sketch the graph.

 16. Verify the sketch you drew for question 15 using a graphing calculator.

17. **Application:** Esther uses a 30-cm by 50-cm piece of cardboard to construct a box with a lid, as shown.

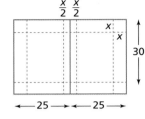

(a) Fold a sheet of paper to make a physical model of the box.

(b) Write an algebraic model for the volume of the box in terms of x.

(c) What value of x produces a box with maximum volume?

(d) What value of x produces a box with a volume of 1052 cm³?

18. The equation $x^3 - 3x^2 - 10x + 24 = 0$ has roots 2, h, and k. Determine a quadratic equation whose roots are $h - k$ and hk.

19. The viscosity, $V(t)$, of a grade of motor oil is given by $V(t) = -t^3 - 3t^2 + 25t + 75$, where t is the temperature in hundreds of degrees Celsius. Determine

(a) the viscosity of the oil at 100°C

(b) the temperature when the viscosity is 75

(c) the temperature when the viscosity is 105

20. **Thinking, Inquiry, Problem Solving:** Many Canadian households consist of one person living alone. The table shows the percent who own and the percent who rent their residences.

Year	1951	1961	1971	1981	1991
Owners (%)	7	8	8	10	14
Renters (%)	9	13	21	36	39

Source: Statistics Canada

(a) Prepare a scatter plot of homeowners living alone, and determine cubic and quartic models that represent the data.

(b) According to the cubic model, when would you expect to see about 36% of homeowners living alone? According to the quartic model, when would you expect to see about 36% of homeowners living alone? Explain your observations. Which model is a better predictor of the future? Why?

(c) Prepare a scatter plot for the number of renters who live alone, and determine both cubic and quartic models for the data.

(d) Determine the percent of renters living alone in 2011, according to both models. Explain your observations.

21. A relationship between x and $f(x)$ is shown.

x	3	4	5	6	7	8
$f(x)$	0	15	48	105	192	315

(a) Determine, algebraically, a polynomial function that represents this relation.

(b) Use the function to solve for x when $f(x) = 1287$.

(c) Confirm your answer graphically.

22. Check Your Understanding: During a normal 5-s respiratory cycle in which a person inhales and then exhales, the volume of air in a person's lungs can be modelled by $V(t) = 0.027t^3 - 0.27t^2 + 0.675t$, where the volume, V, is measured in litres at t seconds.

(a) What restriction(s) must be placed on t?

(b) "How many seconds have passed if the volume of air in a person's lungs is 0.25 L?" Would you answer this question algebraically or by using graphing technology? Justify your decision.

(c) Solve the problem in (b).

C **23.** The table shows the number of people living in collective dwellings, such as houses or motels, or institutions like hospitals, nursing homes, or jails, in Canada from 1961 to 1996.

Year	1961	1966	1971	1976	1981	1986	1991	1996
Population	483 718	463 266	392 695	384 530	405 735	434 370	446 885	449 001

Source: Statistics Canada

The function $P(x) = -636x^4 + 7601x^3 - 18\ 935x^2 - 27\ 774x + 487\ 975$, $0 \le x \le 7$, estimates the population, P, during this time period. The year 1961 corresponds to $x = 0$, 1966 corresponds to $x = 1$, and so on.

(a) Graph $P(x)$. Use the graph to determine when the population was 400 000.

(b) In what years would $P(x) = 0$, if there were no restrictions on x? What does your answer mean? Comment on how likely it would be that $P(x)$ equals 0.

(c) Determine a cubic function that approximates the data.

(d) Graph the cubic function.

(e) Solve the cubic function for a population of 400 000. Compare your results to your answer in (a).

(f) Suppose you could make government policy about collective dwellings. Which model would you use if you had to make a decision that would affect the policy for the next 20 years? Explain.

ADDITIONAL ACHIEVEMENT CHART QUESTIONS

Knowledge and Understanding: Find the real roots of each equation algebraically.

(a) $x^3 - 5x^2 + 8x - 4 = 0$ **(b)** $y^3 + 3y^2 - 3y - 1 = 0$

(c) $3r^3 - r^2 - 2r = 16$

Application: The equation for motion is $s(t) = \frac{1}{2}gt^2 + v_0 t + s_0$, where s is the distance travelled in metres, g is the acceleration due to gravity, t is the time in seconds, v_0 is the initial velocity in metres per second, and s_0 is the initial height in metres. The acceleration due to gravity on Mars is 3.92 m/s^2. Find, to two decimal places, how long it takes an object to hit the surface of Mars if the object is dropped from 1000 m above the surface.

Thinking, Inquiry, Problem Solving: Use any method to solve each equation. Record the number of positive roots for each equation. Give any decimal answers to the nearest hundredth.

(a) $x^3 + 2x^2 - x - 2 = 0$ **(b)** $x^4 - 11x^2 - 12x + 4 = 0$

(c) $2x^4 - x^3 + 6x^2 - 4x - 8 = 0$ **(d)** $x^4 - 2x^3 - 13x^2 + 14x + 24 = 0$

(e) $x^4 - x^3 + 2x^2 - 4x - 8 = 0$

Look at each term in (c). The sign of the coefficient changes to an opposite sign three times as you move from one term to the next: $+2$ to -1, -1 to $+6$, and $+6$ to -4. Find the number of changes in the sign for each equation. Describe the relation between the number of positive roots and the number of changes in sign in a polynomial equation. Test your relation for $2x^4 - 3x^3 + 2x^2 - 6x - 4 = 0$. What do you notice? Do you need to change your relation to fit all polynomial equations? How can you use the relation to solve polynomial equations?

Communication: Anusha is solving a fish population problem by solving a quartic polynomial equation. The answer in the back of the book only shows the number 25 672. Explain to your partner why the other solutions are not there.

The Chapter Problem

Developing a Model for Canada's Population

In this section, you learned to solve polynomial equations. Apply what you learned to answer these questions about The Chapter Problem on page 2.

CP16. When does each equation predict that the population of Canada will be 35 million? Which model is the most likely predictor of the future population of Canada? Explain.

CP17. Which polynomial models have more than one time when the population is 35 million? Does this seem reasonable based on the trend displayed by the data? Explain.

1.7 Solving Polynomial Inequalities

SETTING THE STAGE

The North America automobile industry is affected by the sales of imported vehicles. In 1985, about 30% of passenger cars sold were imports. By 1998, the total was about 20%.

The function $f(x) = 0.018x^4 - 0.435x^3 + 2.915x^2 - 5.049x + 31.820$ is a model of the percentage of imports sold in North America between 1985 and 1998, where x represents the number of years since 1985. During this period, when did the percentage of imports sold in North America exceed 30%?

If the question asked when import sales were exactly 30%, you could use the model and solve $0.018x^4 - 0.435x^3 + 2.915x^2 - 5.049x + 31.820 = 30$, using techniques in the previous section. However, you need to determine when import sales were greater than 30%, so solve $0.018x^4 - 0.435x^3 + 2.915x^2 - 5.049x + 31.820 > 30$.

In this section, you will solve expressions like this one, which is a **polynomial inequality**.

EXAMINING THE CONCEPT

Solving a Polynomial Inequality with Graphing Technology

The solutions to a polynomial inequality form intervals that are sets of numbers that are subsets of the domain of the corresponding function.

Subtract 30 from both sides of the inequality.

$$0.018x^4 - 0.435x^3 + 2.915x^2 - 5.049x + 31.820 - 30 > 30 - 30$$
$$0.018x^4 - 0.435x^3 + 2.915x^2 - 5.049x + 1.820 > 0$$

Determine the solutions to the inequality by graphing the corresponding function $f(x) = 0.018x^4 - 0.435x^3 + 2.915x^2 - 5.049x + 1.820$, where $0 \leq x \leq 13$. Next determine for which x-values in the restricted domain the values of the function are positive. In the graph of the function, look at where the graph lies above the x-axis.

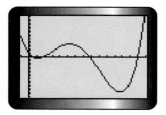

Use graphing technology to graph the function and identify the x-intercepts. Enter $f(x)$ into **Y1** of the equation editor and press $\boxed{\text{ZOOM}}$ $\boxed{0}$. The graph is displayed.

The values of the function are positive where the graph lies above the x-axis. Locate the x-intercepts of the graph. Use the zero operation.

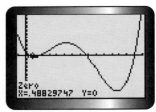

Press $\boxed{\text{2nd}}$ $\boxed{\text{TRACE}}$ and choose **2:zero**. Position the cursor to the left of a zero and press $\boxed{\text{ENTER}}$. Move the cursor to the right of the zero and press $\boxed{\text{ENTER}}$ again. Press $\boxed{\text{ENTER}}$ again to display the zero. Repeat this process for all remaining zeros, except the zero that is to the far right, because it lies outside the restricted domain.

Notice that, on either side of a zero, the function changed its position above or below the *x*-axis.

Zeros and the Sign of a Polynomial Function

There is a possible change in the sign of a polynomial only on either side of a zero. Use the zeros and the domain to determine intervals where a polynomial function is positive and where it is negative.

Using the restricted domain, $0 \leq x \leq 13$, and the zeros, define the intervals where the graph lies above the *x*-axis. The function is positive where $0 \leq x < 0.488$ and $1.899 < x < 7.796$. Round these values and convert them to years, because the variable *x* represents the number of years since 1985. Therefore, import sales exceeded 30% from the start of 1985 to midway through that year and from just before the start of 1987 through to the fourth quarter of 1992.

Solving a Polynomial Inequality Using Graphing Technology

1. Rearrange the inequality so that 0 is on one side.
2. Graph the corresponding polynomial function using graphing technology. Use **ZoomFit** or adjust the window settings accordingly. Ensure that you can see all the zeros and the restricted domain, if necessary, in the window.
3. Locate the zeros of the function in the graph.
4. State the solutions to the inequality. The values of the function that are *greater* than 0 correspond to where the graph lies above the *x*-axis. The values of the function that are *less* than 0 correspond to where the graph lies below the *x*-axis.

EXAMINING THE CONCEPT

Solving a Polynomial Inequality Algebraically

Sometimes you can find the location of the zeros algebraically. In these cases, the polynomial inequality is often factorable.

Example 1   **Solving a Polynomial Inequality Algebraically**

Solve the polynomial inequality $x^2 - 25 > 0$.

Solution

Factor the inequality and solve for x.

$$x^2 - 25 > 0$$
$$(x - 5)(x + 5) > 0$$
$$x - 5 = 0 \text{ or } x + 5 = 0$$
$$x = 5 \text{ or } x = -5$$

These solutions divide the domain into three intervals: x-values to the left of -5, x-values between -5 and 5, and x-values to the right of 5. Express these intervals as $x < -5$, $-5 < x < 5$, and $x > 5$, respectively.

$$x < -5 \qquad -5 < x < 5 \qquad x > 5$$
$$-8 \; -7 \; -6 \; -5 \; -4 \; -3 \; -2 \; -1 \;\; 0 \;\; 1 \;\; 2 \;\; 3 \;\; 4 \;\; 5 \;\; 6 \;\; 7 \;\; 8$$

What is the sign of $(x - 5)(x + 5)$ in each interval? Choose an x-value in each interval. Calculate the sign of each factor using this value. Then multiply the signs to get the sign of $(x - 5)(x + 5)$. Now consider the sign of the value of each factor for a specific x-value in each interval.

	Intervals		
	$x < -5$	$-5 < x < 5$	$x > 5$
Sign of $(x - 5)$	$-$	$-$	$+$
Sign of $(x + 5)$	$-$	$+$	$+$
Sign of $(x - 5)(x + 5)$	$(-)(-) = +$	$(-)(+) = -$	$(+)(+) = +$

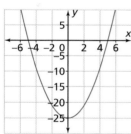

$f(x) = x^2 - 25$

The table shows that $x^2 - 25 > 0$ (positive) on two intervals, $x < -5$ and $x > 5$. The table also shows that $x^2 - 25 < 0$ (negative) on the interval $-5 < x < 5$.

Graph the corresponding function $f(x) = x^2 - 25$ to confirm the analysis. f lies below the x-axis and is negative between $x = -5$ and $x = 5$. f also lies above the x-axis and is positive to the left of -5 and to the right of 5.

• • • • • • • •

In Example 1, there are three intervals, $x < -5$, $-5 < x < 5$, and $x > 5$. Each interval can also be defined in terms of the distance from the origin without regard to direction.

The Definition of Absolute Value

Let a be a real number. The **absolute value** of a, written as $|a|$, is the horizontal distance from a to the origin without regard to direction.

$$|a| = a \text{ if } a \geq 0 \text{ and } |a| = -a \text{ if } a < 0$$

Open dots indicate end points that are not included in the interval. Closed dots indicate end points that are included.

For example, $|5| = 5$ if $a = 5$ and $|-5| = 5$ if $a = -5$. Regardless of whether a is positive or negative, the absolute value of a is always positive.

Using absolute value notation, the interval $-5 < x < 5$ can be defined as $|x| < 5$. Similarly, the notation $|x| > 5$ denotes a pair of intervals, $x < -5$ or $x > 5$.

Example 2 Solving a Polynomial Inequality Using the Quadratic Formula

The population of a city is modelled by $P(t) = 0.5t^2 + 10t + 200$, where $P(t)$ is the population in thousands and t is the time in years. The year 2000 corresponds to $t = 0$. When will the population be less than 330 000?

Solution
To solve this problem, determine where $P(t) < 330$.

$$0.5t^2 + 10t + 200 < 330 \qquad \text{Subtract 330 from both sides.}$$
$$0.5t^2 + 10t + 200 - 330 < 0$$
$$0.5t^2 + 10t - 130 < 0$$

The zeros occur when $0.5t^2 + 10t - 130 = 0$. Use the quadratic formula to solve for t.

$$t = \frac{-b \pm \sqrt{b^2 - 4ac}}{2a}$$

$$t = \frac{-10 \pm \sqrt{(10)^2 - 4(0.5)(-130)}}{2(0.5)}$$

$$t = \frac{-10 \pm \sqrt{360}}{1}$$

$$t = \frac{-10 \pm 6\sqrt{10}}{1}$$

$t = -10 + 6\sqrt{10}$, or about 8.97, and $t = -10 - 6\sqrt{10}$ or about -28.97.

In this case, there is no restricted domain. Negative values for t indicate years before 2000. The roots divide the domain into three intervals: $t < -28.97$, $-28.97 < t < 8.97$, and $t > 8.97$. Substitute a number from each interval and evaluate $0.5t^2 + 10t - 130$.

Intervals		
$t < -28.97$	$-28.97 < t < 8.97$	$t < 8.97$
$0.5(-30)^2 + 10(-30) - 130 = 20$ positive	$0.5(0)^2 + 10(0) - 130 = -130$ negative	$0.5(10)^2 + 10(10) - 130 = 20$ positive

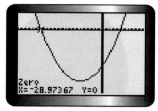

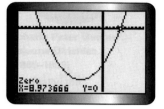

From the table, $0.5t^2 + 10t - 130 < 0$ when $-28.97 < t < 8.97$, which means that the population will be less than 330 000 when $-28.97 < t < 8.97$, or between about 1971 and about 2009.

Check the solution by using a graphing calculator. Graph $P(t) = 0.5t^2 + 10t - 130$ to determine the zeros and the interval where the curve lies below the x-axis.

The population is below 330 000 if $0.5t^2 + 10t - 130 < 0$ or $0.5t^2 + 10t + 200 < 330$, which occurs when $-28.97 < t < 8.97$.

EXAMINING THE CONCEPT

Special Cases When Solving Inequalities

The real zeros or x-intercepts do not always indicate a change in the sign of the polynomial. As well, there are often complex zeros that are not x-intercepts.

Example 3 **A Polynomial Inequality with a Double Root**

Solve $(x^2 - 1)(x^2 + x - 2) \geq 0$ algebraically. Check graphically.

Solution

Factor the inequality.

$$(x^2 - 1)(x^2 + x - 2) \geq 0$$
$$(x - 1)(x + 1)(x - 1)(x + 2) \geq 0$$
$$(x - 1)^2(x + 1)(x + 2) \geq 0$$

The equation $(x - 1)(x - 1)(x + 1)(x + 2) = 0$ has roots 1, 1, -1, and -2. The number 1 is a **double root**, which means that the corresponding function has a turning point at $x = 1$. Order the roots, -2, -1, and 1. Divide the domain into four intervals: $x < -2$, $-2 < x < -1$, $-1 < x < 1$, and $x > 1$. Substitute a test value in each interval.

	Intervals			
	$x < -2$	$-2 < x < -1$	$-1 < x < 1$	$x > 1$
Sign of $(x - 1)^2$	+	+	+	+
Sign of $(x + 1)$	−	−	+	+
Sign of $(x + 2)$	−	+	+	+
Sign of $(x - 1)^2(x + 1)(x + 2)$	$(+)(-)(-) = +$	$(+)(-)(+) = -$	$(+)(+)(+) = +$	$(+)(+)(+) = +$

From the table and the fact that $f(-2) = 0$, $f(-1) = 0$, and $f(1) = 0$, $(x^2 - 1)(x^2 + x - 2) \geq 0$ when $x \leq -2$ and $x \geq -1$.

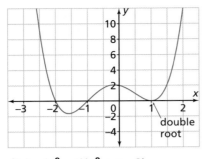

$f(x) = (x^2 - 1)(x^2 + x - 2)$

The corresponding function $f(x) = (x^2 - 1)(x^2 + x - 2)$ is positive for all values of x except those between -2 and -1. In the graph of the function, the graph is above the x-axis for all values of x except between -2 and -1.

• • • • • • • •

Example 4   A Polynomial Inequality with Non-real Roots

Solve $(4 - x^2)(x^2 - 2x + 2) < 0$, and check by graphing.

Solution

Whenever both sides of an inequality are multiplied or divided by a negative number, the inequality sign must be reversed.

Rewrite the inequality by factoring out -1.

$$-(x^2 - 4)(x^2 - 2x + 2) < 0 \qquad \text{Divide both sides by } -1.$$
$$(x^2 - 4)(x^2 - 2x + 2) > 0 \qquad \text{Factor } x^2 - 4.$$
$$(x + 2)(x - 2)(x^2 - 2x + 2) > 0$$

Determine the roots by solving $(x + 2)(x - 2)(x^2 - 2x + 2) = 0$.

For $x + 2 = 0$ and $x - 2 = 0$, $x = -2$ and $x = 2$, respectively.

However, $x^2 - 2x + 2$ has only non-real roots since the discriminant is negative.

$$b^2 - 4ac = (-2)^2 - 4(1)(2)$$
$$= -4$$

So this quartic polynomial has only two real roots, $x = -2$ and $x = 2$. The intervals are then $x < -2$, $-2 < x < 2$, and $x > 2$. Substitute test values and evaluate the intervals.

	Intervals		
	$x < -2$	$-2 < x < 2$	$x > 2$
Sign of $(x + 2)$	$-$	$+$	$+$
Sign of $(x - 2)$	$-$	$-$	$+$
Sign of $(x^2 - 2x + 2)$	$+$	$+$	$+$
Sign of $(x + 2)(x - 2)(x^2 - 2x + 2)$	$(-)(-)(+) = +$	$(+)(-)(+) = -$	$(+)(+)(+) = +$

From the table, $(x + 2)(x - 2)(x^2 - 2x + 2) > 0$, or $(4 - x^2)(x^2 - 2x + 2) < 0$, when $x < -2$ and on $x > 2$.

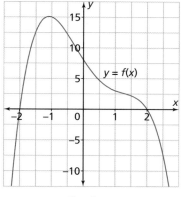

$f(x) = (4 - x^2)(x^2 - 2x + 2)$

The corresponding function $f(x) = (4 - x^2)(x^2 - 2x + 2)$ is negative for all x-values less than -2 and greater than 2. In the graph of the function, the graph is below the x-axis for all values of x where $x < -2$ and $x > 2$.

CHECK, CONSOLIDATE, COMMUNICATE

1. A polynomial function can have real or non-real zeros, which correspond to the roots of the polynomial equation. What type of roots will determine how to divide the domain of the function into intervals?
2. Explain how to use a test value for the independent variable to determine the sign of a polynomial function within a given interval.
3. Which technique can always be used to solve any polynomial inequality, an algebraic approach or a graphing technology approach? Justify your decision and explain.

KEY IDEAS

- Factorable polynomial inequalities can be solved algebraically by determining the roots.
- The roots of a polynomial equation, which correspond to the real zeros of the corresponding function, divide the domain into intervals where the sign of the polynomial might change.
- A test value for the independent variable within each interval helps determine the sign of the polynomial within that interval.
- All polynomial inequalities can be solved graphically. Use graphing technology if a polynomial inequality cannot be factored. Graph the corresponding function and locate the zeros. Determine, visually, the intervals that describe the solution(s) using the zeros and the domain of the function.

1.7 Exercises

A 1. Evaluate.

(a) $|-22|$

(b) $-|-35|$

(c) $|-5-13|$

(d) $|4-7|+|-10+2|$

(e) $\dfrac{|-8|}{-4}$

(f) $\dfrac{|-22|}{|-11|}+\dfrac{-16}{|-4|}$

2. Express using absolute value notation.

(a) $x<-3$ or $x>3$ (b) $-8\le x\le 8$ (c) $x\le -1$ or $x\ge 1$ (d) $x\ne \pm 5$

3. Graph on a number line.

(a) $|x|<8$ (b) $|x|\ge 16$ (c) $|x|\le -4$ (d) $|x|>-7$

4. Rewrite using absolute value notation.

(a)

(b)

(c)

(d)

5. **Knowledge and Understanding:** Solve.

(a) $5(x-1)(x+1)<0$

(b) $(1-2x)(1+4x)\ge 0$

(c) $(2x+1)(x-3)(x+4)>0$

(d) $(1-x)(2-x)(3-x)\ge 0$

(e) $(2x-3)(x+4)(x+5)(x-2)>0$

(f) $(4-3x)(2x-1)(x+3)(x-2)>0$

6. Verify your answers to question 5 with a graphing calculator.

7. Solve each inequality using a graphing calculator.

(a) $x^3+2x^2+4<0$

(b) $-x^3+6x^2-3x-11>0$

(c) $-x^4-2x^3+x^2+4<0$

(d) $x^3-3.7x^2+2.1x>2.15$

(e) $x^3-2.7x^2-2.6x<-1.75$

(f) $x^4-2.1x^3-2.4x^2-x+3<0$

8. Solve algebraically.

(a) $x^2-6x+9\ge 16$

(b) $x^3-9x\ge 0$

(c) $(x^2+x-20)(x^2-2x+7)<0$

(d) $x^3+4x^2+x-6<0$

(e) $x^3-2x^2-5x+6>0$

(f) $x^4-5x^2+4<0$

9. Verify your answers to question 8 with a graphing calculator.

B 10. Let $f(x)=-5(x+2)(x-2)(x+3)$. Graph $f(x)$. Shade the part of the graph that shows $f(x)<0$. What interval does the shaded part represent?

11. Let $f(x)=-2(x-3)(x+3)(x-1)(x+1)$. Graph $f(x)$. Shade the part of the graph that shows $f(x)\ge 0$. What interval does the shaded part represent?

12. Consider the inequality $(x - 3)^2(x + 10)^2 \geq 0$. When will the inequality be negative? Solve algebraically.

13. Verify your answer to question 12 using graphing technology.

14. Consider the inequality $-(1 - 2x)^2(1 + 3x)^2 < 0$. When will the inequality be negative? Solve algebraically.

15. Verify your answer to question 14 using graphing technology.

16. **Communication:** Create a degree-4 polynomial function, $f(x)$, with three zeros and a negative leading coefficient. Graph $f(x)$ and explain how to use the zeros to solve $f(x) < 0$.

17. **Application:** In Canada, hundreds of thousands of cubic metres of wood are harvested each year. The function $f(x) = 1135x^4 - 8197x^3 + 15\ 868x^2 - 2157x + 176\ 608$, $0 \leq x \leq 4$, models the volume harvested, in cubic metres, from 1993 to 1997. In which years was less than 185 000 m^3 harvested?

18. Determine when $f(x) \geq 0$, to two decimal places.
    (a) $f(x) = (x - 2)(x^2 + 3x - 1)$ **(b)** $f(x) = (x^2 + 4x - 3)(x^2 - 3x + 2)$

19. Environment Canada records ozone levels across Canada. The number of days, D, ground level ozone exceeded the national acceptable level of 82 ppb (parts per billon) per hour from 1980 to 1996 can be approximated by $D(x) = -0.0007x^3 - 0.0015x^2 - 0.0494x + 5.3162$, $0 \leq x \leq 16$. Here 1980 is represented by $x = 0$. In which years was the number of days less than three?

20. Solve $-x^4 - 3x^3 + 12x^2 < -22x + 12$. Confirm with an alternative method.

21. **Thinking, Inquiry, Problem Solving:** Determine an expression for $f(x)$ in which $f(x)$ is cubic, $f(x) \geq 0$ when $x \leq 2$, $f(x) < 0$ when $x > 2$, and $f(0) = 4$.

22. Determine an expression for $f(x)$ in which $f(x)$ is a quartic function, $f(x) > 0$ when $-2 < x < 1$, $f(x) < 0$ when $x < -2$ and $x \geq 1$, $f(x)$ has a double root when $x = 3$, and $f(-1) = 96$.

23. A computer software company models the profits on its latest game using $P(n) = -2n^2 + 28n - 90$, where n represents the number of games sold in hundred thousands and P represents the profit in millions of dollars.
    (a) How many games must the company sell to break even?
    (b) When will the company make a profit? lose money?

24. **Check Your Understanding:** Consider $x^3 + 11x^2 + 18x + 10 > 10$.
    (a) What is the equation of the corresponding function that could be graphed and used to solve this inequality?
    (b) Explain how the graph of the corresponding function can be used in this case to solve the inequality.
    (c) Solve this inequality algebraically.

C **25.** **(a)** Evaluate $\dfrac{|2a|}{a}$ for $a < 0$. **(b)** Solve $|x + 4| = 10$.

   (c) Solve $|x - 2| < 5$. **(d)** Solve $|x + 3| > 6$.

   (e) Sketch a graph to show the intersection of $x \leq 20$ and $x \geq -10$. Rewrite the expression using absolute value notation.

26. The graphs of functions $f(x) = x^4 + x^3 - 11x^2 - 9x + 18$ and $g(x) = -x + 3$ intersect. For what values of x, to two decimal places, is the quartic function greater than the linear function?

ADDITIONAL ACHIEVEMENT CHART QUESTIONS

Knowledge and Understanding: Solve each inequality algebraically. Then graph. Shade the parts of the graph that show the solutions.

(a) $x^2 < 2x + 8$ **(b)** $-7x^2 + 15x \geq 9 - x^3$

Application: The total revenue, R, received from selling p items of a product is $R(p) = 42p - 0.015p^2$, where $p \leq 500$. How many items were sold if the revenue was less than $8796?

Thinking, Inquiry, Problem Solving: Solve $x^3 - 13x - 12 \leq 0$. Find three other cubic polynomial inequalities with the same interval solutions. Describe how you found them and why your method works.

Communication: Use words, diagrams, graphs, and/or technology to explain the role of the inequality sign, axes, zeros, domain, and position of the curve when solving polynomial inequalities.

The Chapter Problem
Developing a Model for Canada's Population

In this section, you learned to solve polynomial inequalities. Apply what you learned to answer the following questions about The Chapter Problem on page 2.

CP18. Examine your equations of degree-1, degree-2, degree-3, and degree-4 polynomials for Canada's population.

   (a) What restrictions on the independent variable for each function are necessary to make reasonable predictions?

   (b) What is implied about Canada's population before 1851 if no restrictions are placed on each model?

   (c) What is implied about Canada's population after 2001 if no restrictions are placed on each model?

   (d) By the quartic model, when was Canada's population less than 25 million?

Chapter 1 Review

POLYNOMIAL FUNCTION MODELS

CHECK YOUR UNDERSTANDING

1. What features define a polynomial function?

2. What is the most number of zeros a degree-n polynomial function can have?

3. Sketch a degree-4 polynomial function with
   (a) four zeros   **(b)** three zeros   **(c)** two zeros
   (d) one zero   **(e)** no zeros

4. Why do polynomial functions with an odd degree with no restrictions on the domain have at least one zero?

5. Explain the meaning of a turning point on the graph of a polynomial function.

6. What is the greatest number of turning points in the graph of a degree-n polynomial function? Sketch the graph of a degree-3 polynomial function with the maximum number of turning points and one with the minimum number of turning points.

7. Explain how the end behaviour of a polynomial function is determined by the leading coefficient and degree of the polynomial.

8. Explain how to use the factor theorem to find one factor of a polynomial function. How can you find the remaining factors?

9. A polynomial equation of degree 4 has exactly two real roots. How many other roots are possible? Describe the other roots.

10. Explain how to graphically determine the intervals of the domain where the value(s) of a polynomial function are positive. How are the intervals determined algebraically?

ADDITIONAL REVIEW QUESTIONS BY SECTION

1.1 Polynomial Functions

11. Expand, simplify, and write in standard form. State the degree.
    (a) $f(x) = (2x - 3)(3x + 1)(x + 4)$ **(b)** $f(x) = (x - 1)(2x - 3)^2(x + 2)$
    (c) $f(x) = (2x - 5)^3(3x + 1)$ **(d)** $f(x) = (x - 3)(x^3 + 4x^2 - x + 3)$

12. Determine the equation of the polynomial function of degree 3, with zeros -2, -1, and 4. The graph of this function passes through $(5, -84)$.

13. **(a)** Determine the equation of the function on the left.
    (b) Approximate the intervals in which the function increases and decreases.

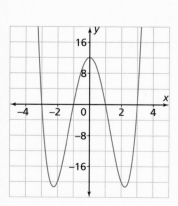

1.2 Investigating the Characteristics of Polynomial Functions

14. Predict the value of the finite difference, then calculate that value.

    (a) $f(x) = 5x^2 - 2x + 3$, second finite difference

    (b) $f(x) = -2x^3 + 3x^2 + 2x - 4$, third finite difference

    (c) $f(x) = 0.5x^4 - 3x^3 + 2x^2 - x + 4$, fourth finite difference

15. Describe the end behaviour and state the zeros of each function.

    (a) 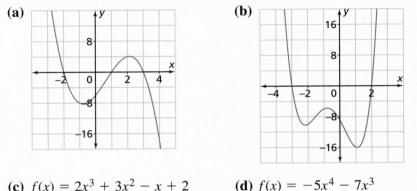   (b)

    (c) $f(x) = 2x^3 + 3x^2 - x + 2$ (d) $f(x) = -5x^4 - 7x^3$

16. Graph each function. Visually approximate the coordinates of the turning points and the intervals in which $f(x)$ increases and decreases.

    (a) $f(x) = x^3 - 3x^2 - 10x + 24$ (b) $f(x) = 0.5x^4 - x^3 - 6.5x^2 + 7x + 12$

1.3 Creating New Polynomial Functions

17. Given $f = \{(0, 6), (1, 3), (4, 7), (5, 8)\}$ and $g = \{(-1, 2), (1, 4), (2, 3), (4, 8), (8, 9)\}$, determine the following.

    (a) $f(x) + g(x)$ (b) $f(x) - g(x)$ (c) $[f(x)][g(x)]$ (d) $f(g(x))$ (e) $g(f(x))$

18. Given $f(x) = 2x^2 - 2x, -2 \le x \le 3$ and $g(x) = -4x, -3 \le x \le 5$, graph the following.

    (a) f (b) g (c) $f + g$ (d) $f - g$ (e) fg

19. Given $f(x) = x^3 - 3x^2 + 2x + 1$ and $g(x) = x - 2$, determine

    (a) $f(g(2))$ (b) $g(f(2))$ (c) $f(g(x))$ (d) $g(f(x))$

20. A housing development begins in 2002 as a 200-m by 100-m parcel of land. Each year its length grows by 50 m and its width grows by 40 m.

    (a) Express the length of the development as a function of time.

    (b) Express the width as a function of time.

    (c) What function represents the area of the development in terms of time?

    (d) If the development continues to grow at the same rate what will be its area in 2010?

1.4 Dividing Polynomials

21. Divide each expression by $x + 2$. State the quotient and remainder.

(a) $2x^3 + 5x^2 - x - 5$ (b) $3x^3 + 13x^2 + 17x + 3$

(c) $2x^4 + 5x^3 - 16x^2 - 45x - 18$ (d) $2x^3 + 4x^2 - 5x - 4$

22. When $2x - 3$ is divided into the dividend, the quotient is $3x^3 + 10x^2 - 27x - 10$, with a remainder of 9. What is the dividend?

23. When $4x^4 - 15x^2 + px + 6$ is divided by $2x + 1$, the remainder is 2. Determine the value of p.

1.5 Factoring Polynomials

24. Use the remainder theorem to determine each remainder.

(a) $(2x^6 + 6x^5 - 3x^3 - 9x^2 + 3x + 1) \div (x + 3)$

(b) $(2x^3 - 9x^2 - 6x + 35) \div (2x - 5)$

25. Show whether $2x + 3$ is a factor of $6x^4 + 23x^3 + 7x^2 - 27x - 9$.

26. Factor fully.

(a) $x^3 - 4x^2 - 11x + 30$ (b) $x^4 - 15x^2 + 10x + 24$

(c) $x^4 - 2x^3 - 7x^2 + 8x + 12$ (d) $12x^3 + 28x^2 - 7x - 5$

(e) $6x^6 + 3x^5 + 2x^2 + x$ (f) $2x^4 - 10x^3 - x^2 + 5x$

1.6 Solving Polynomial Equations

27. Solve algebraically. Confirm the solutions using technology.

(a) $x^3 + 2x^2 = x + 2$ (b) $2x^4 + 11x^3 + 9x^2 - 14x - 8 = 0$

28. Solve algebraically, to two decimal places. Confirm using technology.

(a) $x^3 + x^2 - 11x + 10 = 0$ (b) $x^3 + 5x^2 = 2x + 6$

(c) $2x^4 - 9x^2 - x + 6 = 0$ (d) $x^4 - 13x^2 = -36$

29. What is the equation of a degree-4 polynomial function with zeros 1 and $2 - 3i$ and whose graph passes through $(-1, -72)$?

1.7 Solving Polynomial Inequalities

30. Solve graphically.

(a) $x^3 - 6x^2 + 5x + 12 > 0$ (b) $x^4 - 3x^3 - 3x^2 + 7x + 6 < 0$

(c) $-2x^3 + 7x^2 - 9x + 6 \leq 0$ (d) $-2x^4 + 7x^3 - 19x^2 + 21x - 15 > 0$

31. Solve algebraically and confirm graphically.

(a) $-x^3 - 2x^2 + 5x + 6 > 0$ (b) $x^4 + 2x^3 - 13x^2 - 14x + 24 < 0$

(c) $2x^3 - x^2 + x + 4 < 0$ (d) $2x^4 + 5x^3 + 7x^2 + 7x + 3 < 0$

32. Write using absolute value notation.

(a) $-2 < x < 2$ (b) $-5 \leq x \leq 5$ (c) $x < -3$ or $x > 3$

REVIEW QUESTIONS BY ACHIEVEMENT CHART CATEGORIES

Knowledge and Understanding

33. Which binomials are factors of $f(x) = x^4 + 2x^3 - 25x^2 - 26x + 120$?

(a) $x - 1$ (b) $x - 2$ (c) $x + 3$

(d) $x - 4$ (e) $x + 2$ (f) $x + 5$

34. Divide each polynomial using long division. Check using synthetic division.

(a) $(2x^3 - 3x^2 - 11x + 6) \div (x - 3)$

(b) $(2x^4 + 11x^3 + x^2 - 50x - 24) \div (2x + 1)$

(c) $(x^6 - 4x^3 + 3x^2 - 12) \div (x + 2)$

(d) $(x^4 + 2x^3 - 12x^2 - 8x + 32) \div (x^2 - 4)$

35. Solve for $x, x \in \mathbf{R}$.

(a) $x^3 - 7x - 6 = 0$ (b) $6x^3 - 5x^2 - 3x + 2 = 0$

(c) $64x^3 - 27 = 0$ (d) $2x^3 + 6x^2 - x - 3 = 0$

(e) $2x^4 - x^3 = 8x^2 - x - 6$ (f) $x^5 - x^4 - 4x = -4$

Communication

36. (a) Describe how to determine a cubic polynomial function, given its x-intercepts, and a point that satisfies the function.

(b) Determine the cubic function with x-intercepts -1, 3, and 4. The graph of the function passes through $(5, -24)$.

37. The graph of a cubic polynomial function is shown on the left. Describe the graph in terms of end behaviour, x-intercepts, intervals of increase and decrease, turning points, local maxima and minima, intervals when the function is greater than 0, and intervals when it is less than 0. Approximate values are sufficient.

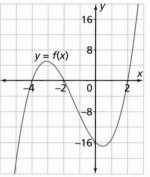

38. Sketch a quartic polynomial function, $f(x)$, in which as $x \to -\infty$, $f(x) \to -\infty$; as $x \to \infty$, $f(x) \to -\infty$; the x-intercepts are 2 and -3; and $f(x) \le 0$ for all x.

Application

39. Prove that $x^3 + y^3 = (x + y)(x^2 - xy + y^2)$ using

(a) multiplication

(b) the factor theorem

40. During a normal five-second respiratory cycle in which a person inhales and then exhales, the volume of air in a person's lungs can be modelled by $V(t) = 0.027t^3 - 0.27t^2 + 0.675t$, where volume, V, is in litres and t is the time in seconds. In this cycle, when is the volume of air in the lungs

(a) at its maximum?   (b) 0.4 L?   (c) more than 0.3 L?

Year	Population (millions)
1950	2555
1955	2780
1960	3039
1965	3346
1970	3708
1975	4088
1980	4457
1985	4855
1990	5284
1995	5691
2000	6080

Source: U.S. Bureau of the Census

41. The population of the world from 1950 to 2000 is shown on the left. Prepare a scatter plot of the data. Model the data using a cubic function. State any restrictions on the domain. Estimate the population in 1963 and 1983. What will the world population be in 2040? Does this seem reasonable according to the growth pattern of the last 50 years? Explain.

Thinking, Inquiry, Problem Solving

42. One root of $3x^3 - 15x^2 + kx - 4 = 0$ is 2. Find k and the other roots.

43. The graph of a quartic function crosses the x-axis at -4 and -2, and touches at $x = 3$. State the equation of the family of curves. Sketch one possible function in this family. Sketch its reflected image in the x-axis. Compare the leading coefficients of the functions. Let the coordinates of the turning point of one of the functions be (a, b). Show that the distance between the turning point of this function and the corresponding turning point of the reflected function is $2|b|$.

44. What is the equation of the quartic function with roots $2 + 3i$ and $1 - 2i$ and whose graph passes through $(-2, 325)$?

Chapter 1 Performance Task

Katie is building a wooden rectangular toy storage box for her younger brother. The box will have an open top and volume of 9 m^3. For design purposes, Katie would like the length of its base to be triple its width. Thick wood for the base costs \$8/m^2 and thinner wood for the sides costs \$5/m^2.

1. Express the cost of wood as a function of the width of the base.

2. What is a reasonable domain and range for the function in this context?

3. Using graphing technology, such as a TI-83 Plus, graph this function with appropriate window settings. Explain why you chose the window settings that you did and comment on the shape of the graph.

4. Locate any maximum and minimum values. Explain what they mean in the context of the problem. What is the cost as the width approaches ∞ and as it approaches −∞? Is this result realistic? Why or why not?

5. If Katie can afford to spend \$144 to make the toy storage box, what must the dimensions of the box be to keep the volume at 9 m^3?

6. What dimensions do you recommend that Katie use? Justify your answer.

Chapter 1 Review Test

POLYNOMIAL FUNCTION MODELS

1. **Knowledge and Understanding**
   - (a) Write the standard form for a general polynomial function and state its degree and leading coefficient.
   - (b) What is the most number of turning points this function can have?
   - (c) What is the most number of zeros this function can have?
   - (d) If the least number of zeros is 1, describe the degree of the polynomial.
   - (e) If a polynomial function is less than 0 for all x, describe the degree and the leading coefficient of the polynomial.

2. **Communication:** Let $f(x) = (x - 3)(x + 4)(x - 1)$.
   - (a) Describe how to graph $f(x)$ without technology.
   - (b) Follow your directions and graph $f(x)$.

3. Divide $6x^3 + x^2 - 12x + 5$ by $2x - 1$. Is the divisor a factor of the dividend?

4. Factor.
   - (a) $2x^3 - 3x^2 - 5x + 6$
   - (b) $8x^3 - 27$
   - (c) $4x^3 - 8x^2 + 3x - 6$

5. Solve for x algebraically.
   - (a) $2x^4 + 7x^3 - 6x^2 = 7x - 4$
   - (b) $2x^3 + x^2 > 8x - 5$

6. The roots and degree of a polynomial function are given. Write the function in standard form.
   - (a) $1, 2, -3$, degree 3
   - (b) $2, -2i$, degree 4

Year	Males	Females
1975	73.1	14.7
1980	83.2	21.7
1985	93.2	30.9
1990	92.7	36.5
1995	84.7	40.8
2000	78.6	46.4

Source: Cancer Bureau, Health Canada

7. **Application:** The incidence of lung cancer in Canadians per 100 000 population is shown on the left.
   - (a) Determine a cubic function to represent the curve of best fit for the male data and for the female data. Determine the number of males and females per 100 000 who had lung cancer in 1983.
   - (b) According to your models, when will more females have lung cancer than males?

8. **Thinking, Inquiry, Problem Solving:** Chris makes an open-topped box from a 30-cm by 30-cm piece of cardboard by cutting out equal squares from the corners and folding up the flaps to make the sides. What are the dimensions of each square, to the nearest hundredth of a centimetre, so that the volume of the resulting box is more than 100 cm^3?

9. The graph of $f(x) = 3x^4 + 14x^3 + px^2 + qx + 24$ has x-intercepts -4 and 2. Determine the function.

2 Exponential and Logarithmic Function Models

Many mathematical relations in the world are nonlinear. In Chapter 1, you explored various polynomial functions. In this chapter, you will investigate another type of nonlinear model. Exponential models are often used to model rapid change. Compound interest, population growth, the intensity of an earthquake, and inflation are just a few examples of exponential change.

An important characteristic of exponential change is the rate at which a quantity increases or decreases. Under the conditions of exponential growth or decay, quantities change at mind-boggling rates. For example, under ideal conditions, a single cell of the bacterium E. coli could grow in a single day to a colony equal in size and weight to the entire planet Earth! Fortunately for us, these ideal conditions do not exist in nature!

In this chapter, you will

- identify the key properties of exponential functions in different forms

- describe the significance of exponential growth or exponential decay in various applications

- decide whether an exponential model is appropriate or not

- create graphical and algebraic exponential models for appropriate data

- solve problems related to models of exponential functions from a range of applications

- relate the logarithmic function to the exponential function

- work with logarithmic equations and expressions

- solve exponential and logarithmic equations

- solve simple problems involving logarithmic scales such as the Richter scale, the pH scale, and the decibel scale

The Chapter Problem

Determining Concentration

It is vitally important that accurate dosages of drugs be prescribed to patients. Pharmaceutical companies extensively research the effects of a drug before determining recommended dosages.

The concentration of a drug in someone's bloodstream normally decreases with time. The exact pattern of the decrease is important. For most drugs, the drug will be ineffective *below* a certain concentration and the drug will be dangerous *above* a certain concentration.

The following data was recorded during two separate experiments involving a single dose of a specific drug:

	Experiment 1	Experiment 2
Concentration at 0 h	1.0 mg/mL	1.5 mg/mL
Concentration at 4 h	0.15 mg/mL	0.25 mg/mL
Concentration at 9 h	0.015 mg/mL	0.021 mg/mL

Suppose that this drug is effective at a minimum concentration of 0.51 mg/mL. The maximum safe concentration is 1.95 mg/mL.

A new dose of the same drug is given to someone else. This dose is given every 6 h. Will the concentration of the drug always be in the effective and safe range with either the 1.0 mg/mL dosage or with the 1.5 mg/mL dosage? If not, give the dosage range that would be safe and effective given the behaviour of the drug.

For help with this problem, see pages 95, 106, 113, 134, and 156.

Chapter Challenges

Challenge 1

Several scales are based on exponents. These scales are called **logarithmic scales**. Logarithmic scales are used to measure the intensity of an earthquake, the intensity of sound, and the hydrogen ion concentration (pH) of solutions. Other logarithmic scales are represented in everyday objects, for example, the frets of a guitar and the analog tuner on a radio.

Choose one everyday object mentioned above or another that you suspect has a logarithmic scale. Through analysis, determine whether there is an aspect of this object that you could represent with a logarithmic scale. You will need to show how you can use logarithms to find the corresponding linear scale.

Challenge 2

Throughout this chapter, you will explore population growth.

What do you know about the population in your area? about the population trends in your school and other schools in the district? You also may be able to obtain population data about your school from the school's office. You may gather data about population by gender or about the population in specific locations in the district, and so on. School boards analyze population data to make decisions about, for example, the number of teachers, schools, and bus routes.

Plot the data by year. You may want to compare data by plotting it in different ways, according to the categories described above. Examine the resulting patterns. Does the data show decline or growth over time? Determine a mathematical model that will fit the patterns in the data.

Report your method and findings. Include tables, graphs, and models. Interpret your findings.

Present your report to the class. You also could write your report as a newspaper article.

Getting Ready

In this chapter, you will be working with models, functions, and equations of exponential and logarithmic functions. These exercises will help you warm up for the work ahead.

1. Write each power with a positive exponent.
   (a) 3^{-4} (b) 7^{-2} (c) a^{-8} (d) x^{-5}

2. Evaluate.
   (a) 2^8 (b) 3^5 (c) $(-8)^3$ (d) -4^2
   (e) -6^{-2} (f) $350(1.02)^3$ (g) $(-2)^{-5}$ (h) $(-1)^{-100}$
   (i) $\left(\frac{2}{3}\right)^2$ (j) $\left(\frac{3}{4}\right)^{-3}$ (k) $5^{-1} + \left(\frac{-4}{9}\right)^2$ (l) $\frac{7}{8} - 4^{-2}$

3. Evaluate to two decimal places where necessary.
   (a) $4^{\frac{1}{2}}$ (b) $(-8)^{\frac{1}{3}}$ (c) $\left(\frac{1}{16}\right)^{\frac{1}{2}}$ (d) $216^{-\frac{1}{3}}$
   (e) $2^{\frac{1}{2}}$ (f) $\left(\frac{5}{6}\right)^{\frac{1}{3}}$ (g) $200^{-\frac{2}{5}}$ (h) $(17.4)^{-\frac{3}{7}}$

4. Write each expression as a power of 2.
   (a) $2^4 \times 2^7$ (b) $2^6 \div 2^{-3}$ (c) $4^2 \div 2^m$ (d) 8^n

5. Evaluate.
   (a) $49^{\frac{1}{2}} + 16^{\frac{1}{4}}$ (b) $16^{\frac{3}{2}} + 16^{-0.5}$
   (c) $\left(\frac{1}{8}\right)^{\frac{1}{3}} - \sqrt[3]{\frac{27}{125}} + 4(8^{-\frac{2}{3}})$ (d) $(2^2 \times 5)^{-1}$
   (e) $\left(\frac{3^{-1}}{2^{-1}}\right)^{-2}$ (f) $(5^0 \times 5^4 \div 5^3)^{-4}$

6. Evaluate each expression for $x = 2$ and $y = -2$.
   (a) $\frac{4x^{-2}y^3}{x^3}$ (b) $(3x^2y^{-3})^{-2}$

7. Simplify.
   (a) $\frac{x^4y^2}{x^2y}$ (b) $\left(\frac{-1}{a}\right)^2(a^4b^2)^5$ (c) $(-d^3)^4\left(\frac{c}{d}\right)^6$ (d) $\left(\frac{x^5}{y^2}\right)^4\left(\frac{y^3}{x}\right)^2$

8. For each equation, make a table of values and sketch the graph.
   (a) $y = 2^x$ (b) $y = 3^x$ (c) $y = (0.5)^x$

9. Solve.
   (a) $y = 1.07^3$ (b) $\left(\frac{m^7}{m^6}\right)^2 = 196$ (c) $(p \times p^2)^3 = 3^9$

   (d) $c^{\frac{2}{3}} = 64$ (e) $3a^{\frac{4}{5}} = 48$ (f) $70 = 35a^2$

10. Solve each equation by guessing and checking.

    (a) $4^x = 60$ **(b)** $6^x = 10$ **(c)** $2.5^x = 200$ **(d)** $1.05^x = 2$

11. Write the first differences and the second differences for each relation. Is the relation linear, quadratic, or other? Write an equation for the relation.

    (a)

x	0	1	2	3	4	5
y	0	2	4	6	8	10

    (b)

x	0	1	2	3	4	5
y	−1	2	5	8	11	14

    (c)

x	0	1	2	3	4	5
y	2	6	18	54	162	486

    (d)

x	0	1	2	3	4	5
y	1	2	4	8	16	32

12. Solve each quadratic equation by factoring or by using the quadratic formula.

    (a) $x^2 + 2x - 15 = 0$ **(b)** $n^2 + 7n - 30 = 0$

    (c) $2y^2 + 9y + 4 = 0$ **(d)** $m^2 - 4 = 0$

    (e) $17x + 5x^2 = -6$ **(f)** $0 = -4.9t^2 + 20.58t + 0.491$

13. Solve for x by making the bases equal and using the exponent laws. If the bases cannot be made equal, guess and check to solve for x, to two decimal places, if necessary.

    (a) $3^x = 27$ **(b)** $2^x = \dfrac{1}{4}$ **(c)** $5^{2x-1} = \dfrac{1}{125}$

    (d) $4(2)^x = 32$ **(e)** $8^x = 16\sqrt[3]{2}$ **(f)** $9^{-x-2} = \left(\dfrac{1}{27}\right)^{x+3}$

14. For each geometric sequence, determine the common ratio, the general term, and t_8.

    (a) $6, -12, 24, -48, \ldots$ **(b)** $1, \dfrac{-2}{3}, \dfrac{4}{9}, \dfrac{-8}{27}, \ldots$

15. Determine the amount that each investment is worth. Use $A = P(1 + i)^n$.

    (a) $1000 invested at 8%/a, compounded annually, for 20 years

    (b) $5340 invested at 2%/a, compounded annually, for 5 years

16. A bacteria culture doubles in size every 15 min. How long will it take for a culture of 20 bacteria to grow to a population of 163 840?

17. Thorium-227 has a half-life of 18.4 days. How much time will a 50-mg sample take to decompose to 12.5 mg?

2.1 Investigating Exponential Models

SETTING THE STAGE

How fast does a rumour spread?

Someone tells three people a rumour. By the end of the next hour, each of these people has told the same rumour to three new people. And at the end of each subsequent hour, each person who was told the rumour has told three other people the rumour, and so on.

1. How many people would be hearing the rumour in the fifth hour?

2. During which hour have about 250 people been told the rumour?

3. Write an algebraic model to represent the total number of people hearing the rumour within a particular hour.

4. Suppose someone tells three people a rumour. But, by the end of the next hour, each of these people has told the same rumour to *four* new people, and so on. Write a new algebraic model to represent this situation.

5. Now suppose someone tells *five* people a rumour. But, by the end of the next hour, each of these people has told the same rumour to *two* new people, and so on. Write a new algebraic model to represent this situation.

In this section, you will examine the exponential model and use it to answer these questions.

EXAMINING THE CONCEPT

Developing the Exponential Model

One way to solve the problem is to start with a table. The variable t represents the number of hours, and N represents the total number of people who are told the rumour by the end of each hour.

t (h)	0	1	2	3	4	5	6
N (number of people told)	3	9	27	81	243	729	2187

This table shows that 729 people were told the rumour in the fifth hour. The table also shows that about 250 people were told the rumour sometime during the fourth hour.

Now develop an algebraic model for the number of people who have been told the rumour in a certain hour. What pattern do you recognize in the data?

Since the number of people triples by the end of each hour, the relation between N and t is exponential. Test the relation $N = 3^t$ as a starting point. At the end of the first hour, $t = 1$ and $3^1 = 3$. But, according to the table, the total number of people who have been told the rumour at the end of the first hour is 9, not 3. Try adding 1 to the exponent.

$$3^{1+1} = 3^2$$
$$= 9$$

Therefore, $N = 3^{t+1}$ seems to fit the data. Try it for other values in the table.

Consider the situation in step 4 of Setting the Stage. Someone tells three people a rumour. By the end of the next hour, each of these people has told the same rumour to *four* new people, and so on. To write a new algebraic expression, first draw a diagram and write another table.

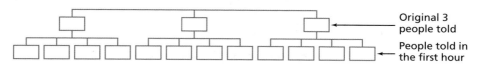

Original 3 people told

People told in the first hour

This diagram represents the number of people who have been told the rumour at $t = 0$ and at $t = 1$.

Hour (t)	Number Who Are Told (N)	Equivalent Expression
0	3	3
1	12	3×4
2	48	3×4^2
3	192	3×4^3
4	768	3×4^4
5	3072	3×4^5
t		3×4^t

Therefore, the number of people, N, who are told the rumour at the tth hour is $N = 3 \times 4^t$.

Compare $N = 3 \times 3^t$ and $N = 3 \times 4^t$. Note that $N = 3 \times 3^t$ is the same as $N = 3^{t+1}$.

For $N = 3 \times 3^t$, three people are first told the rumour. Three people are told the rumour by someone who has already been told the rumour at each stage.

For $N = 3 \times 4^t$, three people are first told the rumour. But four people are told the rumour by someone who has already been told the rumour at each stage.

Therefore, the formula that represents the situation in step 5 of Setting the Stage is $N = 5 \times 2^t$. Five people are first told the rumour. Two people are told the rumour by someone who has already been told the rumour at each stage.

In general, let c be the number of people who are told initially. Let a be the number of people who are told by someone who has already been told the rumour at each stage. Then the model for this situation is $N = c(a)^t$, where N is the number of people who are told the rumour at each stage and t is the number of hours. This situation is an example of **exponential growth**.

Exponential Growth
The general model for **exponential growth** is $y = c(a)^x$, $a > 1$. The quantity a can be called the **growth factor**. The quantity c is the initial amount or population.

In each example, assume smooth exponential growth.

Example 1   Solving Growth Problems

The number of a certain bacteria doubles every hour. The initial population in a culture of this bacteria is 36.

(a) Determine an exponential model for the number of bacteria after t hours.

(b) Determine the number of bacteria after 8 h.

Solution

(a) Use $N = c(a)^t$. Since the initial population is 36, $c = 36$. Since the number of bacteria doubles every hour, the growth rate, a, is 2. Therefore, the exponential model is $N = 36(2)^t$.

(b) Substitute $t = 8$ into $N = 36(2)^t$ to find the number of bacteria after 8 h.

$$N = 36(2)^t \qquad \text{Substitute } t = 8.$$
$$= 36(2)^8 \qquad \text{Evaluate.}$$
$$= 9216$$

Therefore, there are 9216 bacteria after 8 h.
• • • • • • • •

Example 2   Adjusting the Formula

The number of bacteria in a different culture doubles every 2 h. The initial population is again 36. Determine the population after 8 h.

Solution
There are several different ways of looking at this problem.

Method 1
Since the doubling period is every 2 h, there are 4 doubling periods every 8 h. Use $N = 36(2)^t$ and substitute $t = 4$.

$$N = 36(2)^4$$
$$N = 576$$

Therefore, there are 576 bacteria after 8 h.

Method 2
The number of bacteria doubles every 2 h. So, if you start with 1 bacterium, there will be 2 bacteria after 2 h. $N = 2$ and $t = 2$ in the formula $N = c(a)^t$.

Use the information to determine a, the growth rate per hour.

$$N = c(a)^t \qquad \text{Substitute known values.}$$
$$2 = 1(a)^2 \qquad \text{Solve for } a.$$
$$2^{\frac{1}{2}} = a \qquad \text{Write as a radical.}$$
$$a = \sqrt{2}$$

The growth rate per hour is $\sqrt{2}$.

Then substitute $t = 8$ into $N = 36(\sqrt{2})^t$.

$$N = 36(\sqrt{2})^t \qquad \text{Substitute } t = 8.$$
$$= 36(\sqrt{2})^8 \qquad (\sqrt{2})^8 = (2^{\frac{1}{2}})^8 = 2^4 = 16$$
$$= 576$$

Therefore, there are 576 bacteria after 8 h.

The answers produced by either method are the same.

• • • • • • • •

Example 3   Determining Growth Rate and Initial Population

The population of a small town appears to be increasing exponentially. Town planners need a model for predicting the future population. In 1980, the population was 35 000, and in 1990, the population was 57 010.

(a) Create an algebraic model for the town's population growth.

(b) Check your model by using the fact that the population in 1995 was 72 800.

(c) What will the population be in 2010?

Solution

(a) Let the year 1980 be $t = 0$. So, when $t = 0$, $N = 35\ 000$. And, when $t = 10$, $N = 57\ 010$.

Use $N = c(a)^t$ and find the growth rate, a, to the nearest hundredth, and the initial population, c. Substituting $t = 0$ and $N = 35\ 000$,

$$35\ 000 = c(a)^0 \qquad \text{Recall that } a^0 = 1.$$
$$35\ 000 = c$$

The value for c makes sense, since 35 000 is the initial value. Now, to find a, substitute $t = 10$ and $N = 57\ 010$.

$$N = c(a)^t$$
$$57\ 010 = 35\ 000 a^{10} \qquad \text{Divide by 35 000.}$$
$$\frac{57\ 010}{35\ 000} = a^{10} \qquad \text{Take tenth root of both sides.}$$
$$\sqrt[10]{\frac{57\ 010}{35\ 000}} = \sqrt[10]{a^{10}} \qquad \text{Evaluate.}$$
$$a \doteq 1.05$$

Therefore, the growth model for the population, N, is $N = 35\ 000(1.05)^t$, where t is the number of years after 1980.

(b) The year 1995 is 15 years after 1980, so $t = 15$. Substitute $t = 15$ into $N = 35\,000(1.05)^t$.

$$N = 35\,000(1.05)^t \qquad \text{Substitute } t = 15.$$
$$N = 35\,000(1.05)^{15} \qquad \text{Evaluate.}$$
$$N \doteq 72\,763$$

Since this value is close to 72 800, $N = 35\,000(1.05)^t$ appears to be a good model.

(c) For the year 2010, $t = 30$.

$$N = 35\,000(1.05)^t \qquad \text{Substitute } t = 30.$$
$$N = 35\,000(1.05)^{30} \qquad \text{Evaluate.}$$
$$N \doteq 151\,268$$

The population will be about 151 268 in 2010.

• • • • • • • •

In Examples 1, 2, and 3, the quantities increased over time. Quantities can also decrease exponentially. Example 4 illustrates exponential decay.

Example 4 **Using the Growth Formula to Make Predictions**

Three years ago, there were about 2500 fish in Loon Lake. Due to the effects of acid rain, there are about 1945 fish in the lake today. Assume that the decline of the fish population is exponential. Find the population five years from now.

Solution

Use $y = c(a)^x$.

Substitute $c = 2500$, $x = 3$, and $y = 1945$ to find the growth rate, a.

$$y = c(a)^x \qquad \text{Substitute known values.}$$
$$1945 = 2500(a)^3 \qquad \text{Solve for } a^3.$$
$$\frac{1945}{2500} = a^3 \qquad \text{Take the cube root of each side.}$$
$$\sqrt[3]{\frac{1945}{2500}} = \sqrt[3]{a^3} \qquad \text{Evaluate } a, \text{ to the nearest hundredth.}$$
$$a \doteq 0.92$$

Therefore, the formula is $y = 2500(0.92)^x$.

To find the population five years from now, let $x = 8 = (3 + 5)$.

$$y = 2500(0.92)^x \qquad \text{Substitute } x = 8.$$
$$y = 2500(0.92)^8$$
$$y \doteq 1283$$

Therefore, the fish population will be about 1283 in five years.

• • • • • • • •

> ## Exponential Decay
>
> The general model for **exponential decay** is $y = c(a)^x$, $0 < a < 1$.
> The quantity a can be called the **decay factor**. The quantity c is the initial amount or population.

Example 5

Monetary growth and inflation appear to be exponential. For instance, if a population is increasing at the rate of 6% per year, then the rate of growth a is $100\% + 6\% = 106\%$, or 1.06. If the inflation rate is 3%, then a is $100\% + 3\% = 103\%$, or 1.03.

Determining Growth Rates

What is the average annual rate of inflation if a loaf of bread cost $1.19 in 1991 and the same loaf of bread cost $1.50 in 2001?

Solution

To find the growth rate, or the annual rate of inflation, a, use $y = c(a)^x$ and the given information. Round the value of a to the nearest thousandth. Let 1991 be $x = 0$ and 2001 be $x = 10$. The initial amount is $1.19.

$$y = c(a)^x \qquad \text{Substitute } y = 1.50, c = 1.19, \text{ and } x = 10.$$
$$1.5 = 1.19a^{10} \qquad \text{Isolate } a^{10}.$$
$$\frac{1.5}{1.19} = a^{10} \qquad \text{Take the tenth root of each side.}$$
$$\sqrt[10]{\frac{1.5}{1.19}} = \sqrt[10]{a^{10}} \qquad \text{Evaluate.}$$
$$a \doteq 1.023$$

The inflation rate is about $1.023 - 1$, or 2.3%.

CHECK, CONSOLIDATE, COMMUNICATE

1. Give an example of a situation that could be modelled by an exponential relation.
2. Choose a value for a such that $0 < a < 1$. Substitute different values of x in $y = c(a)^x$. Using your results, explain why you can use $y = c(a)^x$, where $0 < a < 1$, to model a situation involving decay or depreciation.
3. For $y = c(a)^x$, explain when a represents the growth factor. Then explain why $a - 1$ represents the rate of growth or inflation.

2.1 Exercises

(A)

1. Evaluate each relation for the given value of x. Answer to four decimal places.

   (a) $y = 2(3)^x$, for $x = 4$ **(b)** $y = 100(1.5)^x$, for $x = 10$

   (c) $y = 25(0.5)^x$, for $x = 8$ **(d)** $y = 2500(0.25)^x$, for $x = 9$

2. Evaluate. Round your answers to two decimal places.

   (a) $\sqrt[3]{\dfrac{1800}{1200}}$ **(b)** $\sqrt[5]{\dfrac{900}{1200}}$ **(c)** $\sqrt[8]{\dfrac{12\,500}{6000}}$ **(d)** $\sqrt[10]{\dfrac{20}{50}}$

3. Solve for a, to two decimal places.

   (a) $81 = a^4$ **(b)** $25 = a^3$

   (c) $100 = 5a^8$ **(d)** $100 = 500a^2$

4. **Knowledge and Understanding:** In a bacterial culture, the number of bacteria doubles each day. The initial population is 150 bacteria. Determine the number of bacteria in the culture after each interval.

   (a) 1 day   **(b)** 10 days   **(c)** 3 days

   (d) t days   **(e)** 2 weeks   **(f)** 30 days

5. The value of a particular investment appears to double every 6 years. The initial amount invested was $5200. The growth of the investment is exponential. Find the value after

   (a) 6 years   **(b)** 12 years   **(c)** 18 years

   (d) 15 years   **(e)** 21 years   **(f)** 25 years

6. Determine the annual inflation or depreciation rate for each case. The variable I represents the initial value, F represents the final value, and t is the number of years.

   (a) $F = I(1.06)^t$

   (b) $F = I(0.98)^t$

   (c) $F = I(1.012)^t$

   (d) $F = I(0.942)^t$

7. Determine the initial value and growth rate for each case.

   (a) $y = 1200(2)^x$

   (b) $y = 3^x$

   (c) $y = 100(1.048)^x$

   (d) $y = 50(5)^x$

8. A tennis ball is dropped from a height of 10 m. Each time the ball touches the ground, it bounces up to about 45% of the maximum height of the previous bounce. Determine its height after five bounces.

9. The value, A, of an investment after t years is given by $A(t) = 1280(1.085)^t$.

   (a) Determine the value of the investment after 5 years and after 10 years.

   (b) What was the initial investment?

   (c) What is the annual interest rate?

   (d) What would be the difference in the value of the investment after 10 years if the interest rate is 7%, rather than the given rate?

B 10. A committee of 20 decides to quickly circulate a petition against the residential development of a neighbourhood park. On the first day, each committee member signs the petition and delivers a copy of the petition to two members of the community. Then each community member signs the petition, copies it, and gives each of the two copies to two other community members. It takes one day to sign, copy, and deliver the petition to two other community members. How many petitions will be in circulation after 30 days?

11. **Communication:** For the linear relation $y = mx + b$ and the exponential relation $y = c(a)^x$, explain what m, a, b, and c represent. Note any similarities and differences.

12. **Application:** The value of a new sports car will depreciate, or decrease, by about 20% at the end of the first year. By the end of the next year, the value of the sports car at the end of the first year will depreciate by 20% again. This pattern continues. Find the value of the car 6 years after it was bought for $38 900.

13. A computer virus attached to an e-mail can spread rapidly. Once the attachment is opened by the person who receives the e-mail, the virus will cause an e-mail with the infected virus to be sent to everyone in the recipient's address book. On average, a person has 15 addresses in his or her address book. One person sends an e-mail with an attached virus every minute to someone else. How many people would receive the virus at the end of three hours?

14. The population of one school in an area of rapid development seems to grow at an exponential rate of 6% per year. What is the school's population in 2002 if it was 920 in 1992?

15. Population growth can be modelled with an exponential function. Mapleville's population was 35 000 in 1990 and 37 500 in 2000. What will be the population in 2008 if this trend continues?

16. You want to buy a new car, and you have investigated the trade-in value of your current car. Three months ago, the trade-in value was $3200. The trade-in value is now $3125. What will be the trade-in value of your car six months from now if it is depreciating exponentially?

17. **Check Your Understanding:** Describe some situations that have exponential patterns. Refer to $y = c(a)^x$, which is the general form of an exponential relation. In what situations will a be between 0 and 1? In what situations will a be greater than 1?

C 18. **Thinking, Inquiry, Problem Solving:** The table describes the cooling of a cup of coffee as it sits on your teacher's desk in the math office.

Time (min)	0	4	8	12	16	20
Temperature (°C)	55	47	40	34	29	25

(a) Calculate a, the cooling factor of the coffee. Round your answer to two decimal places.

(b) Determine an equation for y, the temperature of the coffee in degrees Celsius after t minutes.

(c) Is your model a good predictor of the temperature of the coffee at any point in time? Explain.

19. A photocopier can be set to either enlarge or reduce an image. Using the photocopier in the school's library, Ari chooses a setting of 90% and places a rectangular photograph on the glass of the photocopier. The area of the photograph in the first photocopy will be 90% of the area of the original photograph. Ari takes the photocopy and places it again on the glass of the photocopier. He continues photocopying in this way. What will be the area of the third copy? Express your answer as a percent of the area of the original photograph. Use guess and check to determine when the area will be 50% of the original.

20. Tiziana invests $500 at 5%/a, compounded annually. Ian invests $400 at 6%/a, compounded annually. Estimate when their investments will be equal.

ADDITIONAL ACHIEVEMENT CHART QUESTIONS

Knowledge and Understanding: Suppose that d days from now, the number of bees, N, in a colony is given by $N(d) = 125(2)^{\frac{d}{5}}$.

(a) How many bees were there initially?

(b) After how many days will the number of bees double?

(c) How many bees are there after 14 days?

Application: In general, the value of real estate appreciates over time, while the value of an automobile depreciates over time. Assume that real estate appreciates at the rate of 8%/year. Automobiles depreciate at the rate of 15%/year. If a family currently owns a home with a value of $124 800 and an automobile with a value of $18 500, what will be their value in three years?

Thinking, Inquiry, Problem Solving: A sum of money was invested at a constant interest rate. Interest is compounded annually. After four years, the value of the investment is $619.41. After 10 years, the value of the investment is $854.07.

(a) How much money was invested originally?

(b) Estimate the annual interest rate.

Communication: A new game show called "Double Your Money" is being developed. In this game, contestants will have a certain amount of time to answer eight questions correctly. After a contestant correctly answers a question, he or she can double the money, up to $1000. Draw a diagram to help you explain how to determine the value for the first question.

The Chapter Problem
Determining Concentration

In this section, you studied exponential relations. Apply what you learned to answer these questions about The Chapter Problem on page 82. Assume that, at the end of every hour, 90% of a drug remains in the patient's system. The decrease is exponential.

CP1.   Create an equation for the concentration of the drug that remains in the patient's system after t hours.

CP2.   If the initial concentration is 1.0 mg/mL, what is the concentration after 5 hours? after 3 days? after 2 weeks?

2.2 Graphs of Exponential Functions

SETTING THE STAGE

Recall the rumour situation and the data collected in Setting the Stage in section 2.1.

t (h)	0	1	2	3	4	5	6
N (number of people told)	3	9	27	81	243	729	2187

This situation is an example of exponential growth and describes the **exponential function** $N = 3(3)^t$, where N is the number of people who are told the rumour at the end of the tth hour.

The graph of an exponential function is very different from the graph of a linear or a quadratic function.

To examine the graph of this exponential function, first draw a scatter plot, using discrete data. The graph $N = 3(3)^t$ can be found by drawing the curve of best fit. In this case, the curve passes through each data point.

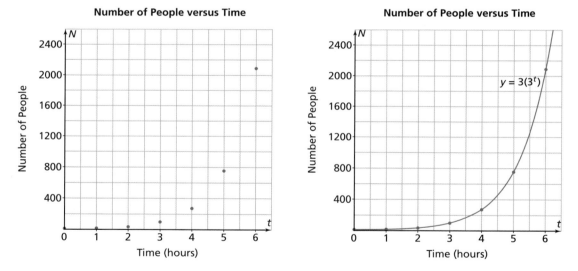

Now suppose that someone tells three people a rumour, but by the end of the next hour, each of these people has told the same rumour to *four* new people, and so on. The exponential model for this situation is $N = 3(4)^t$, where N is the total number of people who have been told the rumour by the end of the tth hour. Graph $N = 3(4)^t$ on the same set of axes and compare the graphs.

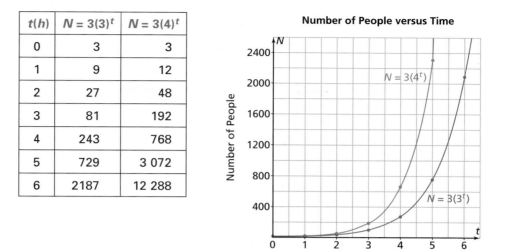

$t(h)$	$N = 3(3)^t$	$N = 3(4)^t$
0	3	3
1	9	12
2	27	48
3	81	192
4	243	768
5	729	3 072
6	2187	12 288

What do the graphs have in common?

In this section, you will examine the common characteristics of the graphs of exponential functions.

EXAMINING THE CONCEPT

Comparing Graphs of Exponential Functions

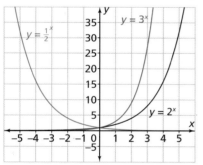

To understand the exponential function, analyze different forms of this function.

Compare the graphs of $y = a^x$, such as $y = 2^x$, $y = 3^x$, and $y = \left(\frac{1}{2}\right)^x$. What is the same, and what is different?

All three graphs are shown. The y-intercept, 1, is the same for all three graphs.

The domain of each function is $\{x \in \mathbf{R}\}$. The range of each function is $\{y \mid y > 0, y \in \mathbf{R}\}$.

When $a > 1$, the exponential function increases. When $0 < a < 1$, the exponential function decreases.

Graphs of $y = a^x$

Exponential functions in the form $y = a^x$, where $a > 0$, have common features. For the graph of any exponential function in this form, the y-intercept is 1. The domain is the set of real numbers and the range is the set of positive real numbers. When $a > 1$, y increases as x increases. When $0 < a < 1$, y decreases as x increases.

Example 1   **Behaviour of an Exponential Function**

(a) Describe the behaviour of $y = 3^x$ and $y = \left(\frac{1}{2}\right)^x$.

(b) Record your descriptions in a table.

Function	End Behaviour as $x \to \infty$	End Behaviour as $x \to -\infty$	Behaviour as $x \to 0$
$y = 3^x$			
$y = \left(\frac{1}{2}\right)^x$			

Solution

(a) Graph $y = 3^x$ and $y = \left(\frac{1}{2}\right)^x$.

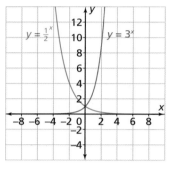

Examine the graph of $y = 3^x$.

As the positive values of x get larger, the values of y get larger in the positive direction. In symbols, as $x \to \infty$, $y \to \infty$.

As the negative values of x get larger, the graph of the function approaches the x-axis and the values of y get closer to 0. In symbols, as $x \to -\infty$, $y \to 0$.

As the value of x approaches 0, the graph of the function approaches 1 and the values of y get closer to 1. In symbols, as $x \to 0$, $y \to 1$.

Examine the graph of $y = \left(\frac{1}{2}\right)^x$.

As the positive values of x get larger, the graph of the function approaches the x-axis and the values of y get closer to 0. In symbols, as $x \to \infty$, $y \to 0$.

As the negative values of x get larger, the values of y get larger in the positive direction. In symbols, as $x \to -\infty$, $y \to \infty$.

As the value of x approaches 0, the graph of the function approaches 1 and the values of y get closer to 1. Therefore, as $x \to 0$, $y \to 1$.

(b)

Function	End Behaviour as $x \to \infty$	End Behaviour as $x \to -\infty$	Behaviour as $x \to 0$
$y = 3^x$	$y \to \infty$	$y \to 0$	$y \to 1$
$y = \left(\frac{1}{2}\right)^x$	$y \to 0$	$y \to \infty$	$y \to 1$

· · · · · · · · ·

The graph of $y = 3^x$ approaches the x-axis as the values of y approach 0.

The graph of $y = \left(\frac{1}{2}\right)^x$ also approaches the x-axis as the values of y approach 0.

An **asymptote** is a line that the curve of a function approaches. In this case, the x-axis is the asymptote for each function.

Behaviour of the Exponential Function $y = a^x$

For the exponential function $y = a^x$,

since $y \to 1$ as $x \to 0$, the y-intercept is 1
if $\boldsymbol{a > 1}$, as $x \to \infty$, $y \to \infty$, and as $x \to -\infty$, $y \to 0$
if $\boldsymbol{0 < a < 1}$, as $x \to \infty$, $y \to 0$, and as $x \to -\infty$, $y \to \infty$

The graph of $y = a^x$, where $a > 0$, has a horizontal asymptote at the x-axis

In Example 1, $y = a^x$ for $a > 1$ and for $0 < a < 1$. How does the function change when $a = 0$, $a = 1$, or $a < 0$?

Example 2

$y = a^x$ when $a = 0$, $a = 1$, or $a < 0$

Describe $y = a^x$ when $a = 0$, $a = 1$, or $a < 0$.

Graph of $y = 0^x$ and $y = 1^x$

Solution
For $a = 0$, $y = 0^x$.

$y = 0$ is the equation of a horizontal line, the x-axis. This function is linear. However, since 0^0 is undefined, there is a hole at $(0, 0)$.

For $a = 1$, $y = 1^x$, or $y = 1$. The graph of this function is the horizontal line $y = 1$. This function is also linear.

One way to examine $y = a^x$ when $a < 0$ is to examine a specific function, for example, $y = (-2)^x$, where $a = -2$. Calculate the value of y for different values of x. Record the results in a table.

x	$y = (-2)^x$
–2	0.25
–1	–0.5
0	1
0.5	no real solution
1	–2
1.5	no real solution
2	4
3	–8

The values for y "jump" from positive to negative where $x = -2$ and $x = -1$, where $x = 0$ and $x = 1$, and where $x = 2$ and $x = 3$. The relation is not defined for $x = 0.5$ and $x = 1.5$. Therefore, the function is not defined for $a \le 0$.

• • • • • • • •

Example 3   **Comparing the Graphs of $y = c(a)^x$**

Compare the graphs of $y = 2^x$, $y = 3(2)^x$, and $y = 3(2)^x + 1$.

Solution

Recall what you know about transformations.

① Start with the graph of $y = 2^x$.

② The graph of $y = 3(2)^x$ is the result of vertically stretching the graph of $y = 2^x$ by a factor of 3.

③ The graph of $y = 3(2)^x + 1$ is the result of vertically translating the graph of $y = 3(2)^x$ 1 unit up.

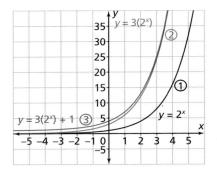

The y-intercept is different for each graph. For the graph of $y = 2^x$, the y-intercept is 1. For the graph of $y = 3(2)^x$, the y-intercept is 3. For the graph of $y = 3(2)^x + 1$, the y-intercept is 4.

The horizontal asymptotes for $y = 2^x$ and $y = 3(2)^x$ are the same, $y = 0$. But the horizontal asymptote for $y = 3(2)^x + 1$ is $y = 1$, because the vertical translation is 1 unit up.

The domain of all three functions is the set of real numbers. The range for $y = 2^x$ and $y = 3(2)^x$ is $\{y \mid y > 0, y \in \mathbf{R}\}$. The range for $y = 3(2)^x + 1$ is $\{y \mid y > 1, y \in \mathbf{R}\}$.

• • • • • • • •

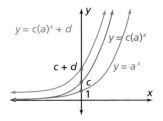

Graphs of $y = c(a)^x + d$

The graphs of $y = c(a)^x$ and $y = c(a)^x + d$ are transformations of the graph of $y = a^x$ and follow the patterns and behaviour of transformations.

Example 4   **Graphing an Exponential Application**

The value, or amount, A, of $200 invested at 8%/a, compounded semiannually, is given by $A = 200(1.04)^{2x}$, where x is the number of years the money has been invested.

(a) Graph this relation by hand or by using graphing technology.

(b) Use the graph to estimate the value of the investment after

      i. 2 years   **ii.** 3.5 years   **iii.** 5.25 years

Solution

(a) First make a table.

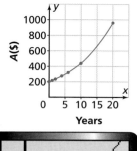

x (years)	0	1	2	4	6	10	20
A ($)	200.00	216.32	233.97	273.71	320.21	438.22	960.20

Draw a scatter plot using the ordered pairs in the table. Draw a smooth curve that connects the points.

You could also use a graphing calculator to graph the function $y = 200(1.04)^{2x}$.

Are the data discrete or continuous? The answer to this question depends on whether the investor can withdraw the full investment at any point or only at the beginning or end of a compounding period. Also, it would depend on whether the interest is calculated as compound interest when it is between compound periods.

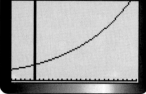

Graph of $y = 200(1.04)^{2x}$

TI-83 Plus Help
For help creating tables for a function, see the Technology Appendix, page 591.

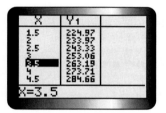

(b) To find the value of the investment after so many years, estimate a value from the graph. You could also find the information in the table created with a graphing calculator.

i. The value of the investment after 2 years is given in the table above.
$A = \$233.97$

ii. After 3.5 years, $A = \$263.19$, as shown in the graphing calculator table.

iii. Estimate the value of the investment after 5.25 years using the graph or the graphing calculator table. After 5.25 years, $A \doteq \$300$. (Note: 5.25 years is between compound periods. So, depending on the terms of the investment, the value of the investment may be the value of A after 5 years.)

• • • • • • • •

Finite Differences of Exponential Functions

Example 5

Create a table for $y = 2^x$. Determine the first and second differences. Discuss any patterns.

Solution

Create a table for $y = 2^x$ and find the first and second differences.

x	y	First Differences	Second Differences
0	1		
1	2	2 − 1 = 1	
2	4	4 − 2 = 2	2 − 1 = 1
3	8	8 − 4 = 4	4 − 2 = 2
4	16	16 − 8 = 8	8 − 4 = 4
5	32	32 − 16 = 16	16 − 8 = 8
6	64	64 − 32 = 32	32 − 16 = 16

In this case, the first and second differences and the original values for y seem to be the same, 1, 2, 4, ... Would this pattern apply to any exponential function? Try $y = 2(3)^x$.

x	y	First Differences	Second Differences
0	2		
1	6	$6 - 2 = 4$	
2	18	$18 - 6 = 12$	$12 - 4 = 8$
3	54	$54 - 18 = 36$	$36 - 12 = 24$
4	162	$162 - 54 = 108$	$108 - 36 = 72$
5	486	$486 - 162 = 324$	$324 - 108 = 216$
6	1458	$1458 - 486 = 972$	$972 - 324 = 648$

The first and second differences are not the same as the values for y.
Each successive number in the first differences increases by a factor of 3.
The second differences follow the same pattern. So the set of first differences and the set of second differences are geometric sequences whose common ratio is also the growth factor of the original exponential function. Each set of differences could also be modelled algebraically.

CHECK, CONSOLIDATE, COMMUNICATE

1. Graph $y = 5^x$ and graph $y = \left(\frac{1}{2}\right)^x$ on the same set of axes.
   On each graph, indicate the y-intercept and the horizontal asymptote.
2. Describe how to transform the graph of $y = 3^x$ to create the graph of $y = 2(3)^x - 1$.
3. Determine the patterns in the first and second differences for $y = 5^x$.

KEY IDEAS

- The exponential function $y = a^x$ has the following characteristics:
  - The domain is the set of real numbers.
  - The function is defined for $a > 0$.
  - The range is the set of positive real numbers.
  - The function either increases or decreases over its domain.
  - The function has a horizontal asymptote, which is the x-axis.
  - The graph has a y-intercept of 1.
  - As $x \to \infty$, $y \to \infty$, and as $x \to -\infty$, $y \to 0$, if $a > 1$.
  - As $x \to \infty$, $y \to 0$, and as $x \to -\infty$, $y \to \infty$, if $0 < a < 1$.

- The graphs of $y = c(a)^x$ and $y = c(a)^x + d$ are transformations of the graph of $y = a^x$.
- The first and second differences calculated from the values of the exponential function $y = c(a)^x$ are distinct exponential functions.

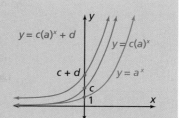

2.2 Exercises

A 1. Graph each function on the same set of axes. Discuss similarities and differences.
   (a) $y = 2^x$
   (b) $y = 3^x$
   (c) $y = 5^x$
   (d) $y = (0.6)^x$
   (e) $y = (0.2)^x$
   (f) $y = \left(\frac{1}{4}\right)^x$

2. Graph each function. State the horizontal asymptote and y-intercept.
   (a) $y = 3(2)^x$
   (b) $y = -2(3)^x$
   (c) $y = -(0.5)^x$
   (d) $y = 4(0.25)^x$
   (e) $y = 200(1.04)^x$
   (f) $y = 0.5(2)^x$

3. Graph each function. State the horizontal asymptote and y-intercept.
   (a) $y = 2^x - 1$
   (b) $y = 3(2)^x$
   (c) $y = -2(0.4)^x - 1$
   (d) $y = 4(0.4)^x + 2$

4. **Knowledge and Understanding:** Graph each function. State the horizontal asymptote, y-intercept, domain, and range.
   (a) $y = 4^x$
   (b) $y = 3(2)^x - 1$
   (c) $y = \left(\frac{1}{5}\right)^x$
   (d) $y = -2^x$
   (e) $y = 5(1.02)^x$
   (f) $y = 5^x + 2$

5. Graph each equation on the same set of axes. Discuss the similarities and differences.
   (a) $y = 3^x$
   (b) $y = -3^x$
   (c) $y = 3^{-x}$

6. The amount of an investment, A, after n years is given by $A(n) = 500(1.08)^n$. Graph this relation. What is the y-intercept, and what does it represent?

7. Graph $y = 10^x$. Use the graph to estimate the value of each expression.
   (a) $\sqrt{10}$
   (b) $10^{1.2}$
   (c) $10^{-0.3}$
   (d) $\sqrt[3]{10}$
   (e) $\sqrt{40}$
   (f) $10^{0.25}$

B 8. **Communication:** Graph $y = 2^x$, $y = 2^x + 3$, $y = 2^x - 1$, and $y = 5(2^x)$ on the same set of axes. The second, third, and fourth graphs are transformations of the graph of $y = 2^x$. Describe each set of transformations.

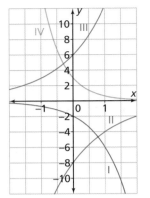

9. Match each function to the corresponding graph, I, II, III, or IV. Give reasons for each choice.

(a) $y = 3(2)^{x+1}$

(b) $y = -2(3)^x$

(c) $y = 3(0.2)^x$

(d) $y = -4(0.5)^{x-1}$

10. As people learn new tasks, they can do them more quickly with practice. In a manufacturing plant, it was determined that the time required to do any manual task decreases exponentially by 5% every month. A new employee initially takes 5 h to make a certain product. How long will this employee take to make the same product after a year on the job? Draw a graph to show the progress over the first year. Extrapolate your graph to show how long this employee will take to do the same task after 5 years. Is your graph an accurate model? Discuss.

11. Copy and complete the table.

	Function	End Behaviour as $x \to \infty$	End Behaviour as $x \to -\infty$	Behaviour as $x \to 0$
(a)	$y = 2^x$			
(b)	$y = (0.1)^x$			
(c)	$y = (1.02)^x$			
(d)	$y = 3^{x+1}$			

12. **Application**: Coffee, tea, and some soft drinks contain caffeine. The metabolism rate of caffeine varies slightly between people. Sue drinks some coffee. After 1 h, 75% of the amount of caffeine remains in her system. At the end of the next hour, 75% of the amount of caffeine at the end of the first hour remains. This pattern continues each hour. Suppose that Sue consumes 60 mg of caffeine.

(a) How much of the original amount remains after

    i. 1 h?   **ii.** 2 h?   **iii.** 4 h?

(b) Create a table and a graph to show the amount of caffeine in Sue's system over time.

(c) Determine an equation for your graph.

(d) Estimate when the amount of caffeine will be less than 1 mg.

13. Create two equations, where $y = a^x$ and $y = \left(\dfrac{1}{a}\right)^x$ and a is an integer greater than 1. Graph the equations. Compare the graphs.

14. Graph the terms of the sequence $-\dfrac{1}{2}, -1, -2, -4, -8, \ldots$. Determine an equation for the value of the nth term. How does this equation compare with what you know about exponential relations?

15. Eileen bought a diamond ring for $5000. The jeweller estimates that the ring's value will increase exponentially by 10% each year.

    (a) Determine an algebraic model where V is the ring's value and t is the number of years since the ring was purchased.

    (b) Graph this model and use it to estimate when the ring's value is double.

16. When light passes through ice, the light's intensity is reduced by 4% for every centimetre of the ice's thickness.

    (a) Determine an algebraic model where T is the ice's thickness and I is the intensity of light.

    (b) Graph this model. Use the graph to estimate the thickness of the ice if the intensity of light passing through the ice is 80%.

17. **Check Your Understanding:** Describe the effect that different values of a have on the graph of $y = a^x$.

C 18. Create a table for $y = 3(4)^x + 1$.

    (a) Find the first differences. Describe the pattern that you see in several ways.

    (b) Find the second differences. Describe the pattern.

19. Find graphical and algebraic solutions for each system of equations.

    (a) $y = 2^{x+2}$ and $y = \left(\frac{1}{2}\right)^{x-1}$

    (b) $y = 2\left(\frac{1}{3}\right)^{-x}$ and $y = 6(9)^{x+1}$

    (c) $y = 1000(0.1)^{2x}$ and $y = 10^x$

20. **Thinking, Inquiry, Problem Solving:** Graphs A and B represent two exponential growth situations. The relations are also shown in the table. **Y1** lists the y-values for one relation and **Y2** lists the y-values for the other relation.

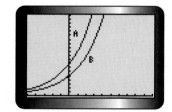   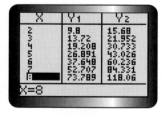

    (a) Which graph, A or B, corresponds to which columns, **X** and **Y1** or **X** and **Y2**, in the table?

    (b) The equation of each graph is in the form $y = c(1.4)^x$. For which graph, A or B, is the value of c greater? Explain your answer.

    (c) Find the value of c for each relation.

ADDITIONAL ACHIEVEMENT CHART QUESTIONS

Knowledge and Understanding: Graph each function. Also state the domain and range, whether the function is increasing or decreasing, the y-intercept, the x-intercept (if it exists), and the horizontal asymptote.

(a) $y = \left(\frac{1}{2}\right)^x$

(b) $y = 2(3)^x$

(c) $y = -4(2)^x$

(d) $y = \frac{1}{2}(3)^x - 2$

Application: An old coin was worth 50¢ originally and has been growing exponentially in value by 15% every year. Predict the coin's value after 3.5 years.

Thinking, Inquiry, Problem Solving: Two investments are made. In one, $2500 is invested at 5% compounded annually. In the other, $2000 is invested at 6% compounded annually. Approximately when will the investments have the same value?

Communication: The number of bacteria in a culture doubles every day. Initially, there are 100 bacteria.

(a) Describe the graph of this relation.

(b) Describe the graph if there were initially 125 bacteria instead of 100. Compare this graph and your graph for (a).

(c) Describe the graph if the number of bacteria tripled instead of doubled. Compare this graph and your graph for (a).

(d) Describe the graph if the number of bacteria doubled every three days instead of every day. Compare this graph and your graph for (a).

The Chapter Problem
Determining Concentration

In this section, you studied exponential functions. Apply what you learned to answer these questions about The Chapter Problem on page 82.

CP3. In section 2.1, you determined an equation for the amount of a drug in a patient's system over time. Draw a graph of the equation that you created.

CP4. Graph the data given for The Chapter Problem on page 82. Does the graph represent an exponential function? How do you know? What is the y-intercept?

2.3 Various Forms of Exponential Functions

SETTING THE STAGE

Now you have seen several examples of exponential growth. In grade 11, you used exponential growth formulas to describe compound interest, growth of bacterial populations, and geometric sequences. Here are some of these formulas:

Compound Interest:

$A = P(1 + i)^n$, where A is the amount, representing a combination of the principal and compounded interest
P is the original principal invested
i is the interest rate per compounding period
n is the number of compounding periods

Doubling period is the time required for a quantity to grow to twice its original amount.

Exponential Growth (involving a doubling period):

$M = c(2)^{\frac{t}{D}}$, where M is the total amount or number
c is the initial amount or number
2 is the growth factor
t is the time
D is the doubling period

Half-life is the time required for a material to decay to one-half of its original mass or quantity.

Exponential Decay (involving half-life):

$M = c\left(\dfrac{1}{2}\right)^{\frac{t}{h}}$, where M is the remaining mass of the decayed material
c is the original mass of the material
$\dfrac{1}{2}$ is the decay factor
t is the time
h is the half-life

Geometric Sequence:

$t_n = a(r)^{n-1}$, where t_n is the nth term of the sequence
a is the first term
r is the common ratio
n is the number of terms

Exponential Function:

$y = c(a)^x$, where y is the total amount or number
c is the initial amount or number
a is the growth factor or decay factor
x is the number of growth periods or decay periods

1. What do all of these formulas have in common?

2. Can you use $y = c(a)^x$ to represent each of the other formulas?

3. Compare the exponential decay formula with $y = c(a)^x$. Which variables are similar?

4. Compare the compound interest formula with $y = c(a)^x$. Which variables are similar?

In this section, you will examine these familiar formulas and look for a common model that represents all of these situations.

EXAMINING THE CONCEPT

Using Exponential Growth and Decay Formulas

Each of the first four formulas can be directly compared with the general exponential function, $y = c(a)^x$.

For instance, compare the compound interest formula and the general exponential function.

Compound Interest:	**General Exponential Function:**
$A = P(1 + i)^n$	$y = c(a)^x$

Both P and c represent the initial value. Both $(1 + i)^n$ and $(a)^x$ are powers, and $(1 + i)$ and a represent the growth factor and are only positive values.

The exponential growth and exponential decay formulas also have initial values, powers, and positive bases.

Example 1   ### Exponential Growth

One bacterium divides into two bacteria every 5 days.

(a) Initially, there are 15 bacteria. How many bacteria will there be in 10 days?

(b) What is the approximate growth rate per day?

Solution

(a) Use the growth formula $M = c(2)^{\frac{t}{D}}$.

$c = 15$, $t = 10$, and $D = 5$

$$
\begin{aligned}
M &= c(2)^{\frac{t}{D}} && \text{Substitute known values.} \\
&= 15(2)^{\frac{10}{5}} && \text{Simplify.} \\
&= 15(2)^2 && \text{Evaluate.} \\
&= 60
\end{aligned}
$$

Therefore, there will be 60 bacteria in 10 days.

(b) To calculate the growth rate per day, use the information in (a) and the general exponential function $y = c(a)^x$.

Then $c = 15$, $x = 10$ (for 10 days), and $y = 60$ (the number of bacteria after 10 days).

$$y = c(a)^x \qquad \text{Substitute known values.}$$
$$60 = 15(a)^{10} \qquad \text{Divide by 15 to isolate } a^{10}.$$
$$\frac{60}{15} = a^{10} \qquad \text{Simplify and find the tenth root of each side.}$$
$$\sqrt[10]{4} = \sqrt[10]{a^{10}} \qquad \text{Evaluate.}$$
$$1.15 \doteq a$$

The growth factor is about 1.15, which means the colony is increasing in size at a rate of 15% per day.

• • • • • • • •

Example 2 **Compound Interest**

Ravinder's parents invested $4000 in an account when he was born. The account pays interest at 6%/a, compounded quarterly. How much money will be in the account on Ravinder's 18th birthday?

Solution

Use the compound interest formula $A = P(1 + i)^n$, where $P = 4000$. The variable i represents the interest rate per compounding period and n represents the number of compounding periods. In this case, there are four compounding periods per year, since interest is compounded quarterly.

So $i = \frac{6\%}{4} = 1.5\%$, or 0.015, and $n = 4 \times 18$, or 72.

$$A = 4000(1.015)^{72} \qquad \text{Evaluate.}$$
$$= 11\ 684.63$$

Therefore, there will be $11 684.63 in the account on Ravinder's 18th birthday.

• • • • • • • •

Example 3 **Exponential Decay**

Archaeologists use carbon-14 dating to estimate the age of relics. All living organisms contain non-radioactive carbon, carbon-12, and radioactive carbon, carbon-14. When an organism dies, the amount of carbon-12 remains the same, but carbon-14 decays exponentially. The half-life of carbon-14 is about 5370 years. Nikolai finds some wood and pottery in a cave. The pottery is thought to be about 8055 years old. Nikolai checks the age of the pottery by carbon dating the wood. If the wood is the same age as the pottery, how much carbon-14 should be in the wood? Express your answer as a percent, to the nearest tenth.

Solution

Apply the decay formula $M = c\left(\frac{1}{2}\right)^{\frac{t}{h}}$, where M is the remaining amount of carbon-14, c is the initial amount, t is the time, and h is the half-life. In this case, $c = 100$, because originally there was 100% of the radioactive material. $t = 8055$ and $h = 5370$. Solve for M.

$$M = 100\left(\frac{1}{2}\right)^{\frac{8055}{5370}} \qquad \text{Simplify.}$$
$$= 100\left(\frac{1}{2}\right)^{1.5} \qquad \text{Evaluate.}$$
$$\doteq 35.4$$

Therefore, about 35.4% of the amount of carbon-14 should remain in the wood.

Another solution is to use $y = c(a)^x$, with $c = 100$, $a = \frac{1}{2}$, and $x = 1.5$, which is the number of decay periods.

CHECK, CONSOLIDATE, COMMUNICATE

1. In what ways are the formulas for compound interest, exponential growth, exponential decay, a geometric sequence, and the exponential function similar?
2. Is there one formula that could be used for all scenarios? Which formula, and why?
3. How does the value of a in $y = c(a)^x$ relate to another variable in each of the other formulas?

KEY IDEAS

- The formulas for determining compound interest, exponential growth, exponential decay, and geometric sequences (on page 107) all correspond to the general exponential function $y = c(a)^x$, where

    y is the final amount or number
    c is the initial amount or number
    a is the growth factor
    x is the number of growth periods

2.3 Exercises

A 1. Which is the best investment if the money in each case is invested for three years?

A: $5000 at 8%/a, compounded monthly; B: $5000 at 8.2%/a, compounded annually; or C: $5000 at 8.1%/a, compounded semiannually

2. The population of a bacteria culture doubles after 1.5 h. An experiment begins with 620 bacteria. Determine the number of bacteria after

(a) 3 h   (b) 6 h   (c) 10 h

(d) 1 day   (e) 3 days   (f) 1 week

3. The half-life of a radioactive material is about 2 years. How much of a 5-kg sample of this material would remain after

(a) 4 years?   **(b)** 3 years?   **(c)** 5.5 years?   **(d)** 18 months?

4. **Knowledge and Understanding:** The population of Littleton is currently 23 000. Assume that Littleton's exponential growth rate is 2% per year.

(a) Copy and complete the table by predicting the population for the next six years.

Time (years)	0	1	2	3	4	5	6
Population	23 000						

(b) Graph the data.

(c) Create an equation to model the data.

(d) Use your equation to predict the population in 10 years.

(e) Use your graph to estimate how long it will take the population to reach 30 000.

(f) Predict Littleton's population after 10 years if the growth rate was 3% rather than 2%.

B 5. **Application:** A population, P, is increasing exponentially. At time $t = 0$ years, the population is 35 000. In 10 years, the population is 44 400.

(a) Find a in $P = k(a)^t$.

(b) Using the value of a that you calculated, write an equation that models the population, P, after t years.

(c) Using your equation, find when the population reaches 100 000.

6. A bacteria culture starts with 3000 bacteria and grows to a population of 12 000 after 3 h.

(a) Find the doubling period.

(b) Find the population after t hours.

(c) Determine the number of bacteria after 8 h.

(d) Determine the number of bacteria after 1 h.

7. The half-life of caffeine in a child's system when a child eats or drinks something with caffeine in it is 2.5 h. How much caffeine would remain in a child's body if the child ate a chocolate bar with 20 mg of caffeine 8 h before?

8. Twelve grams of tritium decays to 9.25 g in 2.5 years. Use a method to estimate the half-life of tritium.

9. A radioactive form of uranium has a half-life of 2.5×10^5 years.

(a) Find the remaining mass of a 1-g sample after t years.

(b) Determine the remaining mass of this sample after 5000 years.

10. **Communication:** Describe the similarities between the various forms of exponential functions. Which do you think is easier to work with—several forms, each describing a certain situation, or the general exponential function? Explain.

11. The half-life of carbon-14 is about 5370 years. What percent of the original carbon-14 would you expect to find in a sample after 2500 years?

12. An old stamp is currently worth $60. The stamp's value will grow exponentially by 15% each year.

    (a) What will be the value of the stamp in eight years?

    (b) When will the stamp be worth three times its initial value?

13. A photocopier, which originally cost $500 000, depreciates exponentially in value by 10% each year.

    (a) What will be the photocopier's value in five years?

    (b) When will the photocopier's value be $175 000? Use guess and check.

14. After an accident at a nuclear power plant, which caused a radiation leak, the radiation level at the accident site was 950 R (roentgens). Five hours later, the radiation level was 800 R. Radiation levels decay exponentially. Calculate the decay factor.

15. Anne bought a new car for $35 000 and sold it five years later for $18 475. Assume that the value of the vehicle depreciates exponentially. Calculate the rate of depreciation per year.

16. Mark invests $500 in a savings plan that pays interest, which is compounded monthly. At the end of 10 years, his initial investment is worth $909.70. What interest rate did the plan pay?

17. **Check Your Understanding:** An exponential function is expressed in the form $y = c(a)^x$. How can you tell whether the relation represents growth or decay?

C 18. An investment triples in value in about nine years. What is the annual interest rate if interest is compounded quarterly?

19. **Thinking, Inquiry, Problem Solving:** The values for world population in the table are estimates.

Year	1750	1800	1850	1900	1950
World Population	7×10^8	9×10^8	1.18×10^9	1.6×10^9	2.5×10^9

    (a) By what percent does the population increase for each 50-year period?

    (b) Create an algebraic model for the data.

    (c) In 2000, the population was 6×10^9. Does this value fit your model? If not, how can you adjust your model so the value fits?

20. The population of a small town increases exponentially. In 1999, the population was 16 000, and in 2002 it was 60 000. What will the population be in 2010?

ADDITIONAL ACHIEVEMENT CHART QUESTIONS

Knowledge and Understanding: The general term of a geometric series is $t_n = 9(3)^{n-1}$.

(a) What is the first term?

(b) What is the common ratio?

(c) What is the 12th term?

(d) Show algebraically that the series represented by $t_n = 9(3)^{n-1}$ is the same as the series represented by $t_n = 3^{n+1}$.

Application: Sabrina invests $1500, which earns interest at 4.5%/a, compounded semiannually. How much more would the investment be worth at the end of three years if the interest was compounded quarterly, not semiannually?

Thinking, Inquiry, Problem Solving: In 1996, Ontario's population was about 10.7 million. Ontario's population will be about 13.7 million in 2016.

(a) Calculate the annual growth rate of Ontario's population.

(b) What would Ontario's population have been in 1980?

(c) What have you assumed for (a) and (b)?

Communication: During an archaeological dig, Selma found a tool that resembled a small hatchet with a wooden handle.

(a) Carbon-14 has a half-life of about 5370 years. Explain what this means.

(b) Create an equation that relates the percent of carbon-14 remaining to the tool's age. Explain what each part of the equation represents.

(c) Explain how you can tell from the equation that the amount of carbon-14 is decreasing.

(d) Explain how you can tell from the equation that the amount of carbon-14 is decreasing exponentially.

The Chapter Problem
Determining Concentration

In this section, you have learned more about the exponential function. Apply what you learned to answer these questions about The Chapter Problem on page 82.

CP5. Assume that, every hour, 90% of the drug remains in the patient's system. What is the half-life of the drug?

CP6. Assume that the half-life of the drug is 2 h. Graph the function and create an algebraic model for the graph.

2.4 The Logarithmic Function

SETTING THE STAGE

Archaeologists use carbon-14 dating to estimate the age of very old objects. The half-life of carbon-14 is about 5370 years. Testing of a particular object shows that 70% of the carbon-14 remains in an object. How old is the object?

Use the exponential decay formula $M = c\left(\frac{1}{2}\right)^{\frac{t}{h}}$.

Substituting known values,

$$70 = 100\left(\frac{1}{2}\right)^{\frac{t}{5370}} \qquad \text{Simplify.}$$

$$0.7 = 1\left(\frac{1}{2}\right)^{\frac{t}{5370}}$$

The next step is to isolate t, but solving for an exponent is difficult at this point. To solve for x in $15 = 5^x$, you could guess and check, using a calculator. Or, you could draw a graph and use the graph to estimate a value for x. However, both of these methods provide only approximate values. In this case, you need a more accurate method to solve for t.

   In this section, you will develop a new function that will enable you to solve exponential equations algebraically.

EXAMINING THE CONCEPT

Defining the Logarithmic Function

To isolate x in the exponential function $y = a^x$, you need to "work backward." In other words, you need to find the inverse function of $y = a^x$.

   This mathematical dilemma was "solved" by John Napier (1550−1617) through the development of the logarithm. The **logarithmic function** is the inverse of the exponential function. You will use the logarithmic function to isolate the exponent.

   Start with the graph of an exponential function. To graph the inverse relation, reflect the original relation in the line $y = x$.

The graph of $y = 2^x$ is reflected in the line $y = x$ to produce the graph of the inverse relation.

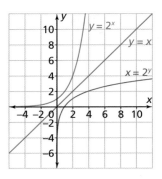

To find the equation of the inverse algebraically, switch x and y. Then isolate x on one side of the equation, if needed.

So, the inverse of $y = 2^x$ is $x = 2^y$.

To express this equation in the form $y = f(x)$, use logarithmic notation.

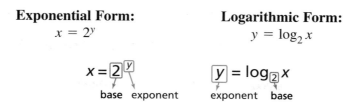

Exponential Form:
$$x = 2^y$$

Logarithmic Form:
$$y = \log_2 x$$

$$x = \boxed{2}^{\boxed{y}} \qquad \boxed{y} = \log_{\boxed{2}} x$$

base exponent $\qquad$ exponent base

The logarithmic form $y = \log_2 x$ is read "y is equal to the logarithm, or log, of x to the base 2." It means "find the exponent." Both forms are equivalent, and contain a base and an exponent.

Definition of a Logarithmic Function

The exponential function $x = a^y$ can be written as the **logarithmic function** $y = \log_a x$, where $a > 0$ and $a \neq 1$. A logarithm is the exponent required on base a to give the value x.

The logarithmic function $x = a^y$ is the inverse of the exponential function $y = a^x$.

Example 1 **Changing between Exponential and Logarithmic Forms**

(a) Write each exponential equation in logarithmic form.

i. $4^3 = 64$ $\qquad\qquad$ **ii.** $25^{\frac{1}{2}} = 5$

(b) Write each logarithmic equation in exponential form.

i. $\log_3 81 = 4$ $\qquad\qquad$ **ii.** $\log_4 1 = 0$

Solution

(a) **i.** $4^3 = 64$ in logarithmic form is $\log_4 64 = 3$

> For $\log_3 81$, ask yourself what exponent would make this statement true: $3^? = 81$. Remember that a logarithm is an exponent.

$\qquad$ **ii.** $25^{\frac{1}{2}} = 5$ in logarithmic form is $\log_{25} 5 = \frac{1}{2}$

(b) **i.** $\log_3 81 = 4$ in exponential form is $3^4 = 81$

$\qquad$ **ii.** $\log_4 1 = 0$ in exponential form is $4^0 = 1$

• • • • • • • •

Example 2 **Evaluating Logarithms**

Evaluate.

(a) $\log_5 125$ $\qquad\qquad$ (b) $\log_2 8$ $\qquad\qquad$ (c) $\log_4 \frac{1}{2}$

Solution

(a) Let $\log_5 125 = y$. Rewrite the equation in exponential form.

$$5^y = 125$$

> To solve $\log_5 125$, ask, "What exponent makes 125 a power of 5?"

Since $5^3 = 125$, $y = 3$.

Therefore, $\log_5 125 = 3$.

(b) $\log_2 8 = 3$, since $2^3 = 8$

(c) Let $\log_4 \dfrac{1}{2} = y$. Rewrite the equation in exponential form.

$$4^y = \frac{1}{2} \qquad\qquad \text{Express } \frac{1}{2} \text{ as a power of 4.}$$

$$4^y = 4^{-\frac{1}{2}}$$

$$\therefore y = -\frac{1}{2}$$

Therefore, $\log_4 \dfrac{1}{2} = -\dfrac{1}{2}$.

• • • • • • • •

Example 3 · Graphing Logarithmic Functions

Graph $y = \log_3 x$. Describe the domain and range, the intercepts, and the asymptotes.

Solution

Recall that the graphs of a function and its inverse are reflections of each other through the line $y = x$.

The graph of $y = \log_3 x$ is the inverse of $y = 3^x$. $y = 3^x$ has a domain of $\{x \mid x \in \mathbf{R}\}$, a range of $\{y \mid y > 0, y \in \mathbf{R}\}$, a y-intercept of 1, and a horizontal asymptote of $x = 0$. $y = \log_3 x$ has a domain of $\{x \mid x > 0, x \in \mathbf{R}\}$, a range of $\{y \mid y \in \mathbf{R}\}$, an x-intercept of 1, and a vertical asymptote of $y = 0$.

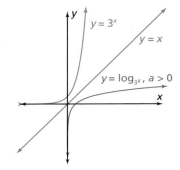

• • • • • • • •

You may have noticed the $\boxed{\text{LOG}}$ key on your calculator. You can use this key to evaluate only a logarithm with base 10, which is called a **common logarithm**.

Base 10 is usually not included in the expression for a common logarithm. For example, $\log 100$ means $\log_{10} 100$.

Example 4 · Working with Common Logarithms

Solve for x. Round your answers to the nearest hundredth, if necessary.

(a) $x = \log 100$ **(b)** $\log 25 = x$ **(c)** $\log x = 0.25$

Solution

(a) $\log 100 = \log_{10} 100$
$$= 2$$

(b) $\log 25 = \log_{10} 25$
$$\doteq 1.40$$

(c) If $\log x = 0.25$, then $\log_{10} x = 0.25$. In exponential form, $10^{0.25} = x$. So $x \doteq 1.78$.

1. Explain the relationship between $y = a^x$ and $y = \log_a x$ in as many ways as you can.
2. Create an expression in exponential form and change it to logarithmic form.
3. What is a common logarithm? Explain. Create a logarithmic expression that can be evaluated with your scientific calculator using the common logarithm.

KEY IDEAS

- A logarithm is an exponent.
- $y = \log_a x$ is read "y is equal to the logarithm, or log, of x to the base a."
- The logarithmic function $y = \log_a x$, where $a \neq 1$ and $a > 0$, can be written as the exponential function $x = a^y$. The function $x = a^y$, or $y = \log_a x$, is the inverse of $y = a^x$.
- $y = \log_a x$ if and only if $x = a^y$.
- To evaluate an expression or solve for a variable, it is often necessary to change between the logarithmic and exponential forms of an expression.
- $\log x$ is a common logarithm and means $\log_{10} x$.

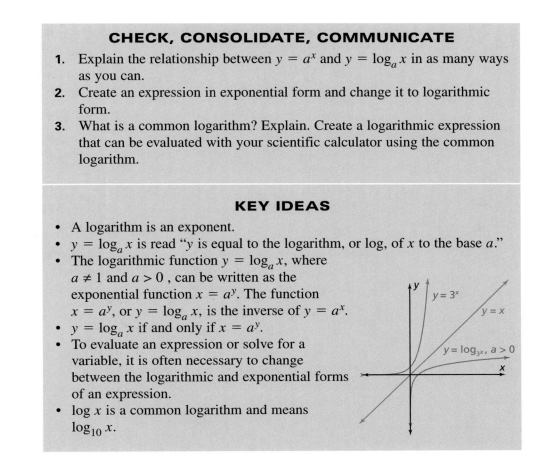

2.4 Exercises

A 1. Copy and complete the table.

Exponential Form	Logarithmic Form
$8 = 2^3$	
	$4 = \log_2 16$
	$3 = \log 1000$
$2^{\frac{1}{2}} = \sqrt{2}$	
	$-3 = \log_2 \frac{1}{8}$
$25^{-\frac{1}{2}} = \frac{1}{5}$	

2. Express in exponential form.
   (a) $\log_5 25 = 2$ (b) $\log_2 16 = 4$ (c) $\log_3 27 = 3$
   (d) $\log_2 0.5 = -1$ (e) $\log_4 2 = \frac{1}{2}$ (f) $\log_7 1 = 0$

3. Express in logarithmic form.
   (a) $2^3 = 8$ (b) $\sqrt{9} = 3$ (c) $10^4 = 10\ 000$
   (d) $3^{-2} = \frac{1}{9}$ (e) $125^{\frac{1}{3}} = 5$ (f) $4^{-\frac{1}{2}} = \frac{1}{2}$

4. Evaluate.
   (a) $\log_3 27$ (b) $\log_4 2$ (c) $\log_5 125 - \log_5 25$
   (d) $\log 1$ (e) $\log_7 \sqrt{7}$ (f) $\log_2 8$
   (g) $\log_4 4$ (h) $\log_3 27 + \log_3 81$ (i) $\log_2 16 - \log_2 32$

5. **Knowledge and Understanding:** Graph each function and its inverse. Describe the domain, the range, and the asymptote of the function and its inverse. State the equation of the inverse function.
   (a) $y = 4^x$ (b) $y = \log_5 x$ (c) $y = (0.5)^x$
   (d) $y = \log_7 x$ (e) $y = 10^x$ (f) $y = \log_4 x$

6. Graph all three functions on the same set of axes. Describe the transformations on the graph of the function in (a) to obtain the graph of the function in (b) and on the graph of the function in (b) to obtain the graph of the function in (c).
   (a) $y = \log_5 x$ (b) $y = 3\log_5 x$ (c) $y = 3\log_5 (x) + 4$

7. Solve for x, to the nearest hundredth.
   (a) $\log 100 = x$ (b) $\log x = 2$ (c) $\log 0.01 = x$
   (d) $\log x = 3.8$ (e) $\log 0.001 = x$ (f) $\log x = 2.5$

B   8. **Communication**
   (a) Describe the graph of $y = \log_a x$ for $a > 1$ and for $0 < a < 1$.
   (b) Explain why $a \neq 1$ in $y = \log_a x$.

9. Graph each function and state its domain and range.
   (a) $y = \log (x + 6)$ (b) $y = \log_5 x$ (c) $y = 2 + \log x$
   (d) $y = -3 \log x$ (e) $y = \log_2 (x + 2)$ (f) $y = \frac{1}{2} \log_3 x - 1$

10. Explain the relationships among the domain, range, and asymptotes of $y = a^x$ and $y = \log_a x$. Use an example to illustrate.

11. **Application:** In section 2.1, the rumour function $N = 3^{t + 1}$ was developed, where t was the time in hours and N was the number of people told during that particular hour. Determine an equation for the inverse function that would give the time if the number of people told that hour was known. Determine, to the nearest minute, how long it would take for 100 people to hear the rumour.

12. Sketch a graph of each of the following:

    (a) $y = \log_2 x$ **(b)** $y = \log_2 (x - 2)$ **(c)** $y = 3 \log_2 (x - 2)$

13. Use a graphing calculator to graph each function in question 12 to test your conjectures.

14. Is $\log_a a^b = b$ true or false? Justify your answer.

15. Match each equation to its graph. Then copy and complete the table.

    (a) $y = \log_4 x$ **(b)** $y = -(2)^x$ **(c)** $y = 4^x$

    (d) $y = (0.5)^x$ **(e)** $y = -\log_2 x$

i.   **ii.**   **iii.**

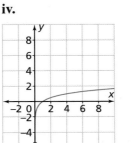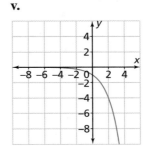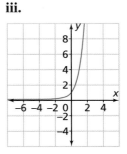

iv.   **v.**

Graph	Equation	x-intercept	y-intercept	End Behaviour as $x \to \infty$	End Behaviour as $x \to -\infty$
i.					
ii.					
iii.					
iv.					
v.					

16. **Check Your Understanding**

    (a) Explain the relationship between a logarithm and an exponent.

    (b) Explain why x is always positive in $y = \log_a x$.

17. For $f(x) = 3^x$,

    (a) determine $f^{-1}(x)$

    (b) determine $(f^{-1} \circ f)(x)$ and $(f \circ f^{-1})(x)$

**John Napier
(1550–1617)**

Scottish mathematician John Napier invented logarithms. The word *logarithm* is composed of the two words *logic* and *arithmetic*. Napier did not develop the natural logarithmic function, but it is occasionally called the Napierian logarithm, in his honour.

18. Find the inverse of each relation.

(a) $y = \sqrt[3]{x}$ (b) $y = 3(2)^x$

(c) $y = (0.5)^{x+2}$ (d) $y = 3 \log_2 (x - 3) + 2$

19. Thinking, Inquiry, Problem Solving: The bacterium *Escherichia coli*, or E-coli, has a doubling period of 0.32 h. If a culture starts with 100 bacteria:

(a) Determine the equation for the number of bacteria, y, in x hours.

(b) Graph this equation.   (c) Graph the inverse.

(d) Find the equation of the inverse. What does this equation represent?

(e) How many hours will pass before there are 450 bacteria in the culture? Use your graph or equation of the inverse to estimate an answer. Explain your method.

20. The half-life of sodium-24 is 15 h.

(a) Copy and complete the table

Amount of Sodium-24 (mg) (x)	100				
Number of Hours (y)	0	15	30	45	60

(b) Graph the ordered pairs in the table.

(c) Determine an equation for your graph.

21. Graph each function and its inverse. State the domain, range, and asymptotes of each. Determine the equation of the inverse.

(a) $y = 3 \log (x + 6)$ (b) $y = -2 \log_5 3x$ (c) $y = 2 + 3 \log x$

(d) $y = 20(8)^x$ (e) $y = 2(3)^{x+2}$ (f) $y = -5^x - 3$

ADDITIONAL ACHIEVEMENT CHART QUESTIONS

Knowledge and Understanding: Evaluate.

(a) $\log 100$ (b) $\log_4 256$ (c) $\log_4 \left(\frac{1}{2} \right)$ (d) $\log_7 1$

Application: The number of bacteria in a dish increases by a factor of 10 every week. If there are initially 50 bacteria in the dish, how long will it take to have 1800 bacteria?

Thinking, Inquiry, Problem Solving

(a) What is the value of $a^{\log_a b}$? Create some examples to help you determine your answer.

(b) How are $\log_a b$ and $\log_b a$ related? Create some examples to help you determine your answer.

Communication

(a) Suppose you are asked to evaluate $\log_a b$. Describe exactly what number you are looking for.

(b) Use your answer in (a) to explain why $\log_5 0$ and $\log_5 (-25)$ have no solution.

2.5 Laws of Logarithms

SETTING THE STAGE

Simplifying logarithmic expressions is like simplifying algebraic expressions. In this section, you will develop some laws for logarithms that you can use for simplifying logarithmic expressions.

EXAMINING THE CONCEPT

Developing the Laws of Logarithms

Recall that logarithms are exponents, Thus, you can apply the laws of exponents to logarithms. Recall the three basic exponent laws.

Exponent Laws

Product Law: $\qquad a^x \times a^y = a^{x+y}$

Quotient Law: $\qquad a^x \div a^y = a^{x-y}$

Power of a Power Law: $\qquad (a^x)^y = a^{xy}$

How do you combine logarithms with the same base? Consider the expression $\log 5 + \log 2$. Is $\log 5 + \log 2 = \log 7$? Or is $\log 5 + \log 2 = \log 10$? The base of $\log 5$ and the base of $\log 2$ is 10. So use your calculator to calculate the sum. $\log 5 + \log 2 = 1$, which means that $\log 5 + \log 2 = \log 10$.

Example 1 **Adding Logarithms with the Same Base**

Express $\log_a m + \log_a n$ as a single logarithm.

Solution
Let $\log_a m = x$ and let $\log_a n = y$. Therefore, $\log_a m + \log_a n = x + y$.
Also, since $\log_a m = x$, $a^x = m$. Since $\log_a n = y$, $a^y = n$.

Therefore,

$$mn = (a^x)(a^y)$$
$$mn = a^{x+y}$$

Rewrite $mn = a^{x+y}$ in logarithmic form.

$\log_a mn = x + y \qquad$ However, from above, $\log_a m = x$ and $\log_a n = y$.
So, $\log_a mn = \log_a m + \log_a n$.

. . . .

Law for Logarithms of Products

$$\log_a mn = \log_a m + \log_a n$$

The log of a product of factors equals the sum of the logs of the factors.

Use the law of logarithms of products to evaluate $\log_6 4 + \log_6 9$.

$$\log_6 4 + \log_6 9 = \log_6 (4)(9) \qquad \text{Simplify.}$$
$$= \log_6 36 \qquad \text{Evaluate.}$$
$$= 2$$

Now find the difference between logs with the same base.

Example 2 **Subtracting Logarithms with the Same Base**

Express $\log_a m - \log_a n$ as a single logarithm.

Solution

Let $\log_a m = x$ and let $\log_a n = y$. Therefore, $\log_a m - \log_a n = x - y$.

Also, since $\log_a m = x$, $a^x = m$. Since $\log_a n = y$, $a^y = n$.

Therefore,

$$\frac{m}{n} = \frac{a^x}{a^y}$$

$$\frac{m}{n} = a^{x - y}$$

Rewrite $\frac{m}{n} = a^{x - y}$ in logarithmic form.

$$\log_a \left(\frac{m}{n}\right) = x - y \qquad \text{However, from above, } \log_a m = x \text{ and } \log_a n = y.$$

So $\log_a \left(\frac{m}{n}\right) = \log_a m - \log_a n$.

· · · · · · · · ·

Law for Logarithms of Quotients

$$\log_a \left(\frac{m}{n}\right) = \log_a m - \log_a n, \; n \neq 0$$

The log of a quotient equals the log of the dividend less the log of the divisor.

Use the law for logarithms of quotients to simplify $\log_2 18 - \log_2 9$.

$$\log_2 18 - \log_2 9 = \log_2 \left(\frac{18}{9}\right) \qquad \text{Simplify.}$$
$$= \log_2 2 \qquad \text{Evaluate.}$$
$$= 1$$

Example 3   **Finding the Logarithm of a Power**

What is the value of $\log_3 9^2$?

Solution
$$\log_3 9^2 = \log_3 81$$
$$= 4$$

Another solution is to use the law for logarithms of products.

$$\log_3 9^2 = \log_3 (9)(9) \qquad \text{Apply the law for logarithms of products.}$$
$$= \log_3 9 + \log_3 9 \qquad \text{Simplify.}$$
$$= 2 \log_3 9 \qquad \text{Evaluate.}$$
$$= 2(2)$$
$$= 4$$

• • • • • • • •

In general, if $p \in \mathbf{N}$ and using the law for logarithms of products,

$$\log_a m^p = \underbrace{\log_a m + \log_a m + \log_a m + \dots + \log_a m}_{p \text{ times}}$$
$$= p \log_a m$$

Law for Logarithms of Powers

$\log_a m^p = p \log_a m$ $(m > 0, p \in \mathbf{R})$

The log of a power equals the exponent of the power times the log of the base of the power.

Now evaluate $2 \log_{10} 2 + 2 \log_{10} 5$.

$$2 \log_{10} 2 + 2 \log_{10} 5 = \log_{10} 2^2 + \log_{10} 5^2 \qquad \text{Use the law for logarithms of powers.}$$
$$= \log_{10} (4)(25) \qquad \text{Use the law for logarithms of products.}$$
$$= \log_{10} 100 \qquad \text{Evaluate.}$$
$$= 2$$

Example 4   **Evaluating the Logarithm of a Power**

Evaluate $\log_2 \sqrt{8}$.

Solution
$$\log_2 \sqrt{8} = \log_2 (8)^{\frac{1}{2}} \qquad \text{Apply the law for logarithms of powers.}$$
$$= \frac{1}{2} \log_2 8 \qquad \text{Evaluate and simplify.}$$
$$= \frac{1}{2} (3)$$
$$= \frac{3}{2}$$

• • • • • • • •

It is often necessary to use the laws of logarithms to solve logarithmic equations.

Example 5   **Solving a Logarithmic Equation**

Solve for x in $\log_3 x = \frac{1}{2}\log_3 36 + \log_3 18 - \log_3 2$.

Solution

Express the right side as a single logarithm with base 3.

$\log_3 x = \frac{1}{2}\log_3 36 + \log_3 18 - \log_3 2$ Use the law for logarithms of powers.

$\log_3 x = \log_3 (36)^{\frac{1}{2}} + \log_3 18 - \log_3 2$ Simplify.

$\log_3 x = \log_3 6 + \log_3 18 - \log_3 2$ Use the law for logarithms of products.

$\log_3 x = \log_3 (6)(18) - \log_3 2$ Use the law for logarithms of quotients.

$\log_3 x = \log_3 \frac{(6)(18)}{2}$ Simplify.

$\log_3 x = \log_3 54$

$\therefore x = 54$

· · · · · · · · ·

Equivalent Logarithms

If $\log_a m = \log_a n$, then $m = n$, provided $a > 0$, and $a \neq 1$.

This result is true only when the logarithms have the same base.

CHECK, CONSOLIDATE, COMMUNICATE

1. Evaluate $\log_8 16 + \log_8 4$.
2. Evaluate $\log 2000 - \log 2$.
3. Express $2\log_3 5 + 3\log_3 2$ as a single logarithm.
4. Give an example to show that the law for logarithms of powers works.

KEY IDEAS

- If m and n are positive numbers, a is a positive number other than 1, and p is any real number, then the following laws hold true:

  Law for Logarithms of Products: $\log_a (mn) = \log_a m + \log_a n$

  Law for Logarithms of Quotients: $\log_a \left(\frac{m}{n}\right) = \log_a m - \log_a n$, $n \neq 0$

  Law for Logarithms of Powers: $\log_a m^p = p\log_a m$

- If $\log_a m = \log_a n$, then $m = n$, provided $a > 0$, and $a \neq 1$.

A 1. Evaluate each expression by first using the laws of logarithms.

(a) $\log_2 320 - \log_2 20$ (b) $\log_2 144 - \log_2 9$

(c) $\log_6 4 + \log_6 9$ (d) $\log 4 + \log 25$

(e) $\log_8 16 + \log_8 32$ (f) $\log_3 27 + \log_3 9$

2. Use the laws of logarithms to expand each expression.

(a) $\log_2 (14 \times 9)$ (b) $\log_5 \left(\frac{735}{40} \right)$

(c) $\log_7 (25)^{\frac{1}{2}}$ (d) $\log_6 (9 \times 8 \times 7)$

(e) $\log_3 (15)^4$ (f) $\log_4 \left(\frac{81}{30} \right)$

3. Evaluate each expression without using a calculator.

(a) $\log 25 + \log 4$ (b) $\log_3 18 - \log_3 6$

(c) $\log_2 8^3$ (d) $\log_3 \sqrt{9}$

(e) $\log_6 3 + \log_6 12$ (f) $2 \log_5 15 - \log_5 9$

(g) $\log_4 32 - \log_4 2$ (h) $\log_2 (32)^4$

4. Evaluate, using the law for logarithms of powers.

(a) $\log_3 \sqrt[3]{9}$ (b) $\log_3 \sqrt[4]{27}$

(c) $\log_6 \sqrt[3]{36}$ (d) $\log_5 \sqrt{125}$

(e) $\log_8 \sqrt[3]{64}$ (f) $\log_4 \left(\frac{1}{16} \right)$

5. **Knowledge and Understanding:** Evaluate and then state the logarithmic law that you used.

(a) $\log_8 6 - \log_8 3 + \log_8 2$ (b) $\log_2 \sqrt[3]{32}$

(c) $\log_3 54 + \log_3 \left(\frac{3}{2} \right)$ (d) $\log_5 \sqrt[5]{125}$

(e) $\log_8 2 + 3 \log_8 2 + \frac{1}{2} \log_8 16$ (f) $\log_2 \left(\frac{1}{8} \right)$

6. Express each expression as a single logarithm.

(a) $3 \log_5 2 + \log_5 7$ (b) $2 \log_3 8 - 5 \log_3 2$

(c) $2 \log_2 3 + \log_2 5$ (d) $\log_3 12 + \log_3 2 - \log_3 6$

(e) $\log_4 3 + \frac{1}{2} \log_4 8 - \log_4 2$ (f) $2 \log 8 + \log 9 - \log 36$

7. Evaluate $\log_2 (8)(32) + \log_7 (49)(\sqrt[4]{7})$.

8. Given $x = \log_2 5$ and $y = \log_2 3$, evaluate each expression in terms of x and y.

(a) $\log_2 15$ (b) $\log_2 0.6$ (c) $\log_2 125$

9. Solve for x.

(a) $\log_2 x = \log_2 5 + \log_2 10$

(b) $\log_3 x = \log_3 18 - \log_3 3$

(c) $\log x = \log 84 + \log 5 - \log 7$

(d) $\log x = 2 \log 4 + 3 \log 3$

(e) $\log_5 x - \log_5 8 = \log_5 6 + 3 \log_5 2$

10. Express as a single logarithm. Assume all variables are positive.

(a) $\log_2 x + \log_2 y + \log_2 z$ (b) $\log_5 u - \log_5 v + \log_5 w$

(c) $\log_6 a - (\log_6 b + \log_6 c)$ (d) $\log_2 x^2 - \log_2 xy + \log_2 y^2$

(e) $1 + \log_3 x^2$ (f) $3 \log_4 x + 2 \log_4 x - \log_4 y$

11. If $\log_3 x = 0.2$, find the value of $\log_3 x\sqrt{x}$.

12. If $\log_a w = \frac{1}{2} \log_a x + \log_a y$, express w in terms of x and y.

13. **Communication:** Explain the similarities between the laws of exponents and the laws of logarithms.

14. Use a calculator to evaluate each expression to two decimal places.

(a) $\log 4^8$ (b) $\log \sqrt{40}$ (c) $\log 9^4$

(d) $\log 200 \div \log 50$ (e) $(\log 20)^2$ (f) $5 \log 5$

15. **Application:** The loudness, L, of a sound is related to the sound's intensity, I, by $L = 10 \log \frac{I}{I_0}$, where L is measured in decibels, I is measured in watts per square metre, and I_0 is the intensity of a barely audible sound. By how many decibels does the loudness increase if the intensity of the sound from a tuning fork is tripled?

16. A barely audible sound has an intensity of $I_0 = 10^{-12}$ W/m^2. Use the formula in question 15 to calculate the loudness of each sound.

(a) a falling pin: $I = 10^{-11}$ W/m^2

(b) quiet conversation: $I = 10^{-6}$ W/m^2

(c) subway: $I = 10^{-3}$ W/m^2

(d) jet at take-off: $I = 1$ W/m^2

17. **Check Your Understanding:** Give an example to show the usefulness of one of the laws of logarithms in evaluating an expression.

18. **Thinking, Inquiry, Problem Solving:** Use graphing technology to draw graphs of

    (a) $y = \log x + \log 2x$ **(b)** $y = \log 2x^2$

    You will notice that the graphs are different. Yet simplifying the first expression using the laws of logarithms produces the second expression. Explain why the graphs are different.

19. Create two logarithmic functions using different expressions. The functions should have the same graph. Demonstrate why the graphs are the same.

20. Create expressions to show each logarithm law.

ADDITIONAL ACHIEVEMENT CHART QUESTIONS

Knowledge and Understanding: Use the logarithm laws to write each expression as a single logarithm. Then evaluate.

(a) $2 \log_3 6 + \log_3 18 - \log_3 24$ **(b)** $\log_4 \sqrt{32} + \log_4 \sqrt{8}$

Application: A rock is classified according to its diameter. A granule has a diameter of 2 mm. A particle of sand has a diameter of $\frac{1}{16}$ mm. How are the logs of the two values related?

Thinking, Inquiry, Problem Solving: Given $\log_3 5 = x$ and $\log_3 2 = y$, write $\log_3 \left(\frac{12}{5} \right)$ in terms of x and y.

Communication: Here is Eldon's solution to a problem. Identify Eldon's mistakes. Explain how Eldon made the mistakes, and correct the solution.

Express $2 \log_2 5 - \log_2 \left(\frac{4}{5} \right) + \frac{1}{2} \log_2 16$ as a single logarithm.

$$2 \log_2 5 - \log_2 \left(\frac{4}{5} \right) + \frac{1}{2} \log 16 = \log_2 5^2 - \log_2 \left(\frac{4}{5} \right) + \log_2 \left(\frac{16}{2} \right)$$
$$= \log_2 25 - \log_2 \left(\frac{4}{5} \right) + \log_2 8$$
$$= \log_2 \left(25 \times \frac{4}{5} \times 8 \right)$$

2.6 Solving Exponential Equations

SETTING THE STAGE

When you drink coffee, tea, or hot chocolate, or eat a chocolate bar, your body absorbs chemicals from these foods. One chemical is caffeine. The amount of caffeine in your bloodstream follows an exponential pattern over time.

After eating a food with caffeine, the highest level of caffeine in the bloodstream occurs in 15 min to 45 min. Then the level of caffeine begins to fall. In adult humans, the half-life for caffeine is about 5 h to 6 h. The length of the half-life is affected by other factors, according to the individual.

The following data shows various half-lives of caffeine in various individuals:

Adult nonsmoker: 5 h to 6 h
Adult smoker: 3.5 h
Woman who is six months pregnant:10 h to 18 h
Newborn baby: 100 h
8-month-old baby: 4 h
6-year-old to 10-year-old child: 2 h to 3 h

The amount of caffeine in different foods varies as well:

Coffee (about 250 mL): 100 mg to 150 mg
Tea (about 250 mL): 50 mg to 75 mg
Hot chocolate (about 250 mL): 50 mg
Cola (about 350 mL): 35 mg to 55 mg
Some analgesic tablets: 30 mg to 50 mg

Jason, who is an adult and a smoker, drinks a cup of coffee. How much caffeine would be in Jason's bloodstream seven hours after drinking the coffee? Melanie, who is an adult and does not smoke, has a cup of tea at 6:00 P.M. When will the amount of caffeine in her bloodstream be less than 2 mg? You will need to create an exponential model for each situation. In this section, you will solve exponential equations algebraically, using logarithms.

EXAMINING THE CONCEPT

Using Logarithms to Solve Exponential Equations

Since Jason drinks a cup of coffee, let 125 mg (the average of 100 mg and 150 mg) be the initial amount of caffeine. With Jason, the half-life of caffeine is 3.5 h. Seven hours have passed since Jason drank the coffee. An appropriate model is $y = c(0.5)^{\frac{t}{h}}$. Substitute the known values. Then solve for y.

$$y = c(0.5)^{\frac{t}{h}}$$
$$= 125(0.5)^{\frac{7}{3.5}}$$
$$= 125(0.5)^2$$
$$= 31.25$$

Therefore, 31.25 mg of caffeine remain in Jason's bloodstream after 7 h.

In Melanie's situation, the initial amount of caffeine is 62.5 mg, and the half-life is 5.5 h. The amount remaining in her bloodstream is 2 mg.

An appropriate model is $y = c(0.5)^{\frac{t}{h}}$. Substitute the known values and solve for t.

An estimate for t can be found either graphically or by guessing and checking with a calculator. An accurate answer can be found algebraically.

$$y = c(0.5)^{\frac{t}{h}}$$
$$2 = 62.5(0.5)^{\frac{t}{5.5}}$$

Before solving for t, examine an example of solving for an exponent in a simpler case.

Example 1   Solving an Exponential Equation Using Logarithms

Solve $5^x = 53$, to the nearest hundredth.

Solution

To solve this equation algebraically, use logarithms.

You could estimate the value of x, which is between 2 and 3, by guessing and checking or using a graph or a table. You could also use a graphing calculator to find the intersection of $y = 5^x$ and $y = 53$.

To solve any equation, you can multiply or divide each side of the equation by a common factor or expression. You can also add or subtract a common factor or expression to each side of the equation. To solve an exponential equation, take the **common logarithm** of each side.

$5^x = 53$	Take the log of both sides.
$\log 5^x = \log 53$	Use the law for logarithms of powers.
$x \log 5 = \log 53$	Isolate x.
$x = \dfrac{\log 53}{\log 5}$	Evaluate using a scientific calculator.
$x \doteq 2.47$	

• • • • • • • •

Example 2   Solving a More Complex Exponential Equation

Now return to Melanie's situation. The initial amount of caffeine is 62.5 mg, and the half-life is 5.5 h. The amount remaining in her bloodstream is 2 mg.

Use $2 = 62.5(0.5)^{\frac{t}{5.5}}$ and solve for t, to the nearest tenth.

$$2 = 62.5(0.5)^{\frac{t}{5.5}} \qquad \text{Divide each side by 62.5.}$$

$$\frac{2}{62.5} = (0.5)^{\frac{t}{5.5}}$$

$$0.032 = (0.5)^{\frac{t}{5.5}} \qquad \text{Take the log of each side.}$$

$$\log (0.032) = \log (0.5)^{\frac{t}{5.5}} \qquad \text{Use the law of logarithms for powers.}$$

$$\log (0.032) = \frac{t}{5.5}\log (0.5) \qquad \text{Divide each side by log (0.5).}$$

$$\frac{\log (0.032)}{\log (0.5)} = \frac{t}{5.5} \qquad \text{Solve for } t.$$

$$5.5\left[\frac{\log (0.032)}{\log (0.5)}\right] = t \qquad \text{Evaluate using a scientific calculator.}$$

$$27.3 \doteq t$$

Therefore, the original amount of caffeine would decay to less than 2 mg in about 27.3 h.

• • • • • • • •

Example 3   **Solving Applications of Exponential Functions**

The value of the Canadian dollar, in a time of inflation, decreased by 10% each year. What is the half-life of the dollar?

Solution

Think of the initial amount as $1.00. Since the decrease each year is 10%, the value of the dollar is 90% of the original value at the end of the first year. For each successive year, the value of the dollar is 90% of the value of dollar at the end of the previous year. The model for the situation is

$$V = 1.00 \times 0.9^t, \text{ where } V \text{ is the value of the dollar after } t \text{ years}$$

To determine when a dollar will be half its original value, let $V = \$0.50$. Solve for t, to the nearest hundredth.

$$0.5 = 1.00 \times 0.9^t \qquad \text{Simplify.}$$
$$0.5 = 0.9^t \qquad \text{Take the log of both sides.}$$
$$\log 0.5 = \log (0.9)^t \qquad \text{Use the law of logarithms for powers.}$$
$$\log 0.5 = t \log (0.9) \qquad \text{Solve for } t.$$
$$\frac{\log 0.5}{\log 0.9} = t$$
$$6.58 \doteq t$$

Therefore, the half-life of the dollar at this time is about 6.58 years.

• • • • • • • •

Example 4   Finding Logarithms with Other Bases

You can use a calculator to evaluate a logarithm with base 10. But how would you evaluate $\log_3 38$?

Solution

Let $\log_3 38 = x$. Change $\log_3 38 = x$ to exponential form.

$$\log_3 38 = x$$
$$3^x = 38 \qquad \text{Take the log of each side.}$$
$$\log 3^x = \log 38 \qquad \text{Apply the law of logarithms for powers.}$$
$$x \log 3 = \log 38 \qquad \text{Isolate } x.$$
$$x = \frac{\log 38}{\log 3} \qquad \text{Evaluate.}$$
$$x \doteq 3.31$$

Therefore, $\log_3 38 \doteq 3.31$.

· · · · · · · ·

To find a logarithm with a base other than 10, for instance, $\log_a x$, $a \neq 10$, do as follows:

Let $\log_a x = y$.

$$\log_a x = y \qquad \text{Change to exponential form. Remember to solve for } y.$$
$$a^y = x \qquad \text{Take the log of each side.}$$
$$\log a^y = \log x \qquad \text{Use the law of logarithms for powers.}$$
$$y \log a = \log x \qquad \text{Isolate } y.$$
$$y = \frac{\log x}{\log a}$$

Evaluating a Logarithm with a Base Other Than 10

In general, $\log_a x = \dfrac{\log x}{\log a}$.

CHECK, CONSOLIDATE, COMMUNICATE

1. Describe the steps for solving a simple exponential equation using logarithms.
2. Explain ways to evaluate a logarithm that is not a common logarithm.

KEY IDEAS

- Any exponential equation can be solved by first taking the log of each side so that you can isolate the exponent.
- To evaluate a log with a base other than 10, use $\log_a x = \dfrac{\log x}{\log a}$.

2.6 Exercises

A 1. Solve for x, to two decimal places.
  (a) $x^2 = 36$ **(b)** $x^4 = 54$ **(c)** $x^3 = 78$
  (d) $x^5 = 105$ **(e)** $x^6 = 340$ **(f)** $x^7 = 210$

2. Solve for x, to two decimal places.
  (a) $3^x = 18$ **(b)** $4^x = 36$ **(c)** $5^x = 164$
  (d) $(0.9)^x = 0.714$ **(e)** $(1.02)^x = 2$ **(f)** $2^x = 10.5$

3. Solve for x, to two decimal places.
  (a) $5^x = 55$ **(b)** $x^{-\frac{3}{4}} = 8$ **(c)** $8^x = 32^5$
  (d) $4^x = \dfrac{1}{8}$ **(e)** $x^{-\frac{2}{3}} = 9$ **(f)** $3^{2x} = 5$

4. Find the roots of each equation, to two decimal places.
  (a) $10^{x-4} = 7$ **(b)** $8^{2x} = 79$ **(c)** $5^{2x+3} = 130$
  (d) $(2x)^4 = 18$ **(e)** $10^{2x-3} = 1500$ **(f)** $-6^{4x-5} = -20$

5. Harry invested $500 at 8.5%/a, compounded annually. This investment is now worth $5000. For how long has the money been invested?

6. Solve for x, to one decimal place.
  (a) $300(2)^x = 1200$ **(b)** $150(1.07)^x = 250$ **(c)** $4200(0.8)^x = 3000$
  (d) $50(2)^{\frac{x}{5}} = 350$ **(e)** $25 = 128(10)^{-0.016x}$ **(f)** $12(9)^{\frac{3x}{2}} = 840$

B 7. **Knowledge and Understanding:** The half-life of radium-226 is 1620 years. After how many years is only 30 mg left if the mass of the original sample was 150 mg?

8. After 15 days, 90% of a radioactive material has decayed. What is the half-life of the material?

9. A sum of money is invested at 7%/a, compounded semiannually. How long will it take for the money to double in value?

10. There are initially 200 bacteria in a culture. After five minutes, the population has grown to 4080 bacteria. Estimate the doubling period.

11. While Jamie was watching the games channel on television, he saw a show called "The $64 000 Pyramid." A contestant wins $125 for answering the first question correctly. Each additional question must be answered correctly to double the winnings. How many questions must be answered correctly altogether to claim the grand prize of $64 000?

12. An investment of $4950 earns 11%/a, compounded semiannually. How long will it take for the investment to grow to $9411?

13. **Communication:** Describe three different techniques for solving $5^x = 90$.

14. Marisa drops a small rubber ball from a height of 6 m onto a hard surface. After each bounce, the ball rebounds to 60% of the maximum height of the previous bounce.

   (a) Create a table to show the height of the ball after each bounce for the first five bounces.

   (b) Graph the relation.

   (c) Create an equation to model the height of the ball as it bounces.

   (d) Estimate the height after 12 bounces from your graph. Verify this result using your equation.

   (e) Use your graph to estimate when the ball's maximum height will be 20 cm. Verify this result using your equation.

15. The McKinney family has a pond in their yard, and water lilies are growing in the pond. The area of the lilies' leaves cover twice as much of the pond as they did 35 days ago. The leaves will completely cover the pond in 80 days if the lilies continue to grow unchecked. The McKinneys want to cut back the lilies when they have covered at most half the area of pond. When is this growth expected to happen?

16. **Application:** A plastic sun visor allows light to pass through but reduces the light's intensity. The light intensity is reduced by 5% if the plastic is 1 mm thick. Each additional millimetre of thickness reduces the light intensity by another 5%.

   (a) Create a table showing the light intensity, as a percent, and the thickness of the plastic.

   (b) Model the relation between the thickness of the plastic and the light intensity using an equation.

   (c) How thick is a piece of plastic that allows only 60% of the original light intensity to pass through?

17. **Check Your Understanding:** What key law of logarithms helps you solve exponential equations?

18. **Thinking, Inquiry, Problem Solving:** An adult nonsmoker has a cup of coffee at 8:00 A.M., another coffee at 11:00 A.M., a cola for lunch at 12:30 P.M., a hot chocolate at 4:00 P.M., and a cup of tea after dinner at 6:00 P.M.

   (a) How much caffeine will be in this adult's bloodstream at 11:00 p.m., when he is trying to fall asleep?

   (b) At what time will the amount of caffeine in his bloodstream be 5 mg?

19. Solve for x, to two decimal places.

   (a) $6^{3x} = 4^{2x-3}$ (b) $(1.2)^x = (2.8)^{x+4}$ (c) $3(2)^x = 4^{x+1}$

20. Determine the point of intersection between the graphs of $y = 5(4)^{2x}$ and $y = 4(2)^{6x}$. Round your answer to three decimal places.

Augustin Louis Cauchy (1789–1857)

Born during the French Revolution, Cauchy was weak and hungry as a child. However, he survived to adulthood and at 22 began his mathematical work, writing over 800 papers on topics ranging from astronomy to mechanics. He was responsible for introducing the concept of rigour to mathematical proofs.

ADDITIONAL ACHIEVEMENT CHART QUESTIONS

Knowledge and Understanding: Solve for x, to one decimal place.

(a) $3^x = 15$

(b) $5^{3x} = \frac{1}{20}$

Application: Jane invests $600 in an account that pays 9%/a, compounded semiannually. After how many years will $1500 be in the account?

Thinking, Inquiry, Problem Solving: Étienne finds if he has more than 25 mg of caffeine in his system when he goes to bed at 11:00 P.M. he cannot sleep. He has one cup of coffee at 9:00 A.M. He likes to have a second cup of coffee later in the day. What is the latest time that he can have the second cup and still fall asleep at 11:00 P.M.? Assume he consumes no other caffeine during the day.

Communication

(a) What properties make an equation exponential?

(b) Use your answer for (a) to determine which of these equations are exponential.
$$-2x = -7, \, 3x = 12, \, \frac{1}{x+2} = 3, \, 4(8)^{x-1} = 6, \, x^{-1} = 5$$

The Chapter Problem
Determining Concentration

In this section, you have learned how to solve exponential equations. Apply what you learned to answer these questions about The Chapter Problem on page 82.

CP7. Assume that the model for the drug is $y = c(0.6)^x$, where x is the number of hours after the dosage is given. If the initial dosage given was 1.2 mg/mL, when will the concentration be 0.51 mg/mL?

CP8. If the next dose of 1.2 mg/mL is given when the concentration reaches 0.51 mg/mL, what will be the concentration in the patient's system after the time interval is repeated and it is time for the next dose?

2.7 Creating Logarithmic Models

SETTING THE STAGE

Many quantities vary so greatly that the largest values are many millions of times greater than the smallest. The energy of earthquakes, the light received from stars, and the hydrogen ion concentration in acids and alkalis can be expressed as very large or very small values.

A very large scale would be needed to measure these quantities. So a scale based on exponents is used. Since exponents are logarithms, such scales are called **logarithmic scales**.

You are already familiar with linear scales. For instance, you have used a ruler, which is a linear scale, to measure distance. The intervals on a ruler are equally spaced, or uniform. The second interval is the same as the tenth interval.

In contrast, the intervals on a logarithmic scale are not equally spaced. A simple example of a logarithmic scale is a piano keyboard. The space on the keyboard between octaves is constant, because each octave has the same number of keys. However, the *frequency* of a note one octave above another is twice the original frequency. As shown in the diagram, the numbers 1, 2, 4, 8, 16, … represent the relative frequencies of the C notes in successive octaves. The sequence 1, 2, 4, 8, … forms a logarithmic scale. The logarithms to base 2 that correspond to the terms in this sequence are 0, 1, 2, 3, 4, … . The numbers in this second sequence are evenly spaced.

Music provides several examples of logarithmic scales. Have you wondered why the spacing between guitar frets is not even? Or why the scale on the tuner of an analog radio is not evenly spaced? These are examples of logarithmic scales.

What other scales are logarithmic? Do all logarithmic scales work in the same way?

In this section, you will investigate some common logarithmic scales.

EXAMINING THE CONCEPT

Working with Earthquakes and the Richter Scale

The amount of energy released by an earthquake can vary enormously. Some minor earthquakes release so little energy that people cannot feel them, while others release the same amount of energy as a billion tonnes of TNT. This range is so great that it is difficult to compare earthquakes on the basis of actual energy released. In 1935, Charles Richter solved this problem by developing the **Richter magnitude scale**. This open-ended scale uses logarithms to compare magnitude.

For example,

True Intensity	Richter Scale Magnitude
10^1	$\log_{10} 10^1 = 1$
10^4	$\log_{10} 10^4 = 4$
$10^{5.8}$	$\log_{10} 10^{5.8} = 5.8$

Suppose the difference between the magnitude of two earthquakes on the Richter scale is 2. Then the stronger earthquake is actually 10^2 or 100 times more intense. The table below compares the Richter magnitude for various examples and earthquakes.

Richter Magnitude	Example, or Epicentre of Earthquake
1.0	Large blast at a construction site
1.5	
2.0	Large quarry or mine blast
2.5	
3.0	
3.5	Less than 3.5: Earthquake generally not felt, but recorded
4.0	
4.5	Average tornado (total energy)
5.0	Quake often felt, but rarely causes damage
5.5	Little Skull Mountain, Nevada, 1992
6.0	Double Spring Flat, Nevada, 1994
6.5	Northridge, California, 1994
7.0	Hyogo-Ken Nanbu, Japan, 1995; Largest thermonuclear weapon
7.5	Landers, California, 1992
8.0	San Francisco, California, 1906
8.5	Anchorage, Alaska, 1964
9.0	Chilean earthquake, 1960
10.0	San-Andreas-type fault circling Earth
12.0	

Example 1   Using the Richter Scale

(a) How many more times intense, to the nearest whole number, was the 1995 earthquake in Hyogo-Ken Nanbu, Japan, that measured 7.0, than the 1992 earthquake in Little Skull Mountain, Nevada, that measured 5.5?

(b) How much more intense is an earthquake that measures 8 on the Richter scale than the average tornado?

Solution

(a) The Japanese earthquake measured 7 on the Richter scale. The Little Skull Mountain earthquake measured 5.5.

Find the difference between the magnitudes. $7 - 5.5 = 1.5$

Therefore, the difference in intensity is $10^{1.5}$.

$$10^{1.5} \doteq 31.6$$

Therefore, the 1995 earthquake in Japan was about 32 times more intense than the 1992 earthquake in Nevada.

(b) According to the table, the average tornado measures 4.5 on the Richter scale. To find the relative intensity of an earthquake measuring 8 on the Richter scale, find the difference. $8 - 4.5 = 3.5$

Therefore, the difference in intensity is $10^{3.5}$.

$$10^{3.5} \doteq 3162$$

Therefore, an earthquake measuring 8 on the Richter scale is 3162 times more intense than the average tornado.

EXAMINING THE CONCEPT

Measuring Sound Intensity

The loudness, L, of a sound is related to the sound's intensity, I, by $L = 10 \log \left(\frac{I}{I_0} \right)$, where L is measured in decibels (dB), I is measured in watts per square metre, and I_0 is the intensity of a barely audible sound. A barely audible sound has an intensity of $I_0 = 10^{-12}$ W/m². As a result, the loudness of a barely audible sound is calculated as follows:

$$L = 10 \log \left(\frac{10^{-12}}{10^{-12}} \right)$$
$$L = 10 \log 1$$
$$L = 10(0)$$
$$L = 0 \text{ dB}$$

The following table compares the actual loudness of some common sounds with their intensity measured in W/m².

Sound	Intensity (W/m²)	Loudness (dB)	Ratio of Intensity to the Intensity at 0 dB $\left(\frac{I}{I_0}\right)$
threshold of sound	10^{-12}	0	1
rustling leaves	10^{-11}	10	10
whisper	10^{-10}	20	100
	10^{-9}	30	1 000
	10^{-8}	40	10 000
conversation	10^{-7}	50	100 000
light traffic	10^{-6}	60	1 000 000
heavy traffic	10^{-4}	80	100 000 000
boiler factory	10^{-2}	100	10 000 000 000
aircraft engine; loud music near amplifiers	10^{0}	120	100 000 000 000
painful to human ear	10^{1}	130+	1 000 000 000 000+

Notice that an increase from 10 dB to 20 dB is actually a tenfold increase in loudness. Loudness and intensity are often used interchangeably.

Example 2 **Using the Sound Intensity Level Scale**

How many times louder is a music concert of 125 dB than a conversation of 53 dB?

Noise pollution is a major threat in our industrialized world. There are very few pain receptors in our ears to warn us that gradual hearing loss may be occurring due to loud noise. Sounds over 90 dB, or even lower levels for prolonged, repeated periods of exposure, can cause permanent damage to the ear. You may have heard a "ringing" in your ears after a loud rock concert, which could signal permanent or temporary hearing loss.

Solution
The difference in the loudness of these two sounds is 72 dB. Substitute this value into the loudness formula.

$$L = 10 \log \left(\frac{I}{I_0}\right)$$
$$72 = 10 \log \left(\frac{I}{I_0}\right)$$
$$7.2 = \log \left(\frac{I}{I_0}\right)$$
$$10^{7.2} = \frac{I}{I_0}$$

The music concert is $10^{7.2}$ or about 15.8 million times as loud as the conversation.

EXAMINING THE CONCEPT

Other Logarithmic Scales

Psychologists use logarithmic scales to measure sense perceptions other than just sound. In chemistry, the pH — the measure of acidity or alkalinity of a substance — is based on a logarithmic scale.

The measure of the acidity of a solution is the number of hydrogen ions, H^+, in a specific volume of the solution. The number of hydrogen ions is measured in moles, and 1 mole $\doteq 6 \times 10^{23}$ particles. The hydrogen ion concentration, measured in moles of H^+ per litre, in most solutions is rather small. For example, the concentration of acid in the stomach is about 0.005 moles of H^+ per litre. Rather than deal with these small numbers, chemists use the **pH scale**, which ranges from 0 to 14.

$$pH = -\log \text{(concentration of } H^+)$$

A pH of 7 is neutral. The pH of an acidic solution ranges from 0 to less than 7. The pH of a basic solution ranges from more than 7 to 14.

Example 3 **Using the pH Scale**

Calculate the pH of each solution, to two decimal places, if necessary.

(a) concentration of $H^+ = 0.0001$ **(b)** concentration of $H^+ = 0.0022$

Solution

(a) $pH = -\log \text{(concentration of } H^+)$ **(b)** $pH = -\log \text{(concentration of } H^+)$
$ pH = -\log (0.0001)$ $ pH = -\log (0.0022)$
$ = 4$ $ \doteq 2.66$

CHECK, CONSOLIDATE, COMMUNICATE

1. Give examples of sequences of numbers that could be used for linear and logarithmic scales.
2. Why are logarithmic scales necessary?

KEY IDEAS

- The intervals on a linear scale are uniform, for example, 2, 4, 6, ... Each successive interval on a logarithmic scale is multiplied by the same factor. For example, in the sequence 2.5, 7.5, 22.5, ... each term is multiplied by 3.
- Logarithmic scales are used to measure quantities that vary greatly. A logarithmic scale is formed from the exponents of the powers that represent measured quantities.

2.7 Exercises

A 1. Which sequences are linear, and which sequences are logarithmic?

    (a) 1, 2.5, 4, 5.5, 7, 8.5, 10, ...   **(b)** 5, 25, 125, 625, ...

    (c) 20, 200, 2000, 20 000, ...   **(d)** 150, 650, 1150, 1650, 2150, ...

2. **Communication:** Discuss the similarities and differences between the Richter scale for earthquake intensity and the decibel scale for sound intensity.

3. Use the decibel scale of sound intensity from page 138 to determine how much more intense the first sound is than the second sound.

    (a) a conversation compared with rustling leaves

    (b) an aircraft engine compared with light traffic

    (c) conversation compared with a whisper

4. Use the Richter scale measurements from page 136 to determine how much more intense the first earthquake was than the second earthquake.

    (a) Chilean earthquake, 1960; at Landers, California, 1992

    (b) at Northridge, California, 1994; at Double Spring Flat, Nevada, 1994

    (c) at Anchorage, Alaska, 1964; at Little Skull Mountain, Nevada, 1992

5. Calculate the pH of each solution, to two decimal places.

    (a) concentration of $H^+ = 0.000\ 32$ **(b)** concentration of $H^+ = 0.000\ 045$

    (c) concentration of $H^+ = 0.0003$ **(d)** concentration of $H^+ = 0.005$

6. **Knowledge and Understanding:** An earthquake scored 2.8 on the Richter scale in city A. At city B, it scored 5.3. How much more intense was the earthquake at city B than the earthquake at city A?

B 7. The sound level of a moving power lawn mower is 109 dB. The noise level in front of the amplifiers at a concert is about 118 dB. How many times louder is the noise at the front of the amplifiers than that of a moving power lawn mower?

8. **Application:** Calculate the number of moles of H^+ per litre for each pH.

    (a) pH $= 2$ **(b)** pH $= 3.8$ **(c)** pH $= 5.6$

9. Find the hydrogen ion concentration of each of the following:

    (a) Lemon juice has a pH of 2.   **(b)** Tomato juice has a pH of 4.1.

    (c) Milk has a pH of 6.6   **(d)** An egg has a pH of 7.8.

    (e) Baking soda has a pH of 8.5.   **(f)** Ammonia has a pH of 11.9.

10. **(a)** Distilled water has a H^+ concentration of 10^{-7} moles per litre. Find the pH of distilled water.

    (b) Drinking water from the tap has a pH between 6.3 and 6.6. Is tap water more or less acidic than distilled water? Explain.

11. The sound level of students talking in the school library is 45 dB. At the same time, the noise level in the cafeteria is 58 dB. How many times louder is the noise in the cafeteria than the sound level in the library?

12. Some scientists use a scale that measures the total amount of energy released by an earthquake. A measure of the Richter scale can be related to the energy of an earthquake by $r = 0.67 \log E - 7.6$, where r is the Richter scale magnitude and E is the energy in ergs.

    (a) What is the magnitude on the Richter scale of an earthquake that releases 3.9×10^{15} ergs of energy?

    (b) How much energy did the Chilean earthquake of 1960 release? This earthquake measured 9.0 on the Richter scale.

13. **Check Your Understanding:** What is the advantage of using a logarithmic scale in certain situations? Use an example to illustrate.

14. When you listen to the sound of a piano or another instrument being played, the size of the difference in pitch between C′ and C″ (an octave above C′) is the same as the difference between C″ and C‴ (an octave above C″). However, as shown in the table, the difference between the frequencies of C′ and C″, measured in Hertz, is not the same as the difference between the frequencies of C″ and C‴.

Note	Number of Semitones Above C′	Frequency (Hz)
C‴	24	1056
B	23	990
A	21	880
G	19	792
F	17	704
E	16	660
D	14	594
C″	12	528
B	11	495
A	9	440
G	7	396
F	5	352
E	4	330
D	2	297
C′	0	264

    (a) Determine and describe the relation between the frequencies of pairs of successive C notes.

(b) What is the frequency of a C note one octave above C''''?

(c) What is the frequency of a C note one octave below C'?

15. You are writing a newspaper article about a recent earthquake that measured 8 on the Richter scale. The same area in which the earthquake occurred experienced an earthquake several years ago that measured 4 on the Richter scale. Many people would think that the new earthquake is twice as intense. Write a paragraph comparing the two earthquakes. Also explain how the Richter scale works. Remember who your audience is!

16. **Thinking, Inquiry, Problem Solving:** The table gives the distances from the sun of different astronomical objects.

Object	Mercury	Venus	Earth	Mars	Jupiter	Saturn	Uranus	Neptune	Pluto	Alpha Centauri	Andromeda Galaxy	quasars
distance (millions of km)	58	108	149	228	778	1426	2869	4495	5900	4.1×10^7	2.4×10^{13}	10^{17}

(a) What problems might you find if you plotted these numbers on a linear scale?

(b) Create a logarithmic scale that you think would be suitable for plotting these distances. Describe how you created the scale.

(c) Plot the points on your scale, and discuss the suitability of the scale for this data. Would you make any adjustments? Why?

ADDITIONAL ACHIEVEMENT CHART QUESTIONS

Knowledge and Understanding: How many times louder is noise that is painful to the human ear than the noise inside a moving car? The sound level of the noise in the moving car is 90 dB.

Application: The pH scale is a logarithmic scale. For each decrease of 1 pH unit, there is an increase of 10 times in acidity.

(a) The pH of a lake's water in the year 2000 is 100 times more acidic than it was in 1950. By how much did the pH decrease?

(b) Distilled water has a pH of 7, and rain water has a pH of 5.7. How much more acidic is rain water than distilled water?

Thinking, Inquiry, Problem Solving: George is hoping to sell two used cars. The El Toro has an interior sound level of 80 dB when the car is driven at 80 km/h. The Grand Elm is half as noisy when it is being driven at the same speed. What is the decibel level inside the Grand Elm?

Communication: Explain the difference between a logarithmic scale and a linear scale. Why is the Richter scale a logarithmic scale?

2.8 Solving Logarithmic Equations

SETTING THE STAGE

🔍 **Explore the concepts in this lesson in more detail using Exploration 3 on p. 563.**

In section 2.7, you used the Richter scale to compare the intensities of earthquakes. You can determine the Richter scale magnitude, R, using

$$R = \log\left(\frac{a}{T}\right) + B$$

where a is the amplitude of the vertical ground motion in microns (μ), T is the period of the seismic wave in seconds, and B is a factor that accounts for the weakening of the seismic waves.

To determine the magnitude of an earthquake, substitute known values into the formula for R. For example, determine the intensity of an earthquake, to the nearest tenth, if the amplitude is 150 μ, the period is 2.4 s, and $B = 2.4$.

$$R = \log\left(\frac{a}{T}\right) + B \qquad \text{Substitute known values.}$$
$$= \log\left(\frac{150}{2.4}\right) + 2.4 \qquad \text{Simplify.}$$
$$= \log 62.5 + 2.4 \qquad \text{Evaluate the log and add 2.4.}$$
$$\doteq 4.2$$

The earthquake measures 4.2 on the Richter scale.

You can learn more about an earthquake if you know the magnitude and some other information about the earthquake.

An earthquake measured 5.5 on the Richter scale, the period was 1.8 s, and $B = 3.2$. Determine the amplitude, a, of the vertical ground motion.

First substitute known values into the formula for R.

$$R = \log\left(\frac{a}{T}\right) + B$$
$$5.5 = \log\left(\frac{a}{1.8}\right) + 3.2$$

The next step is to solve for a.

In this section, you will solve logarithmic equations.

EXAMINING THE CONCEPT

Solving Logarithmic Equations

Sometimes an exponential equation that is difficult to solve becomes easier to solve in logarithmic form. And sometimes a logarithmic equation that is difficult to solve, such as $5.5 = \log\left(\frac{a}{1.8}\right) + 3.2$, becomes easier to solve in exponential form. To solve a logarithmic equation, use what you know about solving equations, the laws for logarithms, and the relation between the exponential and logarithmic forms of an expression.

Now solve for a.

$$5.5 = \log\left(\frac{a}{1.8}\right) + 3.2 \qquad \text{Subtract 3.2 from each side.}$$

$$2.3 = \log\left(\frac{a}{1.8}\right) \qquad \text{Change to exponential form.}$$

$$10^{2.3} = \frac{a}{1.8} \qquad \text{Multiply each side by 1.8.}$$

$$1.8(10^{2.3}) = a \qquad \text{Evaluate.}$$

$$a \doteq 359.1$$

The amplitude of the vertical ground motion was about 359.1 μ.
Different techniques can be used to solve logarithmic equations.

Example 1   **Solving Logarithmic Equations**

Solve:

(a) $\log_x 0.04 = -2$

(b) $\log_5 (2x - 4) = \log_5 36$

Solution

(a) To solve $\log_x 0.04 = -2$, first change the equation to exponential form.

$$\log_x 0.04 = -2$$

$$x^{-2} = 0.04 \qquad \text{Rewrite 0.04 as a fraction.}$$

$$x^{-2} = \frac{1}{25}$$

$$x = 5 \qquad \text{since } 5^{-2} = \frac{1}{25}$$

(b) To solve for x, first recognize that 5 is the base of both logs.
Recall that $m = n$ when $\log_a m = \log_a n$.

$$\log_5 (2x - 4) = \log_5 36$$

$$\therefore 2x - 4 = 36 \qquad \text{Solve for } x.$$

$$2x = 40$$

$$x = 20$$

· · · · · · · ·

Example 2   **Solving Logarithmic Equations Using Laws
of Logarithms**

Solve $\log_3 12 - \log_3 x = \log_3 3$.

Solution

$$\log_3 12 - \log_3 x = \log_3 3 \quad \text{Simplify using the law for logarithms of quotients.}$$

$$\log_3 \frac{12}{x} = \log_3 3$$

$$\therefore \frac{12}{x} = 3 \qquad \text{Isolate } x \text{ and simplify.}$$

$$x\left(\frac{12}{x}\right) = 3x$$

$$12 = 3x$$

$$x = 4$$

· · · · · · · ·

Ensure that you check that the value of x is positive, since the domain of a logarithmic function is the set of positive numbers. In Example 2, the value of x is positive, so the answer is admissible.

Example 3 ### Solving Logarithmic Equations That Involve Quadratics

Solve $\log_6 x + \log_6 (x - 5) = 2$.

Solution

$$\begin{aligned}
\log_6 x + \log_6 (x - 5) &= 2 && \text{Use the law for logarithms of products.} \\
\log_6 x(x - 5) &= 2 && \text{Change to exponential form.} \\
x(x - 5) &= 6^2 && \text{Expand and simplify.} \\
x^2 - 5x - 36 &= 0 && \text{Solve the quadratic. In this case, factor.} \\
(x - 9)(x + 4) &= 0 && \\
x = 9 \text{ or } x &= -4 &&
\end{aligned}$$

To verify the solutions, substitute both x-values into the original equation, $\log_6 x + \log_6 (x - 5) = 2$.

For $x = 9$, both $\log_6 9$ and $\log_6 (9 - 5)$ are defined.

For $x = -4$, both $\log_6 (-4)$ and $\log_6 (-4 - 5)$ are not defined. Therefore, $x = -4$ is inadmissible.

The solution is $x = 9$.

CHECK, CONSOLIDATE, COMMUNICATE

1. Describe the steps for solving each equation.
   (a) $\log_3 x = 5$ (b) $\log_2 (x + 2) = \log_2 15$
   (c) $\log_3 x + \log_3 (x + 2) = 1$
2. Which x-values, -1, 1, or 2, could you substitute into each expression so that you could then evaluate the expression?
   (a) $\log_2 (x - 2)$ (b) $\log_4 (2x + 5)$ (c) $\log_5 (-3x)$

KEY IDEAS

- Solve logarithmic equations using what you know about solving equations, the laws for logarithms, and the relation between the exponential and logarithmic forms of an expression.
- Verify solutions of logarithmic equations. Remember that $y = \log_a x$ is defined when $a > 0$ and $a \neq 1$. Also, since the domain of the function is always positive, x must also be greater than 0.

2.8 Exercises

A 1. Solve.
(a) $\log_x 625 = 4$ (b) $\log_x 5 = -\dfrac{1}{2}$
(c) $\log_x 3 = 2$ (e) $\log_x 27 = \dfrac{3}{2}$
(e) $\log_x 81 = 3$ (f) $\log_x 32 = 5$

2. Solve.
(a) $\log_{\frac{1}{3}} 27 = x$ (b) $\log_{\frac{1}{2}} x = -6$
(c) $\log_3 (x^2 - 1) = 1$ (d) $\log_{\frac{1}{4}} x = -\dfrac{3}{2}$
(e) $\log_{\sqrt{2}} x = -8$ (f) $\log_{\frac{1}{2}} x = -2$

3. Solve.
(a) $\log x = 3 \log 2$ (b) $\log_5 x = \log_5 3 + \log_5 7$
(c) $\log_6 x = \log_6 4 + \log_6 2$ (d) $x = 2 \log_2 6 - \log_2 9$
(e) $\log x = \log 3 + 2 \log x$ (f) $\log_3 x = 3 \log_3 5 - \dfrac{1}{2} \log_3 25$
(g) $\log x^3 = 3 \log 12 - 2 \log 8$ (h) $\log x = \log 500 - \log 5$

4. Solve, to one decimal place.
(a) $\log_{27} \dfrac{1}{3} = x$ (b) $\log_x \sqrt[3]{8} = \dfrac{1}{3}$
(c) $\dfrac{1}{2} \log_3 64 - \log_3 x = \log_3 4$ (d) $\log_2 (3x) + \log_2 x = \dfrac{1}{2} \log_2 81$

5. Determine each value, to two decimal places.
(a) $\log_3 15$ (b) $\log_2 210$
(c) $\log_{12} 540$ (d) $\log_5 0.15$
(e) $\log_{20} 1335$ (f) $\log_4 20$

6. Solve.
(a) $\log_2 x + \log_2 3 = 3$ (b) $\log 2 + \log x = 1$
(c) $\log_5 2x + \dfrac{1}{2} \log_5 9 = 2$ (d) $\log_5 x - \log_5 2 = 2$
(e) $3 \log x - \log 3 = 2 \log 3$ (f) $\log_3 4x + \log_3 5 - \log_3 2 = 4$

B 7. For $\log_7 (x - 2) = 1 - \log_7 (x + 4)$,
   (a) state the restrictions on x in the equation
   (b) solve the equation
   (c) verify your answer

8. **Knowledge and Understanding**: Solve.
   (a) $\log_2 (x + 3) + \log_2 (x - 3) = 4$
   (b) $\log_7 (x + 1) + \log_7 (x - 5) = 1$
   (c) $2 \log_3 x - \log_3 (x - 2) = 2$

9. **Communication**: Describe the strategy or laws for logarithms that you would use to solve each equation.
   (a) $\log_5 (x - 2) = \log_5 (23)$
   (b) $x = 2 \log_2 6 - \log_2 9$
   (c) $\log_{11} x = \log_{11} 3 + \log_{11} 2$

10. Recall that decibels are used to measure the loudness of sound, L, and that $L = 10 \log \left(\frac{I}{I_0} \right)$, where I is the intensity of the sound in W/m^2 and $I_0 = 10^{-12}$ W/m^2.
    (a) Determine the intensity of a teacher speaking in front of the class if the sound level is 45 dB.
    (b) Determine the intensity of the headphones attached to a CD player if the decibel rating is 82.

11. **Application**: The magnitude, R, of an earthquake on the Richter scale is given by $R = \log \left(\frac{a}{T} \right) + B$, where a is the amplitude of the vertical ground motion in microns (μ), T is the period of the seismic wave in seconds, and B is a factor that accounts for the weakening of seismic waves.

    Find the amplitude of the vertical ground motion for an earthquake that measured 6.3 on the Richter scale. $B = 4.2$ and the period of the seismic wave was 1.6 s.

12. Solve $\log (2x + 3) = -\log (3 - x)$ both graphically and algebraically.

13. Light intensity behaves similarly to sound intensity. A large aquarium in a science centre holds various fish and plants. Most of the plants require a light intensity of 4.2 units for strong growth. Light intensity, I, passing through water can be modelled with $I = 10^{1 - 0.13x}$, where x is the depth of the water in metres. Use this equation to find the depth at which the plants will receive the appropriate light.

14. Determine the solution to the system of equations algebraically.

$y = \log_2 (5x + 4)$ and $y = 3 + \log_2 (x - 1)$

15. **Check Your Understanding:** For $y = \log_a x$, decide whether a, x, and y can be positive or negative. Explain your decisions.

C 16. Use graphing technology to solve each equation, to two decimal places.

(a) $\log (x + 3) = \log (7 - 4x)$ (b) $5^x = 3^{x + 1}$

(c) $2 \log x = 1$ (d) $\log (4x) = \log (x + 1)$

17. **Thinking, Inquiry, Problem Solving:** Solve.

$\log_5 (x - 1) + \log_5 (x - 2) - \log_5 (x + 6) = 0$

18. Solve each equation.

(a) $\log_5 (\log_3 x) = 0$ (b) $\log_2 (\log_4 x) = 1$

19. Solve.

(a) $\frac{1}{2} \log_a (x + 2) + \frac{1}{2} \log_a (x - 1) = \frac{2}{3} \log_a 27$

(b) $\log_b (x - 1) + \log_b (x + 2) = \log_b (8 - 2x)$

20. For $f(x) = \log_2 x$ and $g(x) = 4^x$, find

(a) $f(g(3))$ (b) $g(f(2))$ (c) $f(g^{-1}(64))$

ADDITIONAL ACHIEVEMENT CHART QUESTIONS

Knowledge and Understanding: Solve for x.

(a) $\log_x 16 = 4$ (b) $\log_{\left(\frac{1}{2}\right)} x = 3$ (c) $\log_3 \left(\frac{1}{3}\right) = x$

(d) $\log_3 x + \log_3 5 = \log_3 10$ (e) $\log_6 (x - 1) + \log_6 (x + 4) = 2$

Application: Express $\log_2 6$ in terms of common logs. (Hint: Let $\log_2 6 = x$ and solve.)

Thinking, Inquiry, Problem Solving: Given $\log_2 a + \log_2 b = 4$, what are the possible values of a and b?

Communication: Consider the question "Solve $\log_3 x + \log_3 (x + 2) = 1$."

(a) Explain the steps for solving this equation.

(b) What are the restrictions on x? Explain.

2.9 Creating and Applying Exponential and Logarithmic Models

SETTING THE STAGE

Most people have a substance in their blood plasma known as ACAH. ACAH seems to help people recover better from the effects of anesthetics after surgery. Before an operation, a patient whose blood lacks ACAH will be given a transfusion of normal plasma with ACAH. How long will the transfused ACAH remain in the patient's bloodstream?

The data shows how ACAH decreases over time.

Time (days)	0	2	4	6	8	10	12
ACAH	0.94	0.85	0.68	0.61	0.49	0.45	0.39

The minimum safe level of ACAH in the bloodstream is 0.15. Can an individual safely be given an anesthetic after 21 days?

In this section, you will determine an exponential model for given data.

EXAMINING THE CONCEPT

Exponential Models

For a given set of data that shows rapid growth or decay, an exponential model is often the best choice. Recall that graphing technology can be used to help determine the best model for a given set of data.

Example 1 **Creating a Model to Fit the Data**

Graph the given data using graphing technology.

Then test several models. Using graphing technology, perform a linear regression. The resulting linear model is $y = 0.05x + 0.91$, where the values are rounded to two decimal places.

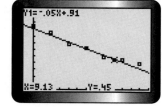

Explore other models for a better fit. Try an exponential model. Using graphing technology again, perform an exponential regression, **0:ExpReg**.

TI-83 Plus Help: For detailed instructions for creating scatter plots and performing exponential regression, see the Technology Appendix on page 594.

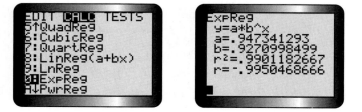

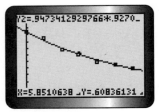

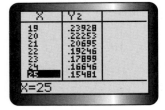

Graph the exponential function.

You can round the values to get the exponential model $y = 0.95(0.93)^x$.

To determine whether the level of ACAH is at least 0.15 after 21 days, use the graph, read a graphing calculator table, or substitute $x = 21$ into the algebraic model.

The graphing calculator table shows that at least 0.15 of ACAH will be in the patient's bloodstream after 21 days.

Verify this result using the model $y = 0.95(0.93)^x$.

$$y = 0.95(0.93)^{21}$$
$$y \doteq 0.21$$

Therefore, since 0.21 is greater than 0.15, the patient will have enough ACAH in his or her system. There will not be enough ACAH in his or her system on the 25th day.

Example 2 Creating a Financial Model

The following data represents the amount of an investment over 10 years. Create the curve of best fit. Determine the average annual interest rate.

Year	0	1	2	3	5	7	10
Amount ($)	10 000.00	10 821.02	11 653.20	12 597.11	14 652.47	17 106.48	21 687.25

Amount versus Years

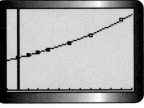

Solution
Creating a scatter plot is a good place to start.

The data could be exponential. Perform an exponential regression on the graphing calculator.

According to the table given, the initial amount is $10 000, not $9993.49, as the calculator indicates. Try $y = 10\ 000(1.08)^x$ as the model.

The equation $y = 10\ 000(1.08)^x$ is a good model. Therefore, the average annual interest rate is about 8%.

Example 3   **Creating a Model without Using Graphing Technology**

Paula is painting the side of a house. After she is finished painting, she scrapes the paintbrush against the lip of a paint can. The paintbrush still contains 120 mL of paint. Paula then puts the brush in a pail containing 1 L of clean paint solvent. She works the paintbrush vigorously until the solution of diluted paint is uniform. She takes the brush out of the pail and lets it drain briefly. The paintbrush still holds 120 mL of solution, which is part paint and part solvent. She repeats washing the paintbrush with a fresh litre of solvent each time.

(a) How much paint is left in the brush after each washing for five washings?

(b) Draw a graph to show the amount of paint that is left after each washing.

(c) Determine how clean you think the brush should be before it is put away. Then determine how many washings would be necessary for a clean brush.

Solution
First make a table.

Initially there are 120 mL of paint on the brush. **After one washing**, the pail contains 1000 mL of solvent and 120 mL of paint. Therefore, the brush will have $\frac{120}{1120}$ of paint. The brush holds 120 mL of liquid, so the brush will have $\frac{120}{1120} \times 120$ mL of paint, which is $\frac{120^2}{1120}$ mL of paint. When Paula puts the brush into fresh solvent the **second** time, the solution will have $\frac{\left(\frac{120^2}{1120}\right)}{1120}$ of paint. The brush will have $\frac{\left(\frac{120^2}{1120}\right)}{1120} \times 120$ mL, or $\frac{120^3}{1120^2}$ mL of paint.

So, after the **third** washing, the brush will have $\frac{120^4}{1120^3}$ mL of paint.

Now create an algebraic model using the pattern in the table on the left.

It appears that $y = \frac{120^{x+1}}{1120^x}$, which, in the form $y = c(a^x)$, is $y = 120\left(\frac{120}{1120}\right)^x$.

x (number of washings)	y (amount of paint)
0	120
1	$\frac{120^2}{1120}$
2	$\frac{120^3}{1120^2}$
3	$\frac{120^4}{1120^3}$

(a) Use the algebraic model to find the amount of paint in the brush after five washings. Round your answer to four decimal places.

$$y = 120\left(\frac{120}{1120}\right)^x \qquad \text{Substitute } x = 5.$$

$$= 120\left(\frac{120}{1120}\right)^5 \qquad \text{Evaluate.}$$

$$= \frac{120^6}{1120^5}$$

$$\doteq 0.0017$$

After five washings, the paintbrush will still have about 0.0017 mL of paint.

(b) See the graph opposite.

(c) Given the answer to (a) and the sharp decrease in the graph, it appears that the brush is "clean" after about three washings.

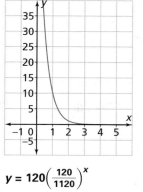

$y = 120\left(\frac{120}{1120}\right)^x$

2.9 Exercises

A 1. **Knowledge and Understanding**: The table shows the value, or the amount, of an investment over time.

(a) Create a model for this data.

(b) Determine the amount of the investment after 10 years.

(c) Determine the annual interest rate.

Year	Amount ($)
0	4000.00
1	4200.00
2	4410.00
3	4630.00
4	4862.03
5	5105.13
6	5360.38

2. The provincial government conducted a study on salmon in a fishery. A scientist measured the oxygen consumption of a salmon at various swimming speeds. The data are recorded in the table.

Speed (m/s)	15	18	20	25	27
Oxygen Consumption (units)	2702	5219	8120	24 250	37 709

(a) Determine graphical and algebraic models for this data.

(b) How much oxygen does the fish consume when it is not moving?

(c) What is the speed of a swimming salmon, consuming 4000 units of oxygen?

3. **Communication**: This section mentions linear and exponential models. What other models do you know? For each model, describe the features of a relation that would indicate that the model might make a good fit.

B **4. Application:** The following data shows the amount of caffeine in Bob's system after drinking a cup of tea containing 40 mg of caffeine:

Number of Hours	0	1	3	4	6
Caffeine (mg)	40	31	17	13	7

(a) Create graphical and algebraic models for this data.

(b) Predict when Bob will have less than 3 mg of caffeine in his system.

(c) What is the half-life of caffeine in Bob's system?

5. The following data represents the growth of a bacteria population over time.

Number of Hours	0	7	12	20	42
Number of Bacteria	850	2250	4500	13500	287 200

(a) Create both graphical and algebraic models for the data.

(b) Determine the doubling period for the population.

6. A class of 30 students conducted an experiment. Each student rolled a die until a 5 or 6 was rolled. Then the student would stop rolling the die. The toss number and "the number of dice remaining" in the class after each toss were recorded as students rolled their dice. The data are shown.

Toss Number	0	1	2	3	4	5	6	7	8
Number of Dice Remaining	30	20	15	11	8	6	4	3	2

(a) Make a scatter plot of this data.

(b) Is a reasonable model of this data the exponential relation $y = c(a)^x$? Explain.

(c) Create an algebraic model for this data. Graph your model.

7. The amount of water vapour in the air is a function of temperature, as shown in the table.

Temperature (°C)	0	5	10	15	20	25	30	35
Saturation (mL of water per m³ of air)	4.847	6.797	9.399	12.830	17.300	23.050	30.380	39.630

(a) Find the growth factors for the saturation row of the table, to the nearest tenth. For example, from 0°C to 5°C, the growth factor is $\frac{6.797}{4.847} \doteq 1.4$. What is the average growth factor?

(b) Write an exponential model for the amount of water vapour as a function of temperature.

(c) Determine the exponential function using exponential regression.

(d) What temperature change will double the amount of water in 1 m³ of air?

8. The table shows how the mass of a chicken embryo inside an egg changes over the first 20 days after the egg is laid.

Days after Egg Is Laid, d	1	4	8	12	16	20
Mass of Embryo (g)	0.0002	0.0500	1.1500	5.0700	15.9800	30.2100

(a) Determine an exponential algebraic model for this data.

(b) By what percent does the embrygo gain mass on a daily basis? Use the model you created for (a).

9. (a) Use a graphing calculator to perform a power regression on the data in question 8. First enter the values for d into **L1**. Change the masses to logarithms. Enter these values into **L2**. Draw a scatter plot. Determine a power model for the data.

(b) Which is better, the exponential model or the power model? Why?

10. **Check Your Understanding:** Write the general equation for an exponential model, and explain what the parts of the equation tell you about the situation being modelled.

11. From 1996 to 2001 (a total of five years), the average price of a new condominium rose 73.4% to $62 000 in Edmonton, 61.1% to $72 500 in Regina, and 37.7% to $144 144 in Toronto. Assume that these growth rates are consistent in the past and in the future. For each city,

(a) graph the cost of a new condominium from 1991 to 2031

(b) use your graph to contrast and compare future condominium prices

(c) determine the average annual increase as a percent, to the nearest tenth

12. **Thinking, Inquiry, Problem Solving**

Revenues in the Sound Recording Industry (in millions of dollars)

	1990	1991	1992	1993	1994[1]
Revenue from the sale of recordings by format[2]	508.7	579.7	633.5	738.0	875.1
Singles (tapes and CDs)	13.1	5.3	5.6	4.8	3.7
Albums	8.9	5.0	2.1	1.2	1.2
Compact discs	204.3	325.5	394.2	507.3	706.3
Tapes (analog)	280.9	243.4	231.4	224.7	×
Other[3]	–	–	×	–	×
Unspecified	1.7	0.5	×	–	–

– nil, zero, or amount too small to be expressed
× data unavailable, not applicable, or confidential
1. The data for 1995 are not strictly comparable to the data for previous years.
2. Figures may not add to totals due to rounding.
3. Other formats, including multimedia in the 1995 survey.

Revenues in the Sound Recording Industry (in millions of dollars)

	1990	1991	1992	1993	1994[1]
Revenue from the sale of recordings by musical category[2]	**508.7**	**579.7**	**633.5**	**738.0**	**875.1**
Popular music/rock[4]	365.4	425.1	453.4	520.8	663.5
Classical and related	41.0	42.2	62.3	63.2	49.5
Jazz	14.9	11.9	19.7	18.0	19.8
Country and folk	35.0	40.5	44.6	61.7	65.4
Children's music	10.3	11.1	17.9	18.9	26.0
Other[5]	42.0	49.0	35.6	55.5	50.9

4. Popular music and rock were classifed as one category in 1995.
5. Includes unspecified data.

Source: Statistics Canada, Culture, Tourism and Centre for Education Statistics

(a) Examine the data for the revenue from CDs from 1990 to 1994. What trend do you see in the data?

(b) Create a scatter plot using this data. Determine an algebraic model.

(c) Comment on the fit of your model.

(d) Use your model to predict the revenue from the sales of CDs in 2010.

(e) Do you think that this trend will continue? Explain.

(f) Choose other data that you believe would fit an exponential model. Create a model, and comment on how well it fits the data.

13. According to Statistics Canada, Canada's population reached 30.75 million on July 1, 2000, an increase of 256 700 from the previous year. The rate of growth for that year was the same as that of the year before. However, both Ontario and Alberta recorded 1.3% growth rates in 2000.

(a) Create algebraic and graphical models for the population growth of Canada. Assume that the rate of growth was the same for every year.

(b) How does the growth rate for Canada's population compare with the growth rate reported by Ontario and Alberta?

ADDITIONAL ACHIEVEMENT CHART QUESTIONS

Knowledge and Understanding: This table shows the value of a particular car over time. What is the initial value of the car? What is the depreciation rate?

Year	0	1	2	3	4
Value ($)	25 000	20 000	16 000	12 800	10 240

Application: This table shows the number of bacteria in a culture.

Day	0	1	2	3	4
Number of Bacteria	300	378	476	600	756

(a) Use graphing technology to graph this data.

(b) Use exponential regression to create an algebraic model of this data.

(c) Using your equation, how many bacteria would you expect after seven days? Use your graph to confirm your answer.

(d) Did the exponential regression produce a reasonable model? Explain.

(e) What is the doubling period? How do you know?

Thinking, Inquiry, Problem Solving: This table shows the amount of caffeine remaining in a person's system over time.

Number of Hours	2	5	7	11
Amount of Caffeine (mg)	36.5	17.3	10.5	3.9

(a) How much caffeine was in the person's system at time $t = 0$?

(b) What is the half-life of caffeine in this person's system?

Communication: Explain how to use a graphing calculator to find the exponential model for a given set of data. How will you decide which type of regression produces the best model?

The Chapter Problem
Determining Concentration

You now know more about creating exponential models and are able to solve The Chapter Problem on page 82. These questions will help to get you started on a model.

CP9. Use the data in Experiment 1 to create both a graphical and an algebraic model of the behaviour of the drug.

CP10. Use the data in Experiment 2 to create both a graphical and an algebraic model of the behaviour of the drug.

CP11. Use the results from the previous two questions to create a suitable model to help you explore and answer other aspects of The Chapter Problem.

Chapter 2 Review

EXPONENTIAL AND LOGARITHMIC FUNCTION MODELS

CHECK YOUR UNDERSTANDING

1. What is the general form of an exponential relation? What do the variables represent?

2. How does the function $y = x^2$ compare with $y = 2^x$? Which relation represents an exponential function? How do you know?

3. Compare an equation modelling exponential growth and an equation modelling exponential decay.

4. What is the graphical relation between exponential functions and logarithmic functions? Graph $y = 5^x$ and $y = \log_5 x$ on the same set of axes to refer to.

5. Explain how to change $3^x = 27$ into logarithmic form.

6. Graph each relation.
   (a) $y = a^x$, $a > 1$
   (b) $y = a^x$, $0 < a < 1$
   (c) $y = \log_a x$, $a > 1$
   (d) $y = \log_a x$, $0 < a < 1$

7. How do the exponent laws compare with the laws of logarithms? List the exponent laws and the logarithm laws.

8. The Richter scale measures the intensitiy of earthquakes. The decibel scale measures sound intensity. The pH scale measures the acidity of a substance. Compare these three scales.

9. When you solve a logarithmic equation, why is it important to always check your solution by substituting the solution(s) into the original logarithmic equation?

10. Name three real-life applications that could be modelled exponentially or logarithmically.

ADDITIONAL REVIEW QUESTIONS BY SECTION

2.1 Investigating Exponential Models

11. The population of a bacterial culture doubles every hour. The initial population is 200. Determine the number of bacteria in the culture after
    (a) 2 h
    (b) 10 h
    (c) n hours

12. The Lim family buys a cottage for $125 000. The value of the property grows exponentially at a rate of 4%/a. What is the property's value after
    (a) 12 years?
    (b) 20 years?
    (c) n years?

13. The town of Greenleaf is growing exponentially at a rate of 4.5% each year. What is the population of Greenleaf now if 15 000 people will be living there in 6 years?

2.2 Graphs of Exponential Functions

14. Compare the graph of $y = 4^x$ with the graph of

    (a) $y = \left(\frac{1}{4}\right)^x$ (b) $y = -4^x$

15. Graph each equation. State the horizontal asymptote, the y-intercept, and the domain and range.

    (a) $y = 3^x$ (b) $y = -4^x$ (c) $y = \left(\frac{1}{2}\right)^x$

    (d) $y = 2(5)^x - 1$ (e) $y = -3(7)^x + 1$ (f) $y = -4\left(\frac{1}{2}\right)^x + 2$

    (g) $y = 6(0.8)^x$ (h) $y = 10(1.03)^x$ (i) $y = 5^{x+2} - 1$

16. Graph $y = 3^x$. Now graph $y = -3^x$, $y = \left(\frac{1}{3}\right)^x$, $y = 3^x + 2$, $y = 3^x - 1$, and $y = 5(3)^x$ on the same set of axes. Describe the transformations on the graph of $y = 3^x$ to create each of the other graphs.

2.3 Various Forms of Exponential Functions

17. Which choice is the best investment for five years?
    (a) $10 000 at 7%/a, compounded annually
    (b) $10 000 at 6.9%/a, compounded semiannually
    (c) $10 000 at 6.8%/a, compounded monthly

18. Due to exponential depreciation, a car is typically worth half of its original value four years after it is purchased new. What is the yearly rate of depreciation?

19. Carbon-14 is a radioactive isotope present in all living things. When a living thing dies, the amount of the isotope at that time starts to decay.

    The function for radioactive decay is $R(t) = R_0\left(\frac{1}{2}\right)^{\frac{t}{h}}$, where R is the radioactivity per gram of carbon-14 at time t after death, R_0 is the radioactivity per gram of carbon at the time of death, and h is the half-life of carbon-14. The half-life of carbon-14 is 5370 years. After 3000 years, how much carbon-14 radioactivity per gram remains in a dead tree?

2.4 The Logarithmic Function

20. Graph the following functions on the same set of axes and compare them:
    (a) $y = \log_3 x$ (b) $y = \log_3 (x + 4)$ (c) $y = \log_3 x + 4$

21. (a) Change to logarithmic form.
         i. $3^7 = 2187$ ii. $8^{\frac{1}{3}} = 2$

    (b) Change to exponential form.
         i. $\log_5 25 = 2$ ii. $\log_{216} \left(\frac{1}{6}\right) = -\frac{1}{3}$

22. Solve for x, to the nearest hundredth.

(a) $\log 1000 = x$ **(b)** $\log 0.000\,01 = x$ **(c)** $\log 37 = x$

(d) $\log x = 1.7$ **(e)** $\log x = 2.5$ **(f)** $\log x = 0.84$

2.5 Laws of Logarithms

23. Write each expression as a single logarithm.

(a) $\log 4 + \log 2$ **(b)** $\log 28 - \log 7$ **(c)** $3 \log 5$

(d) $2 \log_5 16$ **(e)** $\frac{1}{2} \log_4 49$ **(f)** $5 \log 2^{\frac{1}{3}}$

24. Why is $\log_a a = 1$? Use this statement to explain why $\log_a a^x = x$.

25. Evaluate each logarithm. State what logarithmic property you used.

(a) $\log_6 2 + \log_6 3$ **(b)** $\log 300 - \log 3$

(c) $\log_2 24 - \log_2 \left(\frac{3}{4} \right)$ **(d)** $\log_5 25^2$

(e) $\log_3 \sqrt{27}$ **(f)** $\log_3 54 - \log_3 6 + \log_3 \left(\frac{1}{3} \right)$

(g) $\frac{1}{2} \log_7 49$ **(h)** $3 \log_2 \sqrt{8} - 2 \log_2 4$

2.6 Solving Exponential Equations

26. Solve for x, to one decimal place.

(a) $\log_4 56 = x$ **(b)** $7^x = 3^5$ **(c)** $2^x = \frac{1}{20}$ **(d)** $4^{3x} = 9$

27. In 1947, an investor bought Vincent van Gogh's painting *Irises* for $84 000. In 1987, she sold it for $49 million. What was the annual exponential growth rate for this investment?

28. A mummified human body was recently found in a Scandinavian bog. Radioactive carbon dating was used to find the age of the mummy.

The amount of carbon-14 had decayed to $4^{-\frac{1}{3}}$ of its original amount. The half-life of carbon-14 is about 5370 years. For how long has the mummy been dead?

2.7 Creating Logarithmic Models

29. How much more intense is an earthquake measuring 8.1 on the Richter scale than an earthquake measuring 3.9 on the Richter scale?

30. The water in a river has pH 4.9. The water in a lake has pH 7.8. Which is more acidic, and by how many more times?

31. Heavy traffic has a sound level of 82 dB, while a whisper has a sound level of 21 dB. How many times louder is the heavy traffic?

2.8 Solving Logarithmic Equations

32. Solve for x.

   (a) $\log_x 64 = 6$ **(b)** $\log_x 7 = \frac{1}{2}$

   (c) $\log_7 (x^2 - 2) = 1$ **(d)** $\log_{\frac{1}{5}} 625 = x$

33. Solve for x.

   (a) $\log x - \log 3 = 1$ **(b)** $\log_7 x + \log_7 12 = \log_7 8$

   (c) $\log_9 (x - 5) + \log_9 (x + 3) = 1$ **(d)** $2 \log_3 x - \log_3 (x - 2) = 2$

34. Solve for x in $\log_2 (3x + 2) - \log_2 (x - 2) = 3$.

2.9 Creating and Applying Exponential and Logarithmic Models

35. The data represent the value of an investment over time.

Year	0	2	3	5	8	10
Value of Investment ($)	1000	1135	1208	1381	1683	1810

   (a) Determine the average annual interest rate if interest is compounded annually.

   (b) What will the value of the investment be in 20 years if this pattern of growth continues?

36 The table shows the amount of caffeine in Lara's system after she drinks a cup of coffee that has 50 mg of caffeine.

Time (h)	0	1	3	4	7
Caffeine (mg)	50	37	16	10	4

   (a) Create graphical and algebraic models for this data.

   (b) Predict when Lara will have less than 4 mg of caffeine in her system.

   (c) What is the half-life of caffeine in Lara's system?

37. As light passes through a large body of water, for example, a sea, the light's intensity is reduced for every metre of water below the surface. The table shows the light intensity as a scuba diver descends into the water.

Depth of Water (m)	0	10	16	22	32
Light Intensity (%)	100	71	52	38	20

   (a) Draw a scatter plot using this data. Determine an algebraic model.

   (b) How deep is the water when the light intensity is 10%? 0%?

REVIEW QUESTIONS BY ACHIEVEMENT CHART CATEGORIES

Knowledge and Understanding

38. Evaluate.

    (a) $\log_2 64$

    (b) $\log_3 27 \times \log_3 3$

    (c) $\log_9 3$

    (d) $\log_{\frac{1}{2}} 8$

    (e) $\log_8 4$

    (f) $3 \log_2 4$

39. Solve for x.

    (a) $4^{x+2} = 86$

    (b) $\log x = 3 \log 4$

    (c) $5(6)^x = 182$

    (d) $\log_7 x = \frac{1}{3} \log_7 27 + \frac{2}{3} \log_7 8$

    (e) $\log_6 x + \log_6 (x - 5) = 2$

    (f) $3(8)^{2x-1} = 30$

40. At noon, the population of a bacterial culture was 2.4×10^6. At 4 P.M., the population was 6.2×10^7. Assume exponential growth. When will the population be 8.2×10^8?

Application

41. Don drops a ball from a height of 3 m. After each bounce, the ball rebounds to 70% of the ball's maximum height of the previous bounce. Find the height of the ball after the third bounce. Write an expression for the height of the ball, h, in metres after n bounces.

42. DDT is an insecticide that decays slowly. This chemical is sometimes absorbed by plants that are eaten by animals that humans eat. Tests show that about 10% of the initial amount of DDT absorbed by a creek bed disappears after 5 years. How much of the original DDT, as a percent, will remain after 25 years? Assume the creek bed does not absorb any more DDT.

43. The quality of an egg is given by
$N = 100 \log\left[H - \left(\frac{1}{100}\right)\sqrt{g}\,(30W^{0.37} - 100) + 1.9\right]$, where W is the
mass of the egg in grams and g is the acceleration due to gravity (9.8 m/s^2). H is the height of the albumen in millimetres when the egg without a shell and uncooked lies on a flat surface. The variable N, which represents the quality of an egg, is measured in Haugh units. The larger the value of N, the better the egg quality!

    (a) Show that this can be expressed as
$N = 100 \log (H + 5.03 - 0.939W^{0.37})$.

    (b) Compare the quality of an egg with mass 55 g and an albumen height of 8 mm with an egg with mass 43 g and an albumen height of 6.5 mm. Use the formula in (a).

44. In a nuclear test explosion, strontium-90 is released. This element has a half-life of 28 years.

    (a) Graph the decay of strontium-90, expressed as a percent, for a period of 140 years.

    (b) Express the percent of strontium-90 remaining as a function of the number of years.

    (c) What percent of strontium-90 remains after 60 years?

45. Michael puts sugar into a large quantity of water and stirs the mixture. After 3 min, 50% of the sugar has dissolved. How much longer will it take for all but 5% of the sugar to dissolve?

46. (a) In 1987, the world population was 5 billion. Before 1987, the growth rate was about 1.6% each year. Predict the world population in 2027 if the growth rate in 1987 and subsequent years

      i. continues at 1.6% each year

      ii. changes to 3.5% each year

      iii. decreases to 1.1% each year

    Use a graph to help predict in each case. Sketch all three graphs on the same set of axes.

    (b) How are the graphs different? Explain the similarities and the differences.

Communication

47. The compound interest formula $A = P(1 + i)^n$ is an exponential function. State other exponential functions. Explain how each function relates to the general exponential function $y = c(a)^x$.

48. Compare linear models with exponential models. Explain how you choose between the two models for a given set of data.

49. Graph each function on the same set of axes. Describe the similarities and differences. Use transformations.

    (a) $y = \log_2 x$ **(b)** $y = 4 \log_2 x$ **(c)** $y = -4 \log_2 (x) - 4$

Chapter 2 Performance Task

The wind chill index measures the sensation of cold on the human skin. In October 2001, Environment Canada introduced the wind chill index on the right. Each curve represents the combination of air temperature and wind speed that would produce the given wind chill value. For example, a temperature of $-25°C$ and wind speed of 35 km/h produce a wind chill of -40.

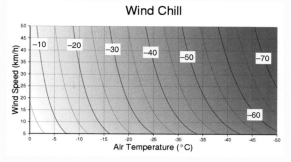

Wind Chill

1. At a wind chill of -35 frostbite is possible after 10 min. Give two combinations of temperature and wind speed that would produce this wind chill.

2. Estimate the maximum wind chill that one could feel at $-20°C$. What are you assuming about the graphs? Does this seem reasonable? Explain.

3. The table gives the wind chill values when it is $-20°C$.

Wind Speed	5	10	15	20	25	30	35	40	45	50	55	60	65	70	75	80
Wind Chill	−24	−27	−29	−31	−32	−33	−33	−34	−35	−35	−36	−37	−37	−37	−38	−38

Source: Environment Canada

(a) Create a graphical model of this data.

(b) Explain why $y = c(a)^x$ will not quite fit the data. Consider the expected range of an exponential function.

(c) Determine whether $y = c(a)^x + b$ will fit the data. Explain why or why not.

(d) Determine an algebraic model for the data. Include all graphs, asymptotes, and equations you used.

4. (a) Use your model from question 3 to predict the wind chill for a wind speed of 0 km/h, 100 km/h, and 200 km/h (hurricane force winds). Comment on the reasonableness of each answer.

5. The actual wind chill formula is
$W = 13.12 + 0.6215 \times T_{air} - 11.37 \times V^{0.16} + 0.3965 \times T_{air} \times V^{0.16}$,
where W is the wind chill index, based on the Celsius temperature scale, T_{air} is the air temperature in °C, and V is the wind speed in kilometres per hour. Is this function model exponential? Explain. Determine the wind chill formula for a temperature of $-20°C$. Comment on how well this model fits the data. How does it compare to your model?

Chapter 2 Review Test

EXPONENTIAL AND LOGARITHMIC FUNCTION MODELS

1. The equation of the graph is in the form $y = c(a)^x$. Is a greater than 1, or is a less than 1? Explain your answer.

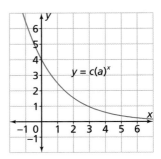

2. Evaluate.

   (a) $\log_{32} 64$

   (b) $\log_{\frac{1}{3}} 27$

   (c) $\log_{\sqrt{5}} 25$

3. **Knowledge and Understanding**: Solve for x, to two decimal places.

   (a) $\log_3 x = 4$

   (b) $\log_{10} x = \log_{10} 3 + 2 \log_{10} x$

   (c) $3.2^x = 45$

   (d) $2 \log_2 x - \log_2 (x - 2) = 3$

4. **Communication**: Graph $y = 3(2)^x$ and $y = 3\left(\frac{1}{2}\right)^x$. Discuss differences and similarities between the two functions.

5. Graph each function. State the domain, range, and asymptote for each function.

   (a) $y = 35(2)^x$

   (b) $y = 3 \log_2 x$

6. How long does it take an investment to double in value if it is invested at 12%/a, compounded semiannually?

7. **Application**: This data represents the number of bacteria in a petri dish at various intervals. Graph the data. Determine a suitable algebraic model. Explain how you created your model.

Time (min)	0	100	250	300	400	700
Number of Bacteria	35	165	1650	3560	16 600	1 685 600

8. **Thinking, Inquiry, Problem Solving**: Helen compared two different strains of bacteria. The bacteria in culture A began with a mass of 35 mg and doubled in mass every 3 h. The bacteria in culture B began with a mass of 85 mg and tripled in mass every 4 h.

   (a) What is the growth rate of each culture?

   (b) When will the cultures have the same mass? Justify your answer in two ways.

Cumulative Review Test 1

ADVANCED FUNCTIONS

1. Identify the intervals in which each function increases and decreases.

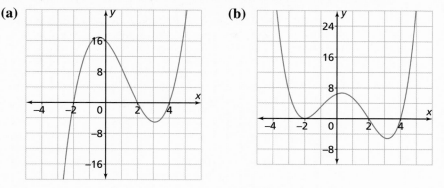

(a)

(b)

2. Graph a polynomial function with degree 5, a negative leading coefficient, three zeros, and four turning points.

3. Simplify.

   (a) $\dfrac{x^3 + x^2 - 5x + 3}{x + 3}$

   (b) $\dfrac{x^4 - 2x^2 + x + 1}{x^2 - 2x + 1}$

4. Graph each function without technology. Describe the shape of each graph.

   (a) $f(x) = x^3 - 7x + 6$

   (b) $f(x) = x^4 - 4x^3 - 7x^2 + 22x + 24$

5. Two factors of the polynomial $4x^4 + 24x^3 + kx^2 + 4x - 15$ are $x + 1$ and $x + 3$. What is the value of k?

6. The life expectancy of a Canadian male born between 1922 and 1992 can be approximated by $f(x) = 0.01x^3 - 0.08x^2 + 2.40x + 58.56$. The life expectancy for Canadian females during the same period is approximated by $f(x) = -0.17x^3 + 1.40x^2 + 0.40x + 60.83$. In each case, $0 \le x \le 70$, $x = 0$ represents 1922, $x = 1$ represents 1932, and so on. Determine the life expectancy of a male and female born in 1972. Who is expected to live longer? Compare the life expectancies of a male born in 1962 and a male born in 1992. Who would be expected to live longer and by how many years? The life expectancy of a female is 74 years. In which year was she born?

7. The US Census Bureau estimates the population of the world from the years 1000 to 1900 as shown in the table. Make a scatter plot of the data and determine a cubic function to represent the population during these years. Use the function to estimate when the population was about 440 million. The function $P(x) = 0.94x^4 - 10.31x^3 + 35.48x^2 - 7.88x + 337.55$, $0 \le x \le 9$, also estimates the population, P, in millions for each hundred-year interval, x. Use this model to estimate when the population was between 500 million and 1400 million.

Year	Population (millions)
1000	345
1100	320
1200	450
1300	432
1400	374
1500	540
1600	579
1700	679
1800	1125
1900	1762

8. Jan Sal, "the Science Gal," cultivates a virus that doubles in size every minute! She places one virus in a 1-L closed jar. One hour later, she finds the jar full. How long will the virus take to fill the 1-L jar if she starts with two viruses? Use an exponential model to solve.

9. Create a table for $y = 2(5^x) - 1$. Find the first differences and the second differences. Describe all the patterns you see in the differences.

10. Solve for x, $x \in \mathbf{R}$. Round to two decimal places if needed.

    (a) $-12 = x^4 - x^3 - 13x^2 + x$ (b) $2x^3 - 5x^2 \geq 28x - 15$

    (c) $10 = 4(2)^{3x-2}$ (d) $\log_2 (8x) = 3 \log_2 x$

11. Find or create examples of exponential and logarithmic functions. Compare these functions according to the characteristics listed in the table. Copy and complete the table.

Characteristics	Exponential Function $y = a^x$	Logarithmic Function $y = \log_a x$
y-intercept		
x-intercept		
asymptote(s)		
domain		
range		

12. Evaluate $\log_3 9 + \log_3 27$ using two different methods. In each method, show one law of logarithms.

13. During the transportation of thorium-243 to a nuclear waste facility, a spill occurred near Springfield. The town was evacuated. None of the town's residents would be allowed to return home until the thorium-243 isotope decayed to one-quarter of its original radioactivity. The half-life of thorium-243 is 24 days. For how long was Springfield evacuated?

14. In 1964, an earthquake in Alaska measured 8.5 on the Richter scale. In 1966, an earthquake in Turkey measured 6.9 on the Richter scale. How many more times intense was the earthquake in Alaska?

15. How is solving a logarithmic equation different from solving an exponential equation?

16. Visit Statistics Canada's Web site at **www.statscan.ca**. Research the sales revenue data for an industry of your choice, for example, agriculture. Or, choose a province or a city in which you are interested and research its population. What types of trends do you see in the data? Create a scatter plot using this data. Determine an algebraic model. Comment on the appropriateness of your model. Use your model to predict the revenue from sales, or the population, 20 years from now.

3 Rates of Change in Polynomial Function Models

Two objects that are moving in tandem and changing velocity at the same rate appear motionless to each other. If an airplane follows the right trajectory, its occupants will experience weightlessness, at least for a short time. The rate of change is a fundamental concept of the branch of mathematics called differential calculus. Many of today's rapid technological advances reflect the importance and diversity of calculus.

In this chapter, you will

- determine and interpret the average rate of change and the instantaneous rate of change for polynomial functions

- estimate and determine the slopes of secant lines and relate the slopes to the average rate of change

- estimate and determine the slope of a tangent line and relate the slope to the instantaneous rate of change

- learn about limits and determine limits of polynomial functions

- examine continuous functions and use limits to determine whether a function is discontinuous

- define the derivative of a function and determine derivatives of polynomial functions

- apply the derivative in real-world situations involving polynomial functions

The Chapter Problem

Average Salaries in Professional Sports

This table shows the average salaries for three major league sports: baseball, hockey, and basketball.

	Average Salary (in thousands of dollars)		
Season	MLB[a]	NHL[b]	NBA[c]
1980	144	108	170
1981	186	120	171
1982	241	110	212
1983	289	118	249
1984	329	120	275
1985	371	144	325
1986	413	158	375
1987	412	172	440
1988	439	188	510

	Average Salary (in thousands of dollars)		
Season	MLB[a]	NHL[b]	NBA[c]
1989	497	211	600
1990	598	271	750
1991	851	368	900
1992	1029	467	1100
1993	1076	562	1300
1994	1168	733	1700
1995	1110	892	1900
1996	1120	981	2100

[a] Source: Major League Baseball Players Association
[b] Source: National Hockey League Players Association
[c] Source: National Basketball Association

(a) Which sport's average salary increased at the fastest rate from 1980 to 1996?

(b) Predict which sport will have the highest average salary in 2005.

(c) For the average salary of each sport, determine when the average salary was increasing the fastest and the slowest.

(d) In 1996, which sport's average salary seems to have increased the most quickly?

(e) Research the average salaries of other sports. Ensure that your research covers the same period. Compare the data and analyze the rates of change. Discuss high or low rates of change that you notice in the data.

After certain lessons in this chapter, you will be asked questions about this problem to help you develop your solution. Keep a record of your work in a project folder or computer file so that you can provide a full solution at the end of the chapter. For help with this problem, see pages 182, 216, 232, and 246.

Chapter Challenges

Challenge 1

A polynomial function is defined by $f(x) = x^3 + 2x^2 - 5x - 6$.

1. Determine the coordinates of four points on the graph of $f(x)$. Choose the points so that the tangent line at each point is a side of the same parallelogram.

2. Determine the equations of the four tangent lines in question 1.

3. Sketch a graph of $f(x)$ and the tangent lines. Also clearly mark the parallelogram on this graph.

Challenge 2

For a certain moving vehicle, the position as a function of time is given by $s = s_0 + v_0 t + \frac{1}{2} a_0 t^2$, where s_0, v_0, and a_0 are constants.

1. Find the initial position.

2. Find the initial velocity.

3. Find the acceleration.

4. A motorist, travelling at 60 km/h, notices a traffic light changing from yellow to red. She applies the brakes 50 m from the white stopping line. What must be the braking deceleration for the vehicle to stop at the white line, if the deceleration is constant?

5. A vehicle's speed is 100 km/h. The braking deceleration is the same as the one you calculated for question 4. At what distance from the white stopping line would the driver need to apply the brakes for the vehicle to stop at the line? Does this distance seem realistic? Explain.

6. Suggest a more reasonable value for braking deceleration for a vehicle travelling at 100 km/h. Use the data and appropriate calculations to support your claim.

Safe Stopping Distances on Dry Pavement

Speed (km/h)	Reaction Time Distance (m)	Braking Distance (m)	Overall Stopping Distance (m)
32	6	6	12
48	9	14	23
64	12	24	36
80	15	38	53
96	18	55	73
112	21	75	96

Getting Ready

In this chapter, you will be working with linear, quadratic, and polynomial equations. You will also analyze quadratic and polynomial functions and their graphs, and examine rates of change.

These exercises will help you warm up for the work ahead.

1. Determine the slope of the line with the given endpoints.

   (a) $(2, 2)$ and $(4, 8)$ **(b)** $(3, -1)$ and $(-4, 6)$

   (c) $(-4, -8)$ and $(-2, -10)$ **(d)** $\left(\frac{1}{2}, \frac{1}{3}\right)$ and $\left(\frac{3}{4}, \frac{1}{2}\right)$

2. Determine the equation of each line in standard form.

   (a) slope of 3, passing through point $(4, 6)$

   (b) slope of $-\frac{2}{3}$, passing through point $(0, 6)$

   (c) passing through points $(2, 7)$ and $(6, 11)$

   (d) parallel to $y = 4x - 6$, passing through point $(2, 6)$

   (e) perpendicular to $y = -5x + 3$, passing through point $(-1, -2)$

3. Expand and simplify.

   (a) $3(2x - 5x^2 + 2)$ **(b)** $3x(2x + 3) - 5x(4x - 7)$

   (c) $(x + 2)(x - 6)$ **(d)** $(x + 2)(3x - 4)$

   (e) $-4(x + 7)^2$ **(f)** $(2x + 3y)(3x + 4y)$

   (g) $5(3 - 2x)(5 + 7x)$ **(h)** $-2(3x + 1)(x - 1)^2$

4. Factor each expression.

   (a) $x^2 + 5x + 6$ **(b)** $a^2 - 6a + 9$ **(c)** $c^2 + 2c - 15$

   (d) $d^2 + 3d - 18$ **(e)** $x^2 - 10x + 16$ **(f)** $m^2 - 5m - 14$

   (g) $c^2 - 15c + 56$ **(h)** $x^2 + 2x - 48$ **(i)** $a^2 + 5a - 36$

5. Factor fully.

   (a) $2s^2 + 4s - 6$ **(b)** $3v^2 + 9v - 30$ **(c)** $3x^2 + 7x + 2$

   (d) $6b^2 + 13b + 6$ **(e)** $d^2 - 16$ **(f)** $9 - a^2$

   (g) $25x^2 - 4$ **(h)** $z^2 + 8z + 16$ **(i)** $4c^2 - 20c + 25$

6. Solve each equation. Round your answers to the nearest hundredth.

   (a) $5x + 6 = 16$ **(b)** $4c + 7 = 2c + 3$

   (c) $4(2x + 3) - 8 = -3(2 - x)$ **(d)** $\frac{2x - 1}{3} = \frac{x + 3}{2}$

   (e) $x^2 - 4x - 32 = 0$ **(f)** $x^2 + 12x + 35 = 0$

   (g) $-2x^2 + 8x - 3 = 0$ **(h)** $3c^2 = 7 - 10c$

   (i) $0 = x^3 - 4x^2 - x + 4$ **(j)** $0 = x^3 + 8x^2 + 17x + 10$

7. If $f(x) = -2x^4 + 3x^2 + 7 - 2x$, evaluate

    (a) $f(2)$ **(b)** $f(-1)$ **(c)** $f\left(\frac{1}{2}\right)$ **(d)** $f(-0.25)$

8. Sketch the graph of each function.

    (a) $g(x) = 3x + 4$ **(b)** $h(x) = 2x^2 - 12x + 19$

    (c) $f(x) = x^3 - 3x^2 - 4x + 12$ **(d)** $h(x) = x^3 - 7x^2 + 4x + 12$

9. Solve each inequality.

    (a) $2x + 5 > 13$ **(b)** $-4x - 2 \le 10$ **(c)** $x^2 < 9$

    (d) $x^2 - 11x + 24 \ge 0$ **(e)** $x^2 + 8x + 15 < 0$ **(f)** $x^2 - x - 56 > 0$

10. Determine the equation of each function.

    (a)   **(b)**

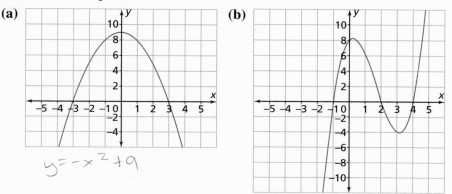

$y = -x^2 + 9$

    (c)

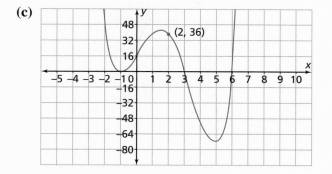

(2, 36)

11. Sam hits a baseball into the air. Eileen uses a motion detector to gather data about the height of the ball. The resulting data is recorded in the table. Find the finite differences. Decide whether the data can be modelled by a linear, a quadratic, a cubic, or a quartic function. Then use the appropriate regression to determine the algebraic model for the data.

Time (s)	0	1	2	3	4	5	6	7
Height (m)	0.5	30.6	50.9	61.4	62.1	53.0	34.1	5.4

3.1 Examining Rates of Change in Polynomial Models

SETTING THE STAGE

 Explore the concepts in this lesson in more detail using Exploration 4 on page 566.

The table shows the results of recording a student's temperature every 5 s.

How can you estimate the rate of change of temperature at exactly 25 s? What problems must you solve to answer this question? In this section you will investigate rates of change of polynomial functions.

Time (s)	Temperature (°F)
0	86.756
5	89.330
10	91.544
15	92.678
20	93.542
25	94.010
30	94.496
35	94.550
40	94.784
45	95.036
50	95.256

EXAMINING THE CONCEPT

Average Rate of Change

Look closely at the temperatures in the table opposite. Every 5 s, the temperature is recorded at an exact time. From 0 s to 50 s, the temperature increases. The amount of temperature increase in each interval, for example, from 5 s to 10 s, is different. So the *rate* of change of temperature is different for different intervals.

The table below shows the first difference and the average rate of change for each 5-s interval. What does the table tell you about the average rates of change?

Time, t (s)	Temperature, T (°F)	First Difference, ΔT (°F)	Average Rate of Change
0	86.756		
5	89.330	89.330 − 86.756 = 2.574	$\frac{2.574}{5} = 0.5148$
10	91.544	91.544 − 89.330 = 2.214	$\frac{2.214}{5} = 0.4428$
15	92.678	92.678 − 91.544 = 1.134	$\frac{1.134}{5} = 0.2268$
20	93.542	93.542 − 92.678 = 0.864	$\frac{0.864}{5} = 0.1728$
25	94.010	94.010 − 93.542 = 0.468	$\frac{0.468}{5} = 0.0936$
30	94.496	94.496 − 94.010 = 0.486	$\frac{0.486}{5} = 0.0972$
35	94.550	94.550 − 94.496 = 0.054	$\frac{0.054}{5} = 0.0108$
40	94.784	94.784 − 94.550 = 0.234	$\frac{0.234}{5} = 0.0468$
45	95.036	95.036 − 94.784 = 0.252	$\frac{0.252}{5} = 0.0504$
50	95.256	95.256 − 95.036 = 0.220	$\frac{0.220}{5} = 0.0440$

The average rates of change of temperature appear to decrease as time increases. The average rate of change is 0.0936°F/s from 20 s to 25 s. The average rate of change is 0.0972°F/s from 25 s to 30 s. So it is difficult to estimate the rate of change at *exactly* 25 s. However, you can use a sequence of average rates of change to estimate the rate of change at an *exact* time.

Average Rate of Change

An average rate of change occurs over an interval between two points.

For the function $y = f(x)$, the **average rate of change** of y with respect to x over the interval from x_1 to x_2 is

$$\frac{\Delta y}{\Delta x} = \frac{y_2 - y_1}{x_2 - x_1}$$

$$= \frac{f(x_2) - f(x_1)}{x_2 - x_1}$$

Example 1   Calculating Average Rates of Change of a Polynomial Model

The height of a model rocket in flight can be modelled by $h(t) = -4.9t^2 + 25t + 2$, where h is the height in metres at t seconds. Determine the average rate of change of the model rocket's height with respect to time during

(a) the first second   **(b)** the second second

Solution

(a) The time interval is $0 \le t \le 1$.

$$\frac{\Delta h}{\Delta t} = \frac{h(1) - h(0)}{1 - 0}$$

$$= \frac{[-4.9(1)^2 + 25(1) + 2] - [-4.9(0)^2 + 25(0) + 2]}{1 - 0}$$

$$= \frac{22.1 - 2}{1}$$

$$= 20.1$$

The average rate of change of height with respect to time is 20.1 m/s during the first second of the model rocket's flight.

(b) The time interval is $1 \le t \le 2$.

$$\frac{\Delta h}{\Delta t} = \frac{h(2) - h(1)}{2 - 1}$$

$$= \frac{[-4.9(2)^2 + 25(2) + 2] - [-4.9(1)^2 + 25(1) + 2]}{2 - 1}$$

$$= \frac{32.4 - 22.1}{1}$$

$$= 10.3$$

The rocket's average rate of change of height with respect to time is 10.3 m/s during the second second of flight.

EXAMINING THE CONCEPT

Instantaneous Rate of Change

In the example of the model rocket, the average rate of change of height is not constant. The average rate of change of height is 20.1 m/s in the first interval, $0 \leq t \leq 1$, and 10.3 m/s in the second interval, $1 \leq t \leq 2$. Examine the table. What happens to the average rate of change during the second interval, from 1 s to 2 s?

Interval	Δh	Δt	Average Rate of Change, $\frac{\Delta h}{\Delta t}$
$1 \leq t \leq 2$	$h(2) - h(1) = 32.4 - 22.1$ $= 10.3$	$2 - 1 = 1$	$\frac{10.3}{1} = 10.3$
$1 \leq t \leq 1.5$	$h(1.5) - h(1) = 28.475 - 22.1$ $= 6.375$	$1.5 - 1 = 0.5$	$\frac{6.375}{0.5} = 12.75$
$1 \leq t \leq 1.1$	$h(1.1) - h(1) = 23.571 - 22.1$ $= 1.471$	$1.1 - 1 = 0.1$	$\frac{1.471}{0.1} = 14.71$
$1 \leq t \leq 1.01$	$h(1.01) - h(1) = 22.251\ 51 - 22.1$ $= 0.151\ 51$	$1.01 - 1 = 0.01$	$\frac{0.15151}{0.01} = 15.151$
$1 \leq t \leq 1.001$	$h(1.001) - h(1) = 22.115\ 195\ 1 - 22.1$ $= 0.015\ 195\ 1$	$1.001 - 1 = 0.001$	$\frac{0.015195}{0.0001} = 15.1951$

What happens to the average rate of change as the time interval *decreases* from $1 \leq t \leq 2$ to $1 \leq t \leq 1.001$?

As Δt gets *smaller*, the average rate of change, $\frac{\Delta h}{\Delta t}$, appears to approach a limiting value of about 15.2 m/s. So the speed, that is, the **instantaneous rate of change** at a specific time, 1 s, is about 15 m/s.

This is written as follows: as $\Delta t \to 0$, $\frac{\Delta h}{\Delta t} \to 15.2$ or $\lim\limits_{\Delta t \to 0} \frac{\Delta h}{\Delta t} = 15.2$;

"lim" means "limit" and "$\Delta t \to 0$" means "the change in t approaches 0."

Instantaneous Rate of Change

An instantaneous rate of change occurs at a single point.

For the function $y = f(x)$, the **instantaneous rate of change** of y with respect to x at point (x_1, y_1) is the limiting value of the average rates of change as the interval between the x-coordinates of points (x_1, y_1) and (x_2, y_2) continuously decreases to 0.

$$\text{instantaneous rate of change} = \lim\limits_{\Delta x \to 0} \frac{\Delta y}{\Delta x}$$

$$= \lim\limits_{x_2 \to x_1} \frac{y_2 - y_1}{x_2 - x_1}$$

$$= \lim\limits_{x_2 \to x_1} \frac{f(x_2) - f(x_1)}{x_2 - x_1}$$

Example 2   Approximating an Instantaneous Rate of Change

David drains the water from a hot tub. The tub holds 1600 L of water. It takes 2 h for the water to drain completely. The volume of water in the tub is modelled by $V(t) = \frac{1}{9}(120 - t)^2$, where V is the volume in litres at t minutes and $0 \le t \le 120$.

(a) Determine the average rate of change of volume during the second hour.

(b) Determine the instantaneous rate of change after exactly 60 min.

Solution

(a) The average rate of change is $\frac{\Delta V}{\Delta t}$ for $60 \le t \le 120$. Therefore, with $t_1 = 60$ and $t_2 = 120$,

$$\frac{\Delta V}{\Delta t} = \frac{V(t_2) - V(t_1)}{t_2 - t_1}$$

$$= \frac{V(120) - V(60)}{120 - 60}$$

$$= \frac{\left[\frac{1}{9}(120 - 120)^2\right] - \left[\frac{1}{9}(120 - 60)^2\right]}{60}$$

$$= \frac{0 - 400}{60}$$

$$\doteq -6.667$$

Time (s)	Volume (L)
0	1600
10	1344
20	1111
30	900
40	711
50	544
60	400
70	278
80	178
90	100
100	44
110	11
120	0

The negative average rate indicates that the volume of water decreases over time.

Δt brace spanning 60 to 120; ΔV brace spanning 60 to 120

The water in the hot tub drains at an average rate of 6.667 L/min during the second hour.

(b) The instantaneous rate of change after 60 min is the limiting value of the average rates of change as the time interval decreases to 0 near 60 min.

$$\text{instantaneous rate of change} = \lim_{\Delta t \to 0} \frac{\Delta V}{\Delta t} \text{ at } t = 60$$

First find a general equation for the average rate of change.

$$\text{average rate of change} = \frac{\Delta V}{\Delta t}$$

$$= \frac{V(t_2) - V(t_1)}{t_2 - t_1}$$

$t_1 = 60$. Next calculate the average rates of change for different values of t_2. Let t_2 start at 61 and decrease toward 60. This table shows the values for $\frac{\Delta V}{\Delta t}$ as Δt approaches 0 near 60 min.

Interval	$\Delta V = V(t_2) - V(t_1)$	$\Delta t = t_2 - t_1$	$\dfrac{\Delta V}{\Delta t}$
$60 \le t \le 61$	$V(61) - V(60) = 386.78 - 400 = -13.22$	$61 - 60 = 1$	-13.22
$60 \le t \le 60.5$	$V(60.5) - V(60) = 393.36 - 400 = -6.64$	0.5	-13.28
$60 \le t \le 60.1$	$V(60.1) - V(60) = 398.668 - 400 = -1.332$	0.1	-13.32
$60 \le t \le 60.01$	$V(60.01) - V(60) = 399.8668 - 400 = -0.133\,322$	0.01	$-13.332\,2$
$60 \le t \le 60.001$	$V(60.001) - V(60) = 399.986\,667 - 400 = -0.013\,333\,22$	0.001	$-13.333\,22$

As Δt approaches 0, $\dfrac{\Delta V}{\Delta t}$ appears to approach -13.3. So -13.3 is the limiting value of the average rates of change.

Therefore, the instantaneous rate of change of volume with respect to time after exactly 60 min is about -13.3 L/min.

• • • • • • • •

Example 3 Instantaneous Rates of Change, Discrete Data, and Graphing Technology

Time (s)	Temperature (°F)
0	86.756
5	89.330
10	91.544
15	92.678
20	93.542
25	94.010
30	94.496
35	94.550
40	94.784
45	95.036
50	95.256

Recall the following question about temperature at the beginning of this section: How can you estimate the rate of change of temperature at exactly 25 s?

Solution
The temperature is measured at 5-s intervals, which means that the data are **discrete**. It also means that you could not calculate an average rate of change for any interval less than 5 s (for example, 3 s) because the temperature changes all the time. Using average rates of change works only when you can calculate the average rate of change at a point that is very close to the point where you want to know the instantaneous rate of change.

So, to estimate the instantaneous rate of change in this case, first find an algebraic model for the data.

Plotting the data shows that a quartic polynomial model might fit the data. Quartic regression produces the following model:

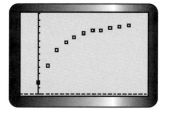 

$$f(x) = -0.000\,001\,45x^4 + 0.000\,289\,53x^3 - 0.020\,306\,15x^2 + 0.643\,623\,31x + 86.717\,776\,22, \text{ for } 0 \le x \le 50$$

Now use average rates of change and the method in Example 2 to estimate the instantaneous rate of change at 25 s.

The following table shows the values of $\frac{\Delta f(x)}{\Delta x}$ as Δx approaches 0 near 25 s.

Interval	$\Delta f(x)$	Δx	$\frac{\Delta f(x)}{\Delta x}$
$25 \leq t \leq 26$	$f(26) - f(25) = 94.151\ 651 - 94.074\ 909 = 0.076\ 742$	$26 - 25 = 1$	0.076 742
$25 \leq t \leq 25.5$	$f(25.5) - f(25) = 94.114\ 232 - 94.074\ 909 = 0.039\ 323$	0.5	0.078 128
$25 \leq t \leq 25.1$	$f(25.1) - f(25) = 94.082\ 931 - 94.074\ 909 = 0.008\ 022$	0.1	0.080 22
$25 \leq t \leq 25.01$	$f(25.01) - f(25) = 94.075\ 715 - 94.074\ 909 = 0.000\ 806$	0.01	0.080 6
$25 \leq t \leq 25.001$	$f(25.001) - f(25) = 94.074\ 990 - 94.074\ 909 = 0.000\ 081$	0.001	0.081

As Δx approaches 0, $\frac{\Delta f(x)}{\Delta x}$ approaches 0.081. The limiting value of the average rates of change is about 0.081°F/s. Therefore, the instantaneous rate of change of temperature with respect to time at 25 s is about 0.081°F/s.

CHECK, CONSOLIDATE, COMMUNICATE

1. Explain the difference between an average rate of change and an instantaneous rate of change.
2. Explain how to use average rates of change to approximate an instantaneous rate of change.
3. Give a real-world example of how to determine an average rate of change and how to determine an instantaneous rate of change.

KEY IDEAS

- The average **rate of change** for any function $y = f(x)$ over the interval between the x-coordinates of points (x_1, y_1) and (x_2, y_2) is

$$\text{average rate of change} = \frac{\text{change in } y}{\text{change in } x}$$

$$= \frac{\Delta y}{\Delta x}$$

$$= \frac{y_2 - y_1}{x_2 - x_1}$$

$$= \frac{f(x_2) - f(x_1)}{x_2 - x_1}$$

- The **instantaneous rate of change** for any function $y = f(x)$ is the limiting value of the sequence of the average rates of change as the interval between the x-coordinates of points (x_1, y_1) and (x_2, y_2) continuously decreases to 0. An instantaneous rate of change occurs at a single point.

$$\text{instantaneous rate of change} = \lim_{\Delta x \to 0} \frac{\Delta y}{\Delta x}$$

$$= \lim_{x_2 \to x_1} \frac{y_2 - y_1}{x_2 - x_1}$$

$$= \lim_{x_2 \to x_1} \frac{f(x_2) - f(x_1)}{x_2 - x_1}$$

3.1 Exercises

A **1.** For $f(x) = x^2$, determine the average rate of change of $f(x)$ with respect to x over each interval.

(a) $1 \leq x \leq 4$ (b) $1 \leq x \leq 3$ (c) $1 \leq x \leq 2$

(d) $1 \leq x \leq 1.5$ (e) $1 \leq x \leq 1.1$ (f) $1 \leq x \leq 1.01$

2. Using your results from question 1, estimate the instantaneous rate of change of $f(x)$ with respect to x at the point where $x = 1$.

3. **(a)** Copy and complete the table. Then estimate the instantaneous rate of change of $f(x) = 5x^2 + 3$ at point (2, 23).

Interval	$\Delta f(x)$	Δx	Average Rate of Change, $\frac{\Delta f(x)}{\Delta x}$
$2 \leq x \leq 3$			
$2 \leq x \leq 2.5$			
$2 \leq x \leq 2.1$			
$2 \leq x \leq 2.01$			

(b) Copy and complete the table. Then estimate the instantaneous rate of change of $f(x) = 5x^2 + 3$ at point (2, 23).

Interval	$\Delta f(x)$	Δx	Average Rate of Change, $\frac{\Delta f(x)}{\Delta x}$
$1 \leq x \leq 2$			
$1.5 \leq x \leq 2$			
$1.9 \leq x \leq 2$			
$1.99 \leq x \leq 2$			

(c) Compare your results for (a) and (b). What do you notice?

4. (a) Determine the average rate of change of $g(x) = 4x^3 - 5x + 1$ over each interval.

    i. $2 \leq x \leq 4$ **ii.** $2 \leq x \leq 3$ **iii.** $2 \leq x \leq 2.5$

    iv. $2 \leq x \leq 2.1$ **v.** $2 \leq x \leq 2.01$ **vi.** $2 \leq x \leq 2.001$

(b) What number do the average rates of change approach in (a)? What does this number represent?

5. Estimate the instantaneous rate of change of each function at the given point.

    (a) $f(x) = 3x^2 + 4x$ at $(1, 7)$ **(b)** $f(x) = -2x^2 - 8$ at $(0, -8)$

    (c) $f(x) = x^3 + x^2$ at $(2, 12)$ **(d)** $f(x) = -x^4 + 1$ at $(3, -80)$

B   **6.** A ball is dropped from the CN Tower and falls to the ground. The function $d(t) = 4.9t^2$ models the distance, d, in metres the ball has travelled after exactly t seconds passes.

(a) Copy and complete the table.

Interval	Δd	Δt	Average Rate of Change, $\frac{\Delta d}{\Delta t}$
$3 \leq t \leq 4$			
$3 \leq t \leq 3.5$			
$3 \leq t \leq 3.1$			
$3 \leq t \leq 3.01$			

(b) Estimate the instantaneous rate of change of distance with respect to time at 3 s.

(c) What is the more common name given to the rate of change you found for (b)?

7. Knowledge and Understanding: The volume of a cubic crystal, grown in a laboratory, can be modelled by $V(x) = x^3$, where V is the volume measured in cubic centimetres and x is the side length in centimetres.

(a) Determine the average rate of change in the volume of the crystal with respect to the side length as each side grows from 4 cm to 5 cm.

(b) Estimate the instantaneous rate of change of volume when the side length is 5 cm.

8. A pebble falls from the top of a cliff that is 180 m high. The pebble's height above the ground is modelled by $h(t) = -5t^2 - 5t + 180$, where h is the height in metres at t seconds since the pebble started to fall.

(a) Find the average rate of change of height between 1 s and 4 s.

(b) Find $h(3)$.

(c) Find the instantaneous rate of change of height at 3 s.

(d) Communication: Explain the meaning of each value you calculated for (a), (b), and (c).

9. The population of a town is modelled by $P(t) = 6t^2 + 110t + 3000$, where P is the population and t is the number of years since 1990.

(a) Find the average rate of change in population between 1995 and 2005.

(b) Find $P(15)$.

(c) Estimate the rate at which the population is changing in 2005.

(d) Explain the meaning of each value calculated.

Time (s)	Height (m)
0.00	20.000
0.50	18.775
1.00	15.100
1.50	8.975
2.00	0.400

10. A stone is dropped from a bridge that is 20 m above a river. The table on the left gives the height of the falling stone above the water's surface.

(a) An algebraic model for the data is the polynomial function $h(t) = -4.9t^2 + 20$, where h is the height above the water, in metres, t is the elapsed time in seconds, and $t \geq 0$. Determine the average rate of change in height with respect to time over the first 2 s.

(b) Estimate the instantaneous rate of change of height with respect to time at 1 s.

Time (s)	Height (m)
0.00	1.5
0.25	3.5
0.50	4.9
0.75	5.7
1.00	5.7
1.25	5.2
1.50	4.1
1.75	2.4
2.00	0.1

11. **Thinking, Inquiry, Problem Solving:** A ball is tossed straight up into the air. Its height is recorded every quarter second and the results are shown on the left.

(a) Create a scatter plot and use quadratic regression to determine an algebraic model for the data.

(b) Determine the average rate of change in height with respect to time over the first half second.

(c) Determine the average rate of change in height with respect to time between 1.00 s and 1.50 s.

(d) Determine the instantaneous rate of change in height with respect to time at 0.50 s and at 1.5 s.

(e) Explain any differences in sign in your answers.

12. **Application:** A miniature golf course adjusted its playing fees each week and collected this data. Estimate the rate at which the revenue is changing with respect to the fee when the playing fee is $3.00.

Playing Fee ($)	2.60	2.80	3.00	3.20	3.40	3.60	3.80
Revenue ($)	1260	1365	1485	1485	1440	1365	1125

13. From a platform tower 10 m high, a diver performs a handstand dive. His height, h, in metres above the water at t seconds can be modelled by $h(t) = 10 - 4.9t^2$. Estimate the rate at which the diver enters the water.

14. A skydiver jumps from an airplane. Before she opens her parachute, she is in free fall. The function $d(t) = 4.9t^2$ models the vertical distance, d, in metres she has travelled at t seconds.

(a) What does the rate of change of distance with respect to time represent? What units are used to measure this rate of change?

(b) Estimate the rate of change at exactly 2 s.

15. The table shows the temperature of an oven as it heats from room temperature to 445°F.

Time (min)	0	1	2	3	4	5	6	7	8	9	10	11	12	13	14
Temperature (°F)	70	125	170	210	250	280	310	335	360	380	400	415	430	440	445

(a) Create a scatter plot of temperature versus time, and draw the curve of best fit.

(b) Determine the average rate of change of temperature over the first five minutes.

(c) Explain what is happening to the instantaneous rate of change at each minute as the oven heats up.

16. (a) Use graphing technology to determine an algebraic model for the data in question 15.

(b) Use a table and the algebraic model to determine an estimate for the instantaneous rate of change at 5 min.

17. Check Your Understanding: Suppose that some real-world situation is modelled by the function $y = f(x)$.

(a) How would you use the equation for $f(x)$ to calculate the average rate of change in x over the interval $a \leq x \leq b$?

(b) How would you use the equation for $f(x)$ to calculate the instantaneous rate of change in x at point $(c, f(c))$?

C **18.** Concentric circles form when a stone is dropped into a pool of water.

(a) What is the average rate of change in the area of one circle with respect to radius as the radius grows from 0 cm to 100 cm?

(b) How fast is the area changing with respect to radius when the radius is 120 cm?

19. The table shows how the volume of a soap bubble increases as its radius increases.

Radius (cm)	1	2	3	4
Volume (cm³)	$\frac{4}{3}\pi$	$\frac{32}{3}\pi$	$\frac{108}{3}\pi$	$\frac{256}{3}\pi$

(a) What is the average rate of change in volume with respect to radius as the soap bubble grows from 2 cm to 4 cm?

(b) At what rate is the soap bubble growing with respect to radius when the radius is 4 cm?

20. A crystal in the shape of a cube is growing in a test tube. Estimate the rate at which the surface area is changing with respect to the side length when the side length of the crystal is 3 cm.

21. A balloon is being inflated. Estimate the rate at which its surface area is changing with respect to the radius when the radius measures 20 cm.

ADDITIONAL ACHIEVEMENT CHART QUESTIONS

Knowledge and Understanding: The distance an airplane has flown at t hours is given by $S(t) = 600t + 30t^2 - 4t^3$, where S is the distance in kilometres and $0 \leq t \leq 5$. Determine the average rate of change in distance over the entire flight. Estimate the instantaneous rate of change in distance at exactly 2 h.

Application: A turtle is swimming directly toward shore. At $t = 0$ s, it is 16.2 cm from shore. At $t = 6$ s, it is 11.4 cm past the shore. The table on the left shows its position from the shoreline over six seconds.

Time (s)	Distance (cm)
0	−16.2
1	−15
2	−11.4
3	−7.8
4	3
5	13.8
6	11.4

(a) Determine the average rate of change of position with respect to time from 2 to 5 s.

(b) Create a scatter plot and use quadratic regression to determine an algebraic model for the data.

(c) Estimate the instantaneous rate of change of the turtle's position at 4 s.

Thinking, Inquiry, Problem Solving

(a) For $h(x) = 3x^2 + 4x + 2$, determine the average rate of change of $h(x)$ with respect to x for the interval $5 \leq x \leq 7$, then find the instantaneous rate of change of $h(x)$ at the midpoint of this interval.

(b) Repeat (a) for the interval $5 \leq x \leq 11$.

(c) Choose a different interval and repeat (a). What can you conclude from your observations?

Communication: Create and share a table that shows the similarities and differences between finding an average rate of change of a polynomial model and finding an instantaneous rate of change of the same polynomial model.

The Chapter Problem
Average Salaries in Professional Sports

Apply what you learned to answer these questions about The Chapter Problem on page 168.

CP1. For each sport, determine the average rate of change in the average salary between 1980 and 1996. For which sport is this rate of change the largest? the smallest?

CP2. Construct a single scatter plot using the data for all three sports. Use different symbols to plot the points for each data set. Draw the curve of best fit for each set of points.

CP3. Do your graphs support your findings from question CP1? Explain.

CP4. For which sport is the rate of change in the average salary in 1996 the largest? the smallest?

3.2 A Closer Look at Rates of Change: The Tangent Problem

SETTING THE STAGE

The average rate of change of a function occurs over an interval of the function's domain. The instantaneous rate of change occurs at a single point.

The slope of the line that is tangent to the graph of the function at this single point represents the instantaneous rate of change. The question "What is the slope of the tangent line to the function's graph at a specific point?" is known as the **tangent problem**, which is fundamental to the branch of mathematics called **calculus**.

How can you determine the equation of the tangent line to the function $f(x) = x^2$ at point $(1, 1)$? In this section we establish the connection between the rates of change of a function and its corresponding graph.

EXAMINING THE CONCEPT

The Tangent Line

In the graphs of the circle and the parabola, a **tangent line** touches exactly one point of the graph at P. For other curves, such as the one in the third diagram, a tangent line touches the graph at the **point of tangency**, P, but it may pass through other points on the graph as well.

Each line is tangent to the curve at point P.

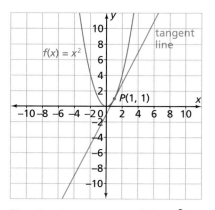

The line is tangent to $f(x) = x^2$ at point $P(1, 1)$.

What information about the tangent line to the function $f(x) = x^2$ do you need to find the equation of this line?

To determine the equation, you must first determine the **slope** of the tangent line. To use the slope formula, $m = \dfrac{y_2 - y_1}{x_2 - x_1}$, you need two points on the line. You know only one point, the point of tangency, that is, $(1, 1)$.

To find the slope of the tangent line, you could graph the function, draw the tangent line at $(1, 1)$, and then find the coordinates of another point on the line. With these two points, you could then calculate the slope. But this slope would only be a rough approximation, because the hand-drawn line and the choice of a second point may be inaccurate.

Example 1 Using Graphing Technology to Approximate the Slope of a Tangent Line

Use a graphing calculator to determine an approximate equation of the tangent line to the function $f(x) = x^2$ at point $(1, 1)$.

Solution

Graph $y = x^2$ using a TI-83 Plus calculator.

Enter the function into the equation editor and graph it in the standard window:

$\boxed{\text{Y=}}$ $\boxed{\text{X,T,$\Theta$,}n}$ $\boxed{x^2}$ $\boxed{\text{ZOOM}}$ $\boxed{6}$

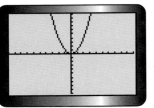

$y = x^2$

Using $\boxed{\text{TRACE}}$ and the arrow keys, position the cursor near the point of tangency, $(1, 1)$, and zoom in (**2:Zoom In**) repeatedly until the visible part of the graph appears to be linear.

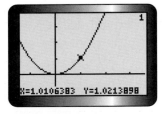

Use point $(1.000\ 664\ 9, 1.001\ 330\ 2)$, which is close to the point of tangency $(1, 1)$, to estimate the slope of the tangent line.

$$m = \frac{\Delta y}{\Delta x}$$
$$= \frac{1.001\ 330\ 2 - 1}{1.000\ 664\ 9 - 1}$$
$$= \frac{0.001\ 330\ 2}{0.000\ 664\ 9}$$
$$= 2.000\ 601\ 594$$

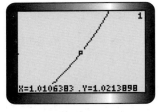

Now find the approximate equation of the tangent line. Use the slope-intercept form, $y = mx + b$, substituting the point of tangency, $(1, 1)$, and the slope, $m = 2.000\ 601\ 594$.

$$\begin{aligned} y &= mx + b & &\text{Substitute.} \\ 1 &= 2.000\ 601\ 594(1) + b & &\text{Solve for } b. \\ b &= -1.000\ 601\ 594 \end{aligned}$$

Zoom in on point $(1, 1)$.

Therefore, an approximate equation of the tangent line is

$$y = 2.000\ 601\ 594x - 1.000\ 601\ 594$$

Although this result is useful, it is still only an approximation.

EXAMINING THE CONCEPT

Using Secants to Find the Slope of the Tangent

A **secant** is a line that passes through two points on the graph of a relation.

In Example 1, you used a specific secant line to estimate the slope of the tangent. By zooming in with a calculator, you found a second point on the graph that was close to the point of tangency.

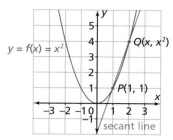

$y = f(x) = x^2$

$Q(x, x^2)$

$P(1, 1)$

secant line

Secant through $P(1, 1)$ and $Q(x, x^2)$

In the graph of $f(x) = x^2$, the secant PQ passes through $P(1, 1)$ and $Q(x, x^2)$. You could create a series of secant lines by changing the x-coordinate of point Q.

Examine the tables. What happens to the slopes of the secant lines, each of which is called PQ, as Q moves closer to the fixed point $P(1, 1)$? Recall that the slope of each secant is m_{PQ}, or $\dfrac{\Delta y}{\Delta x} = \dfrac{x^2 - 1}{x - 1}$.

For points Q to the right of P,

Q	P	Δy	Δx	Slope of Secant PQ
(2, 4)	(1, 1)	$4 - 1 = 3$	$2 - 1 = 1$	$\dfrac{\Delta y}{\Delta x} = \dfrac{3}{1} = 3$
(1.5, 2.25)	(1, 1)	1.25	0.5	2.5
(1.1, 1.21)	(1, 1)	0.21	0.1	2.1
(1.01, 1.0201)	(1, 1)	0.0201	0.01	2.01

For points Q to the left of P,

Q	P	Δy	Δx	Slope of Secant PQ
(0, 0)	(1, 1)	$0 - 1 = -1$	$0 - 1 = -1$	$\dfrac{\Delta y}{\Delta x} = \dfrac{-1}{-1} = 1$
(0.5, 0.25)	(1, 1)	−0.75	−0.5	1.5
(0.9, 0.81)	(1, 1)	−0.19	−0.1	1.9
(0.99, 0.9801)	(1, 1)	−0.0199	−0.01	1.99

In the first table, as Q moves from the right toward P, Δx gets smaller and closer to 0, while the slope of PQ gets smaller and closer to 2. In the second table, as Q moves from the left toward P, Δx gets closer to 0, while the slope of PQ gets larger and closer to 2. So it appears that the slope of the tangent line will be exactly 2 when $\Delta x = 0$.

The slope of the tangent line at $(1, 1)$ is the limiting value of the slopes of the secant lines as Δx approaches 0.

$$\text{slope of the tangent} = \lim_{\Delta x \to 0} \frac{\Delta y}{\Delta x}$$

In this case, where $f(x) = x^2$ and the point of tangency is $P(1, 1)$, the slope is 2.

$$\text{slope of the tangent} = \lim_{\Delta x \to 0} \frac{\Delta y}{\Delta x}$$
$$= 2$$

Definition of Limit

$\lim\limits_{\Delta x \to 0} \dfrac{\Delta y}{\Delta x}$ is called a **limit** and is read "the limit of the change in y with respect to the change in x as the change in x approaches zero."

The limit represents the value that the ratio approaches as Δx gets closer to 0.

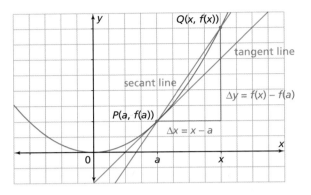

Now apply this method to any point on the graph, $Q(x, f(x))$, and the tangent point, $P(a, f(a))$, of the function $y = f(x)$.

The slope of the secant line PQ is

$$m_{PQ} = \frac{\Delta y}{\Delta x}$$
$$= \frac{f(x) - f(a)}{x - a}$$

The secant line *PQ* will approximate the tangent line as *Q* moves closer to *P*.

Slope of a Secant

The slope of a secant line represents the average rate of change between two points on the graph of a relation.

As Q moves closer to P, x gets closer to a, and the slopes of the corresponding secant lines get closer to the slope of the tangent line at P.

Slope of a Tangent

The slope of the tangent at P is the limiting value of the slopes of the secants, PQ, as point Q approaches point P.

When you use a series of secant lines to determine the slope of the tangent line, you must approach the point of tangency from **both** the left and right sides. When the slopes of the secants approach the same value from both directions, you have found a close approximation of the slope of the tangent line.

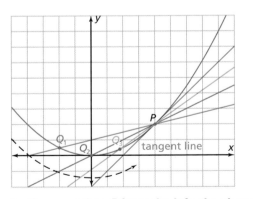

As *Q* approaches *P* from the left, the slope of *QP* increases and approaches the slope of the tangent line.

As *Q* approaches *P* from the right, the slope of *QP* decreases and approaches the slope of the tangent line.

The slope of the tangent line at point $(a, f(a))$ is the limiting value of the sequence of secant slopes as the horizontal interval between the points, $\Delta x = x - a$, continuously decreases to 0. The rate of change at point $(a, f(a))$ is called the **instantaneous rate of change**.

Instantaneous Rate of Change

slope of the tangent = instantaneous rate of change

$$= \lim_{\Delta x \to 0} \frac{\Delta y}{\Delta x}$$

$$= \lim_{x \to a} \frac{f(x) - f(a)}{x - a}$$

Example 2 **Using Secant Lines to Approximate the Slope of a Tangent Line**

Find the equation of the tangent line to $f(x) = 3x^3 + 2x - 4$ at point $(-1, -9)$.

Solution

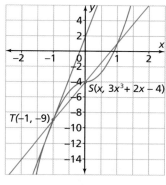

$f(x) = 3x^3 + 2x - 4$

The graph shows $f(x) = 3x^3 + 2x - 4$, the tangent line at point $T(-1, -9)$, and the secant line TS, where S is any point on the graph, $(x, 3x^3 + 2x - 4)$, such that $S \neq T$.

The slope of the secant line TS, m_{TS}, is

$$m_{TS} = \frac{\Delta y}{\Delta x}$$

$$= \frac{f(x_S) - f(x_T)}{x_S - x_T}$$

$$= \frac{[3x^3 + 2x - 4] - [f(-1)]}{x - (-1)}$$

$$= \frac{3x^3 + 2x - 4 - (-9)}{x + 1}$$

$$= \frac{3x^3 + 2x + 5}{x + 1}$$

Now calculate the slope of the secant line.

For example, if S is $(0, -4)$, then

$$m_{TS} = \frac{3(0)^3 + 2(0) + 5}{0 + 1}$$

$$= 5$$

The table shows that, as S gets closer to T from the right, x decreases toward -1, and the value of m_{TS}, which is the slope of the secant line, appears to approach 11.

x	Δx	m_{TS}
0	$0 - (-1) = 1$	5
-0.5	$-0.5 - (-1) = 0.5$	7.25
-0.9	$-0.9 - (-1) = 0.1$	10.13
-0.99	$-0.99 - (-1) = 0.01$	10.91
-0.999	$-0.999 - (-1) = 0.001$	10.991

x	Δx	m_{TS}
−2	−2 − (−1) = −1	23
−1.5	−1.5 − (−1) = −0.5	16.25
−1.1	−1.1 − (−1) = −0.1	11.93
−1.01	−1.01 − (−1) = −0.01	11.09
−1.001	−1.001 − (−1) = −0.001	11.009

Similarly, as S gets closer to T from the left, x increases toward -1, and the value of m_{TS} again approaches 11.

The slope of the tangent line is the limiting value of the slopes of the secant lines. In this case,

$$m_{tangent} = \lim_{S \to T} m_{TS}$$
$$= \lim_{x \to -1} \frac{3x^3 + 2x + 5}{x + 1}$$
$$= 11$$

Use this slope and the point of tangency $(-1, -9)$ to find the equation of the tangent line.

$$y = mx + b \qquad \text{Substitute.}$$
$$-9 = 11(-1) + b \qquad \text{Solve for } b.$$
$$2 = b$$

Therefore, the approximate equation of the tangent line is $y = 11x + 2$. As before, this equation is only an approximation.

• • • • • • • •

Example 3   **Using Secants to Approximate an Instantaneous Rate of Change**

Recall Example 2 in section 3.1.

David drains the water from a hot tub. The tub holds 1600 L of water. It takes 2 h for the water to drain completely. The volume of water in the tub is modelled by $V(t) = \frac{1}{9}(120 - t)^2$, where V is the volume in litres at t minutes and $0 \le t \le 120$.

(a) Determine the average rate of change of volume during the second hour.

(b) Determine the instantaneous rate of change after exactly 60 min.

Solution

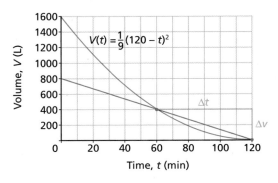

(a) The average rate of change during the second hour is the slope of the secant from $(60, V(60))$ to $(120, V(120))$.

$$\frac{\Delta V}{\Delta t} = \frac{V(120) - V(60)}{120 - 60}$$
$$= \frac{0 - 400}{60}$$
$$\doteq -6.667$$

The water drains at an average rate of 6.667 L/min during the second hour.

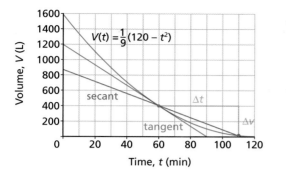

Volume, V (L) vs Time, t (min)

$V(t) = \frac{1}{9}(120 - t^2)$

secant

tangent

Δt

ΔV

(b) The instantaneous rate of change is the slope of the tangent at $(60, V(60))$, or the limiting value of the slopes of the secants that pass through $(60, V(60))$ as Δt approaches 0.

$$\text{instantaneous rate of change} = \lim_{\Delta t \to 0} \frac{\Delta V}{\Delta t}$$

At $t = 60$, the instantaneous rate of change is

$$\lim_{t \to 60} \frac{V(t) - V(60)}{t - 60}$$

Find a general equation for the slope of a secant through $(60, V(60))$ and any other point on the graph $(t, V(t))$, where $t \neq 60$.

$$\frac{\Delta V}{\Delta t} = \frac{V(t) - V(60)}{t - 60}$$

$$= \frac{\left[\frac{1}{9}(120 - t)^2\right] - \left[\frac{1}{9}(120 - 60)^2\right]}{t - 60}$$

$$= \frac{1600 - \frac{240}{9}t + \frac{1}{9}t^2 - 400}{t - 60}$$

$$= \frac{1200 - \frac{240}{9}t + \frac{1}{9}t^2}{t - 60}$$

$$= \frac{10\,800 - 240t + t^2}{9(t - 60)}$$

$$= \frac{t - 80}{9}$$

From the Right	
t	$\frac{\Delta V}{\Delta t}$
61	−13.22
60.5	−13.28
60.1	−13.32
60.01	−13.3322
60.001	−13.33322

From the Left	
t	$\frac{\Delta V}{\Delta t}$
59	−13.44
59.5	−13.39
59.9	−13.34
59.99	−13.3344
59.999	−13.33344

Evaluate the slope of the secant for various values of t close to 60. As t approaches 60 from either direction, the value of $\frac{\Delta V}{\Delta t}$ approaches −13.333. Therefore, the instantaneous rate of change after exactly 60 min is about −13.3 L/min.

We can verify this result with graphing technology. Enter $V(t) = \frac{1}{9}(120 - t)^2$ into Y1 of the equation editor. Adjust the window accordingly. To draw the tangent with the TI-83 Plus, press 2nd PRGM and choose **5:Tangent(**.

Press TRACE and scroll to X=60, then press ENTER. The tangent line is drawn and its equation is displayed.

The slope of the tangent line is −13.3. At 60 min the volume is decreasing at a rate of 13.3 L/min.

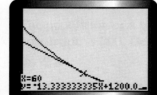

```
DRAW POINTS STO
1:ClrDraw
2:Line(
3:Horizontal
4:Vertical
5:Tangent(
6:DrawF
7↓Shade(
```

X=60
Y=-13.333333335X+1200.0

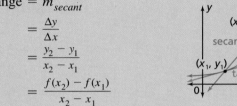
3.2 Exercises

A 1. Determine the slope of the line passing through each pair of points.

(a) $(2, 4)$ and $(6, 8)$ (b) $(-3, -2)$ and $(1, 10)$

(c) $(0, 5)$ and $(-5, 15)$ (d) $(-4, -2)$ and $(-9, -17)$

2. Determine the equation of a line that has slope 4 and passes through $(3, -8)$.

3. Determine the equation of a line that passes through $(6, -1)$ and $(4, -2)$.

4. Estimate the slope of the tangent line in the graph of each function.

(a)

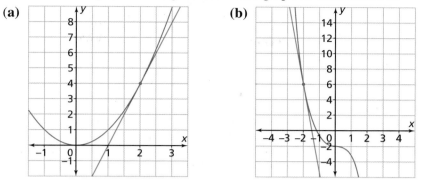

(b)

5. Find the slope of the secant to the graph of $y = x^3 - 4x$ between the points where $x = 1.5$ and $x = 2.5$.

6. (a) Sketch the graph of $f(x) = -x^2$ for $-3 \le x \le 3$.
   (b) Draw the secant line that passes through $(1, -1)$ and $(3, -9)$.
   (c) Calculate the slope of the secant that you drew for (b).
   (d) Draw the tangent line to the curve at $(-2, -4)$ and use the graph to estimate the slope of the tangent.

7. Driving to their cottage, the Burns travelled 85 km in the first hour. After 3 h of continuous driving, they completed the trip, having travelled 276 km in all.
   (a) Determine the average rate of change of distance with respect to time for the entire trip.
   (b) Determine the average rate of change of distance with respect to time during the last two hours.
   (c) What name is usually given to these rates of change?

B 8. Copy and complete the tables to estimate the slope of the tangent to $y = x^2 - 2x - 2$ at point $P(-1, 1)$.

Approaching P from the left,

Q	P	Δx	Δy	Slope of Secant PQ
$(-2, 6)$	$(-1, 1)$	$-2 - (-1) = -1$	$6 - 1 = 5$	$\frac{5}{-1} = -5$
$(-1.5, 3.25)$	$(-1, 1)$			
$(-1.1, ?)$	$(-1, 1)$			
$(-1.01, ?)$	$(-1, 1)$			
$(-1.001, ?)$	$(-1, 1)$			

Approaching P from the right,

Q	P	Δx	Δy	Slope of Secant PQ
(0, ?)	(−1, 1)			
(−0.5, ?)	(−1, 1)			
(−0.9, ?)	(−1, 1)			
(−0.99, ?)	(−1, 1)			
(−0.999, ?)	(−1, 1)			

9. Create a table to estimate the slope of the tangent to $y = x^3 + 1$ at $P(2, 9)$. Be sure to approach P from both directions.

10. For each function, use graphing technology to approximate the slope of the tangent line at the specified point. Then, determine an approximate equation of the tangent line to the curve at the given point.

   (a) $f(x) = 3x^2 + 4x - 5$; (2, 15)
   (b) $f(x) = -x^2 - 2x + 4$; (−1, 5)
   (c) $f(x) = 4x^3 + 2x^2 - 5$; (0, −5)
   (d) $f(x) = -x^4 - 3x^3 - x^2 + 2x + 6$; (−2, 6)

11. The graph of $g(x) = x^3 - 2$ passes through point $T(1, -1)$.

   (a) Determine an algebraic expression that represents the slope of any secant line TS that passes through T and $S(x, x^3 - 2)$.

   (b) Copy and complete the tables.

   i.

x	2	1.5	1.1	1.01	1.001
m_{TS}					

   ii.

x	0	0.5	0.9	0.99	0.999
m_{TS}					

   (c) Use your tables to estimate the slope of the tangent line at $T(1, -1)$.

   (d) Determine the equation of the line tangent to $g(x)$ at $T(1, -1)$.

12. (a) Express, in terms of x, the slope of any secant through (1, 1) on the graph of $y = -x^2 + 2x$.

   (b) Use your expression to evaluate the slope of the secant connecting (2, 0) and (1, 1).

13. Find the slope of the tangent to $y = x^3 + 2x^2 - 8x$ at (2, 0).

14. **Knowledge and Understanding:** The graph of $g(x) = x^3$ passes through (2, 8).

   (a) Determine an algebraic expression that represents the slope of any secant line that passes through (2, 8) and (x, x^3).

   (b) Use a table to estimate the slope of the tangent at (2, 8).

15. Find the equation of the tangent to $y = x^2 - 3x + 1$ at (3, 1).

16. Find the equation of the tangent to $y = x^2 - 7x + 12$ where $x = 2$.

17. **Communication:** Explain the difficulty you encounter when you use a sequence of secant lines to approximate an instantaneous rate of change for a set of discrete data.

18. **Application:** The movement of a certain glacier can be modelled by $d(t) = 0.01t^2 + 0.5t$, where d is the distance in metres that a stake on the glacier has moved, relative to a fixed position, t days after measurements began. Find the rate at which the glacier is moving after 20 days.

19. **Check Your Understanding:** You have studied how secants relate to average rates of change and how tangents relate to instantaneous rates of change. Find a creative way—a diagram, an acronym, or a jingle, for example—to make this easier to remember.

C 20. **Thinking, Inquiry, Problem Solving:** Determine the equation of the line that is perpendicular to the tangent to $y = 5x^2$ at (1, 5).

21. Determine the equation of the line that passes through (2, 2) and is parallel to the line tangent to $y = -3x^3 - 2x$ at (−1, 5).

22. Estimate the instantaneous rate of change of the surface area of a sphere with respect to its radius when the radius is 10 cm.

Sir Isaac Newton (1643–1727)

Isaac Newton made many important contributions to mathematics and physics, including calculus, the Universal Law of Gravitation, and the three laws of motion. He is also responsible for the ridges that appear on the edge of most coins, which he invented when he was in charge of the British Royal Mint. You might want to research to find out why he did this.

ADDITIONAL ACHIEVEMENT CHART QUESTIONS

Knowledge and Understanding: Find the slope of the line tangent to $f(x) = \dfrac{x^2}{2}$ at point (2, 2).

Application: The Happy Face Fix-It shop is having a sales promotion day. A spherical Happy Face balloon is being inflated to float above the shop. The volume, V, of a spherical balloon is $V = \dfrac{4}{3}\pi r^3$. Find the rate at which the volume of the balloon is increasing when the diameter is 2 m.

Thinking, Inquiry, Problem Solving: Consider $y = 5x^2 + 6x + 3$. For what values of x is the slope of the tangent to y negative? positive? zero?

Communication: Let Q_1, Q_2, …, and Q_n be a sequence of points on $f(x)$ and P be a specific point on $f(x)$. Explain, using diagrams and sentences, the meaning of, "The slope of the tangent at P is sandwiched between the slope of the secants Q_1P, Q_2P, …, and Q_nP."

3.3 Limits of Polynomial Functions

SETTING THE STAGE

Explore the concepts in this lesson in more detail using Exploration 5 on page 568.

The tangent problem introduced the concept of the **limit**. So far, you have evaluated the limit of a function $f(x)$ by examining a table for the function as x moves closer to some specific value. In many cases, it is possible to determine the limiting value for the function this way. But do you always need a table to evaluate a limit? Are there other ways to evaluate a limit more easily or efficiently? Is it always possible to find a limit?

In this section we will develop several techniques to determine the limit of any polynomial function.

EXAMINING THE CONCEPT

Evaluating a Limit

The limit of a function $f(x)$ is a mathematical tool for investigating the behaviour of $f(x)$ as the value of x gets closer and closer to some number a.

The Limit of a Function

The notation $\lim_{x \to a} f(x) = L$ is read "the limit of $f(x)$ as x approaches a is L."
It means that the value of the function $f(x)$ approaches the number L ($L \in \mathbf{R}$) as x approaches a from either side.

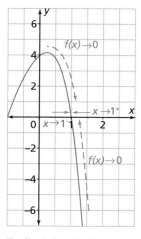

To find the limit of $f(x) = -2x^3 - 4x^2 + 2x + 4$ as $x \to 1$, approach 1 from both sides.

You can use the graph of $f(x) = -2x^3 - 4x^2 + 2x + 4$ to determine $\lim_{x \to 1} (-2x^3 - 4x^2 + 2x + 4)$.

As x approaches 1 from the left (solid green arrow), the values of $f(x)$ (dashed green arrow) get smaller and closer to 0. The notation $x \to 1^-$ means that x is approaching 1 from the left.

As x approaches 1 from the right (solid red arrow), the values of $f(x)$ (dashed red arrow) get larger and closer to 0. The notation $x \to 1^+$ means that x is approaching 1 from the right.

The limit at $x = 1$ is said to *exist* if and only if the value approached from the left is the same as the value approached from the right, that is,

$$\lim_{x \to 1^-} f(x) = \lim_{x \to 1^+} f(x).$$

As x approaches 1 from either direction, $f(x)$ gets closer to 0. Using limit notation, $\lim_{x \to 1} (-2x^3 - 4x^2 + 2x + 4) = 0$.

One-Sided Limits

Left-hand limit: $\lim_{x \to a^-} f(x)$ denotes the limit approaching a from the left side.

Right-hand limit: $\lim_{x \to a^+} f(x)$ denotes the limit approaching a from the right side.

Two-Sided Limit

If $\lim_{x \to a^-} f(x) = L$ and $\lim_{x \to a^+} f(x) = L$, then $\lim_{x \to a} f(x)$ exists and is equal to L.

$\lim_{x \to a} f(x)$ is called a **two-sided limit**.

Example 1 Estimating Limits by Graphing

Determine the limit, if it exists, of each function.

(a) $\lim_{x \to 2} f(x)$ **(b)** $\lim_{x \to 1} g(x)$ **(c)** $\lim_{x \to 0} h(x)$

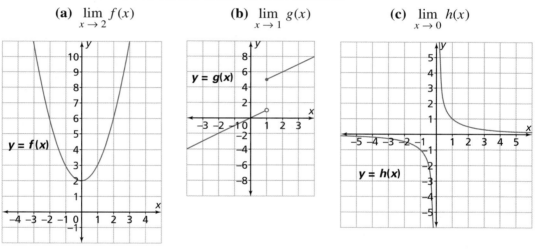

Solution

(a) To determine $\lim_{x \to 2} f(x)$, consider both the left- and right-hand limits.
The graph shows that, as x approaches 2 from the left, the value of $f(x)$ approaches 6, so $\lim_{x \to 2^-} f(x) = 6$. Similarly, as x approaches 2 from the right, the value of $f(x)$ also approaches 6, so $\lim_{x \to 2^+} f(x) = 6$. The left- and right-hand limits both equal 6. Therefore, $\lim_{x \to 2} f(x)$ exists and $\lim_{x \to 2} f(x) = 6$.

A **piecewise function** has different function definitions, depending on the value of the independent variable.

(b) The graph of $g(x)$ consists of two segments, each defined by a different function. This is an example of a piecewise function. The solid dot that marks the end of one segment indicates that that point is included in the function, while the open dot indicates that the point it marks is not included.

As x approaches 1 from the left, the value of $g(x)$ approaches 1. Therefore, $\lim\limits_{x \to 1^-} g(x) = 1$, even though point $(1, 1)$ is not defined for this function.

As x approaches 1 from the right, the value of $g(x)$ approaches 5, so $\lim\limits_{x \to 1^+} g(x) = 5$. Both one-sided limits exist, but they are not equal, so $\lim\limits_{x \to 1} g(x)$ does not exist.

(c) As x approaches 0 from the left, the value of $h(x)$ becomes a larger and larger negative number. Use the symbol for infinity, ∞, to describe the behaviour of the function. So $\lim\limits_{x \to 0^-} h(x) = -\infty$. As x approaches 0 from the right, the value of $h(x)$ becomes a larger and larger positive number, so $\lim\limits_{x \to 0^+} h(x) = \infty$. Neither the left- or right-hand limit exists, so $\lim\limits_{x \to 0} h(x)$ does not exist.

Limits That Fail to Exist

If $\lim\limits_{x \to a^-} f(x) \neq \lim\limits_{x \to a^+} f(x)$, then $\lim\limits_{x \to a} f(x)$ does not exist.

$\bullet\ \bullet\ \bullet\ \bullet\ \bullet\ \bullet\ \bullet\ \bullet$

Example 2 **Finding a Limit from a Table**

For each function, create a table to determine the limit, if it exists.

(a) $\lim\limits_{x \to 3} (x^4 - 2x^2 - 3)$
(b) $\lim\limits_{x \to 0} \dfrac{1}{x^3}$

Solution
In both cases, create two tables, one that includes x-values approaching the limit point from the left and the other with x-values approaching from the right.

(a) Approaching $x = 3$ from the left,   From the right,

x	$x^4 - 2x^2 - 3$
2	5
2.5	23.5625
2.9	50.9081
2.99	59.0452
2.999	59.9041

x	$x^4 - 2x^2 - 3$
4	221
3.5	122.5625
3.1	70.1321
3.01	60.9652
3.001	60.0961

The trends in the tables indicate that $\lim\limits_{x \to 3^-} (x^4 - 2x^3 - 3) \doteq 60$ and $\lim\limits_{x \to 3^+} (x^4 - 2x^3 - 3) \doteq 60$. Therefore, $\lim\limits_{x \to 3} (x^4 - 2x^3 - 3) \doteq 60$

(b) Approaching $x = 0$ from the left,   From the right,

x	$\frac{1}{x^3}$
-1	-1
-0.5	-8
-0.1	$-1\,000$
-0.01	$-1\,000\,000$
-0.001	$-1\,000\,000\,000$

x	$\frac{1}{x^3}$
1	1
0.5	8
0.1	$1\,000$
0.01	$1\,000\,000$
0.001	$1\,000\,000\,000$

As x approaches 0 from the left side, $\frac{1}{x^3}$ becomes a larger and larger negative number. As x approaches 0 from the right side, $\frac{1}{x^3}$ becomes a larger and larger positive number. In limit notation, $\lim_{x \to 0^-} \frac{1}{x^3} = -\infty$ and $\lim_{x \to 0^+} \frac{1}{x^3} = \infty$.

Therefore, the two-sided limit $\lim_{x \to 0} \frac{1}{x^3}$ does not exist.

EXAMINING THE CONCEPT

Continuous and Discontinuous Functions

In Example 2(a), two tables were created to show that $\lim_{x \to 3} (x^4 - 2x^3 - 3) \doteq 60$. Try substituting $x = 3$ directly into the expression.

$$x^4 - 2x^2 - 3 = (3)^4 - 2(3)^2 - 3$$
$$= 81 - 18 - 3$$
$$= 60$$

The result of substituting is the same as the value of the limit. Is this result always true?

In Example 2(b), $\lim_{x \to 0} \frac{1}{x^3}$ does not exist. Substituting $x = 0$ gives $\frac{1}{x^3} = \frac{1}{(0)^3} = \frac{1}{0}$.
Division by 0 is undefined, so direct substitution does not help in this case.

As the following graphs show, the functions in Example 2 are different.

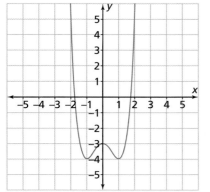

$f(x) = x^4 - 2x^2 - 3$

The graph of $f(x) = x^4 - 2x^2 - 3$ is a curve with no interruptions or breaks. As a result,

$$\lim_{x \to 3} (x^4 - 2x^2 - 3) = \lim_{x \to 3} f(x)$$
$$= f(3)$$
$$= 60$$

In fact, the same result is true for any value $x = a$ in the domain. Therefore, this function is **continuous**.

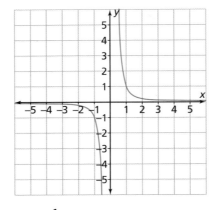

$f(x) = \dfrac{1}{x^3}$

The graph of $f(x) = \dfrac{1}{x^3}$ has a break at $x = 0$ and $f(0)$ is undefined. Therefore, this function is **discontinuous** at $x = 0$.

Continuous Functions

The graph of a continuous function is a smooth curve with no interruptions or breaks.

A function f is **continuous** at a if $\lim\limits_{x \to a} f(x) = f(a)$, that is if all of the following are true:

1. The value a is in the domain of f.
2. $\lim\limits_{x \to a} f(x)$ exists.
3. $\lim\limits_{x \to a} f(x) = f(a)$

A function f is **continuous** if it is continuous at a for all values of a in its domain.

Discontinuous Functions

The graph of a discontinuous function has a break for some value of x.

The function f is **discontinuous** at a, or f has a discontinuity at a, when a is not in the domain of f; that is, $f(a)$ is not defined; when $\lim\limits_{x \to a} f(x)$ does not exist; or when $\lim\limits_{x \to a} f(x) \neq f(a)$.

Example 3   ## Determining Where a Function Is Discontinuous

Is $f(x)$ continuous or discontinuous? If it is discontinuous, state where the discontinuity occurs.

$$f(x) = \begin{cases} x^2 & \text{if } -5 \leq x < 2 \\ x - 2 & \text{if } 2 \leq x < 5 \end{cases}$$

Solution

The function $f(x)$ is a piecewise function. To decide whether it is continuous or not, create a table for each piece and graph the function.

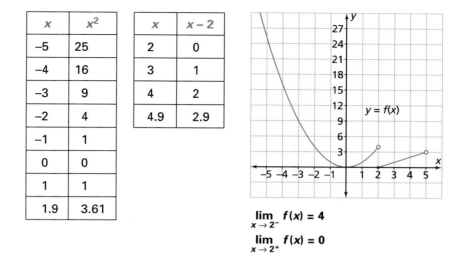

x	x^2
−5	25
−4	16
−3	9
−2	4
−1	1
0	0
1	1
1.9	3.61

x	$x - 2$
2	0
3	1
4	2
4.9	2.9

$$\lim_{x \to 2^-} f(x) = 4$$

$$\lim_{x \to 2^+} f(x) = 0$$

The graph has a break at $x = 2$. The one-sided limits are not equal at $x = 2$. Therefore, $\lim_{x \to 2} f(x)$ does not exist and the function is discontinuous at $x = 2$.

EXAMINING THE CONCEPT

Some Properties of Limits Involving Polynomial Functions

Some Basic Limits

If a and c are real numbers and n is an integer, then

1. $\lim_{x \to a} c = c$
2. $\lim_{x \to a} x = a$
3. $\lim_{x \to a} x^n = a^n$, provided $a \neq 0$ when $n \leq 0$

Example 4 **Evaluating Basic Limits**

Evaluate.

(a) $\lim_{x \to 3} 5$ (b) $\lim_{x \to -2} x$ (c) $\lim_{x \to 4} x^2$

Solution

(a) $\lim_{x \to 3} 5 = 5$ (b) $\lim_{x \to -2} x = -2$ (c) $\lim_{x \to 4} x^2 = 4^2$
$= 16$

• • • • • • • •

The following properties of limits are known as limit laws. More limit laws will be discussed in later chapters.

Algebraic Form	Description	Example
Constant Law If $f(x) = C$ (a constant function), then $\lim\limits_{x \to a} f(x) = \lim\limits_{x \to a} C$ $\phantom{\lim\limits_{x \to a} f(x)} = C$	The limit of a constant function is the constant.	$\lim\limits_{x \to 2} 6 = 6$
Constant Multiplier Law If $\lim\limits_{x \to a} f(x) = L$, then $\lim\limits_{x \to a} [cf(x)] = c \lim\limits_{x \to a} f(x)$ $\phantom{\lim\limits_{x \to a} [cf(x)]} = cL$	The limit of a constant times a function is the constant times the limit of the function.	$\lim\limits_{x \to 3} (5x^2) = 5 \lim\limits_{x \to 3} x^2$ $\phantom{\lim\limits_{x \to 3} (5x^2)} = 5(9)$ $\phantom{\lim\limits_{x \to 3} (5x^2)} = 45$
Sum/Difference Law If $\lim\limits_{x \to a} f(x) = L$ and $\lim\limits_{x \to a} g(x) = M$, then $\lim\limits_{x \to a} [f(x) \pm g(x)] = [\lim\limits_{x \to a} f(x)] \pm [\lim\limits_{x \to a} g(x)]$ $\phantom{\lim\limits_{x \to a} [f(x) \pm g(x)]} = L \pm M$	The limit of a sum or difference is the sum or difference of the limits.	$\lim\limits_{x \to 2} (x^3 + 4x) = \lim\limits_{x \to 2} x^3 + \lim\limits_{x \to 2} 4x$ $\phantom{\lim\limits_{x \to 2} (x^3 + 4x)} = \lim\limits_{x \to 2} x^3 + 4 \lim\limits_{x \to 2} x$ $\phantom{\lim\limits_{x \to 2} (x^3 + 4x)} = 2^3 + 4(2)$ $\phantom{\lim\limits_{x \to 2} (x^3 + 4x)} = 16$

Example 5   **Applying the Limit Laws to a Polynomial Function**

Evaluate $\lim\limits_{x \to 5} (2x^3 + 4x^2 - 3x + 1)$.

Solution

$$\lim\limits_{x \to 5} (2x^3 + 4x^2 - 3x + 1) = \lim\limits_{x \to 5} 2x^3 + \lim\limits_{x \to 5} 4x^2 - \lim\limits_{x \to 5} 3x + \lim\limits_{x \to 5} 1$$
$$= 2 \lim\limits_{x \to 5} x^3 + 4 \lim\limits_{x \to 5} x^2 - 3 \lim\limits_{x \to 5} x + \lim\limits_{x \to 5} 1$$
$$= 2(5)^3 + 4(5)^2 - 3(5) + 1$$
$$= 250 + 100 - 15 + 1$$
$$= 336$$

The limit of $f(x)$ as x approaches a does not always depend on the value of $f(a)$. However, if f is continuous at a, then $\lim\limits_{x \to a} f(x) = f(a)$.

Every polynomial function
$P(x) = a_n x^n + a_{n-1} x^{n-1} + \ldots + a_2 x^2 + a_1 x + a_0, a_n \neq 0$ and $n \in \mathbf{N}$ is continuous. Use direct substitution to determine the limit of a polynomial function: simply evaluate $f(a)$.

Limits of Polynomial Functions

For any polynomial function $P(x)$, $\lim\limits_{x \to a} P(x) = P(a)$.

Example 6   **Determining the Limit of a Polynomial Function**

Find the limit, if it exists.

$$\lim_{x \to -2} (3x^5 - 2x^3 + 6x^2 - 4)$$

Solution

Since $3x^5 - 2x^3 + 6x^2 - 4$ is a polynomial, use direct substitution.

$$
\begin{aligned}
\lim_{x \to -2} (3x^5 - 2x^3 + 6x^2 - 4) &= 3(-2)^5 - 2(-2)^3 + 6(-2)^2 - 4 \\
&= 3(-32) - 2(-8) + 6(4) - 4 \\
&= -96 + 16 + 24 - 4 \\
&= -60
\end{aligned}
$$

CHECK, CONSOLIDATE, COMMUNICATE

1. Explain, in your own words, the limit of a function and describe three different techniques for determining a limit.
2. When does a limit fail to exist? Sketch the graph of a function that you can use to support your argument.
3. What is the difference between the graphs of a continuous function and a discontinuous function? Give an example of a continuous function and a discontinuous function.
4. When can you use direct substitution to determine the limit of a function?

KEY IDEAS

- A limit represents the behaviour of a function $f(x)$ near a specific value of x. The limit of a function can be expressed as $\lim_{x \to a} f(x) = L$. The limit of a function can be determined by examining the graph of the function, examining a table, or, in some cases, using direct substitution.
- $\lim_{x \to a^+} f(x)$ denotes the right-hand limit, approaching a from the right.
  $\lim_{x \to a^-} f(x)$ denotes the left-hand limit, approaching a from the left.
- If $\lim_{x \to a^-} f(x) \neq \lim_{x \to a^+} f(x)$, then $\lim_{x \to a} f(x)$ does not exist.
- If $\lim_{x \to a^-} f(x) = L = \lim_{x \to a^+} f(x) = L$, then $\lim_{x \to a} f(x)$ exists and $\lim_{x \to a} f(x) = L$.
- A function f is continuous at a if $\lim_{x \to a} f(x) = f(a)$. A continuous function is continuous for all values in the function's domain. The graph of this function is a smooth, continuous curve with no holes or breaks. If f is not continuous at a, it is a discontinuous function, with a discontinuity at a.
- Polynomial functions are continuous. For any polynomial function P, $\lim_{x \to a} P(x) = P(a)$.

3.3 Exercises

A **1.** Use the graphs to evaluate the following limits for each function.

    i. $\lim\limits_{x \to 2^+} f(x)$ **ii.** $\lim\limits_{x \to 2^-} f(x)$ **iii.** $\lim\limits_{x \to 2} f(x)$

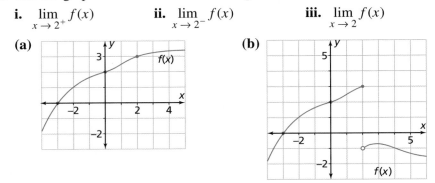

(a)   **(b)**

2. For each function, use tables to examine the function on both sides of the point where $x = 1$. Determine $\lim\limits_{x \to 1} f(x)$, if it exists.

    (a) $f(x) = 8x + 7$ **(b)** $f(x) = 3x^2 - 1$

    (c) $f(x) = -3x + 6x^2$ **(d)** $f(x) = 2x^3 + x^2 - 5x - 3$

3. Invent a function and sketch its graph to satisfy each situation.

    (a) $\lim\limits_{x \to 3} f(x) = 1$

    (b) $\lim\limits_{x \to 0^+} f(x) = 3$ and $\lim\limits_{x \to 0^-} f(x) = -2$

    (c) $\lim\limits_{x \to 0} f(x) = 2$ and $\lim\limits_{x \to \infty} f(x) = 0$

    (d) $\lim\limits_{x \to 2^+} f(x) = -4$ and $\lim\limits_{x \to 2^-} f(x) = 5$

4. Evaluate each limit, if it exists. If it does not exist, explain why not.

    (a) $\lim\limits_{x \to 4} (x^2 + 3)$ **(b)** $\lim\limits_{x \to 2} 3$

    (c) $\lim\limits_{x \to 0} \dfrac{3}{x}$ **(d)** $\lim\limits_{x \to 2} (5x^2 - 4x + 3)$

    (e) $\lim\limits_{x \to -2} (x^4 + 2)$ **(f)** $\lim\limits_{x \to 0} (2x^3 - 4x^2 + 2x - 7)$

    (g) $\lim\limits_{x \to 7} (6x - x^2 + 1)$ **(h)** $\lim\limits_{x \to -3} (-5x^3 - x + 9x^2)$

    (i) $\lim\limits_{x \to 4} \dfrac{2}{x^2}$ **(j)** $\lim\limits_{x \to 2} \left(\dfrac{1}{x^2 - 9} \right)$

B **5.** Evaluate each limit, if it exists.

    (a) $\lim\limits_{x \to 0^+} (x^2 + 3)$ **(b)** $\lim\limits_{x \to 0^-} \dfrac{5}{x^2}$

    (c) $\lim\limits_{x \to 0} \dfrac{1}{x}$ **(d)** $\lim\limits_{x \to 2^+} (3x^2 - 8)$

    (e) $\lim\limits_{x \to 4^-} (7x + 2)$ **(f)** $\lim\limits_{x \to 1^+} (4x^3 + 5x - 7)$

6. Check your answers to question 5 by graphing each function using a graphing calculator.

7. Apply the limit laws to each polynomial function, and evaluate.

(a) $\lim_{x \to 3} (x^3 - 5x^2 + x - 7)$

(b) $\lim_{x \to -2} (3x^4 + 5x^3 - 4x^2 + 3)$

(c) $\lim_{x \to 5} (x^2 + 2x + 5)$

(d) $\lim_{x \to -4} (-3x^3 - 5x - 9)$

(e) $\lim_{x \to 0} (4x^3 - 6x^2 - 8x)$

(f) $\lim_{x \to -6} (x^4 + 9x - 2x^3)$

8. **Knowledge and Understanding**: Evaluate $\lim_{x \to 2} (x^3 - x^2)$ using

(a) a table

(b) a graph

(c) the limit laws

(d) direct substitution

9. For each piecewise function,

   i. sketch a graph of the function

   ii. determine the x-values, if any, at which the function is discontinuous. Find appropriate limits to support your conclusion.

(a) $f(x) = \begin{cases} x & \text{if } x \leq 1 \\ x^2 & \text{if } x > 1 \end{cases}$

(b) $f(x) = \begin{cases} -3x + 2 & \text{if } x < 1 \\ x^2 & \text{if } x \geq 1 \end{cases}$

(c) $f(x) = \begin{cases} -2x & \text{if } x \leq 2 \\ x^2 - 4x + 1 & \text{if } x > 2 \end{cases}$

(d) $f(x) = \begin{cases} x + 1 & \text{if } -10 \leq x \leq 0 \\ -x^2 & \text{if } 0 \leq x \leq 10 \end{cases}$

10. Describe a real-world situation in which the model of this situation is

(a) a continuous function

(b) a discontinuous function

11. **Application**: A downtown parking lot charges \$4 for the first hour (or part of an hour) and \$3 for each additional hour (or part of an hour), up to a daily maximum of \$20.

(a) Sketch a graph of $C(t)$, the cost of parking, as a function of time.

(b) Evaluate $\lim_{t \to 5^+} C(t)$ and $\lim_{t \to 5^-} C(t)$. What significance do these limits have for someone who parks in this lot?

12. The signum function is defined by

$$f(x) = \begin{cases} -1 & \text{if } x < 0 \\ 0 & \text{if } x = 0 \\ 1 & \text{if } x > 0 \end{cases}$$

(a) Sketch the graph of the signum function.

(b) Find each limit, if it exists.

   i. $\lim_{x \to 0^-} f(x)$

   ii. $\lim_{x \to 0^+} f(x)$

   iii. $\lim_{x \to 0} f(x)$

(c) Is $f(x)$ continuous? Explain.

13. Thinking, Inquiry, Problem Solving: For $f(x) = \begin{cases} 5 - x^2 & \text{if } x \le -1 \\ ax + b & \text{if } -1 < x < 1 \\ 2x^2 & \text{if } x \ge 1 \end{cases}$

find a and b such that $\lim\limits_{x \to -1} f(x)$ and $\lim\limits_{x \to 1} f(x)$ exist.

14. Mary says that a continuous function can be drawn without lifting the pencil from the paper. Do you think that this is a valid description? Explain.

15. Describe a situation that might produce each graph.

    (a)   **(b)**   **(c)**

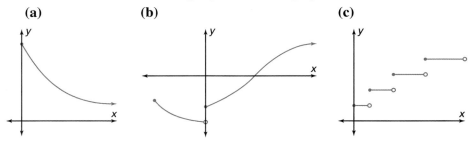

16. Sketch a graph in which $f(x)$ exists at $x = 2$. Also the limit as x approaches 2 from the right exists, but the limit as x approaches 2 from the left does not.

17. Communication

    (a) Sketch the graph of $f(x) = \begin{cases} -3x - 2 & \text{if } x \le 2 \\ x^2 - 5 & \text{if } x > 2 \end{cases}$

    (b) Is $f(x)$ continuous or discontinuous at $x = 2$? Explain.

18. Examine the graph of $f(x)$.

    (a) Find $f(3)$.

    (b) Evaluate $\lim\limits_{x \to 3^-} f(x)$.

    (c) Is $f(x)$ continuous on the interval $-3 < x < 8$? Explain.

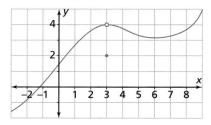

19. (a) Sketch the graph of $y = x^2 + 4x - 5$ and label the point where $x = 0$.

    (b) Find an expression to represent the slope of any secant that passes through the labelled point.

    (c) Find the value of the limit of the secant expression as the value of x approaches 0. What does this value signify?

20. Check Your Understanding: Verify $\lim\limits_{x \to -1} (5x^3 + 5x^2 - 20x + 10) = 30$

    (a) using a table   **(b)** using a graph

    (c) by applying the limit laws   **(d)** by direct substitution

C **21.** Give an example of a real-world situation where the function that models the situation
   (a) has a hole
   (b) has a break
   (c) has an x-value where the function value approaches ∞

22. Find each limit, if it exists.
   (a) $\lim\limits_{x \to 3} |x - 3|$ **(b)** $\lim\limits_{x \to 0} \dfrac{|x|}{x}$ **(c)** $\lim\limits_{x \to -5} \dfrac{|x + 5|}{x + 5}$

23. Find each limit, if it exists.
   (a) $\lim\limits_{x \to \frac{\pi}{2}} \sin x$ **(b)** $\lim\limits_{x \to 0} \cos x$ **(c)** $\lim\limits_{x \to \frac{\pi}{2}} \tan x$

ADDITIONAL ACHIEVEMENT CHART QUESTIONS

Knowledge and Understanding: For the function $f(x) = \begin{cases} -x - 1 & \text{if } 1 < x \le 3 \\ x - 3 & \text{if } 3 < x < 4 \\ -x + 5 & \text{if } 4 \le x < 5 \end{cases}$

(a) evaluate the limits of $f(x)$ at $x = 2, 3, 4,$ and 5 .

(b) tell whether the function is continuous or not. Explain your answer.

Application: A scientific calculator manufacturer can produce 50 000 calculators. The wholesale price is $16.00 for each calculator. The fixed production cost is $9000.00, plus $11.50 per calculator.

(a) Write an expression for
   i. the wholesale revenue, $R(x)$, if x calculators are sold
   ii. the total cost, $C(x)$, of producing x calculators
   iii. the profit, $P(x)$

(b) In each case, find the limit and explain its meaning.
   i. $\lim\limits_{x \to 2000} P(x)$ **ii.** $\lim\limits_{x \to 5000} P(x)$ **iii.** $\lim\limits_{x \to 500} P(x)$

Thinking, Inquiry, Problem Solving: For the function $g(x) = \begin{cases} rx^2 & \text{if } x \le 12 \\ 4x + r & \text{if } x > 12 \end{cases}$

determine a value for r that makes $g(x)$ continuous.

Communication: Explain how $\lim\limits_{x \to a^+} f(x)$ and $\lim\limits_{x \to a^-} f(x)$ can be modelled by a table of values.

3.4 Using Limits to Find Instantaneous Rates of Change—The Derivative

SETTING THE STAGE

In this chapter, you have estimated the instantaneous rate of change of a function by using a sequence of average rates of change, represented by secant lines. Using secants and tables involves a lot of work.

Is there an algebraic technique for calculating instantaneous rates of change accurately and efficiently?

A football is punted into the air. Model the football's height using the polynomial function $f(t) = -4.9t^2 + 16t + 1$, where f represents the height in metres at t seconds. Determine the instantaneous rate of change of height at 1 s, 2 s, and 3 s.

In this section, we will develop an algebraic technique to determine instantaneous rate of change more efficiently.

EXAMINING THE CONCEPT

Developing the Derivative at a Point

You have seen that the instantaneous rate of change at point $P(a, f(a))$ is equal to the slope of the tangent line at that point. The slope of the tangent line is the limiting value of the slopes of the secants, represented by PQ, as point Q approaches point P.

$$\text{slope of the tangent} = \text{instantaneous rate of change}$$
$$= \lim_{\Delta x \to 0} \frac{\Delta y}{\Delta x}$$
$$= \lim_{x \to a} \frac{f(x) - f(a)}{x - a}$$

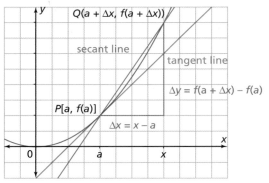

Δx is the interval between the x-coordinates of P and Q, so $\Delta x = x - a$ or $x = a + \Delta x$. The coordinates of Q can be expressed as $(a + \Delta x, f(a + \Delta x))$ and $\Delta y = f(a + \Delta x) - f(a)$.

Therefore,

$$\text{slope of the tangent} = \lim_{\Delta x \to 0} \frac{\Delta y}{\Delta x}$$
$$= \lim_{x \to a} \frac{f(x) - f(a)}{x - a}$$
$$= \lim_{\Delta x \to 0} \frac{f(a + \Delta x) - f(a)}{(a + \Delta x) - a}$$
$$= \lim_{\Delta x \to 0} \frac{f(a + \Delta x) - f(a)}{\Delta x}$$

Secant slope of *QP* approaches tangent slope as $\Delta x \to 0$.

Let $h = \Delta x$, which gives

$$\text{slope of the tangent} = \lim_{h \to 0} \frac{f(a + h) - f(a)}{h}$$

This limit is a keystone of differential calculus, with its own name and notation.

The Derivative at a Point

The derivative of a function f at point $(a, f(a))$ is $f'(a) = \lim_{h \to 0} \frac{f(a + h) - f(a)}{h}$, if this limit exists.

The notation $f'(a)$ is read "f prime of a."

An alternative expression for the derivative is $f'(a) = \lim_{x \to a} \frac{f(x) - f(a)}{x - a}$.

Other notations for the derivative are $f'(x)$, y', $\frac{dy}{dx}$, and $\frac{d}{dx} f(x)$. "d" stands for differential. The derivative at a specific point, $f'(a)$, is also written as $\frac{dy}{dx}\Big|_{x = a}$.

Example 1 **Using the Derivative to Determine the Slope of a Tangent**

(a) Determine the equation of the tangent to the curve defined by $f(x) = -x^2 + 3x - 5$ at point $(4, -9)$.

(b) Sketch the graph of $f(x)$ and the tangent line.

Solution

(a) The derivative can be used to determine the slope of the tangent at $(a, f(a)) = (4, -9)$. Recall that $f'(a) = \lim_{h \to 0} \frac{f(a + h) - f(a)}{h}$.

$$
\begin{aligned}
f'(4) &= \lim_{h \to 0} \frac{f(4 + h) - f(4)}{h} && \text{Subsitute into } f(x).\\
&= \lim_{h \to 0} \frac{[-(4 + h)^2 + 3(4 + h) - 5] - (-9)}{h} && \text{Expand.}\\
&= \lim_{h \to 0} \frac{[-(16 + 8h + h^2) + 3(4 + h) - 5] - (-9)}{h} && \text{Simplify.}\\
&= \lim_{h \to 0} \frac{-16 - 8h - h^2 + 12 + 3h - 5 + 9}{h}\\
&= \lim_{h \to 0} \frac{-h^2 - 5h}{h} && \text{Factor.}\\
&= \lim_{h \to 0} \frac{h^1(-h - 5)}{h^1} && \text{Reduce.}\\
&= \lim_{h \to 0} (-h - 5) && \text{Subsitute } h = 0.\\
&= -(0) - 5\\
&= -5
\end{aligned}
$$

At point $(4, -9)$, the slope of the tangent is -5. Substitute these values into $y = mx + b$ and solve for b.

$$y = mx + b$$
$$-9 = -5(4) + b \qquad \text{Solve for } b.$$
$$b = 11$$

The equation of the tangent is $y = -5x + 11$.

(b) The graph of $f(x)$ is a parabola that opens down. Complete the square to determine the vertex.

$$f(x) = -x^2 + 3x - 5$$
$$= -\left(x^2 - 3x + \frac{9}{4} - \frac{9}{4}\right) - 5$$
$$= -\left(x^2 - 3x + \frac{9}{4}\right) + \frac{9}{4} - \frac{20}{4}$$
$$= -\left(x - \frac{3}{2}\right)^2 - \frac{11}{4}$$

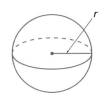

$f(x) = -x^2 + 3x - 5$ and the tangent at $(4, -9)$

The vertex of the parabola is $\left(\frac{3}{2}, -\frac{11}{4}\right)$. The y-intercept is -5. The tangent line passes through $(4, -9)$. The y-intercept is 11.

• • • • • • • •

Example 2 **Using the Derivative to Determine an Instantaneous Rate of Change**

A balloon is inflated by an electric pump. Determine the rate of change of volume with respect to radius when the radius measures exactly 6 cm.

Solution

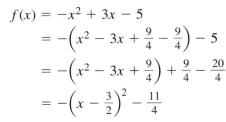

Sphere with radius r

Assume that the balloon is a sphere. The volume, V, of a sphere with radius r is $V(r) = \frac{4}{3}\pi r^3$.

Determine the instantaneous rate of change of volume with respect to radius at $r = 6$ using the derivative $f'(a) = \lim\limits_{h \to 0} \dfrac{f(a + h) - f(a)}{h}$.

$$V'(6) = \lim_{h \to 0} \frac{V(6 + h) - V(6)}{h} \qquad \text{Direct substitution does not work here; the result is } \frac{0}{0}.$$

$$= \lim_{h \to 0} \frac{\left[\frac{4}{3}\pi(6 + h)^3\right] - \left[\frac{4}{3}\pi(6)^3\right]}{h}$$

$$= \lim_{h \to 0} \frac{\left[\frac{4}{3}\pi(6 + h)(6 + h)^2\right] - \left[\frac{4}{3}\pi(216)\right]}{h} \qquad \text{Expand and simplify.}$$

$$= \lim_{h \to 0} \frac{\left[\frac{4}{3}\pi(6 + h)(36 + 12h + h^2)\right] - 288\pi}{h}$$

$$= \lim_{h \to 0} \frac{\frac{4}{3}\pi(216 + 72h + 6h^2 + 36h + 12h^2 + h^3) - 288\pi}{h}$$

$$= \lim_{h \to 0} \frac{\frac{4}{3}\pi(216 + 108h + 18h^2 + h^3) - 288\pi}{h}$$

$$= \lim_{h \to 0} \frac{288\pi + 144\pi h + 24\pi h^2 + \frac{4}{3}\pi h^3 - 288\pi}{h}$$

$$= \lim_{h \to 0} \frac{144\pi h + 24\pi h^2 + \frac{4}{3}\pi h^3}{h} \qquad \text{Factor.}$$

$$= \lim_{h \to 0} \frac{\not{h}^1 \pi(144 + 24h + \frac{4}{3}h^2)}{\not{h}^1} \qquad \text{Reduce.}$$

$$= \lim_{h \to 0} \pi(144 + 24h + \frac{4}{3}h^2) \qquad \text{Evaluate the limit of the polynomial by direct substitution.}$$

$$= \pi[144 + 24(0) + \frac{4}{3}(0)^2]$$

$$= 144\pi$$

$$\doteq 452.39$$

The rate of change of volume with respect to radius is measured in cubic centimetres per centimetre. At a radius of 6 cm, the balloon's volume is changing at an instantaneous rate of about 452.39 cm³/cm.

Note that the result is not reduced to 452.39 cm².

- - - - - - - - -

Interpretation of the Derivative $f'(a)$

The derivative of a function f at point $(a, f(a))$ can be interpreted as either

1. the slope of the tangent line. The slope of the tangent to the graph of $y = f(x)$ at point $(a, f(a))$ is the value of $f'(a)$, the derivative of f at a, or

2. the instantaneous rate of change. The derivative $f'(a)$ is the instantaneous rate of change of $f(x)$ with respect to x when $x = a$.

EXAMINING THE CONCEPT

The Derivative of a Function

The derivative of a function has been defined for a specific point: $f'(a)$ at $(a, f(a))$. If you replace the constant a in $f'(a) = \lim\limits_{h \to 0} \dfrac{f(a + h) - f(a)}{h}$ with the independent variable x, you obtain the definition of the derivative function.

The process of finding the derivative is called **differentiation**.

The Derivative Function

The derivative of the function $f(x)$ is the function $f'(x)$ defined by

$$f'(x) = \lim_{h \to 0} \frac{f(x + h) - f(x)}{h},$$ for all x for which the limit exists.

When you use this limit to determine the derivative of a function, it is called **determining the derivative from first principles**. To evaluate this limit, x is held constant as h approaches 0.

Example 3

Determining the Derivative of a Polynomial Function from First Principles

Determine $f'(x)$ if $f(x) = -2x^3 + x - 6$.

Solution

$$
\begin{aligned}
f'(x) &= \lim_{h \to 0} \frac{f(x + h) - f(x)}{h} && \text{Substitute into } f(x). \\
&= \lim_{h \to 0} \frac{[-2(x + h)^3 + (x + h) - 6] - (-2x^3 + x - 6)}{h} && \text{Expand and simplify.} \\
&= \lim_{h \to 0} \frac{[-2(x^3 + 3x^2h + 3xh^2 + h^3) + (x + h) - 6] + 2x^3 - x + 6}{h} \\
&= \lim_{h \to 0} \frac{-2x^3 - 6x^2h - 6xh^2 - 2h^3 + x + h - 6 + 2x^3 - x + 6}{h} \\
&= \lim_{h \to 0} \frac{-6x^2h - 6xh^2 - 2h^3 + h}{h} && \text{Factor.} \\
&= \lim_{h \to 0} \frac{\cancel{h}^1(-6x^2 - 6xh - 2h^2 + 1)}{\cancel{h}^1} && \text{Reduce.} \\
&= \lim_{h \to 0} (-6x^2 - 6xh - 2h^2 + 1) && \text{Substitute } h = 0. \\
&= -6x^2 - 6x(0) - 2(0)^2 + 1 \\
&= -6x^2 + 1
\end{aligned}
$$

• • • • • • • •

Differentiability and Functions

A function $f(x)$ is **differentiable at a** if $f'(a)$ or, equivalently,

$\lim_{h \to 0} \dfrac{f(a + h) - f(a)}{h}$ exists. If this limit exists for all values of a on an interval in the domain, then $f(x)$ is differentiable on this interval.

For example, the function $f(x) = x^2$ is differentiable on the interval $-\infty < x < \infty$, because $\lim_{h \to 0} \dfrac{f(x + h) - f(x)}{h}$ exists for all values of x in this interval.

Example 4

Determining whether a Function Is Differentiable at a Given Number

Show that $f(x) = \dfrac{-1}{x}$ is not differentiable at $x = 0$.

Solution

Create a table and a graph.

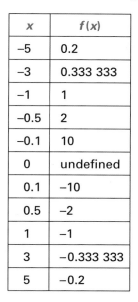

x	f(x)
−5	0.2
−3	0.333 333
−1	1
−0.5	2
−0.1	10
0	undefined
0.1	−10
0.5	−2
1	−1
3	−0.333 333
5	−0.2

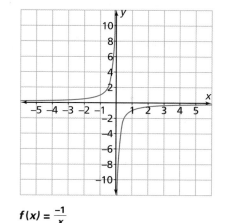

$f(x) = \dfrac{-1}{x}$

$f(x) = \dfrac{-1}{x}$ is differentiable at $x = 0$ if $\displaystyle\lim_{h \to 0} \dfrac{f(0 + h) - f(0)}{h}$ exists.
But $f(0) = \dfrac{-1}{0}$ is not defined. Therefore, the limit is not defined and
does not exist. The function $f(x) = \dfrac{-1}{x}$ is not differentiable at $x = 0$.

• • • • • • • •

Example 5 Using the Derivative to Determine an Instantaneous Rate of Change

Recall the problem in Setting the Stage. A football is punted into the air. Model the football's height using the polynomial function $f(t) = -4.9t^2 + 16t + 1$, where $f(t)$ represents the height in metres at t seconds. Determine the instantaneous rate of change of height at 1 s, 2 s, and 3 s.

Solution

The function $f(t) = -4.9t^2 + 16t + 1$ models the height of the football in metres at t seconds. Therefore, the derivative function, $f'(t)$, models the instantaneous rate of change of height with respect to time, in metres per second. Use the derivative to solve this problem. Find the derivative function from first principles.

$$f'(t) = \lim_{h \to 0} \frac{f(t + h) - f(t)}{h} \qquad \text{Substitute into } f(t).$$

$$= \lim_{h \to 0} \frac{[-4.9(t + h)^2 + 16(t + h) + 1] - [-4.9(t)^2 + 16(t) + 1]}{h} \quad \begin{array}{l}\text{Expand and} \\ \text{simplify.}\end{array}$$

$$= \lim_{h \to 0} \frac{-4.9(t^2 + 2th + h^2) + 16(t + h) + 1 + 4.9t^2 - 16t - 1}{h}$$

$$= \lim_{h \to 0} \frac{-4.9t^2 - 9.8th - 4.9h^2 + 16t + 16h + 1 + 4.9t^2 - 16t - 1}{h}$$

$$= \lim_{h \to 0} \frac{-4.9h^2 - 9.8th + 16h}{h} \qquad \text{Factor.}$$

$$= \lim_{h \to 0} \frac{\overset{1}{\cancel{h}}(-4.9h - 9.8t + 16)}{\underset{1}{\cancel{h}}} \qquad \text{Reduce.}$$

$$= \lim_{h \to 0} (-4.9h - 9.8t + 16) \qquad \text{Substitute } h = 0.$$

$$= -9.8t + 16$$

The instantaneous rate of change of height at time t is given by the derivative function $f'(t) = -9.8t + 16$. Therefore, at the times in question,

$$f'(1) = -9.8(1) + 16 = 6.2 \text{ m/s}$$
$$f'(2) = -9.8(2) + 16 = -3.6 \text{ m/s}$$
$$f'(3) = -9.8(3) + 16 = -13.4 \text{ m/s}$$

At 1 s, the football is travelling up at 6.2 m/s.
At 2 s, it has just started to descend at 3.6 m/s.
At 3 s, it is descending rapidly at 13.4 m/s.

f(t) = −4.9t² + 16t + 1 and the tangents at 1, 2, and 3 s.

CHECK, CONSOLIDATE, COMMUNICATE

1. What limit would you evaluate to determine the derivative of a function $f(x)$ at $x = a$?
2. What limit would you use to determine the derivative of any function $f(x)$?
3. What are two interpretations for the derivative $f'(a)$?
4. What does it mean to say that a function is differentiable on the interval $x_1 \leq x \leq x_2$?

KEY IDEAS

- The derivative of a function f at point $(a, f(a))$ is

$$f'(a) = \lim_{h \to 0} \frac{f(a + h) - f(a)}{h} \text{ or } f'(a) = \lim_{x \to a} \frac{f(x) - f(a)}{x - a}, \text{ if the limit exists.}$$

- The derivative $f'(a)$ can be interpreted as either
  (a) the slope of the tangent line at $(a, f(a))$, or
  (b) the instantaneous rate of change of $f(x)$ with respect to x when $x = a$
- A function $f(x)$ is said to be **differentiable at a** if $f'(a)$ exists. A function is differentiable on an interval if it is differentiable at every number in the interval.
- The derivative function for any function $f(x)$ is given by

$$f'(x) = \lim_{h \to 0} \frac{f(x + h) - f(x)}{h}. \text{ Using this limit to calculate the derivative is}$$

called *determining the derivative from first principles*.
- Other notations for the derivative of the function $y = f(x)$ are $f'(x)$, y', $\frac{dy}{dx}$, and $\frac{d}{dx} f(x)$.

3.4 Exercises

A

1. For each function, find $f(a + h)$ and $f(a + h) - f(a)$.
   (a) $f(x) = 5x - 2$ **(b)** $f(x) = x^2 + 3x - 1$
   (c) $f(x) = x^3 - 4x + 1$ **(d)** $f(x) = x^2 + x - 6$
   (e) $f(x) = -7x + 4$ **(f)** $f(x) = 4 - 2x - x^2$

2. For each function, use the definition of the derivative at a point to find the slope of the tangent at the indicated point.
   (a) $f(x) = 4x + 1$ at $(2, 9)$ **(b)** $f(x) = x^2 + 3x - 5$ at $(-3, -5)$
   (c) $f(x) = 3x^2 - 4x + 5$ at $(1, 4)$ **(d)** $f(x) = x^3 - 2x^2 + 1$ at $(2, 1)$
   (e) $f(x) = 6x - x^2$ at $(4, 8)$ **(f)** $f(x) = \frac{x + 6}{2}$ at $(-4, 1)$

3. Use the limit definition of the derivative to determine $f'(x)$ for each function.
   (a) $f(x) = 2x^2 + 4x$ **(b)** $f(x) = -5x - 8$
   (c) $f(x) = -8x^2 - 3x + 5$ **(d)** $f(x) = 6x^3 - 7x$
   (e) $f(x) = 4 - 10x^2$ **(f)** $f(x) = x^3 + x^2 + x + 1$

4. Determine $\frac{dy}{dx}$ from first principles.
   (a) $y = x^2 - 9$ **(b)** $y = -5x^2 + 6x - 3$
   (c) $y = 2x^3 + 6$ **(d)** $y = -3x^2 - 7x + 2$
   (e) $y = 5x - 12$ **(f)** $y = 5x^3 - 6x^2 + 3x - 2$

B **5.** For $f(x) = x^2 - 6x + 5$, find

    (a) the missing coordinate in $(x, ?)$

    (b) the slope of the tangent where $x = 3$

    (c) the equation of the tangent in (b)

6. **Knowledge and Understanding:** For $y = x^2 + 8x - 6$, determine $\dfrac{dy}{dx}$ from first principles.

7. Find the equation of the tangent for each given x-value.

    (a) $y = x^2 + x - 3$, where $x = 4$

    (b) $y = 2x^2 - 7$, where $x = -2$

    (c) $f(x) = 3x^2 + 2x - 5$, where $x = -1$

    (d) $f(x) = 5x^2 - 8x + 3$, where $x = 1$

    (e) $y = x^2 + 8x + 12$, where $x = -4$

    (f) $f(x) = x^3 + 3x^2 - 2x + 4$, where $x = 1$

8. **(a)** Find the equation of the tangent to the curve of $y = x^2 - 4x + 3$, where $x = 1$.

    (b) Sketch the graph of the function and the tangent.

9. For $f(x) = x^2 - 4x + 1$, find

    (a) the coordinates of point A, where $x = 3$, and of point B, where $x = 5$

    (b) the equation of the secant AB

    (c) the equation of the tangent at A

    (d) the equation of the tangent at B

10. For $f(x) = 2x^2 - 3x - 5$, find $f(3)$ and $f'(3)$. Explain in words and with a diagram the meaning of the value and the derivative function.

11. **Communication:** If a function is not differentiable at $x = a$, what does this mean

    (a) algebraically?   **(b)** graphically?

12. A plane takes off from an airport. The table gives the plane's distance in kilometres from the airport at various times.

Time (h)	0	1	2	3	4	5	6
Distance (km)	0	300	800	1500	2300	2900	3300

    (a) What is the average rate of change of distance with respect to time over the first four hours?

    (b) Determine a possible algebraic model for the data.

    (c) Use your model to estimate the speed of the plane at 3 h after take-off.

13. A tank holds 500 L of liquid, which takes 90 min to drain from a hole in the bottom of the tank. The volume, V, remaining in the tank after t minutes is

$$V(t) = 500\left(1 - \frac{t}{90}\right)^2, \text{ where } 0 \le t \le 90$$

   (a) How much liquid remains in the tank at 1 h?
   (b) What is the average rate of change of volume with respect to time from 0 min to 60 min?
   (c) How fast is the liquid draining at 30 min?

14. **Application:** A population of raccoons moves into a wooded, urban area. At t months, the number of raccoons, P, can be modelled by

$$P(t) = 100 + 30t + 4t^2$$

Determine the rate at which the raccoon population is changing when the initial population has doubled in size.

15. The volume of a sphere is given by $V(r) = \frac{4}{3}\pi r^3$.

   (a) Find the average rate of change of volume with respect to radius as the radius changes from 10 cm to 15 cm.
   (b) Find the rate of change of volume when the radius is 8 cm.

16. **Thinking, Inquiry, Problem Solving:** Find the coordinates of the point of intersection between the lines tangent to the zeros of $g(x) = 4x^3 - 4x^2 + x$.

17. The average annual salary of a professional baseball player can be modelled by the function

$$S(x) = 246 + 64x - 8.9x^2 + 0.95x^3$$

where S represents the average annual salary in thousands of dollars and x is the number of years since 1982. Determine the rate at which the average salary is changing in 2005.

18. A football is kicked up into the air. Its height, h, above the ground in metres at t seconds can be modelled by $h(t) = 18t - 4.9t^2$.

   (a) Determine $h'(2)$.
   (b) What does $h'(2)$ represent?

19. **Check Your Understanding:** Determine the slope of the tangent to the curve $y = 4x^3 - 3x + 6$ at point $(1, 7)$.

C 20. At what point on the graph of $y = x^2 - 4x - 5$ is the tangent parallel to $2x - y = 1$?

21. Determine the coordinates of each point on the graph of $f(x) = 2x^3 - 7x^2 + 8x - 3$ where the tangent line is horizontal.

22. Determine the equations of both lines that are tangent to the graph of $f(x) = x^2$ and pass through point $(1, -3)$.

ADDITIONAL ACHIEVEMENT CHART QUESTIONS

Knowledge and Understanding: Consider the function $y = x^2 - 3x + 1$.

(a) Use first principles to determine the slope of any tangent to the curve of the function at the general point $(x, f(x))$.

(b) Find the equation of the tangent line at the point where $x = 2$.

(c) Sketch the graph of the function and its tangent.

Application: The revenue from DVD movie sales depends on the number sold, S. The formula seems to be $P(S) = 160 - 350S + 5S^2$. Find the rate of change of revenue, $P(S)$, when a store sells 500 DVD movies.

Thinking, Inquiry, Problem Solving: Elizabeth was looking at a calculus book that belonged to her mom when she was in high school. On page 77, she noticed that the answer to a first-principles derivative problem was $f'(x) = 5x^2 + 7x - 3$. Unfortunately, pages 75 and 76 were missing from the book. Elizabeth wondered what the original function $f(x)$ might have been. What are three different possibilities for $f(x)$? How could you check whether each might be correct?

Communication: A classmate says, "The derivative of a cubic polynomial function is a quadratic polynomial function." Is the statement always true, sometimes true, or never true? Defend your choice in words, and provide two examples to support your argument.

The Chapter Problem
Average Salaries in Professional Sports

Apply what you learned to answer these questions about The Chapter Problem on page 168.

CP5. Enter the data on page 168 into lists in a graphing calculator. Enter 0 to 16 for the years representing 1980 to 1996. Enter the salary numbers as they appear in the table. Use regression to determine the equation of a cubic polynomial that models each data set. Verify your equations by creating a scatter plot and graphing the equations.

CP6. For each data set's equation, use the Tangent command in the Draw menu (2nd **DRAW 5:Tangent(**) at various points to approximate where the salaries are increasing the fastest and the slowest.

CP7. Round the coefficients of the cubic regression equations to three decimal places. Then determine their derivatives from first principles.

CP8. Using your derivatives, determine the instantaneous rates of change in 1996.

3.5 Finding Some Shortcuts— The Constant and Power Rules

SETTING THE STAGE

You have seen that the derivative of a function, $f'(x)$, can be determined algebraically from $\lim\limits_{h \to 0} \dfrac{f(x + h) - f(x)}{h}$.

For $f(x) = 2x^{25}$, how easily can you determine $f'(x)$ from first principles by evaluating the limit?

In this section, you will develop some shorter algebraic methods, called *differentiation rules*, for determining the derivative.

EXAMINING THE CONCEPT

Developing the Basic Differentiation Rules

The constant function is represented by a horizontal line.

For $f(x) = c$, where c is a constant, the value of the function is the same for each x-value. Then the instantaneous rate of change is 0.

Derivative of a Constant Function: The Constant Rule

If $f(x)$ is a constant function, that is, $f(x) = c$, then $f'(x) = 0$.

In Leibniz notation, $\dfrac{d}{dx}(c) = 0$.

Proof:
$$f'(x) = \lim_{h \to 0} \frac{f(x + h) - f(x)}{h}$$
$$= \lim_{h \to 0} \frac{c - c}{h}$$
$$= \lim_{h \to 0} 0 = 0$$

Example 1 **Using the Constant Rule**

Differentiate each function.

(a) $f(x) = 9$ (b) $y = -3$ (c) $h(t) = 0.75$ (d) $y = \dfrac{3}{8}$

Solution

(a) $f'(x) = 0$ (b) $\dfrac{dy}{dx} = 0$ (c) $h'(t) = 0$ (d) $y' = 0$

•••••••••

Now find the derivative of functions in the form $f(x) = x^n$, where $n \in \mathbf{N}$. Look for a pattern in the table.

$f(x) = x$	$f(x) = x^2$	$f(x) = x^3$
$f'(x) = \lim_{h \to 0} \dfrac{f(x+h) - f(x)}{h}$	$f'(x) = \lim_{h \to 0} \dfrac{f(x+h) - f(x)}{h}$	$f'(x) = \lim_{h \to 0} \dfrac{f(x+h) - f(x)}{h}$
$= \lim_{h \to 0} \dfrac{(x+h) - x}{h}$	$= \lim_{h \to 0} \dfrac{(x+h)^2 - x^2}{h}$	$= \lim_{h \to 0} \dfrac{(x+h)^3 - x^3}{h}$
$= \lim_{h \to 0} \dfrac{\cancel{h}^1}{\cancel{h}^1}$	$= \lim_{h \to 0} \dfrac{x^2 + 2xh + h^2 - x^2}{h}$	$= \lim_{h \to 0} \dfrac{x^3 + 3x^2h + 3xh^2 + h^3 - x^3}{h}$
$= \lim_{h \to 0} 1$	$= \lim_{h \to 0} \dfrac{2xh + h^2}{h}$	$= \lim_{h \to 0} \dfrac{3x^2h + 3xh^2 + h^3}{h}$
$= 1$	$= \lim_{h \to 0} \dfrac{\cancel{h}^1(2x + h)}{\cancel{h}^1}$	$= \lim_{h \to 0} \dfrac{\cancel{h}^1(3x^2 + 3xh + h^2)}{\cancel{h}^1}$
	$= \lim_{h \to 0} (2x + h)$	$= \lim_{h \to 0} (3x^2 + 3xh + h^2)$
	$= 2x + 0$	$= 3x^2 + 3(0) + 0$
	$= 2x$	$= 3x^2$
$f(x) = x \Rightarrow f'(x) = 1$	$f(x) = x^2 \Rightarrow f'(x) = 2x$	$f(x) = x^3 \Rightarrow f'(x) = 3x^2$

Each derivative follows the pattern $\dfrac{d}{dx}(x^n) = nx^{n-1}$.

Derivative of a Power Function: The Power Rule

If n is a positive integer and $f(x) = x^n$, then $f'(x) = nx^{n-1}$. In Leibniz notation, $\dfrac{d}{dx}(x^n) = nx^{n-1}$.

Proof

Before we prove the power rule, we will establish the identity
$x^n - a^n = (x - a)(x^{n-1} + x^{n-2}a + x^{n-3}a^2 + \ldots + a^{n-1})$, which will be used in the proof.

The sequence $x^{n-1} + x^{n-2}a + x^{n-3}a^2 + \ldots + a^{n-1}$ is a geometric sequence of n terms, where the first term is x^{n-1} and the common ratio is $\dfrac{a}{x}$.

Recall that the sum of a geometric series is

$$S = \frac{a(1 - r^n)}{1 - r} = \frac{x^{n-1}\left[1 - \left(\frac{a}{x}\right)^n\right]}{1 - \frac{a}{x}} = \frac{x^{n-1}\left[\frac{x^n - a^n}{x^n}\right]}{\frac{x-a}{x}} = \frac{x^n - a^n}{x - a}$$

Therefore,

$$(x - a)(x^{n-1} + x^{n-2}a + x^{n-3}a^2 + \ldots + a^{n-1}) = (x - a)\frac{x^n - a^n}{x - a}$$
$$= x^n - a^n$$

Use this result for $f(x) = x^n$:

$$f'(x) = \lim_{h \to 0} \frac{f(x+h) - f(x)}{h}$$

$$= \lim_{h \to 0} \frac{(x+h)^n - x^n}{h}$$

$$= \lim_{h \to 0} \frac{[(x+h) - x][(x+h)^{n-1} + (x+h)^{n-2}x + \ldots + x^{n-1}]}{h} \quad \text{Apply the identity proven above.}$$

$$= \lim_{h \to 0} \frac{\cancel{h}^1[(x+h)^{n-1} + (x+h)^{n-2}x + \ldots + x^{n-1}]}{\cancel{h}^1}$$

$$= x^{n-1} + x^{n-2}x + x^{n-3}x^2 + \ldots + x^{n-1}$$

$$= x^{n-1} + x^{n-1} + x^{n-1} + \ldots + x^{n-1} \quad (n \text{ terms})$$

$$= nx^{n-1}$$

Example 2 **Using the Power Rule**

Determine the derivative of each function.

(a) $f(x) = x^8$ **(b)** $y = x^{12}$ **(c)** $g(t) = t^5$ **(d)** $y = x^{15}$

Solution

(a) $f'(x) = 8x^7$ **(b)** $\dfrac{dy}{dx} = 12x^{11}$ **(c)** $g'(t) = 5t^4$ **(d)** $y' = 15x^{14}$

• • • • • • • •

The power rule is true for all real numbers, n.

The General Power Rule

If n is a real number and $f(x) = x^n$, then $f'(x) = nx^{n-1}$. In Leibniz notation, $\dfrac{d}{dx}(x^n) = nx^{n-1}$.

Example 3 **Using the General Power Rule**

Determine $\dfrac{dy}{dx}$ for each function.

(a) $y = x^{-6}$ **(b)** $y = \sqrt[3]{x^2}$

Solution

(a) $\dfrac{dy}{dx} = -6x^{-6-1}$ **(b)** $\quad y = \sqrt[3]{x^2}$

$\qquad\quad = -6x^{-7}$ $= x^{\frac{2}{3}}$

$\qquad\quad = -6\left(\dfrac{1}{x^7}\right)$ $\dfrac{dy}{dx} = \dfrac{2}{3}\left(x^{\frac{-1}{3}}\right)$

$\qquad\quad = \dfrac{-6}{x^7}$ $= \dfrac{2}{3}\left(\dfrac{1}{x^{\frac{1}{3}}}\right)$

                                                 $= \dfrac{2}{3\sqrt[3]{x}}$

• • • • • • •

If a function is multiplied by a constant, then the constant can be factored out of the differentiation process.

The Constant Multiple Rule

If $g(x) = c f(x)$ and $f(x)$ is differentiable, then $g'(x) = c f'(x)$.
Equivalently, $\frac{d}{dx}[cf(x)] = c\left[\frac{d}{dx}f(x)\right]$.

Proof

$$
\begin{aligned}
g'(x) &= \lim_{h \to 0} \frac{g(x + h) - g(x)}{h} \\
&= \lim_{h \to 0} \frac{cf(x + h) - cf(x)}{h} \\
&= \lim_{h \to 0} c\left[\frac{f(x + h) - f(x)}{h}\right] \\
&= c \lim_{h \to 0} \left[\frac{f(x + h) - f(x)}{h}\right] \\
&= cf'(x)
\end{aligned}
$$

Intuitively, if g is c times as big as f, then g increases or decreases c times as fast as f.

Example 4   **Using the Constant Multiple Rule**

Differentiate each function.

(a) $y = 2x^{25}$

(b) $f(x) = \dfrac{2}{3\sqrt{x}}$

Solution

(a) $\dfrac{dy}{dx} = 2(25)x^{24}$

$\qquad = 50x^{24}$

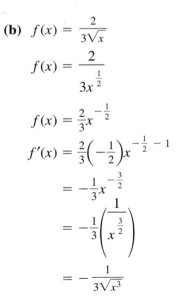

(b) $f(x) = \dfrac{2}{3\sqrt{x}}$

$f(x) = \dfrac{2}{3x^{\frac{1}{2}}}$

$f(x) = \dfrac{2}{3}x^{-\frac{1}{2}}$

$f'(x) = \dfrac{2}{3}\left(-\dfrac{1}{2}\right)x^{-\frac{1}{2} - 1}$

$\qquad = -\dfrac{1}{3}x^{-\frac{3}{2}}$

$\qquad = -\dfrac{1}{3}\left(\dfrac{1}{x^{\frac{3}{2}}}\right)$

$\qquad = -\dfrac{1}{3\sqrt{x^3}}$

• • • • • • • •

Example 5 Using Differentiation Rules in a Tangent Problem

Determine the point on the graph of $f(x) = -3x^3$ where the tangent line at this point is perpendicular to the line $y = 4x - 1$.

Solution

The slope of the given line is 4. Then the slope of the perpendicular tangent line must be $-\frac{1}{4}$.

Any line that is tangent to the curve of $f(x) = -3x^3$ has a slope equal to the derivative, $f'(x)$. Therefore, $f'(x) = -\frac{1}{4}$. Then

$$f'(x) = -9x^2 \qquad \text{Substitute } f'(x) = -\frac{1}{4}.$$
$$-9x^2 = -\frac{1}{4}$$
$$-36x^2 = -1 \qquad \text{Simplify and solve.}$$
$$x^2 = \frac{1}{36}$$
$$x = \pm\frac{1}{6}$$

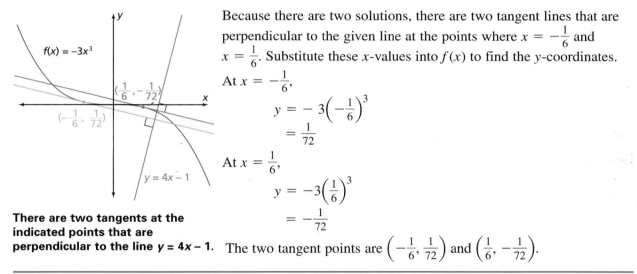

$f(x) = -3x^3$

$\left(\frac{1}{6}, -\frac{1}{72}\right)$

$\left(-\frac{1}{6}, \frac{1}{72}\right)$

$y = 4x - 1$

There are two tangents at the indicated points that are perpendicular to the line $y = 4x - 1$.

Because there are two solutions, there are two tangent lines that are perpendicular to the given line at the points where $x = -\frac{1}{6}$ and $x = \frac{1}{6}$. Substitute these x-values into $f(x)$ to find the y-coordinates.

At $x = -\frac{1}{6}$,

$$y = -3\left(-\frac{1}{6}\right)^3$$
$$= \frac{1}{72}$$

At $x = \frac{1}{6}$,

$$y = -3\left(\frac{1}{6}\right)^3$$
$$= -\frac{1}{72}$$

The two tangent points are $\left(-\frac{1}{6}, \frac{1}{72}\right)$ and $\left(\frac{1}{6}, -\frac{1}{72}\right)$.

CHECK, CONSOLIDATE, COMMUNICATE

1. Explain how to determine $\frac{dy}{dx}$ of the function $y = x^8$.

2. Explain why the derivative of any constant function is always 0.

3. Explain how to determine $f'(x)$ for $f(x) = \frac{4}{x^6}$.

4. Explain how to determine $g'(x)$ for $g(x) = \sqrt[3]{x^5}$.

KEY IDEAS

This table is a summary of the differentiation rules in this section.

Rule	Function Notation	Leibniz Notation
Derivative of a Constant Function	If $f(x) = c$ (a constant) for all x, then $f'(x) = 0$.	$\frac{d}{dx}(c) = 0$
Power Rule	If n is a positive integer and $f(x) = x^n$, then $f'(x) = nx^{n-1}$.	$\frac{d}{dx}(x^n) = nx^{n-1}$
General Power Rule	If n is a real number and $f(x) = x^n$, then $f'(x) = nx^{n-1}$.	$\frac{d}{dx}(x^n) = nx^{n-1}$
Constant Multiple Rule	If $g(x) = cf(x)$, then $g'(x) = cf'(x)$.	$\frac{d}{dx}[cf(x)] = c\left[\frac{d}{dx}f(x)\right]$

3.5 Exercises

A 1. For $f(x) = 3x^2$,
   (a) use first principles to find the derivative, $f'(x)$
   (b) use differentiation rules to confirm your findings for (a)

2. For each function, find $f'(x)$. Answer in power form.

   (a) $f(x) = x^4$

   (b) $f(x) = 8$

   (c) $f(x) = x$

   (d) $f(x) = \frac{3}{4}x^4$

   (e) $f(x) = \frac{1}{2}\sqrt{x}$

   (f) $f(x) = 5x^{-3}$

   (g) $f(x) = \frac{3}{x^2}$

   (h) $f(x) = \frac{3}{\sqrt{x}}$

   (i) $f(x) = \frac{5}{\sqrt[4]{x}}$

   (j) $f(x) = -x^{\frac{3}{2}}$

3. For each function, find $\frac{dy}{dx}$.

   (a) $y = 8$

   (b) $y = 5x$

   (c) $y = 4x^3$

   (d) $y = (-3x)^4$

   (e) $y = \sqrt[3]{x^5}$

   (f) $y = x^{\frac{-1}{3}}$

   (g) $y = -4x^{-2}$

   (h) $y = \frac{2}{3}x^{\frac{3}{2}}$

   (i) $y = \sqrt{x^5}$

   (j) $y = -4.9x^2$

B **4.** Sketch the graph of the derivative of any

    (a) constant function

    (b) linear function

    (c) quadratic function with a positive leading coefficient, such that the graph opens up

    (d) quadratic function with a negative leading coefficient, such that the graph opens down

5. Differentiate.

    (a) $y = 5x^{-2}$ **(b)** $y = 6x^{\frac{1}{2}}$

    (c) $f(x) = 7$ **(d)** $f(x) = \frac{4}{x^5}$

    (e) $y = 0$ **(f)** $g(x) = -6x^3$

    (g) $h(x) = -6x^6$ **(h)** $y = 0.75x^{-0.5}$

    (i) $f(x) = \frac{7}{x^6}$ **(j)** $y = \frac{4}{3}\pi x^3$

6. Knowledge and Understanding: Determine the slope of the tangent to the curve $y = 4x^5$ at point $\left(\frac{1}{2}, \frac{1}{8}\right)$.

7. For $y = \frac{1}{3}x^6$, find the equation of the tangent where $x = 1$.

8. Find the equations of the tangents to the graph of $y = 4x^3$ that have slope 3.

9. For $y = 0.75x^2$, find the rate at which the value of y is changing when $x = 3$.

10. Communication: Rafael tries to find $f'(2)$, where $f(x) = x^5$. He substitutes 2 for x and gets $f(2) = 32$. Then he differentiates 32 and gets 0. Explain why he also gets a mark of 0.

11. An object drops from a cliff that is 150 m high. The distance, d, in metres that the object has dropped at t seconds is modelled by $d(t) = 4.9t^2$.

    (a) Find the average rate of change of distance with respect to time from 2 s to 5 s.

    (b) Find the instantaneous rate of change of distance with respect to time at 4 s.

    (c) Find the rate at which the object hits the ground to the nearest tenth.

12. The motion of an avalanche is described by $s(t) = 3t^2$, where s is the distance in metres travelled by the leading edge of the snow at t seconds.

    (a) Find the distance travelled from 0 s to 5 s.

    (b) Find the rate at which the avalanche is moving from 0 s to 10 s.

    (c) Find the rate at which the avalanche is moving at 10 s.

    (d) How long, to the nearest second, does the leading edge of the snow take to move 600 m?

13. Application: The relative percentage of carbon dioxide, C, in a carbonated soft drink at t minutes can be modelled by $C(t) = \frac{100}{t}$, where $t > 2$. Determine $C'(t)$ and interpret the results at 5 min, 50 min, and 100 min. Explain what is happening.

14. Show that $\frac{dy}{dx} = (a + 4b)x^{a + 4b - 1}$ if $y = \frac{x^{2a + 3b}}{x^{a - b}}$ and a and b are integers.

15. Determine where the graph of each function has a horizontal tangent line.

    (a) $y = x^2$ **(b)** $y = 2x^3$ **(c)** $y = -5x^4$ **(d)** $y = 3x$

16. Find two lines that pass through point $(2, 8)$ and are tangent to the curve $y = x^3$.

17. **Thinking, Inquiry, Problem Solving:** Determine the coordinates of two points of tangency to the curve $y = -2x^2$, given that the corresponding tangent lines intersect at point $(2, 8)$.

18. **Check Your Understanding:** A baseball is dropped from the roof of a school. The distance, f, in metres that the ball has fallen after t seconds is modelled by $f(t) = 4.9t^2$. How far has the ball travelled if it hits the ground at 12.74 m/s? (Note that the derivative of displacement is velocity.)

C 19. Find the equation of a line that passes through $(2, 12)$ and is tangent to the curve $y = 4x^2$.

20. Determine the point on the graph of $g(x) = -3x^4$ where the tangent line is perpendicular to the line $3y + 2x - 15 = 0$.

21. **(a)** Show that the instantaneous rate of change of the area of a circle with respect to the radius is always equal to the circumference of the circle.

    (b) For any sphere with radius r, what is the instantaneous rate of change of the volume with respect to the radius? What is the significance of this result?

Gottfried Wilhelm von Leibniz (1646–1783)

Leibniz was a good example of a *polymath*, a person of great and varied learning. In addition to developing calculus, and developing formal notation for calculus, he also was responsible for combinatorial analysis. Outside of math, he showed genius in many subjects, such as literature, history, law, and politics.

ADDITIONAL ACHIEVEMENT CHART QUESTIONS

Knowledge and Understanding: Consider the function $f(x) = \frac{x^4}{4}$.

Find the equation of the line that is tangent to the curve of $f(x)$ at point $(2, 4)$.

Application: In t months, $0 \le t \le 3$, the estimated number, N, in thousands of passenger vehicles with non-Canadian licence plates entering Ontario will be $N(t) = -t^3 + 13t$. At what rate will the number of vehicles with non-Canadian licence plates enter Ontario two months from now?

Thinking, Inquiry, Problem Solving: For $h(x) = x^{2n - 1}$, $n \in N$ and n is odd. A student says, "The slope of all tangent lines to this curve, at any point on it, will have a positive value." Is this statement always true, sometimes true, or never true? Defend your choice in words and give two examples.

Communication: One of your friends missed the lesson on the constant and power rules for differentiation. Your friend wants to know why the exponent is reduced by 1. Use linear graphical models, quadratic graphical models, and their equations to show why the exponent is reduced by 1.

3.6 Finding Some Shortcuts— The Sum and Difference Rules

SETTING THE STAGE

A cliff diver in Acapulco, Mexico, dives from about 17 m above the water. The function $f(t) = -4.9t^2 + 1.5t + 17$ models the diver's height above the water, in metres, at t seconds. Determine the diver's instantaneous rate of descent with respect to time at intervals of 0.1 s during the first second the diver is in the air.

The instantaneous rate of change of height is given by the derivative of the height function. Can the differentiation rules from the previous section be applied to the polynomial function that models the diver's height?

In this section we will develop the rules to differentiate any polynomial function.

EXAMINING THE CONCEPT

Developing the Sum and Difference Rules

The function $f(t) = -4.9t^2 + 1.5t + 17$ is the sum of three different functions. By defining $b(t) = -4.9t^2$, $c(t) = 1.5t$, and $d(t) = 17$, you can write the original function as $f(t) = b(t) + c(t) + d(t)$. Examine the graph of all four functions.

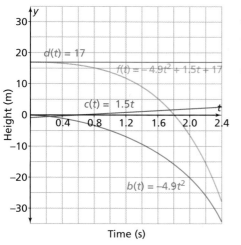

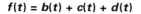

$f(t) = b(t) + c(t) + d(t)$

The function $f(t) = -4.9t^2 + 1.5t + 17$ is equal to the sum of its three component functions, $b(t) = -4.9t^2$, $c(t) = 1.5t$, and $d(t) = 17$, for all real values of t.

But how are the derivatives of the functions related? Is $f'(t)$ equal to the sum of $b'(t)$, $c'(t)$, and $d'(t)$?

Using the differentiation rules from the previous section,

$$b'(t) = \frac{d}{dt}(-4.9t^2) \qquad c'(t) = \frac{d}{dt}(1.5t) \qquad d'(t) = \frac{d}{dt}(17)$$
$$ = 2(-4.9)t^{2-1} \qquad = 1.5 \qquad = 0$$
$$ = -9.8t$$

Summing the derivatives together gives

$$b'(t) + c'(t) + d'(t) = -9.8t + 1.5 + 0$$
$$= -9.8t + 1.5$$

Compare this sum and the derivative of $f(t)$. Determine the derivative $f'(t)$ from first principles.

$$h(t) = -4.9t^2 + 1.5t + 17$$

$$h'(t) = \lim_{h \to 0} \frac{f(t+h) - f(t)}{h}$$

$$= \lim_{h \to 0} \frac{[-4.9(t+h)^2 + 1.5(t+h) + 17] - [-4.9t^2 + 1.5t + 17]}{h}$$

$$= \lim_{h \to 0} \frac{-4.9(t^2 + 2th + h^2) + 1.5(t+h) + 17 - [-4.9t^2 + 1.5t + 17]}{h}$$

$$= \lim_{h \to 0} \frac{-4.9t^2 - 9.8th - 4.9h^2 + 1.5t + 1.5h + 17 + 4.9t^2 - 1.5t - 17}{h}$$

$$= \lim_{h \to 0} \frac{-9.8th - 4.9h^2 + 1.5h}{h}$$

$$= \lim_{h \to 0} \frac{h(-9.8t - 4.9h + 1.5)}{h}$$

$$= \lim_{h \to 0} (-9.8t - 4.9h + 1.5)$$

$$= -9.8t - 4.9(0) + 1.5$$

$$= -9.8t + 1.5$$

The derivative of the original function, $f(t)$, is the sum of the derivatives of the component functions, $b(t)$, $c(t)$, and $d(t)$.

$$f(t) = b(t) + c(t) + d(t)$$
$$= -4.9t^2 + 1.5t + 17$$
$$f'(t) = b'(t) + c'(t) + d'(t)$$
$$= -9.8t + 1.5$$

$$f'(t) = b'(t) + c'(t) + d'(t)$$

The Sum Rule

The derivative of a sum is the sum of the derivatives.

If $h(x) = f(x) + g(x)$ and f and g are both differentiable, then $h'(x) = f'(x) + g'(x)$. In Leibniz notation,

$$\frac{d}{dx}[f(x) + g(x)] = \frac{d}{dx}[f(x)] + \frac{d}{dx}[g(x)].$$

Proof
Let $F(x) = f(x) + g(x)$.

$$h'(x) = \lim_{h \to 0} \frac{F(x+h) - F(x)}{h}$$

$$= \lim_{h \to 0} \frac{[f(x+h) + g(x+h)] - [f(x) + g(x)]}{h} \qquad \text{Rearrange the numerator.}$$

$$= \lim_{h \to 0} \frac{[f(x+h) - f(x)] + [g(x+h) - g(x)]}{h} \qquad \text{Rewrite using the sum rule for limits.}$$

$$= \lim_{h \to 0} \frac{f(x+h) - f(x)}{h} + \lim_{h \to 0} \frac{g(x+h) - g(x)}{h}$$

$$= f'(x) + g'(x)$$

The sum rule can be extended to any number of functions. A corresponding rule also exists for differences.

The Difference Rule

If $h(x) = f(x) - g(x)$ and f and g are both differentiable, then $h'(x) = f'(x) - g'(x)$. In Leibniz notation,

$$\frac{d}{dx}[f(x) - g(x)] = \frac{d}{dx}[f(x)] - \frac{d}{dx}[g(x)].$$

The proof for the difference rule is similar to the proof for the sum rule.

Example 1 **Using the Sum and Difference Rules**

Determine the derivative of each function.

(a) $g(x) = 8x^4 + 6x^2 + 12$ **(b)** $h(x) = 4x^{-2} - 5x^2 - 4x$

Solution
Use the sum and difference rules. Differentiate term by term.

(a) $g'(x) = \dfrac{d}{dx}(8x^4 + 6x^2 + 12)$

$= \dfrac{d}{dx}(8x^4) + \dfrac{d}{dx}(6x^2) + \dfrac{d}{dx}(12)$
$= 32x^3 + 12x + 0$
$= 32x^3 + 12x$

(b) $h'(x) = \dfrac{d}{dx}(4x^{-2} - 5x^2 - 4x)$

$= \dfrac{d}{dx}(4x^{-2}) - \dfrac{d}{dx}(5x^2) - \dfrac{d}{dx}(4x)$
$= -8x^{-3} - 10x - 4$

• • • • • • • •

The Derivative of Any Polynomial Function

For any polynomial function,
$P(x) = a_n x^n + a_{n-1} x^{n-1} + \ldots + a_2 x^2 + a_1 x^1 + a_0$, where $n \in$ **N**,
$P'(x) = na_n x^{n-1} + (n-1)a_{n-1} x^{n-2} + \ldots + 2a_2 x^1 + a_1$.

Example 2 **Determining the Derivative of a Polynomial Function**

Differentiate $y = -5x^4 - 2x^3 + 6x^2 - 9x + 18$.

Solution

$$\frac{dy}{dx} = \frac{d}{dx}(-5x^4 - 2x^3 + 6x^2 - 9x + 18)$$

$= \dfrac{d}{dx}(-5x^4) - \dfrac{d}{dx}(2x^3) + \dfrac{d}{dx}(6x^2) - \dfrac{d}{dx}(9x) + \dfrac{d}{dx}(18)$
$= -20x^3 - 6x^2 + 12x - 9 + 0$
$= -20x^3 - 6x^2 + 12x - 9$

• • • • • • • •

Example 3   Using the Sum and Difference Rules to Determine an Instantaneous Rate of Change

Recall the problem in Setting the Stage.

A cliff diver in Acapulco, Mexico, dives from about 17 m above the water. The function $f(t) = -4.9t^2 + 1.5t + 17$ models the diver's height above the water, in metres, at t seconds. Determine the diver's instantaneous rate of descent with respect to time at intervals of 0.1 s during the first second the diver is in the air.

Solution

Given $f(t)$, which is the height at time t, the instantaneous rate of change of height with respect to time — the rate of descent — is $f'(t)$. In this case,

$$f'(t) = \frac{d}{dt}(-4.9t^2 + 1.5t + 17)$$
$$= -9.8t + 1.5$$

The table shows the rate of descent every 0.1 s during the first second.

Time, t (s)	0.0	0.1	0.2	0.3	0.4	0.5	0.6	0.7	0.8	0.9	1.0
Instantaneous Rate of Descent, $f'(t) = -9.8t + 1.5$ (m/s)	1.5	0.5	-0.5	-1.4	-2.4	-3.4	-4.4	-5.4	-6.3	-7.3	-8.3

A positive rate means the diver is moving up. A negative rate means the diver is moving down. The rate is initially positive because the diver jumps up off the cliff. Between 0.1 s and 0.2 s, the diver starts to fall, and the pull of gravity steadily increases the rate of descent until the diver enters the water.

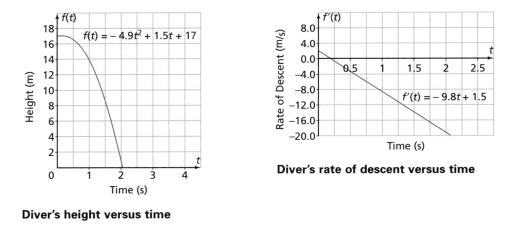

Diver's height versus time

Diver's rate of descent versus time

KEY IDEAS

The table summarizes the differentiation rules developed in this section.

Rule	Function Notation	Leibniz Notation
Sum Rule	If $h(x) = f(x) + g(x)$ and f and g are both differentiable, then $h'(x) = f'(x) + g'(x)$.	$\frac{d}{dx}[f(x) + g(x)] = \frac{d}{dx}[f(x)] + \frac{d}{dx}[g(x)]$
Difference Rule	If $h(x) = f(x) - g(x)$ and f and g are both differentiable, then $h'(x) = f'(x) - g'(x)$.	$\frac{d}{dx}[f(x) - g(x)] = \frac{d}{dx}[f(x)] - \frac{d}{dx}[g(x)]$
Derivative of a Polynomial	If $P(x) = a_n x^n + a_{n-1}x^{n-1} + \ldots + a_2 x^2 + a_1 x^1 + a_0$, where $n \in \mathbf{N}$, then $P'(x) = na_n x^{n-1} + (n-1)a_{n-1}x^{n-2} + \ldots + 2a_2 x^1 + a_1$.	

3.6 Exercises

1. For $y = 3x^2 + 2x - 1$,

    (a) find $\frac{dy}{dx}$ from first principles

    (b) confirm your results for (a) using the rules for differentiation

2. Differentiate.

    (a) $y = 4x^2 + 5x - 2$ **(b)** $y = x^3 - 5x^2 + 2x - 8$

    (c) $y = 3x + 2$ **(d)** $y = -4x^{-2} + 5x - 1$

    (e) $f(x) = 8x + 3$ **(f)** $f(x) = 3x^2 + 2x - 5$

    (g) $f(x) = \frac{3}{x^4} - \frac{2}{x} + 5$ **(h)** $f(x) = 6x^4 - 3x^3 + 9x^2 - 5x + 8$

3. Determine the slope of the tangent line at the given point for each function.

    (a) $y = 3x + 5$ at $(2, 11)$ **(b)** $y = 4x^2 - 3x + 7$ at $(-1, 14)$

    (c) $y = -2x^3$ at $(-2, 16)$

    (d) $y = 5x^4 - 4x^3 + 3x^2 - 6x + 2$ at $(0, 2)$

    (e) $y = -5x^2 + 6x - 3$ at $(0, -3)$ **(f)** $y = -7x^4 - x^2 + 6x$ at $(1, -2)$

4. **(a)** Find the equation of the tangent to the curve of $y = 2x^2 - 5x - 7$ where $x = 1$.

   (b) Draw a sketch of the function and the tangent.

5. **Communication:** Express in your own words the sum and difference rules for differentiation. Use an example to illustrate each rule.

6. **Knowledge and Understanding:** Determine $\dfrac{dy}{dx}$ for the function $y = 5x^4 - 8x^3 + 3x^2 - 6x + 9$.

7. Determine the equation of the tangent to the curve of $y = x^2 - 3x + 1$ at each point.

   (a) $(-1, 5)$ **(b)** $(-2, 11)$ **(c)** $(0, 1)$ **(d)** $\left(\dfrac{1}{2}, -\dfrac{1}{4}\right)$

8. For $f(x) = 3x^2 + 8x - 5$ and $g(x) = 5x^3 + 4x^2 - 5x + 7$, show that

   (a) the derivative of the sum equals the sum of the derivatives

   (b) the derivative of the difference equals the difference between the derivatives

9. Find the equation of the tangent to each curve.

   (a) $y = x^2 - 5x + 4$ where $x = 3$

   (b) $y = 4x^2 + x - 5$ where $x = -\dfrac{1}{2}$

   (c) $f(x) = x^3 - 5x^2 + 6x - 7$ where $x = -1$

   (d) $f(x) = 5x^4 + x^3 - 6x$ where $x = 3$

10. Find the equations of all the tangents to the graph of $f(x) = x^2 - 4x + 25$ that pass through the origin.

11. **Application:** Liquid is flowing out of a tank. The volume, V, in litres remaining after t minutes is given by $V(t) = 1000(20 - t^2)$.

    (a) What is the initial volume of liquid in the tank?

    (b) Over the first two minutes, what is the average rate at which the tank is being emptied?

    (c) At exactly what time is this rate in effect?

    (d) How fast is the liquid leaving the tank at 3 min?

    (e) How long, to the nearest half minute, will the liquid take to drain completely from the tank?

    (f) What is the average rate, to the nearest litre per minute, at which the liquid drains?

12. A business report determines that a company's profit, P, in dollars per month can be expressed as a function of the number of items manufactured, x:

    $$P(x) = -x^3 + 32x^2 + 560x - 9600, \ 0 \le x \le 40$$

    (a) Explain why the y-intercept of the graph is negative.

(b) At what rate is the profit changing when 15 items are manufactured? 35? 26?

(c) What is the profit when 15 items are manufactured? 35? 26?

(d) For what levels of production is the company profitable?

13. Kathy has diabetes. Her blood sugar level, B, one hour after an insulin injection, depends on the amount of insulin, x, in milligrams injected.

$$B(x) = -0.2x^2 + 500, \ 0 \leq x \leq 40$$

(a) Find $B(0)$ and $B(30)$.

(b) Find $B'(0)$ and $B'(30)$.

(c) Interpret your results.

(d) Consider the values of $B'(50)$ and $B(50)$. Comment on the significance of these values. Why are restrictions given for the original function?

14. **(a)** Find coordinates of the points, if any, where each function has a horizontal tangent line.

    i. $f(x) = 2x - 5x^2$

    ii. $f(x) = 4x^2 + 2x - 3$

    iii. $f(x) = x^3 - 8x^2 + 5x + 3$

(b) Suggest a graphical interpretation for each of these points.

15. **Thinking, Inquiry, Problem Solving**: Find numbers a, b, and c so that the graph of $f(x) = ax^2 + bx + c$ has x-intercepts at $(0, 0)$ and $(8, 0)$, and a tangent with slope 16 where $x = 2$.

16. The population, P, of a bacteria colony at t hours can be modelled by

$$P(t) = 100 + 120t + 10t^2 + 2t^3$$

(a) What is the initial population of the bacteria colony?

(b) What is the population of the colony at 5 h?

(c) What is the growth rate of the colony at 5 h?

17. Coffee consumption in the United States can be modelled by
$C(x) = 2.767\ 75 + 0.084\ 794\ 3x - 0.008\ 320\ 58x^2 + 0.000\ 144\ 017x^3$,
where C represents the number of cups consumed per day by the average adult and x represents the number of years since 1955.

(a) How many cups of coffee did the average American adult consume each day in 2000?

(b) What was the rate of change in the number of cups of coffee consumed per adult per day in 2000?

18. **Check Your Understanding**

(a) Determine $f'(3)$, where $f(x) = -6x^3 + 4x - 5x^2 + 10$.

(b) Give two interpretations of the meaning of $f'(3)$.

C **19.** Prove that the tangent to the curve $y = x + 2x^2 - x^4$ at point $(-1, 0)$ is also tangent to the curve at $(1, 2)$.

20. For any point (x, y) on the graph of $y = 3x^2 + 15x - 3$, determine the coordinates of the point on $y = -2x^2 - 5x + 4$ such that the tangents at the two points are parallel.

21. Show that $f(x) = 8x^3 + 7x - 5$ has no tangent line with slope 5.

22. Show that the x- and y-intercepts for any tangent to the curve $y = 16 - 8\sqrt{x} + x$ have a sum of 16.

ADDITIONAL ACHIEVEMENT CHART QUESTIONS

Knowledge and Understanding: Consider the function $f(x) = x^4 - 7x + 12$.
(a) Write the equation of the tangent line at $x = 1$.
(b) Find the coordinates of the point on the function so that the tangent line is perpendicular to $x + 25y - 175 = 0$.

Application: An ant colony was treated with an insecticide and the number of survivors, A, in hundreds at t hours is $A(t) = -t^3 + 5t + 750$.
(a) Find $A'(t)$.
(b) Find the rate of change of the number of living ants in the colony at 10 h.
(c) How many ants were in the colony before it was treated with the insecticide?
(d) How many hours after the insecticide was applied were no ants remaining in the colony?

Thinking, Inquiry, Problem Solving: Suppose that $f(x)$ is a quadratic polynomial function. Where would you find a horizontal tangent line? a vertical tangent line?

Communication: You are writing a self-help manual in calculus. Write the steps for helping readers find the equation of the line that is tangent to the graph of $g(x) = x^4 + 2x^3 - 5x + 2$ where $x = -2$. Explain each step.

The Chapter Problem
Average Salaries in Professional Sports

Apply what you learned to answer this question about The Chapter Problem on page 168.

CP9. Use the cubic regression equations you created for question CP7. Then apply the differentiation rules to verify the derivatives you found for question CP7.

3.7 Polynomial Function Models and the First Derivative

SETTING THE STAGE

This chapter has discussed using the derivative to determine the instantaneous rate of change of a quantity. The derivative has wide application in fields such as economics, science, engineering, and the social sciences. Here is an example:

Suppose a rock is thrown into the air from a bridge 15 m above the water. As it rises and then falls, its height above the water is a function of the time since it was thrown. The height of the rock, in metres, above the water at t seconds can be modelled by the function $h(t) = -4.9t^2 + 12t + 15$.

What is the velocity of the rock when it enters the water?

In this section we will examine applications of the first derivative of a polynomial model.

EXAMINING THE CONCEPT

Polynomial Models Involving Velocity and Speed

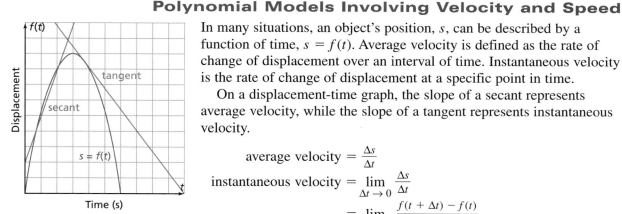

Displacement versus time

In many situations, an object's position, s, can be described by a function of time, $s = f(t)$. Average velocity is defined as the rate of change of displacement over an interval of time. Instantaneous velocity is the rate of change of displacement at a specific point in time.

On a displacement-time graph, the slope of a secant represents average velocity, while the slope of a tangent represents instantaneous velocity.

$$\text{average velocity} = \frac{\Delta s}{\Delta t}$$

$$\text{instantaneous velocity} = \lim_{\Delta t \to 0} \frac{\Delta s}{\Delta t}$$

$$= \lim_{\Delta t \to 0} \frac{f(t + \Delta t) - f(t)}{\Delta t}$$

$$= \lim_{h \to 0} \frac{f(t + h) - f(t)}{h}$$

$$= f'(t)$$

As a result, the derivative of the position function, $s' = f'(t)$, represents the instantaneous velocity of the object at time t. So

$$v(t) = \frac{ds}{dt}$$
$$= s'$$
$$= f'(t)$$

The Difference between Velocity and Speed

The **velocity** of an object measures how fast it is moving and the direction of movement.

Speed is the magnitude or absolute value of the velocity, without regard to direction.

Example 1   **Analyzing the Motion of a Falling Object: Vertical Motion**

A rock is tossed from a bridge 15 m above the water. The height of the rock, h, in metres above the water at t seconds can be modelled by the function $h(t) = -4.9t^2 + 12t + 15$.

(a) Determine the instantaneous velocity at 1 s and at 2 s.

(b) What is the velocity of the rock when it enters the water?

(c) Determine the initial velocity of the rock.

(d) When is the rock at its maximum height? What is the maximum height?

Solution

(a)   instantaneous velocity $= v(t)$

$$= h'(t) \text{ or } \frac{dh}{dt}$$

$$= \frac{d}{dt}(-4.9t^2 + 12t + 15)$$

$$= -9.8t + 12$$

$$
\begin{aligned}
v(1) &= h'(1) \\
&= -9.8(1) + 12 \\
&= 2.2
\end{aligned}
$$

At 1 s, the rock is moving up at 2.2 m/s. (positive velocity = upward movement)

$$
\begin{aligned}
v(2) &= h'(2) \\
&= -9.8(2) + 12 \\
&= -7.6
\end{aligned}
$$

At 2 s, the rock is moving down at 7.6 m/s. (negative velocity = downward movement)

(b) The rock hits the water when $h = 0$. Solve for t when $h = 0$.

$$
\begin{aligned}
h(t) &= -4.9t^2 + 12t + 15 \\
0 &= -4.9t^2 + 12t + 15
\end{aligned}
$$

Solve using the quadratic formula.

$$t = \frac{-b \pm \sqrt{b^2 - 4ac}}{2a}$$

$$= \frac{-12 \pm \sqrt{12^2 - 4(-4.9)(15)}}{2(-4.9)}$$

$$= \frac{-12 \pm \sqrt{144 + 294}}{-9.8}$$

$$= \frac{-12 \pm \sqrt{438}}{-9.8}$$

$$t_1 = \frac{-12 + \sqrt{438}}{-9.8} \doteq \frac{-12 + 20.93}{-9.8} = -0.91$$

$$t_2 = \frac{-12 - \sqrt{438}}{-9.8} \doteq \frac{-12 - 20.93}{-9.8} = 3.36$$

At the time of impact,

$v(t) = v(3.36) = h'(3.36) = -9.8(3.36) + 12 = -20.93$

When it hits the water, the rock is falling at 20.93 m/s.

(c) The initial velocity occurs at $t = 0$:

$v(t) = v(0) = h'(0) = -9.8(0) + 12 = 12$

The rock was thrown upward with an initial velocity of 12 m/s.

(d) A table and graph show the changing velocity.

Time, t	Height, $h(t)$	Velocity, $h'(t)$
0.0	15.0	12.0
0.5	19.8	7.1
1.0	22.1	2.2
1.5	22.0	-2.7
2.0	19.4	-7.6
2.5	14.4	-12.5
3.0	6.9	-17.4

$h(t) = -4.9t^2 + 12t + 15$

Initially, the velocity is positive and the rock is moving up. The velocity starts to decrease. When the velocity is 0, the rock is motionless at its highest point. The velocity becomes a larger and larger negative value until the rock hits the water.

Solve for t when $v(t) = 0$. $v(t) = h'(t)$ and $h'(t) = -9.8 + 12$.

$-9.8t + 12 = 0$

$$t = \frac{-12}{-9.8}$$

$t \doteq 1.2$

The maximum height occurs at 1.2 s. Solve for h at $t = 1.2$.

$$h(t) = -4.9t^2 + 12t + 15$$
$$= -4.9(1.2)^2 + 12(1.2) + 15$$
$$= 22.3$$

The rock reaches a maximum height of 22.3 m.

Example 2 **Analyzing the Motion of a Moving Object: Horizontal Motion**

The position of an object moving along a straight line can be modelled by the function $s(t) = 3t^3 - 40.5t^2 + 162t$, where s is the position in metres at t seconds and $t \geq 0$.

(a) Determine the initial position of the object.

(b) Determine the velocity at 2 s and 5 s.

(c) When is the object stationary?

(d) When is the object advancing? retreating?

(e) Determine the total distance travelled during the first eight seconds of motion.

Solution

(a) The initial position occurs when $t = 0$. Since $s(0) = 0$, the object starts at the origin.

(b) For $v(t)$, the velocity function,

$$v(t) = s'(t) \qquad\qquad v(2) = 9(2)^2 - 81(2) + 162$$
$$= \frac{d}{dt}(3t^3 - 40.5t^2 + 162t) \qquad = 36$$
$$= 9t^2 - 81t + 162 \qquad\qquad v(5) = 9(5)^2 - 81(5) + 162$$
$$= -18$$

At 2 s, the object is moving at 36 m/s. In this type of situation, assume that positive velocity means movement to the right. At 5 s, the object is moving at -18 m/s, that is, at 18 m/s to the left.

(c) The object is stationary when the velocity $v(t) = 0$. Substitute and solve for t.

$$9t^2 - 81t + 162 = 0$$
$$9(t^2 - 9t + 18) = 0$$
$$9(t - 6)(t - 3) = 0$$
$$t = 6 \text{ and } t = 3$$

The object is motionless at exactly 3 s and 6 s.

(d) For the object to be advancing, $v(t) > 0$. Substitute and then solve the inequality.

$$9t^2 - 81t + 162 > 0$$
$$(t - 6)(t - 3) > 0 \qquad \text{The same factorization as in (c).}$$

	Interval		
	$0 \leq t < 3$	$3 < t < 6$	$t > 6$
$t - 6$	$-$	$-$	$+$
$t - 3$	$-$	$+$	$+$
$v(t)$	$(-)(-) = +$	$(-)(+) = -$	$(+)(+) = +$

Since $t \geq 0$, there are three intervals to consider. The object is advancing when $0 \leq t < 3$ and when $t > 6$. The object is retreating when $3 < t < 6$.

(e) The total distance travelled includes both advancing and retreating motion. The total distance is the sum of the absolute distances travelled. The object changes direction at 3 s and at 6 s, and starts at the origin, $s(0) = 0$.

Time, t (s)	Position, s (m) $s(t) = 3t^3 - 40.5t^2 + 162t$	Time Interval	Distance Travelled
3	$s(3) = 3(3)^3 - 40.5(3)^2 + 162(3)$ $= 202.5$	$0 < t < 3$	$\mid s(3) - s(0) \mid = \mid 202.5 - 0 \mid = 202.5$
6	$s(6) = 162$	$3 < t < 6$	$\mid s(6) - s(3) \mid = \mid 162 - 202.5 \mid = 40.5$
8	$s(8) = 240$	$6 < t < 8$	$\mid s(8) - s(6) \mid = \mid 240 - 162 \mid = 78$

The total distance travelled between 0 s and 8 s is
202.5 m + 40.5 m + 78 m = 321 m.

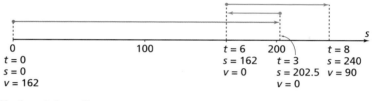

Horizontal motion

EXAMINING THE CONCEPT

Other Rates of Change

Use the derivative to solve problems that involve instantaneous rates of change in a variety of applications. Often in these problems, the independent variable is time t. The variable Q in $Q = f(t)$ is a quantity that varies with time. For example, Q might be

- the size of a population
- the number of dollars in a bank account
- the volume of a balloon being inflated or deflated
- the amount of liquid in a tank that is being filled or drained
- the total distance travelled over an interval of time

Average Rate of Change

The **average rate of change** of Q is the ratio of ΔQ, which is the change in Q, to Δt, which is the change in t. The average rate of change equals the slope of the secant to the curve over the interval Δt.

$$\frac{\Delta Q}{\Delta t} = \frac{f(t + \Delta t) - f(t)}{\Delta t} \quad \text{or} \quad \frac{\Delta Q}{\Delta t} = \frac{f(t_2) - f(t_1)}{t_2 - t_1}$$

Instantaneous Rate of Change

The **instantaneous rate of change** of $Q = f(t)$ at time t is equal to the slope of the tangent line to the curve $Q = f(t)$ at point $(t, f(t))$.

$$\frac{dQ}{dt} = \lim_{\Delta t \to 0} \frac{\Delta Q}{\Delta t} = \lim_{\Delta t \to 0} \frac{f(t + \Delta t) - f(t)}{\Delta t}$$

$$\text{or } \frac{dQ}{dt} = f'(t)$$

The derivative of $Q = f(t)$ represents the instantaneous rate of change at point $(t, f(t))$.

A positive slope corresponds to a rising tangent line, and a negative slope corresponds to a falling tangent line. Therefore,

Q is increasing at time t Q is decreasing at time t

if $\dfrac{dQ}{dt} = f'(t) > 0$ if $\dfrac{dQ}{dt} = f'(t) < 0$

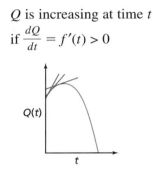

Tangents with positive slope; Q increasing

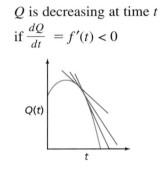

Tangents with negative slope; Q decreasing

Example 3   **Analyzing a Polynomial Population Model**

The world population is growing rapidly, as shown in the data from the World Population Division of the United Nations.

(a) Create a scatter plot and determine a cubic polynomial that models the data.

(b) Determine the average rate of change in the world population between 1960 and 1990.

(c) Determine the rate at which the world population is changing in 1995.

(d) Use graphing technology to analyze the yearly growth rate of the world population since 1990.

Year	1900	1910	1920	1930	1940	1950	1960	1970	1980	1990	1998	1999
World Population (billions)	1.65	1.75	1.86	2.07	2.30	2.52	3.02	3.70	4.44	5.27	5.90	6.00

Solution

(a) Using a TI-83 Plus calculator, enter the year data into **L1** and the world population data into **L2**. Turn the **STAT PLOTS** on to create the scatter plot.

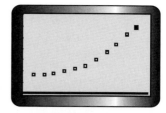

Perform a cubic regression on the data.

Graph the **CubicReg** function.

A cubic polynomial model of this data, for $1900 \leq t \leq 1999$, is
$$f(t) = 0.000\ 001\ 445\ 882\ 6t^3 - 0.007\ 946\ 709\ 3t^2 + 14.539\ 201\ 49t \\ - 8852.482\ 086$$

(b) For the specified period, $t_1 = 1960$ and $t_2 = 1990$.

$$\text{average rate of change} = \frac{f(t_2) - f(t_1)}{t_2 - t_1}$$

$$= \frac{f(1990) - f(1960)}{1990 - 1960}$$

$$\doteq \frac{5.186\ 358\ 8 - 3.099\ 476\ 0}{30}$$

$$\doteq \frac{2.086\ 875\ 9}{30}$$

$$\doteq 0.069\ 562\ 53$$

Between 1960 and 1990, the world population increased by an average of about 70 million people per year.

(c) The instantaneous rate of change is
$$f'(t) = 0.000\ 004\ 337\ 647\ 8t^2 - 0.015\ 893\ 418\ 6t + 14.539\ 201\ 49$$
$$f'(1995) = 0.000\ 004\ 337\ 647\ 8(1995)^2 - 0.015\ 893\ 418\ 6(1995) \\ + 14.539\ 201\ 49$$
$$\doteq 0.095\ 778$$

In 1995, the world population was increasing at the rate of about 96 million per year.

(d) Enter the cubic regression equation, $f(t)$, into **Y1** of the equation editor and its derivative, $f'(t)$, into **Y2**.

Press 2nd TBLSET and
set up a table as shown.

Press 2nd TABLE to
display the table.

Technology Help

The derivative can be entered using the **nDeriv(** operation. For detailed instructions, see page 595 of the Technology Appendix.

The world population is displayed in **Y1** and the yearly growth rate in **Y2**. From 1990 to 2002, the rate at which the population is growing increases every year.

CHECK, CONSOLIDATE, COMMUNICATE

1. What does the derivative of the function represent if the position of an object can be modelled by a function of time?
2. When you throw an object into the air, how can you use a derivative to determine when the object reaches its maximum height?
3. What does a negative rate of change indicate? What does a positive rate of change indicate?

KEY IDEAS

- The **average rate of change** of $Q = f(t)$ is the ratio of the change in Q to the change in t. The average rate of change equals the slope of the secant to the curve over the interval Δt.

$$\frac{\Delta Q}{\Delta t} = \frac{f(t + \Delta t) - f(t)}{\Delta t} \text{ or } \frac{\Delta Q}{\Delta t} = \frac{f(t_2) - f(t_1)}{t_2 - t_1}$$

- The **instantaneous rate of change** of $Q = f(t)$ at time t is equal to the derivative of Q with respect to t. This is equivalent to the slope of the tangent line to the curve $Q = f(t)$ at point $(t, f(t))$.

$$\frac{dQ}{dt} = f'(t)$$

- A positive slope corresponds to a rising tangent line, and a negative slope corresponds to a falling tangent line. Therefore,

  - Q is increasing at time t if $\frac{dQ}{dt}$ or $f'(t) > 0$

  - Q is decreasing at time t if $\frac{dQ}{dt}$ or $f'(t) < 0$

- **Horizontal Motion** If the displacement, $s(t)$, of an object moving horizontally along a line is a function of time, s, the derivative represents the instantaneous velocity $v(t)$.

$$v(t) = \frac{ds}{dt} = s'(t) = f'(t)$$

If $v(t) > 0$, it represents movement to the right of its initial position. If $v(t) < 0$, it represents movement to the left. If $v(t) = 0$, the object is stationary and may be in the process of changing direction.

- **Vertical Motion** If the height of a falling object is a function of time, $h = f(t)$, the derivative represents the instantaneous velocity $v(t)$. If $v(t) > 0$, the object is travelling up. If $v(t) < 0$, the object is falling down. If $v(t) = 0$, the object is at its maximum height.

3.7 Exercises

A **1.** Stand in the centre of an open space, noting your starting position. Take three steps forward, followed by one step back.

   (a) How many steps are you from your starting point? The number of steps is your displacement.

   (b) How many steps have you taken? The number of steps is the distance you travelled.

2. When any object is in motion, three related characteristics of the motion can be measured. Copy and complete the table. Indicate the appropriate units.

Displacement, $f(t)$	Velocity, $f'(t)$	Time, t
	kilometres per hour	
metres		seconds
	metres per minute	
centimetres		seconds

3. For each function, find an expression for the velocity and the value of the displacement and velocity at $t = 5$. Displacement is in metres and time is in seconds. Include the appropriate units in your responses.

   (a) $s(t) = t^2 - 4t + 5$ **(b)** $s(t) = 3t + 7$

   (c) $s(t) = 12$ **(d)** $s(t) = t^3 - 2t^2 + 4t - 1$

B **4.** An object is projected directly up so that its height in metres at time t seconds can be modelled by $h(t) = -0.5t^2 + 9t + 9.1$.

   (a) From what height was the object initially projected?

   (b) What was the initial velocity?

(c) Find the velocity when $t = 2, 5, 9$, and 11 s.

(d) Find the height when $t = 8, 9$, and 10 s.

(e) When does the object return to its initial height?

(f) Sketch the path of the object and a height-versus-time graph of the motion.

5. When a flare is launched from an oceanside hilltop, its height above the water, in metres, at t seconds is described by $h(t) = -4.9t^2 + 16t + 200$.

(a) What is the initial velocity of the flare?

(b) What is the height at launch?

(c) How fast is the flare descending at 6 s after launch?

(d) When does the flare hit the water?

(e) What is its velocity when it hits the water?

6. **Knowledge and Understanding:** A model rocket is launched with an initial velocity of 55 m/s. Its height as a function of time can be modelled by $h(t) = 55t - 4.9t^2$. Determine the maximum height reached by the rocket.

7. The population of a city has been tracked since 1980. The population growth, P, is a function of the number of years after 1980, x.

$$P(x) = 2(x - 20)^3 + 20\ 000,\ 0 \le x \le 40$$

(a) Use your knowledge of transformations to sketch the function.

(b) What is the projected population in 2010?

(c) At what rate is the population growing between 1995 and 2010?

(d) At what rate is the population expected to grow in 2012?

(e) Is the growth rate the same at any other time?

8. An environmental report estimates that acid rain is changing the conditions in a lake so that the fish population in hundreds, f, as a function of t years since 1990 can be described by $f(t) = 1200 + 150t - 15t^2$.

(a) How was the fish population changing in 2000? in 1992? in 1997?

(b) What was the average rate of change in the first five years covered by the report?

(c) If no environmental improvements occur, when will the fish population become 0?

9. A particle moves along a line. The particle's position, s, in metres at t seconds is modelled by $s(t) = 2t^3 - 15t^2 + 36t + 40$, where $t \ge 0$.

(a) Determine the initial position of the particle.

(b) What is the velocity at 1 s? at 5 s?

(c) When is the particle stationary?

(d) When is it advancing? retreating?

(e) Determine the total distance travelled during the first five seconds.

10. A particle moves along a line. The particle's position, s, in centimetres at t seconds is modelled by $s(t) = t^3 - 9t^2 + 24t + 20$, where $t \geq 0$.

(a) What is the total distance travelled by the particle in the first 8 s?

(b) Draw a diagram that illustrates the particle's motion in the first 8 s.

11. The position of a remote-control car as it moves back and forth along a straight path is given in the table.

Time (s)	0	1.0	1.3	2.0	2.3	3.0	3.5	4	4.5	5	5.1	5.3	5.6	6.1
Displacement (m)	78.0	16.0	6.2	–4.0	–4.5	0.0	5.8	10.0	11.6	8.0	5.8	2.4	–7.1	–29.0

(a) Develop an algebraic model for the motion.

(b) Find the initial position of the car compared with the fixed point.

(c) When is the car moving away from the fixed point?

(d) What is the car's velocity at $t = 3$?

(e) What is the average velocity from $t = 1$ to $t = 5$?

12. The table describes the flight of a toy glider launched from a tower on a hilltop. The values for height indicate the number of metres above or below the top of the hill.

Time (s)	0	1	2	3	4	5	6	7	8	9
Height (m)	9.0	5.5	2.5	0.0	–2.0	–3.5	–4.5	–5.0	–5.0	–4.5

Time (s)	10	11	12	13	14	15	16	17	18
Height (m)	–3.5	–2.0	0.0	2.5	5.5	9.0	13.0	17.5	22.5

(a) Find an algebraic model that gives height as a function of time.

(b) Find the initial velocity.

(c) Find the average velocity between 4 s and 7 s.

(d) Find the velocity at 15 s.

(e) Describe the position and direction of the glider at 6 s, 12 s, and 14 s.

13. **Thinking, Inquiry, Problem Solving:** The table shows the percentage of Canadians who are between 15 years old and 19 years old and who smoke.

Year	1981	1983	1985	1986	1989	1991	1994	1995	1996
Males (%)	43.4	39.6	26.7	25.2	22.6	22.6	27.3	28.5	29.1
Females (%)	41.7	40.5	27.7	27.0	23.5	25.6	28.9	29.5	31.0

Source: Health Canada

(a) Determine when the rate of change for male smokers is exactly the same as the rate of change for female smokers.

(b) Is the percentage of smokers increasing or decreasing at the present time? Explain.

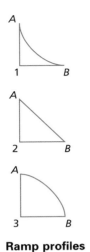

1 A B

2 A B

3 A B

Ramp profiles

14. **Communication:** Each diagram on the left shows the side profile of a different ramp. Imagine a ball rolling down each ramp and stopping at B. For each ramp, A and B are in the same relative positions.

   (a) On which ramp does the ball travel the longest distance? the shortest? Explain your reasoning.

   (b) On which ramp is the ball travelling the fastest one-quarter of the way down the ramp? the slowest? Explain.

   (c) On which ramp will the speed of the ball at the bottom of the ramp be the greatest? the least? Explain.

   (d) For each ramp, sketch a graph of the speed of the ball as a function of time.

15. For each section of the graph, complete the corresponding line in the table. Indicate whether the value of the function in that interval is positive or negative ($+$ or $-$). Also indicate whether the values are increasing or decreasing ($\nearrow$ or $\searrow$) in each interval. Indicate the same information for the derivative.

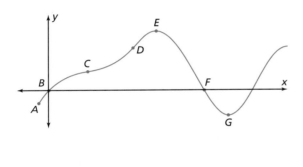

Section	Value of Function		Value of Derivative	
	$+$ or $-$	$\nearrow$ or $\searrow$	$+$ or $-$	$\nearrow$ or $\searrow$
A to B				
B to C				
C to D				
D to E				
E to F				
F to G				

16. **Application:** A bucket that initially held 5 L of water has a leak. After t seconds, the amount of water, Q, in litres remaining in the bucket is represented by $Q(t) = 5\left(1 - \frac{t}{25}\right)^2$.

   (a) How fast, to the nearest hundredth, is the water leaking from the bucket at 3 s?

   (b) How long does it take for all of the water to leak out of the bucket?

   (c) At what rate is the water leaking when the last drop leaks out?

17. An environmental study of a suburban community suggests that, t years from now, the level of carbon monoxide in the air, measured in parts per million, can be modelled by the function $q(t) = 0.05t^2 + 0.2t + 2.7$.

   (a) At what rate will the carbon monoxide level be changing with respect to time two years from now?

   (b) Does this model predict an increase or a decrease in the carbon monoxide level over the long term? Explain.

18. The position, s, in metres of a moving particle is given by $s(t) = 2t^3 - 2t^2 - 5t$, where $t \geq 0$. When does the particle reach a velocity of 8 m/s? Anwer to three decimal places.

19. Check Your Understanding

  (a) Draw a graph that shows an object's displacement increasing over time. What can you say about the object's velocity in this situation?

  (b) Draw a graph that shows the object's displacement decreasing over time. What can you say about the object's velocity in this situation?

C 20. Consider $f(x) = (x - 3)(x + 4)(2x + 15)$. How quickly is the value of the function changing when $x = 1$?

21. (a) For $s(t) = t^2 + 8t$, where s is in metres and t is in seconds, find the average velocity between $t = 2$ and $t = 3$.

  (b) Find the arithmetic average of the velocities at $t = 2$ and $t = 3$.

  (c) Find the instantaneous velocity at $t = 2.5$.

  (d) Repeat (a) to (c) for the displacement function $s(t) = t^3 + 9t$.

  (e) Explain why the three values are equal for the first function but different for the second function.

22. Two objects start from the same location at the same time and move along the same straight path. After t seconds, their displacements from the starting point are given by $f(t) = 2t^2 - 3t$ and $g(t) = 3t - t^2$.

  (a) Determine when the objects have equal velocities.

  (b) What are the velocities when the object's positions are the same?

23. A car is travelling at 80 km/h when the driver applies the brakes to avoid a moose on the road. After t seconds, the car is $s(t) = 80t - 3t^2$ metres from the point where the brakes were first applied. How far does the car travel before it stops?

**Galileo Galilei
(1564–1642)**

Before the time of Galileo, the physical world was described in terms of qualities, such as potentiality. Galileo advanced science by using measurable quantities like time, distance, and mass, to describe things.

ADDITIONAL ACHIEVEMENT CHART QUESTIONS

Knowledge and Understanding: The distance a test car has travelled at t seconds is represented by $d(t) = 12t + t^2$, where d is the distance in metres.

(a) Find the velocity at time t in metres per second.

(b) How fast is the test car travelling at 10 s?

(c) When does the test car reach a velocity of 60 m/s?

Application: A ball is thrown up so that its height is represented by $H(t) = 20t - 5t^2$, where H represents the height in metres after t seconds. After starting to descend, the ball strikes a post at a point 15 m high. Find the rate of descent of the ball at the moment when the ball strikes the post. For how long is the ball rising? falling? Sketch a graph to see if your findings are reasonable.

Thinking, Inquiry, Problem Solving: Two objects, A and B, begin to move from the same starting point, at the same time, and travel along the same straight line. After t seconds, their displacements, in metres, from the starting point are modelled by $s(t) = 2t^2 - 5t + 2$ and $g(t) = -3t^2 + t + 3$, respectively, where $t \geq 0$.

(a) When is A moving faster than B? slower than B?

(b) A comes to a sudden stop. How fast is B travelling at that time?

(c) When does B change directions? How can you tell?

Communication: One of your classmates takes calculus, but not physics. When a problem involving vertical motion is discussed, he has trouble using the function model to find **(a)** the height the object is above a surface, **(b)** the initial velocity at which the object is thrown, and **(c)** at what time the object reaches the ground surface. Create a vertical motion problem. Then use visual models, diagrams, and graphs to clearly explain this problem. Also show how to use the function model to solve this problem.

The Chapter Problem
Average Salaries in Professional Sports

Apply what you learned to answer these questions about The Chapter Problem on page 168.

CP10. Using the derivatives (question CP7), determine the instantaneous rate of change for each season for each data set. (Hint: Consider using a spreadsheet or the lists in a graphing calculator.) When are the salaries increasing the fastest? the slowest?

CP11. Using the cubic regression equations (question CP7), predict the average salary for each league in 2005. How well do you think the model will reflect the actual average salary at that time? Explain.

CP12. Research the average salaries of other sports. Ensure that your research covers the same period. Compare the data, and analyze the rates of change as you did for the original data. Discuss high or low rates of change that you notice in the new data. Write a report to summarize your findings and discuss trends in the new data.

3.8 Polynomial Function Models and the Second Derivative

SETTING THE STAGE

Recall the falling rock problem in section 3.7:

A rock is thrown into the air from a bridge 15 m above the water. As it rises and then falls, its height above the water is a function of the time since it was thrown. The height of the rock, in metres, above the water at t seconds can be modelled by the function $h(t) = -4.9t^2 + 12t + 15$. Is the rock accelerating or decelerating when it enters the water?

In this section we will examine applications of the second derivative of a polynomial function.

EXAMINING THE CONCEPT

Applications Involving the Second Derivative

Acceleration is the rate of change of velocity with respect to time, that is, the derivative of velocity. Velocity is the rate of change of position or displacement with respect to time. As a result, acceleration is the rate of change of the rate of change of position. Then acceleration is the **second derivative** of displacement. The function $s = f(t)$ models the displacement, s, as a function of time t.

$$\text{velocity} = v(t) \qquad \text{and} \qquad \text{acceleration} = a(t)$$
$$= s' \qquad\qquad\qquad\qquad\qquad = v'(t)$$
$$= f'(t) \qquad\qquad\qquad\qquad\quad = s''$$
$$= f''(t)$$

Second Derivative Function

The second derivative is the derivative of the derivative.

$f''(t)$, $\dfrac{d^2s}{dt^2}$, and s'' are all other forms of the second derivative.

Example 1   Determining the Second Derivative

For $y = 8x^3 + 4x^2 - 25x - 23$, determine y''.

Solution
Find the second derivative by differentiating the derivative, using established rules.

$$y' = \frac{d}{dx}(8x^3 + 4x^2 - 25x - 23) \qquad y'' = \frac{d}{dx}(24x^2 + 8x - 5)$$
$$= 24x^2 + 8x - 25 \qquad\qquad\qquad\qquad = 48x + 8$$

Example 2 **Examining the Acceleration of a Falling Object**

A rock is thrown into the air from a bridge 15 m above the water. Its height above the water is a function of the time since it was thrown. The height of the rock, in metres, above the water can be modelled by the function $h(t) = -4.9t^2 + 12t + 15$, where $h(t)$ represents the height in metres at t seconds. What is the rock's acceleration when it enters the water?

Solution

In the graph and the table, you can see that the rock travels up for a time and then changes direction. The height decreases, and the rock enters the water shortly after 3 s.

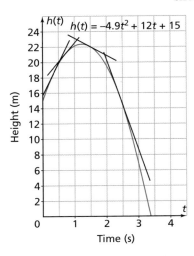

The graph of height versus time with several tangents.

Examine the tangent lines in the graph. The slope of each tangent represents the velocity of the moving rock. Compare the slopes of the tangents. The first slope is positive. The second slope is also positive, but is not as steep as the first. So the velocity is less and the rock is slowing down. The third slope is negative. The fourth slope is also negative, but the magnitude of the fourth slope is greater than the magnitude of the third slope. So the rate of change of height is greater as the rock gets closer to the surface of the water.

t (s)	$h(t)$ (m)	$\Delta h(t)$ (First Differences)
0.00	15.0	2.7
0.25	17.7	2.1
0.50	19.8	1.5
0.75	21.2	0.9
1.00	22.1	0.2
1.25	22.3	−0.4
1.50	22.0	−1.0
1.75	21.0	−1.6
2.00	19.4	−2.2
2.25	17.2	−2.8
2.50	14.4	−3.5
2.75	10.9	−4.0
3.00	6.9	−4.7
3.25	2.2	−5.3
3.50	−3.0	

Since velocity is the rate of change of height, it seems that the stone is gaining speed as it enters the water. The first differences in $h(t)$ (see the table above) confirm that the average speed over intervals of 0.25 s is increasing as the stone approaches the water. Remember that speed is the absolute value of velocity.

Confirm this conjecture by using the derivative. Let $v(t)$ represent the velocity at time t.

$$v(t) = h'(t)$$
$$= \frac{d}{dt}(-4.9t^2 + 12t + 15)$$
$$= -9.8t + 12$$

In the graph of the velocity function, you can see that the velocity changes at a constant rate.

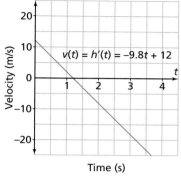

Velocity versus Time

t (s)	$v(t) = h'(t)$ (m/s)	$\Delta v(t)$ (First Differences)
0	12.0	−9.8
1	2.2	−9.8
2	−7.6	−9.8
3	−17.4	−9.8
4	−27.2	

The velocity function is linear. The average rate of change of velocity over each 1-s interval is −9.8. This value is also the slope of the line. The rate of change of velocity, which is the acceleration, at any time t is −9.8.

Again, verify this conjecture using the derivative. Let $a(t)$ represent the acceleration at time t.

Since height is measured in metres and time is measured in seconds, the units for acceleration are metres per second per second, or metres/second², or m/s².

$$
\begin{aligned}
a(t) &= v'(t) \\
&= h''(t) \\
&= \frac{d}{dt}(-9.8t + 12) \\
&= -9.8
\end{aligned}
$$

While it is in the air, the rock is accelerating at all times at the same rate, −9.8 m/s².

In this example, the acceleration is a constant and is called the **acceleration due to gravity**. The fact that it is negative means that any object moving away from Earth slows down, while an object moving toward Earth speeds up.

• • • • • • • •

Example 3   Acceleration and Horizontal Motion

The position at t seconds of a particle moving along a straight line is given by $s(t) = 3t^3 - 40.5t^2 + 162t$, where s is measured in metres and $t \geq 0$.

(a) Determine the acceleration at 6 s.

(b) Determine when the velocity is decreasing.

(c) Determine when the velocity is increasing.

(d) Determine when the velocity is not changing.

Solution

(a) Acceleration is the rate of change of velocity.

- Speed increases when the velocity and the acceleration have the same signs.
- Speed decreases when the velocity and the acceleration have opposite signs.

For example,

- when $a > 0$, a car going forward speeds up and a car going backward slows down
- when $a < 0$, a car going forward slows down and a car going backward speeds up

$$a(t) = v'(t) = s''(t)$$
$$v(t) = \frac{d}{dt}[s(t)] = \frac{d}{dt}(3t^3 - 40.5t^2 + 162t)$$
$$= 9t^2 - 81t + 162$$
$$a(t) = \frac{d}{dt}[v(t)] = \frac{d}{dt}(9t^2 - 81t + 162)$$
$$= 18t - 81$$
$$a(6) = 18(6) - 81$$
$$= 27$$

At 6 s, the velocity is increasing at the rate of 27 m/s^2.

(b) The velocity is decreasing when $a(t) = v'(t) < 0$.

$$18t - 81 < 0$$
$$18t < 81$$
$$t < 4.5$$

Since $t \geq 0$, the velocity is decreasing when $0 \leq t < 4.5$.

(c) The velocity is increasing when $a(t) = v'(t) > 0$.

$$18t - 81 > 0$$
$$18t > 81$$
$$t > 4.5$$

The velocity is increasing when $t > 4.5$.

(d) The velocity is not changing when $a(t) = v'(t) = 0$. Substituting and solving as above gives $t = 4.5$. The velocity is not changing at 4.5 s.

CHECK, CONSOLIDATE, COMMUNICATE

1. Explain how to determine the second derivative of a function.
2. What is the relationship between the position of a moving object and its acceleration?
3. The instantaneous velocity of an object is decreasing. What does this change imply about the object's acceleration?
4. The instantaneous velocity of an object is increasing. What does this change imply about the object's acceleration?

KEY IDEAS

- The derivative of the derivative of a function is called the **second derivative**. Symbols for the second derivative are $f''(x)$, $\frac{d^2y}{dx^2}$, $\frac{d^2}{dx^2}[f(x)]$, or y''.
- Use the second derivative to determine the rate of change of the rate of change of a given function. The most common application of the second derivative is acceleration.

- If the position of an object, $s(t)$, changes as a function of time t, then the **first derivative** of this function **represents the velocity** of the object as a function of time t: $v(t) = s'(t) = \dfrac{ds}{dt}$.
- Acceleration, $a(t)$, is the instantaneous rate of change of velocity with respect to time. **Acceleration is the first derivative of the velocity function and the second derivative of the position function**: $a(t) = v'(t) = s''(t)$ or $a(t) = \dfrac{dv}{dt} = \dfrac{d^2s}{dt^2}$.

3.8 Exercises

A

1. Find the first and second derivatives for each function.
   (a) $f(x) = 20x^4$
   (b) $g(x) = -12x^6 - 3x^2$
   (c) $y = x^4 + 2x^3 - 5x^2 + 6$
   (d) $h(x) = 3x^4 - 4x^3 - 3x^2 - 5$
   (e) $y = 4x^2 - 3x + 2$
   (f) $y = 5x$
   (g) $f(x) = 13$
   (h) $y = 4x^{-3} + 2x^3$

2. For each function, evaluate
   (a) $f'(3)$ if $f(x) = x^4 - 3x$
   (b) $f'(-2)$ if $f(x) = 2x^3 + 4x^2 - 5x + 8$
   (c) $f''(1)$ if $f(x) = -3x^2 - 5x + 7$
   (d) $f''(-3)$ if $f(x) = 4x^3 - 3x^2 + 2x - 6$
   (e) $f'(0)$ if $f(x) = 14x^2 + 3x - 6$
   (f) $f''(4)$ if $f(x) = x^4 + x^5 - x^3$
   (g) $f''\left(\frac{1}{3}\right)$ if $f(x) = -2x^5 + 2x - 6 - 3x^3$
   (h) $f'\left(\frac{3}{4}\right)$ if $f(x) = -3x^3 - 7x^2 + 4x - 11$

3. Find y''.
   (a) $y = -3x^2$
   (b) $y = 4x^4 - 2x + 5$
   (c) $y = 5x^4 - 2x^3 + 7x^2 - 6$
   (d) $y = 7x - 2x^3 + 8x^2 - 15$
   (e) $y = -13x^2 + 2x - 20$
   (f) $y = 14x + 7$
   (g) $y = -22$
   (h) $y = 5x^{-2} + x^3 - 12x$

4. **Knowledge and Understanding:** For $y = -7x^4 - 2x^3 + 5x^2 - 8x + 12$, determine $\dfrac{d^2y}{dx^2}$.

5. The position of an object travelling in a straight line is a function of time, $y = s(t)$, where the position, y, is measured in metres at t seconds. Express each statement as an equation or inequality, using derivative notation.

(a) The object's acceleration is 12 m/s².

(b) The object is 5 m to the left of its initial position.

(c) The velocity is 5 m/s.

(d) The object is travelling toward its initial position.

(e) The object is slowing down.

6. For each displacement function, find the velocity and acceleration at the indicated time. State whether the object is accelerating or decelerating.

(a) $s(t) = -3t^3 + 5t^2 - 6t$ when $t = 3$

(b) $s(t) = (2t - 5)^3$ when $t = 2$

(c) $s(t) = -4.9t^2 + 5t$ when $t = 2$

(d) $s(t) = -4.9t^2 + 20t + 1.5$ when $t = 5$

B 7. The displacement of an object in motion is described by $s(t) = t^3 - 21t^2 + 90t$, where the displacement, s, is measured in metres at t seconds.

(a) Find the displacement at 3 s.

(b) Find the velocity at 5 s.

(c) Find the acceleration at 4 s.

8. A ball is thrown up. Its motion can be described by $h(t) = -4.9t^2 + 6t + 2$, where the height, h, is measured in metres at t seconds.

(a) Find the initial velocity.

(b) When does the ball reach its maximum height?

(c) When does the ball hit the ground?

(d) What is its velocity when it hits the ground?

(e) What is the acceleration of the ball on the way up? on the way down?

9. An object is moving horizontally. The object's displacement, s, in metres at t seconds is described by $s(t) = 4t - 7t^2 + 2t^3$.

(a) Find the velocity and acceleration at $t = 2$.

(b) When is the object stationary? Describe the motion immediately before and after these times.

(c) At what time, to the nearest tenth, is acceleration equal to 0? Describe the motion at that time.

10. **Application:** On the surface of the moon, an astronaut can jump higher, because the force of gravity is less than it is on Earth. When an astronaut jumps, his or her height in metres above the moon's surface can be modelled by $s(t) = t\left(\frac{-5}{6}t + 1\right)$, where t is measured in seconds. What is the acceleration due to gravity on the moon?

11. Create sketches so that each graph in a set corresponds to the other two.

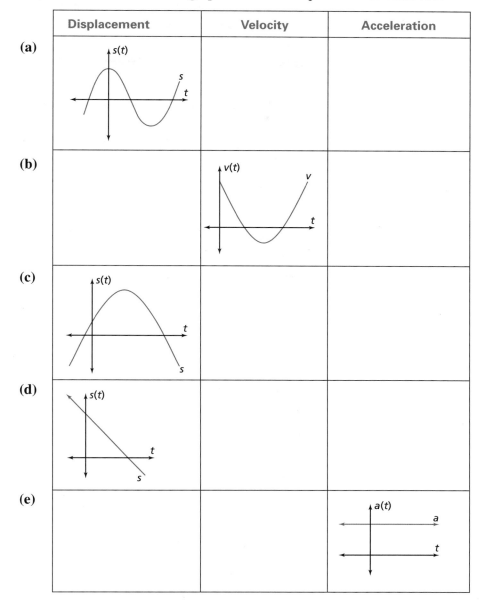

	Displacement	Velocity	Acceleration
(a)	$s(t)$ ... s, t		
(b)		$v(t)$ ... v, t	
(c)	$s(t)$ ... t, s		
(d)	$s(t)$ ... t, s		
(e)			$a(t)$ ... a, t

12. The forward motion of a space shuttle t seconds after touchdown is described by $s(t) = 189t - t^{\frac{7}{3}}$, where s is measured in metres.

(a) What is the velocity of the shuttle at touchdown?

(b) How much time is required for the shuttle to stop completely?

(c) How far does it travel from touchdown to a complete stop?

(d) What is the deceleration eight seconds after touchdown?

13. Fully describe the motion shown in each graph. Refer to *direction*, *displacement*, *velocity*, and *acceleration* and include the words *positive*, *negative*, *increasing*, and *decreasing*.

(a)

(b)

14. **Communication:** A car screeches to a sudden stop at a stop sign. Describe the car's distance from the stop sign, velocity, and acceleration as *positive*, *negative*, *large*, *small*, *increasing*, and *decreasing*. Sketch graphs for this situation that show

   (a) position versus time

   (b) velocity versus time

   (c) acceleration versus time

15. **Thinking, Inquiry, Problem Solving:** A space probe on the surface of Mars conducts several experiments. It launches a small weight and tracks the weight's motion using a motion detector. The table shows the data that the probe collected.

Time (s)	0.0	0.5	1.0	1.5	2.0	2.5	3.0	3.5	4.0	4.5	5.0
Height (m)	0.50	5.01	8.54	11.09	12.66	13.25	12.86	11.49	9.14	5.81	1.50

   (a) Determine the initial velocity of the weight.

   (b) Determine the velocity at which the weight falls to the surface of Mars.

   (c) Determine the force of gravity on Mars.

   (d) If the probe launched the same weight on Earth, with the same initial velocity, how long would the weight take to return to the ground?

16. A particle moves on a vertical line. Its position, s, in metres at t seconds is given by $s(t) = t^3 - 9t^2 + 24t, t \geq 0$.

   (a) Determine the velocity and acceleration functions.

   (b) When is the particle moving up? down?

   (c) Find the distance the particle travels between $t = 0$ and $t = 6$.

   (d) Graph the position, velocity, and acceleration functions for the interval $0 \leq t \leq 6$.

   (e) When is the particle speeding up? slowing down?

17. **Check Your Understanding:** The graphs of f, f', and f'' are shown on the left. Which graphs correspond to which functions? Explain your reasoning.

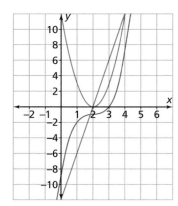

A function and its derivatives

C **18.** The position of an object moving on a straight path at t seconds is given by $s(t) = t^3 - 8t^2 + 9$, where s is the distance from a fixed point in centimetres.

(a) Find the average acceleration from $t = 0$ to $t = 5$.

(b) Find the acceleration at 2.5 s.

(c) What is the graphical significance of your answers for (a) and (b)?

(d) Will your answer for (c) be true for the average acceleration between any two points and the instantaneous acceleration at the midpoint between these two points? Explain.

19. The driver of a vehicle, travelling at 50 km/h, applies the brakes 100 m from a crosswalk. Assuming constant braking deceleration, find the deceleration required to bring the vehicle to a full stop at the crosswalk.

20. For $f(x) = x^3 + 4x^2 - 5x + 2$, determine the point of intersection between the tangent lines of $f(x)$ and $f'(x)$ that occur at $x = -1$.

ADDITIONAL ACHIEVEMENT CHART QUESTIONS

Knowledge and Understanding: A frog leaps along a path that leads to a pond. Its motion is described by $d(t) = 6t + t^2$, where distance, d, is measured in centimetres at t seconds. At 1 s, determine whether

(a) the frog is approaching or moving away from the pond

(b) the frog's acceleration is toward or away from the pond

(c) the frog's velocity is increasing or decreasing

Application: A jet car travelling at 200 m/s needs to stop quickly by steadily increasing the braking force. Assume that $d(t) = 200t - 0.4t^3$. Determine

(a) the stopping distance

(b) the maximum braking deceleration

Thinking, Inquiry, Problem Solving: An object moves horizontally so that its displacement from a starting point, s, can be modelled by $s(t) = -t^3 + 100$, where t represents time and $t \geq 0$.

(a) Determine when the object is speeding up and when it is slowing down. Defend your position.

(b) Suppose the motion of the object is modelled by a quadratic function over time, where $t \geq 0$, and the object is accelerating at a certain time. Will the object ever decelerate? Why or why not? Create one or two quadratic functions to defend your position.

Communication: A classmate sends you an e-mail asking for help on acceleration and deceleration. Write an e-mail to help your classmate understand acceleration. Refer to the motion of a vehicle. Compare the velocity and the acceleration of a vehicle that accelerates from rest. Do the same for deceleration. Use specific values to indicate when a vehicle is not accelerating and not decelerating.

Chapter 3 Review

RATES OF CHANGE IN POLYNOMIAL FUNCTION MODELS

CHECK YOUR UNDERSTANDING

1. What is meant by *rate of change*? Distinguish between average rate of change and instantaneous rate of change.

2. What is the slope of a tangent? How does this slope compare with the slope of a secant?

3. Describe a continuous function and provide an example of one.

4. Explain in your own words the limit of a function.

5. What limit do you use to determine the derivative from first principles?

6. What does the derivative of a function represent?

7. State the following derivative rules in your own words:
   (a) the constant rule   (b) the power rule
   (c) the sum rule   (d) the difference rule

8. State each of the rules in question 7 using differential notation.

9. How do you find the velocity and acceleration of a moving object at position $s(t)$?

10. What is the difference between velocity and speed?

ADDITIONAL REVIEW QUESTIONS BY SECTION

3.1 Examining Rates of Change in Polynomial Models

11. (a) Determine the average rate of change of $f(x) = 2x^3 + 4x - 3$ over each interval.
      i. $1 \leq x \leq 2$ **ii.** $1 \leq x \leq 1.5$ **iii.** $1 \leq x \leq 1.1$
      iv. $1 \leq x \leq 1.01$ **v.** $1 \leq x \leq 1.001$ **vi.** $1 \leq x \leq 1.0001$
    (b) What value do the average rates of change approach? What does this value represent?

12. Estimate the instantaneous rate of change of $f(x) = 4x^2 + 6x - 3$ at $(2, 25)$.

13. An astronaut on the moon throws a stone. Its height, h, in metres above the surface of the moon at t seconds can be modelled by $h(t) = 5 - 0.83t^2$.
    (a) Determine when the stone hits the surface.
    (b) How fast is the stone moving when it hits the surface?

3.2 A Closer Look at Rates of Change: The Tangent Problem

14. **(a)** Use the slopes of a sequence of secants to estimate the slope of the tangent to the graph of $y = x^2 + 4x - 5$ at $P(1, 0)$.

(b) Find the equation of the tangent line.

(c) Draw a sketch showing the original function and the tangent.

15. $A(3, 1)$ and $B(5, 11)$ are points on the graph of $y = x^2 - 3x + 1$.

(a) Find the slope of the line segment between the points.

(b) Find an expression for the slope of any secant through point A. Show that this expression has the same value as the slope you calculated for (a) for $x = 5$.

(c) Use a sequence of x-values approaching 3 from each side to predict the slope of the tangent at $x = 3$.

16. Find the equation of the tangent to the graph of $y = x^2 - 7x + 12$ at the point where $x = 0$. Sketch the function and the tangent on the same axes.

3.3 Limits of Polynomial Functions

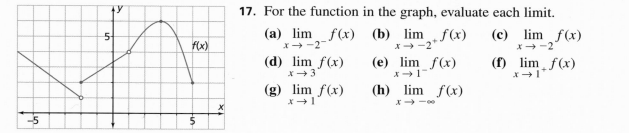

17. For the function in the graph, evaluate each limit.

(a) $\lim\limits_{x \to -2^-} f(x)$ **(b)** $\lim\limits_{x \to -2^+} f(x)$ **(c)** $\lim\limits_{x \to -2} f(x)$

(d) $\lim\limits_{x \to 3} f(x)$ **(e)** $\lim\limits_{x \to 1^-} f(x)$ **(f)** $\lim\limits_{x \to 1^+} f(x)$

(g) $\lim\limits_{x \to 1} f(x)$ **(h)** $\lim\limits_{x \to -\infty} f(x)$

18. Use a table to evaluate each limit.

(a) $\lim\limits_{x \to 2} (5x + 6)$ **(b)** $\lim\limits_{x \to -2} 4x^2$ **(c)** $\lim\limits_{x \to 1} (5x^3 - 2x^2)$ **(d)** $\lim\limits_{x \to 5} x^4$

19. Evaluate each limit.

(a) $\lim\limits_{x \to -2} (3x^2 - 5)$ **(b)** $\lim\limits_{x \to 2} (6x - 8)$

(c) $\lim\limits_{x \to 1} (3x^3 - 8x + 5)$ **(d)** $\lim\limits_{x \to 0} (-6x^2 + 9x + 12)$

(e) $\lim\limits_{x \to -3} (4x - 8x^4)$ **(f)** $\lim\limits_{x \to 2} (5x^3 - x^2 + x + 1)$

(g) $\lim\limits_{x \to 10} (7x - 2x^2 + 10)$ **(h)** $\lim\limits_{x \to 4} (x^3 + 2x + 3x^2 - 6)$

3.4 Using Limits to Find Instantaneous Rates of Change—The Derivative

20. Determine $f'(x)$ from first principles.

(a) $f(x) = 2x^2 + 4$ **(b)** $f(x) = -x^2 + 3x - 7$

(c) $f(x) = 4x^3 - 3x - 2$ **(d)** $f(x) = -4x^2 - 8x + 12$

(e) $f(x) = 6x + 15$ **(f)** $f(x) = 6x^3 + x^2 + 2x - 5$

21. For each function, determine the equation of the tangent line to the graph of the function at the given point.
   (a) $f(x) = 3x^2 + 2x + 1$ at $(0, 1)$ (b) $y = x^2 - 4$ at $(2, 0)$
   (c) $f(x) = x^3 + x - 1$ at $(-1, -3)$ (d) $f(x) = -x^2 + x + 2$ at $(3, -4)$
   (e) $y = x^3 - x^2$ at $(1, 0)$
   (f) $y = 4x^3 + 3x^2 + 2x + 1$ at $(-2, -23)$

22. (a) At what point on the graph of $y = -3x^3 + 2x - 1$ is the tangent parallel to $y = 2x + 10$?

   (b) Sketch the graph of the function and the tangent line.

3.5 Finding Some Shortcuts—The Constant and Power Rules

23. Differentiate.
   (a) $y = 6x^4$
   (b) $y = 10x^{\frac{1}{2}}$
   (c) $f(x) = -8x$
   (d) $g(x) = \dfrac{2}{x^3}$
   (e) $y = 12$
   (f) $g(x) = -8x^{-4}$
   (g) $h(x) = 7x^6$
   (h) $y = -0.5x^{-0.25}$
   (i) $f(x) = \dfrac{8}{\sqrt{x}}$

24. Find the equation of the tangent to the graph of $f(x) = 2x^4$ that has slope 1.

25. The volume of a cube with side length x is $V(x) = x^3$. Find the rate of change of volume with respect to side length if the surface area of the cube is 54 cm^2.

3.6 Finding Some Shortcuts—The Sum and Difference Rules

26. Differentiate.
   (a) $y = 4x^2 - 7x + 8$
   (b) $y = -2x^3 + 4x^2 + 5x - 6$
   (c) $y = 8x + 12$
   (d) $y = 10x^{-2} + 5x^{-1} + 3$
   (e) $f(x) = 4x^4 - 3x^3 + 2x^2 - x + 1$ (f) $f(x) = -11x^2 + 8x - 15$
   (g) $g(x) = \sqrt{x} + \sqrt[3]{x}$
   (h) $f(x) = \dfrac{5}{x^2} - \dfrac{3}{x^3}$

27. Find the equation of the tangent to the curve of each function.
   (a) $y = -3x^2 + 6x + 4$ where $x = 1$
   (b) $y = x^2 - x - 1$ where $x = -2$
   (c) $f(x) = 6x^3 - 2x^2 + 4x - 3$ where $x = -1$
   (d) $f(x) = -2x^4 + 4x^3 - 2x^2 - 8x + 9$ where $x = 3$

28. The estimated population of a bacteria colony is $P(t) = 20 + 61t + 3t^2$, where the population, P, is measured in thousands at t hours.
   (a) What is the estimated population of the colony at 8 h?
   (b) At what rate is the population changing at 8 h?

3.7 Polynomial Function Models and the First Derivative

29. For each displacement formula, find the velocity at t seconds. Then find the displacement in metres and the velocity at 2 s. Answer in appropriate units.

(a) $s(t) = -5t^2 + 6t + 4$ **(b)** $s(t) = 5t + 12$

(c) $s(t) = -4.9t^2 + 20t$ **(d)** $s(t) = 2t^3 - 3t^2 + 5t - 6$

30. A football is kicked with an initial velocity of 6.5 m/s. Its height, h, as a function of time in seconds is given by $h(t) = 0.2 + 16.5t - 4.9t^2$. What is the football's maximum height?

31. The model $C(t) = 90t^2 + 300t + 8200$ projects the circulation of a local newspaper, where t is the number of years since 2000. When will the circulation be growing by about 1200 papers/year?

3.8 Polynomial Function Models and the Second Derivative

32. Find the second derivative for each function.

(a) $f(x) = -15x^4 + 7x$ **(b)** $g(x) = 9x^5 - 4x^3 + 6x - 12$

(c) $y = -3x^4 + 5x^3 + 8x^2 + 14$ **(d)** $h(x) = 3x^2 - 5x + 13$

(e) $y = 17x + 23$ **(f)** $y = 5x - x^2 + 9x^4$

(g) $f(x) = 13$ **(h)** $y = 5x^{-3} + 10x^3$

33. Sam applies the brakes steadily to stop his car, which is travelling at 20 m/s. The position of the car, s, in metres at t seconds is given by $s(t) = 20t - 0.3t^3$. Determine

(a) the stopping distance   **(b)** the stopping time   **(c)** the deceleration at 2 s

34. The position of a particle moving along a horizontal line is described by $s(t) = 2t^3 - 6t^2 + 20t$, where s is measured in metres at t seconds.

(a) When is the acceleration equal to 0?

(b) What are the velocity and displacement when the acceleration is 0?

REVIEW QUESTIONS BY ACHIEVEMENT CHART CATEGORIES

Knowledge and Understanding

35. Evaluate each limit.

(a) $\lim\limits_{x \to 2} (2x^2 - 5x + 8)$ **(b)** $\lim\limits_{x \to -1^+} (-6x^2 + 8x + 2)$

(c) $\lim\limits_{x \to 3^-} (2x^3 - 7x + 10)$ **(d)** $\lim\limits_{x \to 2^-} (x^2 + 4x - 3)$

36. (a) Determine $\dfrac{dy}{dx}$ from first principles for each function.

     i. $y = 8x - 7$ **ii.** $y = -2x^2 + 10x - 5$ **iii.** $y = 4x^3 + 5x^2 + 16x - 25$

(b) Use the differentiation rules to verify your results for (a).

(c) Determine $\dfrac{d^2y}{dx^2}$ for each function in (a).

37. Find the equation of the tangent line to $f(x) = 2x^3 + 5x^2 - 7x - 9$ at $(1, -9)$.

38. (a) Sketch the graph of $f(x) = \begin{cases} -x^2 - 2 & \text{if } x \le 2 \\ x^2 + 2 & \text{if } x > 2 \end{cases}$

(b) Is $f(x)$ continuous or discontinuous at $x = 2$? Explain.

39. The function $N(t) = -0.045t^3 + 2.063t + 2$ models the concentration of a medicine in the body's bloodstream, in parts per million, t hours after the medicine is administered.

(a) Graph the function using technology. Define the restricted domain.

(b) Explain what happens to the concentration, N, of the drug over time.

(c) Graph the derivative. Discuss the significance of positive and negative values of the derivative over the restricted domain.

40. The manager of a transport firm has found that a truck's fuel consumption, in litres per kilometre, is related to its speed, in kilometres per hour, by $C(s) = \dfrac{12.8}{s} + \dfrac{s}{500}$. Prepare some graphs that the manager could show to the drivers to encourage efficient driving habits.

Application

41. The model $P(t) = 2t^2 + 3t + 1$ estimates the population of fish in a reservoir, where P represents the population in thousands and t is the number of years since 2000.

(a) Find the average rate of population change between 2000 and 2005.

(b) Estimate the rate at which the population is changing in 2002.

42. The gas tank in a parked car holds 75 L of gasoline. Gas is leaking from a small hole in the bottom of the tank. The volume, V, of gas remaining in the tank after t minutes can be modelled by $V(t) = 75\left(1 - \dfrac{t}{240}\right)^2$, where $0 \le t \le 240$.

(a) How much gasoline remains in the tank after 1 h?

(b) What is the average rate of change of volume with respect to time during the first two hours?

(c) How fast is the liquid draining after 3 h?

(d) How long does it take for the tank to empty?

43. The team skip slides a curling stone toward the rings at the opposite end of the ice. The stone's position, s, in metres at t seconds can be modelled by $s(t) = 12t - 4t^{\frac{3}{2}}$. How far does the stone travel before it stops? For how long is it moving?

Thinking, Inquiry, Problem Solving

44. Determine the equation of the line that is perpendicular to the tangent to the curve $y = -3x^2 + 1$ at point $(1, -2)$.

45. When a pebble is dropped into a still pond, the ripples in the water move outward in concentric circles. How fast is the area of one circle changing with respect to the radius when the radius is 4 m?

46. Prove that no line can be tangent to the curve $y = x^2$ at two different points.

Chapter 3 Performance Task

Creating and analyzing a model for a set of data helps to make predictions. Use the following data on numbers of tuberculosis (TB) cases to analyze trends and help make predictions.

Year	1925	1930	1935	1940	1945	1950	1955	1960	1965	1970	1975	1980	1985	1990	1995
Number of New, Active, and Relapsed Cases of Tuberculosis in Canada (per 100 000 People)	61	65	81	87	112	85	55	36	30	21	16	12	9	9	8

Figures taken from graph on p. 9 of *Tuberculosis In Canada 1998*. Howard Njoo, Penny Nault, Melissa Phypers. © Minister of Public Works and Government Services Canada 2001

1. Graph the relation of time and number of cases using graphing technology. Be sure to choose a suitable window. Determine whether a cubic function could model the data.

2. (a) Find the average rate of change for the data from 1925 to 1995 and the instantaneous rate of change for the curve of best fit.

(b) Identify all points where the number of cases neither increases nor decreases.

(c) Determine the equation of the tangent to the curve of best fit at 1925 and the equation of the line through the same point, (1925, 61), but with slope equal to the average rate of change.

(d) Graph both lines from (c). Both graphs are meant to illustrate the rate of change of the number of TB cases in Canada. Why are the two lines different? Explain.

(e) Repeat (c) and (d) using 1995 data instead of 1925 data. Which of the two curves illustrates a more optimistic prediction for the spread of tuberculosis after 1995? Which illustrates the more likely prediction? Justify your answers.

3. Determine the second derivative of the curve of best fit. At what point (or points) is the slope, or rate of spread of TB, not changing? Explain with reference to both the first derivative and the second derivative.

4. Two events that significantly affected the growth or decline in the number of TB cases 1925 to the present were the introduction of *chemotherapy*, which occurred shortly after 1940, and the initial spread of *AIDS*, which occurred shortly after 1980. Discuss how these two events are illustrated in the curve of best fit and in the graph of the first derivative.

Chapter 3 Review Test

RATES OF CHANGE IN POLYNOMIAL FUNCTIONS

1. The annual amount of waste taken to a landfill site can be modelled by the function $w(t) = 110(t^2 + 15t + 40)$, where w is measured in tonnes and t is the number of years since 1990. Explain the meaning of each expression in terms of the landfill site.

   (a) $\dfrac{w(10) - w(5)}{10 - 5}$

   (b) $\lim\limits_{t \to 4} \dfrac{w(t) - w(4)}{t - 4}$

2. **Knowledge and Understanding**

   (a) Determine the derivative of $f(x) = 4x^2 + 6x - 8$ from first principles.

   (b) Verify your result in (a) using the differentiation rules.

   (c) Find $f''(x)$.

3. Evaluate.

   (a) $\lim\limits_{x \to -2} (x^2 + 4x - 2)$

   (b) $\lim\limits_{x \to 2^+} \dfrac{1}{x - 2}$

4. Determine the first and second derivatives.

   (a) $y = 7x^2 - 9x + 22$

   (b) $y = -5x^3 + 2x^2 - 8x - 11$

5. **Application:** A study of the afternoon shift at a widget factory shows that the average worker who starts work at 3 P.M. will have completed $\left(-\dfrac{1}{3}x^3 + \dfrac{1}{2}x^2 + 60x\right)$ widgets after x hours. Describe what happens to the assembly rate during an 8-h shift.

6. Find the equation of the tangent at point $(1, 9)$ on the graph of $g(x) = 5x^2 - 6x + 10$.

7. **Thinking, Inquiry, Problem Solving:** Find the two straight lines that are perpendicular to $y = 0.25x$ and tangent to the curve $f(x) = \dfrac{1}{x}$.

8. After a model rocket is launched, its height above the ground can be modelled by $h(t) = -4.9t^2 + 35t + 0.5$, where h is measured in metres at t seconds.

   (a) What is the height of the launching pad?

   (b) What is the initial velocity of the rocket?

   (c) When does the rocket reach its maximum height?

   (d) When is the rocket accelerating? decelerating?

   (e) How long is the rocket's flight?

9. **Communication:** An overseas long-distance telephone call costs $1.05 for the first two minutes and $0.35 for each additional minute or partial minute. Sketch the graph of this function for calls up to 10 min long. Discuss whether this function is continuous or not.

4 Using the Derivative to Analyze Polynomial Function Models

Graphing technology lets you draw the graph of almost any function. However, your view of the function depends entirely on the current window settings. So when you look at a graph on the graphing calculator's window, you might not actually see the most important parts of the graph.

You can sketch the important parts of a function's graph using calculus. The first derivative tells where a function is increasing or decreasing, which leads to identifying its maximum and minimum points.

Optimal solutions to real-world problems often correspond to maximum and minimum values of functions. For example, the goals of most businesses, such as banks, are to maximize profit and minimize cost. You can use calculus to solve many types of optimization problems.

In this chapter, you will

- use the first derivative to determine algebraically the intervals in which a polynomial function is increasing or decreasing

- use the first derivative to determine maximum and minimum values of a polynomial function

- develop tests, using the first and second derivatives, to verify maximum and minimum values

- develop a rule to find the derivative of the product of two polynomial functions

- use the second derivative to determine the intervals in which the graph of a polynomial function is concave up or concave down

- graph a polynomial function using calculus

- solve optimization problems involving real-life applications and polynomial functions

The Chapter Problem

Trends in Post-Secondary Education

Post-secondary education is a priority for many young Canadians. Enrollment in community colleges and universities is at an all-time high. Data from the 1996 Canadian census shows the impact that a post-secondary education can have on future earnings. In 1996, high school graduates earned an average of $22 846. People with a university degree earned an average of $42 054.

Between 1994 and 1998, full-time enrollment at Canadian universities increased by 0.81% to 580 376 students. Community college enrollment grew at a much faster rate, up 6.2% to 403 516 students.

The growth rate for post-secondary programs varies widely. For example, enrollment in mathematics and computer science programs at community colleges increased by 57% between 1994 and 1998. The table shows the number of full-time mathematics and computer science students at Ontario community colleges from 1980 to 1998.

Year	Number of Students
1980	3 401
1983	7 462
1986	4 492
1989	4 288
1992	6 493
1995	7 538
1998	12 699

Source: Statistics Canada

Use the table to answer the following questions:

(a) From 1980 to 1998, when was the enrollment increasing? decreasing?

(b) From 1980 to 1998, when was the enrollment at a maximum? minimum?

In this chapter, you will use the first and second derivatives to analyze an algebraic model of this data. After certain lessons, you will be asked questions about this problem to help you develop your solution. Keep a record of your work in a project folder or computer file so that you can provide a full solution at the end of the chapter.

For help with this problem, see pages 276, 285, 295, and 333.

Chapter Challenges

Challenge 1

Louise is designing a new large-size package for gourmet popcorn. The company that sells the popcorn wants the package to look different from other popcorn packages on a store's shelf. So Louise chooses a prism with a regular hexagonal base for the package.

The cardboard for the top and bottom will be thicker than the cardboard for the sides. The thicker cardboard costs 0.015¢/cm². The other cardboard costs 0.01¢/cm². The volume of the package must be 9000 cm³.

(a) Determine the dimensions that minimize the cost of cardboard for the new package.

(b) Determine the cost of cardboard for the new package.

(c) Is this design more expensive than a design for a square-based box? Justify your answer with appropriate calculations.

(d) What shape would minimize the cost? Justify your answer.

Challenge 2

The graph of a quartic polynomial function has an absolute minimum point at $(1, -27)$. It also has points of inflection at $(2, -16)$ and $(4, 0)$. Determine the equation of this function. Sketch the graph. Justify your answer.

Getting Ready

In this chapter, you will use first and second derivatives to analyze the characteristics of polynomial functions. These exercises will help you warm up for the work ahead.

1. Factor fully.

   (a) $8x^3 - 4x^2$
   (b) $x^2 - 6x - 16$
   (c) $x^2 + 10x + 25$
   (d) $x^3 - 27$
   (e) $x^3 + 8$
   (f) $3x^3 + 5x^2 - 27x - 45$
   (g) $4x^3 + 8x^2 - x - 2$
   (h) $10x^3 - 33x^2 + 23x + 6$

2. Solve each equation, where $x \in \mathbf{R}$.

   (a) $3x + 9 = 0$
   (b) $-2x + 5 = 9$
   (c) $4x - 7 = 10$
   (d) $(x + 2)(x - 4) = 0$
   (e) $(3 + x)(x - 5) = 0$
   (f) $(2x - 1)(3x + 5) = 0$
   (g) $x^2 - 11x + 28 = 0$
   (h) $x^2 - 3x - 54 = 0$
   (i) $6x^2 - x - 12 = 0$
   (j) $5x^2 - 13x - 10 = 0$
   (k) $4x^2 - 3x - 7 = 0$
   (l) $6x^2 - 11x = -5$

3. Solve each equation, where $x \in \mathbf{R}$.

   (a) $0 = 2(x - 3)(x + 5)(x - 7)$
   (b) $0 = (3x + 1)(2x - 5)(x + 2)$
   (c) $x^3 - 7x^2 + 4x + 12 = 0$
   (d) $2x^3 - 9x^2 + 30 = 11x$
   (e) $\dfrac{2}{x} = \dfrac{4}{12}$
   (f) $\dfrac{x^2}{4} = \dfrac{18}{2}$
   (g) $3x^{-2} = 12$
   (h) $x^3 = 64$

4. Solve each inequality algebraically.

   (a) $(x + 5)(x - 4) > 0$
   (b) $(x - 3)(2x + 1) < 0$
   (c) $x^2 - 2x > 35$
   (d) $6x^2 < 35 - 11x$
   (e) $(x + 3)(x - 1)(x - 6) > 0$
   (f) $(2x + 3)(5x - 1)(x + 2) < 0$

5. State each differentiation rule in your own words. Give an example.

   (a) the power rule
   (b) the constant rule
   (c) the sum rule
   (d) the difference rule

6. Determine $\dfrac{dy}{dx}$ for each function.

   (a) $y = 7$
   (b) $y = 4x - 9$
   (c) $y = -5x^2 - 3x + 7$
   (d) $y = 7x^3 + 6x^2 - 9x - 6$
   (e) $y = 5x^4 - 9x^2$
   (f) $y = 3x^{-2} + 4x - 1$
   (g) $y = \dfrac{5}{x} - 7x$
   (h) $y = 2x^4 + 6x^6 + 9x - 12$
   (i) $y = -x^{-3} + x^2 - 6x$
   (j) $y = (3x + 5)^2$

7. Determine $\dfrac{d^2y}{dx^2}$ for each function in question 6.

8. For $f(x) = 4x^4 - 3x^2 + 2x - 1$, find the value.

    (a) $f(1)$ **(b)** $f(0)$ **(c)** $f(-2)$

    (d) $f'(-2)$ **(e)** $f'(0.5)$ **(f)** $f''(3)$

9. Describe the end behaviour of each function as $x \to \infty$ and $x \to -\infty$.

    (a) $f(x) = 2x^2 - 3x + 4$ **(b)** $f(x) = -2x^3 + 4x - 1$

    (c) $f(x) = -5x^4 + 2x^3 - 6x^2 + 7x - 1$

    (d) $f(x) = 6x^5 - 4x - 7$

10. Graph each function.

    (a) $f(x) = 2x + 5$ **(b)** $f(x) = -(x + 4)(x - 2)$

    (c) $f(x) = 2(x + 2)^2 - 3$ **(d)** $f(x) = -3x^2 + 18x - 27$

    (e) $f(x) = (x + 3)(x - 2)(x + 4)$ **(f)** $f(x) = x^3 - 1$

11. In which intervals does each function increase or decrease? Find the coordinates of any turning points. State whether a turning point is a local maximum or a local minimum.

    (a)   **(b)**

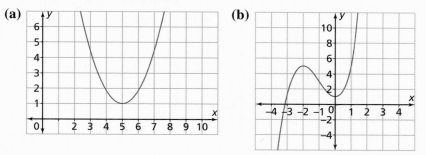

12. Use graphing technology to estimate the intervals on which the function increases or decreases. Also estimate the coordinates of any local maxima or minima points.

    (a) $y = 3x^2 - 9x + 1$ **(b)** $y = x^3 - 5x^2 + 4x - 2$

    (c) $y = x^4 - 2x^3$ **(d)** $y = -2x^5 + 3x^2 + x$

13. Solve using graphing technology.

    (a) $3 = 3x^4 - 2x^2 + 6x$ **(b)** $12 - 3x - 2x^3 = 0$

    (c) $2x^3 + 2x^2 - 5x - 4 < 0$ **(d)** $2x^4 - 8x^2 > 10$

14. For $f(x) = 4x^3 - 2x + 5$, determine the slope of the tangent line at the y-intercept.

15. Determine the equation of the tangent line at the given point.

    (a) $f(x) = 5x^2 - 3x + 2$ at $(1, 4)$

    (b) $f(x) = 4x^3 - 3x + 7$ at $(-1, 6)$

    (c) $f(x) = -2x^4 - x^3 + x$ at $(2, -38)$

    (d) $f(x) = 2x^4 - 3x^3 + 4x^2 - 5x + 6$ at $(0, 6)$

4.1 Analyzing a Polynomial Function: Intervals of Increase and Decrease

SETTING THE STAGE

Explore the concepts in this lesson in more detail using Exploration 6 on page 570.

The terms *increasing* and *decreasing* describe how a function changes over an interval. For example, the temperature usually increases from May to July and decreases from October to December.

The derivative of a function at a specific point is the slope of the tangent line at this point. The slopes, where the function is increasing and where it is decreasing, are different.

In this section, you will use the first derivative to algebraically determine where a function is increasing or decreasing.

EXAMINING THE CONCEPT

Increasing and Decreasing Functions

The values of $y = f(x)$ increase on the open intervals $-\infty < x < a$ and $b < x < \infty$. In these two intervals, the graph of $y = f(x)$ rises from left to right. The function decreases on the open interval $a < x < b$. In this interval, the graph falls from left to right.

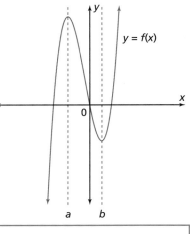

Definition of Increasing and Decreasing Functions

A function $f(x)$ is **increasing** on the interval I ($a < x < b$), if $f(x_1) < f(x_2)$ for all pairs of numbers x_1 and x_2 in I such that $x_1 < x_2$.

A function $f(x)$ is **decreasing** on the interval I ($a < x < b$), if $f(x_1) > f(x_2)$ for all pairs of numbers x_1 and x_2 in I such that $x_1 < x_2$.

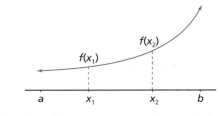

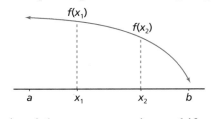

Function f increases on an interval if the values of $f(x)$ increase as x increases.

Function f decreases on an interval if the values of $f(x)$ decrease as x increases.

Example 1   **Determining Intervals of Increase and Decrease Graphically**

State the intervals of increase and decrease.

(a)   **(b)**

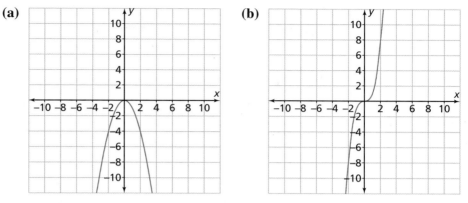

Solution

(a) The graph is rising, and thus increasing, on the interval $-\infty < x < 0$. The graph is falling, and thus decreasing, on the interval $0 < x < \infty$. The graph changes from increasing to decreasing at $x = 0$.

(b) For all values of x, the graph is always rising. Therefore, the function is increasing on the interval $-\infty < x < \infty$.

EXAMINING THE CONCEPT

Using the Derivative to Determine Intervals of Increase or Decrease

The derivative of a function at a point is the slope of the tangent line at that point. How does the derivative change at various points? Study this diagram. Where is the slope of each tangent line positive? negative?

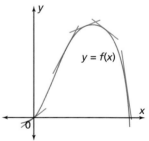

Where $f(x)$ is increasing and $f'(x) > 0$, the slope of each tangent line is *positive*. These lines slope up to the right. Where $f(x)$ is decreasing and $f'(x) < 0$, the slope of each tangent line is *negative*. These lines slope down to the right.

This pattern suggests that you can use the sign of the derivative, $f'(x)$, to determine where a function is increasing or decreasing.

Test for Increasing and Decreasing Functions

If $f'(x) > 0$ for all x in that interval, then f is *increasing* on the interval $a < x < b$.
If $f'(x) < 0$ for all x in that interval, then f is *decreasing* on the interval $a < x < b$.

Example 2 **Using the Derivative to Determine Intervals of Increase or Decrease**

Determine the intervals where each function increases and decreases.

(a) $g(x) = x^2 - 2x + 3$ **(b)** $y = -\frac{2}{3}x^3 + x^2 + 12x - 1$

Solution

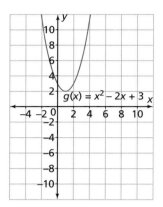

(a) Start by finding the derivative.

$$g'(x) = \frac{d}{dx}(x^2 - 2x + 3)$$
$$= 2x - 2$$

The function $g(x)$ increases when $g'(x) > 0$ and decreases when $g'(x) < 0$.

i. increasing when $2x - 2 > 0$ **ii.** decreasing when $2x - 2 < 0$
$2x > 2$ $2x < 2$
$x > 1$ $x < 1$

The function $g(x)$ is quadratic. The graph of the function is a parabola that opens up. The y-intercept is 3, since $g(0) = 3$. The graph changes direction when $x = 1$ at the vertex $(1, 2)$.

The function $g(x)$ decreases when $x < 1$ and increases when $x > 1$.

(b) The function $y = -\frac{2}{3}x^3 + x^2 + 12x - 1$

increases when $y' > 0$ and decreases when $y' < 0$.

$$y' = \frac{d}{dx}\left(-\frac{2}{3}x^3 + x^2 + 12x - 1\right)$$
$$= 3\left(-\frac{2}{3}\right)x^2 + 2x + 12$$
$$= -2x^2 + 2x + 12 \qquad\qquad \text{Factor.}$$
$$= -2(x^2 - x - 6)$$
$$= -2(x - 3)(x + 2)$$

The function is increasing when $-2(x - 3)(x + 2) > 0$.

$-2(x - 3)(x + 2) = 0$ when $x = 3$ or when $x = -2$.

The numbers 3 and -2 divide the x-axis into three intervals: $x < -2$, $-2 < x < 3$, and $x > 3$.

What is the sign of the derivative for each interval? Choose a value for x in each interval. Substitute this value into each factor and solve. Note the sign. Then multiply the signs to get the sign of the derivative.

	Intervals		
	$x < -2$	$-2 < x < 3$	$x > 3$
-2	$-$	$-$	$-$
$(x - 3)$	$-$	$-$	$+$
$(x + 2)$	$-$	$+$	$+$
Sign of y'	$(-)(-)(-) = -$	$(-)(-)(+) = +$	$(-)(+)(+) = -$
Behaviour of y	decreasing ↘	increasing ↗	decreasing ↘

Notice that the intervals are in order from left to right along the x-axis, so you can see where the function increases or decreases from left to right. This helps when graphing the function.

A graph confirms the analysis.

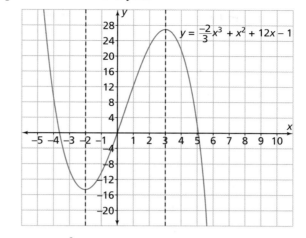

The function $y = -\frac{2}{3}x^3 + x^2 + 12x - 1$ is

- decreasing on $x < -2$
- increasing on $-2 < x < 3$
- decreasing on $x > 3$

• • • • • • • •

Example 3   Using the First Derivative to Analyze a Model

ROXS, a music store, predicts that every dollar increase in the price of any CD will cause sales to decrease by 10 000 units a year. The store now sells 300 000 CDs a year at $15 each.

(a) Develop a model that represents the music store's sales revenue.

(b) Using this model, determine when revenue will increase and when it will decrease.

(c) The store's manager is thinking about raising the price of any CD by $2. At this new price, what is the rate of change in revenue?

Solution

(a) revenue = price × units sold

Let x represent the price increase in dollars. Then price = $(15 + x)$ and units sold = $(300\ 000 - 10\ 000x)$.

$$\begin{aligned} \text{revenue} &= (15 + x)(300\ 000 - 10\ 000x) \\ &= 4\ 500\ 000 - 150\ 000x + 300\ 000x - 10\ 000x^2 \\ &= 4\ 500\ 000 + 150\ 000x - 10\ 000x^2 \end{aligned}$$

Let R represent revenue. The model for sales revenue is

$$R = 4\ 500\ 000 + 150\ 000x - 10\ 000x^2$$

(b) Revenue will increase when $R' > 0$. Revenue will decrease when $R' < 0$.

$$R' = \frac{d}{dx}(4\ 500\ 000 + 150\ 000x - 10\ 000x^2)$$
$$= 150\ 000 - 20\ 000x$$

R is increasing when

$$150\ 000 - 20\ 000x > 0$$
$$\frac{-20\ 000x}{-20\ 000} > \frac{-150\ 000}{-20\ 000}$$
$$x < 7.5$$

R is decreasing when

$$150\ 000 - 20\ 000x < 0$$
$$\frac{-20\ 000x}{-20\ 000} < \frac{-150\ 000}{-20\ 000}$$
$$x > 7.5$$

Revenue will increase if the price is raised by any amount up to \$7.50.
Revenue will decrease if the price is raised by more than \$7.50.

(c) The derivative represents the (instantaneous) rate of change at a point.
To find the rate of change for a price increase of \$2, evaluate $R'(2)$.

$$R'(2) = 150\ 000 - 20000(2)$$
$$= 150\ 000 - 40\ 000$$
$$= 110\ 000$$

Revenue would increase at a rate of \$110 000 per dollar increase in price.

CHECK, CONSOLIDATE, COMMUNICATE

1. How can you estimate, from the graph of a polynomial function, the intervals where the function is increasing? decreasing?
2. What is always true about the slopes of all tangent lines on a section of a curve that is rising? falling?
3. Graph the function that is increasing on the interval $-2 < x < 2$, decreasing on the interval $2 < x < 4$, and increasing on the interval $4 < x < 7$. Draw a smooth curve. Suggest the degree of a polynomial function that fits this description.

KEY IDEAS

- A function $f(x)$ is **increasing** on the open interval $I\ (a < x < b)$ if $f(x_1) < f(x_2)$ for all pairs of numbers, x_1 and x_2, such that $x_1 < x_2$ in I.

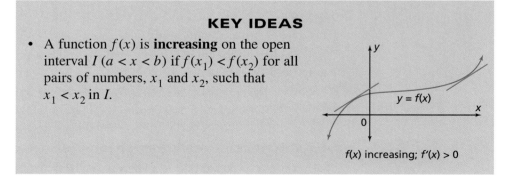

$f(x)$ increasing; $f'(x) > 0$

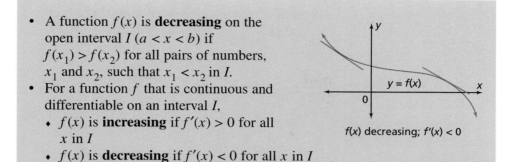

- A function $f(x)$ is **decreasing** on the open interval I $(a < x < b)$ if $f(x_1) > f(x_2)$ for all pairs of numbers, x_1 and x_2, such that $x_1 < x_2$ in I.
- For a function f that is continuous and differentiable on an interval I,
  - $f(x)$ is **increasing** if $f'(x) > 0$ for all x in I
  - $f(x)$ is **decreasing** if $f'(x) < 0$ for all x in I

$y = f(x)$

$f(x)$ decreasing; $f'(x) < 0$

4.1 Exercises

A **1.** Identify the intervals on which the function increases or decreases.

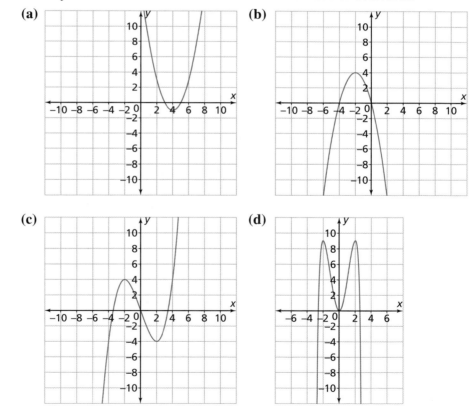

(a)

(b)

(c)

(d)

2. (a) The function $f(x)$ is an increasing function. Its derivative $f'(x)$ is defined for all $x \in \mathbf{R}$. Can any values of $f'(x)$ be negative? Explain.

(b) The function $f(x)$ is a decreasing function. Its derivative $f'(x)$ is defined for all $x \in \mathbf{R}$. Can any values of $f'(x)$ be positive? Explain.

3. Determine the sign of $\dfrac{dy}{dx}$ at points A, B, C, and D.

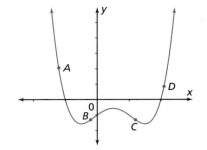

4. Solve for x, $x \in \mathbf{R}$.

(a) $3x + 6 > 0$ (b) $-2x + 8 < 0$

(c) $(x - 5)(x + 2) > 0$ (d) $(3x + 2)(x - 4) < 0$

(e) $x^2 - 81 > 0$ (f) $x^2 - 10x + 24 > 0$

(g) $x^2 - x - 30 < 0$ (h) $8x^2 + 2x - 3 > 0$

(i) $2x^2 - 3x - 20 < 0$ (j) $3x^2 - 11x > 4$

5. For each function $f(x)$, determine $f'(x)$. Also determine when $f'(x) > 0$. State the intervals on which $f(x)$ is increasing.

(a) $f(x) = 2x + 10$ (b) $f(x) = -4x + 9$

(c) $f(x) = x^2 + 3$ (d) $f(x) = -2x^2 - 8$

(e) $f(x) = 4x^2 + 8x$ (f) $f(x) = -5x^2 - 20x + 3$

6. For each function $f(x)$, determine $f'(x)$. Also determine when $f'(x) < 0$. State the intervals on which $f(x)$ is decreasing.

(a) $f(x) = -3x - 12$ (b) $f(x) = 5x + 35$

(c) $f(x) = 3x^2 + 13$ (d) $f(x) = -3x^2 - 12$

(e) $f(x) = 3x^2 + 12x - 2$ (f) $f(x) = -4x^2 - 32x + 5$

B   **7.** Determine the intervals where each function increases and decreases.

(a) $y = 8x + 16$ (b) $y = -3x - 1$

(c) $y = 5$ (d) $y = x^2 + 4x + 1$

(e) $y = 6 - 3x^2$ (f) $y = -x^2 + 2x - 1$

(g) $y = x^3 - 12x + 15$ (h) $y = x^3 - 27x - 10$

(i) $y = -2x^3 + 6x - 2$ (j) $y = x^3 + 2$

8. Determine the intervals where each function increases and decreases.

(a) $y = 2x^4 + 10$ (b) $y = -3x^4 - 12x$

(c) $y = x^4 - 2x^2 - 1$ (d) $y = 3x^4 + 4x^3 - 12x^2$

(e) $y = 2x^2 - \dfrac{1}{4}x^4$ (f) $y = x^4 + x^2 - 1$

9. Knowledge and Understanding: Determine where $g(x) = 2x^3 - 3x^2 - 12x + 15$ is increasing and where it is decreasing.

10. A plastic pop bottle holds 2 L of liquid. In an experiment, a small hole is drilled in the bottom of the bottle. The volume of liquid, V, remaining after t seconds can be modelled by $V(t) = 2 - \frac{t}{5} + \frac{t^2}{200}$, where $t \geq 0$.

 (a) How long does it take for the 2 L of liquid to drain from the bottle?

 (b) Verify that the volume of liquid is always decreasing until the bottle is empty.

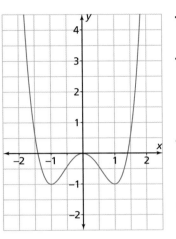

11. **Communication:** Identify the intervals on which the function shown on the left is increasing or decreasing.

12. A slow-pitch pitcher lobs the ball toward home plate. The height of the ball in metres, h, at t seconds can be modelled by $h(t) = -4.9t^2 + 10.5t + 0.2$.

 (a) When is the height of the ball increasing? decreasing?

 (b) When is the velocity of the ball increasing? decreasing?

13. **Application:** The profit, P, in dollars for selling x hamburgers is modelled by $P(x) = 2.44x - \frac{x^2}{20\,000} - 5000$, where $0 \leq x \leq 35\,000$. For what quantities of hamburgers is the profit increasing? decreasing?

14. Graph f if $f'(x) < 0$ when $x < -2$ and when $x > 3$, $f'(x) > 0$ when $-2 < x < 3$, and $f(-2) = 0$ and $f(3) = 5$.

15. Graph f if $f'(x) > 0$ when $x < -3$ and when $x > 1$, $f'(x) < 0$ when $-3 < x < 1$, and $f(-3) = 4$ and $f(1) = 2$.

16. Use an example to show and verify the following: If functions f and g are increasing on an interval I, then $f + g$ must also be increasing on I.

17. The world population from 1900 to 2000 can be modelled by $P(t) = 0.0012t^3 + 0.3197t^2 + 0.2109t + 1688.951$, where P is the population in millions and t is the number of years since 1900. Did the world population ever decrease in the 20th century? Justify your answer.

18. **Thinking, Inquiry, Problem Solving:** After birth, a baby normally loses weight for a few days and then starts gaining. The table shows an infant's weight during the first two weeks.

Day	0	1	2	3	4	5	6	7	8	9	10	11	12	13	14
Weight (kg)	3.14	3.03	2.95	2.80	2.77	2.76	2.79	2.84	2.93	2.95	3.01	3.14	3.32	3.49	3.68

Determine the best polynomial model for this data. Use your model to find the intervals on which the infant's weight is increasing and decreasing.

19. **Check Your Understanding:** A rock is thrown into the air from a bridge. Verify that its height decreases over the interval $1 < t < 2.2$. The height of the rock above the water, h, in metres at t seconds is modelled by $h(t) = -4.9t^2 + 9.8t + 2.1$.

C 20. Determine the intervals in which $f(x) = |x - 2| + 3$ increases and decreases.

21. For the cubic polynomial function $f(x) = ax^3 + bx^2 + cx + d$, where $a \neq 0$, find conditions for a, b, c, and d to ensure that, for $-\infty < x < \infty$, f is always

  (a) increasing   **(b)** decreasing

22. Use calculus to prove that, for any quadratic function $f(x) = ax^2 + bx + c$,

  (a) if $a > 0$, then f is always decreasing when $x < -\dfrac{b}{2a}$ and increasing when $x > -\dfrac{b}{2a}$

  (b) if $a < 0$, then f is always increasing when $x < -\dfrac{b}{2a}$ and increasing when $x > -\dfrac{b}{2a}$

ADDITIONAL ACHIEVEMENT CHART QUESTIONS

Knowledge and Understanding: Determine where the polynomial function $f(x) = 2x^3 - 9x^2 + 12x - 2$ is increasing and decreasing.

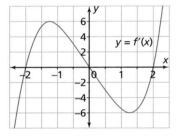

Application: A particle moves along a line. The particle's distance from a fixed point, s, in metres as a function of time, t, in seconds can be modelled by $s(t) = -2t^3 + 6t^2 - 3$, $t \geq 0$. Determine when the particle is moving forward.

Thinking, Inquiry, Problem Solving: Given the graph of $f'(x)$ on the left, determine where $f(x)$ is increasing and decreasing.

Communication: Suppose that you are riding on a Ferris wheel. Sketch a graph that represents your distance above the ground while you are on the Ferris wheel. When does the distance increase? When does the distance decrease?

The Chapter Problem

Trends in Post-Secondary Education

Apply what you learned in this section to answer these questions about The Chapter Problem on page 264.

CP1. Create a scatter plot using graphing technology. The independent variable is the number of years since 1980. Sketch the curve of best fit.

CP2. Using graphing technology, determine the equation of the polynomial that best models the given data.

CP3. Use the mathematical model you found to determine when the enrollment is increasing and decreasing between 1980 and 1998.

4.2 Maximum and Minimum Values of a Polynomial Function

SETTING THE STAGE

How often a person visits the doctor depends on his or her age. The average number of trips to the doctor, f, can be modelled by $f(x) = 6.95 - 0.3x + 0.0083x^2 - 0.000\,02x^3$, where x is the age of the patient in years and $0 < x \leq 100$. At what age are visits to a doctor the least frequent?

The problem asks you to determine the minimum value of a function over a defined interval. The function may have not one but several different minimum or maximum values. How can you tell which minimum value is the *least* minimum value? How can you tell which maximum value is the *greatest* maximum value?

In this section, you will learn how to find any or all of the *extreme* values, or **extrema**, of a polynomial function.

EXAMINING THE CONCEPT

Extreme Values of a Function

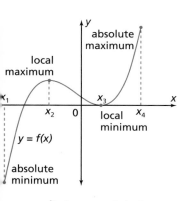

$f(x_4)$ represents both a local and an absolute maximum value on the closed interval $x_1 \leq x \leq x_4$.

When a function changes from increasing to decreasing or from decreasing to increasing, the function has an extreme value. A function may have several extreme values, or extrema. The graph of the function has either a maximum or a minimum point where the function's derivative changes its sign.

Points $(x_1, f(x_1))$ and $(x_3, f(x_3))$ correspond to minimum values of the function.

Points $(x_2, f(x_2))$ and $(x_4, f(x_4))$ correspond to maximum values of the function.

Definition of Local Maximum and Minimum Values

1. Function f has a **local maximum** (or relative maximum) at c if $f(c) \geq f(x)$ for all x sufficiently close to c.

2. Function f has a **local minimum** (or relative minimum) at c if $f(c) \leq f(x)$ for all x sufficiently close to c.

To decide whether a point represents a maximum value or a minimum value, examine some values of the function on each side of the point.

The **absolute maximum value** corresponds to the highest point on the graph of the function. The absolute maximum value is the largest of all local maximum values.

The **absolute minimum value** corresponds to the lowest point on the graph. The absolute minimum value is the smallest local minimum value.

Definition of Absolute Maximum and Minimum Values

1. $f(d)$ is the **absolute maximum value** if $f(d) \geq f(x)$ for all x in the domain of f.

2. $f(d)$ is the **absolute minimum value** if $f(d) \leq f(x)$ for all x in the domain of f.

Example 1   Maximum and Minimum Values: Absolute or Local?

Identify all the maximum and minimum values for each function. Then decide whether these values are local or absolute, or both.

(a) $f(x) = -x^2 + 2$

(b) $g(x) = (x - 2)^3$

(c) $h(x) = x^3 - 3x + 2, \ -2 \leq x \leq 3$

Solution

(a) Graph $f(x) = -x^2 + 2$.

The highest point on the graph is $(0, 2)$, and $f(x) > f(0)$ for all values of x. $(0, 2)$ corresponds to the local, and absolute, maximum point of the function. $f(0) = 2$ is the absolute maximum value.

Since $f(x) \to -\infty$ as $x \to -\infty$ and $f(x) \to -\infty$ as $x \to \infty$, there is no minimum value.

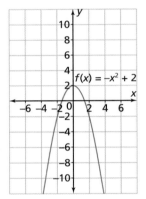

(b) Graph $g(x) = (x - 2)^3$.

The graph shows that $g(x)$ is increasing for all values of x. This function has no maximum or minimum values.

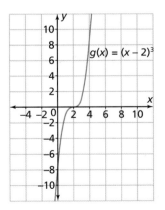

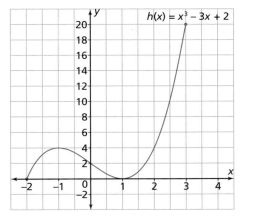

(c) Graph $h(x) = x^3 - 3x + 2$ on the closed interval $-2 \le x \le 3$.

The graph shows that the function has a local minimum value of 0, for $x = -2$ and for $x = 1$. The local minimum value is also an absolute minimum value on this closed interval.

The local maximum values of f on the interval are $f(3) = 20$ and $f(-1) = 4$. The local maximum of 20 is also an absolute maximum on this closed interval.

EXAMINING THE CONCEPT

Critical Numbers and Critical Points

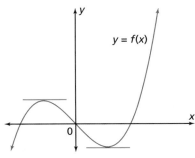

In the graph, the tangent lines at the points corresponding to the extrema are horizontal. So the slope of each tangent line and the value of the derivative is 0.

> ### Definition of a Critical Number of a Polynomial Function
>
> For any polynomial function $f(x)$, a point on the graph of the function where $f'(x) = 0$ is a **critical point**. A **critical number** is a number c in the domain of $f(x)$ such that $f'(c) = 0$.

This definition will be expanded upon in Chapter 5. In a polynomial function, a critical number occurs where the function changes from increasing to decreasing or vice versa.

To locate all the local and absolute extrema of a polynomial function, start by identifying all the critical numbers. A local extremum may occur at a critical number. However, not every critical number leads to a local extremum.

Example 2   **Determining the Critical Numbers**

Find the critical numbers of $f(x) = -\frac{4}{3}x^3 + 3x^2 + 4x + 1$.

Solution
First determine the derivative. Then factor. The critical numbers occur where $f'(x) = 0$.

$$f'(x) = -4x^2 + 6x + 4$$
$$= -2(2x^2 - 3x - 2)$$
$$= -2(2x + 1)(x - 2)$$
$$\therefore 0 = -2(2x + 1)(x - 2)$$
$$x = -\frac{1}{2} \text{ or } x = 2$$

Therefore, the critical numbers are $-\frac{1}{2}$ and 2.

The critical numbers indicate where *possible* extrema can occur. On an interval the absolute extrema will occur at the critical points or at the endpoints of the interval.

Procedure for Finding Absolute Extrema

Follow these steps to find the absolute maximum and maximum values of the function f on a closed interval $a \leq x \leq b$.

1. Determine $f'(x)$. Find all critical numbers of f on the interval $a \leq x \leq b$.
2. Evaluate f at the endpoints a and b and at each critical number c.
3. Compare all the values found for step 2.
   - The largest value is the absolute maximum of f on the interval $a \leq x \leq b$.
   - The smallest value is the absolute minimum of f on the interval $a \leq x \leq b$.

Example 3 **Finding the Extrema on a Closed Interval**

Find the absolute maximum and minimum values of $g(x) = 2x^4 - 8x^3 + 9x^2$, $-2 \leq x \leq 3$.

Solution
First determine the derivative and factor it.

$$g'(x) = 8x^3 - 24x^2 + 18x$$
$$= 2x(4x^2 - 12x + 9)$$
$$= 2x(2x - 3)^2$$

To determine the critical numbers, let $g'(x) = 0$.

$$2x(2x - 3)^2 = 0$$
$$x = 0 \text{ or } x = \frac{3}{2}$$

The critical numbers are 0 and $\frac{3}{2}$.

Evaluate $g(x)$ at the critical numbers and at the x-coordinates of the endpoints of the interval.

$$g(-2) = 2(-2)^4 - 8(-2)^3 + 9(-2)^2 = 132$$
$$g(0) = 2(0)^4 - 8(0)^3 + 9(0)^2 = 0$$
$$g\left(\frac{3}{2}\right) = 2\left(\frac{3}{2}\right)^4 - 8\left(\frac{3}{2}\right)^3 + 9\left(\frac{3}{2}\right) = 3\frac{3}{8}$$
$$g(3) = 2(3)^4 - 8(3)^3 + 9(3)^2 = 27$$

Therefore, the absolute minimum value of g on $-2 \leq x \leq 3$ is $g(0) = 0$.
The absolute maximum value of g on $-2 \leq x \leq 3$ is $g(-2) = 132$.

• • • • • • • •

Example 4   Determining the Extrema of a Polynomial Function Model

Recall the problem in Setting the Stage.

How often a person visits the doctor depends on his or her age. The average number of trips to the doctor, f, can be modelled by $f(x) = 6.95 - 0.3x + 0.0083x^2 - 0.000\,02x^3$, where x is the age of the patient in years and $0 < x \le 100$. At what age are visits to a doctor the least frequent?

Solution

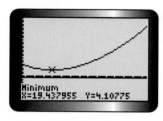

Minimum
X=19.437955   Y=4.10775

To verify this result, use graphing technology. For help with finding the minimum value, see the Technology Appendix on page 592.

$f'(x) = -0.3 + 0.0166x - 0.000\,06x^2$ First find the derivative.

$-0.000\,06x^2 + 0.0166x - 0.3 = 0$ Then find the critical numbers, x, by letting $f'(x) = 0$.

$$x = \frac{-b \pm \sqrt{b^2 - 4ac}}{2a}$$ Solve using the quadratic formula, to the nearest tenth.

$$x = \frac{-0.0166 \pm \sqrt{(-0.0166)^2 - 4(0.000\,06)(-3)}}{2(-0.000\,06)}$$

$x \doteq 19.4$ or $x \doteq 257.2$

Only the critical number 19.4 lies in the defined interval, $0 \le x \le 100$. Evaluate the function at this number and at the end points of the interval, 0 and 100.

$f(0) = 6.95 - 0.3(0) + 0.0083(0)^2 - 0.000\,02(0)^3 = 6.95$

$f(19.4) = 6.95 - 0.3(19.4) + 0.0083(19.4)^2 - 0.000\,02(19.4)^3 \doteq 4.11$

$f(100) = 6.95 - 0.3(100) + 0.0083(100)^2 - 0.000\,02(100)^3 = 39.95$

According to this model, visits to the doctor are at an absolute minimum of about 4 visits per year, when the patient is about 19 years old.

• • • • • • • •

Example 5   Graphing the Derivative Given the Graph of a Function

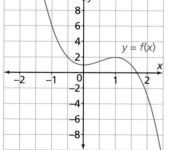

Given the graph of $y = f(x)$, graph $y = f'(x)$.

Solution

A polynomial function f is continuous for all values of x in the domain of f. As a result, the derivative of f, f', must also be continuous for all values of x in the domain of f.

To graph $y = f'(x)$ using the graph of $y = f(x)$, first determine the slopes of the tangent lines, $f'(x_i)$, at certain x-values, x_i. These x-values include zeros, critical numbers, and numbers in each interval where f is increasing or decreasing. Then plot the corresponding ordered pairs on a graph. Draw a smooth curve through these points to complete the graph.

The given graph has a local minimum at $(0, 1)$ and a local maximum at $(1, 2)$. At these points, the tangents are horizontal. Therefore, $f'(0) = 0$ and $f'(1) = 0$.

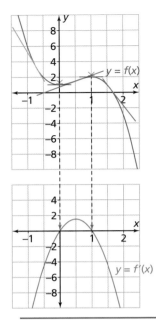

At $x = 0.5$, which is halfway between $x = 0$ and $x = 1$, the slope of the tangent is about 1.5. So $f'(0.5) \doteq 1.5$.

The function $f(x)$ is decreasing when $f'(x) < 0$. The tangent lines show that $f'(x) < 0$ when $x < 0$ and when $x > 1$. Similarly, $f(x)$ is increasing when $f'(x) > 0$. The tangent lines show that $f'(x) > 0$ when $0 < x < 1$.

The shape of the graph of $f(x)$ suggests that $f(x)$ is a cubic polynomial with a negative leading coefficient. Assume this is true. The derivative, $f'(x)$, may be a quadratic function with a negative leading coefficient. If this is the case, the graph of $f'(x)$ is a parabola that opens down.

Plot $(0, 0)$, $(1, 0)$, and $(0.5, 1.5)$ on the graph of $f'(x)$. The graph of $f'(x)$ is a parabola that opens down and passes through these points.

CHECK, CONSOLIDATE, COMMUNICATE

1. Explain the difference between an absolute maximum and a local maximum. Draw a diagram to illustrate your explanation.
2. How does setting each factor of the derivative of a polynomial function $f(x)$ to 0 help you identify all of the x-values that may correspond to maximum or minimum values of $f(x)$?

KEY IDEAS

- The **minimum and maximum values** of a function on an interval are also called the extreme values or extrema. On an interval, a function may have one **extremum** or several **extrema**.
- The largest local maximum value on the entire domain of the function or on a closed interval is the **absolute maximum** value. The smallest local minimum value is the **absolute minimum**.
- Function $f(x)$ is a polynomial function. Its domain is $x \in \mathbf{R}$. Point $(c, f(c))$ is a local extremum. Then $f'(c) = 0$. The number c is a **critical number** of f. Point $(c, f(c))$ is a **critical point** on the graph of f.

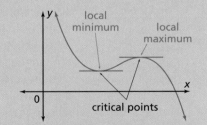

- Find the absolute extrema of a polynomial function $f(x)$ on the interval $a \leq x \leq b$ by finding all critical numbers, c_i, on the interval, and then evaluating $f(a)$, $f(b)$, and all of $f(c_i)$. The largest of these values is the absolute maximum of f on the interval. The smallest value is the absolute minimum.

A 1. Match each graph in the top row with the graph of its derivative function in the bottom row.

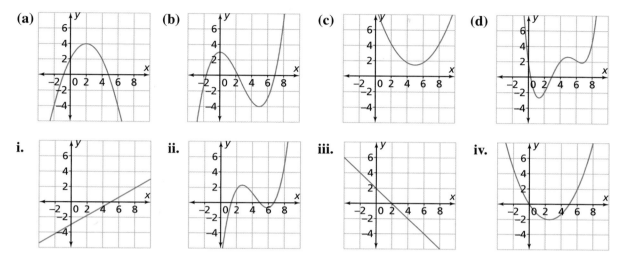

2. For the graph of each function, estimate and graph the derivative function.

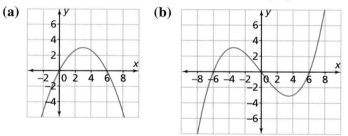

3. Let $f(x) = 5x + 15$.

   (a) Show that $f(x)$ has no critical numbers.

   (b) Find the absolute maximum and minimum values of $f(x)$ on $-3 \le x \le 5$.

4. Let $g(x) = -x^2 + 5$.

   (a) Determine the critical numbers of $g(x)$.

   (b) Find the absolute maximum and minimum values of $g(x)$ on $-1 \le x \le 4$.

5. Find all the critical points of each function.

   (a) $y = 3x^2 + 2$ (b) $y = x^2 + 6x + 7$

   (c) $y = -2x^2 + 16x - 31$ (d) $y = x^3 - 27x$

   (e) $y = x^4 - 4x^2$ (f) $y = 3x^5 - 25x^3 + 60x$

B 6. Find all the absolute maximum and minimum values on each interval.

(a) $f(x) = x^2 - 2x + 3, 0 \le x \le 3$

(b) $f(x) = x^3 - 3x^2, -1 \le x \le 4$

(c) $f(x) = -4x^2 - 16x - 17, -5 \le x \le 0$

(d) $f(x) = x^4 - 2x^2, -2 \le x \le 5$

(e) $f(x) = x^3 + 3x^2 + 1, -2 \le x \le 2$

(f) $f(x) = \frac{1}{3}x^3 - 9x + 5, -4 \le x \le 4$

(g) $f(x) = x^5 - 5x^4 + 100, -1 \le x \le 5$

(h) $f(x) = (x + 2)^2, -3 \le x \le 3$

(i) $f(x) = x^3 - 3x^2 + 3x + 5, -2 \le x \le 3$

(j) $f(x) = 2x^3 + 3x^2 - 36x + 17, -3 \le x \le 3$

7. **Knowledge and Understanding:** Determine the absolute maximum and minimum values of $h(x) = 2x^3 + 3x^2 - 12x$, where $-2 \le x \le 2$.

8. For $f(x) = x^3 + 3x^2 - 45x$ on the interval $-6 \le x \le 4$, find the critical points and the maximum and minimum values. Graph $f(x)$.

9. For $f(x) = x^4 - 18x^2$ on the interval $-4 \le x \le 4$, find the critical numbers and the maximum and minimum values. Graph $f(x)$.

10. The volume, V, of 1 kg of H_2O at temperature t between 0°C and 30°C can be modelled by $V(t) = -0.000\ 067\ 9t^3 + 0.008\ 504\ 3t^2 - 0.064\ 26t + 999.87$. Volume is measured in cubic centimetres. Determine the temperature at which the volume of water is the greatest in the given interval.

11. **Communication:** Explain why $f(x) = ax^3 + bx^2 + cx + d, a \ne 0$, can have two critical numbers, or one critical number, or no critical numbers. Show an example for each case.

12. (a) Graph the cubic function with an absolute minimum at $(-2, -12)$, a local maximum at $(0, 3)$, a local minimum at $(2, -1)$, and an absolute maximum at $(4, 9)$.

    (b) What is the domain of this function?

    (c) Where is the function increasing? decreasing?

13. **Application:** The polynomial function $f(x) = 0.001x^3 - 0.12x^2 + 3.6x + 10$, $0 \le x \le 75$, models the shape of a roller coaster track, where f is the vertical displacement of the track and x is the horizontal displacement of the track. Both displacements are in metres. Determine the absolute maximum and minimum heights along this stretch of track.

14. For $f(x) = x^2 + px + q$, find the values of p and q such that $f(1) = 5$ is an extremum of f on the interval $0 \le x \le 2$. Is this extremum a maximum value or a minimum value? Explain.

15. For $f(x) = x^3 - kx$, where $k \in \mathbf{R}$, find the values of k such that f has

    (a) no critical numbers (b) one critical number (c) two critical numbers

16. **Thinking, Inquiry, Problem Solving:** Find values of a, b, c, and d such that $g(x) = ax^3 + bx^2 + cx + d$ has a local maximum at $(2, 4)$ and a local minimum at $(0, 0)$.

17. **Check Your Understanding:** What points on an interval must you consider to determine the absolute maximum, or minimum, value on the interval? Why?

18. (a) How many critical numbers does a quadratic function have? Explain.

   (b) Show that the critical number for $y = ax^2 + bx + c$, $a \neq 0$, is always the x-coordinate of the vertex of the corresponding parabola.

19. (a) For $y = x^4 - kx^2$, for what values of k, where $k \in \mathbf{R}$, does the function have a single critical number?

   (b) Is there a function in this family with two critical numbers? Justify your answer.

20. For $f(x) = \sin 2x$ and $f'(x) = 2 \cos 2x$, determine the absolute maximum and minimum values of $f(x)$ on the interval $-2\pi \leq x \leq 2\pi$.

ADDITIONAL ACHIEVEMENT CHART QUESTIONS

Knowledge and Understanding: Determine the absolute maximum and minimum values of $f(x) = 2x^4 - 4x^2 + 1$, $-2 \leq x \leq 2$.

Application: The concentration of a drug in a patient's bloodstream is $C(t) = 4t^3 - 33t^2 + 72t$, where C is in milligrams per cubic centimetre and t is the number of hours after the drug is taken. Find the maximum and minimum concentrations during the first four hours, that is, $0 \leq t \leq 4$, after the drug is taken.

Thinking, Inquiry, Problem Solving: Graph $y = f(x)$, where $f(1) = 3$, $f'(1) = 0$, and

(a) $f'(x) > 0$ for $x < 1$, $f'(x) < 0$ for $x > 1$

(b) $f'(x) < 0$ for $x < 1$, $f'(x) > 0$ for $x > 1$

Communication: Use the graph of $y = f'(x)$ to replace the question mark with $<$, $=$, or $>$. Explain your reasoning.

(a) $f(0) ? f(1)$ **(b)** $f(1) ? f(2)$

The Chapter Problem
Trends in Post-Secondary Education

CP4. Use your algebraic model that you found for question CP2 (section 4.1) to determine the critical numbers.

CP5. Use the model to determine the local maximum and minimum enrollments between 1980 and 1998.

CP6. Use the model to determine the absolute maximum and minimum enrollments between 1980 and 1998.

4.3 The First Derivative Test

SETTING THE STAGE

A small rocket is launched as part of an atmospheric study. The onboard digital sensor sends back these measurements of the rocket's height at 5-s intervals.

Time (s)	0	5	10	15	20	25	30
Height (m)	1.5	754.0	1261.5	1524.0	1541.5	1314.0	841.5

What was the maximum height of the rocket?

The table shows that the maximum height is 1541.5 m at 20 s. But how do you know, without graphing, whether this maximum height is the absolute maximum height on the interval?

Identifying the critical numbers of an algebraic model will help determine the absolute maximum, or minimum, value of a function. Every local extremum occurs at a critical number of a polynomial function. But is it also true that every critical number leads to an extremum?

In this section, you will use the first derivative test to determine whether a critical number corresponds to a maximum or minimum value.

EXAMINING THE CONCEPT

Establishing the First Derivative Test

Example 1 **A Critical Number May Not Lead to a Maximum or Minimum**

Show that $f(x) = -x^3 + 1$ has no maximum or minimum values at the critical numbers.

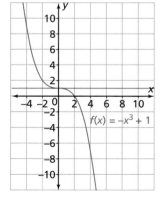

$f(x) = -x^3 + 1$

Solution

To locate the critical numbers, let $f'(x) = 0$.

$$f'(x) = -3x^2$$
$$\therefore \ -3x^2 = 0$$
$$x = 0$$

The only critical point, at $x = 0$, is $(0, f(0)) = (0, -(0)^3 + 1)$, or $(0, 1)$.

Although $(0, 1)$ is a critical point, the graph of $f(x) = -x^3 + 1$ reveals that it does not correspond to an extremum. So the function does not have a maximum, or a minimum, value.

A critical number simply identifies where the slope of the tangent line is 0. So, sometimes a critical number corresponds to an extremum, and sometimes it does not.

A test is needed to determine whether a critical number corresponds to an extremum or not.

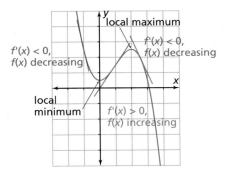

Examine the values of the derivative on both sides of a critical point to decide whether an extremum exists at that point or not.

A local minimum must exist if the graph of the function changes from falling to rising at a critical point. The sign of the derivative changes from negative to positive.

A local maximum must exist if the graph of the function changes from rising to falling at a critical point. The sign of the derivative changes from positive to negative.

The First Derivative Test for Local Extrema

Let c be a critical number of a polynomial function f that is continuous over an interval I.

- If $f'(x)$ changes from negative to positive at c, then point $(c, f(c))$ is a **local minimum point** of f.
- If $f'(x)$ changes from positive to negative at c, then point $(c, f(c))$ is a **local maximum point** of f.
- If $f'(x)$ does not change sign at c, then point $(c, f(c))$ is neither a maximum nor a minimum point.

The First Derivative Test for Absolute Extrema

Let c be a critical number of a function f that is continuous over an interval D, the domain of f.

- If $f'(x)$ is negative for all $x < c$ and $f'(x)$ is positive for all $x > c$, then $f(c)$ is the absolute minimum of f.
- If $f'(x)$ is positive for all $x < c$ and $f'(x)$ is negative for all $x > c$, then $f(c)$ is the absolute maximum of f.

Example 2   **Using the First Derivative Test to Find the Extrema of a Function**

Determine all local extrema of $g(x) = x^3 - 6x^2 + 15$.

Solution

$$g'(x) = 3x^2 - 12x \qquad \text{Determine the derivative and factor.}$$
$$= 3x(x - 4)$$

$$3x(x - 4) = 0 \qquad \text{Find the critical numbers by setting } g'(x) = 0.$$
$$x = 0 \text{ or } x = 4$$

Critical numbers divide the domain, **R**, into three intervals. Use a table to analyze the sign of the derivative and the behaviour of the function in each interval.

	Intervals		
	$x < 0$	$0 < x < 4$	$x > 4$
$3x$	–	+	+
$x - 4$	–	–	+
$g'(x)$	(–)(–) = +	(+)(–) = –	(+)(+) = +
$g(x)$	increasing ↗	decreasing ↘	increasing ↗
	maximum at $x = 0$		minimum at $x = 4$

The sign of the derivative changes from positive to negative at $x = 0$. So $g(x)$ has a local maximum at $(0, g(0)) = (0, 15)$. The sign of the derivative changes from negative to positive at $x = 4$. So $g(x)$ has a local minimum at $(4, g(4)) = (4, -17)$.

EXAMINING THE CONCEPT

Graphing Polynomial Functions with the First Derivative Test

Graphs are important tools for understanding the behaviour of functions and the real-world phenomena that they model. Graphing technology makes analyzing easier, but it is still necessary to understand and interpret the results. The following steps will help you to envision and graph polynomial functions quickly and accurately.

Using the First Derivative Test to Graph $y = f(x)$

1. Determine the derivative, $f'(x)$. Find all critical numbers of f.

2. Substitute each critical number into $f(x)$ to find the y-coordinate of each critical point. Plot the critical points on the coordinate plane.

3. Determine where the function increases or decreases by checking the sign of the derivative on the intervals between the critical numbers.

4. Complete the graph by ensuring that
   - the graph rises on the intervals where $f'(x) > 0$
   - the graph falls where $f'(x) < 0$
   - the graph passes through the critical points
   - the graph has horizontal tangents where $f'(x) = 0$

Example 3　**Graphing a Polynomial Function Using the First Derivative Test**

Graph $f(x) = x^4 - 4x^3 + 4x^2$. Classify all extrema.

Solution

Determine the derivative and factor.

$$\begin{aligned} f'(x) &= 4x^3 - 12x^2 + 8x \\ &= 4x(x^2 - 3x + 2) \\ &= 4x(x - 2)(x - 1) \end{aligned}$$

Find the critical numbers by letting $f'(x) = 0$.

$$4x(x - 2)(x - 1) = 0$$
$$x = 0, x = 2, \text{ or } x = 1$$

Evaluate $f(x)$ at these critical numbers. So the critical points are $(0, 0)$, $(1, 1)$, and $(2, 0)$.

Apply the first derivative test to determine all maximum and minimum values.

	Intervals			
	$x < 0$	$0 < x < 1$	$1 < x < 2$	$x > 2$
$4x$	−	+	+	+
$x - 2$	−	−	−	+
$x - 1$	−	−	+	+
$f'(x)$	$(-)(-)(-) = -$	$(+)(-)(-) = +$	$(+)(-)(+) = -$	$(+)(+)(+) = +$
$f(x)$	decreasing ↘	increasing ↗	decreasing ↘	increasing ↗
	minimum at $x = 0$	maximum at $x = 1$		minimum at $x = 2$

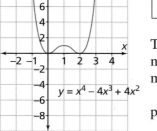

$y = x^4 - 4x^3 + 4x^2$

The first derivative test indicates that $(0, 0)$ and $(2, 0)$ correspond to local minima of $f(x)$ and that $(1, 0)$ corresponds to a local maximum. Both local minima are also absolute minima.

Because the degree of the polynomial is even and the leading coefficient is positive, $f(x) \to \infty$ as $x \to \infty$ and as $x \to -\infty$.

With this information, graph the function.

· · · · · · · ·

Example 4　**Using the First Derivative Test on a Polynomial Model**

Recall the problem in Setting the Stage.

A small rocket is launched as part of an atmospheric study. The onboard digital sensor sends back these measurements of the rocket's height at 5-s intervals.

Time (s)	0	5	10	15	20	25	30
Height (m)	1.5	754.0	1261.5	1524.0	1541.5	1314.0	841.5

What was the maximum height of the rocket?

Solution

To analyze the situation represented by the discrete data, develop an algebraic model. Use graphing technology to create a scatter plot. The points appear to fit a quadratic curve. Perform a quadratic regression to determine the equation for the curve of best fit.

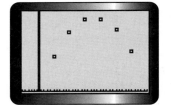

Scatter plot

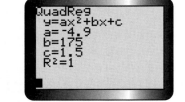

Quadratic regression

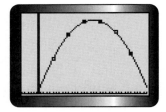

Graph of quadratic model

The equation that models the data is $f(t) = -4.9t^2 + 175t + 1.5$, where f is the height of the rocket in metres at t seconds. Both time and height can only be positive, so the model has a restricted domain: $0 \le t \le 35.72$, since $f(35.72) \doteq 0$.

Find the derivative and the critical numbers, where $f'(t) = 0$.

$$f'(t) = -9.8t + 175$$
$$0 = -9.8t + 175$$
$$t \doteq 17.86$$

Apply the first derivative test.

	Intervals	
	$0 \le t < 17.86$	$17.86 < t \le 35.72$
$-9.8t + 175$	+	−
$f'(t)$	+	−
$f(t)$	increasing ↗	decreasing ↘
	maximum at $t \doteq 17.86$	

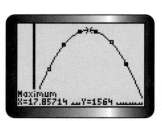

Verify this result using graphing technology.

The rocket achieves its maximum height 17.86 s into the flight. Substitute $t = 17.86$ into $f(t)$ to determine the height at that time.

$$f(17.86) = -4.9(17.86)^2 + 175(17.86) + 1.5$$
$$\doteq 1564$$

The maximum height is about 1564 m.

• • • • • • • •

Example 5   **Graphing a Function Given the Graph of the Derivative**

Consider the graph of $f'(x)$. Graph $f(x)$.

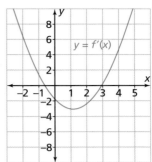

Solution

When the derivative, $f'(x)$, is positive, the graph of $f(x)$ is rising. When the derivative is negative, the graph is falling. In this example, the derivative changes sign at $x \doteq -0.6$ and again at $x \doteq 2.9$. The function $f(x)$ must have a local maximum and a local minimum at these numbers, respectively.

One possible graph of $f(x)$ is shown.

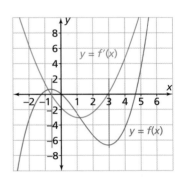

CHECK, CONSOLIDATE, COMMUNICATE

1. Explain how you can use the intervals of increase and decrease to decide whether a local maximum or a local minimum exists at a critical point.
2. Can a local maximum also be an absolute maximum? Explain.
3. A function has a local maximum. What is the sign of the derivative to the left of this value? to the right?
4. A function has a local minimum. What is the sign of the derivative to the left of this value? to the right?

KEY IDEAS

- The critical numbers of a function occur where the slope of the tangent line at the critical point is 0. The first derivative test determines whether an extremum exists at a critical point.
- **The First Derivative Test for Local Extrema**
  Let c be a critical number of a polynomial function f that is continuous over an interval I.

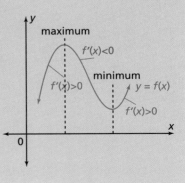

- If $f'(x)$ changes from negative to positive at c, then point $(c, f(c))$ is a local minimum of f.
- If $f'(x)$ changes from positive to negative at c, then point $(c, f(c))$ is a local maximum of f.
- If $f'(x)$ does not change sign at c, then point $(c, f(c))$ is neither a maximum nor a minimum.
- **The First Derivative Test for Absolute Extrema**
  Let c be a critical number of a function f that is continuous over an interval D, the domain of f.
  - If $f'(x)$ is negative for all $x < c$ and $f'(x)$ is positive for all $x > c$, then $f(c)$ is the absolute minimum of f.
  - If $f'(x)$ is positive for all $x < c$ and $f'(x)$ is negative for all $x > c$, then $f(c)$ is the absolute maximum of f.

4.3 Exercises

A **1.** In each graph, which curve represents $y = f(x)$ and which represents $y = f'(x)$? Explain your choice.

(a)

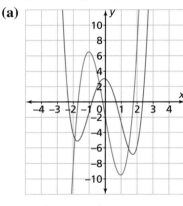

(b)

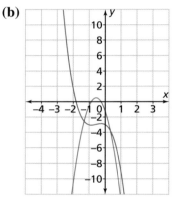

2. Each graph represents a function. Graph the derivative of each function.

(a)

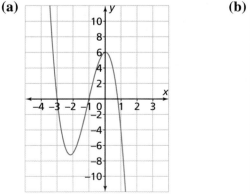

(b)

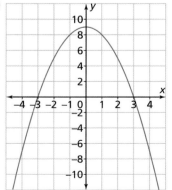

3. Each graph represents the derivative of a function. Graph a possible corresponding function.

(a)

(b)

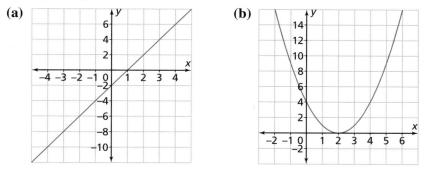

4. As x increases over an interval, $f(x)$ increases and then decreases. Describe the behaviour of $f'(x)$. Sketch a possible graph of $f(x)$. What can you conclude about $f(x)$?

5. A polynomial function has three critical numbers: $x = -2$, $x = 1$, and $x = 4$. State the intervals on the domain created by these numbers.

B 6. For each function, find the critical numbers. Use the first derivative test to identify the local maximum and minimum values.

(a) $g(x) = 2 - 6x - x^2$ (b) $g(x) = 2x^3 - 9x^2 + 12x$

(c) $g(x) = x^3 - 27x - 9$ (d) $g(x) = x^4 - 2x^2 + 10$

(e) $g(x) = 3x^4 - 4x^3 + 2$ (f) $g(x) = 4x^4 - 4x^3 - 2x^2$

(g) $g(x) = x^4 + 2x^3$ (h) $g(x) = 12x^2 - 4x^3$

7. For each function, find the critical numbers. Determine where the function increases and decreases. Decide whether each critical point represents a maximum value, a minimum value, or neither. Use this information to graph the function.

(a) $f(x) = x^2 - 4x + 5$ (b) $f(x) = 10x - x^2$

(c) $f(x) = x^3 - 3x^2 + 2$ (d) $f(x) = x^3 - 3x + 6$

(e) $f(x) = 2x^3 - 6x^2 - 18x + 3$ (f) $f(x) = 2 - x^3$

(g) $f(x) = x^4 + 4x$ (h) $f(x) = x^4 - 6x^2 - 3$

8. **Knowledge and Understanding:** For $f(x) = x^4 - 32x + 4$, find the critical numbers, the intervals on which the function increases and decreases, and all the local extrema. Use graphing technology to verify your results.

9. Sketch a graph of the function g that is differentiable on the interval $-2 \le x \le 5$, decreases on $0 < x < 3$, and increases elsewhere on the domain. The absolute maximum of g is 7 and the absolute minimum is -3. The graph of g has local extrema at $(0, 4)$ and $(3, -1)$.

10. **Communication:** Graph a quartic polynomial function that has four zeros, one absolute minimum, a different local minimum, and one local maximum.

11. Find a value of k that gives $f(x) = kx^2 - 4x + 6$ an absolute maximum at $x = -2$.

12. Find a value of k that gives $f(x) = x^2 + kx + 2$ a local minimum value of 1.

13. A publishing company uses the model $P(x) = 12x - 0.0001x^2 - 10\,000$ to estimate the profit, P, from the sale of x copies of a novel. The maximum print run for this novel is 10 000 books. How many books should be printed to maximize profit?

14. Four congruent squares are cut from the corners of a 5-cm by 8-cm piece of sheet metal. The metal is folded to form a small, open box. The volume, V, of the box is given by $V(x) = 4x^3 - 26x^2 + 40x$, where volume is measured in cubic centimetres and x is the length of each congruent square. What length x will produce a box with maximum volume?

15. **Application:** The table shows the number of students who are absent from a large high school on certain days with the flu. Using a polynomial model, determine when the absences were at a maximum and at a minimum during this two-week period.

Day	0	3	6	9	12	14
Students Away with Flu	96	204	239	172	55	32

16. **Thinking, Inquiry, Problem Solving:** During a rocket's flight, the velocity of the rocket is recorded at 1-s intervals. Use this data to model and graph the rocket's altitude versus time.

Time (s)	0	1	2	3	4	5	6	7	8	9	10
Velocity (m/s)	0	5	10	35	65	90	110	95	55	25	0

Time (s)	11	12	13	14	15	16	17	18	19	20
Velocity (m/s)	−10	−20	−30	−40	−50	−60	−70	−80	−90	0

17. **Check Your Understanding:** Does a function always have a local maximum or minimum at every critical number? Illustrate with one or more examples.

18. A rectangular pen will be built with fencing that costs $25/m. The budget for the project is $1500. What are the dimensions of the pen with the largest possible area?

19. Find the point on the graph of $f(x) = 4x^3 - 3x^2 + 2x - 3$ where the slope of the tangent line represents a minimum.

20. A farmer has 500 bushels of apples to sell to a fruit store. The highest possible price is $10 a bushel. In the past, the farmer has offered a discount of $0.50 per bushel for every 50 bushels the store buys. At what price should the farmer sell the crop to maximize revenue?

21. Find the maximum and minimum slopes of all lines tangent to $y = 2x^3 - 8x^2 + 5x - 4$.

Maria Gaëtana Agnesi
(1718–1799)

Before the 20th Century, only a few women had received credit for their mathematical contributions. Maria Agnesi was one of these women. In the 1740s she wrote a textbook that included differential and integral calculus. By 1748 she was an honorary faculty member of the University of Bologna.

ADDITIONAL ACHIEVEMENT CHART QUESTIONS

Knowledge and Understanding: For $f(x) = 3x^4 - 4x^3$,

(a) determine all critical numbers

(b) determine intervals of increase and decrease

(c) determine local maximum and minimum values

(d) graph $f(x)$

Application: The position, s, of a particle moving along a line and away from a fixed point is given by $s(t) = -2t^3 + 6t^2 - 3$, $t \geq 0$. The position is measured in metres at t seconds. Determine when the particle changes direction.

Thinking, Inquiry, Problem Solving: The graph of $f'(x)$ is shown.

(a) Determine the intervals where $f(x)$ is increasing or decreasing. What are the local extrema?

(b) Graph $f(x)$.

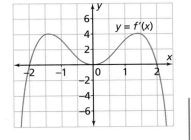

Communication: Must f have a local maximum or minimum at $x = c$ if $y = f(x)$ is differentiable at c and $f'(c) = 0$, where c is a value in the domain of f? Explain.

The Chapter Problem
Trends in Post-Secondary Education

Apply what you learned in this section to answer this question about The Chapter Problem on page 264.

CP7. Use the first derivative test to verify the existence of the local extrema you found for question CP5 using the mathematical model.

4.4 Finding Some Shortcuts— The Product Rule

SETTING THE STAGE

In section 3.6, you saw that the derivative of the sum or difference of two functions was the sum or difference of the derivatives of the two functions. Is it also true that the derivative of the product of two functions is the product of their derivatives?

Consider the function $f(x) = 10x^9$. By the power rule, $f'(x) = 90x^8$. What happens if you factor $f(x)$ and multiply the derivatives of the factors? Let $h(x) = 5x^4$ and $g(x) = 2x^5$, so that $f(x) = h(x)g(x)$.

Differentiating h and g and multiplying gives

$$h'(x)g'(x) = (20x^3)(10x^4)$$
$$= 200x^7$$

Clearly, the results are different. The derivative of a product of two functions is *not* the product of the derivatives. If $f(x) = h(x)g(x)$, then $f'(x) \neq h'(x)g'(x)$.

In this section, you will develop a rule to differentiate the product of two functions.

EXAMINING THE CONCEPT

Deriving the Product Rule

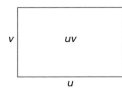

Let u and v represent the functions $f(x)$ and $g(x)$, respectively. Assume that both these functions are positive and differentiable at x. Then write the product $f(x)g(x)$ as uv.

Think of the product uv as the area of a rectangle with dimensions u by v.

Let x change by a small amount, Δx. Then $f(x)$ and $g(x)$ change to $f(x + \Delta x)$ and $g(x + \Delta x)$. In terms of u and v,

$$\Delta u = f(x + \Delta x) - f(x) \text{ and}$$
$$\Delta v = g(x + \Delta x) - g(x)$$

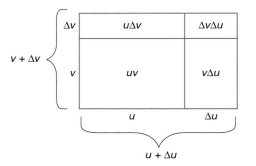

Now think of the product $(u + \Delta u)(v + \Delta v)$ as the area of the largest rectangle on the right, assuming that Δu and Δv are positive.

The change in x causes a change in the area of the original rectangle.

$$\Delta(uv) = (u + \Delta u)(v + \Delta v) - uv$$
$$= uv + u\Delta v + v\Delta u + \Delta u\Delta v - uv$$
$$= u\Delta v + v\Delta u + \Delta u\Delta v$$

Divide $\Delta(uv)$ by Δx to find the rate of change in area with respect to x.

$$\frac{\Delta(uv)}{\Delta x} = \frac{u\Delta v + v\Delta u + \Delta u\Delta v}{\Delta x}$$

$$= u\frac{\Delta v}{\Delta x} + v\frac{\Delta u}{\Delta x} + \Delta u\frac{\Delta v}{\Delta x}$$

Now let $\Delta x \to 0$ to determine an expression for the derivative of the product uv. Apply the limit laws to simplify the expression.

$$\frac{d}{dx}(uv) = \lim_{x \to 0} \frac{\Delta(uv)}{\Delta x}$$

$$= \lim_{\Delta x \to 0} \left(u\frac{\Delta v}{\Delta x} + v\frac{\Delta u}{\Delta x} + \Delta u\frac{\Delta v}{\Delta x} \right)$$

$$= u \lim_{\Delta x \to 0} \frac{\Delta v}{\Delta x} + v \lim_{\Delta x \to 0} \frac{\Delta u}{\Delta x} + \left(\lim_{\Delta x \to 0} \Delta u \right)\left(\lim_{\Delta x \to 0} \frac{\Delta v}{\Delta x} \right)$$

Apply the definition of the derivative. Since u is differentiable at x and therefore continuous, $\Delta u \to 0$ as $\Delta x \to 0$.

$$\frac{d}{dx}(uv) = u\frac{dv}{dx} + v\frac{du}{dx} + 0\left(\frac{dv}{dx} \right)$$

$$\frac{d}{dx}(uv) = u\frac{dv}{dx} + v\frac{du}{dx} \quad \text{or} \quad \frac{d}{dx}(uv) = \frac{du}{dx}v + \frac{dv}{dx}u$$

The result is known as the **product rule** for differentiable functions. Although this derivation assumed positive quantities, the result is true whether u, v, Δu, and Δv are positive or negative. Replace u with $f(x)$ and v with $g(x)$ to express the product rule in another way.

The derivative of the product of two functions is the sum of the derivative of the first function times the second function, plus the derivative of the second function times the first function.

The Product Rule

Given $h(x) = f(x)g(x)$ and $f(x)$ and $g(x)$ are both differentiable, then $h'(x) = f'(x)g(x) + g'(x)f(x)$. In Leibniz notation,

$$\frac{d[h(x)]}{dx} = \frac{d[f(x)]}{dx} \cdot g(x) + \frac{d[g(x)]}{dx} \cdot f(x)$$

Example 1   **Using the Product Rule to Find the Derivative**

Determine the derivative using the product rule.

(a) $y = 3x^4(5x^3 + 5x - 7)$ **(b)** $y = (x^4 - 4x^3 - 2x^2 + 5x + 2)^2$

Solution

(a) Use the product rule. Let $f(x) = 3x^4$ and $g(x) = 5x^3 + 5x - 7$.

$$\frac{dy}{dx} = \frac{d}{dx}[3x^4(5x^3 + 5x - 7)] \qquad \text{Apply the product rule.}$$

$$= \left[\frac{d}{dx}(3x^4)\right](5x^3 + 5x - 7) + \left[\frac{d}{dx}(5x^3 + 5x - 7)\right]3x^4$$

Differentiate polynomials.

$$= 12x^3(5x^3 + 5x - 7) + (15x^2 + 5)3x^4 \qquad \text{Expand and simplify.}$$

$$= 60x^6 + 60x^4 - 84x^3 + 45x^6 + 15x^4$$

$$= 105x^6 + 75x^4 - 84x^3$$

(b) $\quad y = (x^4 - 4x^3 - 2x^2 + 5x + 2)^2$

$$= (x^4 - 4x^3 - 2x^2 + 5x + 2)(x^4 - 4x^3 - 2x^2 + 5x + 2)$$

$$\frac{dy}{dx} = \left[\frac{d}{dx}(x^4 - 4x^3 - 2x^2 + 5x + 2)\right](x^4 - 4x^3 - 2x^2 + 5x + 2)$$

$$+ \left[\frac{d}{dx}(x^4 - 4x^3 - 2x^2 + 5x + 2)\right](x^4 - 4x^3 - 2x^2 + 5x + 2)$$

$$= (4x^3 - 12x^2 - 4x + 5)(x^4 - 4x^3 - 2x^2 + 5x + 2)$$

$$+ (4x^3 - 12x^2 - 4x + 5)(x^4 - 4x^3 - 2x^2 + 5x + 2)$$

$$= 2(x^4 - 4x^3 - 2x^2 + 5x + 2)(4x^3 - 12x^2 - 4x + 5)$$

In both parts of this example, you can also find the derivative without using the product rule. First expand the product and then simplify. Differentiate using the rules for polynomials. This method would be easier for differentiating the product in (a). You will encounter more complex functions later on, where using the product rule is the only practical way to find the derivative.

• • • • • • • •

Example 2   **Using the Product Rule to Find the Equation of a Tangent Line**

Find the equation of the tangent line to $f(x) = (2x + 4)(3x^3 - 3x^2 + x - 2)$ at point $(1, -6)$.

Solution

Differentiate to find the slope of the tangent line. You could expand first before differentiating, but it is easier to use the product rule.

$$f'(x) = \left[\frac{d}{dx}(2x + 4)\right](3x^3 - 3x^2 + x - 2) + \left[\frac{d}{dx}(3x^3 - 3x^2 + x - 2)\right](2x + 4)$$

$$= (2)(3x^3 - 3x^2 + x - 2) + (9x^2 - 6x + 1)(2x + 4)$$

The slope of the tangent line at $x = 1$ is $f'(1)$. In this case, it is easier to substitute $x = 1$ into the derivative before simplifying to obtain the slope.

$$f'(1) = (2)[3(1)^3 - 3(1)^2 + (1) - 2] + [9(1)^2 - 6(1) + 1][2(1) + 4]$$

$$= (2)(-1) + (6)(4)$$

$$= 22$$

Determine the equation by substituting $m = 22$ and point $(1, -6)$ into $y = mx + b$.

$$-6 = 22(1) + b \qquad \text{Solve for } b.$$
$$-28 = b$$

Therefore, the equation of the tangent line is $y = 22x - 28$.

● ● ● ● ● ● ● ●

Example 3 **Using the Product Rule to Graph a Function**

For $f(x) = (4x - 8)(2x^2 + 2x + 4)$, determine the critical numbers, the intervals of increase or decrease, and the extrema, then graph $f(x)$.

Solution

$$f'(x) = \left[\frac{d}{dx}(4x - 8)\right](2x^2 + 2x + 4) + \left[\frac{d}{dx}(2x^2 + 2x + 4)\right](4x - 8)$$
$$= 4(2x^2 + 2x + 4) + (4x + 2)(4x - 8)$$
$$= 24x^2 - 16x$$

To find the critical numbers, solve $f'(x) = 0$.
$$24x^2 - 16x = 0$$
$$8x(3x - 2) = 0$$
$$x = 0 \text{ or } x = \frac{2}{3}$$

	Intervals		
	$x < 0$	$0 < x < \frac{2}{3}$	$x > \frac{2}{3}$
$8x$	−	+	+
$3x - 2$	−	−	+
$f'(x)$	(−)(−) = +	(+)(−) = −	(+)(+) = +
$f(x)$	increasing ↗	decreasing ↘	increasing ↗
	maximum at $x = 0$		minimum at $x = \frac{2}{3}$

Evaluate $f(x) = (4x - 8)(2x^2 + 2x + 4)$ at the critical numbers.

$$f(0) = [4(0) - 8][2(0)^2 + 2(0) + 4]$$
$$= -32$$

$$f\left(\frac{2}{3}\right) = \left[4\left(\frac{2}{3}\right) - 8\right]\left[2\left(\frac{2}{3}\right)^2 + 2\left(\frac{2}{3}\right) + 4\right]$$
$$= -33\frac{5}{27}$$

The function has a local maximum value, $f(0) = -32$ and a local minimum value, $f\left(\frac{2}{3}\right) = -33\frac{5}{27}$. The function is decreasing for $0 < x < \frac{2}{3}$ and increasing for all other values of x, where $x \in \mathbf{R}$. With this information, graph $f(x)$.

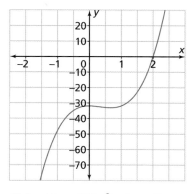

$f(x) = (4x - 8)(2x^2 + 2x + 4)$

CHECK, CONSOLIDATE, COMMUNICATE

1. State the product rule in your own words.
2. For $f(x) = (3x^2 + 5x - 4)(x - 1)$, find the derivative by using the product rule. Then find the derivative by first expanding and then differentiating the polynomial. Verify that the derivatives are the same.

KEY IDEAS

- The product rule for differentiation is summarized below.

Function Notation	Leibniz Notation
Given $h(x) = f(x)g(x)$ and f and g are both differentiable, then $h'(x) = f'(x)g(x) + g'(x)f(x)$.	Given $h(x) = f(x)g(x)$, and f and g are both differentiable, then $\frac{d}{dx}[h(x)] = \frac{d}{dx}[f(x)] \cdot g(x) + \frac{d}{dx}[g(x)] \cdot f(x)$

- In some cases, it is easier to expand and simplify the product before differentiating rather than using the product rule.

4.4 Exercises

A

1. Use the product rule to state the derivative of each function. Write your answers in unsimplified form.
   (a) $f(x) = x(x^3)$
   (b) $h(x) = 2x^2(x^2 - 2x)$
   (c) $f(x) = (3 - 2x^3)(5 + 4x)$
   (d) $y = (3x^2 + 4x - 6)(2x^2 - 9)$
   (e) $g(x) = (4x^4 - 8x^2)^2$
   (f) $y = (4x^3 - 2x^2 + 8x)(-x^2 - 5x + 3)$
2. Let $F(x) = [b(x)][c(x)]$. Express $F'(x)$ in terms of $b(x)$ and $c(x)$.
3. **(a)** Let $f(x) = 5x^4(3x^3 - 4x^2 + 6x - 7)$. Find $f'(x)$ using the product rule.
   (b) Expand $f(x)$ and then find its derivative.
   (c) Compare the results for (a) and (b).

4. (a) Let $y = (3x^2 - 7x)(-5x^2 - 8x + 3)$. Expand the expression and then find its derivative.

(b) Find $\dfrac{dy}{dx}$ using the product rule.

(c) Compare the results for (a) and (b).

B

5. Find the derivative.

(a) $f(x) = (5x^3 - 6x)(x^2 + 7)$

(b) $f(t) = (2t^2 + 4t - 5)(3t + 2)$

(c) $f(x) = (3x^2 - 6x)^2$

(d) $f(x) = x^3(x^2 - 3)(x^2 + 3)$

(e) $f(x) = 5x^{-2}(7 - x^{-3})$

(f) $f(z) = \sqrt{z}(z^4 - 2z)$

(g) $f(t) = \left(2t - t^{\frac{1}{2}}\right)\left(5t^{\frac{3}{2}} + 4t\right)$

(h) $f(z) = z^{-2}\left(z^{\frac{1}{3}} + z^{\frac{2}{3}} + 4\right)$

6. Knowledge and Understanding: For $y = (3x^3 - 2x^2 + x - 1)^2$, find $\dfrac{dy}{dx}$ without first expanding the function.

7. Given $f(x) = g(x)h(x)$, $g(x) = x$, and $h(x) = x^2$, graph $g(x)$, $h(x)$, $f(x)$, and $f'(x)$ on the same set of axes.

8. Determine the slope of the tangent line at the indicated x-value.

(a) $f(x) = (2x - x^2)(x^2 - 1)$ at $x = 1$

(b) $f(x) = (x^2 + 6x - 3)(-4x + 1)$ at $x = -2$

(c) $f(x) = (5x^3 - x)^2$ at $x = 0$

(d) $f(x) = 4x^3(x^2 - 2x + 3)$ at $x = 3$

(e) $f(x) = 2x^{-1}(6x - 2x^{-2})$ at $x = 1$

(f) $f(x) = \sqrt{x}(x^2 - 5x)$ at $x = 4$

9. Find the equation of the tangent to $y = (2x^3 - 4x + 2)(x^2 - 3x + 1)$ at point $(2, -10)$.

10. Find the intervals where $f(x) = (x^2 - 5x + 1)(6x - 2)$ is increasing and where it is decreasing. Round your answers to the nearest hundredth.

11. Determine the local maximum and minimum values of $g(x) = (3x^2 - 6x)(3x^2 + 6x)$, to the nearest hundredth.

12. Communication: Give an example to illustrate this statement: Functions f and g are increasing on an interval I, so $f \times g$ is also increasing on I.

13. Application: A 75-L gas tank has a leak. After t hours, the remaining volume, V, in litres is $V(t) = 75\left(1 - \dfrac{t}{24}\right)^2$, $0 \leq t \leq 24$. Use the product rule to determine how quickly the gas is leaking from the tank when the tank is 60% full of gas.

14. For $f(x) = (2x)(x^2 - 2x + 1)$, determine the critical numbers, the intervals where $f(x)$ is increasing or decreasing, and the extrema. Use this information to graph the function.

15. A tour operator plans to take a 60-seat bus to the next Toronto Maple Leafs home game. In the past, the trip cost $130 per person and the bus was full. Now the tour operator wants to raise the price. She estimates that, for every $5 she raises the price, she will lose two customers. The revenue, R, can be modelled by $R(x) = (130 + 5x)(60 - 2x)$, where x is the number of $5 increases.

(a) What should the ticket price be to maximize revenue?

(b) Will there be any empty seats on the bus?

16. Use the product rule to show that $\frac{d}{dx}(4x^{10}) = 40x^9$, regardless of how $4x^{10}$ is factored.

17. **Check Your Understanding:** Use an example to verify this statement: The derivative of the product of two quadratic functions does not equal the product of the derivatives of the quadratics.

Ⓒ **18. (a)** Find the points on the graph of $y = (x^2 - 4x)(x^2 + 4x)$ at which the tangents are horizontal.

(b) What is the significance of these points?

19. **Thinking, Inquiry, Problem Solving:** Prove that $y' = u'vw + uv'w + uvw'$ if $y = uvw$ and where u, v, and w are differentiable functions of x.

20. Find the equation of a line that is perpendicular, at the point of tangency, to the tangent to $f(x) = (x^3 - 2x^2)(x + 2)$ if the tangent has a slope of -4.

ADDITIONAL ACHIEVEMENT CHART QUESTIONS

Knowledge and Understanding: Let $y = (3x + 1)(x^2 + 4)$. Find $\frac{dy}{dx}$ by

(a) applying the product rule

(b) multiplying the factors first and then differentiating

Application: The function $V(x) = x(10 - 2x)(16 - 2x)$, $0 < x < 5$, models the volume of a box.

(a) Find the extreme values of V.

(b) Interpret the extreme values in terms of the volume of the box.

Thinking, Inquiry, Problem Solving: Suppose u and v are functions of x that are differentiable at $x = 2$. Also $u(2) = 3$, $u'(2) = -4$, $v(2) = 1$, and $v'(2) = 5$. Evaluate each derivative at $x = 2$.

(a) $\frac{d}{dx}(uv)$ **(b)** $\frac{d}{dx}(3u - 2v + 2uv)$

Communication: Write the product rule in words, without using any symbols.

4.5 Finding Optimal Values for Polynomial Function Models

SETTING THE STAGE

The local concert orchestra wants to raise the price of season tickets for next year. Currently, there are 760 season-ticket holders, who paid $200 each. The marketing manager estimates that, for every $10 increase in the season-ticket price, 20 subscribers will not buy a season ticket. What season-ticket price will maximize revenue?

How often do you hear or see the terms *greatest profit, lowest cost, least time, optimum size,* and *shortest distance*? An **optimization problem** requires you to find a maximum or minimum value. In this section, you will develop a strategy for solving optimization problems.

EXAMINING THE CONCEPT

Solving Optimization Problems Involving Polynomial Functions

To learn how to deal with these problems, examine the following examples.

Example 1 **Finding the Maximum Revenue**

Recall the situation in Setting the Stage. What season-ticket price will maximize revenue?

Solution

Let x represent the number of $10 increases in the season-ticket price.
Let R represent the revenue. In this problem, revenue must be maximized.

$$\text{revenue} = \text{price} \times \text{number sold}$$
$$\text{price} = 200 + 10x$$
$$\text{number sold} = 760 - 20x$$
$$R(x) = (200 + 10x)(760 - 20x)$$

Differentiate $R(x)$ using the product rule.

$$R'(x) = \left[\frac{d}{dx}(200 + 10x)\right](760 - 20x) + \left[\frac{d}{dx}(760 - 20x)\right](200 + 10x)$$
$$= (10)(760 - 20x) + (-20)(200 + 10x)$$
$$= 7600 - 200x - 4000 - 200x$$
$$= 3600 - 400x$$

To determine the critical numbers, let $R'(x) = 0$.

$$3600 - 400x = 0$$
$$x = 9$$

Use the first derivative test to verify that a maximum occurs at $x = 9$.

	Intervals	
	$0 \leq x < 9$	$x > 9$
$3600 - 400x$	$+$	$-$
$R'(x)$	$+$	$-$
$R(x)$	increasing ↗	decreasing ↘
	maximum at $x = 9$	

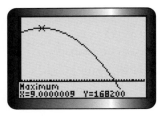

Verify this result with graphing technology.

The revenue is maximized by increasing the season ticket price by $90 to $290.

$$R(9) = [200 + 10(9)][760 - 20(9)]$$
$$= (290)(580)$$
$$= 168\ 200$$

The maximum revenue is $168 200.

• • • • • • • •

Example 2   Finding a Minimum Sum

The math club at Westlane SS held a raffle for a new graphing calculator. The winner had to answer the following skill-testing question without using a calculator:

> Find two numbers that differ by 15. Also, the sum of 5 times the larger number and the square of the smaller number is a minimum.

Solution

For this optimization problem, you need to minimize the sum of two numbers.

Let x represent the larger number and y represent the smaller number. So $y = x - 15$. Let S represent the sum to be minimized.

$$S = 5x + y^2 \qquad \text{Define } S.$$

The right side of the equation has two variables. Substitute $y = x - 15$ to re-express the right side of the equation in terms of one variable.

$$S(x) = 5x + (x - 15)^2 \qquad \text{Substitute and expand.}$$
$$= 5x + x^2 - 30x + 225$$
$$= x^2 - 25x + 225$$

To find the minimum, determine the critical numbers. Differentiate S with respect to x.

$$S'(x) = 2x - 25 \qquad \text{Solve } S'(x) = 0.$$
Then $2x - 25 = 0$
and $x = 12.5$

Use the first derivative test to confirm that the critical number is a minimum.

	Intervals	
	$x < 12.5$	$x > 12.5$
$2x - 25$	$-$	$+$
$S'(x)$	$-$	$+$
$S(x)$	decreasing ↘	increasing ↗
	minimum at $x = 12.5$	

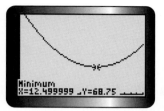

The winner was able to confirm this result using the new calculator.

So 12.5 is the larger of the two numbers. To find the other number, substitute $x = 12.5$ into $y = x - 15$. $y = 12.5 - 15$, or $y = -2.5$. So the smaller number is -2.5.

The sum of the two numbers will be a minimum if the two numbers are 12.5 and -2.5. The minimum sum is $5(12.5) + (-2.5)^2 = 68.75$.

• • • • • • • •

Examples 1 and 2 show a strategy for solving optimization problems.

Strategy for Solving Optimization Problems

1. Understand the problem.

Draw a rough sketch. List the given information and what you must find. List the mathematical concepts that could be used. Write the steps that will lead to the solution.

2. Create a mathematical model of the problem.

Draw and label a new diagram, including all the given information. Identify what you need to find. Identify the relations you will use in the problem. Name the quantity to be optimized. Choose symbols for the quantity to be maximized or minimized, M, and the other unknown quantities in the problem.

3. Plan a solution.

Express M in terms of the other unknowns in the problem. Use the given information to rewrite the original expression as a function of only one variable if the function involves more than one variable. State the domain of this function, $M = f(x)$.

4. Execute the plan.

Determine the derivative of $M = f(x)$. Find the critical numbers. Use the first derivative test to find the absolute maximum or minimum of f.

5. Interpret and evaluate the solution.

Verify that your answer is reasonable. Confirm the degree of accuracy.

6. Generalize your results.

Decide whether your solution can be used for other similar types of problems.

Example 3   **Finding the Maximum Area**

A cattle rancher has purchased five 150-m rolls of wire fencing to build a rectangular corral. She will use all of the fencing. What dimensions will produce the greatest possible area?

Solution

Draw a diagram. Let x represent the width of the corral, y the length, and A the area.

The quantity to be maximized is the area of the rectangle, $A = xy$.

x	$A = xy$

y

$$\text{perimeter} = 2(\text{width}) + 2(\text{length})$$
$$750 = 2x + 2y$$
$$y = 375 - x$$

$A = xy$ contains two variables. Use the information in the problem to eliminate one variable. In this case, the total perimeter is 750 m (5 × 150 m). Solve for y in terms of x.

$$A = x(375 - x)$$
$$= 375x - x^2$$

Substitute $y = 375 - x$ into $A = xy$.

Since A must be positive, $0 \le x \le 375$.

$$A'(x) = 375 - 2x$$
$$0 = 375 - 2x$$
$$x = 187.5$$

Locate the critical numbers.

Use the first derivative test to confirm that a maximum occurs at $x = 187.5$.

	Intervals	
	$0 \le x < 187.5$	$187.5 < x \le 375$
$375 - 2x$	+	−
$A'(x)$	+	−
$A(x)$	increasing ↗	decreasing ↘
	maximum at $x = 187.5$	

To find y, substitute $x = 187.5$ into $y = 375 - x$.

$$375 - 187.5 = 187.5$$

The area will be maximized if the length and width are both 187.5 m. The corral will be a square.

The maximum area will be $(187.5)^2$ m^2, or 35 156.25 m^2.

• • • • • • • •

Verify the answer with graphing technology.

Example 4   Finding the Maximum Volume

A carpenter is building an open box with a square base for holding firewood. The box must have a surface area of 8 m². What dimensions will yield the maximum volume?

Solution

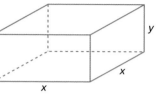

Draw a diagram. The quantity to be maximized is volume. So write an algebraic model to express the box's volume as a function of one dimension.

Let x represent the width of the box, y the height, and V the volume.

$$\text{volume} = \text{length} \times \text{width} \times \text{height}$$
$$V = (x)(x)(y)$$
$$= x^2y$$

The formula for volume contains two variables.

Eliminate one variable. Recall that the total surface area is 8 m² and

$$8 = \text{area of base} + 4(\text{area of one side})$$

Find an expression for y in terms of x.

$$8 = x^2 + 4xy \qquad \text{Solve for } y.$$
$$y = \frac{8 - x^2}{4x}$$

Substitute into the original formula for volume.

$$V = x^2\left(\frac{8 - x^2}{4x}\right)$$
$$= 2x - 0.25x^3$$

Find the critical numbers by solving $V'(x) = 0$.

All dimensions must be positive, so $x \geq 0$.

$$V'(x) = 2 - 0.75x^2$$
$$0 = 2 - 0.75x^2$$
$$x = \pm\sqrt{\frac{2}{0.75}}$$
$$\doteq 1.63$$

Use the first derivative test to confirm that a maximum occurs at $x \doteq 1.63$.

	Intervals	
	$0 \leq x < 1.63$	$x > 1.63$
$2 - 0.75x^2$	+	−
$V'(x)$	+	−
$V(x)$	increasing ↗	decreasing ↘
	maximum at $x \doteq 1.63$	

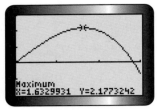

The answer can be verified with graphing technology.

To determine the height of the box, substitute $x = 1.63$ into $y = \frac{8 - x^2}{4x}$, giving $y \doteq 0.82$.

The volume is maximized when the side of the base is 1.63 m and the height is 0.82 m.

The volume is $(1.63)^2(0.82)$ m^3, or about 2.18 m^3.

• • • • • • • •

Example 5   **Finding the Maximum Surface Area**

Cindy makes a candleholder by inscribing a cylinder in a right circular cone. The height of the cone is 15 cm. The radius is 5 cm. Find the dimensions of the cylinder that will maximize its surface area.

Solution

Draw a diagram. Label the key points as shown. $AC = 15$ cm and $CD = 5$ cm.

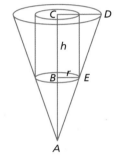

The quantity to be maximized is the surface area of the cylinder, given by

$$A = 2\pi r^2 + 2\pi rh$$

This expression contains two variables: radius, r, and height, h. Eliminate one variable. Note that $h = BC$ and $r = BE$.

$\triangle ACD$ and $\triangle ABE$ are similar, so $\frac{AB}{AC} = \frac{BE}{CD}$. Substitute the given information and simplify. $AB = 15 - h$, $BE = r$.

$$\frac{15 - h}{15} = \frac{r}{5}$$
$$h = -3r + 15$$

$$\begin{aligned} A(r) &= 2\pi r^2 + 2\pi r(-3r + 15) \\ &= -4\pi r^2 + 30\pi r \end{aligned}$$

Substitute the expression for h into the area formula.

$$\begin{aligned} A'(r) &= -8\pi r + 30\pi \\ 0 &= -8\pi r + 30\pi \\ r &= 3.75 \end{aligned}$$

Find the critical numbers by solving $A'(r) = 0$.

Use the first derivative test to confirm that the function has a maximum at $r = 3.75$.

	Intervals	
	$0 \leq r < 3.75$	$r > 3.75$
$A'(r) = -8\pi r + 30\pi$	+	−
$A(r)$	increasing ↗	decreasing ↘
	maximum at $x = 3.75$	

To determine the height of the cylinder, substitute $r = 3.75$ into $h = -3r + 15$, giving $h = 3.75$.

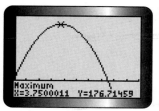

Verify the results with graphing technology.

The surface area will be maximized when the radius and the height are both 3.75 cm. Substitute these into the area formula.

$$A(3.75) = -4\pi(3.75)^2 + 30\pi(3.75)$$
$$\doteq 176.7$$

The maximum area is about 176.7 cm^2.

4.5 Exercises

A

1. Find two positive real numbers whose sum is 70 and whose product is as large as possible.

2. Find two positive real numbers such that the sum of the numbers is 100. The product of the first number and two times the second number should be as large as possible.

3. Find two integers whose difference is 22 and whose product is as small as possible.

4. Find two numbers whose sum is 190 such that the sum of the squares of the two numbers is minimized.

5. A rectangle has a perimeter of 440 cm. What dimensions maximize the rectangle's area?

6. What are the dimensions of a rectangle with an area of 64 m^2 and the smallest possible perimeter?

B 7. A rancher has 1000 m of fencing to enclose two rectangular corrals. The corrals have the same dimensions and one side in common. What dimensions will maximize the enclosed area?

8. **Knowledge and Understanding:** A farmer has 60 m of fencing to enclose a rectangular pen beside a large barn. The farmer uses the wall of the barn as one side of the fence. Find the maximum area that can be enclosed.

9. A builder owns four rectangular building lots, each with an area of 480 m^2. The building lots are beside one another. The builder plans to subdivide the lots. What should be the dimensions of the lots to minimize the fencing cost? The side and back fencing costs $15/m, while the front fencing costs $20/m. The lots must all have the same area.

10. Tom makes an open box from a rectangular piece of metal by cutting equal squares from the four corners and turning up the sides. The piece of metal measures 60 cm by 100 cm. What are the dimensions of the box with the maximum volume?

11. A net enclosure for practising golf shots is open at one end, as shown. Find the dimensions that minimize the amount of netting and that give a volume of 144 m^3. (Netting is required only on the sides, the top, and the far end.)

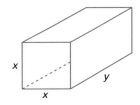

12. Sandy will make a closed rectangular jewellery box with a square base from two different woods. The wood for the top and bottom costs $20/m^2. The wood for the sides costs $30/m^2. Find the dimensions that minimize the wood costs for a volume of 4000 cm^3.

13. **Communication:** Explain to a fellow student how you would find an algebraic model for the following problem: Marie-Hélène makes an open box from a piece of cardboard by cutting equal squares out of all four corners and turning up the sides. The piece of cardboard measures 60 cm by 60 cm. What are the dimensions of each square so that the finished box has maximum volume? (Do not solve the problem yourself.)

14. What is the maximum volume of a right cylinder that has a total surface area of 384π cm^2?

15. A cylindrical can holds 500 mL of sliced peaches. Determine the measurements of the radius and height that minimize the surface area of the can.

16. Use the fact that 355 mL = 355 cm^3 to find the dimensions of the 355-mL soft drink can with the least amount of metal. Compare your results with the dimensions of an actual soft drink can. Suggest some reasons for the differences.

17. **Application:** Mark will make an open rectangular box with a square base from two different materials. The material for the bottom costs $3/m^2. The material for the sides costs $2/m^2. Find the dimensions of the box with the maximum volume that Mark can make for $120.

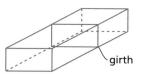

18. Suppose that a courier accepts packages only if the sum of the length and the girth is no more than 300 cm. The girth is the perimeter of the cross section of the package. What is the maximum volume of an acceptable rectangular box with a square cross section?

19. A rectangle with a perimeter of 40 cm is rotated around one of its sides, creating a right cylinder. What is the largest possible volume for this cylinder?

20. An electronics store is selling personal CD players. The regular price for each CD player is $90. During a typical two weeks, the store sells 50 units. Past sales indicate that, for every $1 decrease in price, the store sells five more units during two weeks. Calculate the price that will maximize revenue.

21. Paul is organizing a bus trip to Copps Coliseum in Hamilton. He charges $100 for each ticket. He usually sells 50 tickets. Paul is thinking about reducing the ticket price. He estimates that each $2 decrease will generate one more ticket sale. What should be the ticket price to maximize revenue for this concert?

22. A professional basketball team plays in an arena that holds 20 000 spectators. Average attendance at each game has been 14 000. The average ticket price is $75. Market research shows that, for each $5 reduction in the ticket price, attendance increases by 800. Find the price that will maximize revenue.

23. The landlord of a 40-unit apartment building is planning to increase the rent. Currently residents pay $700/month. Four units are vacant. A real estate agency has found that, in this market, every $25 increase in monthly rent results in one more vacant unit. What rent should the landlord charge to maximize revenue?

24. The right triangle represents a lot with the dimensions shown. Doug wants to build and fence a rectangular dog kennel inside this lot. What is the maximum possible area for the kennel?

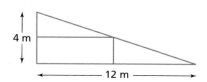

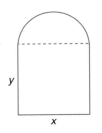

Norman window

25. This Norman window is made up of a semicircle and a rectangle. The total perimeter of the window is 16 m. What is the maximum area?

26. **Thinking, Inquiry, Problem Solving:** A piece of wire 75 m long is divided into two pieces. One piece is used to form a circle. The other piece is used to make a square. Find the lengths of the pieces that minimize the total area of the circle and square.

27. **Check Your Understanding:** List the steps for solving an optimization problem. Describe each step.

C 28. A picture window is in the shape of an equilateral triangle. Each side measures 4 m. Celia will glue a rectangular piece of stained glass on the window so that one side of the rectangle lies on the base of the triangle. Determine the maximum area for the piece of stained glass.

29. What is the maximum volume of a cylinder that can be inscribed in a right cone? The height of the cone is 30 cm and its base is 20 cm.

30. A cylinder is inscribed in a sphere with radius 10 cm. What are the dimensions of the cylinder if its volume is maximized?

ADDITIONAL ACHIEVEMENT CHART QUESTIONS

Knowledge and Understanding: The sum of two positive numbers is 8. Find the minimum value of the sum of the square of one number and the cube of the other number.

Application: A closed rectangular container with a square base must have a volume of 2250 m³. The material for the top and bottom sides of the container will cost $2/m². The material for the sides will cost $3/m². Find the dimensions of the container so that the costs of these materials is minimized.

Thinking, Inquiry, Problem Solving: A piece of cardboard measures 10 cm by 15 cm. Two equal squares, each with sides x centimetres long, are removed from two corners of the side of the piece which measures 10 cm, as shown. Two equal rectangles are removed from the other corners so that the tabs can be folded to form a rectangular box with a lid.

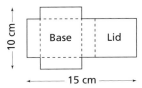

(a) Write a formula for the volume, $V(x)$, of the box.

(b) Find the domain of V for this problem. Graph V over this domain.

(c) Use a graph to find the maximum volume of the box. Also find the value of x that gives the maximum volume.

(d) Confirm the maximum volume and the value of x analytically.

Communication: Show that the dimensions that minimize the surface area of a square-based prism with a fixed volume are equal.

4.6 Rates of Change in Business and Economics

SETTING THE STAGE

In everyday life, a rate of change is usually measured in terms of time. Economists and businesspeople use rates of change as well. Profit, revenue, demand, and price are rates of change that are measured in terms of the number of units produced or sold. The **marginal rate** is also a rate of change, or a derivative.

In this section, you will examine business applications that involve marginal analysis, or analyzing the unit rates of change for profit, revenue, and cost.

EXAMINING THE CONCEPT

The Business Model

Recall the three basic functions for modelling the manufacture of a product.

The Basic Business Model

cost	$C(x)$ = total cost of producing x units
revenue	$R(x)$ = total revenue from the sale of x units
	= (price per unit) $\times x$
profit	$P(x)$ = total profit from the sale of x units
profit = revenue − cost	$P(x) = R(x) - C(x)$

In practice, the price of an item influences the quantity that consumers are willing to buy. The lower the price, the more consumers will buy. The **demand function**, p, is the price at which x units can be sold. Therefore, the revenue function can also be expressed as $R(x) = px$, the product of the demand function and the number of items sold.

Example 1   Defining the Business Functions

A cosmetic company sells 2000 bottles of nail polish a month at a price of $10 each. The company believes that sales will increase by 250 bottles for each $0.25 decrease in price.

(a) Find the demand function.

(b) The model of the cost, C, of producing x bottles is
$C(x) = -0.003x^2 + 9.215x + 5500$. What is the profit function?

(c) How many bottles must the company sell each month to make a profit?

Solution

(a) For each $0.25 decrease in price p from the original $10, the quantity sold, x, increases by 250 from the original 2000. Sales are a function of price.

$$x = 2000 + 250\left(\frac{10 - p}{0.25}\right)$$

$$x = 2000 + 1000(10 - p) \qquad \text{Expand.}$$
$$x = 12\,000 - 1000p \qquad \text{Solve for } p.$$
$$p = 12 - 0.001x$$

(b) profit = revenue − cost
$$P(x) = R(x) - C(x)$$
$$= px - C(x)$$
$$= (12 - 0.001x)x - (-0.003x^2 + 9.215x + 5500)$$
$$= 12x - 0.001x^2 + 0.003x^2 - 9.215x - 5500$$
$$= 0.002x^2 + 2.785x - 5500$$

(c) The company makes a profit when the profit function is positive. So, $P(x) = 0.002x^2 + 2.785x - 5500 > 0$.

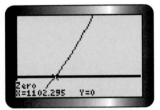

Zero
X=1102.295   Y=0

Solve for x by graphing the function. Note where the x-values are positive. The graph shows that the company will make a profit if more than 1102 bottles are sold each month.

To find the solution algebraically, note that profit changes from negative to positive when cost equals revenue: $C(x) = R(x)$. Substitute the functions for cost and revenue in this equation. Solve using the quadratic formula.

$$-0.003x^2 + 9.215x + 5500 = 12x - 0.001x^2$$
$$0.002x^2 + 2.785x - 5500 = 0$$
$$x = \frac{-2.785 \pm \sqrt{(2.785)^2 - 4(0.002)(-5500)}}{2(0.002)}$$
$$x \doteq -2494.8 \text{ or } x \doteq 1102.3$$

Since x, the quantity sold, must be positive, the company makes a profit if more than 1102 bottles of nail polish are sold.

• • • • • • • •

Definition of the Break-Even Point

At the **break-even point**, profit changes from negative to positive, or vice versa. So, at the break-even point, $P(x) = 0$ and $C(x) = R(x)$.

EXAMINING THE CONCEPT

Marginal Profit, Marginal Revenue, Marginal Cost

These items are the rates of change of profit, revenue, and cost, respectively, of the number of units produced or sold. Use the derivative of each business function to calculate each rate of change.

Marginal cost: $\dfrac{dC}{dx} \doteq$ change in cost of producing one more unit

Marginal revenue: $\dfrac{dR}{dx} \doteq$ change in revenue from selling one more unit

Marginal profit: $\dfrac{dP}{dx} \doteq$ change in profit from selling one more unit

Example 2   **Finding the Marginal Cost**

A maker of penicillin uses $C(x) = 500\,000 + 80x + 0.003x^2$ to model the cost of producing x units of penicillin.

(a) Find the marginal cost at a production level of 10 000 units.

(b) Compare this marginal cost to the difference between the cost of producing 10 000 units and the cost of producing 10 001 units.

Solution

(a) First differentiate.

$$\frac{dC}{dx} = \frac{d}{dx}(500\,000 + 80x + 0.003x^2)$$
$$= 80 + 0.006x$$

The marginal cost at $x = 10\,000$ is

$$\left.\frac{dC}{dx}\right|_{x\,=\,10\,000} = 80 + 0.006(10\,000)$$
$$= 140$$

At $x = 10\,000$, the marginal cost is $140.

(b) For production quantities of 10 000 and 10 001, the actual cost is shown.

$$C(10\,000) = 500\,000 + 80(10\,000) - 0.003(10\,000)$$
$$= \$1\,600\,000$$

$$C(10\,001) = 500\,000 + 80(10\,001) - 0.003(10\,001)$$
$$= \$1\,600\,140.003$$

The cost to produce one more unit, that is, the 10 001th unit, is $1\,600\,140.003 - \$1\,600\,000 = \$140.003$.

• • • • • • • •

Example 3   **Finding the Marginal Revenue**

A fast-food restaurant finds that the demand function, p, based on the monthly sales of x chicken sandwiches is $p = \dfrac{30\,000 - x}{15\,000}$.
What is the marginal revenue for monthly sales of 5000 sandwiches?

Solution
revenue = price $\times$ number sold

$$R(x) = px$$
$$= \left(\frac{30\,000 - x}{15\,000}\right)x$$
$$= 2x - \frac{x^2}{15\,000}$$

To find marginal revenue, determine $R'(x)$.

$$R'(x) = \frac{d}{dx}\left(2x - \frac{x^2}{15\,000}\right)$$
$$= 2 - \frac{2x}{15\,000}$$
$$= 2 - \frac{x}{7500}$$

Evaluate $R'(5000)$.

$$R'(5000) = 2 - \frac{5000}{7500}$$
$$\doteq 1.33$$

For monthly sales of 5000, the revenue increases by about $1.33 per sandwich.

• • • • • • • •

Example 4   Finding the Marginal Profit

At the restaurant in Example 3, the monthly total costs of producing x chicken sandwiches can be modelled by $C(x) = 3500 + 0.76x$. Find the total profit and the marginal profit for 5000, 9300, and 13 000 sandwiches.

Solution

Using the revenue function in Example 3 and $P(x) = R(x) - C(x)$,

• the profit function is $P(x) = 2x - \frac{x^2}{15\,000} - (3500 + 0.76x)$, or
$$P(x) = -\frac{x^2}{15\,000} + 1.24x - 3500$$

• the marginal profit function is $P'(x) = 1.24 - \frac{x}{7500}$

The table shows the profit and marginal profit for the specified demand levels. (The values for marginal profit have been rounded to the nearest hundredth.)

Demand, x (sandwiches/month)	5 000	9 300	13 000
Profit, $P(x)$ ($)	1033.33	2266.00	1353.33
Marginal Profit, $P'(x)$	0.57	0.00	−0.49

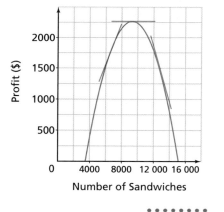

Graph the profit function,

$$P(x) = -\frac{x^2}{15\,000} + 1.24x - 3500$$

The maximum profit occurs when the marginal profit is 0.

When more than 9300 sandwiches are sold, the marginal profit is negative. So producing more than 9300 sandwiches will reduce the profit instead of increasing it!

• • • • • • • •

Example 5   Finding the Maximum Profit

Outdoors Inc. produces handmade wooden kayaks. The owner, who is also the only employee, has determined that $C(x) = 5.125x^2 + 2x + 1500$ models the total costs of making x kayaks. The price is modelled by $p = 1750 - 20x$. What number of kayaks will maximize profits?

Solution

$$P(x) = R(x) - C(x)$$

Expand and simplify the profit function.

$$= px - C(x)$$
$$= (1750 - 20x)x - (5.125x^2 + 2x + 1500)$$
$$= -25.125x^2 + 1748x - 1500$$

$$P'(x) = -50.25x + 1748$$
$$0 = -50.25x + 1748$$
$$x \doteq 34.8$$

Profit is maximized when the marginal profit is 0. Set $P'(x) = 0$ and solve to find the critical numbers.

Apply the first derivative test to ensure that the value at $x = 34.8$ is a maximum.

	Intervals	
	$0 \leq x < 34.8$	$x > 34.8$
$P'(x) = -50.25x + 1748$	+	−
$P(x)$	increasing ↗	decreasing ↘
	maximum at $x = 34.8$	

Outdoors Inc. can maximize profits by making 35 kayaks.

• • • • • • • •

Maximum profit occurs when the marginal revenue equals the marginal cost, that is, when $R'(x) = C'(x)$.

In Example 5, the derivative of the profit function was set to 0 to determine the production level for maximizing profit. Since $P(x) = R(x) - C(x)$, then $P'(x) = R'(x) - C'(x)$, by the difference rule. So $P'(x) = 0$ and $R'(x) - C'(x) = 0$ for maximum profits. Then $R'(x) = C'(x)$.

Businesspeople obviously want to maximize profits, but they also want to reduce production costs. Recall that the average cost of producing an item is

$$\text{average cost} = AC(x)$$
$$= \frac{C(x)}{x}$$

Example 6   **Minimizing Average Cost**

A mountain bike company finds that its cost function is $C(x) = 0.25x^2 + 8x + 3250$ for the Extreme model. What production level minimizes the average cost?

Solution

State and simplify the average cost function, $AC(x)$.

$$AC(x) = \frac{C(x)}{x}$$
$$= \frac{0.25x^2 + 8x + 3250}{x}$$
$$= 0.25x + 8 + 3250x^{-1}$$

Find the derivative and solve $AC'(x) = 0$ to locate the critical numbers.
The number of bikes, x, must be positive, $x \geq 0$.

$$AC'(x) = 0.25 - 3250x^{-2}$$
$$0 = 0.25 - 3250x^{-2}$$
$$\frac{3250}{x^2} = 0.25$$
$$3250 = 0.25x^2$$
$$13\,000 = x^2, x > 0$$
$$114 \doteq x$$

Apply the first derivative test to ensure that the value at $x = 114$ is a minimum.

	Intervals	
	$0 \leq x < 114$	$x > 114$
$\overline{C}'(x) = 0.25 - 3250x^{-2}$	−	+
$\overline{C}'(x)$	decreasing ↘	increasing ↗
	minimum at $x = 114$	

The average cost is minimized when 114 bikes are produced.

CHECK, CONSOLIDATE, COMMUNICATE

1. What does the term *marginal* mean in an economics application?
2. What rate of change does the marginal profit measure?
3. In terms of marginal rates, when does a company break even?
4. When does a company realize maximum profit?

KEY IDEAS

- In terms of producing and selling x units, profit = revenue − cost or $P(x) = R(x) - C(x)$.
- The demand function p defines the relation between the number of units produced or sold, x, and the selling price. Since revenue = price × number of units, $R(x) = px$.
- Marginal profit, marginal cost, and marginal revenue are rates of change with respect to the number of units produced or sold. As a result, they are the derivatives of their respective functions.
- Marginals approximate the extra profit, cost, or revenue associated with the sale or production of one more unit.
- A company breaks even when the revenue from sales equals the cost of production: $R(x) = C(x)$.
- A company realizes maximum profit when the marginal revenue equals the marginal cost: $R'(x) = C'(x)$.

A

1. You are given the cost, $C(x)$, of producing x units of some article and the selling price, p, when x units are produced. Find the revenue function, the profit function, and the average cost function.

Cost Function	Demand Function
(a) $C(x) = 150 + 25x$	$p = 60 - x$
(b) $C(x) = 2500x + 4500$	$p = 5000 - 0.6x^2$
(c) $C(x) = 3000 - 30x + 0.03x^2$	$p = 50 - 0.025x$
(d) $C(x) = 5350 - 45x + 0.05x^2$	$p = 155 - 0.75x$

2. For each business model in question 1, find the marginal cost function, the marginal revenue function, and the marginal profit function.

3. For each case, find the demand function and the restriction on x, where x is the number of items sold.

   (a) A business sells 1000 items a month for $25 each. Research shows monthly sales will increase by 100 items for each $1 decrease in price.

   (b) The Sub Shack sells, on average, 2000 subs each month for $6.00 each. The manager estimates sales will increase by 150 subs for each $0.50 decrease in price.

   (c) The CD Xchange sells about 1500 used CDs each month at a price of $5.00 each. The manager thinks that sales will increase by 30 CDs for each $0.25 decrease in price.

4. For each demand function you found for question 3, find the revenue function and the marginal revenue function.

B

5. A paint company estimates that the cost in dollars, C, of producing x litres of paint per day is $C(x) = 0.0004x^2 + 2x + 2000$.

   (a) Find the marginal cost if 1000 L is produced one day.

   (b) Determine the daily production level that minimizes the average cost.

6. Pizza Express uses $R(x) = 900x - 0.1x^2$ to estimate the monthly revenue in dollars from selling a total of x pizzas at their three locations.

   (a) Find the marginal revenue from selling 3000 pizzas.

   (b) Determine the monthly sales that will maximize revenue.

7. XYZ Sports models the monthly profit in dollars from selling x pairs of cross-training shoes with $P(x) = -2.5x^2 + 5500x + 3000$.

   (a) Find the marginal profit on the sale of 1000 pairs of shoes.

   (b) Determine the monthly sales that will maximize profits.

8. A manufacturer of electronic organizers can make and sell x thousand units if the price, p, in dollars is $p = 600 - 3x$. The manufacturing cost, C, in dollars can be modelled by $C(x) = 8\,000\,000 + 200\,000x + 1000x^2$.

(a) Determine the revenue function.

(b) Determine the profit function.

(c) Calculate the profit on the sale of 30 000 organizers.

(d) Calculate the marginal profit on the sale of 49 000 organizers.

(e) Calculate the maximum profit and the sales needed to realize this profit.

9. **Knowledge and Understanding:** The cost function, C, to produce x thousand units of a product is $C(x) = 100x^2 + 1500x + 50\,000$. The demand function is $p = 50 - x$. Determine the number of units that

(a) corresponds to the minimum average cost

(b) must be sold to maximize profits

10. Through market research, a computer manufacturer found that x thousand units of its new laptop will sell at a price of $2000 - 5x$ dollars per unit. The cost, C, in dollars of producing this many units is $C(x) = 15\,000\,000 + 1\,800\,000x + 75x^2$. Determine the level of sales that will maximize profit.

11. **Communication:** The marginal profit changes from positive to negative on the sale of the $(x + 1)$th unit. What does this change imply about the overall profits of the company? Explain.

12. A manufacturer of designer purses models the monthly production costs, C, in dollars of x purses using $C(x) = 12\,000 + 300x + 0.02x^2$. What production level will minimize the average cost of each purse?

13. An amateur theatre company offers a group discount for its evening performances. For every person in a group of 30 or more, the ticket price decreases by $1.50 from the regular price of $24.00. Determine the size of group that maximizes revenue.

14. A local furniture manufacturer sells cedar patio sets. The company can sell x units each month at price $p = 1000 - x$ in dollars, where the cost, C, of producing x units per day is $C(x) = 3000 + 19x^2$. Determine **(a)** the break-even point and **(b)** the price that will maximize profits.

15. **Application:** A real estate office manages 50 apartments in a downtown building. When the rent is $900 per month, all the units are occupied. For every $25 increase in rent, one unit becomes vacant. On average, each unit requires $75 in maintenance and repairs each month. How much rent should the real estate office charge to maximize profits?

16. The profit of a chewing-gum manufacturer is related to the amount spent on advertising, x, in thousands of dollars by $P(x) = 5500 + 35x - 0.25x^2$. What should the company spend on advertising to maximize its profit?

17. The cost per unit to produce a CD player is $50. The manufacturer charges $85 per unit for orders of 100 or less. To encourage large orders, the manufacturer reduces the price by $0.50 per unit for orders in excess of 100. Determine the order size that maximizes **(a)** revenue and **(b)** profit.

18. EastJet flies an airliner that seats 190 passengers from Sudbury to Ottawa. The ticket price in dollars, p, is $p = 320 - x$ when x seats are sold.

    (a) What price should be advertised to maximize revenue?

    (b) At this price, what percent of the seats will be empty?

19. **Thinking, Inquiry, Problem Solving:** A pharmaceutical company sells an antibiotic in bulk at a price of $75 per unit. The daily production cost in dollars for x units is $C(x) = 100\ 000 + 60x + 0.0025x^2$. The daily production capacity is 2500 units. Should the company adjust this amount? Justify your answer.

20. **Check Your Understanding:** A company estimates that the cost, C, in dollars of producing x units of their product is $C(x) = 500 + 0.5x + 0.002x^2 + 0.0001x^3$. Find the production level that minimizes the average cost.

21. A business manager estimates that $x = 350 - 10p$ units of a product will be sold when the product sells for a price of p dollars. At this level of production, the average cost is modelled by $C(x) = 5 + 0.05x$. What price would maximize profits?

ADDITIONAL ACHIEVEMENT CHART QUESTIONS

Knowledge and Understanding: A firm can sell x units of its product daily at p dollars per unit, where $x = 1000 - p$. The cost, C, of producing x units per day is $C(x) = 3000 + 20x$.

(a) Find the revenue function, $R(x)$.

(b) Find the profit function, $P(x)$.

(c) Assume that maximum production capacity is 500 units per day. How many units must the company produce and sell each day to maximize the profit?

(d) Find the maximum profit.

(e) What price per unit must be charged to obtain the maximum profit?

Application: Suppose you own a 30-unit motel. All units are occupied when you charge $20 a day per unit. For every increase of x dollars in the daily rate, x units are vacant. Each occupied room costs $2 per day to service and maintain. What should you charge per unit to maximize profit?

Thinking, Inquiry, Problem Solving: Prove that the production level at which the average cost is smallest is a level at which the average cost equals the marginal cost.

Communication: The price per unit to charge for a maximum profit is x dollars. Explain how **(a)** an increase and **(b)** a decrease in price creates less profit.

4.7 Sketching Graphs of Polynomial Functions: Concavity

SETTING THE STAGE

> **Explore the concepts in this lesson in more detail using Exploration 7 on page 572.**

The sign of the first derivative of a function, $f'(x)$, tells where the function is increasing and decreasing. For $f'(x) > 0$, the function is increasing and the graph of $f(x)$ is rising. For $f'(x) < 0$, the function is decreasing and the graph of $f(x)$ is falling. You have used the first derivative test to help graph a polynomial function, with critical points and the extrema.

But what is the shape of the curve at the extrema?

In this section, you will examine **concavity**, or curvature, of the function's graph, using the second derivative.

EXAMINING THE CONCEPT

Concavity

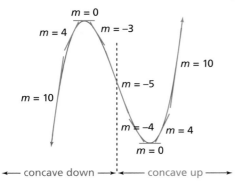

The portion of the graph that is cupped up is **concave up** on an interval. The portion that is cupped down is **concave down** on an interval.

Examine the slopes of the tangents to the curve where the graph is concave down. The slopes 10, 4, 0, and -3 are *decreasing*.

Examine the slopes of the tangents to the curve where the graph is concave up. The slopes -4, 0, 4, and 10 are *increasing*.

The slope of each tangent is the first derivative, f'. So the graph of f is concave up if f' is increasing and concave down if f' is decreasing.

Graphically, the portion of the curve that is concave up lies above all tangent lines. The portion of the curve that is concave down lies below all tangent lines.

Definition of Concavity

Let f be a differentiable function on an open interval I. The graph of f is **concave up** on I if f' is increasing on the interval. The graph of f is **concave down** on I if f' is decreasing.

To determine concavity without seeing a graph, we need an analytic test for finding the intervals on which the derivative is increasing or decreasing. It turns out that we can use the second derivative to determine the intervals in which f' is increasing or decreasing, just as we used the first derivative to determine the intervals in which f is increasing or decreasing.

Test for Concavity

Let $f(x)$ be a differentiable function whose second derivative exists on an open interval I.

1. The graph of $f(x)$ is concave up if $f''(x) > 0$ for all x in I.
2. The graph of $f(x)$ is concave down if $f''(x) < 0$ for all x in I.

A portion of a function can be concave up or down and either increasing or decreasing at the same time. Here are the four possible cases.

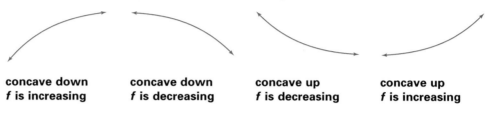

concave down
f is increasing

concave down
f is decreasing

concave up
f is decreasing

concave up
f is increasing

Example 1 **Concavity of a Polynomial Function**

Determine where the graph of the function $f(x) = x^3 + 5x - 2$ is concave up and concave down. Sketch the graph.

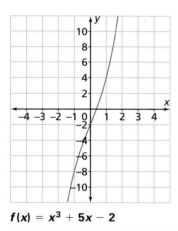

$f(x) = x^3 + 5x - 2$

Solution

$f(x) = x^3 + 5x - 2$, $f'(x) = 3x^2 + 5$, and $f''(x) = 6x$.

The graph of f is concave up when $f''(x) > 0$, $6x > 0$, or $x > 0$.

The graph of f is concave down when $f''(x) < 0$, $6x < 0$, or $x < 0$.

Also, $f'(x) > 0$ for all x, so f is increasing.
The y-intercept is -2, since $f(0) = -2$.

Now graph f.

EXAMINING THE CONCEPT

Points of Inflection

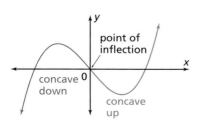

Definition of a Point of Inflection

For any function, a point where the concavity changes—from concave up to concave down or vice versa—is called a **point of inflection**.

At the point of inflection, the slope of the tangent to the derivative changes from increasing to decreasing, or vice versa. So, at the point of inflection, the slope of the tangent line to the first derivative is 0 and the tangent is horizontal. $(f'(x))' = f''(x) = 0$. The second derivative must be 0.

Points of Inflection of a Polynomial Function

A point of inflection is a point on the graph of function $f(x)$ where $f(x)$ changes from concave up to concave down or vice versa. Let $(c, f(c))$ be a point of inflection on the graph of a polynomial function f. Then $f''(c) = 0$ provided that $f''(c)$ exists.

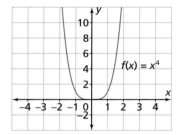

The fact that $f''(x) = 0$ does not mean that $(x, f(x))$ is an inflection point. Even if $f''(x) = 0$ for the continuous function f, there may be no inflection point.

Consider $f(x) = x^4$ at $x = 0$. The second derivative is $f''(x) = 12x^2$ and $f''(0) = 0$. But, at point $(0, 0)$, the concavity does not change. In fact, f is concave up for all real x.

Example 2 Finding the Intervals of Concavity and Points of Inflection

Determine the points of inflection and the intervals of concavity for the graph of $f(x) = 2x^4 - 4x^3$.

Solution

$$f(x) = 2x^4 - 4x^3$$
$$f'(x) = 8x^3 - 12x^2$$
$$f''(x) = 24x^2 - 24x$$
$$= 24x(x - 1)$$

Find $f''(x)$ and factor it.

$$24x(x - 1) = 0$$
$$x = 0 \text{ or } x = 1$$

Solve $f''(x) = 0$ to identify possible inflection points.

Inflection points may occur at $x = 0$ or $x = 1$. Create a table to analyze the second derivative on the three intervals defined by these x-values.

	Intervals		
	$x < 0$	$0 < x < 1$	$x > 1$
$24x$	−	+	+
$x - 1$	−	−	+
$f''(x) = 24x(x - 1)$	$(-)(-) = +$	$(+)(-) = -$	$(+)(+) = +$
$f(x)$	concave up	concave down	concave up
	inflection point at $x = 0$	inflection point at $x = 1$	

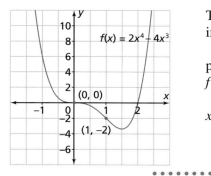

$f(x) = 2x^4 - 4x^3$

(0, 0)

(1, -2)

The graph of the function changes concavity at the two points of inflection, (0, 0) and (1, −2).

Since the degree of $f(x)$ is even and the leading coefficient is positive, the end behaviours are the same. As $x \to \infty$ and $x \to -\infty$, $f(x) \to \infty$.

The table shows that the graph of f is concave up when $x < 0$ and $x > 1$. The graph is concave down when $0 < x < 1$.

• • • • • • • •

Example 3 **Intervals of Concavity, Points of Inflection, and Curve Sketching**

Determine the intervals of increase and decrease, the local maximum and minimum values, the intervals of concavity, and the inflection points, then graph $f(x) = 8x^5 - 5x^4 - 20x^3$.

Solution

$$f'(x) = 40x^4 - 20x^3 - 60x^2 \quad \text{Determine the first derivative, and factor.}$$
$$= 20x^2(x + 1)(2x - 3)$$

$$0 = 20x^2(x + 1)(2x - 3) \quad \text{To find all critical numbers, solve } f'(x) = 0.$$
$$x = 0, x = -1, \text{ or } x = 1.5$$

Apply the first derivative test to determine the local maxima.

	Intervals			
	$x < -1$	$-1 < x < 0$	$0 < x < 1.5$	$x > 1.5$
$20x^2$	+	+	+	+
$x + 1$	−	+	+	+
$2x - 3$	−	−	−	+
$f'(x)$	(+)(−)(−) = +	(+)(+)(−) = −	(+)(+)(−) = −	(+)(+)(+) = +
$f(x)$	increasing ↗	decreasing ↘	decreasing ↘	increasing ↗
	maximum at $x = -1$		minimum at $x = 1.5$	

The function has a local maximum at $f(-1) = 7$ and a local minimum at $f(1.5) = -32.1$. The function is increasing on $x < -1$ and $x > 1.5$, and is decreasing on $-1 < x < 1.5$.

Now analyze the second derivative.

$$f''(x) = 160x^3 - 60x^2 - 120x$$
$$= 20x(8x^2 - 3x - 6)$$

Determine the second derivative, and factor.

$$0 = 20x(8x^2 - 3x - 6)$$
$$x = 0 \text{ or } 8x^2 - 3x - 6 = 0$$

To find where the graph changes concavity, solve $f''(x) = 0$.

Use the quadratic formula to solve $8x^2 - 3x - 6 = 0$.

$$x = \frac{3 \pm \sqrt{(-3)^2 - 4(8)(-6)}}{2(8)}$$

$$x \doteq 1.07 \text{ or } x \doteq -0.70$$

$f''(x) = 0$ when $x = -0.70$, 0, or 1.07. Use a table to analyze the second derivative on the associated intervals.

	Intervals			
	$x < -0.70$	$-0.70 < x < 0$	$0 < x < 1.07$	$x > 1.07$
$20x$	$-$	$-$	$+$	$+$
$8x^2 - 3x - 6$	$+$	$-$	$-$	$+$
$f''(x)$	$(-)(+) = -$	$(-)(-) = +$	$(+)(-) = -$	$(+)(+) = +$
$f(x)$	concave down	concave up	concave down	concave up
	inflection point at $x = -0.70$	inflection point at $x = 0$	inflection point at $x = 1.07$	

$f(x) = 8x^5 - 5x^4 - 20x^3$

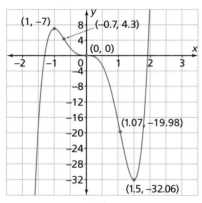

The inflection points are $(-0.70, 4.30)$, $(0, 0)$, and $(1.07, -19.98)$.

The graph of f is concave down on the intervals $x < -0.70$ and $0 < x < 1.07$. It is concave up on the intervals $-0.70 < x < 0$ and $x > 1.07$.

The y-intercept is 0. Since $f(x)$ is an odd-degree polynomial with a positive leading coefficient, the end behaviours are opposite: as $x \to -\infty, f(x) \to -\infty$, and, as $x \to \infty, f(x) \to \infty$.

Plot the points of inflection and the critical points. Then use the intervals of increase and decrease, as well as the intervals of concavity, to sketch the graph.

EXAMINING THE CONCEPT

The Second Derivative Test

The second derivative can be used to locate local maximum and minimum values of a function. Function $f(x)$ must have a local minimum at c if the graph of $f(x)$ is concave up on an interval that contains c and $f'(c) = 0$. Similarly, $f(x)$ must have a local maximum at c if $f(x)$ is concave down on an interval containing c and $f'(c) = 0$.

The Second Derivative Test

For function $f(x)$, where $f'(c) = 0$ and the second derivative, $f''(x)$, exists on an interval containing c:

- If $f''(c) > 0$, then $f(c)$ is a local minimum value.
- If $f''(c) < 0$, then $f(c)$ is a local maximum value.
- If $f''(c) = 0$, then the test fails. Then use the first derivative test.

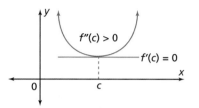

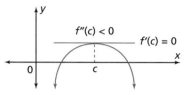

f is concave up; (c, f(c)) is a local minimum point.

f is concave down; (c, f(c)) is a local maximum point.

Example 4 **Using the Second Derivative Test to Find Local Extrema**

Find the local maximum and minimum values of $f(x) = x^3 - 3x^2 - 9x$.

Solution

Find the critical numbers of f by solving $f'(x) = 0$.

$$f'(x) = 3x^2 - 6x - 9$$
$$3x^2 - 6x - 9 = 0$$
$$3(x + 1)(x - 3) = 0$$
$$x = -1 \text{ or } x = 3$$

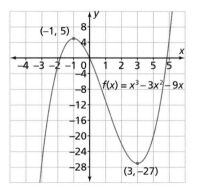

$f''(x) = 6x - 6$ Apply the second derivative test for the critical numbers -1 and 3.

$f''(-1) = -12$ Since $f''(-1) < 0$, $f(-1)$ is a local maximum value.

$f''(3) = 12$ Since $f''(3) > 0$, $f(3)$ is a local minimum value.

The local maximum value of $f(x)$ is $f(-1) = 5$ and the local minimum value of $f(x)$ is $f(3) = -27$.

• • • • • • • •

Example 5   **Graphing the Second Derivative Given the Graph of a Function**

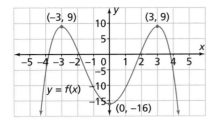

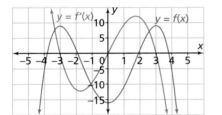

Graph $f''(x)$ given the graph of $f(x)$.

Solution

From the shape of the graph, $f(x)$ appears to be a quartic polynomial with a negative leading coefficient. Then, assuming that $f(x)$ is a quartic polynomial, $f'(x)$ is a cubic polynomial and $f''(x)$ is a quadratic function. The graph of $f''(x)$ is a parabola that opens down.

First sketch the graph of $f'(x)$. The graph of $f(x)$ is rising on the intervals $x < -3$ and $0 < x < 3$. Therefore, $f'(x) > 0$ on $x < -3$ and $0 < x < 3$. Similarly, $f'(x) < 0$ on $-3 < x < 0$ and $x > 3$.

The graph of $f(x)$ has local maximum points at $(-3, 9)$ and $(3, 9)$. So $f'(-3) = 0$ and $f'(3) = 0$. Similarly, $f'(0) = 0$.

Estimate the local maximum and minimum points on the graph of $f'(x)$ and sketch the curve.

Now consider what you know about $f''(x)$.

The graph of $f(x)$ is concave down on $x < -2$ and $x > 2$, so $f'(x)$ is decreasing and $f''(x) < 0$.

The graph of $f(x)$ is concave up on $-2 < x < 2$, so $f''(x) > 0$.

The graph of $f(x)$ has points of inflection at $(-2, 0)$ and $(2, 0)$, so $f''(-2) = 0$ and $f''(2) = 0$.

CHECK, CONSOLIDATE, COMMUNICATE

1. **(a)** The graph of a function is concave up on an interval. Describe the behaviour of the first derivative and the second derivative of this function on the interval.
   (b) The graph of a function is concave down on an interval. Describe the behaviour of the first derivative and the second derivative of this function on the interval.

2. What is a point of inflection? Does one always occur when $f''(x) = 0$? Explain.

3. **(a)** A function has critical number c and $f''(c) > 0$. What can you conclude?
   (b) A function has critical number c and $f''(c) < 0$. What can you conclude?

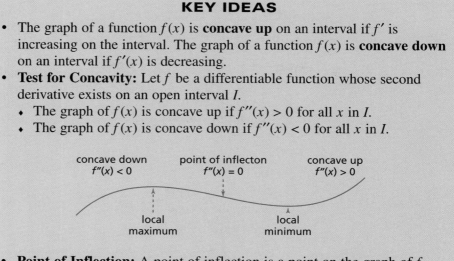

KEY IDEAS

- The graph of a function $f(x)$ is **concave up** on an interval if f' is increasing on the interval. The graph of a function $f(x)$ is **concave down** on an interval if $f'(x)$ is decreasing.
- **Test for Concavity:** Let f be a differentiable function whose second derivative exists on an open interval I.
  - The graph of $f(x)$ is concave up if $f''(x) > 0$ for all x in I.
  - The graph of $f(x)$ is concave down if $f''(x) < 0$ for all x in I.

concave down point of inflecton concave up
$f''(x) < 0$ $f''(x) = 0$ $f''(x) > 0$

local   local
maximum   minimum

- **Point of Inflection:** A point of inflection is a point on the graph of f where the function changes from concave up to concave down or vice versa. $f''(c) = 0$ if $(c, f(c))$ is a point of inflection on the graph of a polynomial function $f(x)$ and $f''(c)$ exists.
- **The Second Derivative Test:** Suppose $f(x)$ is a function where $f'(c) = 0$ and the second derivative of $f(x)$ exists on an interval containing c.
  - If $f''(c) > 0$, then $f(c)$ is a local minimum value.
  - If $f''(c) < 0$, then $f(c)$ is a local maximum value.
  - If $f''(c) = 0$, then the test fails. Use the first derivative test in this case.

4.7 Exercises

A **1.** Each figure includes the graphs of $f(x), f'(x),$ and $f''(x)$.
Which curve is which?

(a)

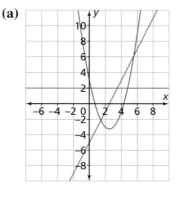

(b)

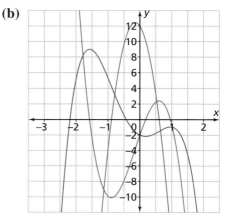

2. Graph $f'(x)$ and $f''(x)$ given the graph of $f(x)$.

(a)

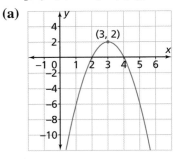

(b)

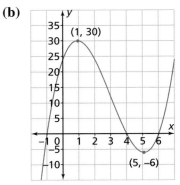

3. Determine the second derivative.

(a) $f(x) = 6x^2 - 8x + 5$

(b) $f(x) = -4x^3 - 9x^2 + 12x - 3$

(c) $y = 5x^4 - 7x^2 + 23x$

(d) $g(x) = 8x^6 + 4x^4 - 3x^2 + 4x - 11$

(e) $y = (2x + 5)(3x - 9)$

(f) $h(x) = (2x - 5)(4x^2 + 10x + 25)$

4. The second derivative of $f(x)$ is given. Determine the intervals of concavity and the x-value for any inflection points. Copy and complete the table.

(a) $f''(x) = 3(x - 4)(x + 2)$

	Intervals		
	$x < -2$	$-2 < x < 4$	$x > 4$
$3(x - 4)$			
$(x + 2)$			
$f''(x)$			
Concavity in the graph of $f(x)$			

(b) $f''(x) = -(2x + 1)(x - 3)(x - 5)$

	Intervals			
	$x < -0.5$	$-0.5 < x < 3$	$3 < x < 5$	$x > 5$
$-(2x + 1)$				
$(x - 3)$				
$(x - 5)$				
$f''(x)$				
Concavity in the graph of $f(x)$				

5. For the graph shown, identify the points or intervals where each derivative is positive, negative, and 0.

(a) $\dfrac{dy}{dx}$ (b) $\dfrac{d^2y}{dx^2}$

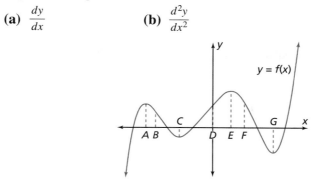

B 6. Find the point of inflection on the curve defined by $y = x^3 + 5$. Show that the tangent line at this point crosses the curve.

7. Determine the intervals of concavity and the points of inflection.

(a) $y = 6x - 2x^2$

(b) $y = 3x^2 + 5x - 1$

(c) $y = 3x^2 - 8x$

(d) $y = x^4 - 6x^2$

(e) $y = x^4 + 4x^3 - 18x^2$

(f) $y = x^4 - 6x^3 + 10$

8. Determine the intervals where the graph of the function is rising or falling, the intervals where the graph is concave up or concave down, the maximum and minimum points, and the points of inflection. Use the information to graph the function.

(a) $y = x^2 + 6x - 10$

(b) $y = 3x^2 - x^3$

(c) $y = x^3 - 3x - 4$

(d) $y = x^3 - 6x^2 + 12x - 8$

(e) $y = 2x^4 - 8x + 2$

(f) $y = \frac{1}{3}x^3 - 9x + 3$

(g) $y = \frac{1}{4}x^4 - 2x^2$

(h) $y = x^4 + 6x^3 - 24x^2 + 26$

(i) $y = x(x - 4)^3$

9. Verify your results for question 8 using graphing technology.

10. **Knowledge and Understanding**: Determine the intervals of concavity and the points of inflection for the graph of
$f(x) = x^4 - 8x^3 + 18x^2 - 16x + 5$.

11. Graph part of a polynomial function that is

    (a) concave down and falling   (b) concave up and rising

    (c) concave down and rising   (d) concave up and falling

12. Graph a function $f(x)$ for which

    (a) $f(3) = f(5) = 0$
    $f'(x) < 0$ if $x < 4$
    $f'(4) = 0$
    $f'(x) > 0$ if $x > 4$
    $f''(x) > 0$ for all x

    (b) $f'(x) > 0$ if $x < -1$
    $f'(x) > 0$ if $x > 3$
    $f'(x) < 0$ if $-1 < x < 3$
    $f''(x) < 0$ if $x < 2$
    $f''(x) > 0$ if $x > 2$

13. **Communication**: Graph a continuous function $f(x)$ for which

    (a) $f''(x) > 0$ for $x < 0$ and $f''(x) > 0$ for $x > 0$

    (b) $f'(x) > 0$ for $x < -1$ and $x > 1$; $f'(x) < 0$ for $-1 < x < 1$

14. **Application**: Show that the point of inflection in the graph of $g(x) = x(x - 6)^2$ lies halfway between the local maximum and minimum points. Is the point of inflection always at the midpoint between the local maximum and minimum points?

15. Determine all extrema of the function. Use the second derivative test to verify, where possible.

    (a) $y = -2x^2 + 12x - 2$ (b) $y = x^2 + 5x - 10$
    (c) $y = x^5 - 5x^3$ (d) $y = 3x^2 - x^3$
    (e) $y = x^4 + 8x^3 + 18x^2$ (f) $y = x^2(2 - x)^2$

16. A manufacturer estimates that it costs $x^3 - 12x^2 + 400x + 600$ dollars to produce x thousand units. What production level will minimize marginal cost?

17. **Thinking, Inquiry, Problem Solving**: Find the inflection points, if any exist, for the graph of $f(x) = (x - c)^n$, for $n = 1, 2, 3$, and 4. What conclusion can you draw about the value of n and the existence of inflection points on the graph of f?

18. **Check Your Understanding**: Can a point of inflection also be a local maximum point or a local minimum point? Explain.

C 19. For $y = x^4 - kx^3 + 10$, find the value of k such that the difference between the x-coordinates of the two inflection points is 2.

20. Prove that the graph of a cubic polynomial function has exactly one inflection point.

21. Prove that the graph of a cubic function with three distinct, real zeros has a point of inflection whose x-coordinate is the average of the three zeros.

ADDITIONAL ACHIEVEMENT CHART QUESTIONS

Knowledge and Understanding: For $f(x) = 2x^3 - 9x^2 + 12x - 2$,

(a) determine the intervals of increase and decrease

(b) determine the local maximum and minimum values

(c) determine the intervals of concavity

(d) determine any inflection points

(e) graph the function

Application: The position, s, of an object moving in a straight line from a fixed point at t seconds is given by $s(t) = t^3 - 9t^2 - 21t - 11$, where $t > 0$ and $s(t)$ is measured in metres.

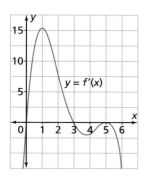

(a) Determine the times when the object is stopped and when it is moving forward. Is the acceleration negative at any time?

(b) At 2 s, is the object speeding up or slowing down? Explain why.

Thinking, Inquiry, Problem Solving: For what values of the constants c and d is $(4, -7)$ a point of inflection on the cubic curve $y = x^3 + cx^2 + x + d$?

Communication: Given the graph of $y = f'(x)$, explain where the graph of $y = f(x)$ has a maximum point, a minimum point, or a point of inflection.

The Chapter Problem
Trends in Post-Secondary Education

Apply what you learned in this section to answer these questions about The Chapter Problem on page 264.

CP8. Determine the second derivative of the mathematical model. Use the second derivative to locate where the graph of the function is concave up and concave down between 1980 and 1998.

CP9. Determine all points of inflection for the graph of the mathematical model.

CP10. Use the second derivative test to verify the existence of the extrema.

CP11. Use all the information you have obtained about the mathematical model to graph it.

Chapter 4 Review

USING THE DERIVATIVE TO ANALYZE POLYNOMIAL FUNCTION MODELS

CHECK YOUR UNDERSTANDING

1. (a) What does $f'(x) > 0$ imply about $f(x)$?
   (b) What does $f'(x) < 0$ imply about $f(x)$?

2. Explain critical numbers and the role they play in identifying maximum and minimum values.

3. Draw a diagram of a polynomial function on an interval with an absolute maximum, an absolute minimum, a local maximum, and a local minimum.

4. Describe the first derivative test. Explain how to use it.

5. State the product rule and give an example.

6. What is an inflection point? How do you identify possible points of inflection?

7. What can you say about the concavity of the graph of $f(x)$ if
   (a) $f''(x) > 0$ on an interval?   (b) $f''(x) < 0$ on an interval?

8. Describe the second derivative test. Explain how to use it.

9. What is meant by *optimization*? Outline a method for solving optimization problems.

10. What is the relation among cost, revenue, and profit? In a business application, what does marginal revenue measure? When is a company's profit maximized?

ADDITIONAL REVIEW QUESTIONS BY SECTION

4.1 Analyzing a Polynomial Function: Intervals of Increase and Decrease

11. Determine the intervals where each function increases and decreases.
    (a) $y = 3x^2 - 12x + 7$ (b) $y = 4x^3 - 12x^2 + 8$
    (c) $y = 10x^4 - 8x^3$ (d) $y = x^4 - 20x^2 + 64$
    (e) $y = 2x^5 - 20x^3 + 50x$ (f) $y = x^4 - 6x^3 - 5x^2$

12. A diver dives from the 3-m springboard. Her height above the water in metres at t seconds is $h(t) = -4.9t^2 + 9.5t + 2.2$.
    (a) When is the height of the diver increasing? decreasing?
    (b) When is the upward velocity of the diver increasing? decreasing?

13. The concentration, C, of a drug injected into the bloodstream t hours after injection can be modelled by $C(t) = \frac{t}{4} + 2t^{-2}$. Determine when the concentration of the drug is increasing and when it is decreasing.

4.2 Maximum and Minimum Values of a Polynomial Function

14. Find the absolute maximum and minimum values.

(a) $f(x) = x^2 - 2x + 6$, $-1 \leq x \leq 7$

(b) $f(x) = x^3 + x^2$, $-3 \leq x \leq 3$

(c) $f(x) = x^3 - 12x + 2$, $-5 \leq x \leq 5$

(d) $f(x) = 3x^5 - 5x^3$, $-2 \leq x \leq 4$

(e) $f(x) = 2x^3 - 3x^2 - 12x$, $-2 \leq x \leq 2$

(f) $f(x) = x^4 - 18x^2$, $-4 \leq x \leq 4$

15. After a football is punted, its height, h, in metres above the ground at t seconds can be modelled by $h(t) = -4.9t^2 + 21t + 0.45$.

(a) Determine the restricted domain of this model.

(b) When does the ball reach its maximum height?

(c) What is the ball's maximum height?

16. Determine the equation of the line tangent to $f(x) = 4x^3 + 12x^2 - 96x$ with the smallest slope on the interval $-4 \leq x \leq 2$.

4.3 The First Derivative Test

17. Graph $y = f'(x)$ for the given function.

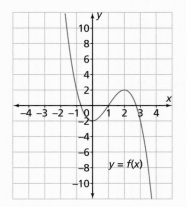

18. For each function $f(x)$,

   i. find the critical numbers

   ii. determine where the function increases and decreases

   iii. determine whether each critical number is at a maximum, a minimum, or neither

   iv. use all the information to sketch the graph

(a) $f(x) = x^2 - 7x - 18$

(b) $f(x) = -2x^3 + 9x^2 + 3$

(c) $f(x) = 2x^4 - 4x^2 + 2$

(d) $f(x) = x^5 - 5x$

(e) $f(x) = x^4 - 8x^3 + 18x^2 + 6$

(f) $f(x) = 3x^5 - 5x^4$

19. For groups of 60 or more, a charter bus company computes total revenue using $R(x) = x[10 - 0.1(x - 60)]$, $x \geq 60$. What size of group will maximize revenue?

4.4 Finding Some Shortcuts—The Product Rule

20. Find the derivative using the product rule.

(a) $f(x) = (4x^2 - 9x)(3x^2 + 5)$

(b) $f(t) = (-3t^2 - 7t + 8)(4t - 1)$

(c) $f(x) = (5x^2 - 3x)^2$

(d) $f(x) = 2x^4(3x^2 - 3x)(2x^2 + 3x)$

(e) $f(x) = 4x^{-3}(4x - 2x^{-2})$

(f) $f(z) = \sqrt{z}(2z^3 - 5\sqrt{z})$

21. Find the equation of the tangent to $y = (5x^2 + 9x - 2)(-x^2 + 2x + 3)$ at $(1, 48)$.

22. For $f(x) = (5x + 3)(x^2 - x - 1)$, determine the critical numbers, the intervals of increase or decrease, and the extrema. Use this information to graph the function.

4.5 Finding Optimal Values for Polynomial Function Models

23. A park ranger has 600 m of floating rope. She is going to enclose a rectangular swimming area, using the beach as one border of the area. Find the maximum area that can be enclosed and the corresponding dimensions.

24. A rectangular box is to be constructed from two different materials. The box will have a square base and open top. The material for the bottom costs $4.25/m^2$. The material for the sides costs $2.50/m^2$. Find the dimensions of the box with the largest volume if the budget is $500 for the material.

25. The landlord of a 50-unit apartment building is planning to increase the rent. Currently, residents pay $850/month and all units are occupied. A real estate agency advises that every $100 increase in rent will result in 10 vacant units. What rent should the landlord charge to maximize revenue?

4.6 Rates of Change in Business and Economics

26. A soft-drink company estimates that the cost, C, in dollars of producing x litres of product per day is $C(x) = 0.0005x^2 + 4x + 4000$.

(a) Find the marginal cost if 5000 L is produced.

(b) Determine the daily production level to minimize the average cost.

27. A publisher can sell x thousand copies of a monthly sports magazine if it sells for $p = 5 - \frac{x}{100}$ dollars. The monthly cost of publishing, C, can be modelled by $C(x) = 8000 - 200x - 0.05x^2$.

(a) Determine the revenue function.

(b) Determine the profit function.

(c) Calculate the profit on the sale of 20 000 magazines.

(d) Calculate the marginal profit on the sale of 30 000 magazines.

(e) Calculate the maximum profit and the sales required to realize the profit.

28. The cost to produce one high-definition TV is $750. The manufacturer charges $1800 per unit for orders of 50 or less. The price will be reduced by $15 per unit for larger orders. Determine the size of order that

(a) maximizes revenue   (b) maximizes profit

4.7 Sketching Graphs of Polynomial Functions: Concavity

29. Determine the intervals of concavity and the points of inflection.

(a) $y = x^3 - 3x^2 - 45x$ (b) $y = 2x^3 - 9x^2 - 108x + 200$

(c) $y = x^4 - 54x^2 + 250$ (d) $y = x^4 - 12x^2$

30. Determine the intervals where each function increases or decreases. Also determine where the graph of the function is concave up or down, the maximum and minimum points, and the points of inflection. Use the information to graph each function.

(a) $y = 2x^2 + 12x + 8$ (b) $y = 2x^3 - 3x^2 - 12x + 3$

(c) $y = 2x^3 - 3x^2 - 36x$ (d) $y = x^4 - 32x$

(e) $y = x^3 + x^2 - 5x + 3$ (f) $y = 3x^5 - 5x^3 + 60x$

31. Use the second derivative test to show that $f(x) = x^3 - 2x^2$ has a local maximum at the origin.

REVIEW QUESTIONS BY ACHIEVEMENT CHART CATEGORIES

Knowledge and Understanding

32. (a) Determine the intervals where $f(x) = x^4 + 4x^3 + 4x^2 + 1$ is increasing and decreasing.

(b) Identify all maximum and minimum values.

33. **(a)** Find the intervals of concavity and all inflection points for the graph of $f(x) = x^3 + 6x^2 + 9x - 3$.

(b) Do you need any more information to graph f? If so, what would be this information?

34. Determine the level of production that will maximize profits if the cost, C, in dollars of producing x units in thousands is $C(x) = \frac{x^2}{8} + 4x - 100$ and the selling price is $p = \frac{80 - x}{2}$.

Communication

35. Explain why the following is false: Let c be a critical number of $f(x)$. Then $f(x)$ has a local maximum or minimum at $f(c)$.

36. $f'(x) < 0$ for all x in the interval $3 \le x \le 10$. Explain why $f(3) > f(6)$.

37. For function $f(x)$, $f'(x)$ is decreasing on an interval. Graph $f(x)$ where
(a) $f'(x) < 0$ **(b)** $f'(x) > 0$

Application

38. An object moves horizontally along a line. Its position from a fixed point can be modelled by $s(t) = t^3 - 6t^2 - 15t + 20$, where s is the displacement in centimetres and t is the time in seconds. Determine the object's maximum velocity on the interval $0 \le t \le 5$.

39. A cylindrical, open container is to be made to hold 2 L (2000 cm³) of liquid. The material for the bottom costs \$0.05/cm². The material for the sides costs \$0.10/cm². What are the dimensions of the least expensive container?

40. A toy manufacturer has determined that the total cost, C, of operating a factory is $C(x) = 0.5x^2 + 45x + 10\ 000$, where x is the number of units produced in thousands. Determine the production level that minimizes the average cost.

Thinking, Inquiry, Problem Solving

41. Graph function $f(x)$ so that
   - points $(-1, 10)$ and $(3, 1)$ are local extrema on the graph
   - $(1, 3)$ is an inflection point
   - the graph is concave down only when $x < 1$
   - the x-intercept is -4 and the y-intercept is 8

42. Prove that an nth-degree polynomial, $f(x) = a_0x^n + a_1x^{n-1} + \ldots + a_n$, $a_0 \neq 0$, has at most $n - 2$ inflection points.

43. Ron is planting a garden all around a rectangular patio. The garden will be 5 m wide, except at the diagonals. The area of the patio must be 150 m². Find the overall dimensions of the garden and patio in which the area of the garden is a minimum.

Chapter 4 Performance Task

A function, f, represents the cash in tens of thousands of dollars of a startup computer company over time (in years), where $t = 0$ represents the year when the company went public, 1997. Cash flow is the net available income of a company. A negative cash flow is the result of expenses exceeding income. It is used with total debt to determine a company's ability to repay loans. Use this graph of $f'(t)$ to help determine information about $f(t)$, the cash of the company.

1. **(a)** Given the graph of $f'(t)$, sketch the graph of $f(t)$ by considering

   i. the years when the cash flow hit its maximum or minimum value

   ii. whether each point value in i. will yield a maximum or a minimum

   iii. the intervals of increase and intervals of decrease

   iv. the location of any possible points of inflection

   v. the intervals of concavity

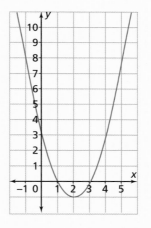

   (b) Compare your sketch with those of your classmates. How must they be the same? In what ways can they differ?

2. **(a)** Determine the equation of $f'(t)$.

   (b) Locate and classify all critical points algebraically. Compare these with your results from question 1.

3. Assume that the company had a cash flow of exactly \$0 only in 1997 and 2000 and that it is predicted to have a cash flow of \$180 000 in 2003.

   (a) Determine the equation(s) of $f(t)$.

   (b) Graph $f(t)$ using graphing technology; include a sketch with your work.

   (c) Compare the results of the graphs of $f(t)$ with the sketch you produced in question 1 and discuss any differences. Explain what each graph means in terms of the cash flow of this company.

Chapter 4 Review Test

USING THE DERIVATIVE TO ANALYZE POLYNOMIAL FUNCTION MODELS

1. Determine the critical numbers and the intervals on which $g(x) = (x^2 - 4)^2$ is increasing or decreasing.

2. **Knowledge and Understanding:** Use the second derivative test to identify all maximum and minimum values of $f(x) = x^3 + \frac{3}{2}x^2 - 7x + 5$ on the interval $-4 \le x \le 3$.

3. At an electronics factory that produces x calculators per day, the daily production cost, C, in dollars is $C(x) = 0.2x^2 + 50x + 200$. The demand function is $120 - 0.5x$. Find the production level that maximizes the daily profit.

4. Use the y-intercept, local extrema, intervals of concavity, and points of inflection to graph $f(x) = 4x^3 + 6x^2 - 24x - 2$.

5. **Application:** The owner of a toy store can purchase yo-yos from the manufacturer for $4.20 each. The owner estimates that 80 will be sold at a price of $8.00 and that 10 more will be sold for every $0.50 decrease in price. What price should be charged to maximize revenue?

6. Use the product rule to determine the derivative.
   (a) $f(x) = (x^3 - 6x)(5x^2 + 7)$
   (b) $g(x) = (2x^3 - 3x^2 - 6x + 1)(4x - 9)$

7. **Thinking, Inquiry, Problem Solving:** A 200-cm length of wire is divided into two pieces. One piece is used to form a circle. The other piece is used to form a square. Find the lengths that make the combined area
   (a) a minimum
   (b) a maximum

8. Determine the equations of the tangent lines at all inflection points on the graph of $f(x) = x^4 - 10x^3 + 36x^2 - 8x + 4$.

9. **Communication:** Explain why the graph of a quadratic function cannot have a point of inflection. Illustrate with an example.

10. A cylindrical pot, without a top, is to have a volume of 1000 cm³. The bottom will be made of copper and the rest of aluminum. Copper is five times as expensive as aluminum. Determine the dimensions that will minimize the cost of the pot.

5 Rates of Change in Rational Function Models

You already know that reciprocal and rational functions behave differently from polynomial functions.

Situations in medicine, the life sciences, and business can be modelled using reciprocal and rational functions.

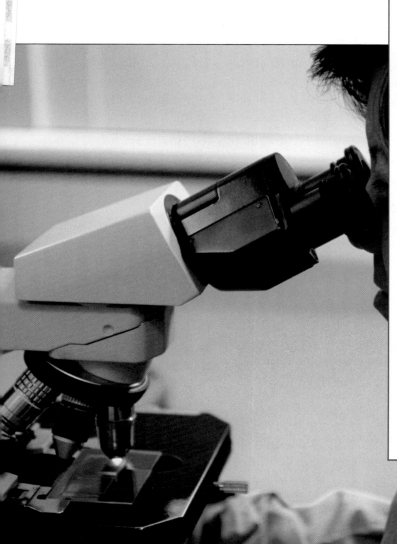

In this chapter, you will

- explore graphs of rational functions with and without graphing technology
- determine the domain, the intercepts, and the asymptotes of a rational function
- determine and use limits of rational functions to describe their behaviour
- identify discontinuous functions and the types of discontinuities they illustrate
- find the derivatives of simple rational functions from first principles
- develop and use the quotient rule to find first and second derivatives of rational functions
- solve problems of rates of change involving rational function models
- identify functions that are not differentiable
- use differential calculus techniques to determine key features of rational function graphs and sketch them by hand
- graph first and second derivatives given the graph of the original function
- graph a function given the graph of its derivative
- solve optimization problems involving rational function models

The Chapter Problem

Designing a Settling Pond

Gold ore is mined in several provinces. Gold ore also contains arsenic, which is very poisonous, even in small quantities. When the gold is separated from the gold ore, the arsenic is released and must be disposed of safely. Often, this is done by treating the arsenic in a "settling" pond. A settling pond allows the debris and particles, such as heavy metals, to settle and neutralizes the harmful chemicals in the water.

(a) Ontario guidelines say that no more than 100 µg (micrograms) of arsenic per litre of discharged water may enter a stream, river, or pond. Suppose that mine water contains 0.5 mg/L of arsenic. The polluted water is collected and flows into a pond at a rate of 2 m³/min. The pond initially contains 5000 m³ of unpolluted water. How will the concentration of arsenic in the pond change with time? After how much time will the concentration of arsenic in the pond be higher than recommended? How are your answers different if the water runs off the mine at 4 m³/min?

(b) A mining company is building a settling pond to catch and treat polluted water. The pond must be large enough to allow debris and particles to settle. The design engineer decides that the pond should be a rectangular prism with an open top and a volume of 5400 m³. The width of the pond should be two times its depth. What dimensions will minimize the amount of lining material needed to line the inside of the settling pond?

For help with this problem, see pages 359, 370, 386, 404, and 418.

Chapter Challenges

Challenge 1

When a toilet is flushed, the water tank behind the toilet empties and then fills up again. During this process, several quantities vary with time. One of these quantities is the height of the water in the tank. Investigate how this height varies with time. Collect height and time data by taking measurements and recording times for your toilet tank at home. Draw a graph to describe the relationship between the height of the water in the tank and the time from before the toilet is flushed to after it has refilled. Discuss the continuity and differentiability of your height function.

Challenge 2

(a) Use calculus to analyze $f(x) = a + \dfrac{b}{x} + cx^n$, where a, b, and c are positive constants, n is a positive integer and $x > 0$. Find the exact point at which the graph of the function has a minimum. Graph the function.

(b) Create two different optimization problems for which the algebraic model $f(x) = a + \dfrac{b}{x} + cx^n$ may be used. Use your results from (a) to solve them.

Getting Ready

In this chapter, you will be working with linear, quadratic, reciprocal, and other functions and their graphs, rational and polynomial expressions, and roots of equations. These exercises will help you warm up for the work ahead.

1. Simplify.

   (a) $(x^2 - 4x - 3) + (4x^2 + 2x + 1)$ (b) $(x^3 - 3x^2 + 2) - (x^2 - 3x + 5)$

   (c) $-x(3x - 4) - 2x(3 - x)$

   (d) $2x^2(3x^3 - 4x + 2) - x^3(2x^3 + x - 5)$

2. Factor.

   (a) $x^2 + 5x - 24$ (b) $2x^2 - 7x - 4$ (c) $3x^2 + 5x - 12$

   (d) $x^3 - 27$ (e) $8x^3 + 125$ (f) $\frac{1}{81}x^4 - 1$

   (g) $x^3 - 2x^2 - 5x + 6$ (h) $2x^3 + 3x^2 - 17x + 12$

   (i) $2x^4 + 7x^3 - 17x^2 - 7x + 15$ (j) $2x^3 + 6x^2 - 4x - 12$

3. For each pair of revenue and cost functions, determine the profit function, the break-even points, and the value of x that maximizes profit.

   (a) $R(x) = -x^2 + 24x$, $C(x) = 12x + 28$

   (b) $R(x) = -2x^2 + 32x$, $C(x) = 6x + 45$

   (c) $R(x) = -3x^2 + 26x$, $C(x) = 8x + 18$

4. Simplify and state restrictions.

   (a) $\dfrac{x^2 - 4x}{3x^2 - 12x}$ (b) $\dfrac{x^2 - x - 20}{3x - 15}$ (c) $\dfrac{x^2 - 7x + 12}{x^2 - x - 12}$

   (d) $\dfrac{2x^2 + 5x - 3}{2x^2 - 7x + 3}$ (e) $\dfrac{2x^3 - 3x^2 - 8x - 3}{2x + 1}$ (f) $\dfrac{x^2 - x - 2}{3x^3 + 2x^2 - 10x - 12}$

5. Simplify.

   (a) $\dfrac{x^2 + 2x + 1}{x} \times \dfrac{x^2 - x}{x^2 - 1}$ (b) $\dfrac{x - 2}{x^3} \div \dfrac{x^2 - 3x + 2}{x^2}$

   (c) $\dfrac{4x}{x^2 - 9} - \dfrac{2}{x + 3}$ (d) $\dfrac{x - 3}{x^2 - 7x + 10} - \dfrac{x + 2}{x^2 - 25}$

   (e) $\dfrac{1}{h}\left(\dfrac{1}{3x + h} - \dfrac{1}{3x}\right)$ (f) $\dfrac{1}{2x + 8} - \dfrac{3x}{(x + 4)^2} + \dfrac{1}{2}$

6. Solve for x.

   (a) $\dfrac{2x + 3}{x - 1} - \dfrac{3}{x} = 2$ (b) $\dfrac{1}{x} = \dfrac{2}{x + 1} + \dfrac{1}{1 - x}$

   (c) $\dfrac{x}{x - 2} + 2 = \dfrac{5x}{x + 2} + \dfrac{3x + 1}{x^2 - 4}$ (d) $\dfrac{2x}{6x + 5} = \dfrac{x + 3}{3x - 1}$

7. Let $f(x) = \dfrac{x^2 - 16}{4x - x^2}$. Evaluate each expression. For what values of x is $f(x)$ undefined?

   (a) $f(1)$ (b) $f(-4)$ (c) $f(-0.0001)$

   (d) $f(3.9999)$ (e) $f(4.0001)$ (f) $f(2)$

8. Find the zeros of $f(x)$.

(a) $f(x) = \frac{1}{4}x^2 - 9$

(b) $f(x) = 10x^2 - 11x - 6$

(c) $f(x) = 3x - 1 + \frac{1}{x+1}$

(d) $f(x) = x^3 + x^2 - 9x - 9$

9. State the domain for each function in question 8.

10. The function $f(x) = \frac{x^2 - 2x + 3}{x}$ can be rewritten as $f(x) = \frac{x^2}{x} - \frac{2x}{x} + \frac{3}{x}$, or $f(x) = x - 2 + \frac{3}{x}$. Rewrite each function in both these ways.

(a) $f(x) = \frac{x^2 - 16}{x}$
(b) $f(x) = \frac{3x^2 + 4x - 5}{x}$
(c) $f(x) = \frac{x^4 + 2x^3 - 8}{x^2}$

11. Write the equation for a horizontal line that passes through
(a) $A(0, 7)$
(b) $B(-2, 5)$
(c) $C(-1, -3)$

12. Write the equation for a vertical line that passes through
(a) $P(2, 0)$
(b) $Q(-4, 5)$
(c) $R(5, -3)$

13. Determine the equation of the axis of symmetry of $f(x)$ and then graph $f(x)$.
(a) $f(x) = (x + 4)(x - 10)$
(b) $f(x) = 2x^2 - 5x$
(c) $f(x) = x^2 + 2x - 15$
(d) $f(x) = 2(x - 3)^2 + 5$

14. The sum of two numbers is 10. What is the largest product of these numbers?

15. It costs SkiGo Travel $225 to run a minibus for one ski trip, plus $30 per passenger. The minibus can seat 22 passengers. SkiGo charges $60 per ticket if the bus is full. For each empty seat, SkiGo increases the ticket price by $5. How many empty seats should the bus run with to maximize profit on one trip?

16. Describe the properties of $f(x) = \frac{1}{x}$. How is $f(x)$ related to $g(x) = x$? Graph $f(x)$ and $g(x)$.

17. For each function, determine the reciprocal, $y = \frac{1}{f(x)}$, and the equations of the vertical asymptotes of $y = \frac{1}{f(x)}$. Verify your results with technology.
(a) $f(x) = 2x$
(b) $f(x) = x - 4$
(c) $f(x) = (x - 3)^2$

18. In each case, graph $y = f(x)$ and $y = \frac{1}{f(x)}$ on the same axes.
(a) $f(x) = x^2 - 4$
(b) $f(x) = -(x + 4)^2 + 1$
(c) $f(x) = (x + 3)^2$

19. Graph $f(x)$. State whether f is continuous or discontinuous.
(a) $f(x) = \begin{cases} 3 & \text{if } 0 \le x \le 2 \\ 2x & \text{if } 2 < x \le 8 \end{cases}$
(b) $f(x) = \begin{cases} 2x - 3 & \text{if } x \le 2 \\ x^2 & \text{if } x > 2 \end{cases}$

5.1 Graphs of Rational Functions

SETTING THE STAGE

Explore the concepts in this lesson in more detail using Exploration 8 on page 575.

An economist for a sporting goods company estimates the revenue and cost functions for the manufacture of a new snowboard. These functions are $R(x) = -x^2 + 10x$ and $C(x) = 4x + 5$, respectively, where x is the number in thousands of snowboards produced.

At the annual shareholders' meeting, the company shareholders ask about the "average profit." What information can the economist determine from the **average profit function** $AP(x) = \dfrac{P(x)}{x}$, where $P(x)$ is the profit function?

In this section, you will examine the characteristics of a new class of functions, like $AP(x) = \dfrac{(-x^2 + 10x) - (4x + 5)}{x}$, called rational functions.

EXAMINING THE CONCEPT

Domain, Range, and Zeros of a Rational Function

The average profit function, $AP(x) = \dfrac{P(x)}{x}$, is an example of a **rational function** because $\dfrac{P(x)}{x}$ is a quotient of two polynomial functions.

Definition of a Rational Function

A **rational function** has the form $h(x) = \dfrac{f(x)}{g(x)}$, where $f(x)$ and $g(x)$ are polynomials.

- The domain of a rational function consists of all real numbers except the zeros of the polynomial in the denominator. $g(x) \neq 0$
- The zeros of $h(x)$ are the zeros of $f(x)$ if $h(x)$ is in simplified form.

Example 1   Finding the Domain and the Intercepts

What is the domain of each rational function? Determine the x-and y-intercepts. Then graph $y = f(x)$ with graphing technology and estimate the range.

(a) $f(x) = \dfrac{7}{x + 2}$ **(b)** $g(x) = \dfrac{x}{x^2 - 3x - 4}$ **(c)** $h(x) = \dfrac{2x^2 + x - 3}{x^2 - 4}$

Solution

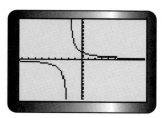

$f(x) = \frac{7}{x+2}$

(a) $f(x) = \frac{7}{x+2}$ is not defined when $x + 2 = 0$.

So the domain is all real numbers except -2, $\{x \mid x \neq -2, x \in \mathbf{R}\}$.
Since the numerator can never be 0, the function has no zeros.
So there is no x-intercept. Since $f(0) = 3.5$, the y-intercept is 3.5.

From the graph, you can see that y can be any real value except 0.
So the range is all real numbers except 0, $\{y \mid y \neq 0, y \in \mathbf{R}\}$.

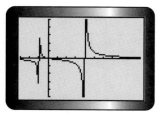

$g(x) = \frac{x}{x^2 - 3x - 4}$

(b) Factor to get $g(x) = \frac{x}{(x+1)(x-4)}$. The function is in simplified form.

The domain is all real numbers except -1 and 4, $\{x \mid x \neq -1, 4, x \in \mathbf{R}\}$.
Since the zero of the function in the numerator is 0, the function has a zero
at $x = 0$. So the x-intercept is 0.

$g(0) = 0$, so the y-intercept is 0. (The graph passes through the origin.)

From the graph, you can see that the range of this function is all real
numbers, $\{y \mid y \in \mathbf{R}\}$.

(c) Factor to get $h(x) = \frac{(2x+3)(x-1)}{(x-2)(x+2)}$. The function is in simplified form.

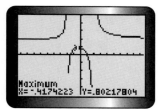

Maximum
X=-.4174223 Y=.80217804

$h(x) = \frac{2x^2 + x - 3}{x^2 - 4}$

The domain is all real numbers except ± 2, $\{x \mid x \neq \pm 2, x \in \mathbf{R}\}$.
The function has zeros at $x = -1.5$ and $x = 1$, so the x-intercepts are -1.5
and 1, respectively. Since $h(0) = \frac{(3)(-1)}{(-2)(2)}$, or 0.75, the y-intercept is 0.75.

From the graph, you can see that the range includes all real numbers less
than about 0.802 or greater than 1.948, $\{y \mid y < 0.802 \text{ or } y > 1.948, y \in \mathbf{R}\}$.
Select **4:maximum** and **3:minimum** from the **Calculate** menu to find the
highest point on the middle portion of the graph and the lowest points on the
other parts of the graph, respectively.

EXAMINING THE CONCEPT

Vertical and Horizontal Asymptotes

The graph of a rational function can have zero or more asymptotes, which may
be vertical, horizontal, or oblique. Oblique means neither vertical nor horizontal.

In Example 1(a), the graph of $f(x)$ gets very close to the vertical line $x = -2$.
When the graph of a function approaches, but does not touch, a vertical line, this
line is called a vertical asymptote. Functions that display this behaviour are said
to have infinite limits.

Vertical Asymptotes

A vertical asymptote occurs when the value of the function increases or
decreases without bound as the value of x approaches a from the left or the
right. In symbols, if $f(x) \to \infty$ or $f(x) \to -\infty$ as $x \to a^-$ or $x \to a^+$,
then $x = a$ is a vertical asymptote.

The graph of a rational function $h(x)$ can behave in four different ways near a vertical asymptote. The four cases are shown here.

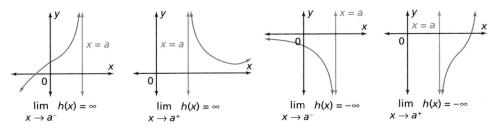

$$\lim_{x \to a^-} h(x) = \infty \qquad \lim_{x \to a^+} h(x) = \infty \qquad \lim_{x \to a^-} h(x) = -\infty \qquad \lim_{x \to a^+} h(x) = -\infty$$

The graph in Example 1(a) also gets very close to the horizontal line $y = 0$ (the x-axis). When a function approaches a horizontal line, this line is called a horizontal asymptote. Functions that display this behaviour are said to have limits at infinity.

Horizontal Asymptotes

A horizontal asymptote occurs when the value of the function approaches a number L as x increases or decreases without bound. In symbols, if $h(x) \to L$ as $x \to \infty$ or as $x \to -\infty$, then $y = L$ is a horizontal asymptote.

The graph of a rational function $h(x)$ can approach a horizontal asymptote in different ways. Some cases are shown here.

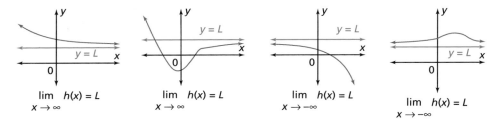

$$\lim_{x \to \infty} h(x) = L \qquad \lim_{x \to \infty} h(x) = L \qquad \lim_{x \to -\infty} h(x) = L \qquad \lim_{x \to -\infty} h(x) = L$$

In section 5.2, you will find the equation of a horizontal asymptote algebraically. But you can also estimate the equation for a horizontal asymptote from the graph of a function or by examining a table for the function. A table is also useful to determine the behaviour of the function on either side of a vertical asymptote.

Example 2

Finding the Equations of Asymptotes

Find the vertical and horizontal asymptotes.

Technology Tip:
You can create a table with a TI-83 Plus calculator. For help, see the Technology Appendix, page 591.

(a) $f(x) = \dfrac{x + 2}{3x - 2}$

(b) $g(x) = \dfrac{4x}{x^2 + 1}$

(c) $h(x) = \dfrac{2 - 3x^2}{1 - x^2}$

(d) $m(x) = \dfrac{5x^2 - 3}{x + 5}$

Solution

(a) $f(x) = \dfrac{x + 2}{3x - 2}$ is undefined when $3x - 2 = 0$ or $x = \frac{2}{3}$. So the line $x = \frac{2}{3}$ is a vertical asymptote.

Create a table to determine the horizontal asymptotes.

$x \to \infty$	
x	**f(x)**
100	0.342 282 ...
500	0.335 113 ...
1 000	0.334 223 ...
5 000	0.333 511 ...
10 000	0.333 422 ...
100 000	0.333 342 ...
700 000	0.333 334 ...

$x \to -\infty$	
x	**f(x)**
−100	0.324 503 ...
−500	0.331 558 ...
−1 000	0.332 445 ...
−5 000	0.333 156 ...
−10 000	0.333 244 ...
−100 000	0.333 324 ...
−700 000	0.333 332 ...

As x increases to very large positive values, $f(x)$ decreases and approaches $\frac{1}{3}$. So the line $y = \frac{1}{3}$ is a horizontal asymptote on the right.

As x decreases to very large negative values, $f(x)$ increases and approaches $\frac{1}{3}$. So the line $y = \frac{1}{3}$ is a horizontal asymptote on the left.

(b) $g(x) = \dfrac{4x}{x^2 + 1}$ is defined for all real values of x, since the denominator can never be 0. So there is no vertical asymptote.

Create a table to determine the horizontal asymptotes.

$x \to \infty$	
x	**g(x)**
100	0.039 996 ...
500	0.008 000 ...
1 000	0.004 000 ...
5 000	0.000 800 ...
10 000	0.000 400 ...
100 000	0.000 040 ...
700 000	0.000 006 ...

$x \to -\infty$	
x	**g(x)**
−100	−0.039 996 ...
−500	−0.008 000 ...
−1 000	−0.004 000 ...
−5 000	−0.000 800 ...
−10 000	−0.000 400 ...
−100 000	−0.000 040 ...
−700 000	−0.000 006 ...

As x increases to very large positive values, $f(x)$ decreases and approaches 0. Therefore, the line $y = 0$ is a horizontal asymptote on the right.

As x decreases to very large negative values, $f(x)$ increases and approaches 0. Therefore, the line $y = 0$ is a horizontal asymptote on the left.

(c) For $h(x) = \dfrac{2 - 3x^2}{1 - x^2}$, first factor the denominator: $h(x) = \dfrac{2 - 3x^2}{(1 - x)(1 + x)}$.

The function $h(x)$ is undefined when $x = \pm 1$. So the lines $x = 1$ and $x = -1$ are vertical asymptotes.

Create a table to determine the horizontal asymptotes.

$x \to \infty$	
x	**h(x)**
100	3.000 100 ...
140	3.000 051 ...
200	3.000 025 ...
500	3.000 004 ...
1000	3.000 001 ...
5000	3.000 000 ...
7000	3.000 000 ...

$x \to -\infty$	
x	**h(x)**
-100	3.000 100 ...
-140	3.000 051 ...
-200	3.000 025 ...
-500	3.000 004 ...
-1000	3.000 001 ...
-5000	3.000 000 ...
-7000	3.000 000 ...

The function $h(x)$ never reaches 3, but the difference between $h(x)$ and 3 becomes very very small. (The number 3 may occur in a graphing calculator table due to rounding.)

The function $h(x)$ appears to quickly reach a limit of 3 as x increases or decreases. Therefore, the line $y = 3$ is a horizontal asymptote on the left and on the right.

(d) The function $m(x) = \dfrac{5x^2 - 3}{x + 5}$ is undefined when $x = -5$. So the line $x = -5$ is a vertical asymptote. Create a table to determine the horizontal asymptotes.

$x \to \infty$	
x	**m(x)**
100	476.162 ...
500	2 475.242 ...
1 000	4 975.121 ...
5 000	24 975.024 ...
10 000	49 975.012 ...
100 000	499 975.001 ...
700 000	3 499 975.000 ...

$x \to -\infty$	
x	**m(x)**
-100	-526.284 ...
-500	-2525.246 ...
-1 000	-5025.122 ...
-5 000	-25 025.024 ...
-10 000	-50 025.012 ...
-100 000	-500 025.001 ...
-700 000	-3 500 025.000 ...

As x increases to very large values, the value of $m(x)$ also increases to very large values. Similarly, as x decreases, the value of $m(x)$ also decreases. The value of $m(x)$ does not approach a limiting value. The function $m(x)$ does not approach a limit. Therefore, there is no horizontal asymptote, on either the left or the right.

Although the functions in Example 2 look alike, their graphs are very different.

(a) $f(x) = \dfrac{x + 2}{3x - 2}$ (b) $g(x) = \dfrac{4x}{x^2 + 1}$ (c) $h(x) = \dfrac{2 - 3x^2}{1 - x^2}$ (d) $m(x) = \dfrac{5x^2 - 3}{x + 5}$

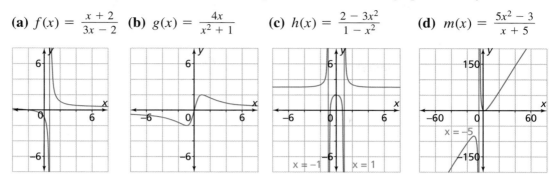

You can get a rough idea of what the graph of a rational function looks like, using information about its domain, the intercepts, and the asymptotes.

Example 3 **Graphing a Rational Function Using the Domain, the Intercepts, and the Asymptotes**

Let $f(x) = \dfrac{x^2}{x^3 - 2x^2 - 5x + 6}$. Find the domain, intercepts, and vertical and horizontal asymptotes. Then use this information to sketch an approximate graph.

Solution

Domain and Vertical Asymptotes: Factor $f(x)$. $f(x) = \dfrac{x^2}{(x + 2)(x - 1)(x - 3)}$

• The domain is the set of all real numbers except -2, 1, and 3, $\{x \mid x \neq -2, 1, 3, x \in \mathbf{R}\}$.
• The lines $x = -2$, $x = 1$, and $x = 3$ are vertical asymptotes.

Intercepts:
• Since the zero for the function in the numerator is 0, the function has a zero at $x = 0$. The x-intercept is 0.
• Since $f(0) = 0$, the y-intercept is 0.

Horizontal Asymptotes: Use tables.

$x \to \infty$			$x \to -\infty$	
x	$f(x)$		x	$f(x)$
100	0.010 209 ...		−100	−0.009 809 ...
500	0.002 008 ...		−500	−0.001 992 ...
1 000	0.001 002 ...		−1 000	−0.000 998 ...
5 000	0.000 200 ...		−5 000	−0.000 200 ...
10 000	0.000 100 ...		−10 000	−0.000 100 ...
100 000	0.000 010 ...		−100 000	−0.000 010 ...
700 000	0.000 001 ...		−700 000	−0.000 001 ...

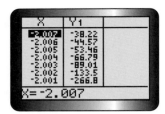

As $x \to -2^-$, $y \to -\infty$

As $x \to -2^+$, $y \to \infty$.

As x increases to very large positive values, $f(x)$ decreases and approaches 0. As x decreases to very large negative values, $f(x)$ increases and approaches 0.

So the line $y = 0$ is a horizontal asymptote on the left and on the right.

You can also use a table to determine how the graph approaches each vertical asymptote. For example, consider the vertical asymptote $x = -2$.
What happens to $f(x)$ as x approaches 2 from the left or the right?
The tables created with the TI-83 Plus calculator, where $\mathbf{Y1} = f(x)$, appear on the left.

Use another table to summarize the behaviour of the function near the vertical asymptotes. It is also helpful to check the sign of $f(x)$ on each side of each asymptote.

As $x \to$	-2^-	-2^+	1^-	1^+	3^-	3^+
Sign of $f(x) = \dfrac{x^2}{(x+2)(x-1)(x-3)}$	$\dfrac{(+)}{(-)(-)(-)}$	$\dfrac{(+)}{(+)(-)(-)}$	$\dfrac{(+)}{(+)(-)(-)}$	$\dfrac{(+)}{(+)(+)(-)}$	$\dfrac{(+)}{(+)(+)(-)}$	$\dfrac{(+)}{(+)(+)(+)}$
$f(x) \to$	$-\infty$	∞	∞	$-\infty$	$-\infty$	∞

Now graph $y = f(x)$.

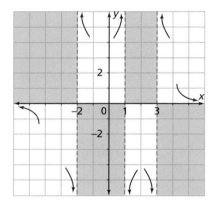

This graph shows the behaviour near the asymptotes.

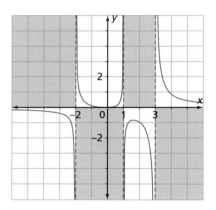

In this graph, the turning points in the middle two sections are estimates.

• • • • • • • •

Example 4   The Average Profit Function

Recall the situation in Setting the Stage:

An economist for a sporting goods company estimates the revenue and cost functions for the manufacture of a new snowboard. These functions are $R(x) = -x^2 + 10x$ and $C(x) = 4x + 5$, respectively, where x is the number in thousands of snowboards produced.

At the annual shareholders' meeting, the company shareholders ask about the "average profit." What information can the economist determine from the **average profit function** $AP(x) = \dfrac{P(x)}{x}$, where $P(x)$ is the profit function?

Solution

$$P(x) = R(x) - C(x)$$
$$= -x^2 + 10x - (4x + 5)$$
$$= -x^2 + 6x - 5$$

So $AP(x) = \dfrac{-x^2 + 6x - 5}{x}$ is the average profit function. Factor the numerator to

get $AP(x) = \dfrac{-(x - 1)(x - 5)}{x}$. So the average profit function has zeros at $x = 1$

and $x = 5$. Recall that $x = 1$ and $x = 5$ are **break-even quantities**. At the corresponding points, revenue equals cost, so profit equals 0.

The graph of the average profit function will have a vertical asymptote at $x = 0$, since this value is the zero of the function in the denominator. Since $AP(x)$ does not approach a limit as x increases or decreases without bound, there is no horizontal asymptote.

It is easier to examine the **end behaviour** if $AP(x)$ is written in another form.

$$AP(x) = \dfrac{-x^2}{x} + \dfrac{6x}{x} - \dfrac{5}{x}$$
$$= -x + 6 - \dfrac{5}{x}$$

When x is very large, $\dfrac{5}{x}$ is very small and has little effect on $AP(x)$. The graph

looks like the line $y = -x + 6$ as $x \to \infty$. The line $y = -x + 6$ is called an **oblique asymptote**.

In this context, the domain is all real numbers greater than 0. Use graphing technology to graph both the function and the oblique asymptote. Restrict the domain to positive x-values by adjusting the window settings.

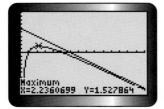

Using **4:maximum** in the **Calculate** menu, calculate the maximum of $AP(x)$.

The greatest average profit per item produced occurs at a production level of about 2236 items.

The zeros of the function occur at $x = 1$ and $x = 5$. So the company's economist can tell shareholders that manufacturing the new snowboard will be profitable at production levels between 1000 and 5000 items. She can also tell them that selling 2236 snowboards will yield the maximum average profit per item. After this maximum level, the average profit decreases. The rate of decrease approaches a steady value as production levels increase.

EXAMINING THE CONCEPT

Oblique Asymptotes

An oblique asymptote is neither horizontal nor vertical, but slanted.

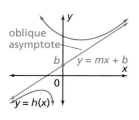
oblique asymptote
b
$y = mx + b$
0
x
y
$y = h(x)$

Oblique Asymptotes

The line $y = mx + b$ is an oblique, or slanted, asymptote to the graph of a rational function $h(x)$, if the vertical distance between the curve $y = h(x)$ and the line $y = mx + b$ approaches 0.

In other words, the difference between $h(x)$ and $mx + b$ approaches 0 as x increases or decreases without bound. So

$$\lim_{x \to \pm\infty} [h(x) - (mx + b)] = 0$$

A rational function $h(x) = \dfrac{f(x)}{g(x)}$ has an oblique asymptote if the degree of $f(x)$ is **one** more than the degree of $g(x)$.

Example 5   **Finding the Equation of an Oblique Asymptote**

Determine the intercepts and asymptotes for $f(x) = \dfrac{x^2 - x - 6}{x - 2}$.

Solution

Factor the numerator: $f(x) = \dfrac{(x + 2)(x - 3)}{x - 2}$. The x-intercepts are -2 and 3.

$f(0) = 3$, so the y-intercept is 3.

As $x \to$	2^-	2^+
Sign of $f(x)$	$\dfrac{(+)(-)}{(-)} = +$	$\dfrac{(+)(-)}{(+)} = -$
$f(x) \to$	∞	$-\infty$

The line $x = 2$ is a vertical asymptote.

As $x \to 2^-, f(x) \to \infty$. As $x \to 2^+, f(x) \to -\infty$.

Since the degree of the numerator is exactly one more than the degree of the denominator, the graph of the function will have an oblique asymptote. To find its equation, use long division to rewrite the function equation.

$$\begin{array}{r} x + 1 \\ x - 2 \overline{\smash{)}\, x^2 - x - 6} \\ \underline{x^2 - 2x} \\ x - 6 \\ \underline{x - 2} \\ -4 \end{array}$$

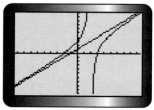

$f(x) = x + 1 - \dfrac{4}{x - 2}$. As $x \to \pm\infty$, $\dfrac{4}{x - 2}$ becomes negligible. So the line $y = x + 1$ is the oblique asymptote.

Check with graphing technology. Enter $\dfrac{(x + 2)(x - 3)}{(x - 2)}$ into **Y1** and $x + 1$ into **Y2** in the equation editor.

• • • • • • • • •

Some rational functions have graphs that approach curves rather than straight lines. Finding the equation of such a curve is the same as finding the equation of an oblique asymptote. Divide the expression in the numerator by the expression in the denominator.

CHECK, CONSOLIDATE, COMMUNICATE

1. What is a rational function? How is the graph of a rational function different from the graph of a polynomial function?
2. Explain how to use the equation of a rational function to determine its domain and its zeros.
3. What are asymptotes? How can you tell from the equation of a rational function what types of asymptotes its graph will have?
4. Explain *end behaviour* and *limit at infinity*. Describe these terms in relation to the asymptotes of a rational function.
5. Describe the steps for sketching the graph of a rational function by hand.

KEY IDEAS

- In the **rational function** $h(x) = \frac{f(x)}{g(x)}$, $f(x)$ and $g(x)$ are polynomials.
- The domain of a rational function consists of all real numbers except the zeros of the polynomial in the denominator. $g(x) \neq 0$
- When $h(x)$ is in simplified form, the zeros of $h(x)$ are the zeros of $f(x)$.
- The graph of a rational function may have vertical, horizontal, or oblique asymptotes. An oblique asymptote is neither vertical nor horizontal, but slanted.
- A **vertical asymptote** occurs at each zero of the function in the denominator if the rational function is in simplified form.
- The line $x = a$ is a **vertical asymptote** if $h(x) \to \infty$ or $h(x) \to -\infty$ as $x \to a^-$ or $x \to a^+$.
- A table is useful for determining whether a function is increasing or decreasing on either side of a vertical asymptote.
- The line $y = L$ is a **horizontal asymptote** for $h(x)$ if the value of $h(x)$ approaches L as x increases or decreases without bound. As $x \to \infty$ or as $x \to -\infty$, $h(x) \to L$. The function is said to have a **limit at infinity**.
- One way of finding the equation for a horizontal asymptote is to examine a table for the function.
- An oblique asymptote is neither horizontal nor vertical; it is slanted.
- A rational function $h(x) = \frac{f(x)}{g(x)}$ has an **oblique asymptote** if the degree of $f(x)$ is one more than the degree of $g(x)$.
- The line $y = mx + b$ is an oblique asymptote in the graph of $y = h(x)$ if the difference between $h(x)$ and $mx + b$ approaches 0 as x increases or decreases without bound.

$$\lim_{x \to \pm\infty} [h(x) - (mx + b)] = 0$$

5.1 Exercises

A *Questions 1 to 6 refer to the following functions. Answer questions 1 to 5 without graphing technology.*

(a) $f(x) = \dfrac{2 + x}{x - 7}$

(b) $f(x) = \dfrac{x}{2x - 8}$

(c) $f(x) = \dfrac{5x^2 - 11x + 2}{x}$

(d) $f(x) = \dfrac{x - 2}{x^2 + 5x + 6}$

(e) $f(x) = \dfrac{x^2 + x - 6}{x + 2}$

(f) $f(x) = \dfrac{x^2 - 9}{x^3 + 4x^2 - x - 4}$

1. Determine the x- and y-intercepts of each function.

2. State the domain for each function.

3. Will the graph of each function have a vertical asymptote? If so, determine the equation for each vertical asymptote.

4. Will the graph of each function have a horizontal asymptote? an oblique asymptote? Give reasons for your answers. Determine the equation of each asymptote.

5. Use the information from questions 1 to 4 to graph each function.

6. Confirm your answers to questions 1 to 5 by graphing each function using graphing technology.

B 7. **Knowledge and Understanding:** For each rational function, determine the zeros and the domain. Write the equation of each asymptote. Then graph the function and estimate the range.

(a) $f(x) = \dfrac{2x - 1}{x + 1}$

(b) $g(x) = \dfrac{x}{x^2 - 4}$

(c) $h(x) = \dfrac{x^2 - 4}{x}$

8. **Communication:** When asked to graph $y = \dfrac{6}{(x + 3)(x - 1)}$, Jean used a graphing calculator to obtain the graph on the left, while La-Toya produced the graph on the right. Whose graph is correct? Explain your answer. Also explain the error that resulted in the incorrect graph.

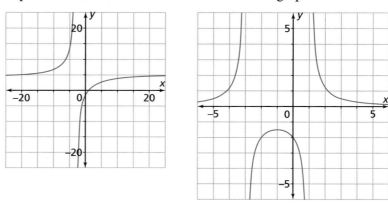

9. What are the asymptotes in the graph of $f(x) = \dfrac{3x}{x - 2}$, $x \neq 2$?
   Graph the function, showing all asymptotes clearly.

10. Use the domain and intercepts, and vertical, horizontal, and oblique asymptotes to graph each function.

    (a) $f(x) = \dfrac{3}{x + 1}$

    (b) $f(x) = \dfrac{5x - 11}{2x + 3}$

    (c) $f(x) = \dfrac{2x + 1}{x^2 - 4x - 5}$

    (d) $f(x) = \dfrac{2x^2 - 5x}{x^2 - 1}$

    (e) $f(x) = \dfrac{x^2 + 4x + 3}{x - 2}$

    (f) $f(x) = \dfrac{x^2}{x^3 - 2x^2 - x + 2}$

11. **Thinking, Inquiry, Problem Solving:** For each case, create a function that has a graph with the given features.

    (a) a vertical asymptote $x = 1$ and a horizontal asymptote $y = 0$

    (b) a vertical asymptote $x = 2$, a horizontal asymptote $y = 0$, no x-intercepts, and y-intercept -2

    (c) two vertical asymptotes $x = -1$ and $x = 3$, horizontal asymptote $y = -1$, and x-intercepts -2 and 4

    (d) a vertical asymptote the y-axis, an oblique asymptote $y = 3x + 1$, and no x- or y-intercepts

12. Functions $R(x) = -2x^2 + 8x$ and $C(x) = 3x + 2$ are the estimated revenue and cost functions for the manufacture of a new product. Determine the average profit function, $AP(x) = \dfrac{P(x)}{x}$. Express this function in two different forms. Explain what can be determined from each form. Restrict the domain of the function to represent the context. What are the break-even quantities?

13. Repeat question 12 for $R(x) = -x^2 + 30x$ and $C(x) = 17x + 36$.

14. Let $f(x) = \dfrac{3x - 1}{x^2 - 2x - 3}$, $g(x) = \dfrac{x^3 + 8}{x^2 + 9}$, $h(x) = \dfrac{x^3 - 3x}{x + 1}$, and

    $m(x) = \dfrac{x^2 + x - 12}{x^2 - 4}$. Explain each of the following:

    (a) Which of these rational functions has a horizontal asymptote?

    (b) Which has an oblique asymptote?

    (c) Which has no vertical asymptote?

    (d) Graph $y = m(x)$, showing the asymptotes and the x- and y-intercepts.

15. The model for the concentration y of a drug in the bloodstream, x hours after it is taken orally, is $y = \dfrac{7x}{x^2 + 2}$. What is the domain of y in this context? What do you know about the graph of y just by looking at the equation? Graph the function. Describe what happens to the concentration of the drug over 24 consecutive hours. Does the model seem reasonable?

16. Any function f for which $f(-x) = f(x)$ is called an **even** function. An even function is symmetric about the y-axis. For example, $f(x) = x^2$ is an even function. Any function f for which $f(-x) = -f(x)$ is called an **odd** function. An odd function is symmetric about the origin. $f(x) = \dfrac{1}{x}$ is an odd function. Find two rational functions that are even and two that are odd.

17. A farmer wants to experiment with a new corn plant. She has enough seed for an area of 216 m². She wants to fence a rectangular plot. This plot will be divided into two equal parts by another fence parallel to one side. What dimensions for the largest rectangle will minimize the amount of fencing? Let x represent the length of the rectangle.

(a) The area is 216 m². Now express the width of the largest rectangle in terms of x.

(b) Express the total length of fencing in terms of x.

(c) Describe the relation between the perimeter and x.

18. (a) Enter the perimeter function in question 17 into a graphing calculator. Describe the graph. What is the domain of the perimeter function in the context of this problem?

(b) Trace or use the correct item in the **Calculate** menu to determine the smallest possible perimeter. How much fencing will the farmer need?

19. **Check Your Understanding:** What makes a function rational? Explain how you would determine the domain, any zeros, and any asymptotes for any rational function. Use examples to illustrate your explanation.

C **20.** **Application:** A rectangular garden, 21 m² in area, will be fenced to keep out rabbits and skunks. Find the dimensions that will require the least amount of fencing if one side of the garden is already protected by a barn.

21. Use long division to rewrite $f(x) = \dfrac{2x^3 - 7x^2 + 8x - 5}{x - 1}$ in the form $f(x) = ax^2 + bx + c + \dfrac{k}{x-1}$. What does this tell you about the end behaviour of the function? Graph the function. Include all asymptotes in your graph. Write the equations of the asymptotes.

22. For what values of x is $\dfrac{x+4}{x+1} < \dfrac{x-2}{x-4}$ true? Use graphs as well as algebra in your solution.

ADDITIONAL ACHIEVEMENT CHART QUESTIONS

Knowledge and Understanding: Let $f(x) = \dfrac{2x^2 + 2}{x^2 + x - 2}$.

(a) Without using graphing technology, determine the zeros, the asymptotes, and the domain. Graph the function.

(b) Use a calculator to check the graph and estimate the range.

Application: A manufacturer of cardboard drink containers wants to construct a closed rectangular container that has a square base. The container must hold 0.1 L (100 cm³). Let S be the surface area of the box and x be the length of a side of the square base. Show that $S(x) = 2x^2 + \dfrac{400}{x}$ for $x > 0$. Graph S versus x for $x > 0$. Estimate the dimensions of the container that will require the least amount of material for its manufacture.

Thinking, Inquiry, Problem Solving: Find an equation in the form $y = \dfrac{k}{x^2 + bx + c}$ so that its graph closely matches the one shown. Check your work with graphing technology.

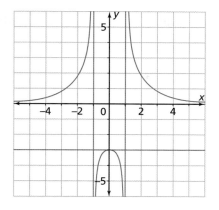

Communication: Explain what a horizontal asymptote is and how to find one for a given function.

The Chapter Problem
Designing a Settling Pond

Apply what you learned in this section to answer these questions about The Chapter Problem on page 342.

CP1. **(a)** How many micrograms are in a milligram?
(b) How many litres are in 1 m³?
(c) How many micrograms of arsenic enter the pond during one minute?

CP2. **(a)** After t minutes,
   i. how much arsenic has entered the pond?
   ii. how much water, in total, is in the pond?
(b) Write a function to describe the concentration of arsenic in the pond at time t.

CP3. What kind of function is the concentration function?

CP4. Determine the domain and intercepts.

CP5. Repeat questions CP2 to CP4 for a water runoff rate of 4 m³/min.

5.2 Limits and End Behaviour of Rational Functions

SETTING THE STAGE

An important function used by economists is the **average cost function** $AC(x) = \frac{C(x)}{x}$, where $C(x)$ is the cost of producing x items.

At a small clothing company, the estimated cost function for producing a new line of jeans is $C(x) = x^2 - 4x + 5$, where x is the number of pairs of jeans produced, in thousands.

What happens to the average cost if the number of pairs of jeans produced approaches 0? What happens to the average cost if the number of pairs of jeans produced becomes very large? What do the answers to these questions mean in economic terms?

In this section, you will use your knowledge of limits to answer these questions and develop techniques for finding limits of rational functions.

EXAMINING THE CONCEPT

Finding Limits of Rational Functions

To find the limit of a rational function, sometimes you can use direct substitution.

Finding Limits of Rational Functions by Substitution

Let $h(x) = \frac{f(x)}{g(x)}$ be a rational function. Let a be any real number that is in the domain of h. Then the limit of $h(x)$ as x approaches a is

$$\lim_{x \to a} h(x) = \frac{f(a)}{g(a)}, \text{ if } g(a) \neq 0$$

Example 1   **Finding the Limit of a Rational Function**

Find each limit.

(a) $\displaystyle\lim_{x \to 2} \frac{x^2 + 3x + 6}{x + 2}$

(b) $\displaystyle\lim_{x \to 2} \frac{x^2 - 3x}{x - 2}$

Solution

(a) Determine whether $f(x)$ exists at $x = 2$. Attempt to evaluate $f(2)$.

$$\lim_{x \to 2} \frac{x^2 + 3x + 6}{x + 2} = \frac{2^2 + 3(2) + 6}{2 + 2}$$

$$= 4$$

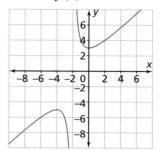

Therefore, $f(x)$ does exist at $x = 2$ and

$$\lim_{x \to 2} \frac{x^2 + 3x + 6}{x + 2} = 4.$$

As with polynomial functions, you can also estimate the limit from the graph of the function.

(b) Determine whether $f(x)$ exists at $x = 2$. Attempt to calculate $f(2)$.

$$\lim_{x \to 2} \frac{x^2 - 3x}{x - 2} = \frac{2^2 - 3(2)}{2 - 2}$$

$$= \frac{-2}{0}$$

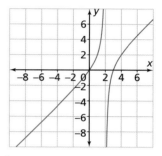

$f(2)$ is undefined. Graph the function and estimate.

As x approaches 2 from the left, $f(x)$ increases without bound. In symbols, as $x \to 2^-$, $f(x) \to \infty$.
As x approaches 2 from the right, $f(x)$ decreases without bound. In symbols, as $x \to 2^+$, $f(x) \to -\infty$. The limit at $x = 2$ does not exist. You cannot use substitution to find the limit because $f(2)$ does not exist.

• • • • • • • •

For Example 1(b), the line $x = 2$ is a vertical asymptote. You can write $\lim_{x \to 2^-} f(x) = \infty$ and $\lim_{x \to 2^+} f(x) = -\infty$. These limits are infinite limits.

In this case, there is no limit to $f(x)$ as x approaches 2 from either the left or the right.

Example 2   **Rational Functions and Infinite Limits**

Evaluate.

(a) $\lim_{x \to 0} \frac{1}{x}$
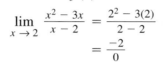
(b) $\lim_{x \to 0} \frac{1}{x^2}$

Solution

(a) The line $x = 0$ is a vertical asymptote. At $x = 0$, the function is undefined. Examine a table of values for $f(x) = \frac{1}{x}$ on either side of 0.

from the left			from the right	
x	$f(x) = \frac{1}{x}$		x	$f(x) = \frac{1}{x}$
−0.005	−200		0.005	200
−0.003	−333.$\dot{3}$		0.003	333.$\dot{3}$
−0.002	−500		0.002	500
−0.001	−1 000		0.001	1 000
−0.0001	−10 000		0.0001	10 000
0	undefined		0	undefined

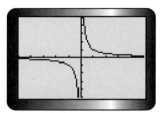

−4.7 ≤ x ≤ 4.7, −5 ≤ y ≤ 5

As $x \to 0^-$, $f(x) \to -\infty$. As $x \to 0^+$, $f(x) \to \infty$.

So $\lim\limits_{x \to 0^-} \frac{1}{x} = -\infty$ and $\lim\limits_{x \to 0^+} \frac{1}{x} = \infty$

The one-sided limits are not the same, so the limit does not exist.
The graph confirms the analysis.

(b) The line $x = 0$ is a vertical asymptote. At $x = 0$, the function is undefined.
Examine a table of values for $f(x) = \frac{1}{x^2}$ on either side of 0.

from the left			from the right	
x	$f(x) = \frac{1}{x^2}$		x	$f(x) = \frac{1}{x^2}$
−0.005	40 000		0.005	40 000
−0.003	111 111.$\dot{1}$		0.003	111 111.$\dot{1}$
−0.002	250 000		0.002	250 000
−0.001	1 000 000		0.001	1 000 000
−0.0001	100 000 000		0.0001	100 000 000
0	undefined		0	undefined

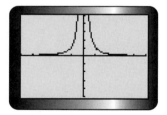

−4.7 ≤ x ≤ 4.7, −5 ≤ y ≤ 5

As $x \to 0^-$, $f(x) \to \infty$. As $x \to 0^+$, $f(x) \to \infty$.

So $\lim\limits_{x \to 0^-} \frac{1}{x^2} = \infty$, $\lim\limits_{x \to 0^+} \frac{1}{x^2} = \infty$, and $\lim\limits_{x \to 0} \frac{1}{x^2} = \infty$.

The limit does not exist. The graph confirms the analysis.

· · · · · · · ·

In Example 1(b), $f(x) = \frac{x^2 - 3x}{x - 2}$ is undefined at $x = 2$ because division
by 0 is undefined. Substituting $x = 2$ yields $\frac{-2}{0}$, which is meaningless.
It was necessary to use a graph or table to estimate the limit.

Substituting $x = a$ to find $\lim\limits_{x \to a} h(x) = \frac{f(a)}{g(a)}$ may also result in the

indeterminate form $\frac{0}{0}$. To find the limit in this case, first factor the rational
function.

Example 3   **The Indeterminate Form of a Limit**

Find $\lim\limits_{x \to -1} \dfrac{x^3 + 1}{x + 1}$.

Solution

Substitute $x = -1$.

$$\lim_{x \to -1} \frac{x^3 + 1}{x + 1} = \frac{(-1)^3 + 1}{-1 + 1}$$

$$= \frac{-1 + 1}{-1 + 1}$$

$$= \frac{0}{0}$$

x	f(x)
−1.003	3.009
−1.002	3.006
−1.001	3.003
−1.000	undefined
−0.999	2.997
−0.998	2.994
−0.997	2.991

Substituting $x = -1$ yields the indeterminate form $\dfrac{0}{0}$.

First examine the behaviour of $f(x) = \dfrac{x^3 + 1}{x + 1}$. Create a table and graph $y = f(x)$. Use values close to -1 on both sides.

$f(x)$ seems to approach 3 as x approaches -1 from the left or the right.

Verify that the limit is 3 algebraically. First factor. Then divide out the common factor.

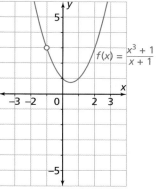

$$\lim_{x \to -1} \frac{x^3 + 1}{x + 1} = \lim_{x \to -1} \frac{\overset{1}{\cancel{(x + 1)}}(x^2 - x + 1)}{\underset{1}{\cancel{(x + 1)}}} \quad \text{Factor and reduce. } x \neq -1.$$

$$= \lim_{x \to -1} (x^2 - x + 1) \quad \text{Substitute.}$$

$$= (-1)^2 - (-1) + 1 \quad \text{Evaluate.}$$

$$= 3$$

EXAMINING THE CONCEPT

Limits at Infinity and Models for End Behaviour

The graph of a function has a horizontal asymptote if the function has a finite limit, L, as $x \to \pm\infty$. The equation of the horizontal asymptote is $y = L$.

Example 4   **Finding a Limit at Infinity**

Let $h(x) = \dfrac{5x^2 - 3x + 4}{2x^2 + x - 7}$. Find the equation of the horizontal asymptote.

Solution

First consider $\lim\limits_{x \to \infty} \dfrac{5x^2 - 3x + 4}{2x^2 + x - 7}$ and $\lim\limits_{x \to -\infty} \dfrac{5x^2 - 3x + 4}{2x^2 + x - 7}$. Finding either limit by substituting ∞ or $-\infty$ gives another **indeterminate form**, $\dfrac{\infty}{\infty}$. So it appears there is no finite limit. But here are two methods for finding the equation of the horizontal asymptote in this case.

Method 1: Examine the end behaviour.
For small values of $|x|$, the graph of
$f(x) = 5x^2 - 3x + 4$ is different from the graph
of $m(x) = 5x^2$.

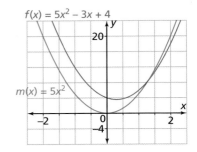

For large values of $|x|$, the graphs are almost the
same. The values of the last two terms do not
significantly affect the value of the leading term
when x is large. $m(x)$ is an **end-behaviour model**
for $f(x)$.

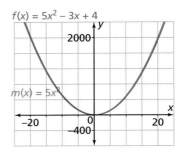

Similarly, $g(x) = 2x^2 + x - 7$ is almost the same as $n(x) = 2x^2$ for large values
of $|x|$. So $n(x)$ is an end-behaviour model for $g(x)$.

Therefore, $k(x) = \dfrac{m(x)}{n(x)} = \dfrac{5x^2}{2x^2} = \dfrac{5}{2}$ is an end-behaviour model for $h(x)$. The

function $k(x)$ is valid for large values of $|x|$. Thus, $h(x) = \dfrac{5x^2 - 3x + 4}{2x^2 + x - 7}$ behaves

like $k(x) = \dfrac{5}{2}$ when $|x|$ is large. The equation of the horizontal asymptote is $y = \dfrac{5}{2}$.

Method 2: Divide the numerator and denominator by the highest power of x in
the denominator.

$$\lim_{x \to \infty} \frac{5x^2 - 3x + 4}{2x^2 + x - 7} = \lim_{x \to \infty} \frac{\frac{5x^2}{x^2} - \frac{3x}{x^2} + \frac{4}{x^2}}{\frac{2x^2}{x^2} + \frac{x}{x^2} - \frac{7}{x^2}}$$

$$= \lim_{x \to \infty} \frac{5 - \frac{3}{x} + \frac{4}{x^2}}{2 + \frac{1}{x} - \frac{7}{x^2}}$$

$$= \frac{\lim\limits_{x \to \infty} 5 - \lim\limits_{x \to \infty} \frac{3}{x} + \lim\limits_{x \to \infty} \frac{4}{x^2}}{\lim\limits_{x \to \infty} 2 + \lim\limits_{x \to \infty} \frac{1}{x} - \lim\limits_{x \to \infty} \frac{7}{x^2}}$$
Use the sum and quotient laws
for limits.

$$= \frac{5 - 0 + 0}{2 + 0 - 0}$$
$\lim\limits_{x \to \pm\infty} \dfrac{1}{x^n} = 0$, for whole-

$$= \frac{5}{2}$$
number values of n.

The line $y = \dfrac{5}{2}$ is a horizontal asymptote on the right.

Similarly, $\lim\limits_{x \to -\infty} \dfrac{5x^2 - 3x + 4}{2x^2 + x - 7} = \dfrac{5}{2}$ by the same process, and $y = \dfrac{5}{2}$ is a horizontal asymptote on the left.

Verify the results by graphing $y = f(x)$.

• • • • • • • • •

Method 2 of the above solution used a law for limits that is required when working with rational functions.

Quotient Law for Limits

If a, L, and M are real numbers and $\lim\limits_{x \to a} f(x) = L$ and $\lim\limits_{x \to a} g(x) = M$, then

$$\lim_{x \to a} \dfrac{f(x)}{g(x)} = \dfrac{\lim\limits_{x \to a} f(x)}{\lim\limits_{x \to a} g(x)}$$

$$= \dfrac{L}{M}, \ M \neq 0$$

Example 5   **Limits and the Average Cost Function**

At a small clothing company, the estimated cost function for producing a new line of jeans is $C(x) = x^2 - 4x + 5$, where x is the number of pairs of jeans produced, in thousands.

What happens to the average cost if the number of pairs of jeans produced approaches 0? What happens to the average cost if the number of pairs of jeans produced becomes very large? What do the answers to these questions mean in economic terms?

Solution

The average cost function is $AC(x) = \dfrac{x^2 - 4x + 5}{x}$.

Because of the context, the domain of this function is restricted, $\{x \mid x \geq 0, x \in \mathbf{R}\}$. To answer the questions, consider $\lim\limits_{x \to 0^+} \dfrac{x^2 - 4x + 5}{x}$ and $\lim\limits_{x \to \infty} \dfrac{x^2 - 4x + 5}{x}$.

x	$\dfrac{x^2 - 4x + 5}{x}$
1	2
0.5	6.5
0.3	12.9$\dot{6}$
0.2	21.2
0.1	46.1
0.001	4996
0.0001	49 996
0	undefined

Since division by 0 is undefined, you cannot substitute $x = 0$ to evaluate the first limit. The line $x = 0$ is a vertical asymptote. Create a table of values where $x \to 0^+$. From the table it is apparent that evaluating the average cost function at very small values of x means that $\lim\limits_{x \to 0^+} \dfrac{x^2 - 4x + 5}{x} = \infty$.

As the number of items produced approaches 0, the average cost per pair of jeans increases without bound. This conclusion does make sense!

The start-up costs for a new process will be high if a new plant and machinery are needed. The average cost is the cost of producing so many items divided by the number of items. So the average cost per item should be very large if the number of items is small.

x	$\dfrac{x^2 - 4x + 5}{x}$
10	6.5
100	96
1 000	996
10 000	9996
100 000	99 996
1 000 000	999 996

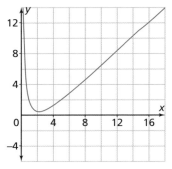

Substituting ∞ to evaluate the second limit gives the indeterminate form $\dfrac{\infty}{\infty}$. Divide by the highest power of x in the denominator.

$$\lim_{x \to \infty} \frac{x^2 - 4x + 5}{x} = \lim_{x \to \infty} \frac{\dfrac{x^2}{x} - \dfrac{4x}{x} + \dfrac{5}{x}}{\dfrac{x}{x}}$$
$$= \lim_{x \to \infty} \left(x - 4 + \frac{5}{x} \right)$$
$$= \infty$$

Therefore, the limit does not exist. The line $y = x - 4$ is an oblique asymptote. Examining a table of values for large values of x, $f(x)$ is about 4 less than x for large values. So $y = x - 4$ is an end-behaviour model.

The average cost per pair of jeans increases without bound as the number of pairs of jeans produced becomes very large.

In economic terms, it would not make sense to go ahead to make this new product if the number of items to be produced is very small or very large. In either case, the average cost per item would be very large. From the graph, the average cost per pair of jeans seems to be the least if between 2000 and 3000 pairs of jeans are produced. The company should aim to produce this much if the demand for the product exists.

CHECK, CONSOLIDATE, COMMUNICATE

1. What are the steps for finding the limit of a rational function?
2. Explain what *undefined* and *indeterminate* mean with respect to a rational function.
3. How do you use limits to determine the equation of **(a)** a vertical asymptote? **(b)** a horizontal asymptote? **(c)** an oblique asymptote?

KEY IDEAS

- If $h(x) = \dfrac{f(x)}{g(x)}$ is a rational function and a is any real number, then

$$\lim_{x \to a} h(x) = \frac{f(a)}{g(a)}, g(a) \neq 0$$

To find the limit of a rational function at a, substitute $x = a$ if the function is defined at $x = a$.

When $g(a) = 0$ and $f(a) \neq 0$, the line $x = a$ is a vertical asymptote. The limit of $h(x)$ as x approaches a from the left or the right does not exist. Use a graph or a table to determine whether $h(x) \to \infty$ or whether $h(x) \to -\infty$ as x approaches a from the left or the right.

- Substituting $x = a$ can yield the **indeterminate form** $\dfrac{0}{0}$. In this case, first factor both the numerator and the denominator, if possible. Then divide out common factors. Finally, substitute to find the limit.

- When you are finding a limit at infinity, substituting can yield another indeterminate form $\frac{\infty}{\infty}$. To find the limit in this case, find an end-behaviour model. Or, divide the functions in the numerator and denominator by the highest power of x in the denominator. Use limit rules to evaluate the limit.
- The graph of a function has a horizontal asymptote if the function has a finite limit at infinity.

5.2 Exercises

A **1.** Find each limit.

(a) $\displaystyle\lim_{x \to -2} \frac{8}{x + 4}$

(b) $\displaystyle\lim_{x \to 3} \frac{x + 1}{x - 5}$

(c) $\displaystyle\lim_{x \to -1} \frac{(x - 4)(1 - x)}{x - 3}$

(d) $\displaystyle\lim_{x \to -5} \frac{2x^2 - 3x + 1}{x^2 - 5}$

(e) $\displaystyle\lim_{x \to 2} \frac{x - 2}{x^2 + x - 1}$

(f) $\displaystyle\lim_{x \to 3} \frac{1 - \frac{2}{x}}{1 - \frac{4}{x^2}}$

 2. Verify your answers for question 1 using a graphing calculator.

3. Let $f(x) = \dfrac{x^2 + 1}{x - 3}$. Copy and complete the table. Use the table to estimate the limit as $x \to 3^-$ and as $x \to 3^+$ of $f(x)$. Does $\displaystyle\lim_{x \to 3} f(x)$ exist? Explain.

x	2.9	2.99	2.999	3	3.001	3.01	3.1
$f(x)$							

4. Let $g(x) = \dfrac{1}{(3 - x)^2}$. Copy and complete the table. Use the table to estimate the limit as $x \to 3^-$ and as $x \to 3^+$ of $g(x)$. Does $\displaystyle\lim_{x \to 3} g(x)$ exist? Explain.

x	2.9	2.99	2.999	3	3.001	3.01	3.1
$g(x)$							

5. Use a table to find each limit. Confirm your answer using technology.

(a) $\displaystyle\lim_{x \to 1^+} \frac{1}{x - 1}$

(b) $\displaystyle\lim_{x \to 1^-} \frac{1}{x - 1}$

(c) $\displaystyle\lim_{x \to 4^-} \frac{1}{4 - x}$

(d) $\displaystyle\lim_{x \to 4^+} \frac{1}{4 - x}$

(e) $\displaystyle\lim_{x \to -2^-} \frac{x}{x + 2}$

(f) $\displaystyle\lim_{x \to -2^+} \frac{x}{x + 2}$

6. Explain why you cannot substitute to evaluate each limit.

(a) $\displaystyle\lim_{x \to 0} \frac{1}{x^2}$

(b) $\displaystyle\lim_{x \to 0} \frac{(3 + x)^2 - 9}{x}$

(c) $\displaystyle\lim_{x \to 4} \frac{\frac{1}{x - 5} + 1}{x - 4}$

(d) $\displaystyle\lim_{x \to \infty} \frac{3x - 2x^3 - 3x^4}{3x^3 - 5x^4}$

7. Determine each limit .

(a) $\lim\limits_{x \to 0} \dfrac{x + 3x^2}{4x}$

(b) $\lim\limits_{x \to 1} \dfrac{1 - x^2}{1 - x}$

(c) $\lim\limits_{x \to 3} \dfrac{x^2 - 9}{2x - 6}$

(d) $\lim\limits_{x \to -1} \dfrac{x^2 - x - 2}{x + 1}$

(e) $\lim\limits_{x \to 3} \dfrac{x^2 - 4x + 3}{x^2 - 9}$

(f) $\lim\limits_{x \to -2} \dfrac{x^3 + 8}{x + 2}$

(g) $\lim\limits_{x \to 0} \dfrac{4x^3 + 9x^2}{2x^4 - 15x^2}$

(h) $\lim\limits_{x \to 0} \dfrac{\frac{1}{5 + x} - \frac{1}{5}}{x}$

(i) $\lim\limits_{h \to 0} \dfrac{(4 + h)^2 - 16}{h}$

(j) $\lim\limits_{x \to 2} \dfrac{x^2 - 4x + 4}{x^3 - 4x}$

(k) $\lim\limits_{x \to -2} \dfrac{\frac{1}{1 + x} + 1}{2x + x^2}$

(l) $\lim\limits_{x \to 0} \dfrac{27 + (x - 3)^3}{x}$

B

8. Find the vertical asymptote(s) for the graph of each function. Describe the behaviour of $f(x)$ to the left and right of each vertical asymptote.

(a) $f(x) = \dfrac{x - 1}{x + 2}$ VA = -2

(b) $f(x) = \dfrac{1}{9 - x^2}$

(c) $f(x) = \dfrac{x^2 - 4}{3x + 9}$ VA = -3

(d) $f(x) = \dfrac{2 - x}{3x^2 - 13x - 10}$

9. Describe how to find, in as many ways as possible, the horizontal asymptote for the graph of $f(x) = \dfrac{6x^2 - 5}{2x^2 + 3}$.

10. Find each limit.

(a) $\lim\limits_{x \to \infty} \dfrac{5x + 3}{4x}$

(b) $\lim\limits_{x \to \infty} \dfrac{4x^2 - 3x + 2}{3x^2 + x - 5}$

(c) $\lim\limits_{x \to \infty} \dfrac{1 + 3x^3 - 6x^5}{2x^5 - x^4 + x^2}$

(d) $\lim\limits_{x \to \infty} \dfrac{2 + 3x^2}{x^3 - 5x}$

(e) $\lim\limits_{x \to \infty} \dfrac{x^6 + 3}{x^5 - 2x^3 - 1}$

(f) $\lim\limits_{x \to \infty} \dfrac{x^2 - 3x - 10}{(x + 2)^2}$

(g) $\lim\limits_{x \to \infty} \dfrac{x^2 - x - 6}{x^2 - 9}$

(h) $\lim\limits_{x \to \infty} \left(3x - 5 + \dfrac{2}{x - 1} \right)$

11. **Communication:** Vitaly said that $\lim\limits_{x \to 5} \dfrac{x^2 - 2x - 15}{x - 5}$ does not exist since the function is undefined when $x = 5$. Show that the actual value of the limit is 8. Explain Vitaly's mistake.

12. Find each limit, if it exists. If the limit does not exist, explain why.

(a) $\lim\limits_{x \to 5} \dfrac{5 - x^2}{4x}$

(b) $\lim\limits_{x \to 3} \dfrac{x}{x^2 - 9}$

(c) $\lim\limits_{x \to -2} \dfrac{x^2 - x - 6}{x + 2}$

(d) $\lim\limits_{x \to \infty} \dfrac{3x - 2x^3 - 3x^4}{3x^2 - 5x^4}$

13. **Knowledge and Understanding:** For each function, determine any vertical or horizontal asymptotes and describe its behaviour on each side of any vertical asymptote.

(a) $f(x) = \dfrac{3x - 1}{x + 5}$

(b) $g(x) = \dfrac{x^2 + 3x - 2}{(x - 1)^2}$

(c) $h(x) = \dfrac{x^2 + x - 6}{x^2 - 4}$

(d) $m(x) = \dfrac{5x^2 - 3x + 2}{x - 2}$

14. **Application:** When Laura went to a "temp" agency for a summer job, the pay scheme was explained as shown in the margin on the next page.

Pay Scheme	
Day 1	$59.00
Day 2	$59.50
Day 3	$59.66
Day 4	$59.75
Day 5	$59.80

Laura wants to know if she will eventually earn $60 per day. The employer replies that she uses the formula $p(x) = \dfrac{60x - 1}{x}$ to calculate the pay for day x.

(a) Under this pay scheme, will Laura ever earn $60 a day?

(b) Under a new scheme, where $p(x) = \dfrac{60.05x - 1}{x}$, will Laura ever earn $60 a day?

15. The value of a car in dollars x years after it is bought is modelled by
$$f(x) = \frac{18\,000 + 5x}{2 + 0.5x} + 80.$$ Determine

(a) the value of the car when it was new

(b) the value of the car after five years

(c) what happens to the car's value as x increases

(d) the scrap value of the car (the least value the car can have)

16. The function $g(x) = 5x^2$ is an end-behaviour model for $p(x) = 5x^2 - 3x + 4$ (Example 4).

Function $k(x)$ is a **right-end-behaviour model** for $f(x)$ if and only if
$$\lim_{x \to \infty} \frac{f(x)}{k(x)} = 1.$$

Function $k(x)$ is a **left-end-behaviour model** for $f(x)$ if and only if
$$\lim_{x \to -\infty} \frac{f(x)}{k(x)} = 1.$$

Verify that $k(x) = 5x^2$ is an end-behaviour model for $f(x) = 5x^2 - 3x + 4$ by evaluating the limits in the definition.

17. Find an end-behaviour model for each function. Identify any horizontal asymptotes.

(a) $f(x) = \dfrac{x + 1}{2x^2 + 3x - 4}$

(b) $f(x) = \dfrac{4x^2 - x - 3}{x^2 + 2}$

18. **Thinking, Inquiry, Problem Solving:** Let $\lim_{x \to a} f(x) = 0$, and $\lim_{x \to a} g(x) = \infty$. What, if anything, can you say about $\lim_{x \to a} [f(x) \times g(x)]$? Investigate these three limits for each pair of functions. Create some of your own.

(a) $f(x) = \dfrac{2}{x}$, $g(x) = 2x$, as $x \to 0$

(b) $f(x) = \dfrac{1}{x - 3}$, $g(x) = (x - 3)^2$, as $x \to 3$

(c) $f(x) = \dfrac{4}{(1 - x)^3}$, $g(x) = x - 1$, as $x \to 1$

19. **Check Your Understanding:** When can you *not* substitute to find a limit of a rational function? Use examples in your explanation.

C **20.** For $f(x) = \dfrac{x^2 - 16}{x - 4}$, show that $\lim_{x \to 4} f(x)$ is 8. In what interval does the value of $f(x)$ lie for the interval $3.99 \le x \le 4.01$?

21. For the function $f(x) = \dfrac{4x}{x-1}$,

    (a) for what value of x is $f(x) = 6$?

    (b) what values of x make $\left| f(x) - 6 \right| \le 0.01$ true?

    (c) what values of x make $\left| f(x) - 6 \right| \le 0.001$ true?

22. For $\lim\limits_{x \to 0} f(x) = 0$ and $\lim\limits_{x \to 0} g(x) = 0$, does $\lim\limits_{x \to 0} \dfrac{f(x)}{g(x)}$ exist? Explain with examples.

ADDITIONAL ACHIEVEMENT CHART QUESTIONS

Knowledge and Understanding: Find each limit, if it exists. If it does not exist, explain why.

(a) $\lim\limits_{x \to \infty} \dfrac{6x^3 - 3x + 1}{2x^3 + x^2 - 5}$ **(b)** $\lim\limits_{x \to -2} \dfrac{x}{x^2 - x - 6}$ **(c)** $\lim\limits_{x \to -\infty} \dfrac{2x^2 + 3x}{x - 1}$

Application: Suppose the number of houses in a new subdivision after t months of development is modelled by $N(t) = \dfrac{1000t^3}{100 + t^3}$, where N is the number of houses and $t \ge 0$.

(a) How many houses will be in the subdivision when the development is complete?

(b) After how many years is the subdivision fully developed?

Thinking, Inquiry, Problem Solving: If $\lim\limits_{x \to \infty} f(x) = \infty$ and $\lim\limits_{x \to \infty} g(x) = \infty$, does $\lim\limits_{x \to \infty} \dfrac{f(x)}{g(x)}$ exist? Explain with examples.

Communication: Explain why $\lim\limits_{x \to \infty} \dfrac{mx + b}{x^2 + 5x + 1} = 0$ for any $m, b \in \mathbf{R}$.

The Chapter Problem
Designing a Settling Pond

Apply what you learned in this section to answer these questions about The Chapter Problem on page 342.

CP6. What kind(s) of asymptotes do the graphs of the arsenic concentration functions have? Determine their equations.

CP7. In each case, what will happen to the concentration of arsenic in the pond in the long run?

CP8. Graph each function.

CP9. By using your graphs, or otherwise, determine the times at which the concentration of arsenic reaches 100 µg/L.

5.3 Continuity of Rational Functions

SETTING THE STAGE

Explore the concepts in this lesson in more detail using Exploration 9 on page 576.

The demand for a new music CD is described by

$$D(p) = \begin{cases} \dfrac{1}{p^2} & \text{if } 0 < p \le 15 \\ 0 & \text{if } p > 15 \end{cases}$$

where D is the demand for the CD at price p in dollars.

Where is the demand function continuous?

A polynomial function is continuous for all values of the domain. In this section, you will examine how asymptotes and other features of rational functions affect the continuity of rational functions.

EXAMINING THE CONCEPT

Continuity at a Point

A function $f(x)$ is continuous at $x = a$ if and only if $\lim\limits_{x \to a} f(x) = f(a)$. For the function to be continuous at $x = a$, the following three conditions must be true:

1. $\lim\limits_{x \to a} f(x)$ exists

2. $f(a)$ exists (or is defined)

3. $\lim\limits_{x \to a} f(x) = f(a)$

Example 1 Finding Points of Continuity and Discontinuity

Find all numbers, $x = a$, for which each function is discontinuous. For each discontinuity, state which of the three conditions for continuity are not satisfied.

(a) $f(x) = \dfrac{x}{(x + 1)^2}$ **(b)** $g(x) = \dfrac{x^2 - 9}{x - 3}$

(c) $h(x) = \begin{cases} 2x^4 - 3x^3 - x^2 + x - 1 & \text{if } x \le 2 \\ \dfrac{x^2 + 2x - 3}{x - 1} & \text{if } x > 2 \end{cases}$

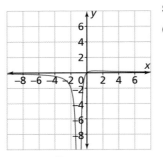

$f(x) = \frac{x}{(x+1)^2}$, discontinuous at $x = -1$

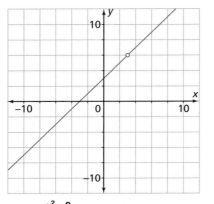

$g(x) = \frac{x^2-9}{x-3}$, discontinuous at $x = 3$

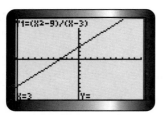

Solution

(a) The function is in simplified form. The denominator, $(x + 1)^2$, is 0 when $x = -1$. The function is discontinuous at $x = -1$. The line $x = -1$ is a vertical asymptote. $f(-1)$ does not exist and $\lim\limits_{x \to -1} f(x)$ does not exist. Conditions 1 and 2 are not satisfied.

(b) First, factor.

$$g(x) = \frac{x^2 - 9}{x - 3}$$
$$= \frac{(x - 3)(x + 3)}{(x - 3)}$$
$$= x + 3 \quad \text{if } x \neq 3$$

The denominator is 0 when $x = 3$. The graph of the simplified function is the line $y = x + 3$. But the graph of the original function has a hole at $x = 3$. $g(3)$ does not exist. Condition 2 is not satisfied.

(c) $h(x) = \begin{cases} 2x^4 - 3x^3 - x^2 + x - 1 & \text{if } x \leq 2 \\ \dfrac{x^2 + 2x - 3}{x - 1} & \text{if } x > 2 \end{cases}$

When $x < 2$, $h(x)$ is the polynomial $2x^4 - 3x^3 - x^2 + x - 1$. Since a polynomial is continuous for all values in its domain, this function is continuous for $x < 2$.

When $x > 2$, $h(x)$ is the rational function $\dfrac{x^2 + 2x - 3}{x - 1}$. Since a rational function is discontinuous only if the denominator equals 0, (in this case, when $x = 1$) this function is continuous for $x > 2$.

The only place where the function might be discontinuous is at $x = 2$. The function is continuous at $x = 2$ if $\lim\limits_{x \to 2} h(x) = h(2)$.

Since $h(2) = 2(2)^4 - 3(2)^3 - (2)^2 + (2) - 1 = 5$, $h(2)$ is defined.

And $\lim\limits_{x \to 2^-} h(x) = \lim\limits_{x \to 2^-} (2x^4 - 3x^3 - x^2 + x - 1)$
$$= 2(2)^4 - 3(2)^3 - (2)^2 + (2) - 1$$
$$= 5$$

Since $h(x) = \dfrac{x^2 + 2x - 3}{x - 1}$ if $x > 2$, $\lim\limits_{x \to 2^+} h(x) = \lim\limits_{x \to 2^+} \dfrac{x^2 + 2x - 3}{x - 1}$
$$= \frac{(2)^2 + 2(2) - 3}{(2) - 1}$$
$$= 5$$

The one-sided limits are the same, so $\lim\limits_{x \to 2} h(x) = 5$. Also $\lim\limits_{x \to 2} h(x) = h(2)$ and $h(2) = 5$.

All three conditions for continuity are satisfied at $x = 2$. $h(x)$ is continuous for all values of its domain.

• • • • • • • •

Example 2   **Examining a Jump Discontinuity**

The demand for a new music CD is described by $D(p) = \begin{cases} \dfrac{1}{p^2} & \text{if } 0 < p \le 15 \\ 0 & \text{if } p > 15 \end{cases}$,

where D is the demand for the CD at price p in dollars.
Determine where the demand function is continuous.

Solution

For $0 < p < 15$, $D(p) = \dfrac{1}{p^2}$ is continuous for all values of p in this interval.

For $p > 15$, $D(p) = 0$. $D(p) = 0$ is continuous for all values of p such that $p > 15$.

When $p = 15$, $D(15) = \dfrac{1}{15^2} = \dfrac{1}{225}$, so $D(15)$ is defined.

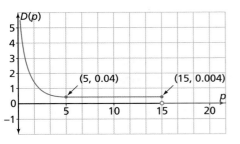

$$\lim_{p \to 15^-} D(p) = \lim_{p \to 15^-} \frac{1}{p^2} = \frac{1}{225}$$

$$\lim_{p \to 15^+} D(p) = \lim_{p \to 15^+} 0 = 0$$

Since the one-sided limits are not the same, $\lim_{p \to 15} D(p)$ does not exist.

The graph of the function has a break or "jump" at $p = 15$.

The demand function has a **jump discontinuity** at $p = 15$.

• • • • • • • •

A discontinuity is a **jump discontinuity** when the one-sided limits exist but are not equal. Sometimes, if a discontinuity is a hole in an otherwise continuous graph, it can be removed by redefining the function at that point.

Example 3   **Removing a Discontinuity**

Determine the point of discontinuity for $f(x) = \dfrac{x^2 + 3x - 10}{x - 2}$.
Then redefine the function to remove the discontinuity.

Solution

Factor the numerator.

$$f(x) = \frac{x^2 + 3x - 10}{x - 2}$$

$$= \frac{{}^1(x - 2)(x + 5)}{(x - 2)_1}$$

$$= x + 5, x \ne 2$$

Use a table and graph $y = f(x)$.

x	f(x)
−3	2
−2	3
−1	4
0	5
1	6
2	undefined
3	8
4	9

The function has a discontinuity at $x = 2$. The discontinuity is represented by a hole in the graph. $f(2)$ is not defined.

However, as x approaches 2 from either side, $f(x)$ approaches 7.

$$\lim_{x \to 2^-} f(x) = \lim_{x \to 2^+} f(x) = 7, \text{ so } \lim_{x \to 2} f(x) = 7$$

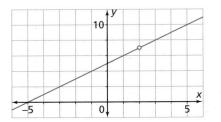

The function will satisfy the conditions for continuity at $x = 2$ if the function is defined so that $f(2) = 7$.

$$\text{Define } f(x) = \begin{cases} \dfrac{x^2 + 3x - 10}{x - 2} & \text{if } x \neq 2 \\ 7 & \text{if } x = 2 \end{cases} \quad \text{to remove the discontinuity.}$$

· · · · · · · ·

The Continuity of Rational Functions

Rational functions are continuous at every point where they are defined, so they are continuous on their domain. However, rational functions are undefined at the zeros of their denominator. At these points they have either removable discontinuities (holes) or vertical asymptotes.

Example 4   **Determining Continuous Functions**

Which functions in examples 1, 2, and 3 are continuous?

Solution

In Example 1, the functions in parts (a) and (b) are discontinuous because each one has a discontinuity. The function in (c) is continuous since it is continuous at every point in its domain.

In Example 2, the demand function is not continuous since it has a discontinuity at $p = 15$.

In Example 3, the original function is not continuous since it has a discontinuity, but the redefined function is continuous since it is continuous at every point in its domain.

CHECK, CONSOLIDATE, COMMUNICATE

1. Describe, with examples, where a rational function can be discontinuous.
2. What is a removable discontinuity, and how is it removed?
3. Give three examples of continuous rational functions and three examples of functions that are not continuous. Explain why the latter three are not continuous.

KEY IDEAS

- A rational function $h(x) = \dfrac{f(x)}{g(x)}$ is continuous at $x = a$ if $g(a) \neq 0$.
- A rational function in simplified form has vertical asymptotes at the zeros of the denominator.

- The graph of a rational function will have a hole at $x = a$ if $(x - a)$ is a common factor of the functions in the numerator and denominator.
- A discontinuity is a **jump discontinuity** when the one-sided limits exist but are not equal.
- A removable discontinuity can be removed by redefining the function at the point of discontinuity to make the function continuous.
- Rational functions are continuous on their domain, but may have points of discontinuity at the zeros of their denominators that result in holes or vertical asymptotes.

5.3 Exercises

A

1. Each function has a discontinuity at $x = 2$. In each case, state which of the continuity conditions are not satisfied.

   (a) $f(x) = \dfrac{x^2 + x - 6}{x - 2}$

   (b) $f(x) = \begin{cases} \dfrac{x^2 + x - 6}{x - 2} & \text{if } x \neq 2 \\ 2 & \text{if } x = 2 \end{cases}$

   (c) $f(x) = \dfrac{x^2 - x + 6}{x - 2}$

2. For each function, find any points of discontinuity. State which of the conditions of continuity are not satisfied.

   (a) $f(x) = \dfrac{1}{(x + 3)^2}$ **(b)** $f(x) = \dfrac{x + 1}{x^2 - 4x - 5}$ **(c)** $f(x) = \dfrac{1}{x^2 - 1}$

3. Sketch each function. Determine any discontinuities.

   (a) $f(x) = \dfrac{2}{x - 3}$ **(b)** $f(x) = 2x - \dfrac{1}{x + 1}$ **(c)** $f(x) = \dfrac{x^2 - 9}{x + 3}$

   (d) $f(x) = \dfrac{4x^2 - x^4}{x^2 - 4}$ **(e)** $f(x) = \dfrac{x + 2}{x^2 - 3x - 10}$ **(f)** $f(x) = \dfrac{x^2 - x - 6}{x - 3}$

4. Determine whether each function is continuous at $x = -1$ or not. Justify your decision.

   (a) $f(x) = \begin{cases} \dfrac{x^2 - 1}{x + 1} & \text{if } x \neq -1 \\ -2 & \text{if } x = -1 \end{cases}$

   (b) $f(x) = \begin{cases} \dfrac{1}{x + 1} & \text{if } x \neq -1 \\ 0 & \text{if } x = -1 \end{cases}$

5. **Knowledge and Understanding:** Determine where each function is continuous.

   (a) $f(x) = \dfrac{3x}{x - 4}$ **(b)** $g(x) = \dfrac{x^2 - x - 12}{x^2 - 16}$ **(c)** $h(x) = \begin{cases} \dfrac{x}{x - 3} & \text{if } x < 2 \\ x - 4 & \text{if } x \geq 2 \end{cases}$

B   **6. Communication:** Explain the difference between saying that $f(x)$ is continuous at $x = a$ and saying that $\lim\limits_{x \to a} f(x)$ exists.

7. Determine where each function is continuous.

(a) $f(x) = \dfrac{x}{x^2 + x}$ (b) $f(x) = \dfrac{x}{x^2 - 1}$ (c) $f(x) = \dfrac{x - 4}{x^2 - 16}$

8. Show that $f(x) = \dfrac{x^2 + 3x - 4}{x + 4}$ has a discontinuity at $x = -4$.

How must $f(-4)$ be defined to make $f(x)$ continuous?

9. Define $f(1)$ so that $f(x) = \dfrac{x^2 - 1}{x - 1}$ is continuous for all values of x.

10. Where possible, define each function so that it is continuous for all values of x.

(a) $f(x) = \dfrac{x^2 - 9}{x - 3}$ (b) $f(x) = \dfrac{x - 2}{x^2 - 4}$

11. Application: For what values of a does $f(x) = \dfrac{x^2 + x + a}{x^2 + 2x - 3}$ have a removable discontinuity? For each value of a, redefine the function to make it continuous.

12. For $f(x) = \begin{cases} \dfrac{2}{x^2 + 1} & \text{if } x < 0 \text{ or } x > 1 \\ x & \text{if } 0 \le x \le 1 \end{cases}$

(a) sketch $f(x)$

(b) determine where the function is continuous

13. Determine where each function is continuous.

(a) $f(x) = \dfrac{1}{x^2}$ (b) $f(x) = \dfrac{x}{x^2 + 1}$ (c) $f(x) = \dfrac{x^2 - 4}{x - 2}$

(d) $f(x) = \dfrac{x - 1}{1 - x}$ (e) $f(x) = \dfrac{x + 1}{x^2 - 4x - 5}$

(f) $f(x) = \begin{cases} \dfrac{x}{4} & \text{if } x \le 2 \\ \dfrac{1}{x} & \text{if } x > 2 \end{cases}$ (g) $f(x) = \begin{cases} \dfrac{x^2 + 2x - 3}{x^2 - 1} & \text{if } x \ne \pm 1 \\ 2 & \text{if } x = 1 \end{cases}$

14. Thinking, Inquiry, Problem Solving: Define a function that has a removable discontinuity at $x = -2$ and a jump discontinuity at $x = 3$.

15. Which functions in questions 12, 13, and 14 are continuous? Give reasons for your answers.

16. Let $f(x) = \begin{cases} x^2 & \text{if } x < 1 \\ \dfrac{A}{x + 3} & \text{if } x \ge 1 \end{cases}$. Find A if the function is continuous at $x = 1$.

17. Check Your Understanding: What are the conditions for continuity at a point, and at what points are rational functions continuous? Explain, with an example, the steps for finding the points of discontinuity for a rational function.

C **18.** What must be true about A and B for $f(x) = \begin{cases} \dfrac{Ax - B}{x - 2} & \text{if } x \leq 1 \\ 3x & \text{if } 1 < x < 2 \\ Bx^2 - A & \text{if } x \geq 2 \end{cases}$

if the function is continuous at $x = 1$ but discontinuous at $x = 2$?

19. Use graphs to show whether the following is true or not:

A function that is continuous at every x-value on the interval $a < x < b$ will take on every value between $f(a)$ and $f(b)$ on $a < x < b$. But a function that is not continuous on $a < x < b$ might not take on every value between $f(a)$ and $f(b)$ in $a < x < b$.

ADDITIONAL ACHIEVEMENT CHART QUESTIONS

Knowledge and Understanding: Find the points of discontinuity, if any.

(a) $f(x) = \dfrac{x}{x^2 + 1}$

(b) $f(x) = \dfrac{x - 4}{x^2 - 16}$

(c) $f(x) = \begin{cases} 2x + 3 & \text{if } x \leq 4 \\ 7 + \dfrac{16}{x} & \text{if } x > 4 \end{cases}$

(d) $f(x) = \begin{cases} \dfrac{3}{x - 1} & \text{if } x \neq 1 \\ 3 & \text{if } x = 1 \end{cases}$

Application: A student parking lot at a university charges \$2 for the first half hour (or any part) and \$1 for each subsequent half hour (or any part) up to a daily maximum of \$10.

(a) Graph cost as a function of the time parked.

(b) Using a graph, discuss the meaning of discontinuities to a student who parks in the student parking lot.

Thinking, Inquiry, Problem Solving: Create the graph of a function so that it is not continuous at $x = 3$ and so that the function becomes continuous at $x = 3$ if its value at $x = 3$ is changed from $f(3) = 1$ to $f(3) = 0$.

Communication: Determine whether each function is continuous or not. Explain your reasoning.

(a) your exact height as a function of time

(b) the cost of a taxi ride in your city as a function of the distance travelled

(c) the volume of a melting ice cube as a function of time

(d) the Earth's population as a function of time

5.4 Rate of Change of a Rational Function—The Quotient Rule

SETTING THE STAGE

Polluted water flows at a rate of 3 m^3/min into a pond. The pond initially holds 10 000 m^3 of unpolluted water. The concentration of pollutant in the polluted water is 9 kg/m^3. The concentration of pollutant, c, in the pond at t minutes is modelled by $c(t) = \frac{27t}{10\ 000 + 3t}$, where c is measured in kilograms per cubic metre. What is the domain of this function? At what rate is the concentration changing after one hour? one day? one week? What is the average rate of change of $c(t)$ in the first week? What will happen to the concentration of pollutant in the long run?

In this problem, the rate at which the concentration of pollutant is changing at time t is given by the derivative $c'(t)$. In this section, you will develop techniques that will enable you to determine the derivative of a rational function.

EXAMINING THE CONCEPT

The Derivative of a Rational Function

Recall that the derivative of $f(x)$ is $f'(x) = \lim\limits_{h \to 0} \frac{f(x + h) - f(x)}{h}$ for all x for which the limit exists.

Example 1 **Finding the Derivative of a Rational Function from First Principles**

For $c(t) = \frac{27t}{10\ 000 + 3t}$, find $c'(t)$ from first principles.

Solution

$$c'(t) = \lim_{h \to 0} \frac{c(t + h) - c(t)}{h}$$

$$= \lim_{h \to 0} \frac{1}{h}\left[\frac{27(t + h)}{10\ 000 + 3(t + h)} - \frac{27t}{10\ 000 + 3t} \right] \quad \text{Find a common denominator.}$$

$$= \lim_{h \to 0} \frac{1}{h}\left\{ \frac{27(t + h)(10\ 000 + 3t) - 27t[10\ 000 + 3(t + h)]}{[10\ 000 + 3(t + h)](10\ 000 + 3t)} \right\} \quad \text{Expand the numerator.}$$

It is important to note that the derivative of a quotient of two differentiable functions is not the quotient of the derivatives.

$$= \lim_{h \to 0} \frac{27}{h}\left\{ \frac{10\ 000t + 3t^2 + 10\ 000h + 3ht - (10\ 000t + 3t^2 + 3ht)}{[10\ 000 + 3(t + h)](10\ 000 + 3t)} \right\} \quad \text{Simplify.}$$

$$= \lim_{h \to 0} \frac{27}{h}\left\{ \frac{10\ 000h}{[10\ 000 + 3(t + h)](10\ 000 + 3t)} \right\} \quad \text{Simplify.}$$

$$= \lim_{h \to 0} \frac{270\ 000}{[10\ 000 + 3(t + h)](10\ 000 + 3t)} \quad \text{Evaluate the limit.}$$

$$= \frac{270\ 000}{(10\ 000 + 3t)^2}$$

There is a simpler way of finding the derivative for a rational function.

The Quotient Rule for Derivatives

Let $h(x) = \dfrac{f(x)}{g(x)}$. If both $f'(x)$ and $g'(x)$ exist, the derivative of $h(x)$ is

$$h'(x) = \frac{f'(x)g(x) - g'(x)f(x)}{[g(x)]^2}, \text{ where } g(x) \neq 0.$$

In Leibniz notation, $\dfrac{d}{dx}\left(\dfrac{f(x)}{g(x)}\right) = \dfrac{\left[\frac{d}{dx}f(x)\right]g(x) - \left[\frac{d}{dx}g(x)\right]f(x)}{[g(x)]^2}$, $g(x) \neq 0.$

The rule in words: The derivative of the top times the bottom minus the derivative of the bottom times the top all over the bottom squared.

Proof
The rule for finding the derivative of the quotient of two functions follows from the product rule for derivatives. Suppose that there are functions f and g, and that $g(x) \neq 0$. Then, $\dfrac{f(x)}{g(x)}$ defines a quotient of the two functions.

Let $\qquad\qquad h(x) = \dfrac{f(x)}{g(x)}$ $\qquad\qquad$ Multiply both sides by $g(x)$.

$\qquad\qquad g(x)h(x) = f(x)$ $\qquad\qquad$ Differentiate both sides with respect to x.

$g'(x)h(x) + h'(x)g(x) = f'(x)$ $\qquad$ Solve for $h'(x)$.

$\qquad\qquad h'(x) = \dfrac{f'(x) - g'(x)h(x)}{g(x)}$ $\qquad$ Substitute $h(x) = \dfrac{f(x)}{g(x)}$.

$\qquad\qquad = \dfrac{f'(x) - g'(x)\frac{f(x)}{g(x)}}{g(x)}$ $\qquad$ Multiply both the numerator and the denominator by $g(x)$.

$\qquad\qquad h'(x) = \dfrac{f'(x)g(x) - g'(x)f(x)}{[g(x)]^2}$

Example 2   Using the Quotient Rule

Find the derivative of each rational function using the quotient rule. Verify with graphing technology.

(a) $y = \dfrac{2x + 5}{3x - 1}$ $\qquad$ **(b)** $y = \dfrac{x^3 - 3}{1 + 4x^2}$ $\qquad$ **(c)** $y = \dfrac{x^2}{(x + 2)(x - 3)}$

Technology Help:
For help with using the numerical derivative operation, nDeriv(, see page 595 of the Technology Appendix.

Solution
Use the quotient rule to find the derivative. To verify, graph the derivative function you found with the TI-83 Plus by entering the function into **Y1** of the equation editor. Then enter the numerical derivative of the original function as **Y2**. Both functions should yield the same graph.

(a) Apply the quotient rule with $f(x) = 2x + 5$ and $g(x) = 3x - 1$.

$$\frac{dy}{dx} = \frac{f'(x)g(x) - g'(x)f(x)}{[g(x)]^2}$$

$$= \frac{2(3x - 1) - (3)(2x + 5)}{(3x - 1)^2}$$

$$= \frac{6x - 2 - 6x - 15}{(3x - 1)^2}$$

$$= \frac{-17}{(3x - 1)^2}$$

$-4.7 \le x \le 4.7; -5 \le y \le 5$

(b) $f(x) = x^3 - 3$ and $g(x) = 1 + 4x^2$

$$\frac{dy}{dx} = \frac{f'(x)g(x) - g'(x)f(x)}{[g(x)]^2}$$

$$= \frac{(3x^2)(1 + 4x^2) - (x^3 - 3)(8x)}{(1 + 4x^2)^2}$$

$$= \frac{3x^2 + 12x^4 - 8x^4 + 24x}{(1 + 4x^2)^2}$$

$$= \frac{4x^4 + 3x^2 + 24x}{(1 + 4x^2)^2}$$

$$= \frac{x(4x^3 + 3x + 24)}{(1 + 4x^2)^2}$$

$-4.7 \le x \le 4.7; -5 \le y \le 5$

(c) Here $f(x) = x^2$ and $g(x) = (x + 2)(x - 3)$. Use the product rule to find $g'(x)$.

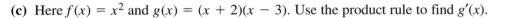

$$\frac{dy}{dx} = \frac{f'(x)g(x) - g'(x)f(x)}{[g(x)]^2}$$

$$= \frac{(2x)(x + 2)(x - 3) - [(1)(x - 3) + (x + 2)(1)]x^2}{[(x + 2)(x - 3)]^2}$$

$$= \frac{(2x)(x^2 - x - 6) - x^2(2x - 1)}{(x + 2)^2(x - 3)^2}$$

$$= \frac{2x^3 - 2x^2 - 12x - 2x^3 + x^2}{(x + 2)^2(x - 3)^2}$$

$$= \frac{-x^2 - 12x}{(x + 2)^2(x - 3)^2}$$

$$= \frac{-x(x + 12)}{(x + 2)^2(x - 3)^2}$$

$-4.7 \le x \le 4.7; -5 \le y \le 5$

• • • • • • • •

For most functions that are quotients, the derivative function is also a quotient. Use the quotient rule again to find the second derivative.

Example 3 **Finding the Second Derivative of a Rational Function**

An object moves along a straight line. The object's position, s, at t seconds is modelled by $s(t) = \frac{5t}{t^2 + 1}$. When does the object change direction? What is its acceleration at that instant?

Solution

When the object changes direction, its velocity, $s'(t)$, changes sign.

The velocity function is $v(t) = s'(t)$.

$$s'(t) = \frac{(5)(t^2 + 1) - (2t)(5t)}{(t^2 + 1)^2}$$

$$= \frac{5 - 5t^2}{t^4 + 2t^2 + 1} \text{ or } \frac{5(1 - t)(1 + t)}{t^4 + 2t^2 + 1}$$

$s'(t) = 0$ when $t = \pm 1$. But $t \geq 0$, so the negative root is inadmissible.

The velocity changes sign when $t = 1$. The object changes direction after exactly one second.

The acceleration function is $a(t) = v'(t) = s''(t)$.

$$s''(t) = \frac{-10t(t^4 + 2t^2 + 1) - (4t^3 + 4t)(5 - 5t^2)}{(t^4 + 2t^2 + 1)^2}$$

$$= \frac{-10t^5 - 20t^3 - 10t - (20t^3 - 20t^5 + 20t - 20t^3)}{[(t^2 + 1)^2]^2} \quad \text{Simplify.}$$

$$= \frac{10t^5 - 20t^3 - 30t}{(t^2 + 1)^4} \quad \text{Factor.}$$

$$= \frac{10t(t^4 - 2t^2 - 3)}{(t^2 + 1)^4}$$

$$= \frac{10t(t^2 - 3)(t^2 + 1)}{(t^2 + 1)^4} \quad \text{Simplify.}$$

$$= \frac{10t(t^2 - 3)}{(t^2 + 1)^3}$$

Therefore, $s''(1) = \dfrac{10(1 - 3)}{(2)^3}$, or -2.5.

The object's acceleration at the instant it changes direction is -2.5 units/s^2.

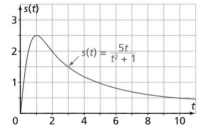

Graph the position function. When $t = 1$, the object has stopped briefly. Before $t = 1$, the object was moving away from a point. After $t = 1$, the object is moving toward the point. Velocity is represented by the slopes of tangent lines to this graph. At the maximum point on the graph, the slope of the tangent line is 0. The velocity is decreasing before $t = 1$. And the velocity is decreasing after $t = 1$. The graph is concave down at its peak. The acceleration is negative.

• • • • • • • •

Example 4 **Analyzing the Pollution Problem**

Recall the original problem in Setting the Stage:

   Polluted water flows at a rate of 3 m^3/min into a pond. The pond initially holds 10 000 m^3 of unpolluted water. The initial concentration of pollutant in the polluted water is 9 kg/m^3. The concentration of pollutant, c, in the pond at t minutes is modelled by $c(t) = \dfrac{27t}{10\ 000 + 3t}$.

(a) What is the domain of this function?

(b) At what rate is the concentration changing after one hour? one day? one week?

(c) What is the average rate of change of $c(t)$ in the first week?

(d) What will happen to the concentration of pollutant in the long run?

Solution

(a) Since t represents time, the domain of $c(t) = \dfrac{27t}{10\ 000 + 3t}$ is restricted to all real numbers greater than or equal to 0, $\{t \mid t \geq 0, t \in \mathbf{R}\}$.

(b) Find the derivative.

$$c'(t) = \frac{27(10\ 000 + 3t) - (3)(27t)}{(10\ 000 + 3t)^2} \qquad \text{Simplify.}$$

$$= \frac{270\ 000}{(10\ 000 + 3t)^2}$$

You could find these values more quickly using **nDeriv(**, which is accurate to five decimal places.

At 1 h, $t = 60$, and $c'(60) \doteq 0.0026$.

At 1 h, the concentration is increasing at about 0.0026 kg/m³/min.

After one day, $t = 1440$, and $c'(1440) \doteq 0.0013$.

After one day, the concentration is increasing at about 0.0013 kg/m³/min.

After one week, $t = 10\ 080$, and $c'(10\ 080) \doteq 0.0002$.

After one week, the concentration is increasing at about 0.0002 kg/m³/min. The rate at which the concentration is increasing decreases over time.

(c) The average rate of change of $c(t)$ in the first week is $\dfrac{c(10\ 080) - c(0)}{10\ 080 - 0}$, or about 0.0007 kg/m³/min.

(d) To determine what happens to the concentration of pollutant in the long run, find $\lim\limits_{t \to \infty} c(t)$.

$$\lim_{t \to \infty} \frac{27t}{10\ 000 + 3t} = \lim_{t \to \infty} \frac{\frac{27t}{t}}{\frac{10\ 000}{t} + \frac{3t}{t}}$$

$$= \frac{27}{0 + 3}$$

$$= 9$$

The concentration will approach the concentration of the polluted water entering the pond.

Of course, this conclusion assumes that the pond has an infinite capacity, which is not a reasonable assumption!

The pond would actually overflow into the surrounding area and the water would drain away into the ground or into any nearby creeks, carrying the pollution farther afield.

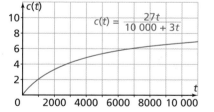

Graph concentration versus time. The slopes of the tangent lines decrease over time. The curve seems to approach a limiting value.

CHECK, CONSOLIDATE, COMMUNICATE

1. Use an example to show that the derivative of a rational function is not the same as the quotient of the derivatives of its numerator and denominator.
2. Compare the quotient rule to the product rule. What is similar about the two rules? What is different?
3. Why might you need to find the first and second derivatives of a rational function? Give an example of a rational function. Then find the first and second derivatives.

KEY IDEAS

- The derivative of a quotient of two differentiable functions is not the quotient of their derivatives.
- The **quotient rule** is a rule for finding the derivative of a rational function.

  Let $h(x) = \dfrac{f(x)}{g(x)}$. If both $f'(x)$ and $g'(x)$ exist, the derivative of $h(x)$ is

  $$h'(x) = \frac{f'(x)g(x) - g'(x)f(x)}{[g(x)]^2} \text{ where } g(x) \neq 0.$$

- The quotient rule in Leibniz notation is

  $$\frac{d}{dx}\left(\frac{f(x)}{g(x)}\right) = \frac{\left[\frac{d}{dx}f(x)\right]g(x) - \left[\frac{d}{dx}g(x)\right]f(x)}{[g(x)]^2}, \ g(x) \neq 0.$$

5.4 Exercises

A

1. Find the derivative of each rational function from first principles.

   (a) $f(x) = \dfrac{x}{3-x}$ **(b)** $g(x) = \dfrac{x-2}{1+x}$ **(c)** $h(x) = \dfrac{3x^2 - 2}{x}$

2. Use the quotient rule to find $f'(x)$ for each function.

   (a) $f(x) = \dfrac{x-3}{x+3}$ **(b)** $f(x) = \dfrac{3x^4}{x^2 - 6}$

   (c) $f(x) = \dfrac{x^3 - 2x}{x^2 + x + 1}$ **(d)** $f(x) = \dfrac{(x+4)(x-5)}{2x(x+3)}$

   (e) $f(x) = \dfrac{x^3}{1-x}$ **(f)** $f(x) = \dfrac{ax - b}{cx - d}$

   (g) $f(x) = \dfrac{x^2 - 1}{2x + 3}$ **(h)** $f(x) = \dfrac{5x^4 + 9}{x + 2}$

   (i) $f(x) = \dfrac{1 + x^4}{x^2}$ **(j)** $f(x) = \dfrac{5 - \frac{1}{x}}{x - 3}$

3. Verify your answers for question 2 by graphing $\mathbf{Y1} = f'(x)$ and $\mathbf{Y2} = \mathbf{nDeriv}\, f(x)$ in the same window.

4. Find $\dfrac{dy}{dx}$.

(a) $y = \dfrac{x + 6}{(x + 1)^2}$

(b) $y = \dfrac{5x^3}{2(x - 3)}$

(c) $y = \dfrac{(x + 1)(x - 4)}{(x - 2)}$

(d) $y = \dfrac{x - 5}{(3x + 1)(3x - 2)}$

5. When asked to find the derivative of $f(x) = \dfrac{x^5 - 2x}{x^2}$, Vassili used the quotient rule. Instead of using the quotient rule, Kelly divided each term in the numerator by the denominator and then simplified. Then she found the derivative of each term. Find the derivative using each method. Explain which method you prefer, and why.

6. Knowledge and Understanding: Find the equation of the tangent to the graph of $f(x) = \dfrac{x}{3 - 2x}$ at the point where $x = 1$.

7. Find an equation for the tangent to the graph of the function at the given value of x.

(a) $f(x) = \dfrac{x}{x + 3}; x = -5$

(b) $f(x) = \dfrac{2x + 5}{5x - 1}; x = -1$

8. Find the point(s) where the tangent to the curve is horizontal.

(a) $f(x) = \dfrac{5x}{x^2 + 1}$

(b) $f(x) = \dfrac{x^2 - 2x + 4}{x^2 + 4}$

9. An object moves along a straight line. The object's position at time t is given by $s(t)$. Find the position, velocity, acceleration, and speed at the specified time.

(a) $s(t) = \dfrac{2t}{t + 3}; t = 3$

(b) $s(t) = t + \dfrac{5}{t + 2}; t = 1$

10. Communication: An object moves along a straight line so that its position, s, at t seconds is given by $s(t) = \dfrac{t^2 + 2t + 5}{t + 2}$. Does the object change direction at any time? Justify your answer.

11. The position, s, of an object that moves in a straight line at time t is given by $s(t) = \dfrac{t}{t^2 + 8}$. Determine when the object changes direction.

12. Salt water has a concentration of 10 g of salt per litre. The salt water flows into a large tank that initially holds 500 L of pure water. Twenty litres of the salt water flow into the tank per minute. Show that the concentration of salt, c, in the tank at t minutes is given by $c(t) = \frac{10t}{25 + t}$, where c is measured in grams per litre. What is the rate of change of c with respect to t?

13. Application: The concentration, c, of a drug in the blood t hours after the drug is taken orally is given by $c(t) = \frac{5t}{2t^2 + 7}$. When does the concentration reach its maximum value?

14. At a manufacturing plant, productivity is measured by the number of items, p, produced per employee per day over the previous 10 years. Productivity is modelled by $p(t) = \frac{25t}{t + 1}$, where t is the number of years measured from 10 years ago. Determine the rate of change of p with respect to t.

15. Find $\frac{dy}{dx}$ for $y = \frac{x^2 - 1}{2x^2 + 1}$. Determine the values of x for which $\frac{dy}{dx}$ is positive.

16. Functions u and v are differentiable functions of x, and $y = \frac{u}{v}$. Determine $\frac{dy}{dx}$ from first principles.

17. The radius of a circular juice blot on a piece of paper towel t seconds after it was first seen is modelled by $r(t) = \frac{1 + 2t}{1 + t}$, where r is measured in centimetres. Calculate

(a) the radius of the blot when it was first observed

(b) the time at which the radius of the blot was 1.5 cm

(c) the rate of increase of the area of the blot when the radius was 1.5 cm

(d) According to this model, will the radius of the blot ever reach 2 cm? Explain your answer.

18. Check Your Understanding: The function $P(t) = \frac{30(7t + 9)}{3t + 2}$ models the population, in thousands, of a town t years since 1985. Determine the first and second derivatives. What information do these two derivative functions give? Explain using numerical examples. Describe the population of this town.

C **19.** Find the equations of the tangents from the origin to the graph of $y = \frac{x + 8}{x + 6}$. Sketch the function and the tangent lines.

20. Thinking, Inquiry, Problem Solving: Choose a simple polynomial function in the form $f(x) = ax + b$. Use the quotient rule to find the derivative of the reciprocal function $\frac{1}{ax + b}$. Repeat for other polynomial functions, and devise a rule for finding the derivative of $\frac{1}{f(x)}$. Confirm your rule using first principles.

**Pierre de Fermat
(1601–1665)**

Pierre de Fermat
treated mathematics as
an interesting hobby,
rather than as a
profession. He made
contributions in
calculus, number
theory, and optics. Do
some research on
Fermat's Last Theorem.
Why is it appropriate
that this note on
Fermat is in the
margin of a math text?

ADDITIONAL ACHIEVEMENT CHART QUESTIONS

Knowledge and Understanding: Determine the derivative for $f(x) = \frac{x^2 - 1}{x^2 + 1}$.
Verify your answer by graphing the derivative and using **nDeriv(** for $f(x)$.

Application: The position function of a particle moving in a straight line is
$s(t) = \frac{10t^2}{32 + t^2}$, where $0 \le t \le 10$. When is the velocity a maximum?

Thinking, Inquiry, Problem Solving: The graph of $f(x) = \frac{ax + b}{(x - 1)(x - 4)}$ has a
horizontal tangent line at $(2, -1)$. Find a and b. Check using a graphing
calculator.

Communication: A shirt manufacturer has records that show that the unit cost,
C, per shirt produced by a worker is given by $C(t) = \frac{15 + 0.6t}{5t}$, where t is the
number of hours worked per day. Find approximate values for $C''(t)$ at $t = 1$, 3,
5, and 7. Describe what the numbers tell you about the cost per shirt.

The Chapter Problem
Designing a Settling Pond

Apply what you learned in this section to answer these questions about
The Chapter Problem on page 342.

CP10. Determine the first and second derivatives of the first
concentration function.

CP11. At what rate is the concentration changing after one hour? one
day? one week? What is the average rate of change in the first
week?

CP12. Repeat questions CP10 and CP11 for the second concentration
function.

5.5 Differentiability of Rational and Other Functions

SETTING THE STAGE

Explore the concepts in this lesson in more detail using Exploration 10 on page 578.

A function f is differentiable at $x = a$ if $f'(a)$ exists. A polynomial function is differentiable at every number in the domain. Consider two questions.

- Are there functions for which the derivative does not exist at one or more numbers in the domain?
- If so, what properties of these functions cause the derivative not to exist at these numbers?

In this section, you will examine the differentiability of rational functions as well as other types of functions.

EXAMINING THE CONCEPT

Differentiating a Rational Function

If $f'(a)$ exists, then $\displaystyle\lim_{h \to 0} \frac{f(a + h) - f(a)}{h}$ exists. Both the one-sided limits exist and are equal: $\displaystyle\lim_{h \to 0^-} \frac{f(a + h) - f(a)}{h} = \lim_{h \to 0^+} \frac{f(a + h) - f(a)}{h}$. Also, you can draw a tangent line at $x = a$ if $f'(a)$ exists.

corner

cusp

The Differentiability of a Function

A function is not differentiable at $x = a$ when

1. the graph of the function has a discontinuity at a
2. the graph of the function has a corner or a cusp
3. the line $x = a$ is a vertical tangent

In the next three examples, you will examine each case in more detail.

Example 1 **Functions Whose Derivatives Do Not Exist Because of a Discontinuity or a Restricted Domain**

Explain why each function is not differentiable at $x = 3$.

(a) $f(x) = \dfrac{x + 1}{x - 3}$
(b) $g(x) = \dfrac{x^2 - 9}{x - 3}$

(c) $h(x) = \sqrt{3 - x}$
(d) $m(x) = \begin{cases} 3x - 1 & \text{if } x \le 3 \\ 1 & \text{if } x > 3 \end{cases}$

Solution

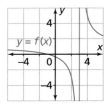

(a) $f(x) = \dfrac{x+1}{x-3}$

This function is not defined at $x = 3$.

The line $x = 3$ is a vertical asymptote. The function is discontinuous at $x = 3$.

You cannot draw a tangent line at $x = 3$. $f'(3)$ does not exist.

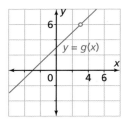

(b) $g(x) = \dfrac{x^2 - 9}{x - 3}$

This function is not defined at $x = 3$.

The graph has a hole at $x = 3$. The function is discontinuous at $x = 3$.

You cannot draw a tangent line at $x = 3$. $g'(x)$ does not exist.

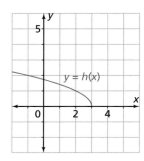

(c) $h(x) = \sqrt{3 - x}$

This function is not defined for $x > 3$, so $f(3 + h)$ is not defined.

$$\lim_{h \to 0^+} \frac{f(3 + h) - f(3)}{h} \text{ does not exist.}$$

$$\lim_{h \to 0^-} \frac{f(3 + h) - f(3)}{h} = -\infty.$$

Since these limits are not equal, $h'(3)$ does not exist.

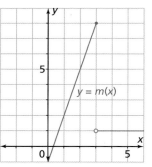

(d) $m(x) = \begin{cases} 3x - 1 & \text{if } x \leq 3 \\ 1 & \text{if } x > 3 \end{cases}$

The one-sided limits as $x \to 3$ are not the same. That is,

$\lim\limits_{x \to 3^-} m(x) \neq \lim\limits_{x \to 3^+} m(x)$. The function is discontinuous at $x = 3$.

$m'(3)$ does not exist.

· · · · · · · ·

Example 2   **A Function Whose Derivative Does Not Exist at a Corner in Its Graph**

Let $f(x) = |x - 1|$. Is this function differentiable at $x = 1$?

x	f(x)
–3	4
–2	3
–1	2
0	1
1	0
2	1
3	2
4	3

Solution

Create a table for the function. Then graph the function.

The graph has a corner at $(1, 0)$.

$$\lim_{h \to 0^-} \frac{f(1 + h) - f(1)}{h} = -1$$

$$\lim_{h \to 0^+} \frac{f(1 + h) - f(1)}{h} = 1$$

Since these limits are not the same, $f'(1)$ does not exist.

The slope changes abruptly from -1 to 1 at $(1, 0)$. You cannot draw a unique tangent line at this point.

The function is not differentiable at $x = 1$.

• • • • • • • •

An extreme case of a corner is a **cusp**. A cusp occurs where the slopes of the secant lines approach ∞ from one side and $-\infty$ from the other side.

Example 3   **A Function Whose Derivative Does Not Exist at a Cusp in Its Graph**

Where is $f(x) = (3x - 6)^{\frac{2}{3}}$ differentiable?

x	f(x)
–3	6.0822
–2	5.2415
–1	4.3267
0	3.3019
1	2.0801
2	0.0000
3	2.0801
4	3.3019
5	4.3267

Solution

Make a table. (The values for the function in the table are rounded to four decimal places.) Then graph the function.

$$\lim_{h \to 0^-} \frac{f(2 + h) - f(2)}{h} = -\infty, \text{ but}$$

$$\lim_{h \to 0^+} \frac{f(2 + h) - f(2)}{h} = \infty$$

So, $f'(2)$ does not exist.

The graph has a cusp at $(2, 0)$.

The function is not differentiable at $x = 2$.

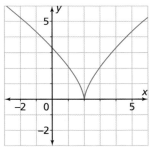

• • • • • • • •

Example 4   **A Function with a Vertical Tangent**

Show that $f(x) = \sqrt[3]{x - 1}$ is not differentiable at $x = 1$.

Solution

Make a table. (The values for the function in the table are rounded to four decimal places.) Then graph the function.

x	f(x)
-4	-1.7100
-3	-1.5874
-2	-1.4422
-1	-1.2599
0	-1.0000
1	0.0000
2	1.0000
3	1.2599
4	1.4422

A tangent line can be drawn at point (1, 0).

However, this tangent is vertical, so its slope is undefined. The slope does not exist, and $f'(1)$ does not exist. The function is not differentiable at $x = 1$.

• • • • • • • •

Maximum and minimum values can occur at corners and cusps. At these points, the derivative does not exist. To account for all critical points, we must also consider the points where the derivative does not exist. Points of inflection can occur at corners. Also, vertical tangents occur at points of inflection. To account for all points of inflection, we must also consider where the second derivative does not exist.

Critical Points and Points of Inflection

For any function $f(x)$, at a critical number $f'(c) = 0$ or $f'(c)$ does not exist. At a point of inflection, $f''(c) = 0$ or $f''(c)$ does not exist.

You may have noticed that the descriptions of differentiability and continuity are similar. In fact, they are closely connected. Every differentiable function is also continuous.

Continuity and Differentiability

The function $f(x)$ is continuous at $x = a$ if $f(x)$ is differentiable at $x = a$.

Example 5 **Showing That a Differentiable Function Is Also Continuous**

Show that $f(x)$ is continuous at $x = a$ if $f(x)$ is differentiable at $x = a$.

Solution
Show that $\lim_{h \to 0} f(a + h) = f(a)$, which means $\lim_{h \to 0} [f(a + h) - f(a)] = 0$.

For $h \neq 0$ and $(a + h)$ in the domain of the function,

$$\lim_{h \to 0} [f(a + h) - f(a)] = \lim_{h \to 0} \left[\frac{f(a + h) - f(a)}{h} \times h \right]$$

$$= \left[\lim_{h \to 0} \frac{f(a + h) - f(a)}{h} \right] \times (\lim_{h \to 0} h)$$

$$= f'(a) \times 0$$

$$= 0$$

So f is continuous at $x = a$ if $f'(a)$ exists.

5.5 Exercises

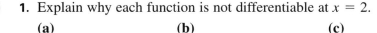

A 1. Explain why each function is not differentiable at $x = 2$.

(a)   (b)   (c)

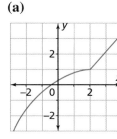 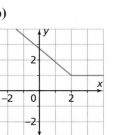 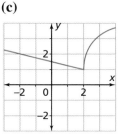

2. Where is each function
   i. differentiable?
   ii. continuous but not differentiable?
   iii. neither continuous nor differentiable?

   (a)   **(b)**   **(c)**

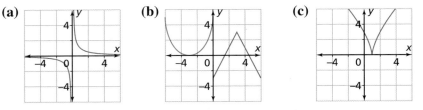

3. Each function is *not* differentiable at $x = 1$. Determine whether the reason is a discontinuity, a corner, a cusp, or a vertical tangent.

   (a) $f(x) = \dfrac{x^2 - 1}{x - 1}$

   (b) $f(x) = \dfrac{1}{2}\left|1 - x\right| + 1$

   (c) $f(x) = \dfrac{x + 4}{x - 1}$

   (d) $f(x) = (x - 1)^{\frac{2}{3}}$

   (e) $f(x) = 2\sqrt{1 - x}$

   (f) $f(x) = (x - 1)^{\frac{1}{3}}$

B   4. Explain why each function is not differentiable at the given x-value(s).

   (a) $f(x) = \dfrac{1}{(3 - x)^2}$ at $x = 3$

   (b) $f(x) = \dfrac{x - 4}{16 - x^2}$ at $x = \pm 4$

   (c) $f(x) = \sqrt[3]{(2x - 5)^2}$ at $x = 2.5$

   (d) $f(x) = \dfrac{2}{3}\left|4 - 5x\right| - 1$ at $x = 0.8$

   (e) $f(x) = \dfrac{2x - 1}{4x - 9}$ at $x = 2.25$

   (f) $f(x) = 5\sqrt{3 - 2x}$ at $x = 1.5$

   (g) $f(x) = \sqrt[3]{5 - 4x}$ at $x = 1.25$

   (h) $f(x) = \begin{cases} \dfrac{x^2 - 4}{x - 2} & \text{if } x \leq 2 \\ 6 - x & \text{if } x > 2 \end{cases}$

5. **Knowledge and Understanding:** Determine which functions are differentiable at $x = 1$. Give reasons for your choices.

   (a) $f(x) = \dfrac{3x}{1 - x^2}$

   (b) $g(x) = \dfrac{x - 1}{x^2 + 5x - 6}$

   (c) $h(x) = \sqrt[3]{(x - 2)^2}$

   (d) $m(x) = \left|3x - 3\right| - 1$

6. Find all x-values for which each function is differentiable. Explain your answers.

   (a) $f(x) = \dfrac{x^3 + 1}{x^2 - 3x - 4}$

   (b) $f(x) = 1 - 4|2 - x|$

   (c) $f(x) = \dfrac{2 - 3x}{x - 1}$

7. At what x-values is each function *not* differentiable? Explain.

   (a) $f(x) = \dfrac{3}{4x^2 - x}$ (b) $f(x) = \dfrac{x^2 - x - 6}{x^2 - 9}$ (c) $f(x) = \sqrt{x^2 - 7x + 6}$

8. **Communication**: Explain, with an example, why a function whose graph has a cusp is not differentiable at the point where the cusp occurs.

9. (a) Explain why $f(x) = \dfrac{1}{x - 1}$ and $g(x) = \dfrac{1}{(x - 1)^2}$ are not differentiable at $x = 1$.

   (b) Use a graphing calculator to obtain nDeriv($f(x)$, x, 1, 0.0001) and nDeriv($g(x)$, x, 1, 0.0001).

   (c) Explain your results for (b) by calculating $\dfrac{f(a + h) - f(a - h)}{2h}$ and

   $\dfrac{g(a + h) - g(a - h)}{2h}$ for $a = 1$ and $h = 0.0001$.

   (d) Find the derivatives of other functions at x-values where the functions are not differentiable using the **nDeriv(** operation. Explain each erroneous result using the function definition

   nDeriv($f(x)$, x, a, h) $= \dfrac{f(a + h) - f(a - h)}{2h}$.

10. **Application**: Determine whether the derivative of $f(x) = \begin{cases} \dfrac{1}{x} & \text{if } x < 1 \\ 1 & \text{if } x \geq 1 \end{cases}$ exists at $x = 1$.

11. Use the limit definition of the derivative to show that $f'(3)$ does not exist for $f(x) = |x - 3|$.

12. **Check Your Understanding**: Explain, with examples, the three ways in which a function may not be differentiable at $x = a$.

13. Let $f(x) = \begin{cases} 2x + b & \text{if } x < 1 \\ \dfrac{a}{x + 1} & \text{if } x \geq 1 \end{cases}$

   (a) Find a relation between a and b if the function is continuous for all values of x.

   (b) Find the values of a and b that make the function both continuous and differentiable for all values of x.

14. Repeat question 13 for $f(x) = \begin{cases} 5 - x & \text{if } x < 2 \\ \dfrac{ax + 2}{bx - 1} & \text{if } x \geq 2 \end{cases}$

15. Thinking, Inquiry, Problem Solving: You have seen that a function that is differentiable is continuous. Investigate whether the converse is true: is a function differentiable at $x = a$ if the function is continuous at $x = a$? Give examples to support your arguments.

ADDITIONAL ACHIEVEMENT CHART QUESTIONS

Knowledge and Understanding: Find all values of x for which the function is differentiable.

(a) $y = \dfrac{x^3 - 8}{x^2 - 4x - 5}$

(b) $h(x) = \sqrt[3]{3x - 6} + 4$

(c) $y = x|x|$

(d) $g(x) = \begin{cases} (x + 1) & \text{if } x \leq 0 \\ 2x + 1 & \text{if } 0 < x < 3 \\ (4 - x)^2 & \text{if } x \geq 3 \end{cases}$

Application: Use the limit definition of the derivative to show that $f'(5)$ does not exist for $f(x) = |x - 5|$.

Thinking, Inquiry, Problem Solving: Let $f(x) = \begin{cases} 3x^2 & \text{if } x \leq 1 \\ ax + b & \text{if } x > 1 \end{cases}$

where a and b are constants.

(a) What is the relation between a and b if the function is continuous for all x?

(b) Find the unique values for a and b that will make the function both continuous and differentiable.

Communication: Explain why $f(x) = \begin{cases} 0 & \text{if } -1 \leq x < 0 \\ 2 & \text{if } 0 \leq x \leq 1 \end{cases}$

is not the derivative of any function on the interval $-1 \leq x \leq 1$.

5.6 Finding Optimal Values for Rational Function Models

SETTING THE STAGE

Erin and Tony are creating rectangular banners for the companies attending a convention. Each banner must have a coloured border and a white centre. The width of the border will be 20 cm at the top and bottom and 15 cm along the sides. Because of the number of companies and the available wall space, each banner must have an area of 2.43 m². What are the dimensions of a banner if the area of the white centre is maximized?

In this section, you will revisit optimization problems. But you will use rational functions to model these problems.

EXAMINING THE CONCEPT

Solving Optimization Problems

The first step in solving an optimization problem is to understand the problem. You might ask yourself the following questions about the situation in Setting the Stage:

- What quantity is to be optimized?
- What is fixed and what can vary?
- How can the shape of a banner change if the banner is a rectangle with a fixed area?
- How many variables do you need?

You have solved problems like this one before by testing values in a spreadsheet. Or you have created an algebraic model and tested values for the model with graphing technology. Now you can verify these solutions using calculus.

Example 1   Solving the Banner Problem

Solution

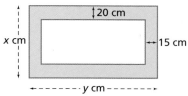

Create an algebraic model. Organize the information in a diagram.

Let the width and length of the banner be x and y, respectively.

Both x and y vary but not independently.

The area of the banner is 2.43 m² or 24 300 cm², so $xy = 24\ 300$.

Use this to express y in terms of x. $y = \dfrac{24\ 300}{x}$

The area of the white part is to be maximized. Now write an expression for this area in terms of x.

The white part is $(x - 40)$ centimetres wide and $(y - 30)$ centimetres long.

The area of the white part is

$$A = (y - 30)(x - 40)$$ Replace y with $\frac{24\,300}{x}$.

$$= \left(\frac{24\,300}{x} - 30\right)(x - 40)$$

$$= 24\,300 - \frac{972\,000}{x} - 30x + 1200$$

$$= 25\,500 - \frac{972\,000}{x} - 30x$$

What is the domain of A? From the equation, $x \neq 0$.

From the diagram, $x \geq 40$ and $y \geq 30$, so
$$\frac{24\,300}{x} \geq 30$$
$$24\,300 \geq 30x$$
$$810 \geq x$$

The restricted domain of A is $\{x \mid 40 \leq x \leq 810, x \in \mathbf{R}\}$.

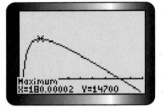

$40 \leq x \leq 180$;
$-5000 \leq y \leq 24\,300$

In the graph, the optimal value for A occurs when the graph has a horizontal tangent. At this point, the slope is 0 and $A'(x) = 0$.

You could estimate the maximum value using graphing technology.

The maximum value of A occurs when $x \doteq 180$. Use the first derivative test to calculate the value of x algebraically.

Solve for x algebraically. Differentiate $A(x)$ term by term. Apply the quotient rule to $\frac{972\,000}{x}$.

$$A'(x) = 0 - \left[\frac{(0)x - (1)972\,000}{x^2}\right] - 30$$

$$= \frac{(1)972\,000}{x^2} - 30$$

The optimal value for A occurs when $A'(x) = 0$.

$$0 = \frac{972\,000}{x^2} - 30$$ Isolate the term containing x.

$$30 = \frac{972\,000}{x^2}$$ Multiply both sides by x^2.

$$x^2 = \frac{972\,000}{30}$$ Simplify.

$$x^2 = 32\,400$$ Take the square root of both sides.

$$x = \pm\sqrt{32\,400} \text{ or } \pm 180$$

Since $40 \leq x \leq 810$, the negative root is inadmissable. $x = 180$

Use the first derivative test to verify that a maximum occurs when $x = 180$.

	Intervals	
	$40 \leq x < 180$	$180 < x \leq 810$
$A'(x)$	+	−
$A(x)$	increasing ↗	decreasing ↘
	maximum at $x = 180$	

The first derivative test confirms a maximum value at $x = 180$ since $A'(x)$ changes from positive to negative. When $x = 180$, $y = \frac{24\,300}{180}$, or 135.

To maximize the area of the white centre, the banner should be 180 cm long and 135 cm wide, or 1.80 m by 1.35 m.

• • • • • • • •

Here are the steps for solving optimization problems.

Solving Optimization Problems

1. Read the problem carefully. What needs to be maximized or minimized? What is fixed and what can vary?

2. Draw a diagram, if needed. Assign variable names. Note any relations between variables.

3. Create an algebraic model by expressing the quantity to be maximized or minimized as a function of only one variable. Use the relations from step 2.

4. Note the domain of the new function. Graph the function using graphing technology, if possible.

5. Find where the derivative of the function is 0 or where it does not exist. Use the first derivative test or the second derivative test to find maximum or minimum values. Also evaluate the function at the endpoints of the domain. These values may be more extreme than any local maximum or minimum. This calculation is especially important if a graph is not available.

6. Interpret your solution in the context of the problem. Answer the question posed in the problem!

Example 2 **Minimizing the Cost of Materials for a Juice Can**

Helena is designing a cylindrical can. The can will hold 280 mL of juice. The metal for the side of the can costs $0.75/m². The metal for the top and bottom, which is thicker, costs $1.40/m². The side of the can is one rectangular sheet. The circular top and bottom are stamped out from another rectangular sheet. The unused metal from this rectangle is donated to a charity. The charity exchanges the scrap metal for money. What dimensions for the can will minimize the cost of materials?

Solution

The volume of the can is fixed. The can must be a cylinder. But the radius and height can vary. You must find the combination of radius and height that will minimize the cost of metal for the can.

Let the radius of the can be r centimetres. Let the height be h centimetres.

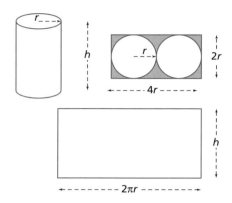

These quantities do not vary independently, since the volume of the can is 280 cm³.

$V_{\text{cylinder}} = \pi r^2 h$

$$280 = \pi r^2 h \quad \text{Solve for } h.$$

$$h = \frac{280}{\pi r^2}$$

(It is easier to isolate h than r.)

The total cost is the cost of metal for the side and the cost of metal for the top and bottom. Each cost depends on the area of metal used.

Metal for the side costs $0.75/m², and metal for the the top and bottom costs $1.40/m².

$$\text{Area of rectangle for side} = 2\pi rh \qquad \text{Replace } h \text{ with } \frac{280}{\pi r^2}.$$

$$= 2\pi r\left(\frac{280}{\pi r^2}\right) \qquad \text{Simplify.}$$

$$= \frac{560}{r}$$

Area of rectangle for top and bottom $= (4r)(2r) = 8r^2$

The cost of metal for one can is
$$C(r) = \frac{1}{10^4}\left[0.75\left(\frac{560}{r}\right) + 1.40(8r^2)\right]$$

$$= \frac{420}{r} + 11.20r^2$$

The domain of this function is $\{r \mid r > 0, r \in \mathbf{R}\}$. A graphing calculator can be used to estimate when the cost is minimized. The cost is minimized when $r \doteq 2.7$ cm.

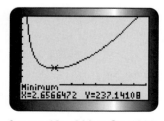

Minimum
X=2.6566472   Y=237.14108

$0 \le r \le 10; -200 \le C \le 1000$

Calculate and verify by finding the derivative.

$$C'(r) = \frac{1}{10^4}\left(\frac{-420}{r^2} + 22.4r\right)$$

$C'(r)$ is defined for all r in the domain of the function.

Let $C'(r) = 0$.

$$\frac{-420}{r^2} + 22.4r = 0$$

$$22.4r = \frac{420}{r^2} \qquad \text{Multiply both sides by } r^2 \text{ and divide by 22.4.}$$

$$r^3 = \frac{420}{22.4} \qquad \text{Simplify.}$$

$$r^3 = 18.75 \qquad \text{Take the cube root of both sides.}$$

$$r \doteq 2.7$$

	Intervals	
	$0 \le r < 2.7$	$r > 2.7$
$C'(r)$	$-$	$+$
$C(r)$	decreasing ↘	increasing ↗
	minimum at $r = 2.7$	

The first derivative test verifies that $f(2.7)$ is a local minimum. $f(2.7) \doteq 12.6$

Therefore, to minimize the cost of metal for the juice can, the radius of the pop can should be 2.7 cm and its height should be 12.6 cm.

• • • • • • • •

Extra care is needed when the domain is restricted in some way.

Example 3   **Minimizing the Operating Costs of Driving a Truck**

On the highway, a truck burns fuel at a rate of $\left(0.003x + \frac{3}{x}\right)$ litres per kilometre when its speed is x kilometres per hour. Fuel costs $0.65/L. The driver is paid $16/h. What steady speed will minimize the operating costs for a 400-km trip on a highway where the posted speed limit is 90 km/h?

Solution

The quantity to be minimized is the operating cost of the truck.

$$\text{operating cost} = \text{cost of fuel} + \text{cost of driver}$$

On a 400-km trip, the truck will use

$\left[400\left(0.003x + \frac{3}{x}\right)\right]$ litres of fuel. The fuel costs $0.65\left[400\left(0.003x + \frac{3}{x}\right)\right]$.

The cost of the driver depends on the time the trip takes. Let t be the time of the trip in hours.

The distance to be travelled is fixed. The speed of the truck and the time for the trip are variable.
Distance = speed × time, if the speed is steady.

$$\text{distance} = \text{speed} \times \text{time}$$
$$400 = x \times t \qquad \text{Solve for } t.$$
$$\frac{400}{x} = t$$

The driver costs $16 \times \dfrac{400}{x}$.

So, the operating cost is

$$C(x) = 0.65\left[400\left(0.003x + \frac{3}{x}\right)\right] + \left(16 \times \frac{400}{x}\right) \qquad \text{Expand.}$$

$$= 0.78x + \frac{780}{x} + \frac{6400}{x} \qquad\qquad\qquad \text{Simplify.}$$

$$= 0.78x + \frac{7180}{x}$$

The domain of the function is $\{x \mid 0 < x \le 90, x \in \mathbf{R}\}$, since the speed limit is 90 km/h.

$C'(x) = 0.78 - \frac{7180}{x^2}$ is defined for all x in the domain of the function.

Let $C'(x) = 0$.

$$0.78 - \frac{7180}{x^2} = 0 \qquad\qquad \text{Isolate the term containing } x.$$

$$0.78 = \frac{7180}{x^2} \qquad\qquad \text{Multiply both sides by } x^2.$$

$$x^2 = \frac{7180}{0.78} \qquad\qquad \text{Simplify and take the square root of both sides.}$$

$$x \doteq \pm95.9$$

However, neither root is in the domain of the function. In this case, the minimum value occurs at an end point of the domain.

Calculate $C(0)$ and $C(90)$.

$C(0)$ is undefined. $\qquad\qquad\qquad C(90) = 0.78(90) + \frac{7180}{90}$

$$\doteq 149.98$$

Graphing the function verifies the analysis. The function decreases over its entire domain. The minimum value occurs outside its domain. A steady speed of 90 km/h will minimize the operating costs within the restricted domain.

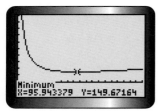

Minimum
X=95.943379   Y=149.67164

$0 < x \le 200; -200 \le y \le 1000$ Does the length of the trip affect the optimal speed?

CHECK, CONSOLIDATE, COMMUNICATE

1. How do you use derivatives to solve an optimization problem?
2. Why is the domain of the function that represents the quantity to be optimized important?
3. How can a calculus solution help you with a graphing calculator solution? How can a graphing calculator help you with a calculus solution?

KEY IDEAS

- Apply the steps, introduced in Chapter 4 and refined on page 397, to solve an optimization problem using calculus.

A 1. For what values of x does $f(x) = 4x^2 + \dfrac{27}{x}$ have a maximum or minimum value? Give reasons for your answer.

2. Determine the smallest possible perimeter for a rectangle with an area of 36 cm^2. What are the dimensions of the rectangle in this case?

3. A rectangular carrot patch of area 20 m^2 is to be fenced. One side of the patch is already protected by a barn. Find the dimensions that will use the least amount of fencing.

4. A rectangular vegetable garden will have an area of 96 m^2. The garden will be enclosed by a fence and divided into two equal parts by another fence parallel to one side. Determine the dimensions of the garden so that the total length of fence is minimized. What length of fencing will be needed?

5. A goat farmer needs to enclose a rectangular field. The area of the field will be 600 m^2. The farmer will use an existing wall as one side of the enclosure. The cost of fencing for the other three sides is $24/m. Find the dimensions of the rectangular field that will minimize the cost of the fence.

6. A rectangular rose garden will be surrounded on three sides by a brick wall and by a fence on the fourth side. The area of the garden will be 1000 m^2. The cost of the brick wall is $192/m. The cost of the fencing is $48/m. Find the dimensions of the garden so that the cost of the materials is as small as possible.

7. **Application:** An indoor swimming pool enclosure will have a rectangular floor area of 4800 m^2. Three walls of the pool will be glass and one will be brick. The cost per linear metre of constructing a glass wall is two times the cost of constructing a brick wall. Find the dimensions of the floor area that will minimize the cost of building the walls.

8. The rectangular floor area of a supermarket must be 3750 m^2. Three walls will be cement blocks. The other wall will be glass. The cost per *linear* metre of constructing a glass wall is two times the cost of constructing a cement-block wall. Find the dimensions of the floor area that will minimize the cost of building the walls.

9. A rectangular pigpen will be surrounded by a fence and then divided into two sections by a block wall. The area of the pigpen must be 32 m^2. Fencing costs $20/m. The block wall costs $40/m. What should be the dimensions of the pigpen to minimize the costs?

10. Torstein plans to sail his boat on a trip of 200 km at a constant speed. When the speed of his boat is v kilometres per hour, the cost is $\$\left(2.5v^2 + \dfrac{10\,000}{v}\right)$ each hour. Find the speed at which the ship should travel so that the cost of the trip is minimized.

11. The printed area of a page in a book will be 81 cm². The margins at the top and bottom of the page will each be 3 cm deep. The margins at the sides of the page will each be 2 cm wide. What page dimensions will minimize the amount of paper?

12. Stuart is designing an advertising flyer. The flyer will be rectangular and its area will be 120 cm². The margins will be 2.5 cm wide at the top and bottom and 1.5 cm wide at the sides. What should be the dimensions of the flyer so that the area with print will be as large as possible?

13. A company needs to create a box with a square base and no top. The volume of the box must be 500 cm³. What should be the dimensions of the box to minimize the amount of material that will be used to make it?

14. The volume of a rectangular box will be 15 m³. The box has a square base and top. The material for the base costs \$7.50/m². The material for the top costs \$2.50/m² and for the sides \$4.50/m². Find the dimensions that will minimize the cost of materials for the box.

15. A closed rectangular box will be made so that it has a square base. The volume must be 5000 cm³. The material for the bottom costs twice as much as the material for the sides and top. Find the dimensions of the box so that the cost of materials is minimized.

16. Sindy is building a rectangular wooden toy chest so that its length is two times its width. She has picked pine for the top, front, and two sides of the chest. She will use fibreboard for the back and bottom. The chest must have a volume of 0.3 m³. Pine costs twice as much as fibreboard. Find the dimensions that will minimize the cost of the chest.

17. **Knowledge and Understanding:** A soup manufacturer wants to sell its soups in 500-mL cans. The metal for the top and bottom costs \$1.20/m². The metal for the side costs \$0.40/m². After the circles for the top and bottom are cut out of a rectangle, the remaining metal will be scrapped. Find the dimensions of the can that will minimize the cost of materials.

18. Mary is making a cylindrical oil drum. The drum must hold 1.8 m³ of a liquid. The drum must be taller than it is wide, but no more than 1.8 m tall. What are the dimensions of the drum that uses the least amount of material?

19. A closed rectangular box with a square base is to be constructed to the following specifications. The volume must be 1 m³, the area of the base must not exceed 2 m², and the height of the box must not exceed 0.6 m. Determine the dimensions for **(a)** minimal surface area; **(b)** maximum surface area.

20. **Communication:** Why are solutions to optimization problems so important in everyday life? Give examples of people or organizations that rely on such solutions.

21. On the highway, a truck burns fuel at a rate of $\left(0.004x + \frac{2}{x}\right)$ litres per kilometre when travelling at x kilometres per hour. Fuel costs $0.68/L and the driver is paid $18/h. What steady speed will minimize the operating costs for a 350-km trip on a highway where speed laws require $40 \leq x \leq 100$?

22. A light-fitting manufacturer estimates that x table lamps are sold each week at p dollars each where $p(x) = 125 - 1.6x$. The estimated cost of production is $C(x) = 0.2x^2 + 15x + 500$. Determine the production level that produces the maximum profit. At what production level is the average cost per item a minimum?

23. Stellar Steel can produce x tonnes of regular-quality steel and y tonnes of super-quality steel per day, where $y = \frac{40 - 5x}{10 - x}$. The market price for regular quality steel is half the market price for super-quality steel. How many tonnes of regular-quality steel should the company produce to maximize revenue?

24. Stan needs to move some excess topsoil from his farm. He can hire a dump truck and a driver for $60/h. The driver will take 30 min to deliver a load of topsoil and return to the farm. One person will take 40 h to load the truck with soil. Labourers get $18/h (whether they are loading the truck with soil or waiting for the truck to return). How many labourers should Stan hire to minimize the cost per load? What is the minimum cost?

25. **Check Your Understanding:** Create a packaging problem. Use it to describe the steps for solving optimization problems.

ⓒ 26. **Thinking, Inquiry, Problem Solving:** In Example 3, the speed that minimized the cost of operating a truck on a 400-km trip was determined. Investigate whether the length of the trip affects the optimal speed. Determine the optimal speed for several different distances. Generalize your results.

27. Determine the most economical proportions for a closed cylindrical can that will hold 1 L of liquid.

28. An estimated cost function is $C(x) = a + bx^2$, where a and b are positive constants. Determine the value(s) of x that minimize(s) average cost.

29. The total cost function for producing x items is $C(x)$. The average cost per item is $AC(x) = \frac{C(x)}{x}$. Show that if the average cost is minimal then $AC(x) = C'(x)$.

30. Two sources of heat are placed s metres apart at points A and B. The intensity of heat, $I(x)$, at point P between A and B is modelled by $I(x) = \frac{a}{x^2} + \frac{b}{(s-x)^2}$, where x is the distance in metres between P and A, a is the intensity of the heat source at A, and b is the intensity of the heat source at B. At what point P between A and B will the temperature be the lowest?

ADDITIONAL ACHIEVEMENT CHART QUESTIONS

Knowledge and Understanding: A landscape architect plans to enclose a 800-m² rectangular region in a botanical garden. She will use shrubs costing $27/m along three sides and fencing costing $15/m along the fourth side. Find the minimum total cost.

Application: Your metal-works company has been contracted to design and build a 24-m³, square-based, open-topped, rectangular steel holding tank for a paper company. The tank will be made by welding thin stainless steel plates together along their edges. Craig, a structural engineer, has been hired to design the tank. Help Craig by finding the dimensions that will minimize the mass of the tank.

Thinking, Inquiry, Problem Solving: A juice can in the shape of a right circular cylinder will have a capacity of 355 cm³. Find the dimensions of the can that will use the least amount of material for the top, bottom, and side. What is the ratio of height to diameter for this can?

Communication: You could determine, using calculus, that the height of a can must be equal to the diameter so that the material that makes up the can is minimized. Suggest reasons why so many products sold in cans do not follow this model.

**John Wallis
(1616–1703)**

The work of English mathematician John Wallis influenced both Newton and Leibniz in their development of calculus.

The Chapter Problem
Designing a Settling Pond

Apply what you learned in this section to answer these questions about The Chapter Problem on page 342.

CP13. Draw a diagram of the settling pond described in (b) of The Chapter Problem. Let the depth of the pond be x metres. Write expressions for the width and length of the pond in terms of x.

CP14. Write a function that describes the surface area of the inside of the pond. What is the domain of this function?

CP15. Determine the value of x that minimizes this surface area.

5.7 Sketching Graphs of Rational Functions

SETTING THE STAGE

Suppose that the percentage of people using a new computer model t years after its introduction to the market is modelled by $p(t) = \frac{100t^2}{t^2 + 500}$, where p is the percentage of people and is expressed as a percent. After how long does the growth rate in the percentage of people stop increasing and begin to decrease? Why might the answer to this question be useful to the company that markets the new computer model?

To answer the first question, a specific point on the graph of the function must be determined.

A graphing calculator will help estimate this point, but using calculus will give an exact answer. In this section, you will revisit the calculus techniques in Chapter 4 used to analyze polynomial functions. You will apply these techniques to analyze rational functions.

EXAMINING THE CONCEPT

Sketching Graphs of Rational Functions

You have sketched the graphs of rational functions by first finding the domain, intercepts, and asymptotes. You have also learned how to find the extreme values of a function and the intervals where the function increases and decreases. You can also determine the concavity of a graph and how to find the points of inflection.

Using all of this information, you can sketch the complete graph of a rational function without technology.

Example 1   **Analyzing the Graph of a Rational Function**

Without graphing technology, graph $f(x) = \frac{5x}{x^2 + 1}$.

Solution

1. Analyze $f(x)$.

Use the equation of the function to find the domain, the intercepts, and the asymptotes.

Domain
There are no restrictions on the domain. The domain is the set of all real numbers, $\{x \mid x \in \mathbf{R}\}$.

Intercepts
- The zero of the function occurs when the numerator is 0, so the function has one zero at $x = 0$. The x-intercept is 0.
- $f(0) = 0$, so the y-intercept is 0.

Asymptotes
- There are no vertical asymptotes since the denominator can never be equal to 0.

$$\lim_{x \to \infty} \frac{5x}{x^2 + 1} = \lim_{x \to \infty} \frac{\frac{5x}{x^2}}{\frac{x^2}{x^2} + \frac{1}{x^2}} = \frac{0}{1 + 0} = 0, \text{ so } y = 0 \text{ (the } x\text{-axis) is a}$$

horizontal asymptote on the right, and

$$\lim_{x \to -\infty} \frac{5x}{x^2 + 1} = \lim_{x \to -\infty} \frac{\frac{5x}{x^2}}{\frac{x^2}{x^2} + \frac{1}{x^2}} = \frac{0}{1 + 0} = 0, \text{ so } y = 0 \text{ is a horizontal}$$

asymptote on the left.
- There are no oblique asymptotes, since the highest power of x in the numerator is not one more than the highest power of x in the denominator.

Symmetry
Will the graph of the function be **symmetric**? Because of the x^2 in the denominator, the denominator will always be positive. Therefore, the sign of $f(x)$ is determined by the sign of the numerator. In fact, $f(-x) = -f(x)$. So the graph will be symmetric about the origin. The shape of the graph on the left of the origin will be the same as that on the right of the origin. But one side will appear to be upside down.

The graph will approach the x-axis from above on the right and from below on the left.

Critical Numbers

2. Analyze $f'(x)$.

Use $f'(x)$ to find any critical numbers.
Apply the quotient rule to find $f'(x)$.

At a **critical number** c, $f'(c) = 0$ or $f'(c)$ does not exist.

$$f'(x) = \frac{5(x^2 + 1) - (2x)(5x)}{(x^2 + 1)^2}$$

$$= \frac{5(1 - x^2)}{(x^2 + 1)^2}$$

$f'(x) = \dfrac{5(1 - x)(1 + x)}{(x^2 + 1)^2}$ is defined for all real x-values.

$f'(x) = 0$ when the numerator is 0. $x = \pm 1$, so -1 and 1 are critical numbers.

Intervals of Increase and Decrease

In this case, the sign of $f'(x)$ is completely determined by the numerator, the product $(1 - x)(1 + x)$, since the denominator $(x^2 + 1)^2$ is always positive.

- The function is increasing on the interval $a < x < b$ if $f'(x) > 0$ for all x in that interval.
- The function is decreasing on the interval $a < x < b$ if $f'(x) < 0$ for all x in that interval.

	Intervals		
	$x < -1$	$-1 < x < 1$	$x > 1$
$1 - x$	$+$	$+$	$-$
$1 + x$	$-$	$+$	$+$
y'	$(+)(-) = -$	$(+)(+) = +$	$(-)(+) = -$
y	decreasing ↘	increasing ↗	decreasing ↘

f is decreasing when $x < -1$, increasing on $-1 < x < 1$, and decreasing when $x > 1$.

- $f(c)$ is a local minimum value if $f'(x)$ changes from negative to positive at c.
- $f(c)$ is a local maximum value if $f'(x)$ changes from positive to negative at c.

Local Maximum and Minimum Values

From the above table, you can see that $f'(x)$ changes from negative to positive at $x = -1$, which means the graph has a local minimum at $f(-1) = -2.5$.

$$\left(f(-1) = \frac{5(-1)}{(-1)^2 + 1} = -2.5 \right)$$

The sign of $f'(x)$ changes from positive to negative at $x = 1$, which means the graph has a local maximum at $f(1) = 2.5$.

Concavity and Points of Inflection

3. Analyze $f''(x)$.

Now determine f''. First expand f'. $f'(x) = \dfrac{5 - 5x^2}{x^4 + 2x^2 + 1}$

- The graph of the function is concave up when $f'(x)$ is increasing i.e. when $f''(x) > 0$.
- The graph of the function is concave down when $f'(x)$ is decreasing i.e. when $f''(x) < 0$.
- At a point of inflection the graph changes from concave up to concave down or vice versa. $f''(c) = 0$ or $f''(c)$ does not exist.

$$f''(x) = \frac{-10x(x^4 + 2x^2 + 1) - (5 - 5x^2)(4x^3 + 4x)}{(x^4 + 2x^2 + 1)^2} \quad \text{Use the quotient rule.}$$

$$= \frac{-10x(x^4 + 2x^2 + 1) - (20x)(1 - x^4)}{(x^4 + 2x^2 + 1)^2} \quad \text{Simplify.}$$

$$= \frac{10x(-x^4 - 2x^2 - 2 + 2x^4)}{[(x^2 + 1)^2]^2}$$

$$= \frac{10x(x^4 - 2x^2 - 3)}{(x^2 + 1)^4} \quad \text{Factor.}$$

$$= \frac{10x(x^2 - 3)(x^2 + 1)}{(x^2 + 1)^4} \quad \text{Simplify.}$$

$$= \frac{10x(x^2 - 3)}{(x^2 + 1)^3}$$

In this case, $f''(x)$ is defined for all real values of x.

$f''(x) = 0$ when the numerator equals 0. Let $10x = 0$ or $x^2 - 3 = 0$. Then $x = 0$ or $x = \pm\sqrt{3}$. Points of inflection may occur at $x = 0$ and $x = \pm\sqrt{3}$.

Create a table to analyze the second derivative on the four intervals defined by these x-values.

	Intervals			
	$x < -\sqrt{3}$	$-\sqrt{3} < x < 0$	$0 < x < \sqrt{3}$	$x > \sqrt{3}$
$10x$	$-$	$-$	$+$	$+$
$x^2 - 3$	$+$	$-$	$-$	$+$
$(x^2 + 1)^3$	$+$	$+$	$+$	$+$
$f''(x)$	$\dfrac{(-)(+)}{(+)} = -$	$\dfrac{(-)(-)}{(+)} = +$	$\dfrac{(+)(-)}{(+)} = -$	$\dfrac{(+)(+)}{(+)} = +$
$f(x)$	concave down $\cap$	concave up $\cup$	concave down $\cap$	concave up $\cup$

The graph is concave up on $-\sqrt{3} < x < 0$ and on $x > \sqrt{3}$.

The graph is concave down on $x < -\sqrt{3}$ and on $0 < x < \sqrt{3}$.

The graph changes from concave down to concave up at $x = \pm\sqrt{3}$. The graph changes from concave up to concave down at $x = 0. f\left(\pm\sqrt{3}\right) = \frac{\pm5\sqrt{3}}{4}$, or about ±2.2, and $f(0) = 0$, so the estimated points of inflection are $(-1.7, -2.2)$, $(0, 0)$, and $(1.7, 2.2)$. Putting all the information together, graph $f(x) = \frac{5x}{x^2 + 1}$.

4. Sketch the graph.

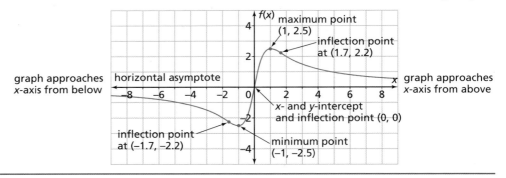

To sketch the graph of a rational function, follow these steps:

Apply these steps in the next example.

Sketching the Graph of a Rational Function

1. Use the function to
- determine the domain and any discontinuities
- determine the intercepts
- find any asymptotes

2. Use the first derivative to
- find the critical numbers
- determine where the function is increasing and where it is decreasing
- identify any local maxima or minima

3. Use the second derivative to
- determine where the graph is concave up and where it is concave down
- find any points of inflection

4. Calculate the values of y corresponding to critical points and points of inflection. Use the information from steps 1 to 3 to sketch the graph.

Example 2   **Curve Sketching**

Without graphing technology, sketch the graph of $f(x) = \frac{x^2 - 3x}{x - 4}$.

Solution

1. Analyze f(x).   In factored form, $f(x) = \frac{x(x - 3)}{x - 4}$.
- The domain of the function is $\{x \mid x \neq 4, x \in \mathbf{R}\}$.
- The x-intercepts are 0 and 3. The y-intercept is 0. (The graph passes through the origin.)

- Let the denominator equal 0. The line $x = 4$ is a vertical asymptote.
  $f(3.999) = -3995.001$. So, as $x \to 4^-, f(x) \to -\infty$.
  $f(4.001) = 4005.01$. So, as $x \to 4^+, f(x) \to \infty$.

  As $x \to \pm\infty, f(x) \to -\infty$, and there is no horizontal asymptote.

  Since the highest power of x in the numerator is exactly one more than the highest power of x in the denominator, the graph of the function will have an oblique asymptote. By long division, $f(x) = x + 1 + \dfrac{4}{x-4}$. The line $y = x + 1$ is an oblique asymptote.

2. Analyze $f'(x)$.

$$f'(x) = \frac{(2x - 3)(x - 4) - (x^2 - 3x)(1)}{(x - 4)^2}$$

$$= \frac{x^2 - 8x + 12}{(x - 4)^2}$$

$$= \frac{(x - 2)(x - 6)}{(x - 4)^2} \qquad \text{(in factored form)}$$

- $f'(x)$ is defined for all values of x in the domain of the function.
- $f'(x) = 0$ when $x = 2$ and when $x = 6$, so 2 and 6 are critical numbers.
- For intervals of increase and decrease, note that $(x - 4)^2$ is always positive, so consider only factors of the numerator. Also recall that $f'(4)$ does not exist.

	Intervals			
	$x < 2$	$2 < x < 4$	$4 < x < 6$	$x > 6$
$x - 2$	−	+	+	+
$x - 6$	−	−	−	+
$f'(x) = \dfrac{(x-2)(x-6)}{(x-4)^2}$	$(-)(-) = +$	$(+)(-) = -$	$(+)(-) = -$	$(+)(+) = +$
$f(x)$	increasing ↗	decreasing ↘	decreasing ↘	increasing ↗
	maximum at $x = 2$		minimum at $x = 6$	

- The function is increasing when $x < 2$ and when $x > 6$. The function is decreasing when $2 < x < 4$ and when $4 < x < 6$.
- The function has a local maximum at $f(2) = 1$ and a local minimum at $f(6) = 9$.

3. Analyze $f''(x)$.

$$f''(x) = \frac{8(x - 4)}{(x - 4)^4} = \frac{8}{(x - 4)^3}, \text{ and } x \neq 4$$

- $f''(x)$ is defined for all values of the domain of the original function.
- $f''(x) \neq 0$ for any value of x.
- The sign of the factor $(x - 4)$ in the denominator determines the sign of $f''(x)$, since the numerator is always positive.

Intervals	$x < 4$	$x > 4$
$x - 4$	−	+
$f''(x) = \dfrac{8}{(x-4)^3}$	$\dfrac{(+)}{(-)} = -$	$\dfrac{(+)}{(+)} = +$
$f(x)$	concave down ∩	concave up ∪

- The graph is concave up on $x < 4$ and concave down on $x > 4$.
- There are no points of inflection. Since $x = 4$ is not part of the domain of f, the line $x = 4$ is a vertical asymptote.

4. Sketch the graph.

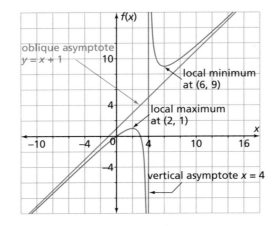

· · · · · · · ·

For applications, you must often consider one or more specific points on the graph of a function.

Example 3

Examining Growth Rate

Recall the problem in Setting the Stage:

Suppose that the percentage of people using a new computer model t years after its introduction to the market is modelled by $p(t) = \dfrac{100t^2}{t^2 + 500}$, where p is the percentage of people and p is expressed as a percent. After how long does the growth rate in the percentage of people stop increasing and begin to decrease? Why might the answer to this question be useful to the company that markets the new computer model?

Solution

The growth rate in the percentage of people is measured by $p'(t)$.

The growth rate is increasing when $p'(t)$ is increasing and $p''(t)$, is positive.

The growth rate is decreasing when $p'(t)$ is decreasing and $p''(t)$ is negative.

Find the point of inflection at which $p''(t)$ changes from positive to negative.

Check the domain and intercepts. Find any asymptotes. $p'(t)$ and $p''(t)$ will not be defined at a vertical asymptote, and the curve may have different concavity on each side of such an asymptote.

1. Analyze p(t).

- Since t represents time, the domain is the set of all real numbers greater than or equal to 0.
- The x- and y-intercepts are both 0. (The graph passes through the origin.)
- There are no vertical or oblique asymptotes. The line $y = 100$ is a horizontal asymptote on the right. This asymptote makes sense since $p(t)$ represents a percent.

2. Analyze $p'(t)$.

$p'(t) = \dfrac{200t(t^2 + 500) - 100t^2(2t)}{(t^2 + 500)^2} = \dfrac{100\,000t}{(t^2 + 500)^2}$ and is defined for all values of t in the domain of p.

$p'(t) = 0$ when $t = 0$. The growth rate in the percentage of people starts at 0.

3. Analyze $p''(t)$.

To determine $p''(t)$, first expand $p'(t)$.

$$p'(t) = \frac{100\,000t}{(t^2 + 500)^2}$$

$$p''(t) = \frac{100\,000(t^4 + 1000t^2 + 250\,000) - (4t^3 + 2000t)100\,000t}{[(t^2 + 500)^2]^2}$$

$$= \frac{-300\,000t^4 - 100\,000\,000t^2 + 25\,000\,000\,000}{[(t^2 + 500)^2]^2}$$

$$= \frac{100\,000(250\,000 - 1000t^2 - 3t^4)}{(t^2 + 500)^4}$$

$$= \frac{100\,000(500 - 3t^2)(500 + t^2)}{(t^2 + 500)^4}$$

$$= \frac{100\,000(500 - 3t^2)}{(t^2 + 500)^3}$$

$p''(t)$ is defined for all values of t in the domain of $p(t)$.

$p''(t) = 0$ when $t = \sqrt{\dfrac{500}{3}}$ or about 12.9. Ignore the negative root, since $t \geq 0$.

The factor $(500 - 3t^2)$ determines the sign of $p''(t)$, since the denominator will always be positive.

	Intervals	
	$0 < t < \sqrt{\dfrac{500}{3}}$	$t > \sqrt{\dfrac{500}{3}}$
$500 - 3t^2$	$+$	$-$
$p''(t) = \dfrac{100\,000(500 - 3t^2)}{(t^2 + 500)^3}$	$\dfrac{(+)(+)}{(+)} = +$	$\dfrac{(+)(-)}{(+)} = -$
$p(t)$	concave up $\cup$	concave down $\cap$

The inflection point occurs at $t = \sqrt{\dfrac{500}{3}}$. The graph changes from concave up to concave down. The growth rate in the percent of people stops increasing and starts decreasing after about 12 years and 11 months.

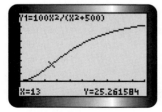

You could also trace, using a graphing calculator, to find the estimated point at which the graph changes from concave up to concave down. However, use the second derivative to find the exact value.

The company that makes the new computer model may need to adjust production levels as the market declines. The company should also develop new products to make and sell to keep their plants busy.

• • • • • • • •

You can use the features of the graph of a function to graph its derivative functions.

Example 4   Using the Graph of a Function to Graph Its First and Second Derivatives

The graph of $f(x)$ is shown. Use this graph to sketch the graphs of $f'(x)$ and $f''(x)$.

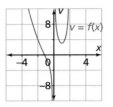

Solution
Draw axes for the graphs of $f'(x)$ and $f''(x)$ beneath the graph of $f(x)$.
Examine the graph of $f(x)$.

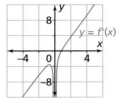

Asymptotes:
- Since the y-axis is a vertical asymptote, $f'(x)$ and $f''(x)$ are undefined at $x = 0$. $f(x)$ has a discontinuity at $x = 0$, so the graphs of $f'(x)$ and $f''(x)$ will have vertical asymptotes.

Critical Points:
- The graph of $f(x)$ has a local minimum at point $(1, 3)$ ($f(1) = 3$), so $f'(1) = 0$ and $f''(x)$ will be positive.
- The graph of $f(x)$ has a point of inflection at a point on the x-axis between -2 and -1, so $f''(x) = 0$ at this value. Since the graph of $f(x)$ changes from concave up to concave down at this x-value, the sign of $f''(x)$ also changes from positive to negative here.

Also, since $f''(x)$ is 0 at this x-value, the graph of $f'(x)$ will have a local maximum or minimum, and since the sign of $f''(x)$ changes from positive to negative, it must be a local maximum point.

Slope and Intervals of Increase and Decrease:
- $f(x)$ is decreasing for $x < 0$ and for $0 < x < 1$, so $f'(x)$ will be negative for x on these intervals.
- $f(x)$ is increasing for all $x > 1$, so $f'(x)$ will be positive for $x > 1$.

As $x \to 0^-$ and as $x \to 0^+$, the slope $\to -\infty$.

Concavity:
The graph of f is concave up for all $x > 0$, so f'' is positive for all $x > 0$.
Sketch the graphs of f' and f'' using all of this information.
• • • • • • • •

Sometimes you may have data about the derivative of a function rather than data about the function itself. What can you learn about a function's graph from the graph of its derivative?

Example 5   Sketching the Graph of a Function from the Graph of Its Derivative Function

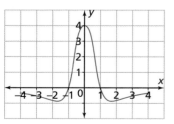

Here is the graph of $f'(x)$, the derivative of $f(x)$, for $-4 < x < 4$.

(a) For what x-values between -4 and 4 is $f(x)$ increasing? decreasing?

(b) At what x-values does the graph of $f(x)$ have local maximum or minimum points? Justify your answers.

(c) For what values of x is the graph of $f(x)$ concave up? concave down? Explain.

(d) Sketch a possible graph for $f(x)$ if $f(0) = 0$.

Solution

(a) $f'(x) > 0$ if $f(x)$ is increasing. From the graph of $f'(x)$, $f'(x) > 0$ on $-1 < x < 1$.

$f'(x) < 0$ if $f(x)$ is decreasing. From the graph of $f'(x)$, $f'(x) < 0$ on $-4 < x < 1$ and on $1 < x < 4$.

(b) At a local maximum or minimum, $f'(x) = 0$. From the graph, the zeros for $f'(x)$ occur at $x = \pm 1$.

At $x = -1$, $f'(x)$ changes from negative to positive, so the graph of $f(x)$ will have a local minimum point at $x = -1$.

At $x = 1$, $f'(x)$ changes from positive to negative, so the graph of $f(x)$ will have a local maximum point at $x = 1$.

(c) $f''(x)$ is positive and $f'(x)$ is increasing where the graph of $f(x)$ is concave up. From the graph, $f'(x)$ is increasing between $x \doteq -1.7$ and $x = 0$ and again between $x \doteq 1.7$ and $x = 4$. The graph of f will be concave up on $-1.7 < x < 0$ and on $1.7 < x < 4$.

$f''(x)$ is negative and $f'(x)$ is decreasing where the graph of $f(x)$ is concave down. From the graph of $f'(x)$, the graph of $f(x)$ will be concave down on $-4 < x < -1.7$ and on $0 < x < 1.7$.

(d) Now sketch a possible graph for $f(x)$.

Since $f'(x)$ exists for all x-values between -4 and 4, $f(x)$ must be continuous in this interval.

The value of the slope at different x-values can be read directly from the graph of $f'(x)$. For example, the slope of $f(x)$ is 4 when $x = 0$. Also, as x approaches -4 or 4, the slope is negative and close to 0.

Given that $f(0) = 0$, a possible graph for $f(x)$ is shown on the left.

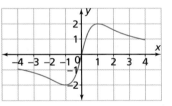

CHECK, CONSOLIDATE, COMMUNICATE

1. Explain why you might not use a graph created with graphing technology to correctly answer an application problem.
2. What information can you get from $f(x)$, $f'(x)$, and $f''(x)$ to help sketch the graph of $f(x)$?
3. How can you sketch the graph of a function from the graph of its derivative?

KEY IDEAS

- The first and second derivatives of a rational function give information about the shape of the function's graph.
- The number c is a **critical number** if
  - $f(c)$ exists, that is, c is in the domain of the function and
  - $f'(c) = 0$ or $f'(c)$ does not exist.
- The function is increasing for all x-values in an interval if $f'(x) > 0$ on that interval.

- The function is decreasing for all x-values in an interval if $f'(x) < 0$ on that interval.
- Let c be a critical number for a continuous function.
  - $f(c)$ is a local maximum if the sign of $f'(x)$ changes from positive to negative at c.
  - $f(c)$ is a local minimum if the sign of $f'(x)$ changes from negative to positive at c.
- The graph of the function is concave up when $f'(x)$ is increasing and when $f''(x) > 0$.
- The graph of the function is concave down when $f'(x)$ is decreasing and when $f''(x) < 0$.
- A point of inflection is a point at which the graph changes from concave up to concave down or vice versa.
- At a point of inflection, $f''(x) = 0$ or $f''(x)$ does not exist.
- Apply the steps for analyzing the features of any function to help sketch its graph. These steps are introduced on page 408.

5.7 Exercises

A *Questions 1 to 7 refer to the following functions:*

(a) $f(x) = \dfrac{x-1}{x^2}$

(b) $f(x) = \dfrac{2x}{x^2+1}$

(c) $f(x) = \dfrac{x}{x-2}$

(d) $f(x) = \dfrac{x-5}{3} - \dfrac{3}{x-5}$

1. Determine the domain and intercepts for each function.

2. Find the equations of all asymptotes for each function.

3. Find the first derivative. Determine the critical numbers for each function.

4. Find the intervals on which the functions are
   i. increasing   **ii.** decreasing

5. Find the second derivative. Determine the interval(s) on which the graph of each function is
   i. concave up   **ii.** concave down

6. Identify all local maximum and minimum points and any points of inflection for the graph of each function.

7. Use your results from questions 1 to 6 to sketch the graph of each function.

8. Verify the sketches you created for question 7 using graphing technology. Are any of the graphs symmetric about the y-axis or about the origin? How could you use the function equation to determine symmetry?

B **9. Knowledge and Understanding:** For $f(x) = \dfrac{x^2 + 3x + 9}{x}$,

  (a) show that $f'(x) = 1 - \dfrac{9}{x^2}$ and $f''(x) = \dfrac{18}{x^3}$

  (b) without graphing technology, use the information provided by the original function and its first and second derivatives to sketch the graph of the original function

10. For $f(x) = \dfrac{4(x-1)}{x^2}$, show that $f'(x) = \dfrac{4(2-x)}{x^3}$ and $f''(x) = \dfrac{8(x-3)}{x^4}$.

Use the function and its derivatives to determine the domain, intercepts, asymptotes, intervals of increase and decrease, and concavity, and to locate any critical points and points of inflection. Then use this information to sketch the graph of the original function.

11. For $f(x) = \dfrac{1}{1+x^2}$, show that $f'(x) = \dfrac{-2x}{(1+x^2)^2}$ and $f''(x) = \dfrac{2(3x^2-1)}{(1+x^2)^3}$.

Follow the steps for analyzing the graph of a function to sketch $f(x)$.

12. Determine the first and second derivatives for each function. Then analyze each function and sketch its graph.

  (a) $f(x) = x + \dfrac{9}{x}$ (b) $f(x) = \dfrac{x^2 - 1}{x^3}$ (c) $f(x) = \dfrac{x}{(x-2)^2}$

  (d) $f(x) = \dfrac{1}{x^2 - 4x}$ (e) $f(x) = \dfrac{x+1}{x+2}$ (f) $f(x) = x + \dfrac{1}{3x^3}$

  (g) $f(x) = \dfrac{x^2}{x-1}$ (h) $f(x) = \dfrac{2x}{4x-3}$ (i) $f(x) = \dfrac{x^2 - 1}{x^2 + 1}$

  (j) $f(x) = \dfrac{3x}{3+x}$ (k) $f(x) = \dfrac{x}{x^2 + 2}$ (l) $f(x) = \dfrac{x^2 - x}{x+1}$

13. The concentration, c, of a certain drug in the bloodstream t hours after it is taken orally is modelled by $c(t) = \dfrac{5t}{2t^2 + 5}$. Analyze the function and sketch its graph. After how long does the concentration begin to decrease? How does the rate of change of the concentration vary over time?

14. The position, s, of a particle moving along a straight line at t seconds is described by $s(t) = \dfrac{5t^2}{10 + t^2}$, where $0 \le t \le 10$.

  (a) Analyze the function and sketch its graph.

  (b) After what time does the particle stop speeding up and start to slow down?

  (c) When is the velocity greatest?

  (d) Sketch the graph of the velocity function.

15. Application: The population, p, of frogs in a newly created conservation area is modelled by $p(t) = 50 + \dfrac{2500t^2}{25 + t^2}$, where t is the time in years since the opening of the area. Analyze the model. According to this model,

  (a) how many frogs will populate this area in the long run?

  (b) when is the frog population increasing most rapidly?

  Sketch the graph of the frog population.

16. Let $R(x)$ be a revenue function. $R'(x)$ is the *marginal revenue*. Its value at any point is a measure of the estimated additional revenue from selling one more item. Suppose the demand equation for a certain product is $p(x) = \dfrac{5}{1 + x^2}$, where x is the number of items sold in thousands, and p is the price in dollars. When does the marginal revenue reach its lowest value? What feature of the graph of the revenue function occurs at this point?

17. Given the following results of the analysis of a function, sketch a possible graph for the function:

    (a) $f(0) = 0$, the horizontal asymptote is $y = 2$, the vertical asymptote is $x = 3$, $f'(x) < 0$ and $f''(x) < 0$ for $x < 3$; $f'(x) < 0$ and $f''(x) > 0$ for $x > 3$.

    (b) $f(0) = -6$, the horizontal asymptote is $y = -2$, the vertical asymptote is $x = -4$; $f'(x) > 0$ and $f''(x) > 0$ for $x < -4$; $f'(x) > 0$ and $f''(x) < 0$ for $x > -4$.

18. Use the features of each function's graph to sketch the graphs of its first and second derivatives.

    (a)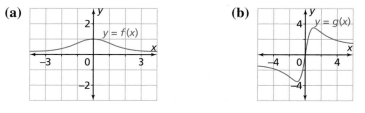

    (b)

19. A function's derivative is shown in each graph. Use the graph to sketch a possible graph for the original function.

    (a)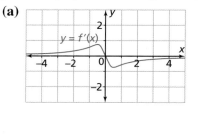

    (b)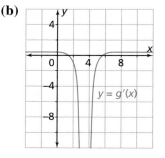

20. **Communication:** The graphs of a function and its derivatives, $y = f(x)$, $y = f'(x)$, and $y = f''(x)$, are shown in each graph. Which is which? Explain how you can tell.

    (a)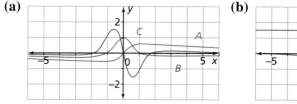

    (b)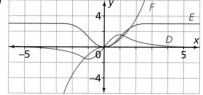

21. Decide whether each statement is true or false. Explain and give examples to support your decisions.

    (a) Function $f(x)$ has a local maximum or a local minimum when $x = 3$ if $f'(3) = 0$.

    (b) The graph of a rational function has a horizontal asymptote.

    (c) The graph of $f(x)$ has a point of inflection when $x = 2$ if $f''(2) = 0$.

22. **Check Your Understanding:** Without graphing technology, sketch the graph of $f(x) = \dfrac{x^2 + 3x}{x - 1}$ using information about the function and its derivatives. Explain each step in the analysis.

C **23.** The graph of the function $f(x) = ax^2 + \dfrac{b}{x}$ has a horizontal tangent at point $(1, 3)$. Find a and b, and show that $f(x)$ has a local minimum value at $x = 1$.

24. "If a continuous function has a local maximum value and a local minimum value, then the graph of the function must have a point of inflection between these two extrema." Do you agree with this comment? Explain with examples.

25. Create a rational function so that, in the graph of this function,

    (a) the y-axis and the line $y = 1$ are asymptotes

    (b) the x-intercept is at $x = 1$

26. Create a rational function for which

    i. the graph passes through $(0, 4)$

    ii. $\lim\limits_{x \to \pm\infty} f(x) = 0$

    iii. $\lim\limits_{x \to a^{\pm}} f(x) \neq \infty$, for any value of a in the domain

27. **Thinking, Inquiry, Problem Solving**

    (a) Sketch the graph of a function that satisfies these conditions.

        i. $f'(x) < 0$ and $f''(x) < 0$ for $x < -3$ and for $3 < x < 6$

        ii. $f'(x) > 0$ and $f''(x) < 0$ for $-3 < x < 3$

        iii. $f'(x) < 0$ and $f''(x) > 0$ for $x > 6$

        iv. $\lim\limits_{x \to -\infty} f(x) = 0,\ \ \lim\limits_{x \to -3^-} f(x) = -\infty,\ \ \lim\limits_{x \to -3^+} f(x) = -\infty$, and $\lim\limits_{x \to \infty} f(x) = 0$

        v. $f(0) = 0$

    (b) Label all the features of the graph.

ADDITIONAL ACHIEVEMENT CHART QUESTIONS

Knowledge and Understanding: Let $f(x) = \dfrac{3x^2 - 4x - 4}{x^2}$.

(a) Determine the first and second derivatives; the domain, intercepts, and asymptotes; intervals of increase and decrease and any critical points; and concavity and points of inflection.

(b) Use the information from (a) to sketch $f(x)$. Check your work with graphing technology.

Application: If a polio epidemic broke out in a small community with no vaccine, the fraction of the population that would be infected after t months could be modelled by $f(t) = \dfrac{64t^2}{(4 + t)^4}$, $0 \le t \le 5$. Graph the function, showing all essential features. When is the largest fraction of people infected? When is the epidemic spreading most rapidly? Show the results on your graph.

Thinking, Inquiry, Problem Solving: Graph a function $f(x)$ for which $\lim\limits_{x \to 0^+} f(x) = -\infty$; for $x < 0$, $f(x) = -1$ and $f'(x) = 0$; $f(1) = 0$; for $x > 0$, the only point at which $f'(x) = 0$ is $(2, 2)$; $f''(3) = 0$; and $\lim\limits_{x \to \infty} f(x) = 1$.

Communication: The growth in sales of a new product often follows a life-cycle curve like the one shown. Describe the growth pattern. When will the sales experience the most rapid growth?

The Chapter Problem
Designing a Settling Pond

Apply what you learned in this section to answer these questions about The Chapter Problem on page 342.

CP16. For each concentration function, **(a)** determine any critical numbers and **(b)** determine intervals of increase or decrease.

CP17. Determine where the graph of each concentration function is concave up or concave down. Are there any points of inflection? Explain.

CP18. Use the information from questions CP16 and CP17 to refine the graphs you made for question CP8.

CP19. (a) Write a report that describes the buildup of arsenic in a pond if water contaminated with arsenic runs into it. Discuss the effect that the water runoff rate has on the buildup of arsenic in the pond.
(b) In your report, also recommend the dimensions of a settling pond that will minimize material costs. Illustrate your report with your graphs and calculations.

Chapter 5 Review

RATES OF CHANGE IN RATIONAL FUNCTION MODELS

CHECK YOUR UNDERSTANDING

1. What is a rational function? Describe in what ways the graphs of rational functions are different from the graphs of polynomial functions.

2. What are the steps for finding a limit of a rational function if substitution fails?

3. How do you determine the equation of **(a)** a vertical asymptote? **(b)** a horizontal asymptote? **(c)** an oblique asymptote?

4. What kinds of discontinuities do rational functions have? When can a discontinuity be removed, and how is this done?

5. State the rule for determining the derivative of a rational function, in symbols and in words. What is this rule called?

6. In what ways can a function fail to have a derivative at a point?

7. Who might need to determine an optimal value? What are the steps for solving an optimization problem using calculus?

8. How can you use the equation of a rational function and its first and second derivatives to sketch the graph of the function by hand?

9. How do you use the graph of a function to sketch the graph of its first derivative? How do you use the graphs of a function's first and second derivatives to sketch the graph of the function?

10. A function is continuous at a point if the function is differentiable at that point. However, a continuous function may not be differentiable at one or more points. Explain, using examples and limit concepts.

ADDITIONAL REVIEW QUESTIONS BY SECTION

5.1 Graphs of Rational Functions

11. Determine the domain and the x- and y-intercepts for each rational function.

(a) $f(x) = \dfrac{3 - x}{x + 1}$

(b) $f(x) = \dfrac{2x}{3x - 7}$

(c) $f(x) = \dfrac{4x^2 - 17x - 15}{x}$

(d) $f(x) = \dfrac{2x - 3}{2x^2 + x - 3}$

(e) $f(x) = \dfrac{3x^2 - 7x + 2}{3x - 1}$

(f) $f(x) = \dfrac{x^2 - 1}{x^3 + 2x^2 - 4x - 8}$

12. Which of the functions in question 11 have

    (a) a vertical asymptote?

    (b) a horizontal asymptote?

    (c) an oblique asymptote?

    Give reasons for your answers. Determine the equation of each asymptote. Then sketch the graph for each function.

13. The estimated revenue and cost functions for the manufacture of a new product are $R(x) = -2x^2 + 15x$ and $C(x) = 5x + 8$. Express the *average profit function, $AP(x) = \dfrac{P(x)}{x}$*, in two different forms. Explain what can be determined from each form. What is the domain of the function in this context? What are the break-even quantities?

5.2 Limits and End Behaviour of Rational Functions

14. Evaluate each limit, where it exists. If a limit does not exist, explain why.

    (a) $\displaystyle\lim_{x \to 3} \frac{6 - x^2}{2x}$

    (b) $\displaystyle\lim_{x \to 2} \frac{2x}{x^2 - 4}$

    (c) $\displaystyle\lim_{x \to -4} \frac{2x^2 + 5x - 12}{x + 4}$

    (d) $\displaystyle\lim_{x \to \infty} \frac{1 - 2x^3 - 4x^6}{5x^2 - 2x^6}$

15. Determine the equations of any vertical or horizontal asymptotes for each function. Describe the behaviour of the function on each side of any vertical asymptote.

    (a) $f(x) = \dfrac{x - 5}{2x + 1}$

    (b) $g(x) = \dfrac{x^2 - 4x - 5}{(x + 2)^2}$

    (c) $h(x) = \dfrac{x^2 + 2x - 15}{9 - x^2}$

    (d) $m(x) = \dfrac{2x^2 + x + 1}{x + 4}$

16. Find each limit.

    (a) $\displaystyle\lim_{x \to \infty} \frac{3 - 2x}{3x}$

    (b) $\displaystyle\lim_{x \to \infty} \frac{x^2 - 2x + 5}{6x^2 + 2x - 1}$

    (c) $\displaystyle\lim_{x \to \infty} \frac{7 + 2x^2 - 3x^3}{x^3 - 4x^2 + 3x}$

    (d) $\displaystyle\lim_{x \to \infty} \frac{5 - 2x^3}{x^4 - 4x}$

    (e) $\displaystyle\lim_{x \to \infty} \frac{2x^5 - 1}{3x^4 - x^2 - 2}$

    (f) $\displaystyle\lim_{x \to \infty} \frac{x^2 + 3x - 18}{(x - 3)^2}$

    (g) $\displaystyle\lim_{x \to \infty} \frac{x^2 - 4x - 5}{x^2 - 1}$

    (h) $\displaystyle\lim_{x \to \infty} \left(5x + 4 - \frac{7}{x + 3}\right)$

5.3 Continuity of Rational Functions

17. Find any points of discontinuity for each function. State which conditions of continuity are not satisfied.

    (a) $f(x) = \dfrac{x}{(x - 5)^2}$

    (b) $f(x) = \dfrac{5}{x^2 + 9}$

    (c) $f(x) = \dfrac{x - 2}{x^2 - 8x + 12}$

    (d) $f(x) = \begin{cases} x^3 - 3x^2 + 2x + 4 & \text{if } x \le 0 \\ \dfrac{x^2 - x + 12}{x + 3} & \text{if } x > 0 \end{cases}$

18. Determine whether or not each function is continuous at $x = -2$.

(a) $f(x) = \begin{cases} \dfrac{1}{x+2} & \text{if } x \neq -2 \\ 0 & \text{if } x = -2 \end{cases}$

(b) $f(x) = \begin{cases} \dfrac{x^2 - x - 6}{x+2} & \text{if } x \neq -2 \\ -5 & \text{if } x = -2 \end{cases}$

19. Define each function so that it is continuous for all real numbers.

(a) $f(x) = \dfrac{x^2 - 4}{x + 2}$

(b) $f(x) = \dfrac{x^2 + x - 12}{x - 3}$

5.4 Rate of Change of a Rational Function — The Quotient Rule

20. Use the quotient rule to find $f'(x)$ for each function.

(a) $f(x) = \dfrac{x + 4}{x - 1}$

(b) $f(x) = \dfrac{2x^3}{x^2 - 3}$

(c) $f(x) = \dfrac{x^3 - x}{2x^2 + x - 1}$

(d) $f(x) = \dfrac{(x + 1)(x - 2)}{3x(x + 4)}$

(e) $f(x) = \dfrac{x^4}{2 - x}$

(f) $f(x) = \dfrac{ax + b}{cx - d}$

(g) $f(x) = \dfrac{x^2 - 4}{3x + 1}$

(h) $f(x) = \dfrac{2x^5 + 3}{x - 2}$

(i) $f(x) = \dfrac{1 - x^4}{x^3}$

(j) $f(x) = \dfrac{1 - \dfrac{3}{x}}{x - 5}$

21. The position of an object moving along a straight line at time t is given by s. Find the position, velocity, and acceleration at the specified time.

(a) $s(t) = \dfrac{3t}{t + 4}; t = 2$

(b) $s(t) = 2t + \dfrac{4}{t + 1}; t = 1$

22. The amount of money a family saves is a function, $S(x)$, of its income, x. The *marginal propensity to save* is $S'(x)$. Find the marginal propensity to save if $S(x) = \dfrac{1.5x^2}{5(x + 45\,000)}$.

5.5 Differentiability of Rational and Other Functions

23. Explain why each function is not differentiable at $(2, 3)$.

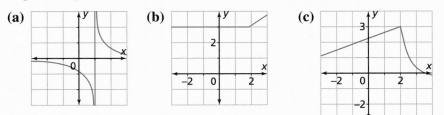

(a) **(b)** **(c)**

24. Each function is *not* differentiable at $x = 2$. Determine whether the reason is a discontinuity, a corner, a cusp, or a vertical tangent.

(a) $f(x) = \dfrac{x^2 - 4}{x - 2}$

(b) $f(x) = \dfrac{1}{2}|2 - x| + 1$

(c) $f(x) = \dfrac{x+6}{x-2}$

(d) $f(x) = (x-2)^{\frac{2}{3}}$

(e) $f(x) = 2\sqrt{4-2x}$

(f) $f(x) = (0.5x-1)^{\frac{1}{3}}$

25. Determine whether each function is differentiable at $x = -1$. Give reasons for your choices.

(a) $f(x) = \dfrac{7x}{1-x^2}$

(b) $g(x) = \dfrac{x+1}{x^2-3x-4}$

(c) $h(x) = \sqrt[3]{(x-1)^2}$

(d) $m(x) = |x+1| - 1$

5.6 Finding Optimal Values for Rational Function Models

26. Craig is designing a rectangular poster that will have an area of 3750 cm². The margins at the top and bottom are 12.5 cm wide. The margins at the sides are 7.5 cm wide. What should be the dimensions of the poster if the area of print should be as large as possible?

27. A health drink manufacturer wants to sell its product in 400-mL cans. The metal used for the top and bottom of a can costs \$1.50/m². The metal used for the side costs \$0.50/m². The metal left over after the circles for the top and bottom of one can are cut out of one rectangle will be scrapped. Find the dimensions of the can that will minimize the cost of materials.

28. A closed rectangular box with a square base will be made as follows. The volume must be 0.9 m³. The area of the base must not exceed 1.8 m². The height of the box must not exceed 0.75 m. Determine the dimensions for **(a)** minimal surface area and **(b)** maximum surface area.

5.7 Sketching Graphs of Rational Functions

29. For $f(x) = \dfrac{5x}{(x-1)^2}$, show that $f'(x) = \dfrac{-5(x+1)}{(x-1)^3}$ and $f''(x) = \dfrac{10(x+2)}{(x-1)^4}$. Use the function and its derivatives to determine the domain, intercepts, asymptotes, intervals of increase and decrease, and concavity, and to locate any turning points and points of inflection. Use this information to sketch the graph of f.

30. Determine the first and second derivatives for each function. Then analyze each function and sketch its graph.

(a) $f(x) = \dfrac{1-2x^2}{x^3}$

(b) $f(x) = \dfrac{x}{(x-3)^2}$

(c) $f(x) = \dfrac{x+2}{x+3}$

(d) $f(x) = 2x + \dfrac{1}{x^3}$

(e) $f(x) = \dfrac{x}{2-3x}$

(f) $f(x) = \dfrac{x^2-1}{x^2+2}$

(g) $f(x) = \dfrac{2x}{x^2+1}$

(h) $f(x) = \dfrac{x^2-x}{x+2}$

31. The graphs of a function and its derivatives are shown. Which is which? Explain how you can tell.

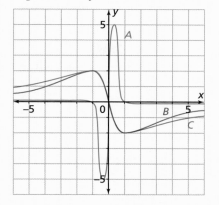

REVIEW QUESTIONS BY ACHIEVEMENT CHART CATEGORIES

Knowledge and Understanding

32. Evaluate each limit, if it exists. If the limit does not exist, explain why.

(a) $\displaystyle\lim_{x \to -2} \frac{3x}{2 + x^2}$

(b) $\displaystyle\lim_{x \to 1} \frac{x + 1}{x^2 - 1}$

(c) $\displaystyle\lim_{x \to 2} \frac{x^2 + 4x - 12}{x^2 - 4}$

(d) $\displaystyle\lim_{x \to \infty} \frac{2x^5 - 3x^4 + 5x}{3x^3 - 7x^5}$

33. Find the equation of the tangent line to the graph of $f(x) = \dfrac{8x^2 - 3}{x^2 + 4}$ at the point where $x = -1$.

34. For $f(x) = \dfrac{x^2 + 3}{x - 1}$,

(a) show that $f'(x) = \dfrac{x^2 - 2x - 3}{(x - 1)^2}$ and $f''(x) = \dfrac{8}{(x - 1)^3}$

(b) use the information given by $f(x)$ and its derivatives to graph $f(x)$ without graphing technology

Communication

35. Let $f(x) = \dfrac{-x - 3}{x^2 - 5x - 14}$, $g(x) = \dfrac{x - x^3}{x - 3}$, $h(x) = \dfrac{x^3 - 1}{x^2 + 4}$, and

$r(x) = \dfrac{x^2 + x - 6}{x^2 - 16}$. How can you can tell from its equation which of these functions has

(a) a horizontal asymptote?

(b) an oblique asymptote?

(c) no vertical asymptote?

Explain. Determine the equations of all asymptote(s) for each function. Describe the behaviour of each function close to its asymptotes.

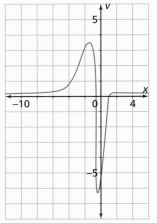

36. The function $c(t) = \dfrac{7t}{2t^2 + 1}$ represents the concentration, $c(t)$, of a drug in the bloodstream t hours after it is taken orally. Determine $c'(t)$ and $c''(t)$. Explain, using numerical examples, the information these two derivative functions provide.

37. The graph of $y = f'(x)$ is shown on the left. Sketch possible graphs for $y = f(x)$ and $y = f''(x)$. Explain how you sketched the graphs.

Application

38. For what values of A does $f(x) = \dfrac{x^2 + 2x + A}{x^2 - 4x - 5}$ have a removable discontinuity? For each value of A, redefine the function to make it continuous.

39. The concentration of a pollutant in polluted water is 2 g/L. The polluted water flows into a large tank that initially holds 800 L of pure water. Ten litres of polluted water per minute flow into the tank. Determine the concentration of pollutant in the tank after t minutes. Describe how this concentration is changing after 3 hours; after 12 hours. What assumptions do you need to make?

40. A rectangular wooden bedding chest will be built so that its length is 2.5 times its width. The top, front, and two sides of the chest will be oak. The back and bottom of the chest will be aromatic cedar. The volume of the chest must be 0.5 m³. Oak costs 1.5 times as much as cedar. Find the dimensions that will minimize the cost of the chest.

Thinking, Inquiry, Problem Solving

41. Suppose $p(x)$ and $q(x)$ are rational functions and $\lim\limits_{x \to +\infty} [p(x)] = \infty$ and $\lim\limits_{x \to \infty} [q(x)] = \infty$. Is it always true that $\lim\limits_{x \to \infty} [p(x) - q(x)] = 0$? Investigate using different functions for $p(x)$ and $q(x)$.

42. Rolle's theorem states: Let f be differentiable on $a < x < b$ and continuous on $a \le x \le b$. If $f(b)$ and $f(a)$ are both 0, there is at least one number c in $a < x < b$ for which $f'(c) = 0$. Does $f(x) = \dfrac{x^2 - 9x + 8}{x}$ satisfy Rolle's theorem on any interval? If so, what are the values of a, b, and c?

43. For function $f(x)$, $f''(x)$ is continuous and positive for all values of x, and $f(x)$ is negative for all values of x. For $g(x) = \dfrac{1}{f(x)}$, show that $g(x)$ is always concave down.

Chapter 5 Performance Task

The position of a flare, shot straight up in the air, relative to the ground is given by $s(t) = \dfrac{-125(t^2 - 15t)}{t + 1}$, where s is height in metres and t is time in seconds.

1. Determine the domain and intercepts of the function. Identify which points are in the domain of the *function* but not in the domain of the trajectory of the flare.

2. (a) Identify all asymptotes of $s(t)$: vertical, horizontal, and oblique.

   (b) Suggest a simpler function that can be used to model $s(t)$ after the first 6 s of flight. How close to $s(t)$ is this function at 6 s? 15 s?

   (c) The model suggested in part (b) is considered *reasonably accurate*, at any given time, if it is within 10 m of $s(t)$. After what point in time is the model from part (b) considered *reasonably accurate*? Explain whether or not you think the new model is a good substitute for $s(t)$.

3. Examine the end behaviour and continuity of $s(t)$ by determining $\lim\limits_{t \to -1} s(t)$ and $\lim\limits_{t \to \infty} s(t)$. Explain how the continuity and end behaviour of the function relate to the trajectory of the flare.

4. Use the quotient rule to determine the first and second derivative of $s(t)$. Is $s(t)$ differentiable at all points within the domain of the function? Is $s(t)$ differentiable within all points of the trajectory?

5. Determine the maximum height reached by the flare using $s(t)$, the first derivative ($v(t)$), and the second derivative ($a(t)$). Verify that the height you have determined is the maximum height and not the minimum height.

6. Determine the maximum velocity reached by examining the graph of the flare $v(t)$ using graphing technology. Can this value be found by setting the first derivative of $v(t) = 0$ (that is, $a(t) = 0$) and solving for t? Explain.

7. Graph $s(t)$ without technology. Use only the information you have determined from questions 1 to 6.

Chapter 5 Review Test

RATES OF CHANGE IN RATIONAL FUNCTION MODELS

1. Let $p(x) = \dfrac{3x^3 - 5}{4x^2 + 1}$, $q(x) = \dfrac{3x - 1}{x^2 - 2x - 3}$, $r(x) = \dfrac{x^2 - 2x - 8}{x^2 - 1}$, and $s(x) = \dfrac{x^3 + 2x}{x - 2}$.

   (a) For each function, determine its asymptotes and identify their type (vertical, horizontal, or oblique).

   (b) Graph $y = r(x)$, showing clearly the asymptotes and the intercepts.

2. **Knowledge and Understanding:** Evaluate each limit, if it exists. If it does not exist, explain why.

   (a) $\displaystyle\lim_{x \to 0} \frac{4}{x + 2}$

   (b) $\displaystyle\lim_{x \to 4} \frac{x}{16 - x^2}$

   (c) $\displaystyle\lim_{x \to 1} \frac{x^5 - 1}{x^2 - 1}$

   (d) $\displaystyle\lim_{x \to \infty} \frac{1 - 3x^3 - 2x^5}{5x^5 - 8x^4}$

3. Describe the discontinuities, if any, for each function.

   (a) $f(x) = |x + 3|$

   (b) $f(x) = \dfrac{x + 2}{x^2 - 5x - 14}$

4. **Application:** The population of Newton is modelled by $P(t) = \dfrac{20(4t + 3)}{2t + 5}$, where $P(t)$, the population, is measured in thousands and t is the time in years since 1990.

   (a) Is the population increasing or decreasing? Justify your answer.

   (b) Determine the rate of change of the population in 1996 to three decimal places.

   (c) The town will need its own transit system if the population exceeds 50 000. Will Newton's population ever exceed 50 000? Explain.

5. **Thinking, Inquiry, Problem Solving:** Determine the equations of the two tangents to the curve $y = \dfrac{x}{(1 - x)^2}$ that pass through $(1, 1)$.

6. At what values of x is each function *not* differentiable? Explain.

   (a) $f(x) = \dfrac{7}{2x - 1}$

   (b) $f(x) = \dfrac{x^2 - 5x - 6}{x^2 - 1}$

7. A cylindrical vat must hold 5 m³ of liquid cake mix. The vat must be wider than it is tall, but no more than 3 m in diameter. What dimensions will use the least amount of material?

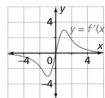

8. For $f(x) = \dfrac{x^3 + 8}{x}$, determine the domain, intercepts, asymptotes, intervals of increase and decrease, and concavity. Locate any critical points and points of inflection. Use this information to sketch the graph of $f(x)$.

9. **Communication:** Explain how you can use this graph of $y = f'(x)$ to sketch a possible graph of the original function $y = f(x)$.

Cumulative Review Test 2

DIFFERENTIAL CALCULUS: POLYNOMIAL AND RATIONAL FUNCTIONS

1. For each function, find the derivative, find all critical numbers, and state the intervals of increase and decrease.

   (a) $y = 6x^2 + 12$ **(b)** $y = -5x^2 + 20x + 2$

   (c) $y = 6x^2 + 16x - 40$ **(d)** $y = 2x^3 - 24x$

   (e) $y = -2x^4 + 4x^2$ **(f)** $y = \dfrac{x^4}{2} + \dfrac{x^3}{3} - \dfrac{13x^2}{2} + 6x - 1$

2. The graph of $f(x) = 2x^2 - 3x + 1$ passes through $T(0, 1)$. Determine the equation of the tangent line at T.

3. Evaluate.

   (a) $\displaystyle\lim_{x \to 2} (3x^3 - 2x^2 + 5)$ **(b)** $\displaystyle\lim_{x \to -1} (5x^2 - 6x + 7)$

   (c) $\displaystyle\lim_{x \to 4} (-6x + 8)$ **(d)** $\displaystyle\lim_{x \to -3} (-3x^4 + 3x^2 - 1)$

   (e) $\displaystyle\lim_{x \to -3} (5x^3 + 2x^2 + 3x - 10)$ **(f)** $\displaystyle\lim_{x \to 8} (x^5 - 9x^3 - 2x)$

4. When an arrow is shot into the air, its height, h, in metres after t seconds can be modelled by $h(t) = 42t - 4.9t^2$. Determine
   $$\lim_{h \to 0} \frac{[42(3 + h) - 4.9(3 + h)^2] - [42(3) - 4.9(3)^2]}{h}.$$ What does this represent?
   At what rate is the arrow's height changing with respect to time at exactly 4 s?

5. If an object were dropped from the observation deck of the Skylon Tower in Niagara Falls, Ontario, the distance in metres from the deck at t seconds would be described by $d(t) = 4.9t^2$. Find the average rate of change of distance with respect to time from $t = 1$ to $t = 3$. Find the instantaneous rate of change of distance with respect to time at 2 s. The height of the deck is 146.9 m. How fast would the object be moving when it hits the ground?

6. The model $G(t) = t^2 + 6t + 105$ is an estimate of the gross domestic product (GDP), G, of a certain country in billions of dollars, where t is the number of years since 2000. According to the model, how fast will the GDP be changing in 2010?

7. The position of an object moving along a horizontal line at t seconds is $s(t) = \dfrac{t^3}{3} - 4t^2 + 12t + 10$, where $s(t)$ is in metres and $t \geq 0$. Determine the initial position of the object. Determine the velocity at 1 s and 4 s. When is the object stationary? Determine when the object is advancing and when it is retreating. Determine the total distance travelled during the first 7 s.

8. A hockey player shoots a puck from the blue line. The position, $s(t)$, of the puck, in metres, from the blue line is $s(t) = 64t - \dfrac{3}{4}t^{\frac{4}{3}}$ at t seconds. Is the puck accelerating or decelerating 1 s after it is shot? Justify your answer.

9. A rectangular box is to have a volume of 7200 cm^3. The length of the box is three times the width. Determine the height of the box with the smallest total surface area.

10. The annual "Lobsterama" supper has always filled a hall that can seat 500 people. In the past, tickets cost $30 per person, but the organizers want to raise the price. They estimate that ticket sales will drop by 10 for every $1 the price is raised. The revenue, R, can be modelled by $R(x) = (30 + x)(500 - 10x)$, where x is the price increase in dollars. What ticket price will maximize revenue? Will there be any empty seats at this price?

11. Research has shown that the profit, P, for a cosmetics manufacturer is related to the amount spent on advertising, x thousands of dollars, by $P(x) = 15\ 200 + 40x - 0.1x^2$. How much should the company spend to maximize their profit?

12. Find the derivative of each rational function from first principles. Then verify your results using the quotient rule.

(a) $f(x) = \dfrac{2x}{1 - x}$ (b) $f(x) = \dfrac{x - 1}{x + 3}$ (c) $f(x) = \dfrac{2x^2 - 1}{3x}$

13. The value of a car, t years after it is bought, is modelled by $V(t) = \dfrac{21\ 000 + 8t}{1 + 0.5t} + 150$. State the domain of $V(t)$, determine any intercepts and asymptotes, and sketch the function. What will the car be worth in the long run?

14. In each case, find an end-behaviour model. Identify any horizontal asymptotes.

(a) $f(x) = \dfrac{x - 2}{3x^2 - 2x - 1}$ (b) $f(x) = \dfrac{3x^2 - x + 7}{x^2 - 3}$

15. Define a function that has a removable discontinuity at $x = 4$ and a jump discontinuity at $x = -1$.

16. Explain why the derivative of $f(x) = \begin{cases} \dfrac{1}{x} & \text{if } x < 1 \\ x & \text{if } x \geq 1 \end{cases}$ does not exist at $x = 1$

but the derivative of $f(x) = \begin{cases} \dfrac{1}{x} & \text{if } x < 1 \\ 2 - x & \text{if } x \geq 1 \end{cases}$ does exist at $x = 1$.

17. Custom Chairs estimates that it can sell x chairs per week at p dollars each. The demand function is $p = 205 - 1.2x$. The cost of production is estimated by $C(x) = 0.25x^2 + 18x + 625$. Determine the production level that produces the maximum profit. At what production level is the average cost per item a minimum?

18. The demand equation for a certain product is $p = \dfrac{7}{2 + x^2}$, where p is the price in dollars and x is the number of items sold in thousands. When does the marginal revenue reach its lowest value? What feature of the graph of $R(x)$ occurs at this point?

6 Rates of Change in Composite Function Models

In this course, you have analyzed the behaviour of polynomial and rational functions such as $g(x) = 2x^4 - 8x^3 + 9x^2$, $h(x) = 5x^{-2}(7 - x^3)$, and $s(t) = \dfrac{5t}{t^2 + 1}$. You have learned to differentiate these functions and to use the derivative to solve problems and analyze the behaviour of the function.

You have also seen that a polynomial function can depend on another polynomial function. For example, the flow of exports to the United States is a function of the value of the Canadian dollar. Also, the value of the dollar is a function of time. So, the relation between exports and time is a third function, and is a composition of the other two. The rate of change of either component affects the rate of change of the third function. Finding relations between functions is an important skill in analyzing functions.

In this chapter, you will

- learn about the composition of two functions in various situations

- use composition of functions to model transformations and to reinforce an understanding of inverse functions

- decompose complex functions into simpler functions to find the derivative

- develop a rule for differentiating composite functions in algebraic, numerical, and graphical contexts

- practise differentiating products, quotients, and powers of polynomials

- use calculus to analyze and graph composite functions

- find derivatives of relations where $f(x)$ is not defined explicitly

- solve optimization and related rate problems involving complex relations

The Chapter Problem

Tides on the Bay of Fundy

The Bay of Fundy in New Brunswick is famous for its powerful tides and the Reversing Falls on the St. John River. In the bay, the water falls and rises about 14 m every 12.5 h. One hundred billion tons of water flow with every tide. The tremendous flow of water in and out of the bay churns up nutrients and plankton, which are food for several species of whales. The Bay of Fundy is one of the best places in the world to view whales. When the tides recede, many different shorebirds feed in the mudflats.

The table shows the depth of water in the St. John harbour over a day and a half as predicted by a computer model.

Time (h:min)	Tide Mark	Depth (m)
02:37	low tide	1.65
08:45	high tide	6.80
15:00	low tide	1.86
21:12	high tide	7.35
27:40	low tide	1.43
33:48	high tide	6.98

Assume that the slope of the floor of the bay in that area is a constant 1:20. Determine the maximum rate at which the water receded down the beach during that period.

List the reasons why different people might depend on a computer model in this area, and consider how such a model might be developed.

After certain lessons, you will be asked questions about this problem to help you develop your solution. Keep a record of your work in a project folder or computer file so that you can provide a full solution at the end of the chapter.

For help with this problem, see pages 445 and 457.

Chapter Challenges

Challenge 1

A *clepsydra* is an ancient type of clock that uses water to keep time. The vessel in the diagram has a small opening in the bottom. Torricelli's law states that the rate at which water flows from the opening is proportional to the square root of the depth of the water above the opening. The shape of the vessel in the diagram is based on $y = ax^4$. The curve is rotated around the y-axis to form a bowl. Show that this bowl serves as a clepsydra in which the depth of the water decreases at a constant rate.

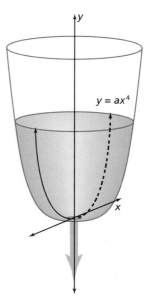

$y = ax^4$

Challenge 2

One challenge of designing a microprocessor is to find efficient ways to approximate common mathematical functions. One way of approximating trigonometric functions is by using polynomial models.

Show that $f(x) = x - \dfrac{x^3}{3!} + \dfrac{x^5}{5!} - \dfrac{x^7}{7!} + \dfrac{x^9}{9!}$ is a good model for $\sin x$ on $0 \le x \le \dfrac{\pi}{2}$ by comparing graphs and tables for values of $x, f(x)$, and $\sin x$ on this interval. Describe how to reasonably approximate the value of $\sin x$ for x-values outside this domain.

Use the relations between the trigonometric functions to find approximations for $\cos x$ and $\tan x$.

Compare the graph of the derivative of $f(x)$ with the graphs of the other trigonometric functions. Extend and explore these relations. Use these relations to create other approximations, or models, for the trigonometric functions.

Getting Ready

In this chapter, you will work with the composition of functions, inverses, and their graphs; find the slope of the tangent at various points; revisit differentiation rules and learn new ones; and apply these concepts to real-life situations. These exercises will help you warm up for the work ahead.

1. Find the slope of each line, using $m = \dfrac{y_2 - y_1}{x_2 - x_1}$. Which line has the steepest slope? How do you know?

   (a) a line passing through $(-10, 5)$ and $(10, 50)$

   (b)

x	y
−2	−7
−1	−4
0	−1
1	2
2	5

   (c)

   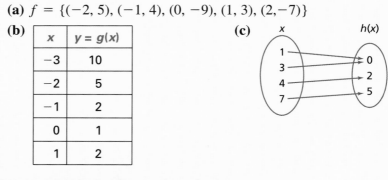

2. Find the inverse of each function. Write the inverse in the same way the function is presented. State the domain and range of each function and its inverse. What do you notice?

   (a) $f = \{(-2, 5), (-1, 4), (0, -9), (1, 3), (2, -7)\}$

   (b)

x	y = g(x)
−3	10
−2	5
−1	2
0	1
1	2

   (c)

3. State the domain and range of each function.

   (a)   **(b)**   **(c)**

   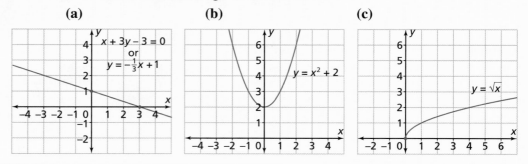

(d) $f(x) = x^4 - 5x^3 - 3$

(e) $g(s) = s^2 + (s - 1)^8$

(f) $h(x) = \frac{x + 1}{2x^7 - 1}$

(g) $k(t) = \frac{\sqrt[3]{t}}{(t - 1)^2}$

(h) $m(u) = \sqrt{\frac{u - 2}{6 + u}}$

(i) $p(a) = |a^3 - a|$

4. Find the inverse of each function algebraically. Express your answer in function notation.

(a) $f(x) = 2x - 3$

(b) $g(x) = -4x^2 + 3x + 2$

(c) $h(x) = 3\sqrt{x + 1}$

(d) $k(x) = \frac{x + 1}{4}$

(e) $q(x) = -x^3 - 1$

(f) $r(x) = \sqrt{x^2 - 16}$

5. **(a)** Graph the three circles on the same set of axes. Compare the graphs.

    i. $x^2 + y^2 = 4$ **ii.** $x^2 + y^2 = 8$ **iii.** $x^2 + y^2 = 1$

  (b) Graph the three ellipses on the same set of axes. Compare the graphs.

    i. $\frac{x^2}{25} + \frac{y^2}{64} = 1$ **ii.** $x^2 + 4y^2 = 100$ **iii.** $\frac{x^2}{9} + \frac{y^2}{4} = 1$

6. Differentiate.

(a) $f(x) = 7$

(b) $f(x) = \sqrt{x}$

(c) $f(x) = 2\pi + 4x$

(d) $f(x) = x^{23}$

(e) $f(x) = 2x^2 + 1$

(f) $f(x) = -3x^4 - 3x + 4$

(g) $f(x) = x^{\frac{4}{3}}$

(h) $f(x) = 5x^7 + 3x^6 - 2x^4 + 5x - 3$

(i) $f(x) = \frac{x^2 - 2x + 4}{6}$

(j) $f(x) = x^2 - \frac{2}{x}$

(k) $f(x) = (x^2 + 3)(3x - 1)$

(l) $f(x) = \frac{x + 1}{x^2 + 2}$

(m) $f(x) = (\sqrt{x} + 2)(x^6 - 4x^3 + 7x - 3)$

(n) $f(x) = (\sqrt[3]{x} + 3)\left(\frac{1}{x} - 6\right)$

(o) $f(x) = \frac{1}{10 - 0.1x^3}$

7. The cost function of operating a small business is given by $C(x) = -x^4 + 16x^3 - 5$.

  (a) Find where the cost is increasing and where it is decreasing.

  (b) Find all critical points and points of inflection.

  (c) Determine the intervals of concavity.

  (d) Graph the function.

8. The function $s(t) = 3t^2 + 5t - 1$ models the distance an object travels, where s represents the distance in metres at t seconds. Find

  (a) the velocity, $v(t)$

  (b) the acceleration, $a(t)$

  (c) the average velocity of the object over the first three seconds

9. Find the equation of the tangent line of each function at the given point.

  (a) $f(x) = 1 - x^4 - x^8$ at $x = 2$ **(b)** $g(t) = 4 - 3t^{-3} + 6t^2$ at $t = -1$

  (c) $v(a) = (a + 1)(\sqrt{a} + 1)$ at $a = 4$ **(d)** $n(x) = \frac{-4}{x^4 + 3}$ at $x = \frac{1}{3}$

6.1 Composition of Functions

SETTING THE STAGE

🔍 **Explore the concepts in this lesson in more detail using Exploration 11 on page 579.**

Recall that **composition** was introduced as the result of substituting one polynomial function, f, into another, g. The result is another polynomial function, $f \circ g$.

Definition of a Composite Function

The composite function $f \circ g$ is defined by $(f \circ g)(x) = f(g(x))$.

The notation $f \circ g$ is read "f follows g" or "the composition of f and g."

To evaluate $f(g(x))$, first evaluate $g(x)$ and then evaluate f at the number $g(x)$.

The input-output diagram shows the composite function $f \circ g$.

To determine the output of $f \circ g$, use the output of g as the input of f.

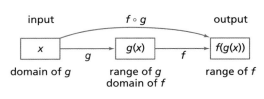

Input-output diagram of $f \circ g$.

You can think of a composite function in this way: a change in one quantity produces a change in a second quantity, which in turn produces a change in a third quantity. For example, in many Northern Ontario communities, the human population affects the wolf population, which in turn affects the rabbit population. When the human population *increases*, the local wolf population *decreases*, because the wolves tend to avoid humans. The *decrease* in the wolf population leads to an *increase* in the rabbit population, since rabbits are eaten by wolves. What would happen to the rabbit population if the human population decreased?

This population example illustrates the idea of composition. However, other factors influence the populations of humans, wolves, and rabbits.

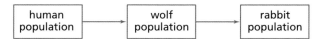

Can you use composition to combine functions that are not polynomials? Can you combine a function and its inverse? Do the properties for polynomial composite functions apply to other composite functions as well? In this section, you will extend your understanding of composition to include polynomial, rational, inverse, and other functions.

EXAMINING THE CONCEPT

Composition Involving Functions Represented by Discrete Data

Before combining, or composing, different types of functions, you should understand some basic properties of composite functions.

Example 1 **Composition of Functions Defined by Tables**

x	g(x)
−1	2.5
0	3
1	−2
2	0
3	1
4	−3

x	f(x)
−1	4
0	3
1	2
2	1
3	0
4	−1

Functions f and g are defined in the tables on the left.
Create a table for $f \circ g$.

Solution

For $f \circ g$, start with the table for g. Recall the input-output diagram. The values for x are the inputs. The outputs are the values for $g(x)$. These outputs become the inputs for f. So the second column of the first table becomes the first column for the second table shown here. Now treat each value for $g(x)$ as an input for f. Find the values for $f(g(x))$, if they exist, in the second table below. For example,

$$x \xrightarrow{g} g(x) \xrightarrow{f} f(g(x))$$

$$2 \xrightarrow{g} 0 \xrightarrow{f} 3$$

$$4 \xrightarrow{g} -3 \xrightarrow{f} \text{undefined}$$

To obtain the table for $f \circ g$, choose the rows in the other tables where x, $g(x)$, and $f(g(x))$ are all defined.

x	g(x)
−1	2.5
0	3
1	−2
2	0
3	1
4	−3

→

g(x)	f(g(x))
2.5	undefined
3	0
−2	undefined
0	3
1	2
−3	undefined

x	(f ∘ g)(x)
0	0
2	3
3	2

• • • • • • • •

The Domain and Range of $f \circ g$

The composition of two functions exists only where the range of the first function overlaps, or is contained in, the domain of the second function.

The domain of $f \circ g$ is a subset of the domain of g. The range of $f \circ g$ is a subset of the range of f.

What happens when a function is composed with its inverse? Recall that the inverse function "undoes" the effect of the original function. As a result, the domain of the original function becomes the range of the inverse. The range of the original function becomes the domain of the inverse.

Example 2   **Composition of a Discrete Function and Its Inverse**

For function g in Example 1, find $g \circ g^{-1}$ and $g^{-1} \circ g$.

Solution

Rewrite g as a set of ordered pairs.

$$g = \{(-1, 2.5), (0, 3), (1, -2), (2, 0), (3, 1), (4, -3)\}$$

Therefore, $g^{-1} = \{(2.5, -1), (3, 0), (-2, 1), (0, 2), (1, 3), (-3, 4)\}$
$$g^{-1} \circ g = \{(-1, -1), (0, 0), (1, 1), (2, 2), (3, 3), (4, 4)\}$$
$$g \circ g^{-1} = \{(2.5, 2.5), (3, 3), (-2, -2), (0, 0), (1, 1), (-3, -3)\}$$

In this example, $(g^{-1} \circ g)(x) = x$ for all x in the domain of g and
$(g \circ g^{-1})(x) = x$ for all x in the domain of g^{-1}.

The next example shows that this pattern is not always true.

• • • • • • • •

Example 3   **Composition of Discrete Relations**

The arrow diagrams on the right represent
relations k and k^{-1}. Draw an arrow diagram
for $k^{-1} \circ k$. Explain why $(k^{-1} \circ k)(x) = x$ is
not true for all x in the domain of k. What
condition would guarantee that, in general,
$(f^{-1} \circ f)(x) = x$ for all x in the domain of f?

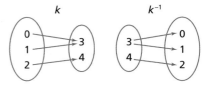

Solution

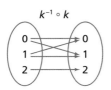

The arrow diagram for $k^{-1} \circ k$ is shown on the left. Note that $(0, 0) \in k^{-1} \circ k$
and $(0, 1) \in k^{-1} \circ k$, so the relation is not a function.

So, $(k^{-1} \circ k)(x) \neq x$ for all x in the domain of k. Note that while k is a function,
k^{-1} is not.

• • • • • • • •

The Composition of a Function and Its Inverse

If both f and f^{-1} are functions, then
- $(f^{-1} \circ f)(x) = x$ for all x in the domain of f, and
- $(f \circ f^{-1})(x) = x$ for all x in the domain of f^{-1}.

EXAMINING THE CONCEPT

Algebraic Composition Involving Functions

The examples so far have shown some properties of composite functions defined
by ordered pairs or discrete data. In section 1.3, you composed algebraically a
polynomial function with another polynomial function. Now extend composition
to include other types of functions that are defined algebraically.

Example 4   Algebraic Composition of Functions

Let $f(x) = 2x + 3$ and $g(x) = \frac{5x + 1}{2x - 3}$. Determine $(g \circ f)(x)$ and $(f \circ g)(x)$.

Solution

In most cases, the function defined by $g \circ f$ is a different function than that defined by $f \circ g$.

By definition, $(g \circ f)(x) = g(f(x))$.

$$(g \circ f)(x) = g(f(x))$$
$$= g(2x + 3)$$
$$= \frac{5(2x + 3) + 1}{2(2x + 3) - 3}$$
$$= \frac{10x + 16}{4x + 3}$$

By definition, $(f \circ g)(x) = f(g(x))$.

$$(f \circ g)(x) = f(g(x))$$
$$= f\left(\frac{5x + 1}{2x - 3}\right)$$
$$= 2\left(\frac{5x + 1}{2x - 3}\right) + 3$$
$$= \frac{10x + 2}{2x - 3} + \frac{3(2x - 3)}{2x - 3}$$
$$= \frac{10x + 2 + 6x - 9}{2x - 3}$$
$$= \frac{16x - 7}{2x - 3}$$

• • • • • • • •

Example 4 shows an important relationship to remember when working with composite functions: You may often need to restrict the domain of a composite function to ensure that it is defined.

Example 5   The Domain and Range of a Composite Function

Let $h(x) = 3x + 12$ and $k(x) = \sqrt{x}$. What are the domain and range of $k \circ h$?

Solution

Substitute the expression for $h(x)$ into the expression for k.

$$(k \circ h)(x) = k(h(x))$$
$$= k(3x + 12)$$
$$= \sqrt{3x + 12}$$

The expression for $k \circ h$ is defined only if $3x + 12 \geq 0$ or $x \geq -4$. The value of the expression can be any real number y such that $y \geq 0$. Therefore, the domain of $k \circ h$ is $\{x \mid x \geq -4, x \in \mathbf{R}\}$. The range is $\{y \mid y \geq 0, y \in \mathbf{R}\}$.

Note: In this example, h is applied first. Since the domain of h is $\mathbf{R}$, you might think that the domain of $k \circ h$ is also $\mathbf{R}$. But since the output from h is also the input to k, there are restrictions on the domain of the composite function.

• • • • • • • •

Sometimes it is useful to know the actual functions that have been combined to create a composite function. The process of determining these functions is called **decomposition**.

Example 6   **Decomposing a Composite Function**

Let $h(x) = (x^2 + 6)^5 - 9$. Find two functions f and g such that $h(x) = f(g(x))$.

Solution
Think of applying one function (the *inner* function) first and applying the other (the *outer* function) next. To evaluate $h(x)$, you would first evaluate $x^2 + 6$. So choose $g(x) = x^2 + 6$ as the inner function. The next step is to raise $u = g(x)$ to the power 5 and subtract 9, so take $f(u) = u^5 - 9$ as the outer function.

With $g(x) = x^2 + 6$ and $f(x) = x^5 - 9$, then
$f(g(x)) = f(x^2 + 6) = (x^2 + 6)^5 - 9$.

Note that this is just one of many possible solutions.

• • • • • • • •

Example 7   **Composition of a Function and Its Inverse**

Given $h(x) = 2x - 3$, determine $h^{-1}(x)$, $(h \circ h^{-1})(x)$, and $(h^{-1} \circ h)(x)$.

Solution
Recall that you can find the inverse function by switching x and y and solving for y. Thus, $y = 2x - 3$ becomes $x = 2y - 3$. Solving $x = 2y - 3$ for y gives $y = \frac{x + 3}{2}$. Therefore, $h^{-1}(x) = \frac{x + 3}{2}$.

Now find $(h \circ h^{-1})(x)$ and $(h^{-1} \circ h)(x)$.

$$(h \circ h^{-1})(x) = h(h^{-1}(x))$$
$$= h\left(\frac{x + 3}{2}\right)$$
$$= 2\left(\frac{x + 3}{2}\right) - 3$$
$$= x$$

$$(h^{-1} \circ h)(x) = h^{-1}(h(x))$$
$$= h^{-1}(2x - 3)$$
$$= \frac{(2x - 3) + 3}{2}$$
$$= x$$

• • • • • • • •

This result seems logical for any function f and its inverse, f^{-1}. Since the inverse function "undoes" the original function, the composition $f^{-1} \circ f$ maps the domain of f onto the range of f, then back onto the domain of f. The net result of composing a function with its inverse function (or vice versa) is to map the domain of the original function onto itself.

The function $f(x) = x$ is called the **identity function**.

The Composition of a Function and Its Inverse

As you saw earlier, provided that both f and f^{-1} are functions,
$(f^{-1} \circ f)(x) = (f \circ f^{-1})(x) = x$.

1. Why is it reasonable that $f \circ g$ is read "f follows g"?
2. When do points in $g \circ f$ exist? Explain.
3. Why is $(a, a) \in f^{-1} \circ f$ if $(a, b) \in f$?
4. Let $f(x) = \sqrt{x}$ and $g(x) = x + 1$. Why is $\{x \mid x \geq -1, x \in \mathbf{R}\}$ the domain of $f \circ g$?

KEY IDEAS

- $f \circ g$ is the **composite** function of f and g. The composite function is defined by $(f \circ g)(x) = f(g(x))$. To determine $(f \circ g)(x)$, replace x with $g(x)$ in the expression for $f(x)$.
- Let $(a, b) \in g$ and $(b, c) \in f$. Then $(a, c) \in f \circ g$. A point in $f \circ g$ exists where an element in the range of g is also in the domain of f. The function $f \circ g$ exists only when the range of g overlaps the domain of f.

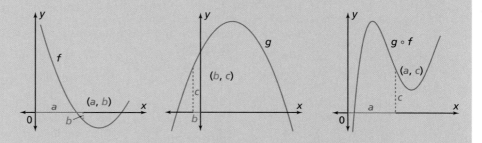

- The domain of $f \circ g$ is a subset of the domain of g. Find the domain of $f \circ g$ by examining $f \circ g$ and comparing the domain of f with the range of g.
- If $(a, b) \in f$, then $(b, a) \in f^{-1}$. So, $(a, a) \in f^{-1} \circ f$ and $(b, b) \in f \circ f^{-1}$.
- If both f and f^{-1} are functions, then $(f^{-1} \circ f)(x) = x$ for all x in the domain of f, and $(f \circ f^{-1})(x) = x$ for all x in the domain of f^{-1}.

6.1 Exercises

A

1. **(a)** Let $f = \{(0, 1), (1, 3), (2, 5), (3, 7)\}$ and $g(x) = 2x + 1$. Evaluate

    i. $(g \circ f)(0)$ **ii.** $(g \circ f)(1)$ **iii.** $(g \circ f)(2)$ **iv.** $(g \circ f)(3)$

    v. $(g \circ f)(4)$ **vi.** $(f \circ g)(0)$ **vii.** $(f \circ g)(1)$ **viii.** $(f \circ g)(2)$

   (b) Determine the domain of $f \circ g$.   **(c)** Graph $y = (f \circ g)(x)$.

   (d) Determine the domain of $g \circ f$.   **(e)** Graph $y = (g \circ f)(x)$.

2. (a) Let $f(x) = 3x - 1$ and $g(x) = 5 - 2x$. Determine

    i. $(f \circ g)(x)$ **ii.** $(f \circ g)(0)$ **iii.** $(f \circ g)(-1)$ **iv.** $(f \circ g)(2)$

    v. $(g \circ f)(x)$ **vi.** $(g \circ f)(0)$ **vii.** $(g \circ f)(-1)$ **viii.** $(g \circ f)(2)$

  (b) Solve $(f \circ g)(x) = (g \circ f)(x)$.

3. Let $f = \{(1, 2), (2, 3), (3, 5), (4, 7)\}$ and $g = \{(1, 4), (2, 3), (3, 1)\}$.
Express each composite as a set of ordered pairs.

  (a) $g \circ f$ **(b)** $f \circ g$ **(c)** $f^{-1} \circ f$ **(d)** $g \circ g^{-1}$

4. (a) Let $f(x) = x^2$ and $g(x) = x + 2$. Determine

    i. $(f \circ g)(x)$ **ii.** $(g \circ f)(x)$

  (b) Solve $(f \circ g)(x) = (g \circ f)(x)$.

5. Let $f(x) = 3x - 5$. Show that $(f \circ f^{-1})(x) = x$.

6. Knowledge and Understanding: Let $f(x) = x^2 - 3x$ and $g(x) = \sqrt{x}$.
Determine

  (a) $(f \circ g)(5)$ **(b)** $(g \circ f)(x)$ **(c)** the domain of $g \circ f$

7. For each function h, find two functions f and g such that $h(x) = f(g(x))$.

  (a) $h(x) = \sqrt{x^2 + 6}$ **(b)** $h(x) = (5x - 8)^6$

  (c) $h(x) = 2^{(6x + 7)}$ **(d)** $h(x) = \dfrac{1}{x^3 - 7x + 2}$

  (e) $h(x) = \sin^2(10x + 5)$ **(f)** $h(x) = \sqrt[3]{(x + 4)^2}$

B

8. Copy and complete the table.

Point on f	Point on g	Point on $f \circ g$
	(3, 4)	(3, 1)
(1, 5)	(2, 1)	
(0, −1)	(1, ■)	
(■, 5)	(■, 1)	(0, ■)
(3, ■)		(−1, 3)

9. Given the graphs of f and g,

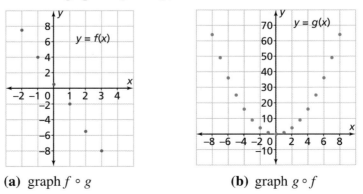

  (a) graph $f \circ g$ **(b)** graph $g \circ f$

10. (a) Let $f = \{(-2, 1), (0, 4), (1, 2), (4, 5)\}$ and $g(x) = \sqrt{x - 3}$. Evaluate

    i. $(f \circ g)(3)$ **ii.** $(f \circ g)(4)$ **iii.** $(f \circ g)(7)$

  (b) Determine the domain of $f \circ g$.

  (c) Graph $f \circ g$.

  (d) Evaluate

    i. $(g \circ f)(0)$ **ii.** $(g \circ f)(-2)$ **iii.** $(g \circ f)(7)$

  (e) Determine the domain of $g \circ f$.

  (f) Graph $g \circ f$.

11. Let $f(x) = 2x + 3$ and $g(x) = ax - 2$.

  (a) Create a table for f if $-2 \le x \le 2$, $x \in \mathbf{I}$, and $a = 3$.

  (b) Add columns for g and $g \circ f$ to your table.

  (c) Graph f, g, and $g \circ f$. Highlight the point on each graph that corresponds to the point on the graph of f where $x = -2$.

  (d) Repeat (a) to (c) for $a = 2$, $a = -1$, and $a = -3$.

  (e) Describe the effect of changing the value of a on the graph of $g \circ f$.

12. Communication:

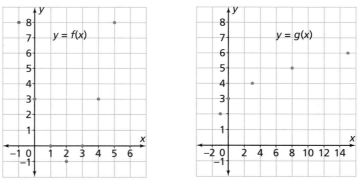

  (a) Given the graphs of f and g, graph $f \circ g$.

  (b) Graph $g \circ f$.

  (c) How do your graphs show that f and g are not inverses of each other?

13. Given the graph of $y = f(x)$ on the right and the functions $g(x) = 2x + 1$, $h(x) = -x + 3$, and $k(x) = (g \circ f \circ h)(x)$,

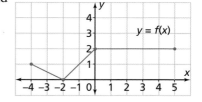

  (a) evaluate

    i. $k(5)$ **ii.** $k(7)$ **iii.** $k(3)$

    iv. $k(-2)$ **v.** $k(0)$ **vi.** $k(6)$

  (b) graph $y = k(x)$

  (c) explain how transforming the graph of $y = f(x)$ can create the graph of $y = k(x)$

14. Given the graph of $y = f(x)$ on the right and the functions below, match the correct composition with each graph. Justify your choices.

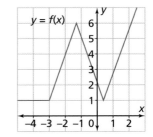

$g(x) = x + 3$ $h(x) = 0.5x$ $k(x) = -x$

$m(x) = 2x$ $n(x) = -0.5x$ $p(x) = x - 3$

(a) $y = f \circ g(x)$ **(b)** $y = f \circ h(x)$ **(c)** $y = f \circ k(x)$

(d) $y = f \circ m(x)$ **(e)** $y = f \circ n(x)$ **(f)** $y = f \circ p(x)$

(g) $y = g \circ f(x)$ **(h)** $y = h \circ f(x)$ **(i)** $y = k \circ f(x)$

(j) $y = m \circ f(x)$ **(k)** $y = n \circ f(x)$ **(l)** $y = p \circ f(x)$

i.

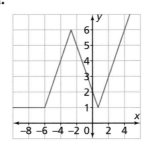

ii.

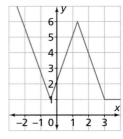

iii.

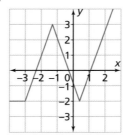

iv.

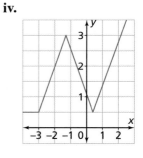

v.

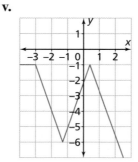

vi.

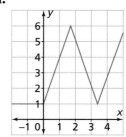

15. (a) Let $f(x) = 2x - 1$ and $g(x) = x^2$. Determine $(f \circ g)(x)$.

(b) Graph f, g, and $f \circ g$ on the same set of axes.

(c) Describe the graph of $f \circ g$ as a transformation of the graph of $y = g(x)$.

16. (a) Let $f(x) = 2x - 1$ and $g(x) = 3x + 2$. Determine $(f \circ g)(x)$.

(b) Graph f, g, and $f \circ g$ on the same set of axes.

(c) Draw the input-output diagram for $f \circ g$.

(d) Describe the graph of $f \circ g$ as a transformation of the graph of $y = g(x)$.

(e) Describe the graph of $f \circ g$ as a transformation of the graph of $y = f(x)$.

17. Let $f(x) = 2(x - 1)$, $g(x) = x^2$, and $h(x) = \sqrt{3x + 2}$. Find the domain and range of $h \circ g \circ f$.

18. Let $f(x) = ax^2 + bx + c$ and $g(x) = mx + n$, where $a, b, c, m, n \in \mathbf{R}$.

(a) Determine $(f \circ g)(x)$.

(b) Determine $(g \circ f)(x)$.

(c) What can you conclude about the composition of a linear function with a quadratic function?

19. For each pair of functions, find $f(g(x))$ and $g(f(x))$.

(a) $f(x) = 1 - x^2$ and $g(x) = 2x + 5$

(b) $f(x) = 5x$ and $g(x) = \sqrt{4x + 2}$

(c) $f(x) = \sqrt{x^2 - 2}$ and $g(x) = x^2 + 2$

(d) $f(x) = x^2 + 1$ and $g(x) = \dfrac{1}{x}$

(e) $f(x) = x^3 - 4$ and $g(x) = \sqrt[3]{x + 4}$

(f) $f(x) = \sin x$ and $g(x) = x^2 + 2$

(g) $f(x) = 2x^2 + 3x - 2$ and $g(x) = x^{\frac{1}{2}}$

(h) $f(x) = \dfrac{2x - 1}{5x}$ and $g(x) = x^2$

20. Let $f(x) = x - 3$. Determine

(a) $(f \circ f)(x)$

(b) $(f \circ f \circ f)(x)$

(c) $(f \circ f \circ f \circ f)(x)$

(d) f composed with itself n times

21. Thinking, Inquiry, Problem Solving: Let $f(x) = x^2 - 3x$. Determine $g(x)$ so that $(f \circ g)(x) = x^2 + x - 2$.

22. Check Your Understanding: Show that the composition of any two linear functions is a linear function.

C **23.** Nadia collected the data in the table on the left using a CBR after a ball was dropped.

(a) Enter the data into **L1** and **L2** using a TI-83 Plus. Graph the relation.

(b) Without looking at the graph, how do you know that the relation is not linear?

(c) Use regression to find the equation of the quadratic of best fit.

(d) Is this equation a good model? Justify your answer.

Time (s)	Height (m)
0.0	3.0
0.2	2.8
0.4	2.2
0.6	1.2
0.8	0.0

You can use the TI-83 Plus to estimate different regression models, but often the model does not perfectly fit the data. A common method in data analysis is to transform one variable until the graph becomes linear. In this case, observe that *time* increases by a constant, but *height* decreases by a larger amount in each successive observation. This suggests a transformation that compresses *height* or expands *time*.

(e) Calculate the square root of each entry in **L2** (*height*) and store the values in **L3**.

(f) Graph the square root of *height* versus *time*. Does this relation appear to be linear? Calculate the correlation coefficient for the relation. What can you conclude?

(g) Calculate the square of each *time*-value in **L1** and store the results in **L3**.

(h) Graph *height* versus *time*^{2}. Does this relation appear to be linear? Calculate the correlation coefficient. What can you conclude?

(i) Let *h* represent *height* and *t* represent *time*. Express $h(t)$ as the composition of two other functions.

24. **Application:** The number of bicycles, *n*, sold at one store in a week is a function of the price, *p*, in dollars. So $n(p) = \dfrac{5(360 - p)}{p - 80}$ for $p > 80$.

The store's cost, *c*, in dollars for each bike is a function of the number of bikes the store sells each week. So $c(n) = 0.002(n + 2)^2 + 80$.

(a) Evaluate $n(100)$ and $n(180)$. Why are these values reasonable in this situation?

(b) Evaluate $c(8)$ and $c(48)$. Why are these values reasonable in this situation?

(c) Evaluate the cost of each bicycle to the store if the selling price is $120.

(d) Determine the store's profit per bicycle if the selling price is $120.

(e) Evaluate the total profit if the selling price is $120.

(f) Express the cost of each bike to the store as a function of the selling price.

(g) Express the total profit in terms of the functions *c* and *n* and the variable *p*.

(h) Use graphing technology to graph total profit versus price.

ADDITIONAL ACHIEVEMENT CHART QUESTIONS

Knowledge and Understanding: Given $f(x) = \dfrac{x+3}{2}$ and $g(x) = \sqrt{-4x+1}$, find

(a) $(f \circ g)(-2)$

(b) the value of x such that $(g \circ f)(x) = 10$

(c) the domain of $(f \circ g)(x)$

(d) the range of $(g \circ f)(x)$

Application: A banquet hall charges \$975 to rent a reception room, plus \$25.95 per person. This month, the hall is offering a discount of 30% off the total bill. Express the discounted cost as a function of the number of people attending a reception.

Thinking, Inquiry, Problem Solving: The function $f(x) = (2x + 3)^7$ is the composition of two functions, $g(x)$ and $h(x)$. Find at least two different pairs of functions $g(x)$ and $h(x)$ such that $f(x) = (g \circ h)(x)$.

Communication: Send an e-mail message to a classmate explaining how to find the domain of $(f \circ g)(x)$, where $f(x) = 5x + 7$ and $g(x) = \sqrt{x}$. Then, to check that person's understanding, ask your classmate to reply with an explanation of how to find the domain of $(g \circ f)(x)$.

The Chapter Problem
Tides on the Bay of Fundy

Apply what you learned in this section to answer these questions about The Chapter Problem on page 430.

CP1. Convert the times in the tide table on page 430 into decimal numbers. Graph the depth of water in the bay versus time. Draw a smooth curve through the points.

CP2. Use the graph to estimate the time and rate at which the water level was falling when it was falling most quickly.

CP3. Assume that the floor of the bay slopes at a constant ratio of 1:20. Express the distance the water flows up the beach in terms of depth.

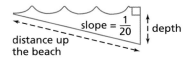

CP4. The depth of water in the bay is a function of time. The distance the water flows up the beach is a function of the depth. Express the distance the water flows up the beach as a composition of functions.

6.2 Rates of Change for Composite Functions—The Chain Rule

SETTING THE STAGE

Explore the concepts in this lesson in more detail using Exploration 12 on page 581.

In the previous section, you saw that a composite function can be created from two or more functions. What is the relation between the rates of change of the original functions and of the composite? In this section, you will learn how the rate of change of a composite function depends on the characteristics of its component functions.

EXAMINING THE CONCEPT

The Chain Rule

Evan is a telephone solicitor. He is paid $1.50 for every newspaper subscription he sells. Recently, his sales have been increasing at a rate of 4 per day. At what rate is Evan's total pay increasing?

The graphs show the situation.

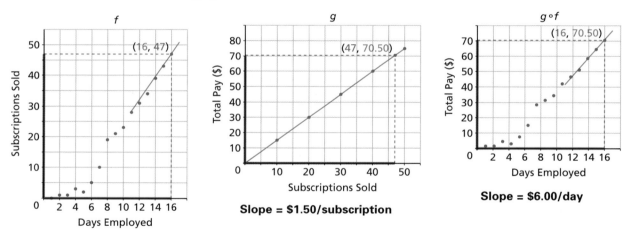

The number of subscriptions sold is a function, f, of the days Evan is employed. His pay is a function, g, of the number of subscriptions he sells. The third function is the composite of the first two functions.

To answer the question "At what rate is Evan's total pay increasing?" assume that the functions are linear, at least in the recent past. The current rate of change of 4 subscriptions per day has been steady for the past few days. The pay rate of $1.50 per subscription applies to any number of subscriptions.

When the number of subscriptions increases by 4 each day, Evan's daily pay increases by $1.50 × 4, or $6.00. So Evan's total pay increases by $6.00 per day.

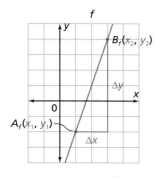

f

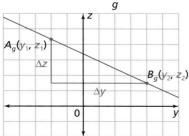

g

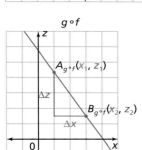

g ∘ f

rate of change in pay = rate of pay per subscription × rate of change in subscriptions sold

= \$1.50/subscription × 4 subscriptions/day

= \$6.00/day

The rate of \$6.00 per day corresponds to the slope of the third graph. Also compare "4 subscriptions/day" and "\$1.50/subscription" to the slopes of the other graphs.

The relation between the rates of change of two functions and their composite function is always true if the functions are linear.

The three diagrams on the left show two points A and B on f and the corresponding points on g and $g \circ f$. All of the functions are linear. Because the graphs all use the same scale, Δx, Δy, and Δz are the same in all diagrams.

$$\text{slope of } A_f B_f \times \text{slope of } A_g B_g = \frac{\Delta y}{\Delta x} \times \frac{\Delta z}{\Delta y}$$

$$= \frac{\Delta z}{\Delta x}$$

$$= \text{slope of } A_{g \circ f} B_{g \circ f}$$

Rates of Change and the Composition of Linear Functions

The slope of the composite of two linear functions is the product of the slopes of the two functions. Therefore, the rate of change of the composite of two linear functions is the product of the rates of change of these two functions.

This relation is also true even when the two functions and their composite are nonlinear. The slope at each point on the composite will depend on the slopes of the graphs of the component functions. Recall that the slope of a function at any point is the slope of the tangent line to the curve at that point.

Rates of Change and the Composition of Functions

The slope of the tangent at any point on the graph of a composite function is the product of the slopes of the tangents to the graphs of the two component functions. Therefore, the rate of change of the composite of two functions is the product of the rates of change of these two functions.

If $f(a) = b$ and $g(b) = c$, then the slope of the tangent to $g \circ f$ at (a, c) equals $f'(a) \cdot g'(b)$.

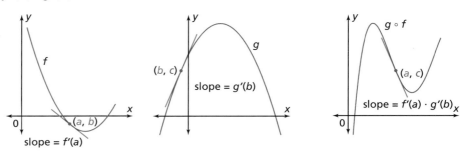

Is there a method for differentiating composite functions?

Example 1 — Developing the Chain Rule

Recall the relations that exist among the numbers of humans, wolves, and rabbits. An increase in the human population means a decrease in the wolf population. This decrease means an increase in the rabbit population. Let x be the human population in thousands in an area. Let u be the number of wolves in the area. So, a simple model of this relation is $u = g(x) = 50 - \frac{x}{4}$. Let y be the number of rabbits, which is a function of u, the wolf population. A simple model for this relationship is $y = f(u) = 1000 - 15u$.

(a) Use these models to determine the function that relates the rabbit population to the human population.

(b) Determine the rate at which each population is changing. Discuss how these rates are related.

Solution

(a) The diagram shows how the composite function $f(g(x))$ represents the relation between the human population and the rabbit population.

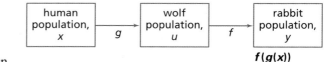

$f(g(x))$

$$y = f(u)$$
$$= 1000 - 15u$$
$$= 1000 - 15\left(50 - \frac{x}{4}\right)$$
$$= 250 + \frac{15x}{4}$$

$y = f(u)$ is the outer function. Substitute the expression for the inner function, $u = 50 - \frac{x}{4}$, into the expression for the outer function.

The composite function $y = (f \circ g)(x) = 250 + \frac{15x}{4}$ defines the relation between the human population and the rabbit population.

(b) Because these functions are linear, their rates of change are constant: the slope of the tangent line to the curve at any point will be constant. The derivative $\frac{du}{dx}$ is the rate of change in the wolf population, u, with respect to the human population, x.

$$\frac{du}{dx} = \frac{d}{dx}\left(50 - \frac{x}{4}\right) = -\frac{1}{4}$$ (When the human population increases by 4000, the wolf population decreases by 1.)

$\dfrac{dy}{du}$ is the rate of change in the rabbit population, y, with respect to the wolf population, u.

$$\frac{dy}{du} = \frac{d}{du}(1000 - 15u) = -15$$ (When the wolf population increases by 1, the rabbit population decreases by 15.)

$\dfrac{dy}{dx}$ is the rate of change in the rabbit population, y, with respect to the human population, x.

$$\frac{dy}{dx} = \frac{d}{dx}\left(250 + \frac{15x}{4}\right) = \frac{15}{4}$$ (When the human population increases by 4000, the rabbit population increases by 15.)

So the relation between the rates of change of these linear functions is $\dfrac{dy}{dx} = \dfrac{dy}{du} \cdot \dfrac{du}{dx}$. In this case, $\dfrac{15}{4} = (-15)\left(-\dfrac{1}{4}\right)$. The relation between these rates of change is not coincidental.

· · · · · · · · ·

Recall that $y = (f \circ g)(x)$. The derivative of the composite function is

$$(f \circ g)'(x) = f'(g(x)) \cdot g'(x)$$

This relation is called the **chain rule**.

The Chain Rule

$\dfrac{dy}{dx} = \dfrac{dy}{du} \cdot \dfrac{du}{dx}$, provided that $\dfrac{dy}{du}$ and $\dfrac{du}{dx}$ exist.

Therefore, if $h(x) = (f \circ g)(x)$, then $h'(x) = f'(g(x)) \cdot g'(x)$.

In Leibniz notation, $\dfrac{d[h(x)]}{dx} = \dfrac{d[f(g(x))]}{d[g(x)]} \cdot \dfrac{d[g(x)]}{dx}$.

A Proof of the Chain Rule

Let y be a function of u, that is, $y = f(u)$. Let u be a function of x, that is, $u = g(x)$. So $y = f(u) = f(g(x))$ is a function of x. Suppose f and g are differentiable. Then a change in x, Δx, will produce a change in u, Δu, which will in turn produce a change in y, Δy. By the definition of the derivative,

$$\frac{dy}{dx} = \lim_{\Delta x \to 0} \frac{\Delta y}{\Delta x}$$ Multiply the numerator and the denominator by Δu.

$$= \lim_{\Delta x \to 0} \left(\frac{\Delta y}{\Delta u} \cdot \frac{\Delta u}{\Delta x}\right)$$ provided $\Delta u \neq 0$

$$= \lim_{\Delta x \to 0} \frac{\Delta y}{\Delta u} \cdot \lim_{\Delta x \to 0} \frac{\Delta u}{\Delta x}$$ since f and g are differentiable

$$= \lim_{\Delta u \to 0} \frac{\Delta y}{\Delta u} \cdot \lim_{\Delta x \to 0} \frac{\Delta u}{\Delta x}$$ $\Delta u \to 0$ as $\Delta x \to 0$, since g is differentiable, hence continuous

$$= \frac{dy}{du} \cdot \frac{du}{dx}$$ from the definition of the derivative

Exceptions to this proof can be dealt with using other techniques, but are beyond the scope of this course. The chain rule is a powerful tool in calculus. Up to this point, you could differentiate polynomial functions and the product or quotient of polynomials. You have seen that the chain rule works for a composite function composed of two linear functions. With the chain rule, you can differentiate very complex functions by expressing them as composites of simpler functions.

Example 2   **Applying the Chain Rule**

Determine $\frac{dy}{dx}$ if $y = (2x - 5)^3$.

Solution

$$\frac{dy}{dx} = \frac{d}{dx}[(2x - 5)^3] \qquad\qquad \text{Apply the chain rule.}$$

$$\frac{dy}{dx} = \frac{d[(2x - 5)^3]}{d[(2x - 5)]} \cdot \frac{d[(2x - 5)]}{dx}$$

$$= 3(2x - 5)^2(2)$$

$$= 6(2x - 5)^2$$

In this example, it is easy to expand the original function, y, and find the derivative using the rules for polynomials. Expand the original function.

$$y = (2x - 5)^3$$

$$= (2x - 5)(2x - 5)^2$$

$$= (2x - 5)(4x^2 - 20x + 25)$$

$$= 8x^3 - 60x^2 + 150x - 125$$

So, $\frac{dy}{dx} = 24x^2 - 120x + 150$.

Using the chain rule, we found that $\frac{dy}{dx} = 6(2x - 5)^2$, which is equivalent to this answer. The result can be verified by expanding one answer or factoring the other.

In many other cases, it may not be possible or advisable to first expand and then simplify the function. The chain rule is a powerful alternative.

Example 2 shows a very common application of the chain rule. In this example, the chain rule is combined with the power rule. Recall the power rule: $\frac{d}{dx}(x^n) = nx^{n-1}$. The power rule lets you differentiate v^n with respect to v, provided v is a variable and n is a constant. It does *not* allow you to differentiate v^n with respect to anything other than v.

The Chain Rule with the Power Rule

$$\frac{d}{dx}[(g(x)^n)] = \frac{d[(g(x))^n]}{d(g(x))} \cdot \frac{d[g(x)]}{dx}$$

$$= n[g(x)]^{n-1} \cdot g'(x), \text{ where } n \text{ is a constant.}$$

To remember the steps, think "take the derivative of the 'outer' function multiplied by the derivative of the 'inner' function."

Example 3   **Differentiating a Radical Function**

Let $r = \sqrt{1 + (c - 3)^2}$. Determine $\dfrac{dr}{dc}$.

Solution

Simplifying gives $r = \sqrt{c^2 - 6c + 10}$ or $r = (c^2 - 6c + 10)^{\frac{1}{2}}$. The equation contains a simple power, which allows you to apply the chain rule with the power rule.

$$\dfrac{dr}{dc} = \dfrac{d}{dc}[(c^2 - 6c + 10)^{\frac{1}{2}}] \qquad \text{Apply the chain rule with the power rule.}$$

$$= \dfrac{d[c^2 - 6c + 10]^{\frac{1}{2}}}{d(c^2 - 6c + 10)} \cdot \dfrac{d(c^2 - 6c + 10)}{dc} \qquad \text{Find the "inner" and "outer" derivatives.}$$

$$= \left[\dfrac{1}{2}(c^2 - 6c + 10)^{-\frac{1}{2}}\right] \cdot (2c - 6) \qquad \text{Simplify.}$$

$$= \dfrac{c - 3}{\sqrt{c^2 - 6c + 10}}$$

Therefore, $\dfrac{dr}{dc} = \dfrac{c - 3}{\sqrt{c^2 - 6c + 10}}$.

• • • • • • • •

Example 4   **Differentiating Quotients with Constant Numerators**

Find $g'(t)$ where $g(t) = \dfrac{9}{(3t - 7)^4}$.

Solution

Rewrite $g(t)$ using a negative exponent.

$$g(t) = 9(3t - 7)^{-4} \qquad \text{Apply the chain rule with the power rule.}$$

derivative of
the inner function

$$g'(t) = [(-4)(9)(3t - 7)^{-4 - 1}](3)$$

derivative of the outer function

$$g'(t) = -108(3t - 7)^{-5}$$

$$= -\dfrac{108}{(3t - 7)^5}$$

• • • • • • • •

Example 5   **Using the Chain Rule with Functions Defined in Tables**

Let $f = b \circ k$. Use the information in the table to evaluate $f(-2)$ and $f'(-2)$.

x	$b(x)$	$k(x)$	$b'(x)$	$k'(x)$
-2	4	5	0.100	-0.100
1	1	4	-5.684	-2.045
2	-2	2	0.000	-1.678
4	2	1	0.665	-0.400
5	5	-2	10.357	-7.309

Algebraic Solution

To find $f(-2)$, substitute directly from the table. Substitute first into the inner function, k, and then into the outer function, b.

$$f(-2) = b \circ k(-2)$$
$$= b(k(-2))$$
$$= b(5)$$
$$= 5$$

Use the chain rule to find $f'(x)$ and $f'(-2)$.

$$f(x) = (b \circ k)(x) \qquad \text{Apply the chain rule.}$$
$$= b(k(x))$$
$$f'(x) = b'(k(x)) \cdot k'(x)$$

$$f'(-2) = b'(k(-2)) \cdot k'(-2) \qquad \text{Evaluate the formula using values}$$
$$= b'(5) \cdot (-0.100) \qquad \text{from the table.}$$
$$= 10.357(-0.100)$$
$$= -1.0357$$

Graphical Solution

Graph functions k and b.

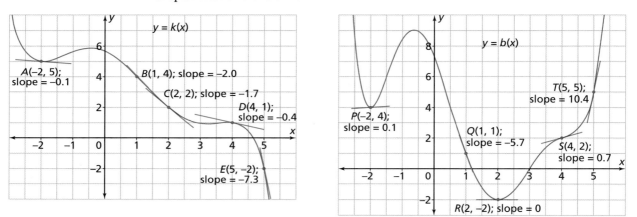

Note that $k(-2) = 5$ and $b(5) = 5$. Therefore, the relevant points on the graphs are $A(-2, 5)$ and $T(5, 5)$. The slopes of the tangents to the curve at these points are -0.1 and 10.4, respectively. Therefore, the slope of the composite function is

$$f'(-2) = b'(5) \cdot k'(-2)$$
$$= 10.4(-0.100)$$
$$= -1.04$$

KEY IDEAS

- **The Chain Rule:** $\dfrac{dy}{dx} = \dfrac{dy}{du} \cdot \dfrac{du}{dx}$, provided that $\dfrac{dy}{du}$ and $\dfrac{du}{dx}$ exist.

  Therefore, if $h(x) = (f \circ g)(x)$, then

  $h'(x) = f'(g(x)) \cdot g'(x)$ (function notation)

  or

  $\dfrac{d[h(x)]}{dx} = \dfrac{d[f(g(x))]}{d[g(x)]} \cdot \dfrac{d[g(x)]}{dx}$ (Leibniz notation)

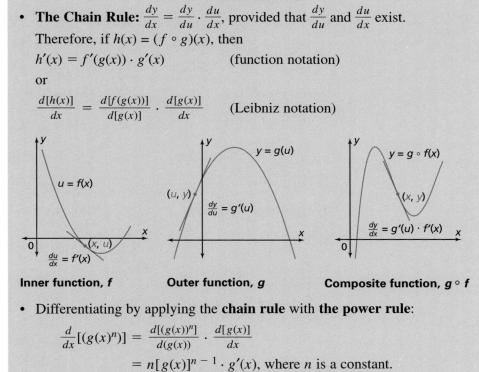

| Inner function, *f* | Outer function, *g* | Composite function, *g* ∘ *f* |

- Differentiating by applying the **chain rule** with **the power rule**:

$$\frac{d}{dx}[(g(x)^n)] = \frac{d[(g(x))^n]}{d(g(x))} \cdot \frac{d[g(x)]}{dx}$$
$$= n[g(x)]^{n-1} \cdot g'(x), \text{ where } n \text{ is a constant.}$$

6.2 Exercises

A

1. **(a)** Let $f(x) = (3x + 5)^4$. Determine $f'(x)$.

   (b) Let $y = (2 - x)^3$. Determine $\dfrac{dy}{dx}$.

2. **(a)** Let $f(x) = \dfrac{-2}{(5 + 3x)^4}$. Determine $f'(x)$.

   (b) Let $y = \dfrac{3}{(1 - 2x)^3}$. Determine $\dfrac{dy}{dx}$.

3. **(a)** Let $f(x) = \sqrt{3x + 15}$. Determine $f'(x)$.

   (b) Let $y = \sqrt{9x^2 - 6x + 1}$. Determine $\frac{dy}{dx}$.

4. **(a)** Let $f(x) = \frac{1}{\sqrt{4x^2 - x}}$. Determine $f'(x)$.

   (b) Let $y = \frac{5}{\sqrt[3]{(2x - 5)^2}}$. Determine $\frac{dy}{dx}$.

B 5. Let $y = u^3 + 6u$, where $u = 2x^4 + 3x^2 - 2$. Find $\frac{dy}{dx}$.
   Leave your answer in terms of u and x.

6. Use the chain rule to differentiate each function.

   (a) $f(x) = (4x - 8)^3$ **(b)** $g(x) = (4x^2 + 2x - 3)^5$

   (c) $y = 5(12 - 6x)^{\frac{1}{5}}$ **(d)** $h(x) = \sqrt{x^3 - 4x^2 + 6x}$

   (e) $y = \sqrt[3]{x^2 - 2x}$ **(f)** $f(x) = \sqrt{(x^2 - 1)^3}$

   (g) $g(x) = (2x^2 + 7x - 6)^{-4}$ **(h)** $y = \frac{1}{(5 - x)^2}$

   (i) $h(x) = \frac{-4}{(6x + x^3)^5}$ **(j)** $y = \frac{1}{\sqrt{7x^3 - x^2}}$

   (k) $f(x) = \frac{5}{\sqrt[5]{6x^4 - 2x}}$ **(l)** $g(x) = (2 + \sqrt{x})^3$

7. Given $h = f \circ g$, $g(2) = 5$, $g'(2) = 3$, and $f'(5) = -2$, determine $h'(2)$.

8. Let $f(x) = \frac{2}{\sqrt{x} + 1}$. Determine $f'(0)$.

9. Given $h = g \circ f$, where f and g are continuous functions, use the information in the table to evaluate $h(-1)$ and $h'(-1)$.

x	$f(x)$	$g(x)$	$f'(x)$	$g'(x)$
-1	1	18	-5	-15
0	-2	5	-1	-11
1	-1	-4	3	-7
2	4	-9	7	-3
3	13	-10	11	1

10. Given $f(x) = (x - 3)^2$, $g(x) = \frac{1}{x}$, and $h(x) = f(g(x))$, determine $h'(x)$.

11. Let $g(x) = \frac{8}{(2x + 3)^2}$. Determine the slope of the tangent line to the curve at point $(-1, 8)$.

12. Given $f(x) = (x + 1)^2$, $g(x) = \frac{1}{x}$, and $h(x) = g(f(x))$, determine the intervals in which h is increasing.

13. **Communication:** The graph of $y = f(x)$ and the tangents at $x = 0$ and $x = 10$ are shown. Function g is defined by $g(x) = \sqrt{f(x)} + 10$, evaluate $g'(0)$. Justify your answer.

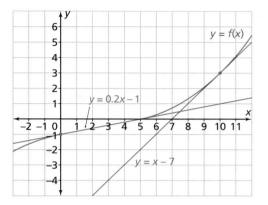

14. The function $s(t) = (t^2 + t)^{\frac{2}{3}}$, $t \geq 0$, represents the displacement, s, in metres of a particle moving along a straight line after t seconds.

   (a) Determine $v(t)$ and $a(t)$.

   (b) Find the average velocity during the first five seconds.

   (c) Determine the velocity at exactly 5 s.

   (d) Find the average acceleration during the first five seconds.

   (e) Determine the acceleration at exactly 5 s.

15. A ball of paper falls from the top of the CN Tower. Its height, h, above the ground in metres after t seconds is given by $h(t) = 603 - \sqrt{t^2 + 9}$, $t \geq 0$.

   (a) Determine the average velocity of the ball during the first four seconds after its release.

   (b) Determine the initial velocity (at $t = 0$).

   (c) Sketch a graph of the velocity of the ball at time t. Explain the graph.

16. **Knowledge and Understanding:** Let $f(x) = \dfrac{2x}{\sqrt{x^2 + 1}}$. Determine $f'(x)$ and $f''(x)$.

17. **Application:** The displacement, s, of an object moving along a straight line is given by $s(t) = \dfrac{5t}{2t + 1}$ for all t, where $t \geq 0$. Describe the motion of the object.

18. For the graph of $y = (4 - x^2)^3$, determine the coordinates of all points of inflection.

19. For $y = (x^2 - 1)^3 + 5(x^2 - 1)^2 + 1$, determine $\dfrac{dy}{dx}$.

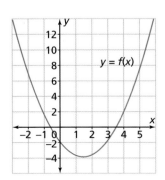

20. Given $g(x) = [f(x)]^2 - 3$ and the graph of $y = f(x)$ shown on the left, graph $y = g'(x)$.

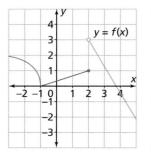

21. The graph of $y = f(x)$ is shown on the left. Assume that $g(x) = 2x - 1$ and $h = f \circ g$.

   (a) For what values of x is h defined?

   (b) For what values of x is h' defined?

22. Given $f(x) = \dfrac{2x}{x^2 + 1}$, determine the intervals on which the graph of $y = f(x)$ is concave up.

23. **Thinking, Inquiry, Problem Solving:** Consider the graph of $y = f(x)$. Here are the equations of the tangent lines at the given points:

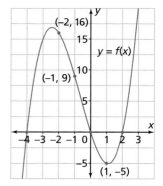

at $(-2, 16)$	$y = -4x + 8$
at $(-1, 9)$	$y = -9x$
at $(1, -5)$	$y = -x - 4$
at $(-4, 0)$	$y = 24x + 96$
at $(0, 0)$	$y = -8x$
at $(2, 0)$	$y = 12x - 24$

For $g(x) = [f(x) - 3]^2$, construct a table and graph $y = g'(x)$.

C **24.** Given $y = f(x)$, then $f(a) = a$ and $f'(a) = b$.
Let $g = f \circ f \circ f \circ f \circ f \circ f \circ f \circ f \circ f \circ f$. Determine $g'(a)$.

25. The graph of $y = (ax + b)^c$, where a, b, and c are real constants, has a tangent line at $(3, 27)$ defined by $y = 18x - 135$. The graph also has a point of inflection, $(-1.5, 0)$. Determine a, b, and c.

ADDITIONAL ACHIEVEMENT CHART QUESTIONS

Knowledge and Understanding: Determine $\dfrac{dy}{dx}$ for each function.

(a) $y = (6x + 7)^4$ **(b)** $y = \sqrt{3x^2 - 1}$

Application: While a balloon is being inflated, the radius increases at a rate of 0.02 m/s. Find the rate of increase of volume with respect to time when the radius is 50 cm.

Thinking, Inquiry, Problem Solving: A function $h(x)$ is even if $h(-x) = h(x)$. A function $r(x)$ is odd if $r(-x) = -r(x)$. List three even functions and three odd functions that must be differentiated using the chain rule. Find the derivatives of the even functions. What type of function is each derivative? Find the derivatives of the odd functions. What type of function is each derivative? How could you show your result for any even or odd function?

Communication: Some students use the following memory aid to recall the chain rule: "Multiply the derivative of the outer function by the derivative of the inner function." Create two different mnemonics to help remember the chain rule.

The Chapter Problem

Tides on the Bay of Fundy

Apply what you learned in this section to answer these questions about The Chapter Problem on page 430.

CP5. Refer to questions CP1 to CP4 on page 445. Express the rate at which the water recedes from the beach in terms of the rate at which the depth of the water in the bay changes.

CP6. Estimate the maximum rate at which the water recedes from the beach.

CP7. You could approximate the depth of water in the bay using a sine curve. Enter the time and depth values into lists on a TI-83 Plus calculator. Plot the data. Experiment with transformations of $y = \sin x$ to match the data as closely as possible.

CP8. Determine the mean high tide and the mean low tide. Estimate the amplitude. Find the mean period length. Estimate the period. Use the data to arrive at a reasonable sinusoidal model for the depth of the water versus time. Plot your model.

CP9. Enter the sinusoidal function values for each time in another list on the TI-83 Plus. Then subtract these values from the depth values to create a new list. Perform a quartic regression on this new list and the list that has the time values.

CP10. Modify your sine model by adding the quartic function you found in CP9. Plot this function. Compare this plot to the plot of the original data. What is the same? different? Describe what you see.

CP11. Use your refined model to approximate the maximum rate at which the depth is decreasing. Use a graphing calculator table. At what time does this maximum rate occur?

CP12. Use the numerical derivative function, **nDeriv(**, with your model to plot the derivative. At what point is the derivative a maximum?

6.3 Differentiation Techniques: Combining the Differentiation Rules

SETTING THE STAGE

In the previous section, you used the chain rule to differentiate. In this section, you will extend this rule to more complex functions. You will need to apply many of the differentiation rules in different combinations. Sometimes decomposing a complex function into simpler functions can help you to differentiate the function.

EXAMINING THE CONCEPT

Combining Differentiation Rules

At this point, you know how to differentiate many simple functions by applying these rules:

the constant rule $\qquad \dfrac{d}{dx}(c) = 0$

the constant multiple rule $\qquad \dfrac{d}{dx}[cf(x)] = c\dfrac{d}{dx}[f(x)]$

the power rule $\qquad \dfrac{d}{dx}(x^n) = nx^{n-1}$

the sum and difference rules $\qquad \dfrac{d}{dx}[f(x) \pm g(x)] = \dfrac{d}{dx}[f(x)] \pm \dfrac{d}{dx}[g(x)]$

the product rule $\qquad \dfrac{d}{dx}[f(x) \cdot g(x)] = \dfrac{d}{dx}[f(x)] \cdot g(x) + \dfrac{d}{dx}[g(x)] \cdot f(x)$

the quotient rule $\qquad \dfrac{d}{dx}\left[\dfrac{f(x)}{g(x)}\right] = \dfrac{\dfrac{d}{dx}[f(x)] \cdot g(x) - \dfrac{d}{dx}[g(x)] \cdot f(x)}{[(g(x)]^2}$

the chain rule $\qquad \dfrac{d}{dx}[f(g(x))] = \dfrac{d[f(g(x))]}{d[g(x)]} \cdot \dfrac{d[g(x)]}{dx}$

the chain rule with power rule $\quad \dfrac{d}{dx}[g(x)^n] = n[g(x)]^{n-1} \cdot \dfrac{d}{dx}[g(x)]$, where n is a constant

Differentiating a complex function often means rewriting it in terms of the sum, difference, product, quotient, or power of polynomials.

The first step of differentiating $r = \sqrt{1 + (c - 3)^2}$ in Example 3 in the last section was to simplify the expression under the radical. Simplifying first is not always the best approach. Sometimes it is better to decompose a function into simpler functions.

Example 1 **Differentiating Using Decomposition**

Use decomposition to determine $\dfrac{dr}{dc}$.

Solution

The sequence of operations helps determine the order in which to differentiate. The last operation to be performed is the first operation to be dealt with when differentiating. First express the radical as a power.

$$r = \sqrt{1 + (c - 3)^2} = [1 + (c - 3)^2]^{\frac{1}{2}}$$

r can be defined using three different functions: $f(c) = c - 3$, $g(v) = 1 + v^2$, and $h(u) = u^{\frac{1}{2}}$, where $v = c - 3$, $u = 1 + v^2$, and $r = u^{\frac{1}{2}}$.

Therefore, $r = h(u) = h(g(v)) = h(g(f(c)))$.

$$f'(c) = 1 \quad g'(v) = 2v \quad h'(u) = \frac{1}{2}u^{-\frac{1}{2}}$$

Differentiate each component function with respect to its independent variable.

$$\frac{dr}{dc} = h'(g(f(c))) \cdot g'(f(c)) \cdot f'(c)$$

Apply the chain rule to find $\frac{dr}{dc}$.

$$= \frac{1}{2}[g(f(c))]^{-\frac{1}{2}} \cdot 2f(c) \cdot 1$$

Substitute the expression for each derivative.

$$= \frac{1}{2}[g(c - 3)]^{-\frac{1}{2}} \cdot 2(c - 3)$$

$$= \frac{1}{2}[1 + (c - 3)]^{-\frac{1}{2}} \cdot 2(c - 3)$$

Simplify.

$$= \frac{c - 3}{\sqrt{1 + (c - 3)^2}}$$

• • • • • • • •

As you become more comfortable with the chain rule, you can simplify how you find the derivative. Here is a general rule for finding the derivative of a composite function $f(g(x))$, where the inner function g and the outer function f are differentiable.

$$\frac{d}{dx}[f(g(x))] = f'(g(x)) \cdot g'(x)$$

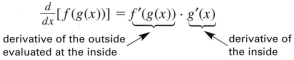

derivative of the outside evaluated at the inside

derivative of the inside

The next four examples show some techniques for determining the derivatives of functions involving products, quotients, and composites.

Example 2 **The Derivative of a Complex Product**

Determine $f'(x)$, where $f(x) = (x^2 + 3)^4(4x - 5)^3$.

Solution

Apply the product rule and the chain rule.

$$f'(x) = \frac{d}{dx}[(x^2 + 3)^4] \cdot (4x - 5)^3 + \frac{d}{dx}[(4x - 5)^3] \cdot (x^2 + 3)^4$$

$$= [4(x^2 + 3)^3(2x)] \cdot (4x - 3)^3 + [3(4x - 5)^2(4)] \cdot (x^2 + 3)^4 \quad \text{Simplify.}$$

$$= 8x(x^2 + 3)^3 \cdot (4x - 5)^3 + 12(4x - 5)^2 \cdot (x^2 + 3)^4 \quad \text{Factor.}$$

$$= 4(x^2 + 3)^3(4x - 5)^2[2x(4x - 5) + 3(x^2 + 3)] \quad \text{Simplify.}$$

$$= 4(x^2 + 3)^3(4x - 5)^2(11x^2 - 10x + 9)$$

• • • • • • • •

Example 3 **The Derivative of a Complex Quotient**

Determine $g'(x)$, where $g(x) = \dfrac{2x}{\sqrt[3]{x^2 + 4}}$.

Solution

$$g(x) = \frac{2x}{\sqrt[3]{x^2 + 4}} = \frac{2x}{(x^2 + 4)^{\frac{1}{3}}}$$

Express $g(x)$ with a rational exponent.

$$g(x) = \frac{\dfrac{d}{dx}[2x] \cdot (x^2 + 4)^{\frac{1}{3}} - \dfrac{d}{dx}\left[(x^2 + 4)^{\frac{1}{3}}\right] \cdot (2x)}{\left[(x^2 + 4)^{\frac{1}{3}}\right]^2}$$

Apply the quotient rule and the chain rule.

$$= \frac{(2)(x^2 + 4)^{\frac{1}{3}} - \left[\dfrac{1}{3}(x^2 + 4)^{-\frac{2}{3}}(2x)\right](2x)}{(x^2 + 4)^{\frac{2}{3}}}$$

Factor the numerator.

$$= \frac{1}{3}(x^2 + 4)^{-\frac{2}{3}}\left[\frac{6(x^2 + 4) - (4x^2)}{(x^2 + 4)^{\frac{2}{3}}}\right]$$

Simplify.

$$= \frac{2x^2 + 24}{3(x^2 + 4)^{\frac{4}{3}}}$$

Another way to differentiate a quotient is to express it as a product using a negative exponent. In this case, $g(x) = (2x)(x^2 + 4)^{-\frac{1}{3}}$. Often this makes it easier to find and simplify the derivative. Try to write expressions in terms of the sum, difference, product, and powers of polynomials.

• • • • • • • •

Example 4 **The Derivative of a Complex Power**

Determine the derivative of $g(x) = \left(\dfrac{1 + x^2}{1 - x^2}\right)^{10}$.

Solution

There are several approaches to this problem. You could decompose the function and express it as $g(x) = \dfrac{(1 + x^2)^{10}}{(1 - x^2)^{10}}$, and then apply the quotient rule and the chain rule. Or you could express the function as the product $g(x) = (1 + x^2)^{10}(1 - x^2)^{-10}$, and then apply the product and the chain rules. In this case we will use the chain rule with the power rule, where $\dfrac{1 + x^2}{1 - x^2}$ is the inner function.

$$g'(x) = \frac{d\left[\left(\frac{1+x^2}{1-x^2}\right)^{10}\right]}{d\left(\frac{1+x^2}{1-x^2}\right)} \cdot \frac{d}{dx}\left(\frac{1+x^2}{1-x^2}\right)$$ Apply the chain rule and the quotient rule

$$g'(x) = 10\left(\frac{1+x^2}{1-x^2}\right)^9 \frac{d}{dx}\left(\frac{1+x^2}{1-x^2}\right)$$

$$= 10\left(\frac{1+x^2}{1-x^2}\right)^9\left[\frac{2x(1-x^2) - (-2x)(1+x^2)}{(1-x^2)^2}\right]$$ Expand.

$$= 10\left(\frac{1+x^2}{1-x^2}\right)^9\left[\frac{2x - 2x^3 + 2x + 2x^3}{(1-x^2)^2}\right]$$ Simplify.

$$= 10\left(\frac{1+x^2}{1-x^2}\right)^9\left[\frac{4x}{(1-x^2)^2}\right]$$

$$= \frac{40x(1+x^2)^9}{(1-x^2)^{11}}$$

· · · · · · · ·

Example 5 Differentiating a Complex Function

Determine the derivative of $f(t) = \left(\dfrac{\sqrt[3]{5+3t}}{1-t^2}\right)^2$.

Solution

Express $f(t)$ as a product of simpler functions. Express the radical as a power and the quotient as a product, and then apply the exponent law for power of a power.

$$f(t) = \left[(5+3t)^{\frac{1}{3}}(1-t^2)^{-1}\right]^2$$ Express the radical as a power and express the quotient as a product.

$$= (5+3t)^{\frac{2}{3}}(1-t^2)^{-2}$$ Simplify.

When you differentiate a complex function, apply the differentiation rules in the order that is opposite to the order of operations. In this example, the last operation is the multiplication of two expressions, so apply the product rule first.

$$f(t) = (5+3t)^{\frac{2}{3}}(1-t^2)^{-2}$$ Apply the product rule and then the chain rule.

$$f'(t) = \frac{d}{dt}\left[(5+3t)^{\frac{2}{3}}\right](1-t^2)^{-2} + \frac{d}{dt}[(1-t^2)^{-2}](5+3t)^{\frac{2}{3}}$$

$$= \frac{2}{3}(5+3t)^{-\frac{1}{3}}(3)(1-t^2)^{-2} + (-2)(1-t^2)^{-3}(-2t)(5+3t)^{\frac{2}{3}}$$

$$= 2(5+3t)^{-\frac{1}{3}}(1-t^2)^{-2} + 4t(1-t^2)^{-3}(5+3t)^{\frac{2}{3}}$$ Simplify and factor.

$$= 2(5+3t)^{-\frac{1}{3}}(1-t^2)^{-3}[(1-t^2) + 2t(5+3t)]$$

$$= 2(5+3t)^{-\frac{1}{3}}(1-t^2)^{-3}(1-t^2+10t+6t^2)$$ Rewrite using positive exponents.

$$= \frac{2(5t^2+10t+1)}{(5+3t)^{\frac{1}{3}}(1-t^2)^3}$$

This method avoids introducing new variables, but it may lead to more minor errors. You should choose the approach that works best for you.

TI-83 Plus Help:
See the
Technology Appendix
on page 595 for details
about this function.

You can check the reasonableness of a solution by comparing the graph of $f'(x)$ with the graph of $y = f(x)$ that you could draw using the TI-83 Plus and the numerical derivative function, **nDeriv(**.

CHECK, CONSOLIDATE, COMMUNICATE

1. Which differentiation rules would you use and in which order would you use them to find $f'(t)$ if $f(t) = \dfrac{(\sqrt{2t + 3} + 5)^3 + 2t}{1 + t^2}$? Explain.

2. Why would you *not* use the chain rule with the power rule to differentiate $y = 2^x$?

3. What is another rule or rules that you could use instead of the quotient rule for differentiating most complex functions?

KEY IDEAS

- When differentiating a complex expression, rewrite functions as combinations of simpler functions and, if possible,
  - express each radical as a power
  - apply the exponent law of a power of a power
  - express each product (or quotient) as the product of two expressions
- When you differentiate a complex function, apply the differentiation rules in the order that is opposite to the order of operations.
- There are often several approaches for differentiating complex functions. Choose the method that works best for you.

6.3 Exercises

A

B

1. Given $u = s^2 - 1$, $y = \dfrac{2}{u}$, and $s = 3 - x$, determine each derivative.

   (a) $\dfrac{du}{ds}$ **(b)** $\dfrac{dy}{du}$ **(c)** $\dfrac{ds}{dx}$ **(d)** $\dfrac{dy}{dx}$, evaluate at $x = 1$

2. **Communication:** Copy the graph of $u = f(x)$. On the same set of axes, graph the derivative of $g(x) = [f(x)]^2 - 4$ without sketching g first. Justify your graph.

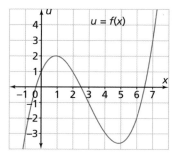

3. Given $f(x) = \dfrac{1}{x}$ and $g(x) = \dfrac{1}{x^2 - 3x}$,

   (a) express g as the composition of f and another function

   (b) use this composition to determine $g'(x)$

4. Given $f(x) = \dfrac{(2x - 3)^2 + 5}{2x - 3}$,

   (a) express f as the composition of two simpler functions

   (b) use this composition to determine $f'(x)$

5. Given $g(x) = \sqrt{2x - 3} + 5(2x - 3)$,

   (a) express f as the composition of two simpler functions

   (b) use this composition to determine $g'(x)$

6. Determine the derivative of each function.

   (a) $f(x) = (2x - 5)^3(3x^2 + 4)^5$

   (b) $g(x) = (8x^3)(4x^2 + 2x - 3)^5$

   (c) $y = (5 + x)^2(4 - 7x^3)^6$

   (d) $h(x) = \dfrac{6x - 1}{(3x + 5)^4}$

   (e) $y = \dfrac{(2x^2 - 5)^3}{(x + 8)^2}$

   (f) $f(x) = \dfrac{-3x^4}{\sqrt{4x - 8}}$

   (g) $g(x) = \left(\dfrac{2x + 5}{6 - x^2}\right)^4$

   (h) $y = \left[\dfrac{1}{(4x + x^2)^3}\right]^3$

   (i) $h(x) = \dfrac{-4\sqrt{3x + 2}}{(2x - x^3)^2}$

   (j) $y = \sqrt{\dfrac{x^2 + 1}{x^2 - 1}}$

   (k) $f(x) = [2x + (3x^2 - 5x)^3]^5$

   (l) $g(x) = \sqrt{2x + \sqrt{x^3}}$

7. (a) Let $y = \dfrac{\sqrt{x}}{\sqrt{x} + 1}$. Determine $\dfrac{dy}{dx}$. (b) Let $y = \dfrac{\sqrt{2x + 1}}{\sqrt{x} + 3}$. Determine $\dfrac{dy}{dx}$.

8. For $y = 3\{x - [x - 3(x + 2)^2]^{-1}\}$, determine $\dfrac{dy}{dx}$.

9. **Knowledge and Understanding:** Let $s = 3 - 2t - [t^{-2} - (3t + 5)^4]^5$. Determine $\dfrac{ds}{dt}$.

10. **Application:** Consider $y = f(x)$ and $g(x) = \sqrt{f(x)}$. Given $f'(a) = 0$, $f(a) > 0$, and $f''(a) > 0$, prove that g has a relative minimum at $x = a$.

11. Given $f(t) = \left(\dfrac{\sqrt[3]{1 - 2t}}{1 + t^2}\right)^2$, determine $f'(0)$.

12. Let $y = -2(x + [2x - 5(x - 2)^3]^{-1})$. Determine $\dfrac{dy}{dx}$.

13. Given $f(x) = 3x - 1$ and $g(x) = \sqrt{[f(x)]^2 - 1}$, determine $g'(x)$.

14. Find the equation of the tangent line to the curve $y = 4x^2(3x^2 - 5x)^3$ at point $(2, 128)$.

15. Given $f(x) = 5 - \dfrac{1}{\sqrt{x^2 - 1}}$, determine the intervals on which f is decreasing.

16. Let $f(x) = \left(\sqrt{x - 2}\right)(2x + 5)^{-1}$. Determine the extreme points on its graph.

x	$f(x)$	$g(x)$	$f'(x)$	$g'(x)$
-1	1	18	-5	-15
0	-2	5	-1	-11
1	-1	-4	3	-7
2	4	-9	7	-3
3	13	-10	11	1

17. Determine the point on the graph of $y = 2\sqrt{x}$ that is closest to point $(6, 0)$.

18. Let $h(x) = [g(f(x))]^2$, where f and g are continuous functions. Use the table on the left to evaluate $h(-1)$ and $h'(-1)$.

19. **Check Your Understanding:** Determine the slope of the tangent line to the graph of $f(x) = \left(\dfrac{x}{x+1}\right)^4$ at point $(0, 0)$.

20. Let $h(x) = f(g(x))$. Prove that $h''(x) = f''(g(x))[g'(x)]^2 + g''(x)f'(g(x))$.

21. Let $f(x) = \dfrac{1}{1+x}$ and $g(x) = \dfrac{1}{1 + \cfrac{1}{1 + \cfrac{1}{1 + \cfrac{1}{1+x}}}}$.

  (a) Express $g(x)$ as a composition.

  (b) Use the decomposition above to determine $g'(x)$.

22. **Thinking, Inquiry, Problem Solving:** The illumination of a point is inversely proportional to the square of the distance from the point to the light source. Two identical 10-m high light posts are 30 m apart. A person walks from one post to the other at 1 m/s. Determine the point where the illumination is greatest. At what point between the posts is the illumination weakest?

23. Find a so that the curve $y = \sqrt{ax^2 - 4}$ has a tangent with slope 2 at the point where $x = 2$.

ADDITIONAL ACHIEVEMENT CHART QUESTIONS

Knowledge and Understanding: Given $y = \dfrac{5x}{\sqrt{(2x+3)^3}}$, find $\dfrac{dy}{dx}$.

Application: A rectangle has dimensions $(2x + 3)^4$ and $(5 - \sqrt{6x})^3$. The rectangle's area increases or decreases, depending on the value of x. Find the rate of change of the area of the rectangle when $x = 5$. Determine whether the area is increasing or decreasing as x increases.

Thinking, Inquiry, Problem Solving: Suppose that k is a rational number, where $h(x) = x^{-k}$ and $f(x) = (x + k)^k$. Show $\dfrac{d}{dx}[h(x) \cdot f(x)] = \dfrac{d}{dx}[h(x)] \cdot \dfrac{d}{dx}[f(x)]$. Find two other pairs of functions whose derivatives have the same property.

Communication: A student found the following problem in his mother's old calculus textbook: "Find a formula for $\dfrac{d}{dx}[h(g(r(x)))]$." How would you express this formula in words or in a diagram so you can quickly remember how to find the derivative?

6.4 Finding Optimal Values for Composite Function Models

SETTING THE STAGE

You have used calculus to solve many real-world problems involving polynomial, rational, and now composite functions. In these problems, you are often asked to minimize distance, time, or cost. For example,

George wants to run a power line to a new cottage being built on an island that is 400 m from the shore of a lake. The main power line ends 3 km away from the point on the shore that is closest to the island. The cost of laying the power line under water is twice the cost of laying the power line on land. How should George place the line to minimize the overall cost?

In this section, you will revisit the techniques you learned for solving optimization problems in Chapters 4 and 5. You will apply these techniques to composite function models.

EXAMINING THE CONCEPT

Solving Optimization Problems Involving the Chain Rule

Before solving the power line problem, consider some simpler examples. Recall the strategy for solving optimization problems in section 4.5 on page 305.

Example 1   **Minimizing a Distance**

Which points on the graph of $y = 9 - x^2$ are closest to point $(0, 6)$?

Solution

Graph the function and point $(0, 6)$. The sketch shows that there are two points at a minimum distance from $(0, 6)$.

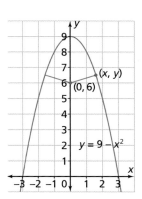

Any point on the graph can be represented by $(x, 9 - x^2)$. The distance, d, between this point and $(0, 6)$ is given by $d(x) = \sqrt{(x - 0)^2 + [(9 - x^2) - 6]^2}$.

After simplifying, $d(x) = \sqrt{x^4 - 5x^2 + 9}$. You can find the point on the graph that is closest to $(0, 6)$ by finding the value of x that minimizes

$$d(x) = \sqrt{x^4 - 5x^2 + 9} \text{ or } d(x) = (x^4 - 5x^2 + 9)^{\frac{1}{2}}.$$

You could use graphing technology to estimate the minimum value. Use calculus to solve the problem algebraically and determine the exact solution.

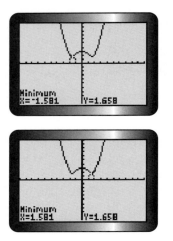

$$d'(x) = \frac{d}{dx}\left[(x^4 - 5x^2 + 9)^{\frac{1}{2}}\right]$$ Apply the chain rule.

$$= \frac{d(x^4 - 5x^2 + 9)^{\frac{1}{2}}}{d(x^4 - 5x^2 + 9)} \cdot \frac{d}{dx}(x^4 - 5x^2 + 9)$$

$$= \frac{1}{2}(x^4 - 5x^2 + 9)^{-\frac{1}{2}} \cdot \frac{d}{dx}(x^4 - 5x^2 + 9)$$

$$= \frac{1}{2(x^4 - 5x^2 + 9)^{\frac{1}{2}}} \cdot (4x^3 - 10x)$$ Factor the numerator.

$$= \frac{2x(2x^2 - 5)}{2(x^4 - 5x^2 + 9)^{\frac{1}{2}}}$$ Simplify.

$$= \frac{x(2x^2 - 5)}{\sqrt{x^4 - 5x^2 + 9}}$$

    The derivative is a rational expression. To find the critical numbers, determine where $d'(x) = 0$ or $d'(x)$ does not exist. The only case in which $d'(x)$ cannot exist is when the denominator, $\sqrt{x^4 - 5x^2 + 9}$, is equal to 0. However, this case cannot occur, as is shown below.

$$x^4 - 5x^2 + 9 = \left(x^2 - \frac{5}{2}\right)^2 + \frac{11}{4}$$ Complete the square.

For all $x \in \mathbf{R}$, $\left(x^2 - \frac{5}{2}\right)^2 \geq 0$.

$$\therefore \left(x^2 - \frac{5}{2}\right)^2 + \frac{11}{4} > 0$$

$$\therefore \sqrt{x^4 - 5x^2 + 9} > 0.$$

Thus, $d'(x)$ is defined for all values of $x \in \mathbf{R}$. Also, $d'(x) = 0$ when the numerator, $x(2x^2 - 5)$, equals 0; that is, when $x = 0$ or $x = \pm\sqrt{\frac{5}{2}}$.

Solving $x = 0$ and $2x^2 - 5 = 0$ produces the critical numbers. Therefore, the critical numbers are $x = -\sqrt{\frac{5}{2}}$, $x = 0$, and $x = \sqrt{\frac{5}{2}}$. Apply the first derivative test to find the critical numbers that represent a local minimum.

	Intervals			
	$x < -\sqrt{\frac{5}{2}}$	$-\sqrt{\frac{5}{2}} < x < 0$	$0 < x < \sqrt{\frac{5}{2}}$	$x > \sqrt{\frac{5}{2}}$
x	$-$	$-$	$+$	$+$
$(2x^2 - 5)$	$+$	$-$	$-$	$+$
$\sqrt{x^4 - 5x^2 + 9}$	$+$	$+$	$+$	$+$
$d'(x)$	$\frac{(-)(+)}{(+)} = -$	$\frac{(-)(-)}{(+)} = +$	$\frac{(+)(-)}{(+)} = -$	$\frac{(+)(+)}{(+)} = +$
$d(x)$	decreasing $\searrow$	increasing $\nearrow$	decreasing $\searrow$	increasing $\nearrow$
	minimum at $x = -\sqrt{\frac{5}{2}}$	maximum at $x = 0$	minimum at $x = \sqrt{\frac{5}{2}}$	

The first derivative test verifies that a local minimum occurs when $x = -\sqrt{\dfrac{5}{2}}$ or $x = \sqrt{\dfrac{5}{2}}$. These values correspond to the minimum distance. Substitute them into the original function $y = 9 - x^2$ to get the minimum distance, which is the corresponding value of the function.

$$y = 9 - \left(-\sqrt{\dfrac{5}{2}}\right)^2 \quad \text{and} \quad y = 9 - \left(\sqrt{\dfrac{5}{2}}\right)^2$$

$$= 9 - \dfrac{5}{2} \qquad\qquad = 9 - \dfrac{5}{2}$$

$$= \dfrac{13}{2} \qquad\qquad\quad = \dfrac{13}{2}$$

The two points closest to $(0, 6)$ on the graph of $y = 9 - x^2$ are $\left(-\sqrt{\dfrac{5}{2}}, \dfrac{13}{2}\right)$ and $\left(\sqrt{\dfrac{5}{2}}, \dfrac{13}{2}\right)$.

Note that in this case, the calculator cannot be used to determine an exact solution, but can be used to check the reasonableness of the solution by evaluating $\sqrt{\dfrac{5}{2}}$ and comparing with the graphs above.

• • • • • • • •

Example 2

Deciding When Two Moving Objects Are Closest to Each Other

A north–south highway intersects an east–west highway at point P. A vehicle crosses P at 1:00 p.m., travelling east at a constant speed of 60 km/h. At the same instant, another vehicle is 5 km north of P, travelling south at 80 km/h. Find the time when the two vehicles are closest to each other and the distance between them at that time.

Solution

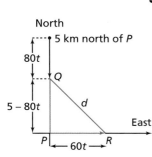

Draw a diagram. Let the x- and y-axes be the highways, and let P be at the origin. The slower vehicle is travelling away from P, while the faster vehicle is travelling toward P.

Let t be the number of hours after 1:00 P.M.

At time t, the slower vehicle is $60t$ kilometres east of P, and the faster vehicle is $(5 - 80t)$ kilometres north of P.

The quantity to be minimized is the distance between the two vehicles, d. From the diagram and using the Pythagorean theorem,

$$d^2 = (5 - 80t)^2 + (60t)^2$$
$$d^2 = 25 - 800t + 10\,000t^2$$
$$d = \sqrt{25 - 800t + 10\,000t^2}$$

$$\therefore d(t) = (25 - 800t + 10\,000t^2)^{\frac{1}{2}}$$

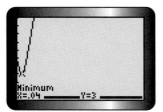

You can estimate the solution graphically, as shown. The minimum distance, approximately 3 km, occurs at $t = 0.04$.

Use calculus to calculate the exact solution algebraically. Applying the chain rule and the power rule,

$$d'(t) = \frac{d(25 - 800t + 10\,000t^2)^{\frac{1}{2}}}{d(25 - 800t + 10\,000t^2)} \cdot \frac{d}{dt}(25 - 800t + 10\,000t^2)$$

$$= \frac{1}{2}(25 - 800t + 10\,000t^2)^{-\frac{1}{2}} \cdot \frac{d}{dt}(25 - 800t + 10\,000t^2)$$

$$= \frac{1}{2}(25 - 800t + 10\,000t^2)^{-\frac{1}{2}} \cdot (-800 + 20\,000t)$$

$$= \frac{-800 + 20\,000t}{2(25 - 800t + 10\,000t^2)^{\frac{1}{2}}}$$

$$= \frac{-400 + 10\,000t}{\sqrt{25 - 800t + 10\,000t^2}}$$

Critical numbers occur when $d'(t) = 0$ or is undefined. Note that the denominator equals $\sqrt{(100t - 4)^2 + 9}$, which is always greater than 0; therefore, the derivative is always defined. So, $d'(t) = 0$ when the numerator equals 0.

$$\therefore 0 = -400 + 10\,000t$$
$$t = 0.04$$

Use the first derivative test to verify that $t = 0.04$ represents a local minimum.

	Intervals	
	$0 \le t < 0.04$	$t > 0.04$
$-400 + 10\,000t$	$-$	$+$
$\sqrt{25 - 800t + 10\,000t^2}$	$+$	$+$
$d'(t)$	$\frac{(-)}{(+)} = -$	$\frac{(+)}{(+)} = +$
$d(t)$	decreasing $\searrow$	increasing $\nearrow$
	minimum at $x = 0.04$	

The first derivative test confirms that a local minimum occurs when $t = 0.04$. In this case, the calculator gives the exact solution.

The distance between the vehicles is minimized at this time. The value $t = 0.04$ means 0.04 h, or $0.04 \times 60 = 2.4$ min, or 2 min 24 sec.

Evaluate d when $t = 0.04$ to determine the minimum distance.

$$d(0.04) = \sqrt{25 - 800(0.04) + 10\,000(0.04)^2}$$
$$= 3$$

The two vehicles are closest to each other when they are 3 km apart at exactly 1:02:24 P.M.

• • • • • • • •

Example 3   **Minimizing the Cost of an Electrical Power Line**

Recall the problem in Setting the Stage.

George wants to run a power line to a new cottage being built on an island that is 400 m from the shore of a lake. The main power line ends 3 km away from the point on the shore that is closest to the island. The cost of laying the power line under water is twice the cost of laying the power line on land. How should George place the line to minimize the overall cost?

Solution

Sketch a diagram of the situation. The cable will run along the shore, enter the water at some point, and continue straight to the island.

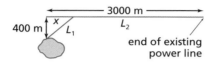

Let x represent the distance between the point on the shore closest to the island and the point where the cable enters the water. Let L_1 represent the length of cable underwater and L_2 the length of cable on land. Therefore, the total cost to lay the cable is $C = 2L_1 + L_2$. Minimize this quantity, C.

From the diagram, $L_2 = 3000 - x$ and $(L_1)^2 = x^2 + 400^2$, so $L_1 = \sqrt{x^2 + 160\ 000}$. Substituting in the expression for C gives

$$C(x) = 2(\sqrt{x^2 + 160\ 000}) + (3000 - x)$$

$$\therefore\ C(x) = 2(x^2 + 160\ 000)^{\frac{1}{2}} + (3000 - x)\quad 0 \le x \le 3000$$

You can estimate the minimum value using graphing technology.

Now use calculus to calculate the exact solution algebraically.
Using the difference and chain rules,

$$C'(x) = \frac{d}{dx}\left[2(x^2 + 160\ 000)^{\frac{1}{2}}\right] + \frac{d}{dx}(3000) - \frac{d}{dx}(x)$$

$$C'(x) = \frac{d[2(x^2 + 160\ 000)^{\frac{1}{2}}]}{d(x^2 + 160\ 000)} \cdot \frac{d(x^2 + 160\ 000)}{dx} + 0 - 1$$

$$= \left[2\left(\frac{1}{2}\right)(x^2 + 160\ 000)^{-\frac{1}{2}} \cdot \frac{d}{dx}(x^2 + 160\ 000)\right] - 1$$

$$= \left[(x^2 + 160\ 000)^{-\frac{1}{2}} \cdot 2x\right] - 1$$

$$= \frac{2x}{\sqrt{x^2 + 160\ 000}} - 1$$

Critical numbers occur when $C'(x)$ equals 0 or is undefined. In this case, the denominator is always greater than 0, so $C'(x)$ is defined for all x where $0 < x < 3000$. Solve for x to determine where $C'(x) = 0$.

$$\frac{2x}{\sqrt{x^2 + 160\ 000}} - 1 = 0 \qquad \text{Add 1 to each side.}$$

$$\frac{2x}{\sqrt{x^2 + 160\ 000}} = 1 \qquad \text{Multiply each side by } \sqrt{x^2 + 160\ 000}.$$

$$2x = \sqrt{x^2 + 160\ 000} \qquad \text{Square both sides.}$$

$$4x^2 = x^2 + 160\ 000 \qquad \text{Isolate } x^2.$$

$$3x^2 = 160\ 000 \qquad \text{Solve for } x.$$

$$x = \pm\sqrt{\frac{160\ 000}{3}}$$

$$x \doteq 230.94 \qquad \text{Since } x \geq 0, \text{ the negative solution is inadmissible.}$$

Intervals		
	$0 \leq x < 230.94$	$230.94 < x \leq 3000$
$C'(x)$	−	+
$C(x)$	decreasing ↘	increasing ↗
	minimum at $x = 230.94$	

The first derivative test confirms that a global minimum occurs at $x \doteq 230.94$. This value is the distance from the point on the shore closest to the island to the point where the cable enters the water. This distance will minimize the cost of installing the cable. Using this value, calculate L_1 and L_2.

$$L_1 \doteq \sqrt{(230.94)^2 + 160\ 000} \qquad L_2 \doteq 3000 - 230.94$$
$$\doteq 461.88 \qquad\qquad\qquad = 2769.06$$

The total cost of laying the cable is minimized if about 2769.06 m are placed along the shore and 461.88 m are placed underwater.

CHECK, CONSOLIDATE, COMMUNICATE

1. Why do optimization problems involving distance often result in using the chain rule?
2. Suppose you have found the model for a problem. Is determining the optimal values of a composite function different from determining the optimal values for polynomial and rational functions? Explain your answer in terms of techniques.

KEY IDEAS

- The properties of the derivative that you use to solve optimization problems involving composite functions are the same as those you apply to polynomial and rational functions.
- Use the strategy for solving optimization problems, outlined in Chapters 4 and 5 on pages 305 and 397, to also solve problems involving composite function models.

6.4 Exercises

(A) **1.** Find the point on the line $y = 6x + 8$ that is closest to the origin, $(0, 0)$.

2. What point on the graph of $f(x) = x^2$ is closest to $(2, 0.5)$?

3. Find the point on the curve $2y^2 = 4(x + 1)$ that is closest to the origin.

4. Ship A, sailing due east at 8 km/h, sights ship B 5 km to the southeast when ship B is sailing due north at 6 km/h. How close to each other will the two ships be when they pass?

5. Mike, who is standing on the deck of a yacht that is travelling due west at 6 km/h, sees a sailboat sailing southwest at 4 km/h, 3 km northwest of the yacht. How close to each other do these boats get?

6. **Knowledge and Understanding:** Determine the points on the curve $y = \sqrt{x}$, $0 \le x \le 1$, that are **(a)** closest to and **(b)** farthest from point $(2, 0)$.

(B) **7.** A passenger jet is travelling due north at 400 km/h, while a cargo plane, 2 km to the northwest, is travelling east at 300 km/h. The altitude of the cargo plane is 1000 m lower than the altitude of the passenger jet. What will be the minimum separation between the two aircraft?

8. A truck travelling west at 100 km/h is 250 km due east of a sports car going north at 120 km/h. When will the vehicles be closest to each other? What is the minimum distance between them?

9. A boat leaves a dock at 2:00 P.M., heading west at 15 km/h. Another boat heads south at 12 km/h and reaches the same dock at 3:00 P.M. When were the boats closest to each other?

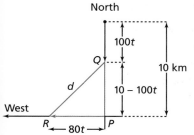

10. **Communication:** Devise an optimization problem based on the diagram on the left.

11. A woman lives on an island 2 km from the mainland. Her fitness club is 4 km along the shore from the point closest to the island. To get to the fitness club, she paddles her kayak at 2 km/h. Once she reaches the shore, she jogs at 4 km/h. Determine where she should land to reach her fitness club in the shortest possible time.

12. A dune buggy is on a straight desert road, 40 km north of Dustin City. The vehicle can travel at 45 km/h off the road and 75 km/h on the road. The driver wants to get to Gulch City, 50 km east of Dustin by another straight road, in the shortest possible time. Determine the route he should take.

13. Suppose you are swimming in a lake and find yourself 200 m from shore. You would like to get back to the spot where you left your towel, which is at least 200 m down the beach, as quickly as possible. You can walk along the beach at 100 m/min, but you can swim at only 50 m/min. To what point on the beach should you swim to minimize your total travelling time?

14. The owners of a small island want to bring in electricity from the mainland. The island is 80 m from a straight shoreline at the closest point. The nearest electrical connection is 200 m along the shore from that point. It costs twice as much to install cable across water than across land. What is the least expensive way to install the cable?

15. Application: Bill owns an oil well located 400 m from a road. Bill wants to connect the well to a storage tank 1200 m down the road from the well. It costs $35/m to lay pipe along the road and $50/m to lay it elsewhere. How should the pipeline be laid to minimize the total cost?

16. Thinking, Inquiry, Problem Solving: Find the dimensions of the rectangle of maximum area that can be inscribed in the ellipse $\dfrac{x^2}{16} + \dfrac{y^2}{9} = 1$.

17. Check Your Understanding: Is the strategy for solving optimization problems different for rational and composite function models? Explain.

C **18.** An offshore oil well is in the ocean at a point 5 km from the closest point on a straight shoreline. The oil must be pumped from the well to a storage facility on shore. The storage facility is 15 km away from the point on shore that is closest to the well. It costs $100 000/km to lay pipe underwater and $75 000/km over land. How should the pipeline be situated on the shore to minimize the cost?

19. Prove that (1, 0) is the closest point on the circle $x^2 + y^2 = 1$ to (2, 0).

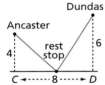

20. Two towns, Ancaster and Dundas, are 4 km and 6 km, respectively, from an old railroad line that has been made into a bike trail. Points C and D on the trail are the closest points to the two towns, respectively. These points are 8 km apart. Where should a rest stop be built to minimize the length of new trail that must be built from both towns to the rest stop?

ADDITIONAL ACHIEVEMENT CHART QUESTIONS

Knowledge and Understanding: A north–south highway intersects an east–west highway at point P. A vehicle passes P at 3:00 P.M., travelling east at a constant speed of 100 km/h. At the same instant, another vehicle passes 2 km north of P, travelling south at 80 km/h. Find the time when the two vehicles are closest to each other and when the distance between them is minimal.

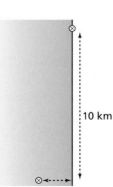

Application: Millie is in a boat 2 km from a straight shoreline and wants to reach a point on the shore 10 km north of her present position, as shown in the diagram. She can row at 5 km/h and jog at 8 km/h. Calculate the position on the shoreline to which she should row to reach the destination in the shortest time.

Thinking, Inquiry, Problem Solving: Find the area of the largest rectangle that can be inscribed in a circle with radius r.

Communication: To solve an optimization problem, you set the derivative of the function that models the problem to 0 and solve the resulting equation. Why?

6.5 Sketching Graphs of Composite Functions

SETTING THE STAGE

In previous chapters, you used calculus to analyze and sketch the graphs of polynomial and rational functions. The first derivative helps identify the intervals in the domain where the function increases or decreases and locate any maximum or minimum values. Use the second derivative to determine the concavity of the graph, along with points of inflection. Recall that rational functions have asymptotes, while polynomial functions do not. Composite functions may or may not have asymptotes.

In this section, you will use the first and second derivatives to analyze the behaviour of composite functions.

EXAMINING THE CONCEPT

Analyzing and Graphing a Composite Function

Recall these steps for graphing a polynomial function or a rational function, $f(x)$.

1. From the equation for $f(x)$,
   - determine the domain and any discontinuities
   - determine the intercepts
   - find any asymptotes

2. From the equation for $f'(x)$,
   - find the critical numbers
   - determine the intervals of increase and decrease
   - identify any local maximum or minimum values

3. From the equation for $f''(x)$,
   - determine where the graph is concave up and where it is concave down
   - find any points of inflection

4. Use the information from steps 1 to 3 to graph the function.

You will apply these same steps to graph composite functions.

Example 1   **Analyzing the Graph of a Radical Function**

(a) For $f(x) = \sqrt{x^2 - 4}$, determine $f'(x)$ and $f''(x)$.

(b) Discuss the domain, asymptotes, critical numbers, intervals of increase or decrease, local extrema, concavity, and points of inflection.

(c) Graph the function.

Solution

(a) $f(x) = \sqrt{x^2 - 4}$ Express the function with a rational exponent.

$\quad\quad = (x^2 - 4)^{\frac{1}{2}}$ Differentiate using the chain rule.

$$f'(x) = \frac{d(x^2-4)^{\frac{1}{2}}}{d(x^2-4)} \cdot \frac{d}{dx}(x^2 - 4)$$

$$= \frac{1}{2}(x^2 - 4)^{-\frac{1}{2}} \cdot \frac{d}{dx}(x^2 - 4)$$

$$= \frac{1}{2}(x^2 - 4)^{-\frac{1}{2}}(2x) \quad\quad \text{Simplify.}$$

$$= \frac{x}{\sqrt{x^2 - 4}} \quad\quad \text{Express as a product so you can use the product rule.}$$

$$= (x^2 - 4)^{-\frac{1}{2}}(x)$$

$$f''(x) = \frac{d}{dx}\left[(x^2 - 4)^{-\frac{1}{2}}\right] \cdot (x) + \frac{d}{dx}(x) \cdot (x^2 - 4)^{-\frac{1}{2}} \quad \begin{array}{l}\text{Apply the} \\ \text{product rule.}\end{array}$$

$$= -\frac{1}{2}(x^2 - 4)^{-\frac{3}{2}}(2x)(x) + (1)(x^2 - 4)^{-\frac{1}{2}} \quad \begin{array}{l}\text{Apply the chain rule} \\ \text{with the power rule.}\end{array}$$

$$= -\frac{1}{2}(x^2 - 4)^{-\frac{3}{2}}[2x^2 - 2(x^2 - 4)] \quad \text{Factor out } -\frac{1}{2}(x^2 - 4)^{-\frac{3}{2}}.$$

$$= \frac{-4}{\sqrt{(x^2 - 4)^3}}$$

1. Analyze f(x).

(b) Since $f(x) = \sqrt{x^2 - 4}$, f is undefined when $x^2 - 4 < 0$.

The domain of f is $\{x \mid |x| \geq 2, x \in \mathbf{R}\}$. The x-intercepts are 2 and -2.

As $x \to \pm\infty$, $f(x) \to \infty$. There are no asymptotes.

2. Analyze f'(x).

Critical numbers occur when $f'(x) = 0$ or when $f'(x)$ is undefined. In this case, $f'(x) = \frac{x}{\sqrt{x^2 - 4}}$, suggesting that the critical numbers are ± 2 and 0. Recall that $f(x)$ is undefined for $-2 < x < 2$, so 0 does not have to be considered.

Therefore, the intervals of increase and decrease are $x < -2$ and $x > 2$. Apply the first derivative test to locate any local extrema.

	Intervals	
	$x < -2$	$x > 2$
x	–	+
$\sqrt{x^2 - 4}$	+	+
$f'(x)$	$\frac{(-)}{(+)} = -$	$\frac{(+)}{(+)} = +$
$f(x)$	decreasing ↘	increasing ↗

For $x < -2$, $f(x)$ is decreasing. For $x > 2$, $f(x)$ is increasing. Since $f(x)$ is undefined for $-2 < x < 2$, and $f(x)$ decreases to $x = -2$ and increases beyond $x = 2$, $f(-2) = 0$ and $f(2) = 0$ are absolute minima.

3. Analyze $f''(x)$.

Now consider the second derivative and concavity. Possible points of inflection occur when $f''(x) = \dfrac{-4}{\sqrt{(x^2-4)^3}} = 0$ or when $f''(x)$ is undefined, that is, at $x = \pm 2$.

Analyze the second derivative on the same intervals to determine where the graph of $f(x)$ is concave up or concave down.

	Intervals	
	$x < -2$	$x > 2$
-4	$-$	$-$
$\sqrt{(x^2-4)^3}$	$+$	$+$
$f''(x)$	$\dfrac{(-)}{(+)} = -$	$\dfrac{(-)}{(+)} = -$
$f(x)$	concave down	concave down

When $x < -2$ and $x > 2$, the graph of $f(x)$ is concave down. There are no points of inflection.

4. Sketch the graph.

(c)

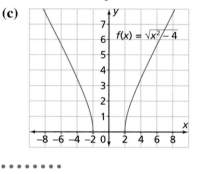

$f(x) = \sqrt{x^2 - 4}$

• • • • • • • • •

Example 2   **Analyzing the Graph of a Rational Function**

(a) For $f(x) = \dfrac{18(1-x)}{(x+3)^2}$, determine $f'(x)$ and $f''(x)$.

(b) Determine the domain, asymptotes, critical numbers, intervals of increase or decrease, local extrema, concavity, and points of inflection.

(c) Graph the function.

Solution

(a) $f(x) = \dfrac{18(1-x)}{(x+3)^2}$ Express the fraction as a product so you can use the product rule.

$\qquad = 18(1-x)(x+3)^{-2}$

Determine the first derivative.

$$f'(x) = 18\left(\frac{d}{dx}(1-x) \cdot (x+3)^{-2} + \frac{d}{dx}[(x+3)^{-2}] \cdot (1-x)\right)$$
$$= 18[(-1)(x+3)^{-2} + (-2)(x+3)^{-3}(1-x)]$$
$$= 18[-(x+3)^{-2} - 2(x+3)^{-3}(1-x)]$$
$$= 18(x+3)^{-3}[-(x+3) - 2(1-x)]$$
$$= 18(x+3)^{-3}(x-5)$$

Determine the second derivative.

$$f''(x) = 18\left(\frac{d}{dx}[(x+3)^{-3}] \cdot (x-5) + \frac{d}{dx}(x-5) \cdot (x+3)^{-3}\right)$$
$$= 18[-3(x+3)^{-4}(x-5) + (1)(x+3)^{-3}]$$
$$= 18(x+3)^{-4}[-3(x-5) + (x+3)]$$
$$= 18(x+3)^{-4}(-2x+18)$$
$$= -36(x+3)^{-4}(x-9)$$

(b) The domain is $\{x \mid x \neq -3, x \in \mathbf{R}\}$. $f(1) = 0$, so the graph crosses the x-axis at $x = 1$.

As $x \to \pm\infty$, $f(x) \to 0$. Therefore, the x-axis is the horizontal asymptote.

If $x > 1$, then $f(x) < 0$. Therefore, as $x \to \infty$, the graph must approach the x-axis from below.

As $x \to -\infty$, $f(x) > 0$. Therefore, the graph must approach the x-axis from above as $x \to -\infty$. $f(-3)$ is undefined.

As $x \to -3$ (from either side), $f(x) > 0$ and $f(x) \to \infty$. Therefore, there is a vertical asymptote at $x = -3$.

2. Analyze f'(x).

The critical numbers occur when $f(x)$ is defined and $f'(x) = \dfrac{18(x-5)}{(x+3)^3} = 0$ or when $f'(x)$ is undefined. In this case, the critical number may be $x = 5$ since a vertical asymptote occurs at $x = -3$. (Note that, as $x \to \pm\infty$, $f'(x) \to 0$, which confirms that there is a horizontal asymptote.)

The vertical asymptote and the critical number divides the domain into three intervals, $x < -3$, $-3 < x < 5$, and $x > 5$.

Apply the first derivative test for the intervals in the table to find any local extrema.

	Intervals		
	$x < -3$	$-3 < x < 5$	$x > 5$
$18(x-5)$	$-$	$-$	$+$
$(x+3)^3$	$-$	$+$	$+$
$f'(x)$	$\frac{(-)}{(-)} = +$	$\frac{(-)}{(+)} = -$	$\frac{(+)}{(+)} = +$
$f(x)$	increasing ↗	decreasing ↘	increasing ↗
	vertical asymptote at $x = -3$		minimum at $x = 4$

When $x < -3$ and $x > 5$, $f(x)$ is increasing. When $-3 < x < 5$, $f(x)$ is decreasing.

A local maximum does not exist at $x = -3$ since the line $x = -3$ is a vertical asymptote. By the first derivative test, there is a local minimum at $x = 5$, and $f(5) = \dfrac{18(1-5)}{(5+3)^2} = -1.125$.

3. Analyze $f''(x)$.

Now consider the second derivative. Possible points of inflection occur when $f''(x) = -\dfrac{36(x - 9)}{(x + 3)^4} = 0$ or when $f''(x)$ is undefined, that is, at $x = -3$ and $x = 9$. However, $f(-3)$ is undefined, so there can be no point of inflection there.

Analyze the second derivative to determine concavity.

	Intervals		
	$x < -3$	$-3 < x < 9$	$x > 9$
$-36(x - 9)$	+	+	−
$(x + 3)^4$	+	+	+
$f''(x)$	$\dfrac{(+)}{(+)} = +$	$\dfrac{(+)}{(+)} = +$	$\dfrac{(-)}{(+)} = -$
$f(x)$	concave up	concave up	concave down
	vertical asymptote at $x = -3$		point of inflection at $x = 9$

When $x < 9$, $x \neq -3$, the graph of $f(x)$ will be concave up. When $x > 9$, the graph of $f(x)$ will be concave down. The graph will have a point of inflection at $x = 9$. Since $f(9) = \dfrac{18(1 - 9)}{(9 + 3)^2} = -1$, the point of inflection is $(9, -1)$.

4. Sketch the graph.

(c)

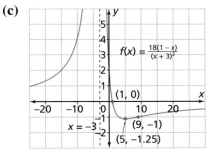

$f(x) = \dfrac{18(1 - x)}{(x + 3)^2}$

$(1, 0)$

$x = -3$

$(9, -1)$

$(5, -1.25)$

6.5 Exercises

A For each function, use the techniques shown in this section to sketch the graph of the function. Use $f(x)$ to find the domain, intercepts, and asymptotes. Use $f'(x)$ to find the critical numbers, intervals of increase or decrease, and local extrema. Use $f''(x)$ to find concavity and points of inflection.

1. $f(x) = (x - 1)^{\frac{1}{3}}$

2. $f(x) = (x - 4)^{\frac{2}{3}}$

3. $f(x) = \sqrt{x + 5}$

4. $f(x) = \sqrt{(x + 3)^2}$

5. $f(x) = \dfrac{15}{x + 3}$

6. $f(x) = (2x - 4)^{-2}$

7. $f(x) = (x^3 + x)^2$

8. $f(x) = (x^2 - 9)^2$

9. $f(x) = x(x^2 - 12)$

10. $f(x) = x\sqrt{4 - x}$

11. $f(x) = \dfrac{x}{(x - 2)^2}$

12. $f(x) = \dfrac{x}{\sqrt{x^2 - 1}}$

13. $f(x) = \dfrac{(x - 1)^2}{(x + 1)^3}$

14. $f(x) = (x^2 + 1)^2(x^2 - 1)^3$

15. $f(x) = \left(\dfrac{x - 2}{x + 3}\right)^2$

6.6 Implicit Differentiation

SETTING THE STAGE

Up to this point, you have differentiated functions defined explicitly by equations in the form $y = f(x)$. For example, in $y = 4x^2 + 6x - 7$, y is isolated on one side, and y is expressed *explicitly* as a function of x. In the relation $x^2 + y^2 = 9$, y is expressed *implicitly* as a function of x.

In this section, you will learn how to find the derivative of an **implicit function**, where the dependent variable cannot be easily isolated.

EXAMINING THE CONCEPT

Implicit Differentiation

Recall that $x^2 + y^2 = 9$ defines a circle with radius 3. This is an example of an **implicit relation**, because the dependent variable is not isolated or explicitly defined in terms of the independent variable.

In this case, you can solve for y to define y explicitly in terms of x.

$$y^2 = 9 - x^2$$
$$y = \pm\sqrt{9 - x^2}$$

Two different functions define y in terms of x: $y = \sqrt{9 - x^2}$ and $y = -\sqrt{9 - x^2}$. Differentiate each function.

$$y = \sqrt{9 - x^2} \qquad\qquad\qquad y = -\sqrt{9 - x^2}$$
$$= (9 - x^2)^{\frac{1}{2}} \qquad\qquad\qquad = -(9 - x^2)^{\frac{1}{2}}$$
$$\frac{dy}{dx} = \frac{d(9 - x^2)^{\frac{1}{2}}}{d(9 - x^2)} \cdot \frac{d}{dx}(9 - x^2) \qquad \frac{dy}{dx} = \frac{d(9 - x^2)^{\frac{1}{2}}}{d(9 - x^2)} \cdot \frac{d}{dx}(9 - x^2)$$
$$= \frac{1}{2}(9 - x^2)^{-\frac{1}{2}}\frac{d}{dx}(9 - x^2) \qquad = -\frac{1}{2}(9 - x^2)^{-\frac{1}{2}}\frac{d}{dx}(9 - x^2)$$
$$= \frac{1}{2}(9 - x^2)^{-\frac{1}{2}}(-2x) \qquad\quad = -\frac{1}{2}(9 - x^2)^{-\frac{1}{2}}(-2x)$$
$$= \frac{-x}{\sqrt{9 - x^2}} \qquad\qquad\qquad = \frac{x}{\sqrt{9 - x^2}}$$
$$= -\frac{x}{y} \qquad\qquad\qquad\qquad = -\frac{x}{y}$$

So the derivative of y with respect to x for $x^2 + y^2 = 9$ is $\frac{dy}{dx} = -\frac{x}{y}$.

In this case, it was possible to differentiate *explicitly*. To do so required solving for y and then differentiating two separate functions.

In many common situations, isolating the variable may be difficult or impossible. For example, consider $x^2 + 2xy + 3y^3 = 27$. Isolating y would be very difficult. You need a new method—**implicit differentiation**—to find the derivative of this type of relation.

Taking the derivative is an operation in the same way that multiplying is an operation. You can take the derivative of each side of an equation, just as you would apply any other algebraic operation to each side.

Taking the derivative of each side of an equation allows you to find derivatives in situations where it may be impossible to isolate a variable.

Example 1   **Implicit Differentiation**

Given $x^2 + y^2 = 9$, determine $\frac{dy}{dx}$.

Solution

$$x^2 + y^2 = 9$$

To find $\frac{dy}{dx}$, take the derivative of each side of the equation with respect to x.

$$\frac{d}{dx}(x^2 + y^2) = \frac{d}{dx}(9)$$

Differentiate each term with respect to x.

$$\frac{d}{dx}(x^2) + \frac{d}{dx}(y^2) = \frac{d}{dx}(9)$$

Use the chain rule to differentiate y^2, since y is a function of x.

$$2x + \frac{d(y^2)}{dy} \cdot \frac{dy}{dx} = 0$$

$$2x + 2y\frac{dy}{dx} = 0$$

Isolate $\frac{dy}{dx}$.

$$2y\frac{dy}{dx} = -2x$$

$$\frac{dy}{dx} = \frac{-2x}{2y}$$

Simplify.

$$\frac{dy}{dx} = -\frac{x}{y}$$

The resulting derivative is identical to the derivatives of $y = \sqrt{9 - x^2}$ and $y = -\sqrt{9 - x^2}$. Implicit differentiation gave the same results with less work.

. . . .

Example 2   **Evaluating the Derivative of an Implicit Relation**

Determine $\frac{dy}{dx}\Big|_{x = 0}$ if $x^2 + 2xy + 3y^2 = 27$.

Solution

$$\frac{d}{dx}(x^2 + 2xy + 3y^2) = \frac{d}{dx}(27)$$

Take the derivative of each side with respect to x.

$$\frac{d}{dx}(x^2) + \frac{d}{dx}(2xy) + \frac{d}{dx}(3y^2) = 0$$

Differentiate each term with respect to x.

$$2x + \left(2y + 2x\frac{dy}{dx}\right) + 6y\frac{dy}{dx} = 0$$

Use the product rule to differentiate $2xy$. Use the chain rule to differentiate all y-terms.

$$2x\frac{dy}{dx} + 6y\frac{dy}{dx} = -2x - 2y \quad \text{Factor out } \frac{dy}{dx}.$$

$$\frac{dy}{dx}(2x + 6y) = -2x - 2y \quad \text{Isolate } \frac{dy}{dx}.$$

$$\frac{dy}{dx} = \frac{-2x - 2y}{2x + 6y} \quad \text{if } x \neq -3y$$

$$\frac{dy}{dx} = \frac{-x - y}{x + 3y}$$

Now evaluate the derivative at $x = 0$. But to evaluate $\frac{dy}{dx} = \frac{-x - y}{x + 3y}$, you need values for both x and y. So substitute $x = 0$ into the original equation, $x^2 + 2xy + 3y^2 = 27$, and solve for y.

At $x = 0$,

$$(0)^2 + 2(0)y + 3y^2 = 27$$
$$3y^2 = 27$$
$$y^2 = 9$$
$$y = 3 \text{ or } y = -3$$

At $(0, 3)$,

$$\frac{dy}{dx} = \frac{-0 - 3}{0 + 3(3)}$$
$$= -\frac{1}{3}$$

At $(0, -3)$,

$$\frac{dy}{dx} = \frac{-0 - (-3)}{0 + 3(-3)}$$
$$= -\frac{1}{3}$$

• • • • • • • •

Example 3   **Implicit Differentiation of an Elliptical Relation**

Determine the equation of the tangent to the ellipse defined by $4x^2 + y^2 - 8x + 6y = 12$ at the point or points where $x = 3$.

Solution

$$\frac{d}{dx}(4x^2 + y^2 - 8x + 6y) = \frac{d}{dx}(12) \qquad \text{Take the derivative of each side with respect to } x.$$

$$8x + \frac{d}{dx}(y^2) - 8 + \frac{d}{dx}(6y) = 0 \qquad \text{Use the chain rule to differentiate all } y\text{-terms.}$$

$$8x + \frac{d}{dy}(y^2) \cdot \frac{dy}{dx} - 8 + \frac{d}{dy}(6y) \cdot \frac{dy}{dx} = 0$$

$$8x + (2y) \cdot \frac{dy}{dx} - 8 + (6) \cdot \frac{dy}{dx} = 0$$

$$2y \cdot \frac{dy}{dx} + 6 \cdot \frac{dy}{dx} = -8x + 8 \qquad \text{Factor out } \frac{dy}{dx}.$$

$$\frac{dy}{dx}(2y + 6) = -8x + 8 \qquad \text{Isolate } \frac{dy}{dx}.$$

$$\frac{dy}{dx} = \frac{-8x + 8}{2y + 6}$$

$$\frac{dy}{dx} = \frac{-4x + 4}{y + 3}$$

With the derivative in this form, you need to know both x and y to evaluate the derivative at a point, so substitute $x = 3$ into the original equation and solve for y.

At $x = 3$,

$$4(3)^2 + y^2 - 8(3) + 6y = 12$$
$$y^2 + 6y = 0$$
$$y(y + 6) = 0$$
$$y = 0 \text{ or } y = -6$$

The two different y-values indicate two points on the graph where $x = 3$: $(3, 0)$ and $(3, -6)$. Substitute each point into the equation for the derivative. Then find the equations of the tangent lines.

$$\frac{dy}{dx}\Big|_{(3, 0)} = \frac{-4(3) + 4}{0 + 3} = -\frac{8}{3}$$

The equation of the tangent line at $(3, 0)$ is

$$y = -\frac{8}{3}(x - 3)$$
$$y = -\frac{8}{3}x + 8$$

$$\frac{dy}{dx}\Big|_{(3, -6)} = \frac{-4(3) + 4}{-6 + 3} = \frac{8}{3}$$

The equation of the tangent line at $(3, -6)$ is

$$y = \frac{8}{3}(x - 3) - 6$$
$$y = \frac{8}{3}x - 14$$

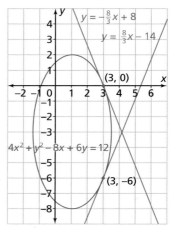

· · · · · · · ·

Example 4   **Finding the Derivative of the Inverse Function**

Let f be defined by $y = x^3 + 2x - 7$. Determine the derivative of f^{-1} with respect to x.

Solution

The inverse function, f^{-1}, is defined by

$$x = y^3 + 2y - 7$$ Differentiate each side with respect to x.

$$\frac{d}{dx}(x) = \frac{d}{dx}(y^3 + 2y - 7)$$

$$1 = \frac{d}{dy}(y^3) \cdot \frac{dy}{dx} + \frac{d}{dy}(2y) \cdot \frac{dy}{dx}$$

$$1 = 3y^2 \cdot \frac{dy}{dx} + 2 \cdot \frac{dy}{dx}$$ Factor out $\frac{dy}{dx}$.

$$1 = \frac{dy}{dx}(3y^2 + 2)$$ Isolate $\frac{dy}{dx}$.

$$\frac{1}{3y^2 + 2} = \frac{dy}{dx}$$

Note that $f(x) = x^3 + 2x - 7$, so $f'(x) = 3x^2 + 2$. Do you see the connection between the derivative of the function and its inverse?

KEY IDEAS

- A valid equation results when you differentiate each side of an equation.
- When y is an implicit function of x, differentiate each side of the function's equation and then isolate the derivative. Follow these steps for **implicit differentiation**:
    1. Differentiate each side of the equation with respect to x.
    2. Collect all terms with $\dfrac{dy}{dx}$ on one side of the equation, and group all other terms on the other side of the equation.
    3. Factor out $\dfrac{dy}{dx}$ from the expression where it appears.
    4. Solve for $\dfrac{dy}{dx}$ by dividing each side of the equation by the factor that does not contain $\dfrac{dy}{dx}$.
- Values of both the independent and the dependent variables are usually needed to evaluate a derivative after implicit differentiation.

6.6 Exercises

A
1. Differentiate each term with respect to x.
   - **(a)** x^3
   - **(b)** $5x^4$
   - **(c)** y
   - **(d)** y^3
   - **(e)** $5y^6$

2. Differentiate each term with respect to x.
   - **(a)** xy
   - **(b)** $2x^4y$
   - **(c)** x^2y^2
   - **(d)** $5x^2y^3$
   - **(e)** $-2x^4y^6$

3. Given $2p + 7c = 8$, determine $\dfrac{dp}{dc}$ by implicit differentiation.

4. Show, explicitly and implicitly, that the derivative of $xy = 1$ is $\dfrac{dy}{dx} = -\dfrac{1}{x^2}$.

B
5. Use implicit differentiation to find $\dfrac{dy}{dx}$.
   - **(a)** $x^2 + y^2 = 4$
   - **(b)** $x^2 - y^2 = 9$
   - **(c)** $x^3 + y^3 = 8$
   - **(d)** $\sqrt{x} + \sqrt{y} = 1$
   - **(e)** $x^2 - xy + y^2 = 4$
   - **(f)** $x^2y + y^2x = -4$
   - **(g)** $x^2y^3 + y = x$
   - **(h)** $x^3 - 4x^2y + 3xy^2 = 20$

6. Find the slope of the tangent to the curve at the given point.

(a) $x^2 + y^3 + 4x - y = 0$; $(0, 0)$ **(b)** $x^2 + 2y^2 = 3$; $(-1, -1)$

(c) $x^2 - y^3 - 5y^2 + 2 = 0$; $(4, -3)$ **(d)** $x^2 + 4xy + y^2 = 22$; $(3, 1)$

(e) $x^3 + y^3 = y + 21$; $(3, -2)$ **(f)** $x^2 + 2xy = y^3$; $(1, -1)$

7. Determine the equation of the tangent to the curve $\frac{1}{x} + \frac{1}{y} = 6$ at point $(0.25, 0.5)$.

8. What is the slope of the tangent to the circle $(x - 3)^2 + (y + 2)^2 = 25$ at point $(0, 2)$?

9. Let $x^2 + 3xy - y^2 = -3$. Find the slope of the tangent to the curve at $(2, -1)$.

10. Consider point $P(2, -6)$ and parabola $y = x^2 - 3x$. Point Q is the point on the parabola that is closest to P. Prove that PQ is perpendicular to the tangent to the parabola at Q.

11. At 10 A.M., a 747 jet is travelling east at 800 km/h. At exactly the same time, a smaller plane is 25 km due east of the 747 at the same altitude, travelling south at 600 km/h. At what time are the planes closest to each other?

12. **Knowledge and Understanding:** Let $9(x - 1)^2 + 16(y + 3)^2 = 144$.

Show that $y'' = \frac{-81}{16(y + 3)^3}$.

13. **Application:** In a computer game, the motion of a car is enhanced by showing the headlights on a building when the car approaches the building. The headlights form a parabola on the road. As the car approaches the building, the beam narrows. The equation of the parabola is $y = x^2 - 4x + c$, where $c < 0$ and $\frac{dc}{dt} = 14$. The x-axis represents the wall. Let length be measured in metres and time in seconds. Determine the rate at which the width of the beam is narrowing when $c = -14$.

14. **Communication:** Let $x^2 + y^2 = 16$. Determine $\frac{dy}{dx}$ in two ways: with and without implicit differentiation. Which method do you prefer? Justify your choice.

15. Let a hyperbola be defined by $9x^2 - 4y^2 = -19$. Determine the slope of the tangent to the curve at $(3, 5)$.

16. Given $\sqrt{x + y} - 2x = 1$, determine $\frac{dy}{dx}$.

17. Let $(x + y)^3 = 12x$. Determine $\frac{dy}{dx}$.

18. Let $xy - 3y^2 = 0$.

(a) Determine $\frac{dy}{dx}$.   **(b)** Graph the relation.

19. Given $x^2 + 2y^2 - 6x + 12y - 104 = 0$, determine $\frac{dy}{dx}$.

20. Assume that $PV = k$ for a gas in a sealed container. P represents pressure, V represents volume, and k is a constant.

    (a) Determine $\frac{dP}{dV}$.

    (b) Justify your formula for $\frac{dP}{dV}$ in terms of the rate of change of pressure with respect to change in volume.

21. Let $x(x + 2y) = 16$. Determine $\frac{dy}{dx}$.

22. **Check Your Understanding:** For any circle whose centre is the origin, $x^2 + y^2 = r^2$, show that $\frac{dy}{dx} = -\frac{x}{y}$, for any radius.

C **23.** **Thinking, Inquiry, Problem Solving:** The cross section of a log is roughly elliptical. Let the width and length of the cross-sectional area be $2a$ and $2b$, respectively. Then the equation of the ellipse is $\frac{x^2}{a^2} + \frac{y^2}{b^2} = 1$. Find the dimensions of the rectangular beam of maximum volume that can be cut from the log.

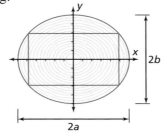

24. Let $x^3 + y^3 = 1$. Show that $\frac{d^2y}{dx^2} = -\frac{2x}{y^5}$.

25. Show that there are no real numbers x and y that satisfy the equation $x^2 + y^2 = 6y - 10$.

Hypatia of Alexandria (Egypt) (370–415)

In her day, Hypatia was an enormously popular and successful mathematics professor. Her writings included a textbook called *On Conics of Apollonius*, which summarized all that was known about conics at the time. Do some research on what happened to Hypatia.

ADDITIONAL ACHIEVEMENT CHART QUESTIONS

Knowledge and Understanding: Find $\frac{dy}{dx}$, using implicit differentiation.

    (a) $16x^2 + 9y^2 = 10$ **(b)** $xy^3 = 8$ **(c)** $(x + 1)^2 + (y - 3)^2 = 9$

Application: Find the equation of the line with positive slope that is tangent to the ellipse $\frac{x^2}{9} + \frac{y^2}{4} = 1$ at $x = 2$.

Thinking, Inquiry, Problem Solving: The equation of a curve is $y^2 + x^2 = 4x - 3$. Determine the equations of the two lines tangent to the curve that also pass through the origin.

Communication: Create a function that is defined explicitly and then differentiate it. Create a function that is defined implicitly and then differentiate it. Explain when implicit differentiation is useful.

6.7 Related Rate Models

Explore the concepts in this lesson in more detail in Exploration 13 on page 584.

SETTING THE STAGE

You have used the chain rule to find $\dfrac{dy}{dx}$ implicitly. You can also use the chain rule to find the rates of change of two or more related quantities that are changing with respect to time. For example, as water drains from a funnel, the volume of water, V, the radius of the water's surface, r, and the level of the water, h, are all functions of time. These three quantities are also related to one another.

Joanne conducts an experiment by letting water drain from a cone-shaped funnel. She uses a graduated cylinder and a timer to measure how quickly the water drains from the funnel. Joanne wants to know the rate at which the water level in the funnel dropped.

In this section, you will use the chain rule to solve problems involving related rates of change.

EXAMINING THE CONCEPT

Solving Related Rate Problems

Joanne's experiment involves **related rates**. The rate at which the water level drops is related to the rate at which the water drains from the funnel, which has a radius of 5.44 cm and a height of 13.6 cm. In related rate problems, you often have to find the rate of change of one variable given the rate of change of some other variable. Understanding the relations between the variables allows you to solve these problems.

Thirty seconds after Joanne's experiment starts, the water level in the funnel is 10 cm, the radius of the water's surface is 4 cm, and the water is draining at a rate of 2.5 mL/s. How fast is the water level dropping?

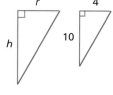

$$\frac{r}{4} = \frac{h}{10}$$
$$\therefore r = \frac{4}{10}h$$
$$r = \frac{2}{5}h$$

Let V represent the volume of water in the funnel, h the depth of water, r the radius of the surface, and t the time in seconds.

Given: At $t = 30$ s, $\dfrac{dV}{dt} = -2.5$ mL/s. (The rate is negative since volume is decreasing with time.)

Evaluate: $\dfrac{dh}{dt}$ at $t = 30$.

The variables are related by the formula for the volume of a cone, $V = \dfrac{\pi}{3}r^2h$. At $t = 30$ s, $h = 10$ cm and $r = 4$ cm. By the properties of cones and similar triangles, $r = \dfrac{2}{5}h$, for any positive value of h. Therefore, you can simplify the volume formula so that it has only one variable.

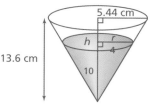

$$V = \frac{\pi}{3}r^2 h$$

$$V = \frac{\pi}{3}\left(\frac{2}{5}h\right)^2 h$$

$$V = \frac{\pi}{3}\left(\frac{4}{25}h^2\right)h$$

$$V = \frac{4\pi}{75}h^3$$

$$\doteq 0.168h^3$$

Use this formula to find a relation between $\frac{dV}{dt}$ and $\frac{dh}{dt}$.

$$V = 0.168h^3 \qquad \text{Differentiate both sides with respect to } t.$$

$$\frac{dV}{dt} = \frac{dV}{dh} \cdot \frac{dh}{dt} \qquad \text{Apply the chain rule.}$$

$$\frac{dV}{dt} = \frac{d}{dh}(0.168h^3) \cdot \frac{dh}{dt}$$

$$\frac{dV}{dt} = (0.504h^2)\frac{dh}{dt}$$

Now substitute the known values for $\frac{dV}{dt}$ and h at $t = 30$ s.

$$-2.5 = 0.504(10^2)\left(\frac{dh}{dt}\right) \qquad \text{Solve for } \frac{dh}{dt}.$$

$$\frac{dh}{dt} \doteq -0.05$$

Thus, at 30 s, the water level in the funnel is dropping at a rate of about 0.05 cm/s.

Strategy for Solving Related Rate Problems

A common mistake in solving related rate problems is to substitute variable information before differentiating. Substitute only constant values before differentiating.

- Define variables for any quantities that vary with time. Define distances relative to a fixed point, where possible. Identify other quantities as constants.
- Draw and label a diagram showing all variables and constants.
- Express all given information in terms of variables and the derivatives of variables. Express the rate to be determined as a derivative.
- Find an equation that relates the variables used in the given derivatives and the derivative to be determined. This may require finding several equations and then substituting.
- Substitute all *constant* quantities into the equation *before* differentiating.
- Differentiate with respect to time, and then evaluate the derivative for a specific instant in time.

Example 1 **Ripples in a Pond**

A pebble is dropped into a pond. The resulting ripples form concentric circles. The radius of the outermost circle increases at the constant rate of 10 cm/s. Determine the rate at which the area of disturbed water is changing when the radius is 50 cm.

Solution

Let r represent the radius of the circle of disturbed water and A the area of this circle.

Given: $\frac{dr}{dt} = 10$ cm/s (The rate is positive since the radius is increasing with time.)

Evaluate: $\frac{dA}{dt}$ when $r = 50$ cm.

In this case, variables r and A are related by the formula for the area of a circle, $A = \pi r^2$.

$$A = \pi r^2 \qquad \text{Differentiate both sides with respect to } t.$$

$$\frac{dA}{dt} = \frac{dA}{dr} \cdot \frac{dr}{dt} \qquad \text{Apply the chain rule.}$$

$$\frac{dA}{dt} = \frac{d}{dr}(\pi r^2) \cdot \frac{dr}{dt}$$

$$= 2\pi r \cdot \frac{dr}{dt} \qquad \text{Substitute } \frac{dr}{dt} = 10.$$

$$= 2\pi r (10)$$

$$= 20\pi r \qquad \text{This is the derivative at any time.}$$

If $r = 50$, then $\frac{dA}{dt} = 20\pi(50) = 1000\pi$.

When the radius is 50 cm, the area of the disturbed water is increasing at a rate of 1000π cm²/s.

· · · · · · · ·

Example 2 **Related Rates Involving Distance**

Sandy is standing on a 10-m ladder leaning against a wall when the foot of the ladder starts to slide away from the wall at 0.5 m/s. Determine the rate at which the top of the ladder is sliding down the wall when the foot of the ladder is 6 m from the wall.

Solution

Sketch a diagram. Define variables for distances, relative to a fixed point.

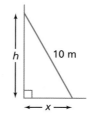

Let h represent the height of the top of the ladder and x the distance from the wall to the foot of the ladder. Both x and h are measured in metres. Let t represent the time in seconds since the ladder started to slip.

Given: $\frac{dx}{dt} = 0.5$ m/s (The rate is positive because x is increasing.)

Evaluate: $\frac{dh}{dt}$ when $x = 6$ m.

Find an equation relating x and h. You will want to differentiate this equation with respect to t to show a relation between $\frac{dh}{dt}$ and $\frac{dx}{dt}$.

Using the Pythagorean theorem,

$$10^2 = h^2 + x^2 \qquad \text{Differentiate both sides with respect to } t.$$

$$\frac{d}{dt}(10^2) = \frac{d}{dt}(h^2) + \frac{d}{dt}(x^2) \qquad \text{Use the chain rule.}$$

$$0 = \frac{d(h^2)}{dh} \cdot \frac{dh}{dt} + \frac{d(x^2)}{dx} \cdot \frac{dx}{dt}$$

$$0 = 2h\frac{dh}{dt} + 2x\frac{dx}{dt} \qquad \text{Substitute the known value, } \frac{dx}{dt} = 0.5.$$

$$0 = 2h\frac{dh}{dt} + 2x(0.5) \qquad \text{Isolate } \frac{dh}{dt}.$$

$$\frac{dh}{dt} = -\frac{x}{2h}$$

To evaluate the derivative when $x = 6$, as required, solve for the missing variable h. Use $10^2 = h^2 + x^2$.   If $x = 6$, then

$$10^2 = h^2 + 6^2 \qquad\qquad\qquad \frac{dh}{dt} = -\frac{6}{2(8)}$$

$$h^2 = 64 \qquad\qquad\qquad\qquad\qquad\; = -\frac{3}{8}$$

$$h = 8 \text{ (since } h \geq 0)$$

The negative value for the derivative means that the height is decreasing as time increases. When the foot of the ladder is 6 m from the wall, the top of the ladder is falling at $\frac{3}{8}$ m/s.

• • • • • • • •

Example 3   **Another Related Rate Problem Involving Distance**

A police cruiser is approaching an intersection when the officer hears a report of a car speeding along the cross street. The police car is 100 m from the intersection, travelling at 30 m/s. The other car is 200 m past the intersection, travelling at 27 m/s. The roads are at right angles. At what rate is the distance between the two cars closing?

Solution

Let t represent the time in seconds since the car crossed the intersection.

Let p represent the distance in metres from the police car to the intersection.

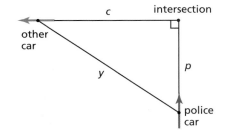

Let c represent the distance from the intersection to the other car.

Let y represent the distance between the two vehicles.

Given: $\frac{dc}{dt} = 27$ m/s, $\frac{dp}{dt} = -30$ m/s   ($\frac{dc}{dt}$ is positive since c is increasing, and

$\frac{dp}{dt}$ is negative since p is decreasing.)

Evaluate: $\frac{dy}{dt}$ when $c = 200$ m and $p = 100$ m.

Find an equation relating c, p, and y. Use the Pythagorean theorem.

$$y^2 = c^2 + p^2.$$ Differentiate both sides with respect to t.

$$\frac{d}{dt}(y^2) = \frac{d}{dt}(c^2) + \frac{d}{dt}(p^2)$$ Apply the chain rule.

$$\frac{d}{dy}(y^2) \cdot \frac{dy}{dt} = \frac{d(c^2)}{dc} \cdot \frac{dc}{dt} + \frac{d(p^2)}{dp} \cdot \frac{dp}{dt}$$

$$2y\frac{dy}{dt} = 2c\frac{dc}{dt} + 2p\frac{dp}{dt}$$ Divide both sides by 2. Substitute the known constants, $\frac{dc}{dt} = 27$ and $\frac{dp}{dt} = -30$.

$$y\frac{dy}{dt} = c(27) + p(-30)$$ Isolate $\frac{dy}{dt}$.

$$\frac{dy}{dt} = \frac{27c - 30p}{y}$$

Use the values of c, p, and y described in the problem to evaluate the derivative. The values of c and p are $c = 200$ m and $p = 100$ m. Calculate the value of y.

$$y^2 = 200^2 + 100^2$$
$$y = \sqrt{50\ 000}$$
$$\doteq 223.6 \qquad \text{(since } y \geq 0)$$

Now substitute into the derivative $\frac{dy}{dt}$.

$$\frac{dy}{dt} = \frac{27(200) - 30(100)}{223.6}$$
$$\doteq 10.7$$

The positive value means the distance between the two vehicles is increasing, not decreasing. At the moment when the police car is 100 m from the intersection, the distance between the vehicles is increasing by about 10.7 m/s.

• • • • • • • • •

Example 4   **Related Rates and Volume**

At 1:00 P.M. on a hot summer day, the temperature is 27°C and rising by 2°C/h. A balloon filled with air has a volume of 0.01 m³. The air pressure inside the balloon remains constant at 120 kPa because the balloon expands or contracts, depending on the temperature. Determine the rate at which the volume of the balloon is increasing at 1:00 P.M. Note that $\frac{PV}{T} = k$, where P is the pressure, V is the volume, T is temperature in kelvin (27°C = 300K), and k is a constant.

Solution
Let t represent the elapsed time in hours after 1:00 P.M.

Given: $P = 120$ kPa, and when $t = 0$, $\frac{dT}{dt} = 2$, $V = 0.01$ m³, and $T = 300$ K

Evaluate: $\frac{dV}{dt}$ when $t = 0$

Starting with $\frac{PV}{T} = k$, at $t = 0$, we have $P = 120$, $T = 300$, and $V = 0.01$.

$$\therefore \quad \frac{120(0.01)}{300} = k$$
$$0.004 = k \qquad \text{where } k \text{ is constant}$$

Note that all the constant values were substituted to find a relation between the variables in the problem. We were given $\frac{dT}{dt}$ at a specific time and asked to determine $\frac{dV}{dt}$ at that time. There is a relation between V and t, so differentiate with respect to t.

The other constant value is $P = 120$.

$$\therefore \frac{120V}{T} = 0.004$$

Thus, at any time t, we have $V = \frac{0.004}{120}T = \frac{T}{30\,000}$.

From $\qquad V = \frac{T}{30\,000}$, $\qquad$ Differentiate both sides with respect to t. The result gives the derivative of V with respect to t in terms of another derivative.

$$\frac{dV}{dt} = \frac{dV}{dT} \cdot \frac{dT}{dt}$$

$$\frac{dV}{dt} = \frac{1}{30\,000} \cdot \frac{dT}{dt}$$

At $t = 0$, it is given that $\frac{dT}{dt} = 2$.

Therefore,

At $t = 0$, $\quad \frac{dV}{dt} = \frac{1}{30\,000}(2)$

$$= \frac{1}{15\,000}$$

You cannot assume that $\frac{dT}{dt}$ is constant. You only know its value at exactly 1:00 P.M., in this case, $t = 0$. Similarly, the value for $\frac{dV}{dt}$ is valid only at $t = 0$.

At 1:00 P.M., the volume of the balloon is increasing at $\frac{1}{15\,000}$ m^3/h.

CHECK, CONSOLIDATE, COMMUNICATE

1. Why is $xy = 6$ and $\frac{dx}{dt} = 3$ enough information to determine $\frac{dy}{dt}$ when $x = 6$?

2. If $\frac{dy}{dt} = -2$, why is it incorrect to conclude that y is always decreasing at a rate of -2?

KEY IDEAS

- To solve related rate problems, do the following:
  - identify and define all relevant variables (quantities that vary with time)
  - define distances relative to a fixed point, where possible
  - draw a diagram
  - express all given and required information in terms of the variables and derivatives of the variables
  - find an equation (or equations) relating the variables that appear in the given or required derivatives
  - substitute constant values and relations between variables
  - differentiate with respect to time
  - substitute information that is valid at a specific time to evaluate the derivative
  - carefully interpret the signs of derivatives

6.7 Exercises

A For questions 1 to 4, assume that x and y are differentiable functions of t. Then determine the indicated values of $\frac{dy}{dt}$ and $\frac{dx}{dt}$.

Equation:	**Find:**	**Given:**
1. $y = \sqrt{x}$	**(a)** $\frac{dy}{dt}$ when $x = 3$	$\frac{dx}{dt} = 4$
	(b) $\frac{dx}{dt}$ when $x = 30$	$\frac{dy}{dt} = 2$
2. $y = x^2 - 3x$	**(a)** $\frac{dy}{dt}$ when $x = 2$	$\frac{dx}{dt} = 3$
	(b) $\frac{dx}{dt}$ when $x = 1$	$\frac{dy}{dt} = 5$
3. $xy = 4$	**(a)** $\frac{dy}{dt}$ when $x = 10$	$\frac{dx}{dt} = 20$
	(b) $\frac{dx}{dt}$ when $x = 5$	$\frac{dy}{dt} = -2$
4. $x^2 + y^2 = 9$	**(a)** $\frac{dy}{dt}$ when $x = 3$, $y = 0$	$\frac{dx}{dt} = 6$
	(b) $\frac{dx}{dt}$ when $x = 0$, $y = -3$	$\frac{dy}{dt} = -2$

5. Let $y\frac{dx}{dt} + 2x\frac{dy}{dt} = 6$. What information do you need to evaluate $\frac{dy}{dt}\Big|_{x\,=\,2}$?

6. Determine $\frac{dy}{dt}$ if $x + 2y = 4$ and $\frac{dx}{dt} = 3$.

B **7. (a)** Determine an expression for $\frac{dy}{dt}$ if $x^2 + 2y^2 = 8$ and $\frac{dx}{dt} = 3$.

(b) What additional information would you need to evaluate $\frac{dy}{dt}$?

8. Point P moves from left to right along the x-axis at 2 units/second. At the instant when $x = 4$, at what rate is the point directly above P on the parabola $y = x^2 - 3x + 5$ moving up or down?

9. Knowledge and Understanding: A point is moving along the right branch of a hyperbola defined by $4x^2 - y^2 = 64$. What is $\frac{dy}{dt}$ when the point is at $(5, -6)$ and $\frac{dx}{dt} = 3$?

10. Differentiate each relation with respect to time.

(a) $A = \pi r^2$ **(b)** $V = \frac{4}{3}\pi r^3$ **(c)** $A = 4\pi r^2$

(d) $x^2 + y^2 = r^2$ **(e)** $V = \pi r^2 h$ **(f)** $A = 2\pi r^2 + 2\pi rh$

11. How fast is the area of a circular oil spill increasing when its radius is 50 m, if the radius is increasing at 0.1 m/s?

12. The radius of a melting snowball is decreasing at a rate of 2 cm/h. Determine the rate at which the volume of snow is decreasing when the radius is 10 cm.

13. The surface area of a sphere is decreasing at a constant rate of 2π cm^2/s. At what rate is the volume of the sphere decreasing at the instant when the radius is 2 cm?

14. A conical icicle melts at a rate of 1.2 cm^3/h. At 10:00 A.M., the icicle is 25 cm long and 4 cm in diameter at its widest point. The icicle keeps the same proportions as it melts. Determine the rate at which its length is decreasing at 10:00 A.M.

15. **Communication**: When an inflated balloon is released, it expels air at a nearly constant rate. Describe how the balloon accelerates. Support your answer as completely as possible.

16. **Application**: A circular oil spill is spreading so that $\frac{dr}{dt} = 1430r^{-1.5}$, where r is the radius in metres of the area covered in oil at t hours since the spill occurred. Determine the rate at which the area is growing when the area is 500.0 m^2.

17. Sand forms a conical pile as it falls from a conveyor belt onto the ground. The diameter of the base of the cone is always four times the height of the pile. The sand is falling at 0.1 m^3/s.

    (a) Graph the volume of the sand in the pile versus time. Justify your graph.

    (b) Graph the height of the pile versus time. Justify your graph.

    (c) Determine $\frac{dh}{dt}$.

    (d) Explain how your formula in (c) is consistent with your graph in (b).

    (e) How fast is the height increasing when the pile contains 200 m^3 of sand?

18. A trough has an isosceles trapezoidal cross section as shown in the diagram. Water is draining from the trough at 0.2 m^3/s.

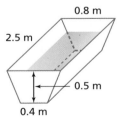

    (a) At what rate is the surface area of the water decreasing?

    (b) At what rate is the water's depth decreasing when the depth is 0.2 m?

19. An image of a box on a computer screen is changing shape so that the length is decreasing at 2 cm/s and the width is increasing at 8 cm/s. Originally, the box was 20 cm long, 12 cm wide, and 16 cm high. The front face retains its original proportions as the box changes shape.

(a) Determine a formula for the rate of change of the area of the front face.

(b) Determine a formula for the rate of change of the volume of the box.

(c) Determine the rate at which the volume is changing after 5 s.

(d) State the formula for the rate of change of volume with respect to time.

(e) Sketch a graph of volume versus time.

20. A line is defined by $x + 2y = 10$. A second line is defined by $x - 2y = 5k$, where k increases by 2 units/second. P is the point where the two lines intersect.

(a) Describe the motion of P.

(b) Determine the rate at which the x-coordinate of P is increasing when P is at $Q(8, 1)$.

(c) Determine the rate at which the y-coordinate of P is increasing when P is at Q.

(d) Determine the coordinates of P exactly 0.01 s after it passes Q.

(e) Determine the distance P moves in the 0.01 s after it passes Q.

(f) Estimate the rate at which P is moving as it passes Q.

(g) Can you think of another way to determine the rate at which P is moving when it passes Q?

21. The table lists the annual unit sales and the number of employees at a Canadian cell phone company over five years.

Year	Cell Phones Sold	Employees
1997	56 000	121
1998	62 000	115
1999	58 000	110
2000	53 000	102
2001	40 000	85

(a) Develop an algebraic model for cell phone sales as a function of the year. Explain.

(b) You might expect the number of employees to be a function of the number of cell phones sold. Determine a reasonable algebraic model for this interpretation.

(c) Express the number of employees as a function of the year, using your answers to the previous parts of this question. Compare this model with the actual values.

(d) Express the instantaneous rate of change in the number of employees as a function of time. Compare this model with the actual values.

(e) Are these models reasonable? Justify your answer.

22. The relation between the number of products sold, n, and the price, $\$p$, is modelled by $pn = k$, where k is a constant. When Marissa set the price of her lemonade to 50¢ a glass, she sold 100 glasses.

(a) How many glasses would she sell if she raised the price to 75¢ a glass?

(b) The cost of the ingredients to make a glass of lemonade is a function of time, modelled by $c(t) = -10^{-6}t(t - 365)(t - 50) + 15$, where c is the cost per glass in cents and t is the day of the year. Is this model reasonable? Explain.

23. A strong wind is blowing when Eduardo is flying a kite. He notices that the kite string will maintain a constant angle with the ground (about 60°) if he releases the string at 0.5 m/s. At what rate is the kite's altitude increasing when he has let out 100 m of string?

24. A weather balloon is rising vertically at a rate of 4 m/s. An observer stands 100 m from the point where the balloon was released. How fast is the distance between the observer and the balloon changing when the balloon is 120 m high?

25. At noon, a truck is 250 km due east of a car. The truck is travelling west at a constant speed of 60 km/h, while the car is travelling north at 100 km/h.

(a) At what rate is the distance between the vehicles changing at time t, in hours?

(b) What is the minimal distance between the car and the truck?

26. A sailor in a boat 10 km off a straight coastline wants to reach a point 20 km along the coast in the shortest possible time. Toward what point on the shore should he head if he can row at 4 km/h and run at 12 km/h?

27. A 1.7-m tall man walks away from a 9-m high streetlight at 0.8 m/s. How fast is the end of his shadow moving when he is 20 m from the lamppost?

28. **Thinking, Inquiry, Problem Solving:** A penny lies on the bottom of a 2-m deep pool. Jaclyn, whose eyes are 1.8 m above the surface of the water, sees the image of the penny 3.2 m from the edge of the pool, where she is standing. Fermat's principle states that light follows the path that minimizes the time to get from the object to the observer's eyes. The indices of light refraction in air and water are 1.02 and 1.333, respectively. The speed of light through a medium is its speed in a vacuum, c m/s, divided by the index of refraction. Determine the actual location of the penny on the bottom of the pool. Verify your answer using Snell's law.

29. **Check Your Understanding:** Outline a procedure for solving related rate problems.

C 30. Coffee is poured at a uniform rate of 3 cm^3/s into a cup whose inside is shaped like a truncated cone. The upper and lower radii of the cup are 4 cm and 2 cm, respectively. The height of the cup is 6 cm. How fast will the level of coffee be rising when the coffee is halfway up the cup? (Hint: Extend the diagram to form a cone.)

31. The altitude of a right circular cone increases at the same rate as the radius of its base decreases. At a certain instant, the altitude is 30 cm and the rate of change of the volume is 0. What is the base radius at this time?

ADDITIONAL ACHIEVEMENT CHART QUESTIONS

Knowledge and Understanding: The circumference of a circle is decreasing at a rate of 3 m/s. Determine the rate at which the area is changing when the circumference is 30 m.

Application: Two planes originated from the same airport. One plane is travelling at 260 km/h due east. The other is travelling at 230 km/h due south. What is the rate of change of the distance between the two planes when they are 30 km and 50 km, respectively, from the airport?

Thinking, Inquiry, Problem Solving: During a recent meteor storm, scientists observed that a meteor's burn rate was proportional to the surface area at any point in time as the meteor entered the atmosphere. Assuming that meteors are spherical in shape, how would you convince a classmate that the radius of each meteor was decreasing at a constant rate?

Communication: Hannah drew a diagram to represent two vehicles approaching an intersection at right angles. She differentiated the change in position of each vehicle over time and found the values to be negative at a particular time. She also differentiated the distance between the vehicles with respect to time and found this value to be negative at the same point in time. Explain what the negative values mean in both situations.

Emilie De Breteuil (1706–1749)

Emilie de Breteuil translated Isaac Newton's work on calculus into French, which helped his ideas to gain importance in Europe. She was also a confidant of the French philosopher Voltaire.

Chapter 6 Review

RATES OF CHANGE IN COMPOSITE FUNCTION MODELS

CHECK YOUR UNDERSTANDING

1. What is meant by "the composition of two functions"?

2. When you see the notation $f \circ g$, which function do you apply first? Explain.

3. Describe how you can determine the domain and range of $f \circ g$ if you know the domain and range of both f and g.

4. What would you expect the result of $f \circ f^{-1}$ to be? Explain.

5. Suppose you know that a function is the composition of two other functions. Can you determine those functions uniquely? Explain.

6. Describe how to find the slopes of tangents to a composite function from the graphs of the component functions.

7. Under what conditions is the derivative of u^n equal to nu^{n-1}?

8. Show how to differentiate a composite function using the chain rule.

9. When you apply several differentiation rules to differentiate a complex function, how can the order of operations help determine the sequence in which you must apply the rules?

10. Give an example of an explicit function and an implicit relation. Differentiate both.

11. Describe how to differentiate an implicit relation.

12. Describe a general strategy for solving related rate problems.

ADDITIONAL REVIEW QUESTIONS BY SECTION

6.1 Composition of Functions

13. Express $\{(1, 2), (3, 4), (4, 5)\}$ as the composition of two functions.

14. Let $f(x) = 2(x - 1)^2 - 3$ and $g(x) = \pm\sqrt{\dfrac{x + 3}{2}} + 1$.

    (a) Determine $(g \circ f)(x)$.   (b) Determine $(f \circ g)(x)$.

    (c) Describe the relation between f and g.

15. Let $f(x) = 3(x - 2)(x + 5)$ and $g(x) = \dfrac{1}{x}$. Determine the domain of $g \circ f$.

6.2 Rates of Change for Composite Functions— The Chain Rule

16. Differentiate.

    (a) $f(x) = (4x^2 + 3x)^5$ **(b)** $g(x) = \sqrt{10x^2 - 5x}$

    (c) $h(x) = \dfrac{7}{(4x^3 - 6x^2)^3}$ **(d)** $y = \dfrac{1}{\sqrt[3]{(x + 5)^2}}$

17. Let $f(x) = \sqrt{1 + x^3}$. Determine the slope of the tangent to the curve at $(2, 3)$.

18. Find the intervals on which $y = \dfrac{1}{(x^2 + 1)^2}$ is increasing and decreasing.

6.3 Differentiation Techniques: Combining the Differentiation Rules

19. Differentiate.

    (a) $f(x) = (6x^2 - 5x)^5(2x - 1)^4$ **(b)** $g(x) = 6x^2\sqrt{3x^3 - x^2}$

    (c) $h(x) = \dfrac{(2x + 5)^2}{(4x^3 - 6x^2)^3}$ **(d)** $y = \left(\dfrac{3x^2 - 5}{x - 1}\right)^5$

20. Given $P(t) = [2t + 5(t^2 - 5t)^3]^{0.5} - 3$, determine $\dfrac{dP}{dt}$.

21. Determine the maximum and minimum values of $g(x) = x(x^2 - 3)^3$.

6.4 Finding Optimal Values for Composite Function Models

22. Which points on the graph of $y = x^2$ are closest to point $\left(2, \dfrac{1}{2}\right)$?

23. A pickup truck is 30 km due west of an SUV and is travelling east at a constant speed of 70 km/h. Meanwhile, the SUV is going south at 90 km/h. When will the truck and the SUV be closest to each other? What is the minimum distance between them?

24. Carl is installing cable at a new house. The main cable is on another street. Part of the cable will cross the lawn to the street in front of the house. The rest of the cable will be installed inside a conduit to connect to the main cable on the other street. The house is 12 m from the conduit at the closest point. The other street is another 50 m along the conduit line. It costs $4.50/m to install cable across the front lawn. It costs $1.80/m to install cable in the conduit. Determine the point on the conduit where the cable should be connected from the house.

6.5 Sketching Graphs of Composite Functions

For each function, determine the first and second derivatives. Use the derivatives and any other appropriate information to analyze and sketch the graph.

25. $f(x) = (x - 1)^3 - 1$ **26.** $f(x) = \dfrac{16x}{(x + 4)^2}$

27. $f(x) = \left(\dfrac{x + 1}{x}\right)^2$ **28.** $f(x) = x\sqrt{9 - x^2}$

6.6 Implicit Differentiation

29. Given $a^2 + b^2 = c^2$, determine $\dfrac{da}{dt}$ when $a = 5$, $b = 12$, and $c = 13$, if $\dfrac{db}{dt} = 3$ and

    (a) c is a constant   **(b)** $\dfrac{dc}{dt} = 3$ **(c)** $c(t) = t^2 - 3t$

30. Let $x^2 + 4y^2 = 6xy$.

    (a) Determine $\dfrac{dy}{dx}$ and $\dfrac{dx}{dy}$.   **(b)** Simplify $\dfrac{dy}{dx} \cdot \dfrac{dx}{dy}$.

31. Determine the equation of the tangent line to $x^3 + y^2 - 3xy = 17$ at $(1, 1)$.

6.7 Related Rate Models

32. A hot-air balloon is held down by ropes from points on the ground 20 m from the spot directly under the balloon. To control the elevation of the balloon, the ropes are gradually released or pulled in. At $t = 0$, the balloon is 30 m in the air. If the ropes are being pulled in at 0.5 m/s,

    (a) sketch a graph of the height of the balloon versus time

    (b) determine the rate at which the balloon is descending when it is 10 m off the ground

33. A children's baseball diamond is a square with 20-m sides. A girl steals second base, running at 4 m/s.

    (a) Graph the distance between the catcher (at home plate) and the runner versus time.

    (b) Determine the rate at which the distance between the catcher and the runner is increasing when the runner is 4 m from second base.

34. Two cars approach a right-angle intersection, one travelling north at 60 km/h and the other travelling east at 80 km/h. When the faster car is 5 km from the intersection, the slower car is 3 km from the intersection. How fast is the distance between the two cars changing?

REVIEW QUESTIONS BY ACHIEVEMENT CHART CATEGORIES

Knowledge and Understanding

35. Given $f = \{(0, 3), (1, 2), (2, 0), (3, -1)\}$ and $g(x) = 2x + 1$,

    (a) evaluate **i.** $(g \circ f)(0)$, **ii.** $(g \circ f)(2)$, and **iii.** $(g \circ f)(3)$.

    (b) determine the domain of $g \circ f$

    (c) graph $g \circ f$

36. Let $f(x) = \dfrac{2x - 1}{(3x + 2)^2}$. Determine $f'(x)$ and $f''(x)$.

37. A particle moves on the curve of an ellipse defined by $5x^2 + 4y^2 = 120$ in such a way that its x-coordinate is given by $x(t) = t(4 - t)$ for $0 \le t \le 4$, and t is in seconds. Determine the rate at which the y-coordinate is changing at the instant the particle passes point $(2, 5)$.

Communication

38. (a) Give an example of two functions f and g for which $f \circ g \neq g \circ f$. Explain why this is possible.

(b) Is it possible for $f \circ g$ to be equal to $g \circ f$? Give an example.

39. Let $f(2) = 5, f'(2) = 3, f(4) = 6, f'(4) = 7, g(5) = 1, g'(5) = -2$, $g(6) = 2, g'(6) = 4$, and $k = g \circ f$. Determine $k'(2)$. Show your solution to this problem with graphs of suitable functions.

40. The volume of a spherical balloon is decreasing at a constant rate. Sketch graphs of the volume, surface area, and radius of the balloon versus time. Support your graphs with analysis.

Thinking, Inquiry, Problem Solving

41. Given $f(x) = \dfrac{1}{x}$ and $g(x) = \dfrac{6x^2 + 1}{2x - 4}$, express g as a composition of f with another function.

42. At a large company, the marginal profit is given by
$$m(x) = \frac{x^3 + 100\,000x - 112x^2 + 400}{x}, \quad x \geq 0,$$
where x represents the number of widgets made, in thousands. Determine the values of x for which the marginal profit is increasing.

43. A researcher estimates that the total number of jobs in Burlington that depend on Canadata Corp. is proportional to the square of the number of people directly employed by Canadata. The number of employees at Canadata is modelled by $n(t) = 0.02t^2 + 27t + 120$, where t is the number of years since the company opened in July 1992. When the company first opened, researchers estimated that a total of 720 new jobs were created in Burlington, including the 120 employees at Canadata. Determine the rate at which jobs will be created in July 2006.

Application

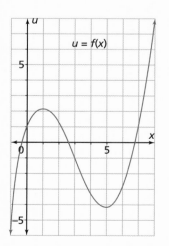

$u = f(x)$

44. Let $\dfrac{d}{dx}(\sin x) = \cos x$ and $f(x) = 2\sin(3x + \pi) + 1$. Determine the slope of the tangent to the graph of f when $x = \dfrac{\pi}{2}$.

45. Copy the graph of $u = f(x)$. Let a second function g be defined by $g(x) = [f(x)]^2 + 1$.

(a) Without graphing g first, sketch the graph of $g'(x)$ on the same set of axes.

(b) For what values of x will g have local extrema?

46. A cylindrical mass of clay is compressed vertically so that its height decreases at a constant rate. The volume remains constant and the clay retains its cylindrical shape as the clay is compressed. Determine a formula for the instantaneous rate of change of height. Describe other information that is necessary to evaluate this rate.

Chapter 6 Performance Task

Create a model to determine the growth rate of a plant. You can choose to do the experiment yourself or to use the given data. If you do it yourself, grow a bean plant in a cup with seeds, soil or cotton. You will need to give your plant soil, water, and sunlight. Record the height of your bean plant every 12 h (for instance at 7:45 A.M. and 7:45 P.M.). Create a table like this one.

Time (hours)	0	12	24	36	...
Height of Bean Plant (cm)	0	0	0	0.1	...

1. Grow the bean plant for three weeks and record the data. For students not performing the experiment, use Sarah's bean plant data below. At the end of three weeks, graph your data and draw a curve of best fit. Which type of curve best describes your scatter plot data: linear, quadratic/parabolic, square root, exponential, hyperbolic, or other?

2. Determine an equation for your curve by looking for patterns, trial-and-error, or using graphing technology to estimate different regression models.

3. Find the rate of change of growth of your bean plant, in general, as well as at an instant in time of your choice.

4. Determine the maximum height that your plant will attain and when this height will be attained.

Time (hours)	0	12	24	36	48	60	72	84
Height of Bean Plant (cm)	0	0	0	0	0	0	0	0
Time (hours)	96	108	120	132	144	156	168	180
Height of Bean Plant (cm)	0	0	0	0	0.1	0.2	0.2	1.0
Time (hours)	192	204	216	228	240	252	264	276
Height of Bean Plant (cm)	2.4	5.0	10.2	12.0	13.2	14.5	15.5	16.1
Time (hours)	288	300	312	324	336	348	360	372
Height of Bean Plant (cm)	17.2	18.0	19.5	20.0	20.5	21.0	21.8	22.2

Chapter 6 Review Test

RATES OF CHANGE IN COMPOSITE FUNCTION MODELS

1. The graphs of functions f and g are shown. Graph $f \circ g$.

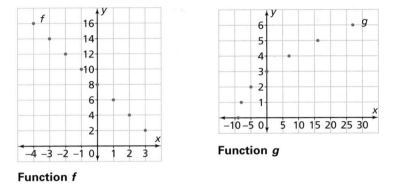

Function f

Function g

2. Differentiate using the chain rule.

   (a) $y = (3x + 5x^2)^4$

   (b) $f(x) = \dfrac{6x}{(x + 1)^2}$

   (c) $g(x) = \sqrt{2x - 8}$

   (c) $y = \left(\dfrac{3x + 5}{x - 1}\right)^4$

3. **Knowledge and Understanding:** Let $f(x) = x$, $g(x) = (x - 3)^2 - 4$, and $k = f \circ g$. Determine the domain of k. Evaluate $k'(5)$.

4. Let $f(x) = \sqrt[3]{\dfrac{2x + 1}{x - 3}}$. Determine $f'(0)$.

5. Determine the derivative of $3x^2 - 5y^3 + 4x^2y = 10$.

6. **Communication:** The sum of the square roots of x and y is 6. The variable x is decreasing at 3 units/second.

   (a) Determine a formula for $\dfrac{dy}{dt}$.

   (b) Graph y versus t and x versus t.

   (c) Explain how your answer to (a) corresponds with your graphs in (b).

7. **Thinking, Inquiry, Problem Solving:** As a volcano erupts, the height increases 20% faster than the rate at which the radius increases. The volcano retains a conical shape during the eruption. At a certain moment, lava is ejected at 1200 m³/h, the radius of the base of the mountain is 1 km, and the height is 500 m. Determine the rate at which the height is increasing at that moment.

8. A spherical balloon is inflated so that the volume increases at 7.5 m³/min. At what rate is the diameter increasing when the radius is 5 m? when the volume is 50 m³?

7 Rates of Change in Exponential and Logarithmic Function Models

In Chapter 2, you used exponential and logarithmic functions to model many situations. This chapter introduces other exponential and logarithmic functions.

In this chapter, you will examine the derivatives of exponential and logarithmic functions. You will also analyze exponential rates of growth and decay in more detail.

In this chapter, you will

- be introduced to a special number, *e*

- discover new exponential and logarithmic functions that relate to *e*

- determine the derivatives of exponential and logarithmic functions

- determine tangents to exponential and logarithmic curves

- solve problems involving exponential and logarithmic functions

- determine and analyze the key features of exponential and logarithmic graphs

- create exponential and logarithmic models for given applications and analyze those models

- pose questions that can be solved by analyzing exponential and logarithmic models and using the techniques of differential calculus

The Chapter Problem

Rabbit Population

A dozen rabbits were released into the open on a farm in Australia over 100 years ago. Because the rabbits had no natural enemies, the population increased exponentially to over one hundred million in 1999. This large population has affected, and continues to affect, the natural vegetation and crops. People have tried to control the rabbit population over time using different methods. These attempts have slowed the rate of growth from time to time, but have failed to control the ever-growing rabbit population.

The following data models the growth of another rabbit population in a similar case.

(a) Create algebraic and graphical models of the data. Describe any patterns that you see.

(b) Determine the intervals of increase and decrease and the maximum and minimum values of the function. Find the points of inflection.

(c) What does the graph of the data tell about the population growth rates?

(d) Compare the growth rates in different intervals.

(e) Predict the rabbit population in 2020.

(f) When was the original pair of rabbits introduced in this case?

Year	Rabbit Population
1955	650
1958	2 180
1960	5 300
1961	8 200
1962	12 400
1965	35 500
1968	66 300
1975	91 600
1980	92 900
1986	92 800
1990	93 100

Write a report. Discuss the population patterns. Include the solutions to the above questions.

After certain lessons in this chapter, you will be asked questions about this problem to help you develop your solution. Keep a record of your work in a project folder or computer file so that you can provide a full solution at the end of the chapter.

For help with this problem, see pages 514, 521, 536, 543, and 550.

Chapter Challenges

Challenge 1

The Kilauea volcano, on the south slope of Mauna Loa in Hawaii, is one of the most active on Earth. Its current eruption began in January 1983. As of January 2000, it has produced 1.9 km³ of lava, has covered 102 km², and has added 205 ha to the southern shore. There are no signs that the current eruption will come to an end anytime soon.

When a volcano erupts, the speed at which the lava flows varies. When the lava is warm, it flows quite quickly. The distance that the lava has moved over time can be modelled by

$$y = 11.7(2 - e^{-0.105t})$$

where y is the distance in kilometres and t is the numbers of hours since the lava started flowing.

(a) Graph this function.

(b) Determine $\dfrac{dy}{dt}$.

(c) What does $\dfrac{dy}{dt}$ represent?

(d) How far has the lava moved at 0.5 h? 1 h? 2 h? 5 h?

Challenge 2

Suppose the annual rate of inflation is about 2%. This rate is compounded continuously. You have invested $45 000 in a savings account that pays 2.5%/a, compounded quarterly. How much money will you actually earn on your investment after 10 years?

Getting Ready

1. Express in exponential form.

   (a) $\log_2 64 = 6$ **(b)** $\log_5 1 = 0$

   (c) $\log_3 27 = 3$ **(d)** $\log_a x = y$

   (e) $\log_2 \left(\frac{1}{8}\right) = -3$ **(f)** $\log 100 = 2$

2. Express in logarithmic form.

   (a) $10^4 = 10\ 000$ **(b)** $3^{-2} = \frac{1}{9}$

   (c) $2^3 = 8$ **(d)** $10^{-3} = 0.001$

   (e) $a^x = y$ **(f)** $\sqrt{81} = 9$

3. Evaluate.

   (a) $\log_3 9$ **(b)** $\log 1000$

   (c) $\log_2 \sqrt{2}$ **(d)** $\log_5 1$

   (e) $\log 0.1$ **(f)** $\log_5 \sqrt{125}$

   (g) $\log_4 192 - \log_4 3$ **(h)** $\log_2 112 - \log_2 7$

4. Graph each function. State the domain and range.

   (a) $y = 3(2)^x$ **(b)** $y = -4(0.5)^x$

   (c) $y = 200(1.06)^{2x}$ **(d)** $y = 3^{-x} + 4$

5. Graph each function. State the domain and range.

   (a) $y = \log_2 x$ **(b)** $y = \log x$

   (c) $y = 3 - \log_3 x$ **(d)** $y = -(\log 2x)$

6. Write each expression as a single logarithm.

   (a) $\log_2 3x + \log_2 2x$ **(b)** $\log 45 - \log 9$

   (c) $3 \log x + \log 3x$ **(d)** $2 \log x + 3 \log y - 4 \log z$

7. Find the first and second derivatives of each function.

   (a) $y = 3x^3 + 4x^2 - 5x + 5$ **(b)** $y = 2\sqrt{x}$

   (c) $y = \frac{3x^3}{2x + 1}$ **(d)** $y = x^3(3x + 2)$

   (e) $y = (2x^2 + 3x + 1)^4$ **(f)** $y = \frac{2x}{(x - 1)^3}$

8. Evaluate each log, to two decimal places.

   (a) $\log_2 56$ **(b)** $\log_3 103$

   (c) $\log_5 15$ **(d)** $\log_{0.5} 1.4$

   (e) $\log_4 1.02$ **(f)** $\log 60$

9. Graph each function and its inverse.

(a) $y = 4^x$

(b) $y = \log_2 x$

(c) $y = 10^x$

(d) $y = \log_5 x$

(e) $y = (0.5)^x$

(f) $y = \log x$

10. Solve for x, to two decimal places.

(a) $3^x = 56$

(b) $9^{x+2} = 3^{3x-3}$

(c) $x = \log_2 5$

(d) $4^{2x+1} = 98$

(e) $15 = \log_3 x$

(f) $2 \log_3 x - \log_3 (x - 2) = 2$

(g) $\log_2 x^2 = \log_2 9 + \log_2 16$

(h) $\log_2 (x + 6) - \log_2 (x - 3) = 3$

11. The half-life of carbon-14 is about 5730 years. How much of a 12-g sample will remain after 4500 years?

12. Amy invests $4000 at 8%/a, compounded quarterly. How long will it take for the $4000 to grow to $5000?

13. The population of a city was 40 000 in 1980. The population grew exponentially to 76 000 in 1995. When did the population reach 100 000?

14. Let $f(x)$ and $g(x)$ be functions, with $g(x) \neq 0$. State the derivative of each function.

(a) $F(x) = f(x) \cdot g(x)$

(b) $F(x) = \dfrac{f(x)}{g(x)}$

(c) $F(x) = f(g(x))$

(d) $F(x) = cf(x)$

15. Discuss each function in terms of

i. domain

ii. intercepts

iii. asymptotes

iv. intervals of increase and decrease

v. local maximum and minimum values

vi. concavity

Then graph the function.

(a) $f(x) = 2x^3 + 3x^2$

(b) $f(x) = \dfrac{x^2}{x + 4}$

(c) $f(x) = \sqrt{2x - 4}$

(d) $f(x) = \dfrac{x}{x^2 + 1}$

7.1 Introducing a Special Number, e

SETTING THE STAGE

 Explore the concepts in this section in more detail using Exploration 14 on page 586.

You know π and i are special numbers. You have calculated the area and circumference of a circle using the formulas $A = \pi r^2$ and $C = \pi d$. You have also solved quadratic equations and found complex roots, for example, $2 + i$ and $2 - i$, where $i^2 = -1$. The number e is also a special number.

The letter e honours the Swiss mathematician Leonard Euler (1707–1783), whose last name is pronounced *oiler*. Euler also developed the symbol π. He was the first to use the symbol i to represent imaginary numbers.

In this section, you will develop an understanding of the significance and usefulness of the special number e.

EXAMINING THE CONCEPT

Defining the Number e

π and e are both irrational numbers.

Locate the e^x key on your calculator. Use 1 for x and calculate the value of e. The numerical value of e is 2.718 281 828 … .

There are several ways to describe e. One way is to define e as a limit.

---

e as a Limit

$e = \lim\limits_{x \to \infty} \left(1 + \dfrac{1}{x}\right)^x$. This limit is called the **Fundamental Limit of Calculus**.

---

x	$y = \left(1 + \dfrac{1}{x}\right)^x$
1	2
2	2.25
3	2.3704
…	…
100	2.7048
1 000	2.7169
100 000	?

This limit suggests that as x gets larger without bound, the value of $\left(1 + \dfrac{1}{x}\right)^x$ approaches the number e. To find this limit, make a table of values of $y = \left(1 + \dfrac{1}{x}\right)^x$ and sketch the graph. Create the table by hand or by using the TI-83 Plus calculator.

As you can see, y approaches a limiting value. This number, which is e, is 2.718 281 828 … .

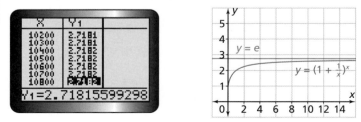

x	$y = (1 + x)^{\frac{1}{x}}$
−1.0	undefined
−0.1	2.867 971 99
−0.01	2.731 999 03
−0.001	2.719 642 22
−0.0001	2.718 417 76
0	undefined
0.00001	2.718 268 24
0.0001	2.718 145 93
0.001	2.716 923 93
0.01	2.704 813 83
0.1	2.593 742 46
1.0	2.0

A second limit can also be used to define e, $e = \lim_{x \to 0} (1 + x)^{\frac{1}{x}}$.

Creating a table or graph of $y = (1 + x)^{\frac{1}{x}}$ verifies this.

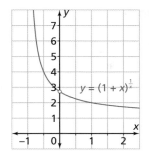

In both the table and graph, $y \to e$ as $x \to 0$. e often appears as a base in algebraic models for exponential growth and exponential decay. To investigate why, first graph some of these models.

Example 1

The Graph of $y = e^x$

Graph each function.

(a) $y = e^x$ **(b)** $y = 2e^x$ **(c)** $y = 3 - e^x$

Solution

(a) Start with a table.

Now plot the ordered pairs from the table. The function has a horizontal asymptote $y = 0$ and y-intercept of 1.

x	$y = e^x$
−1	0.37
0	1
1	2.72
2	7.39

The graphs of two of these functions, $y = e^x$ and $y = 2e^x$, behave like the graph of the exponential function $y = c(a)^x$, $a > 1$.

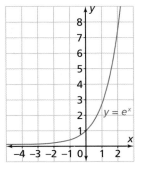

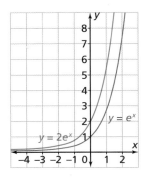

(b) The graph of $y = 2e^x$ on the left is the result of vertically stretching the graph of $y = e^x$ by a factor of 2. The horizontal asymptote remains $y = 0$, but the y-intercept is now 2.

(c) The graph of $y = 3 - e^x$ on the right is the result of reflecting the graph of $y = e^x$ in the x-axis and vertically translating the graph of $y = e^x$ up 3 units. The horizontal asymptote is $y = 3$ and the y-intercept is 2.

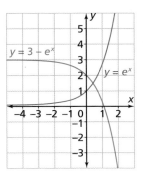

The number e is commonly used in applications involving exponential growth, such as compound interest.

Example 2 **Using the Limit Definition of e for Continuously Compounded Interest**

Find the amount that $1000 will grow to after two years if the money is invested at 10%/a,

(a) compounded annually　　　　　　**(b)** compounded quarterly

(c) compounded n times a year　　　　**(d)** compounded continuously

Solution

In all cases, $P = 1000$.

Recall the formula for compound interest, $A = P(1 + i)^n$, where P is the original principal, i is the interest rate per compounding period, and n is the number of compounding periods.

(a) $i = 10\%$, or 0.1, and $n = 2$ (two years).

$$A = 1000(1.1)^2 \qquad \text{Evaluate.}$$
$$= 1210$$

Therefore, the investment will be worth $1210.00 at the end of two years.

(b) $i = \dfrac{10\%}{4} = 2.5\%$ or 0.025, and $n = 4 \times 2$, or 8.

$$A = 1000(1.025)^8 \qquad \text{Evaluate.}$$
$$= 1218.40$$

Therefore, the investment will be worth $1218.40 at the end of two years.

(c) Interest is compounded n times each year. So $i = \dfrac{10\%}{n}$, or $\dfrac{0.1}{n}$, and the total number of compounding periods is $2n$.

$$A = 1000\left(1 + \frac{0.1}{n}\right)^{2n}$$

(d) When interest is compounded continuously, the number of compounding periods per year increases without bound, $n \to \infty$. So the amount is

$$A = \lim_{n \to \infty} 1000\left(1 + \frac{0.1}{n}\right)^{2n}$$

Let $\dfrac{0.1}{n} = \dfrac{1}{m}$. Then $n = 0.1m$ and $2n = 0.2m$.

$$A = \lim_{m \to \infty} 1000\left(1 + \frac{1}{m}\right)^{0.2m}$$
$$= 1000 \lim_{m \to \infty} \left(1 + \frac{1}{m}\right)^{0.2m}$$

Recall $\lim\limits_{x \to \infty} \left(1 + \dfrac{1}{x}\right)^x = e.$

$$= 1000\left[\lim_{m \to \infty} \left(1 + \frac{1}{m}\right)^m\right]^{0.2}$$
$$= 1000e^{0.2}$$
$$= 1221.40$$

Therefore, the value of the investment, with continuously compounded interest, is $1221.40.

• • • • • • • •

Amount and Continuous Compound Interest

$A = P(e)^{in}$ determines the amount, A, that an initial principal P will grow to under continuous compound interest. i is the interest rate and n is the number of years.

How does $A = P(e)^{in}$ compare with $y = c(a)^x$?

Example 3   **Application of Continuous Compound Interest**

Find the amount, or value, of \$10 000 if the money is invested at 8.5%/a for 15 years, and the interest is compounded continuously.

Solution

Use $A = P(e)^{in}$, where $P = 10\ 000$, $i = 8.5\%$, or 0.085, and $n = 15$.

$$
\begin{aligned}
A &= P(e)^{in} \\
&= 10\ 000 e^{(0.085)(15)} \\
&= 10\ 000 e^{1.275} \\
&\doteq 35\ 787.01
\end{aligned}
$$

Therefore, \$10 000 will grow exponentially to \$35 787.01 at the end of 15 years if interest is compounded continuously.

**Leonhard Euler
(1707–1783)**

Euler contributed to almost every branch of mathematics, and was one of the first people to use calculus to solve real-life problems. He wrote on many topics, including physics, optics, magnetism, astronomy, and shipbuilding. Even in the last 17 years of his life, when he was blind, he continued to write long papers on mathematics.

CHECK, CONSOLIDATE, COMMUNICATE

1. What is an irrational number?
2. Explain how to estimate the numerical value of e using the limit definitions for e.
3. How is interest that is continuously compounded different from interest that is compounded every half year? every quarter year?

KEY IDEAS

- e is an irrational number like π.
- e can be defined using two different limits.
  - $e = \lim\limits_{x \to \infty} \left(1 + \dfrac{1}{x}\right)^x$ is called the **Fundamental Limit of Calculus**.
  - $e = \lim\limits_{x \to 0} (1 + x)^{\frac{1}{x}}$
- The formula for continuous compound interest is $A = P(e)^{in}$, where P is the principal amount invested, i is the interest rate, and n is the number of years.

7.1 Exercises

(A) 1. **Knowledge and Understanding:** Find the amount $100 grows to if invested at 10%/a for 12 years and interest is compounded continuously.

2. Graph $y = e^x$. On the same set of axes, graph each function. Describe each new graph in terms of the transformations applied on $y = e^x$.

   (a) $y = -e^x$ **(b)** $y = 2e^x + 1$ **(c)** $y = 3 - e^x$

3. The numbers π and e are irrational. Use a calculator to answer these questions.

   (a) Compare $\pi^4 + \pi^5$ with e^6. **(b)** Which is larger, e^π or π^e?

(B) 4. Graph each function and state the domain and range.

   (a) $y = 2e^x - 1$ **(b)** $y = 3e^{-x}$
   (c) $y = 4 - e^x$ **(d)** $y = e^{2x}$

5. Use graphing technology to graph $y = (1 + x)^{\frac{1}{x}}$.

   (a) Determine $\lim\limits_{x \to 0} (1 + x)^{\frac{1}{x}}$.

   (b) What does this limit represent?

6. Amy invests $5000 at 6%/a, compounded continuously.

   (a) Determine an equation for the value of this investment over t years.

   (b) Graph the value of this investment for a period of 25 years.

   (c) At what time will the investment double in value? Use your graph to estimate the answer.

7. Use graphing technology to graph $y = \left(1 + \dfrac{1}{x}\right)^x$.

   (a) Determine $\lim\limits_{x \to \infty} \left(1 + \dfrac{1}{x}\right)^x$.

   (b) What does this limit represent?

8. **Application:** Many bridges have arches that resemble parabolas but are not quite parabolic. This kind of shape is called a catenary curve. You can make a catenary curve if you hold a rope by both ends, one end in each hand, and let the rope swing freely. One model for a catenary curve is

$$y = \frac{a}{2}\left(e^{\frac{x}{a}} + e^{-\frac{x}{a}}\right)$$

where a is a real, nonzero constant.

   (a) Create an equation for a catenary curve by letting $a = 2$, so

   $y = \left(e^{\frac{x}{2}} + e^{-\frac{x}{2}}\right)$. Graph this function. Compare the graph with the shape of a parabola.

(b) Determine the equation of a parabola that approximates the catenary curve in (a).

(c) Substitute different values of a into $y = \frac{a}{2}\left(e^{\frac{x}{a}} + e^{-\frac{x}{a}}\right)$. Determine how the value of a changes the shape of a catenary curve.

9. **Thinking, Inquiry, Problem Solving:** Explain how e can be equal to two different limits, that is, $e = \lim_{x \to \infty} \left(1 + \frac{1}{x}\right)^x$ and $e = \lim_{x \to 0} (1 + x)^{\frac{1}{x}}$.

   Compare $\left(1 + \frac{1}{x}\right)^x$ and $(1 + x)^{\frac{1}{x}}$.

10. The rapid growth in the population of a type of insect is given by $P(t) = 5000e^{0.02t}$, where t is the number of days.

    (a) What is the initial population ($t = 0$)?

    (b) How many insects will there be after a week?

    (c) How many insects will there be after a month (30 days)?

11. If the average inflation rate for the next 30 years is 3% each year, how much will a coffee cost when you are 35 years old if a cup is $1.25 now?

12. **Communication**

    (a) Another expression for e is $e = 1 + \frac{1}{1!} + \frac{1}{2!} + \frac{1}{3!} + \frac{1}{4!} + \frac{1}{5!} + \cdots$.

    Evaluate this expression using four, five, six, and seven consecutive terms of this expression. (Note: 2! is read "two factorial." $2! = 2 \times 1$ and $5! = 5 \times 4 \times 3 \times 2 \times 1$)

    (b) Explain why the expression for e in (a) is a special case of
    $$e^x = 1 + \frac{x^1}{1!} + \frac{x^2}{2!} + \frac{x^3}{3!} + \frac{x^4}{4!} + \cdots .$$ What is the value of x?

13. **Check Your Understanding:** List everything you know about e and $y = e^x$.

C 14. Graph $y = e^x$.

    (a) Draw a tangent to the curve at the point where $x = 0, 1, 2, 3, 4,$ and 5. Use your estimation skills to draw each tangent.

    (b) Estimate the slope of each tangent using slope $= \frac{\text{rise}}{\text{run}}$. Copy and complete the table.

x	y	Estimated Slope of Tangent at (x, y)
0	1	
1	e (2.718 281 828 ...)	
2		
3		
4		
5		

    (c) Discuss any patterns that you see in the table.

15. Show that $e^x = \lim\limits_{n \to \infty} \left(1 + \dfrac{x}{n}\right)^n$.

ADDITIONAL ACHIEVEMENT CHART QUESTIONS

Knowledge and Understanding: A sum of money was invested at 8%/a for six years and interest was compounded continuously. If $808 had accumulated, how much was invested?

Application: Geils invested $600 for five years at 5%/a compounded quarterly. How much more interest would she have earned if she had invested the money at 5%/a compounded continuously?

Thinking, Inquiry, Problem Solving: A substance was injected into a patient's system. The amount of the substance left in the patient's system after d days is modelled by $y = 65e^{-0.45d}$.

(a) Find $\lim\limits_{d \to \infty} 65e^{-0.45d}$.

(b) Explain what the result in (a) represents, and why the limit produced the answer it did.

Communication: Describe the graphs of $y = e^x$, $y = e^{-x}$, and $y = -e^x$. Include a discussion of when the functions are increasing and decreasing, as well as stating the asymptotes.

The Chapter Problem
Rabbit Population

Apply what you learned in this section to answer these questions about The Chapter Problem on page 504.

CP1. Graph the ordered pairs in the table about the rabbit population on page 504.

CP2. In Chapter 2, you modelled populations with $y = c(a)^x$. Do you think this model will work for a portion of the data? If so, which portion? Explain.

CP3. Create a model using $y = c(a)^x$ to fit this portion of the data.

7.2 The Derivative of $y = e^x$

SETTING THE STAGE

You can define e in a few ways, and you know some formulas involving e. You have also graphed functions with base e and described transformations of these graphs.

Why is e used as a base in exponential functions? What is the derivative of $y = e^x$? In this section, you will differentiate exponential functions with base e.

EXAMINING THE CONCEPT

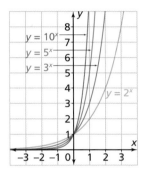

The Exponential Function $y = e^x$ and Its Derivative

In Chapter 2, you graphed the exponential function $y = a^x$. The graph on the left shows the graphs of $y = 2^x$, $y = 3^x$, $y = 5^x$, and $y = 10^x$. All of the graphs pass through point $(0, 1)$.

Where would you draw the graph of $y = e^x$ in the diagram? Recall that e is between 2 and 3.

Using this diagram and a ruler, you could estimate the slope of the tangent to each of these curves at point $(0, 1)$. You would see that the slope of the tangent at $(0, 1)$ becomes greater as a in $y = a^x$ becomes greater. You might also see that, for $y = 2^x$, the slope of the tangent appears to be less than 1. For $y = 3^x$, the slope of the tangent appears to be greater than 1.

In the graph of $y = e^x$, the slope of the tangent at $(0, 1)$ is 1.

What is the slope of the tangent to the curve of $y = e^x$ at other points?

Recall that one interpretation of the derivative is the slope of the tangent to the curve at a point.

Example 1 The Derivative of $y = e^x$

Find the derivative of $y = e^x$ by examining the graph of $y = e^x$.

Solution

Examine the slope of the tangent to $y = e^x$ at any point on the graph.

Let $P(0, 1)$ and $Q(h, e^h)$ be two points on the graph.

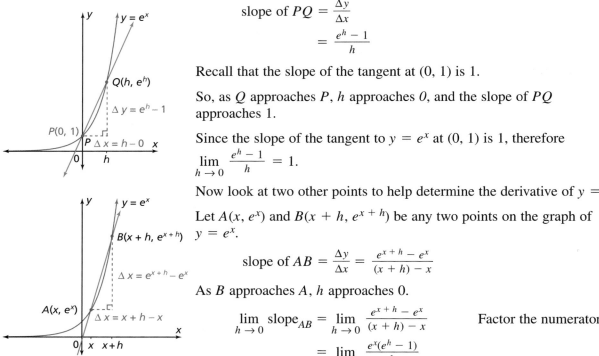

$$\text{slope of } PQ = \frac{\Delta y}{\Delta x}$$

$$= \frac{e^h - 1}{h}$$

Recall that the slope of the tangent at $(0, 1)$ is 1.

So, as Q approaches P, h approaches 0, and the slope of PQ approaches 1.

Since the slope of the tangent to $y = e^x$ at $(0, 1)$ is 1, therefore

$$\lim_{h \to 0} \frac{e^h - 1}{h} = 1.$$

Now look at two other points to help determine the derivative of $y = e^x$.

Let $A(x, e^x)$ and $B(x + h, e^{x+h})$ be any two points on the graph of $y = e^x$.

$$\text{slope of } AB = \frac{\Delta y}{\Delta x} = \frac{e^{x+h} - e^x}{(x + h) - x}$$

As B approaches A, h approaches 0.

$$\lim_{h \to 0} \text{slope}_{AB} = \lim_{h \to 0} \frac{e^{x+h} - e^x}{(x + h) - x} \qquad \text{Factor the numerator.}$$

$$= \lim_{h \to 0} \frac{e^x(e^h - 1)}{h}$$

$$= e^x \left(\lim_{h \to 0} \frac{e^h - 1}{h} \right) \qquad \lim_{h \to 0} \frac{e^h - 1}{h} = 1$$

$$= e^x(1) \qquad \text{Evaluate.}$$

$$= e^x$$

$$\therefore \frac{d}{dx}(e^x) = e^x$$

· · · · · · · ·

The Derivative of $y = e^x$

The derivative of $y = e^x$ is $y' = e^x$, or $\dfrac{dy}{dx} = e^x$.

In Leibniz notation, $\dfrac{d[e^x]}{dx} = e^x$.

The function $y = e^x$ has a special property. The slope of the tangent at each point on the curve is the value of the function at that point.

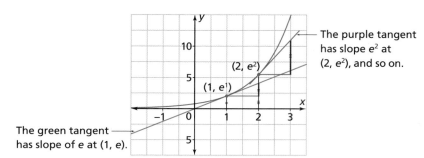

The purple tangent has slope e^2 at $(2, e^2)$, and so on.

The green tangent has slope of e at $(1, e)$.

In this graph of $y = e^x$, the slope of the tangent at each point is the same as the y-coordinate of the point.

You can find the derivatives of other exponential functions with base e using the fact that $\frac{d}{dx}(e^x) = e^x$, along with other derivative rules.

Example 2 **Finding Derivatives of Other Functions Involving e^x**

Find the derivative of $y = e^{3x}$.

Solution

To find the derivative of $y = e^{3x}$, use the chain rule.

$$\frac{dy}{dx} = \frac{d(e^{3x})}{dx} \qquad\qquad \text{Apply the chain rule.}$$

$$= \frac{d(e^{3x})}{d(3x)} \cdot \frac{d(3x)}{dx}$$

$$= e^{3x} \cdot 3$$

$$= 3e^{3x}$$

· · · · · · · ·

The Derivative of a Composite Function Involving $y = e^x$

If $y = e^{f(x)}$, then $\frac{dy}{dx} = f'(x)e^{f(x)}$. In Leibniz notation,

$$\frac{d}{dx}[e^{f(x)}] = \frac{d[e^{f(x)}]}{d[f(x)]} \cdot \frac{d[f(x)]}{dx} = e^{f(x)} \cdot f'(x) \text{ or } f'(x) \cdot e^{f(x)}.$$

Example 3 **Products and Quotients with $y = e^x$**

Find the derivative of $y = (3x^2)(e^{2x})$.

Solution

To find the derivative of $y = (3x^2)(e^{2x})$, use the product rule.

$$y = (3x^2) \times (e^{2x}) \qquad\qquad \text{Apply the product rule.}$$

$$\frac{dy}{dx} = \frac{d(3x^2)}{dx}(e^{2x}) + \frac{d(e^{2x})}{dx}(3x^2) \qquad\qquad \text{Find the derivatives.}$$

$$= (6x)(e^{2x}) + (2)e^{2x}(3x^2) \qquad\qquad \text{Simplify.}$$

$$= 6xe^{2x} + 6x^2e^{2x} \qquad\qquad \text{Factor.}$$

$$= 6xe^{2x}(1 + x)$$

· · · · · · · ·

Example 4 **Equations of Tangents**

Find the equation of the tangent line to the curve $y = 2xe^{2x} + 2$ at $x = 0$.

Solution

First find the derivative of y.

$$y = (2x)(e^{2x}) + 2 \qquad\qquad \text{Use the product and sum rules.}$$

$$\frac{dy}{dx} = \frac{d(2x)}{dx}(e^{2x}) + \frac{d(e^{2x})}{dx}(2x) + \frac{d}{dx}(2)$$

$$= (2)e^{2x} + (2)(e^{2x})(2x) + 0$$

$$= 2e^{2x} + 4xe^{2x} \qquad\qquad \text{Factor out } 2e^{2x}.$$

$$= 2e^{2x}(1 + 2x)$$

Next find the slope of the tangent. Substitute $x = 0$ into $\frac{dy}{dx}$.

$$\frac{dy}{dx}\Big|_{x=0} = 2e^{2(0)}[1 + 2(0)]$$

$$= 2$$

Therefore, the slope of the tangent is 2. To find the equation of the tangent, you need another point on the tangent curve. Find the point on the curve where $x = 0$, since this point will also be on the tangent.

$$y = 2xe^{2x} + 2 \qquad\qquad \text{Substitute } x = 0.$$

$$= 2(0)e^0 + 2 \qquad\qquad \text{Evaluate.}$$

$$= 2$$

So the tangent has slope 2 and passes through point $(0, 2)$. Now find the y-intercept, b, in the point-slope form $y = mx + b$, where $m = 2$.

$$y = 2x + b \qquad\qquad \text{Substitute } x = 0 \text{ and } y = 2.$$

$$2 = 2(0) + b \qquad\qquad \text{Solve for } b.$$

$$b = 2$$

Therefore, the equation of the tangent is $y = 2x + 2$.

$\cdots\cdots\cdots\cdots$

Example 5   **Analyzing Functions Involving $y = e^x$**

Determine where $y = (x + 1)^4 e^{-x}$ is increasing or decreasing. Then graph the function.

Solution

To determine where the function is increasing or decreasing, first find the derivative.

$$y = (x + 1)^4 e^{-x} \qquad\qquad \text{Use the product rule to differentiate.}$$

$$y' = 4(x + 1)^3 e^{-x} - e^{-x}(x + 1)^4 \qquad \text{Factor out } e^{-x}(x + 1)^3.$$

$$= e^{-x}(x + 1)^3 [4 - (x + 1)]$$

$$= e^{-x}(x + 1)^3 (4 - x - 1)$$

$$= e^{-x}(x + 1)^3 (3 - x)$$

To find the critical numbers, let $y' = 0$.

The critical numbers occur when $e^{-x} = 0$, $x + 1 = 0$, and $3 - x = 0$.

But $e^{-x} \neq 0$, so $e^{-x} = 0$ has no solution.

Therefore, the critical numbers are -1 and 3, which divide the domain into three intervals.

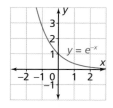

$e^{-x} = \frac{1}{e^x}$

The function $y = e^{-x}$ has a horizontal asymptote $y = 0$.

$\lim\limits_{x \to \infty} e^{-x} = 0$, but $e^{-x} \neq 0$.

Use a table to analyze the derivative and the behaviour of the function in the given intervals.

	Intervals		
	$x < -1$	$-1 < x < 3$	$x > 3$
e^{-x}	+	+	+
$(x + 1)$	–	+	+
$(3 - x)$	+	+	–
$y' = e^{-x}(x + 1)^3(3 - x)$	$(+)(-)(+) = -$	$(+)(+)(+) = +$	$(+)(+)(-) = -$
y	decreasing ↘	increasing ↗	decreasing ↘
	minimum at $x = -1$	maximum at $x = 3$	

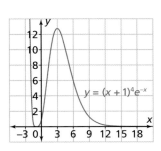

$y = (x + 1)^4 e^{-x}$

Use this information to sketch the graph of $y = (x + 1)^4 e^{-x}$.

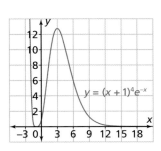

CHECK, CONSOLIDATE, COMMUNICATE

1. Explain why the height of the curve of $y = e^x$ at a point equals the slope of the tangent at that point.
2. Explain how to apply the chain rule to find the derivative of $y = e^{2x+1}$.

KEY IDEAS

- For $y = e^x$, $\dfrac{dy}{dx} = e^x$. Equivalently, $\dfrac{d(e^x)}{dx} = e^x$.
- For $y = e^{f(x)}$, $\dfrac{dy}{dx} = f'(x)e^{f(x)}$. Equivalently, $\dfrac{d[e^{f(x)}]}{dx} = f'(x) \cdot e^{f(x)}$.
- The height of the curve of $y = e^x$ at a point equals the slope of the tangent at that point.
- The rules for differentiating functions, such as the product, quotient, and chain rules, also apply to exponential functions.

7.2 Exercises

A 1. Find the derivative.

(a) $y = e^{2x}$ (b) $y = e^{x + 2}$ (c) $y = 2e^x$

(d) $y = 6 - e^x$ (e) $y = e^x$ (f) $y = 2e^{-x}$

(g) $y = 2x + 3e^x$ (h) $y = e^{2 + 3x}$ (i) $y = 7e^{5x}$

2. For each function, find $f'(x)$ at the given value of x.

   (a) $f(x) = e^{3x}$, $x = 1$
   (b) $f(x) = e^{1-2x}$, $x = 0$
   (c) $f(x) = 2e^{-x}$, $x = 2$
   (d) $f(x) = (e^x + 1)^2$, $x = 0$

3. **Knowledge and Understanding:** Differentiate each function.

   (a) $y = 2xe^x$
   (b) $y = xe^x - e^x$
   (c) $y = 3e^x \times e^{-x}$

   (d) $y = x^4 e^x$
   (e) $y = \dfrac{e^x}{x}$
   (f) $y = x^2 e^x$

   (g) $y = \dfrac{2x^2}{e^x}$
   (h) $y = xe^{-2x}$
   (i) $y = \dfrac{e^x}{x + 2}$

B

4. **Application:** A radioactive substance decays in such a way that the amount left after t years is given by $A = 100\,e^{-0.3t}$. The amount, A, is expressed as a percent. Find the function, A', that describes the rate of decay. What is the rate of decay when 50% of the substance is gone?

5. Find the equation of the tangent to the curve $y = e^{-x}$ at the point where $x = -1$. Graph the original curve and the tangent.

6. For each function, **i.** state the domain and range of the function, **ii.** find $f'(x)$, **iii.** determine the intervals of increase and decrease, and **iv.** graph the function.

   (a) $f(x) = e^{\sqrt{x}}$ (b) $f(x) = e^{-2x}$ (c) $f(x) = 3e^{2x}$ (d) $f(x) = e^x + e^{-x}$

7. Find the equation of the tangent to the curve $y = 2 - e^{-x}$ at the point where $x = 1$. Graph the original curve and the tangent.

8. Given $f(x) = xe^x$, find all x-values for which $f'(x) > 0$. What is the significance of this?

9. Find the equation of the tangent to $y = 2 - xe^x$ at the point where $x = 0$.

10. **Communication:** Is $y = e^x$ the only function that is its own derivative? Give some examples to justify your answer.

11. For $y = x^2 e^{-x}$, find the intervals of increase and decrease. Graph $y = x^2 e^{-x}$.

12. Copy and complete the table.

Exponential Curve	Point through Which Curve Passes	Slope of Tangent at Point
$y = e^x$	(0, 1)	
$y = e^x$	$(3, e^3)$	
	(0, 1)	2
$y = e^{x+2}$		e^3

13. Find the first and second derivatives for each function.

   (a) $y = -3e^x$
   (b) $y = xe^{2x}$
   (c) $y = e^x(4 - x)$

14. Differentiate.

   (a) $y = (2 + 3e^{-x})^3$ (b) $y = x^e$ (c) $y = e^{e^x}$ (d) $y = (1 - e^{5x})^5$

15. **Check Your Understanding:** Explain how to differentiate $y = 2xe^{2x}$.

16. Find the coordinates of the point at which the slope of the tangent is 0 for each function.

(a) $y = xe^x$ (b) $y = -xe^x$ (c) $y = (3 - x^2)e^x$

17. Use implicit differentiation to find the derivative of $x + e^{xy} = y$.

18. **Thinking, Inquiry, Problem Solving**

(a) For $y = e^x$, determine the equations of the tangents at the points where $x = 0$, $x = 1$, $x = 2$, and $x = 3$.

(b) Describe the pattern in the series of equations.

(c) Develop a general formula for the equation of the tangent to $y = e^x$ at $x = a$.

ADDITIONAL ACHIEVEMENT CHART QUESTIONS

Knowledge and Understanding: Find the derivative of each function.

(a) $y = e^x$ (b) $y = e^{x-1}$ (c) $y = (3x^4)e^{\frac{x}{2}}$ (d) $y = \dfrac{e^{\sqrt{x-1}}}{4x + 5}$

Application: The atmospheric pressure, p, varies with the altitude, a, above the Earth's surface. For altitudes less than 10 km, the pressure can be modelled by $p = 760e^{-0.125a}$, where a is in kilometres. At 4.3 km above the Earth's surface, is the pressure increasing or decreasing?

Thinking, Inquiry, Problem Solving: In a medical test, a patient was injected with two different drugs, A and B. The amount, in milligrams, of each drug remaining in the patient's body after d days is modelled by $y_A = 50e^{-0.7d}$ and $y_B = 75e^{-\frac{d}{2}}$. Which drug decays faster after two days?

Communication: Explain in detail how to find the equation of the line tangent to $y = 3x^2e^{-2x}$ when $x = 2$.

The Chapter Problem
Rabbit Population

Apply what you learned in this section to answer these questions about The Chapter Problem on page 504.

CP4. This section introduced a new model $y = c(e)^{kx}$. Fit this model to the rabbit population data.

CP5. Is the model a good fit? Does the model fit all data?

CP6. What is the rate of change in the population growth, if this rate of change exists?

7.3 The Natural Logarithm and Its Derivative

SETTING THE STAGE

Recall from Chapter 2 that the logarithmic function is the inverse of the exponential function. For example, $y = \log_2 x$ is the inverse of $y = 2^x$. The function $y = e^x$ also has an inverse, $y = \log_e x$. The function $y = \log_e x$ can be written as $y = \ln x$.

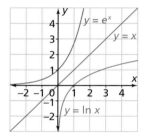

Definition of the Natural Logarithm

The function $y = \ln x$ is the logarithmic function with base e and is called the natural logarithm function. As a result, it is equivalent to $x = e^y$. $y = \ln x$ is the inverse of $y = e^x$.

What types of properties does the natural logarithm function have? Does this function behave like other logarithmic functions? What is the derivative of this function? In this section, you will investigate the characteristics of the natural logarithm function and determine differentiation techniques involving this function.

EXAMINING THE CONCEPT

The Natural Logarithm

Begin by looking at the natural logarithm function from a numerical viewpoint.

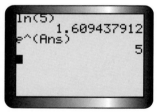

Evaluate the natural logarithm of a number using your calculator. For example, find $\ln 5$ using your calculator. The graphing calculator screen shows that $\ln 5$ is about 1.609 437 912. The screen also shows that $e^{\ln 5} = 5$, or $e^{1.609\ 437\ 912\ \cdots} = 5$, and that $y = \ln x$ and $y = e^x$ are inverses of one another.

Evaluate $\ln 2$, $\ln 5$, and $\ln 10$ using your calculator. How are these values related?

Evaluate $\ln 2$ and $\ln 2^{10}$. How are these values related?

The laws for logarithms that you learned in Chapter 2 apply to natural logarithms.

$$\ln ab = \ln a + \ln b$$
$$\ln \left(\frac{a}{b}\right) = \ln a - \ln b$$
$$\ln a^p = p \ln a$$

Example 1   **Solving Exponential Equations Involving *e***

Solve for x.

$$e^{x + 2} = 18.56$$

Solution

To solve this exponential equation, change it to logarithmic form.

exponential form	logarithmic form
$e^{x + 2} = 18.56$	$\ln 18.56 = x + 2$

Therefore, $x = \ln 18.56 - 2$, or about 0.921.

EXAMINING THE CONCEPT

Finding the Derivative of *y* = ln *x*

What is the derivative of the natural logarithm, $y = \ln x$?

You will find it helpful to change $y = \ln x$ to exponential form.

Since $y = \ln x$ is the same as $y = \log_e x$, $x = e^y$.

$$x = e^y \qquad \text{Use implicit differentiation to differentiate with respect to } x.$$

$$\frac{d(x)}{dx} = \frac{d(e^y)}{dx} \qquad \text{Use the chain rule.}$$

$$\frac{d(x)}{dx} = \frac{d(e^y)}{dy} \times \frac{dy}{dx} \qquad \text{Simplify.}$$

$$1 = e^y \times \frac{dy}{dx} \qquad \text{Solve for } \frac{dy}{dx}.$$

$$\frac{dy}{dx} = \frac{1}{e^y} \qquad \text{Recall that } x = e^y.$$

$$\frac{dy}{dx} = \frac{1}{x}$$

The Derivative of *y* = ln *x*

If $y = \ln x$, then $\frac{dy}{dx} = \frac{1}{x}$. In Leibniz notation, $\frac{d[\ln (x)]}{dx} = \frac{1}{x}$.

Example 2   **Finding the Derivative of a Function Involving the Natural Logarithm**

Find $\frac{dy}{dx}$ for $y = \ln x^4$.

Solution

You can think of $y = \ln x^4$ as the composite function $y = f(g(x))$, where $f(x) = \ln x$, and $g(x) = x^4$. As a result, use the chain rule.

$$y = \ln x^4$$

$$\frac{dy}{dx} = \frac{d[\ln x^4]}{dx}$$
Use the chain rule.

$$= \frac{d(\ln x^4)}{d(x^4)} \cdot \frac{d(x^4)}{dx}$$
Simplify.

$$= \frac{1}{x^4} \cdot 4x^3$$

$$= \frac{4}{x}$$

• • • • • • • •

Generalizing, we apply results of Example 2 to any natural logarithmic function.

The Derivative of a Composite Function Involving $y = \ln x$

If $y = \ln (f(x))$, then $\dfrac{dy}{dx} = \dfrac{1}{f(x)} \cdot f'(x)$ or $\dfrac{dy}{dx} = \dfrac{f'(x)}{f(x)}$.

In Leibniz notation, $\dfrac{d[\ln (f(x))]}{dx} = \dfrac{d[\ln (f(x))]}{d[f(x)]} \cdot \dfrac{d[f(x)]}{dx} = \dfrac{f'(x)}{f(x)}$.

An alternative solution is to first simplify using the laws of logarithms.

So rewrite $y = \ln x^4$ as $y = 4 \ln x$.

$$\frac{dy}{dx} = 4\left(\frac{1}{x}\right)$$

$$= \frac{4}{x}$$

Example 3 **Finding the Derivative without Using the Quotient Rule or the Product Rule**

Given $y = \ln \dfrac{x + 3}{x^3}$, find $\dfrac{dy}{dx}$.

Solution
First use the laws of logarithms to expand the expression.

$$y = \ln (x + 3) - \ln (x^3)$$
Differentiate each term using the chain rule.

$$\frac{dy}{dx} = \left[\frac{d[\ln (x + 3)]}{d(x + 3)} \cdot \frac{d(x + 3)}{dx} \right] - \left[\frac{d(\ln x^3)}{d(x^3)} \cdot \frac{d(x^3)}{dx} \right]$$
Simplify.

$$= \left[\frac{1}{x + 3} \cdot 1 \right] - \left[\frac{1}{x^3} \cdot (3x^2) \right]$$
Simplify further.

$$= \frac{1}{x + 3} - \frac{3}{x}$$
Find the common denominator.

$$= \frac{x - 3(x + 3)}{x(x + 3)}$$
Multiply and collect like terms in the numerator.

$$= \frac{-2x - 9}{x(x + 3)}$$

You could also find the derivative in this case using the quotient rule.

• • • • • • • •

Example 4

Using the Natural Logarithm to Find Logarithms with Other Bases

A scientific or graphing calculator can be used to find an approximate value of a logarithm only when the base is 10 or *e*.

Find $\log_3 6$ using the natural logarithm.

Solution

Let $\log_3 6 = y$.

$$\log_3 6 = y \qquad \text{Change to exponential form.}$$
$$3^y = 6 \qquad \text{Take the ln of each side.}$$
$$\ln 3^y = \ln 6$$
$$y \ln 3 = \ln 6$$
$$y = \frac{\ln 6}{\ln 3}$$
$$y \doteq 1.63$$

Use this example to determine a general formula for finding $\log_b x$.

Let $y = \log_b x$.

$$y = \log_b x \qquad \text{Change to exponential form.}$$
$$b^y = x \qquad \text{Take the ln of each side.}$$
$$\ln b^y = \ln x$$
$$y \ln b = \ln x \qquad \text{Solve for } y.$$
$$y = \frac{\ln x}{\ln b}$$

Evaluating Logarithms without a Base of 10

$$\log_b x = \frac{\ln x}{\ln b} \quad \text{or} \quad \log_b x = \frac{\log x}{\log b}$$

This method evaluates a logarithm with a different base by using the logarithm to the base 10 or the base *e*.

CHECK, CONSOLIDATE, COMMUNICATE

1. Give an example of each of the three laws of natural logarithms.
2. Find $\log_3 28$ using two methods, one with the natural logarithm, ln, and one with the logarithm, log. Compare your results.
3. Logarithmic and exponential functions work together. Find a problem in this section or elsewhere that requires you to use both functions to solve the problem.

- The laws of logarithms also hold true for the natural logarithm, ln.
  - $\ln (ab) = \ln a + \ln b$
  - $\ln \dfrac{a}{b} = \ln a - \ln b$
  - $\ln a^p = p \ln a$
- If $y = \ln x$, then $\dfrac{dy}{dx} = \dfrac{1}{x}$. If $y = \ln (f(x))$, then $\dfrac{dy}{dx} = \dfrac{f'(x)}{f(x)}$.

  Equivalently, $\dfrac{d[\ln (x)]}{dx} = \dfrac{1}{x}$ and $\dfrac{d[\ln (f(x))]}{dx} = \dfrac{f'(x)}{f(x)}$.
- Rules for finding derivatives, such as the product, quotient, and chain rules, also apply to exponential functions.
- To evaluate a logarithm without a base of 10, use $\log_b x = \dfrac{\ln x}{\ln b}$ or $\log_b x = \dfrac{\log x}{\log b}$.

7.3   Exercises

(A)   **1.** Solve for x, to three decimal places. First change each function to logarithmic form.

    (a) $e^x = 5$ **(b)** $e^x = 16$ **(c)** $e^{2x} = 12$

    (d) $e^x + e^x = 8$ **(e)** $e^{x-2} = 28$ **(f)** $e^{x+1} = 5$

2. Differentiate.

    (a) $y = \ln 3x$ **(b)** $y = \ln (x + 2)$ **(c)** $y = \ln x^3$

    (d) $y = \ln \sqrt{x}$ **(e)** $y = \ln 3x^4$ **(f)** $y = \ln (2x - 5)$

    (g) $y = \ln (3x^5)$ **(h)** $y = \ln (3x)^5$ **(i)** $y = \ln x^6$

    (j) $y = \ln x^{-2}$ **(k)** $y = \ln (8x^3 + 4)$ **(l)** $y = 6 \ln (x^2 + 3x)$

3. Use your calculator to help answer these questions. Explain each result.

    (a) Evaluate $\ln 2$, $\ln 3$, and $\ln 6$. How are your results related?

    (b) Evaluate $\ln 20$, $\ln 5$, and $\ln 4$. How are your results related?

    (c) Evaluate $\ln 3$ and $\ln 3^5$. How are your results related?

4. Express as a single natural logarithm.

    (a) $\ln 6 + \ln 4$ **(b)** $\ln 5 + \ln 8$ **(c)** $\ln 40 - \ln 5$

    (d) $4 \ln 23$ **(e)** $\ln 81 - \ln 3$ **(f)** $2 \ln 18 - \ln 9$

5. Verify your answers to question 4 with a calculator.

6. Solve for x, to three decimal places.

(a) $e^x = 16$

(b) $\ln (x - 1)^2 = 4$

(c) $e^{2x} = 125$

(d) $\ln x = 2$

7. **Knowledge and Understanding:** Find $\dfrac{dy}{dx}$ for each function.

(a) $y = \sqrt{\ln x}$

(b) $y = \dfrac{\ln x}{x^3}$

(c) $y = \ln e^{3x}$

(d) $y = \ln 6x + \ln 2x$

(e) $y = x^4 \ln x$

(f) $y = \dfrac{\ln 6x}{\ln 2x}$

(g) $y = \ln 10x^8$

(h) $y = \ln x + \ln x^2 + \ln x^3 + \ln x^4$

(i) $y = \ln (8x^2 + 2)^4$

(j) $y = \sqrt{e} \ln 3$

(k) $y = \ln 3x^7$

(l) $y = (e^{2x})(\ln x^3)$

8. Express as a single logarithm.

(a) $2 \ln x + \ln 2x$

(b) $3 \ln 4x^2 - 2 \ln x$

(c) $2 \ln 3x + 3 \ln (2x - 1)$

(d) $2 \ln x + 3 \ln y$

(e) $\left(\dfrac{1}{2}\right) \ln x - \left(\dfrac{1}{3}\right) \ln y$

(f) $-5 \ln 2x + 6 \ln x$

9. Show that $\log e = \dfrac{1}{\ln 10}$.

10. **Communication:** Determine which is greater: $1 + 3 \ln 2$ or $\ln 8e$. Justify your answer.

B **11.** State the domain of each function. Graph the function.

(a) $y = \ln x + 2$

(b) $y = \ln (x + 2)$

(c) $y = \ln x^2$

(d) $y = 1 - \ln x$

12. **Application:** Choose a strategy to show that $\ln x \leq 1 - x$ for $x \geq 1$.

13. Find $\dfrac{dy}{dx}$ for each function.

(a) $y = x^3 \ln 2x$

(b) $y = (\ln 6x)(\ln 2x)$

(c) $y = \dfrac{\ln x}{2x^3 - 4}$

(d) $y = \ln \left(\dfrac{2x^2 - 3}{2x^3} \right)$

(e) $y = (x + \ln x)^2$

(f) $y = \dfrac{\ln x}{(x + 3)^3}$

(g) $y = e^{x \ln x}$

(h) $y = 3\left(\ln \sqrt{2x + 3} \right)^2$

14. Find the equation of the tangent line to the curve $y = \ln 2x$ at the point where $x = \dfrac{e}{2}$. Graph $y = \ln 2x$ and this tangent at that point.

15. Graph $f(x) = \ln x^2$. Find the equation of the tangent at the point where $x = 3$. Graph the tangent and f.

16. Solve $\ln x = 2 - x$ using graphing technology.

17. You can use the laws of logarithms to verify that $\ln x^2 = 2 \ln x$. Compare the domains of $y = \ln x^2$ and $y = 2 \ln x$.

18. Use graphing technology to verify your comparison in question 17.

19. Find the derivative of each function. Describe the methods for finding them.
(a) $y = \ln 2x^3$
(b) $y = \ln (2x)^3$
(c) $y = (\ln 2x)^3$

20. Find the equation of the tangent to $y = x \ln x$
(a) at $x = e$
(b) that has slope 3

21. Use graphing technology to graph the original function and the two tangents in question 20.

22. Find the second derivative of
(a) $y = \ln x$
(b) $y = \ln x^4$

23. A calculus teacher can estimate the mathematical knowledge, K, that an average student retains over t months using

$$K(t) = 100 - 15 \ln t$$

In this equation, K is measured as a percent.
(a) Graph this function.
(b) How much knowledge does an average student retain after two months?
(c) How much knowledge does an average student retain after a year?
(d) In 25 years, when you are helping your children with their calculus homework, how much of your calculus knowledge will you have retained?
(e) Find $K'(t)$ for $t = 6$, 12, and 24. Is the rate of retention increasing or decreasing?

24. Let $f(x) = \ln (x^2 e^x)$.
(a) Determine $f'(x)$ by first using the laws of logarithms to "expand" the expression.
(b) Determine $f'(x)$ without first simplifying.
(c) Compare the results. Which method do you prefer? Why?

25. **Check Your Understanding:** Compare the slope of the tangent to $y = e^x$ at $(0, 1)$ with the slope of the tangent to $y = \ln x$ at $(1, 0)$. Explain.

26. Use implicit differentiation to find $\dfrac{dy}{dx}$ for each function.

(a) $\ln (xy) = 2 - x - y$ **(b)** $\ln y + 2x = 1$

(c) $\ln (x + y) = 1$ **(d)** $\ln x + \ln y = x$

27. Thinking, Inquiry, Problem Solving: A typical AM radio dial shows that the distances between the numbers are not equal. In fact, the distances decrease as the frequency increases. The distance from 53 to each other frequency varies logarithmically with the frequency. This distance is given by $y = m + n \ln x$, where y is the distance in centimetres, x is the frequency, and m and n are constants.

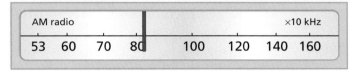

(a) Create a table for each frequency shown. Measure the distance with a metric ruler, to the nearest tenth of a centimetre.

(b) Determine the values for m and n in the equation $y = m + n \ln x$ for the dial shown. Create an equation for the distances in this particular dial. Determine how well your equation fits your table for (a).

(c) Find the derivative and the instantaneous rates of change of the distances with respect to the frequency. Is the function increasing or decreasing?

28. For $f(x) = \ln (\ln x)$,

(a) find $f'(x)$

(b) state the domains of $f(x)$ and $f'(x)$

ADDITIONAL ACHIEVEMENT CHART QUESTIONS

Knowledge and Understanding: Find the derivative of each function.

(a) $y = 6 \ln x$ **(b)** $y = -\ln 9 - x^2$

(c) $y = (\ln 4x)^2$ **(d)** $y = e^{-3x} \ln (2x^5)$

Application: Vasco is going to invest a sum of money for five years at 4.5%/a interest compounded continuously. How long will it take the money to double in value?

Thinking, Inquiry, Problem Solving: Find the maximum and/or minimum point of $y = \dfrac{\ln x}{x}$.

Communication: Explain why the graph of $y = \ln 2x$ is a vertical translation of the graph of $y = \ln x$.

7.4 Differentiating Other Logarithmic and Exponential Functions

SETTING THE STAGE

Many exponential growth formulas do not always have e as a base.

Nadia counts 300 bacteria in a culture at the start of an experiment.

The population will double every two hours. Then $y = 300(2)^{\frac{x}{2}}$ describes the number of bacteria at the end of x hours.

What is the derivative of $y = 300(2)^{\frac{x}{2}}$?

You know how to find the derivative of the natural logarithm function (base e). But what is the derivative of $y = \log_2 x$? The base of this function is 2, not e.

In this section, you will learn how to differentiate a logarithmic function or an exponential function that has a base other than e.

EXAMINING THE CONCEPT

Differentiating a Logarithmic Function Where the Base Is Not e

To differentiate the general logarithmic function $y = \log_a x$, $a > 0$, $a \neq 1$ recall that you can "change the base" by using $\log_a x = \frac{\ln x}{\ln a}$.

To find the derivative, let $y = \frac{\ln x}{\ln a}$.

$$\frac{dy}{dx} = \frac{d\left(\frac{\ln x}{\ln a}\right)}{dx} \qquad \ln a \text{ is a constant.}$$

$$= \frac{1}{\ln a} \times \frac{d(\ln x)}{dx}$$

$$= \frac{1}{\ln a} \times \frac{1}{x}$$

$$= \frac{1}{x \ln a}$$

The Derivative of the Logarithmic Function $y = \log_a x$

If $y = \log_a x$, $a > 0$, then $\frac{dy}{dx} = \frac{1}{x \ln a}$. $(a \neq 1)$

In Leibniz notation, $\frac{d[\log_a x]}{dx} = \frac{1}{x \ln a}$.

Example 1 Finding the Tangent at a Point for a Logarithmic Function

Find the tangent to $y = \log_2 x$ at $(8, 3)$. Graph the curve and the tangent.

Solution

First find the derivative of $y = \log_2 x$.

$$\frac{dy}{dx} = \frac{1}{x \ln 2}$$

The derivative represents the slope of the tangent line.
Now substitute $x = 8$ to find the slope of the tangent at $(8, 3)$.

$$\left. \frac{dy}{dx} \right|_{x=8} = \frac{1}{8 \ln 2}$$

The equation of the tangent at point $(8, 3)$ has the form $y = \frac{1}{8 \ln 2}x + b$.

Substitute $x = 8$ and $y = 3$ into the equation and solve for b.

$$y = \frac{1}{8 \ln 2}x + b \qquad \text{Substitute.}$$

$$3 = \frac{1}{8 \ln 2}(8) + b \qquad \text{Simplify and solve for } b.$$

$$3 - \frac{1}{\ln 2} = b \qquad \text{Evaluate.}$$

$$b \doteq 1.56$$

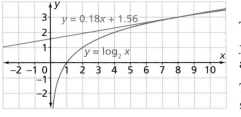

Therefore, the slope, m, is $\frac{1}{8 \ln 2}$, or about 0.18, and the y-intercept, b, is about 1.56. The equation of the tangent is approximately $y = 0.18x + 1.56$.

The original function, $y = \log_2 x$, and the tangent at $(8, 3)$ are shown on the graph.

• • • • • • • •

You can find the derivatives of other logarithmic functions using the fact that $\frac{d}{dx}(\log_a x) = \frac{1}{x \ln a}$, along with other derivative rules.

Example 2   Finding Derivatives of Other Functions Involving $\log_a x$

Find the derivative of $y = \log_5 (3x + 2)^4$.

Solution

To find the derivative of $y = \log_5 (3x + 2)^4$, use the chain rule.

$$\frac{dy}{dx} = \frac{d}{dx}[\log_5 (3x + 2)^4)] \qquad \text{Apply the chain rule.}$$

$$= \frac{d[\log_5 (3x + 2)^4)]}{d[(3x + 2)^4]} \cdot \frac{d[(3x + 2)^4)]}{d(3x + 2)} \cdot \frac{d(3x + 2)}{dx} \qquad \text{Differentiate.}$$

$$= \frac{1}{(3x + 2)^4 \ln 5} \cdot 4(3x + 2)^3(3) \qquad \text{Simplify.}$$

$$= \frac{12(3x + 2)^3}{(3x + 2)^4 \ln 5} \qquad \text{Simplify.}$$

$$= \frac{12}{(3x + 2) \ln 5}$$

• • • • • • • •

The Derivative of a Composite Function Involving $\log_a x$

If $y = \log_a f(x)$, $a > 0$, then $\dfrac{dy}{dx} = \dfrac{1}{f(x)\ln a}\cdot f'(x)$ or $\dfrac{dy}{dx} = \dfrac{f'(x)}{f(x)\ln a}$.

In Leibniz notation, $\dfrac{d[\log f(x)]}{dx} = \dfrac{d[\log f(x)]}{d[f(x)]}\cdot\dfrac{d[f(x)]}{dx} = \dfrac{f'(x)}{f(x)\ln a}$.

EXAMINING THE CONCEPT

Finding the Derivative of $y = a^x$, $a > 0$

To find the derivative of $y = a^x$, use what you know about the derivatives of exponential and logarithmic functions.

Since you know the derivative of $y = \ln x$, use the natural logarithm function to start.

$$y = a^x \qquad \text{Take the ln of each side.}$$
$$\ln y = \ln a^x$$
$$\ln y = x \ln a \qquad \text{Differentiate each side with respect to } x.$$
$$\frac{d(\ln y)}{dx} = \frac{d(x \ln a)}{dx}$$
$$\frac{d(\ln y)}{dy} \times \frac{dy}{dx} = \ln a$$
$$\frac{1}{y} \times \frac{dy}{dx} = \ln a \qquad \text{Solve for } \frac{dy}{dx}.$$
$$\frac{dy}{dx} = y \ln a \qquad \text{Substitute } y = a^x.$$
$$\frac{dy}{dx} = a^x \ln a$$

The Derivative of the Exponential Function $y = a^x$

If $y = a^x$, $a > 0$, then $\dfrac{dy}{dx} = a^x \ln a$. In Leibniz notation, $\dfrac{d[a^x]}{dx} = a^x \ln a$.

Example 3

Finding the Derivative of an Exponential Function

Find the derivative of

(a) $y = 5^x$ (b) $y = 5^{2x-3}$

Solution

(a) $y = 5^x$ Use the derivative for $y = a^x$.

         $\dfrac{dy}{dx} = 5^x \ln 5$

(b) To differentiate $y = 5^{2x-3}$, use the chain rule and the derivative for $y = a^x$.

$$y = 5^{2x-3}$$

$$\frac{dy}{dx} = \frac{d(5^{2x-3})}{d(2x-3)} \cdot \frac{d(2x-3)}{dx} \qquad \text{Simplify.}$$

$$= 2(5^{2x-3})(\ln 5)$$

· · · · · · · · ·

The Derivative of a Composite Function Involving $y = a^x$

If $y = a^{f(x)}$, $a > 0$, then $\dfrac{dy}{dx} = a^{f(x)} \cdot \ln a \cdot f'(x)$.

In Leibniz notation, $\dfrac{d[a^{f(x)}]}{dx} = \dfrac{d[a^{f(x)}]}{d[f(x)]} \cdot \dfrac{d[f(x)]}{dx} = a^{f(x)} \cdot \ln a \cdot f'(x)$.

Example 4 ## Find the Rate of Change in Growth

Recall the situation in Setting the Stage. The number of bacteria, y, in a culture is given by $y = 300(2)^{\frac{x}{2}}$, where x is the number of hours. Determine the rate of change in the growth of the population at

(a) 2 h   **(b)** 6 h   **(c)** 20 h

Solution
To find the rate of change, find the derivative of $y = 300(2)^{\frac{x}{2}}$.

$$y = 300(2)^{\frac{x}{2}} \qquad \text{Use the chain rule.}$$

$$\frac{dy}{dx} = \frac{d\left[300(2)^{\frac{x}{2}}\right]}{dx}$$

$$= \frac{d\left[300(2)^{\frac{x}{2}}\right]}{d\left(\frac{x}{2}\right)} \cdot \frac{d\left(\frac{x}{2}\right)}{dx}$$

$$= \left(2^{\frac{x}{2}} \times 300 \ln 2\right) \cdot \frac{1}{2}$$

$$= (150 \ln 2)\left[(2)^{\frac{x}{2}}\right]$$

To find the rate of change at each time, substitute each x-value into the derivative function.

At 2 h, the rate of change will be 300 ln 2, or about 208 bacteria per hour.

At 6 h, the rate of change will be 1200 ln 2, or about 831.8. So, at 6 h, the rate of change will be about 832 bacteria per hour.

At 20 h, the rate of change will be 153 600 ln 2, or about 106 467.4. So, at 20 h, the rate of change will be about 106 468 bacteria per hour.

CHECK, CONSOLIDATE, COMMUNICATE

1. Why is $\ln a$ a constant?
2. How are the derivatives of $y = a^x$ and $y = \log_a x$ like the derivatives of $y = e^x$ and $y = \ln x$? How are they different?

KEY IDEAS

- If $y = \log_a x$, $a > 0$, then $\dfrac{dy}{dx} = \dfrac{1}{x \ln a}$. Equivalently, $\dfrac{d[\log_a x]}{dx} = \dfrac{1}{x \ln a}$.

- If $y = \log_a f(x)$, $a > 0$, then $\dfrac{dy}{dx} = \dfrac{f'(x)}{f(x) \ln a}$.

  Equivalently, $\dfrac{d[\log_a f(x)]}{dx} = \dfrac{f'(x)}{f(x) \ln a}$.

- If $y = a^x$, $a > 0$, then $\dfrac{dy}{dx} = a^x \ln a$. Equivalently, $\dfrac{d[a^x]}{dx} = a^x \ln a$.

- If $y = a^{f(x)}$, $a > 0$, then $\dfrac{dy}{dx} = a^{f(x)} \cdot \ln a \cdot f'(x)$.

  Equivalently, $\dfrac{d[a^{f(x)}]}{dx} = a^{f(x)} \cdot \ln a \cdot f'(x)$.

- When differentiating a function that involves a logarithmic or exponential function, use the above rules, along with the sum, difference, product, quotient, and chain rules.

7.4 Exercises

A 1. Differentiate.

(a) $y = 5^x$ (b) $y = (0.47)^x$ (c) $y = (52)^{2x}$

(d) $y = 5(2)^x$ (e) $y = 4(e)^x$ (f) $y = -2(10)^{3x}$

2. Find $\dfrac{dy}{dx}$ for each function.

(a) $y = \log_2 x$ (b) $y = \log_3 x$ (c) $y = 2 \log_4 x$

(d) $y = -3 \log_7 x$ (e) $y = -(\log x)$ (f) $y = 3 \log_6 x$

3. **Knowledge and Understanding:** Find $\dfrac{dy}{dx}$ for each function.

(a) $y = \log_3 (x + 2)$ (b) $y = 4^{2x + 1}$ (c) $y = \log_8 (2x)$

(d) $y = -3 \log_3 (2x + 3)$ (e) $y = 400(2)^{x + 3}$ (f) $y = 8^{2x + 5}$

(g) $y = \log_{10} (5 - 2x)$ (h) $y = 10^{2 - 3x}$ (i) $y = \log_8 (2x + 6)$

(j) $y = 100(1.02)^x$

4. Paula invests \$1200 at 12%/a, compounded annually.

(a) What is the amount of the investment after five years?

(b) Determine the equation for $A(t)$, the amount after t years.

(c) Determine an equation for the rate of change of the money's value.

(d) What is the rate of change of the value at five years?

B 5. Differentiate.

(a) $y = x^5 \times (5)^x$

(b) $y = \log_7 (x^2 + x + 1)$

(c) $y = 3^x \log_3 x$

(d) $y = \dfrac{2^{4x}}{x^3}$

(e) $y = 2x \log_4 x$

(f) $y = 3.2(10)^{0.2x}$

(g) $y = 2^x \ln x$

(h) $y = x(3x)^{x^2}$

(i) $y = 3^{\ln x}$

(j) $y = \dfrac{\log_5 3x^4}{5^{2x}}$

6. Jim invests $5000 at 8%/a, compounded annually.

(a) Determine the equation for the amount, $A(t)$, after t years.

(b) Determine an equation for the rate of change of the money's value.

(c) Determine the rate of change of the value at 10 years.

(d) Suppose that interest was compounded quarterly rather than annually. What would be the rate of change at 10 years?

7. Find the equation of the tangent to the curve $y = 3(2^x)$ at the point where $x = 3$.

8. Find the equation of the tangent to the curve $y = 10^x$ at point $(1, 10)$.

9. **Application:** A certain radioactive material decays exponentially. The percent, P, of the material left after t years is given by $P(t) = 100(1.2)^{-t}$.

(a) Determine the half-life of the substance.

(b) How fast is the substance decaying at the point where the half-life is reached?

10. For each function, find $f'(x)$. State the domains of $f(x)$ and $f'(x)$.

(a) $f(x) = \log (5 - 2x)$

(b) $f(x) = 50(1.02)^{4x}$

(c) $f(x) = \log_3 (x^2 - 4)$

(d) $f(x) = \ln (3^x)$

11. Find the equation of the tangent to the curve $y = x \log x$ at the point where $x = 10$. Graph the function and the tangent.

12. Graph $y = 3^x$ and its inverse.

(a) Find the equation of the tangent to the curve $y = 3^x$ at point $(2, 9)$.

(b) Find the equation of the tangent to the inverse at point $(9, 2)$.

(c) Graph both tangents on the same set of axes.

13. $1000 is invested in a savings account that pays 6%/a, compounded annually.

(a) Find the derivative $A'(t)$ of the function.

(b) At what rate is the amount growing at the end of 2 years? 5 years? 10 years?

(c) Is the rate constant?

(d) Determine the ratio of $\dfrac{A'(t)}{A(t)}$ for each value that you determined for $A'(t)$.

(e) What do you notice?

14. Find the equation of the tangent to the curve $y = 2^{-x^2}$ at the point on the curve where $x = 0$. Graph the curve and the tangent at that point.

15. **Check Your Understanding:** Let $y = \log_b u$. Show that $\frac{dy}{dx} = \left(\frac{1}{u \ln b}\right)\frac{du}{dx}$.

C **16.** **Communication:** Explain why the derivative of $y = \log_a kx$, $k > 0$, is $y' = \dfrac{1}{x \ln a}$, for any value of k.

17. **Thinking, Inquiry, Problem Solving:** Determine whether the slope of the graph of $y = 3^x$ at point $(0, 1)$ is greater than the slope of the graph of $y = \log_3 x$ at point $(1, 0)$. Include graphs with your solution.

ADDITIONAL ACHIEVEMENT CHART QUESTIONS

Knowledge and Understanding: Find the derivative of each function.

(a) $y = \log_4 (3x + 1)$ **(b)** $y = x^2 \log_5 x$ **(c)** $y = \log e^x$

(d) $y = 3^{x-1}$ **(e)** $y = 6\left(\dfrac{1}{2}\right)^{-4x}$ **(f)** $y = \log_2 (5x - 1)^3$

Application: At the same time, Rani invests \$500 at 6% compounded semiannually and Pius invests \$500 at 5% compounded quarterly. Whose investment is growing at a faster rate in the 4th year?

Thinking, Inquiry, Problem Solving: A particle's distance in metres from a fixed point at time t seconds is given by $s(t) = t \log_6 t$, $t \geq 0$. Is the distance increasing or decreasing at $t = 15$? How do you know?

Communication: Explain why the identity $\dfrac{d(\log_a x)}{dx} = \dfrac{1}{x} \log_a e$ is the same as the identity $\dfrac{d(\log_a x)}{dx} = \dfrac{1}{x \ln a}$.

The Chapter Problem
Rabbit Population

Apply what you learned in this section to answer these questions about The Chapter Problem on page 504.

In section 7.1 (question CP3), you created a model using $y = c(a)^x$ for a portion of the data.

CP7. Find an equation for the rate of change for your model.

CP8. What is the rate of change of the rabbit population at 5 years? at 10 years?

CP9. How do these rates of change compare with the rate of change that you calculated for question CP6 in section 7.2?

CP10. Which model, $y = c(a)^x$, or the one for the rate of change, is a better fit? Or, are both models the same?

7.5 Sketching Graphs of Exponential and Logarithmic Functions

SETTING THE STAGE

Vitamin C is a nutrient in foods that helps make your body strong. For instance, vitamin C is essential for healthy teeth, gums, and bones. Vitamin C can also help your immune system.

Some people take vitamin C tablets. After a person takes a tablet, the concentration of vitamin C in the person's system rises rapidly and then drops off.

Assume an adult takes a 500-mg tablet of vitamin C. The concentration of vitamin C is given by

$$y = 190t \times (0.65)^t$$

where y is the concentration in parts per million and t is the number of hours after the tablet is taken.

What does the graph of this function look like? When is the concentration of vitamin C the highest? How fast is the concentration changing at 2 h? at 8 h? at 16 h? Suppose a chemist wanted to make a "time-release" vitamin C tablet. What is the algebraic model for the concentration in this case?

In this section, you will use the calculus techniques developed with polynomial, rational, and composite functions to analyze and sketch the graphs of exponential and logarithmic functions.

EXAMINING THE CONCEPT

Graphing Exponential and Logarithmic Functions

Start by graphing the function.

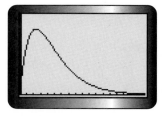

The graph shows that the concentration of vitamin C reaches a maximum after a few hours. Then the concentration rapidly decreases and levels off.

Using the first and second derivatives of the concentration function will help you gather more accurate information.

Examples 1 and 2 discuss this situation.

Example 1 **Finding the Maximum and Minimum Values**

When is the concentration of vitamin C in an adult's system at a maximum?

Solution

To find the maximum concentration, determine the first derivative, $\dfrac{dy}{dt}$.

Then let $\dfrac{dy}{dt} = 0$ and solve for t.

$$y = 190t \times (0.65)^t$$

$$\frac{dy}{dt} = \frac{d[190t(0.65)^t]}{dt} \qquad\qquad \text{Use the product rule.}$$

$$= \frac{d(190t)}{dt} \cdot (0.65)^t + \frac{d[(0.65)^t]}{dt}\,(190t) \qquad \begin{array}{l}\text{Use the derivative for } y = a^x \\ \text{for the second term.}\end{array}$$

$$= (190)(0.65)^t + (0.65)^t \ln 0.65(190t) \qquad \text{Factor.}$$

$$= (190)(0.65)^t(1 + t \ln 0.65) \qquad\qquad \text{Set the derivative} = 0.$$

$$0 = (190)(0.65)^t(1 + t \ln 0.65)$$

Only the last factor can equal 0. Set $(1 + t \ln 0.65)$ equal to 0 and solve for t.

$$1 + t \ln 0.65 = 0$$

$$t = \frac{-1}{\ln 0.65} \qquad \text{Evaluate.}$$

$$t \doteq 2.321$$

Verify using the first derivative test.

	Intervals	
	$0 \le t < 2.321$	$t > 2.321$
$190(0.65)^t$	+	+
$1 + t \ln 0.65$	+	−
$\dfrac{dy}{dt}$	(+)(+) = +	(+)(−) = −
y	increasing ↗	decreasing ↘
	maximum at $t \doteq 2.321$	

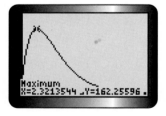

Maximum
X=2.3213544 Y=162.25596

The maximum value of $y \doteq 162.256$ and occurs when $t \doteq 2.321$.

Therefore, the maximum concentration occurs after about 2.321 h and is 162.256 parts per million. Graphing technology can be used to verify the results.

• • • • • • • •

Example 2 **Finding Rates of Change**

How fast is the concentration changing at 2 h? 8 h? 16 h?

Solution

To find the rate of change, evaluate the derivative at $t = 2$, 8, and 16.

At $t = 2$,

$$\frac{dy}{dt}\Big|_{t=2} = (190)(0.65)^2(1 + 2 \ln 0.65)$$
$$\doteq 11.11$$

The rate of change at 2 h is about 11.11 ppm/h (parts per million each hour).

At $t = 8$,

$$\frac{dy}{dt}\Big|_{t=8} = (190)(0.65)^8(1 + 8 \ln 0.65)$$
$$\doteq -14.81$$

The rate of change at 8 h is about -14.81 ppm/h (parts per million each hour).

At $t = 16$,

$$\frac{dy}{dt}\Big|_{t=16} = (190)(0.65)^{16}(1 + 16 \ln 0.65)$$
$$\doteq -1.14$$

The rate of change at 16 h is about -1.14 ppm/h (parts per million each hour).

The graph and the calculated rates of change verify that the rate of change increases to the maximum and then decreases rapidly and levels off.

• • • • • • • •

Example 3 **Determining Critical Numbers and Points of Inflection**

Determine the critical numbers and points of inflection for $y = x^2 e^{-2x}$.

Solution

To find the critical numbers, determine the first derivative. Use the product rule.

$$y' = (2x)\,(e^{-2x}) + (-2)(e^{-2x})(x^2)$$

Simplify and set the derivative equal to 0.

$$0 = 2xe^{-2x}(1 - x)$$

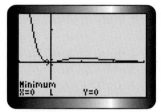

So $x = 0$ or $x = 1$.

Therefore, the critical numbers are 0 and 1.

Examine the graph to verify some of these results.

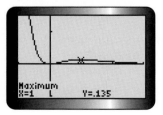

To determine the points of inflection, find the second derivative.

$$y' = 2xe^{-2x} - 2x^2e^{-2x} \qquad \text{Use the product rule to differentiate each term.}$$
$$y'' = 2e^{-2x} + (-2)\,e^{-2x}(2x) - [(4x)(e^{-2x}) + (-2)e^{-2x}(2x^2)] \quad \text{Simplify.}$$
$$y'' = 2e^{-2x} - 4xe^{-2x} - 4xe^{-2x} + 4x^2e^{-2x} \qquad \text{Simplify.}$$
$$y'' = 2e^{-2x} - 8xe^{-2x} + 4x^2e^{-2x} \qquad\qquad \text{Factor and let } y'' = 0.$$
$$0 = 2e^{-2x}(1 - 4x + 2x^2)$$

Therefore, $1 - 4x + 2x^2 = 0$.

Use the quadratic formula to solve for x.

$$x = \frac{-(-4) \pm \sqrt{(-4)^2 - 4(2)(1)}}{2(2)}$$

$$= \frac{4 \pm 2\sqrt{2}}{4}$$

$$= 1 \pm \frac{\sqrt{2}}{2}$$

$$x \doteq 1.71 \text{ or } x \doteq 0.29$$

Therefore, possible points of inflection are about $(1.71, 0.096)$ and $(0.29, 0.047)$. To confirm these points, examine the concavity of the original function using the second derivative.

	Intervals		
	$x < 0.29$	$0.29 < x < 1.71$	$x > 1.71$
$2e^{-2x}$	+	+	+
$1 - 4x + 2x^2$	+	−	+
y''	$(+)(+) = +$	$(+)(-) = -$	$(+)(+) = +$
y	concave up ∪	concave down ∩	concave up ∪
	inflection point at $x \doteq 0.29$		inflection point at $x \doteq 1.71$

The analysis confirms that the function's concavity changes at $x \doteq 0.29$ and $x \doteq 1.71$. Points $(0.29, 0.047)$ and $(1.71, 0.096)$ are inflection points.

• • • • • • • •

Example 4   **Analyzing and Graphing Logarithmic Functions**

Determine the domain, critical numbers, and intervals of increase and decrease of $y = \ln (x^2 - 3)$.

Solution
To determine the domain, recall that $x^2 - 3$ must be positive. This occurs when

$$x^2 - 3 > 0$$
$$x^2 > 3$$
$$x < -\sqrt{3} \text{ or } x > \sqrt{3}$$

The domain is $\{x \,|\, x < -\sqrt{3} \text{ or } x > \sqrt{3}, x \in \mathbf{R}\}$.

To find the critical numbers, take the first derivative using the chain rule.

$$y = \ln (x^2 - 3)$$

$$\frac{dy}{dx} = \frac{d[\ln (x^2 - 3)]}{d(x^2 - 3)} \times \frac{d(x^2 - 3)}{dx}$$

$$= \frac{1}{x^2 - 3} \times 2x$$

$$= \frac{2x}{x^2 - 3}$$

The critical numbers occur when $\frac{dy}{dx}$ equals 0 or is undefined.

$$0 = \frac{2x}{x^2 - 3}$$
$$0 = 2x$$
$$x = 0$$

Intervals		
	$x < -\sqrt{3}$	$x > \sqrt{3}$
$2x$	–	+
$x^2 - 3$	+	+
$\dfrac{dy}{dt}$	$\dfrac{(-)}{(+)} = -$	$\dfrac{(+)}{(+)} = +$
y	decreasing ↘	increasing ↗

$\dfrac{dy}{dx} = 0$ when $x = 0$ and is undefined when $x = \pm\sqrt{3}$. However, these numbers are not in the domain. There are no critical numbers. Determine the intervals of increase and decrease by examining the sign of $\dfrac{dy}{dx}$ for values of x on each side of $x = -\sqrt{3}$ and $x = \sqrt{3}$. The interval $-\sqrt{3} < x < \sqrt{3}$ is omitted since the original function is undefined on this interval.

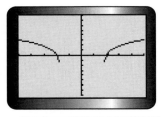

Therefore, the domain is $\{x \mid x < -\sqrt{3}$ or $x > \sqrt{3}, x \in \mathbf{R}\}$, the critical numbers are $x = \pm\sqrt{3}$, and the function is decreasing when $x < -\sqrt{3}$ and increasing when $x > \sqrt{3}$.

CHECK, CONSOLIDATE, COMMUNICATE

1. How do you find the critical numbers for a function? What can you tell from the critical numbers?
2. What information does the second derivative give you?

KEY IDEAS

- To analyze exponential and logarithmic functions, use the same curve-sketching techniques used for polynomial, rational, and composite functions.
- Logarithmic functions are defined only for positive real numbers.

7.5 Exercises

A 1. State the domain and range of each function.
   (a) $y = e^x + x$ (b) $y = x - \ln x$
   (c) $y = 3^{x + 1}$ (d) $y = \log_2 (x) + 2$

2. For each function in question 1, find the intervals of increase and decrease, and then graph the function.

3. **Knowledge and Understanding:** Find the maximum and minimum values of each function. Graph each function.
   (a) $y = e^x + 2$ (b) $y = xe^x + 3$
   (c) $y = 2xe^{2x}$ (d) $y = 3xe^{-x} + x$

4. On what intervals is $y = 3x^2 - \ln x$ increasing or decreasing? Graph the function.

5. Find the maximum and minimum values of each function. Graph each function.

   (a) $y = 2x - \ln x$ (b) $y = x^2 \ln x$

   (c) $y = \ln (x - 1)$ (d) $y = \ln (x - 1)^2$

6. Find the maximum value of $y = \dfrac{\ln x}{x}$.

7. Find the first and second derivatives of each function.

   (a) $y = 2^{3x}$ (b) $y = 7^{x^4}$

   (c) $y = \log_2 (x - 1)$ (d) $y = \log (2x - 3)$

B   8. For $y = 2x^2e^x$, discuss concavity. Graph the function.

9. **Communication:** Explain and show why the graph of the exponential function $y = c(e)^x$ has no points of inflection.

10. Discuss each function in terms of its domain, intercepts, asymptotes, intervals of increase and decrease, local maximum and minimum values, and concavity. Then use this information to graph the function.

    (a) $y = \ln (2 - x^2)$ (b) $y = x^2e^x$ (c) $y = e^{\frac{1}{x}}$

11. Find all maximum and minimum values of $y = xe^x + 3e^x$.

12. **Application:** You have just walked out the front door of your home. You notice that it closes quickly at first and then closes more slowly. In fact, a model of the movement of a closing door is given by $d(t) = 200t(2)^{-t}$, where d is the number of degrees between the door frame and the door at t seconds.

    (a) Graph this relation.

    (b) Determine when the speed of the closing door is increasing and decreasing.

    (c) Determine the maximum speed of the closing door.

    (d) At what point would you consider the door closed?

13. **Check Your Understanding:** Show that $y = e^x$ and $y = \ln x$ are always increasing.

C   14. (a) For $f(x) = \ln (e^{-2} + e^x)$, prove that $f(x)$ increases for all x.

    (b) What is the equation of the inverse function?

15. **Thinking, Inquiry, Problem Solving:** The velocity of a car is given by $v(t) = 120(1 - 0.85^t)$. Graph the function. Describe the acceleration of the car.

16. Discuss $y = x^{\ln x}$ in terms of its domain, intercepts, asymptotes, intervals of increase and decrease, local maximum and minimum values, and concavity. Then use this information to graph the function.

ADDITIONAL ACHIEVEMENT CHART QUESTIONS

Knowledge and Understanding: Find the maximum and/or minimum values and the points of inflection of each function. Sketch each graph.

(a) $y = e^{x^2}$ **(b)** $y = 3x + e^{-x}$ **(c)** $y = \frac{1}{2}xe^{\frac{1}{2}x}$ **(d)** $y = 3x^2 - \ln x$

Application: A dish of bacteria is infected with a disease. The equation

$N(d) = (15d)e^{\frac{-d}{5}}$ models the number of bacteria, N, that will be infected after d days.

(a) Sketch the graph.

(b) Use the equation to determine how many days will pass before the maximum number of bacteria will be infected.

(c) Use the equation to determine the maximum number of bacteria that will be infected.

(d) Use your graph to confirm your results in (b) and (c).

(e) Graph this relation on the graphing calculator to confirm your results in (a), (b), and (c).

Thinking, Inquiry, Problem Solving: In this section, the concentration of vitamin C was modelled by the equation $y = 190t(0.65)^t$. In this model, the level of vitamin C rises rapidly and drops off rapidly. Ideally, chemists would prefer the concentration to reach its maximum level with the same quickness, but to decrease at a slower rate. Create an algebraic model that would do this. Verify your model in several ways.

Communication

(a) Explain how to find the maximum and/or minimum values and the points of inflection of $y = (\ln x)^2$.

(b) How will you know if your maximum or minimum values are local or absolute?

The Chapter Problem
Rabbit Population

Apply what you learned in this section to answer these questions about The Chapter Problem on page 504.

CP11. Describe the graphs of $y = c(a)^x$ or $y = c\,(e)^{kt}$.

CP12. How does your graph of the original full set of data compare with a graph of $y = c(a)^x$ or $y = c(e)^{kt}$? What is the same? different?

CP13. For which parts of the graph is the model a good fit? a poor fit?

7.6 Models of Exponential Growth

SETTING THE STAGE

Explore the concepts in this section in more detail using Exploration 15 on page 587.

In Chapter 2, the exponential growth function is modelled by $y = c(a)^x$. In this chapter, the exponential growth function is modelled by $y = c(e)^{kx}$. Why is this growth function more meaningful than $y = c(a)^x$?

In this section, you will investigate the properties of the exponential growth function $y = c(e)^{kx}$.

EXAMINING THE CONCEPT

Modelling Growth Using $y = c(e)^{kx}$

Look at an example that uses $y = c(e)^{kx}$ to model growth.

Example 1 **Finding the Growth Factor and the Rate of Change**

A weight-loss program claims that, after the first two days, weight loss is exponential. The weight loss is expressed as a percent of the client's changing weight. John is participating in this weight-loss program. His weight is 98 kg four days after he starts the program. After 20 days, his weight is 95 kg.

(a) What will his weight be after 40 days?

(b) How fast is John losing weight? Express this value as a percent per day of weight loss.

Solution

First determine a model for weight loss. Use $y = c(e)^{kt}$ and the information about John's weight to find the values of k and c.

The variable c represents his initial weight after the first two days.

After four days, which is two days after the first two days, $98 = c(e)^{2k}$.

At 20 days, which is 18 days after the first two days, $95 = c(e)^{18k}$.

Divide the two equations.

$$\frac{95}{98} = \frac{c(e)^{18k}}{c(e)^{2k}}$$

$$\frac{95}{98} = e^{16k} \qquad \text{Take the ln of each side.}$$

$$\ln \frac{95}{98} = \ln e^{16k} \qquad \text{Recall that } \ln(e^a) = a.$$

$$\ln \frac{95}{98} = 16k \qquad \text{Solve for } k.$$

$$\frac{\ln \frac{95}{98}}{16} = k \qquad \text{Evaluate.}$$

$$k \doteq -0.002$$

The value of k is about -0.002.

Substitute $k = -0.002$ to find the value of c.

$$98 = c(e)^{-0.002(2)}$$

$$c = \frac{98}{e^{-0.002(2)}}$$

$$c \doteq 98.4$$

Therefore, a model for John's weight loss is $w(t) = 98.4e^{-0.002t}$.

(a) To find John's weight after 40 days, which is 38 days after the first two days, substitute $t = 38$ into $w(t) = 98.4e^{-0.002t}$.

$$w(38) = 98.4e^{-0.002t}$$
$$= 98.4e^{-0.002(38)}$$
$$\doteq 91.2$$

John will weigh about 91.2 kg after 40 days on the weight-loss program.

(b) To find John's rate of change of weight loss, find the derivative of $w(t) = 98.4e^{-0.002t}$.

$$\frac{dw}{dt} = (98.4e^{-0.002t})(-0.002)$$

This derivative is the original function w multiplied by the value of k.

In other words,

$$\frac{dw}{dt} = kw(t), \text{ where } w(t) = 98.4e^{-0.002t}$$

So John's weight is decreasing at a rate that is proportional to his weight at a given point in time. k represents the value of proportionality. And John's rate of weight loss at a given point in time is 0.2% of his weight at that time.

For example, after four days, the rate of weight loss is 0.002×98, or 0.196 kg/day. After 20 days, the rate of weight loss is 0.002×95, or 0.19 kg/day.

In this case, $y = c(e)^{kx}$ and $\frac{dy}{dx} = ky$. Is this always true?

• • • • • • • •

Example 2   **Finding the Derivative of $y = c(e)^{kx}$**

Find the derivative of $y = c(e)^{kx}$.

Solution

$$y = c(e)^{kx}$$ Take the derivative of each side.

$$\frac{dy}{dx} = \frac{d[c(e)^{kx}]}{dx}$$ Apply the chain rule.

$$= \frac{d[c(e)^{kx}]}{d(kx)} \times \frac{d(kx)}{dx}$$ Recall that c is a constant.

$$= c(e)^{kx} \times (k)$$

$$= (k)c(e)^{kx}$$ Substitute $y = c(e)^{kx}$.

$$= ky$$

• • • • • • • •

The Rate of Change of $y = c(e)^{kx}$

The rate of change of a natural exponential function is proportional to the function. In other words, for $y = c(e)^{kx}$, $\dfrac{dy}{dx} = ky$.

Example 3 **Using the Proportional Relation**

A town's population grows at a rate that is proportional to the population at that point in time. The constant of proportionality is 0.0085. In how many years will a population of 36 000 grow to 40 000?

Solution

Use $y = c(e)^{0.0085t}$. Substitute $c = 36\ 000$ and $y = 40\ 000$ to find t.

$$40\ 000 = 36\ 000e^{0.0085t} \qquad \text{Divide by 36 000 and simplify.}$$

$$\frac{10}{9} = e^{0.0085t} \qquad \text{Take the ln of each side.}$$

$$\ln \frac{10}{9} = \ln e^{0.0085t}$$

$$\ln \frac{10}{9} = 0.0085t \qquad \text{Divide by 0.0085.}$$

$$t = \frac{\ln \frac{10}{9}}{0.0085} \qquad \text{Evaluate.}$$

$$t \doteq 12.4$$

Therefore, the population will grow to 40 000 in about 12.4 years.

• • • • • • • •

Sometimes you may need to adjust the exponential growth formula for some relations. Newton's Law of Cooling is another example of exponential growth. Newton's Law of Cooling states that the rate of change in temperature of an object is proportional to the temperature difference between the object and its surroundings. The corresponding function is

$$T - S = (T_0 - S)e^{kt}$$
$$T = (T_0 - S)e^{kt} + S$$

In this formula, T represents the final temperature of the object, T_0 represents the initial temperature of the object, S is the temperature of the surroundings, k is a constant, and t is time.

Example 4 **Newton's Law of Cooling**

Imagine that it is June. You are sitting outside in a sunny area studying calculus. Your book reaches a temperature of 30°C. When you bring your book indoors (22°C), 20 min pass before the book cools to 25°C. How much more time will pass before the book reaches 22.5°C?

Solution

Use $T = (T_0 - S)e^{kt} + S$. Substitute $T = 25$, $T_0 = 30$, $t = 20$, and $S = 22$. Solve for k.

$$25 = (30 - 22)e^{20k} + 22$$

$$25 = 8e^{20k} + 22 \qquad \text{Isolate the term that contains } k.$$

$$3 = 8e^{20k} \qquad \text{Divide both sides by 8.}$$

$$0.375 = e^{20k} \qquad \text{Take the ln of each side.}$$

$$\ln 0.375 = 20k \qquad \text{Divide by 20.}$$

$$\frac{\ln 0.375}{20} = k \qquad \text{Evaluate.}$$

$$k \doteq -0.049$$

Therefore, the model in this case is $T = 8e^{-0.049t} + 22$.
Now find t when $T = 22.5$.

$$22.5 = 8e^{-0.049t} + 22 \qquad \text{Isolate the term that contains } t.$$

$$0.5 = 8e^{-0.049t} \qquad \text{Divide both sides by 8.}$$

$$\frac{1}{16} = e^{-0.049t} \qquad \text{Take the ln of each side.}$$

$$\ln \frac{1}{16} = -0.049t \qquad \text{Divide by } -0.049.$$

$$\frac{\ln \frac{1}{16}}{-0.049} = \frac{-0.049t}{-0.049} \qquad \text{Evaluate.}$$

$$t \doteq 56.6$$

It will take the book 56.6 min, from the time it is brought indoors, to cool from 30°C to 22.5°C. The book has already been indoors for 20 min, so it will take another $56.6 - 20 = 36.6$ min to cool to 22.5°C.

• • • • • • • •

As you can see from Newton's Law of Cooling, the model for exponential growth, $y = c(e)^{kx}$, is useful for some cases but should be adjusted for others. For instance, the growth of a population can be restricted by limited space, disease, or lack of food, which means that the model representing this growth should be adjusted.

Example 5   **Logistic Equation for Inhibited Growth**

The logistic equation $P(t) = \dfrac{A}{1 + be^{-kt}}$ is a function that models a population in which the growth is initially rapid but eventually levels off. The growth of a bacterial culture can be modelled using the logistic equation using $A = 6$, $b = 6$, and $k = 0.3$. $P(t)$ is the mass of the culture in grams.

(a) What is the initial mass of the culture?

(b) What is the instantaneous rate of growth?

(c) Graph $P(t)$ with graphing technology. Show that the mass of this culture can never be more than 6 g.

Solution

Using the logistic equation and substituting the given information yields

$$P(t) = \frac{6}{1 + 6e^{-0.3t}}.$$

(a) To find the initial mass, let $t = 0$.

$$P(0) = \frac{6}{1 + 6e^{-0.3(0)}}$$

$$= \frac{6}{1 + 6}$$

$$= \frac{6}{7}$$

Therefore, the initial mass is $\frac{6}{7}$ g, or about 0.857 g.

(b) Find the derivative to find the instantaneous rate of growth.

$$P(t) = \frac{6}{1 + 6e^{-0.3t}} = 6(1 + 6e^{-0.3t})^{-1}$$

$$\frac{dP}{dt} = (6)(-1)(1 + 6e^{-0.3t})^{-2}(-0.3)(6e^{-0.3t})$$

$$= 10.8(e^{-0.3t})(1 + 6e^{-0.3t})^{-2}$$

$$= \frac{10.8(e^{-0.3t})}{(1 + 6e^{-0.3t})^2}$$

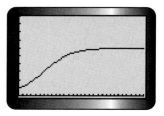

(c) Graph $P(t)$.

The graph levels off at a value of about 6. So the mass of the culture can never be more than 6 mg.

CHECK, CONSOLIDATE, COMMUNICATE

1. Explain the meaning of "the rate of change is proportional to the original function."
2. Given $y = c(e)^{kx}$, for what values of k will the function represent growth? For what values of k will the function represent decay?

KEY IDEAS

- The rate of change of a natural exponential function is proportional to the function. In other words, for $y = c(e)^{kx}$, $\frac{dy}{dx} = ky$.

- Newton's Law of Cooling

  $T = (T_0 - S)e^{kt} + S$, where T represents the final temperature of the object, T_0 represents the initial temperature of the object, S is the temperature of the surroundings, and k is a constant.

- The **logistic equation** $P(t) = \frac{A}{1 + be^{-kt}}$ is a good model for a population with rapid growth. The growth eventually levels off due to restricting factors such as lack of food, natural predators, disease, and so on.

7.6 Exercises

A   **1. Knowledge and Understanding:** Differentiate.

    (a) $y = 35e^x$ **(b)** $y = 25e^{2x}$ **(c)** $y = 15e^{-0.2x}$

    (d) $y = 350e^{1.4x}$ **(e)** $y = 1500e^{1.08x}$ **(f)** $y = 200e^{-0.15x}$

2. A bacterial culture starts with 240 bacteria. At the end of 1.5 h, the estimated count is 25 000. Assume a normal pattern of exponential growth.

    (a) Find the number of bacteria at the end of t hours.

    (b) Find the rate of change of growth after four hours.

3. Communication: For $y' = 0.02y$, explain in words what the rate of change of growth means. Create an equation for the corresponding function, y.

B   **4. Application:** After five years, $3000 grows to $5000. What will be the amount after eight years if the interest rate remains the same?

5. Karen packs her lunch each morning at 7:00 A.M. and includes a frozen juice box ($-10°C$). At school, the lunch sits in her locker at room temperature ($20°C$) until lunch (12:00 noon). At 10:00 A.M., the juice is still frozen ($-2°C$). Will the juice be above freezing ($0°C$) at lunch?

6. George takes a hot loaf of bread out of the oven and allows it to cool. The initial temperature of the loaf when it is pulled from the oven is $100°C$. After 5 min, the loaf has cooled to $75°C$. If the room temperature is $25°C$, find the temperature of the loaf after another 5 min have passed.

7. An object is in a room with an air temperature of $22°C$. The object cools from $50°$ to $40°$ in 28 min. How much time will pass before the object's temperature cools to $30°$?

8. Check Your Understanding: The function $y = e^x$ is its own derivative. But this function is not the only one that has this property. Show that, for every value of c, $y = c(e)^x$ has the same property.

C   **9.** The data in the table represents a car's velocity, $v(t)$, t seconds after the driver steps on the brake.

Time (s)	Velocity (km/h)
2	31
4	20
6	14
8	9
10	5

    (a) Create an algebraic model for this data.

    (b) Determine when the driver has stopped the car.

    (c) Determine the velocity at 7 s.

    (d) What was the initial velocity when the brakes were first applied?

    (e) Find the acceleration function. Use this function to determine when the velocity is increasing and decreasing.

10. **Thinking, Inquiry, Problem Solving:** The population of a type of fish in a bay grows at the rate of 2%/year if no fishing occurs. However, about 150 fish each year are taken by fishers. There are about 4500 fish in the bay in January 2002. Find

   (a) the number of fish in the bay in January 2003

   (b) an equation to represent the number of fish in the bay t years after January 2002

   (c) an equation for the rate at which the fish population is growing

ADDITIONAL ACHIEVEMENT CHART QUESTIONS

Knowledge and Understanding: Determine the derivative of each function.

(a) $y = 2e^x$ **(b)** $y = 30e^{-2x}$ **(c)** $y = \frac{1}{5}e^{0.025x}$

Application: The half-life of a substance is 75 days. Initially there are 500 mg of this substance.

(a) How much of the substance remains after 60 days?

(b) What is the rate of decrease of the amount of the substance after 60 days?

(c) When will 100 mg of the substance remain?

Thinking, Inquiry, Problem Solving: A thermometer has been inside a roast cooking in the oven. Just before the thermometer was removed from the roast, it read 180°C. The thermometer is removed and left on the kitchen counter to cool before putting it in the dishwasher. After 25 min, it has cooled to 160°C. If the room's temperature is 20°C, what will the temperature of the thermometer be 15 min later?

Communication: The equation $y = c(e)^{kt}$ models an exponential relation.

(a) Explain what the restriction is on k. Why does t not have the same restriction?

(b) For what values of k will the equation model an exponential growth? Explain why. How does that compare with knowing how $y = c(a)^x$ will model an exponential growth?

(c) For what values of k will the equation model an exponential decay? Explain why. How does that compare with knowing how $y = c(a)^x$ will model an exponential decay?

The Chapter Problem
Rabbit Population

Apply what you learned in this section to answer this question about The Chapter Problem on page 504.

CP14. Determine whether any of the models in this section would fit the rabbit population data.

Chapter 7 Review

RATES OF CHANGE IN EXPONENTIAL AND LOGARITHMIC FUNCTION MODELS

CHECK YOUR UNDERSTANDING

1. State the Fundamental Limit of Calculus. Explain how it is derived.
   Use this theorem to evaluate $\lim_{x \to 0} (1 + x)^{\frac{1}{x}}$.

2. State the properties of functions and their inverses in general.
   Rewrite each of these properties for $y = e^x$ and $y = \ln x$.

3. State the general derivatives of each of the following:
   (a) $y = e^x$ **(b)** $y = \ln x$ **(c)** $y = e^{f(x)}$ **(d)** $y = \ln (f(x))$

4. State the general derivatives of each of the following:
   (a) $y = a^x$ **(b)** $y = \log_a x$ **(c)** $y = a^{f(x)}$ **(d)** $y = \log_a (f(x))$

5. Write down all the steps for curve sketching. Create an exponential function, and follow your steps to graph it.

6. Name as many real-life situations as you can think of that model exponential growth or decay. Choose one, and design a realistic problem based on this model. Then solve the problem.

7. Given $y = c(e)^{kx}$, for what values of k will the function represent growth? For what values of k will the function represent decay?

8. Write the laws of logarithms using a logarithm with base e (ln).

REVIEW QUESTIONS BY SECTION

7.1 Introducing a Special Number, e

9. Graph each function.
   (a) $y = e^x$ **(b)** $y = 40(e)^x$ **(c)** $y = e^{x + 2}$
   (d) $y = e^{3x}$ **(e)** $y = -2e^x - 1$

10. Find the value of \$2500 after four years if the money is invested at 10%/a,
    (a) compounded annually **(b)** compounded quarterly
    (c) compounded n times each year **(d)** compounded continuously

11. You have probably noticed that the air pressure in a plane varies. The atmospheric pressure, y, varies with the altitude, x kilometres, above Earth. For altitudes up to 10 km, the pressure in millimetres of mercury (mm Hg) is given by $y = 760e^{-0.125x}$. What is the atmospheric pressure
    (a) 5 km above Earth? **(b)** 7 km above Earth?
    (c) 9 km above Earth?

7.2 The Derivative of $y = e^x$

12. Find the derivative of each function.

(a) $y = e^{5x}$ **(b)** $y = e^{-3x}$ **(c)** $y = 7e^{\frac{1}{7}x}$

(d) $y = x^3 e^{-2x}$ **(e)** $y = \dfrac{e^{4x}}{x^2 + 1}$ **(f)** $y = (x - 1)^2 e^x$

(g) $y = (x - e^{-x})^2$ **(h)** $y = \dfrac{e^x - e^{-x}}{e^x + e^{-x}}$ **(i)** $y = \sqrt{2 - e^x}$

13. A certain radioactive substance decays exponentially over time. The amount of a sample of the substance that remains, P, after t years is given by $P = 100e^{-5t}$, where P is expressed as a percent.

(a) Find the function of the rate of change, $\dfrac{dP}{dt}$.

(b) What is the rate of decay when 50% of the original sample has decayed?

14. Find the equation of the tangent line to the curve $4e^{xy} = 2x + y$ at point $(0, 4)$.

7.3 The Natural Logarithm and Its Derivative

15. Solve for x, to three decimal places, if needed.

(a) $e^x = 12$ **(b)** $2^{x - 4} = 5$

(c) $e^{1 - 6x} = 5$ **(d)** $2^{3^x} = 4$

16. Differentiate.

(a) $y = \ln (2x + 1)$ **(b)** $f(x) = \ln (\ln x)$

(c) $y = \ln (9 - x^2)$ **(d)** $y = x^3 \ln (2 - x^2)$

(e) $g(x) = \sqrt{\ln x}$ **(f)** $h(x) = \ln \sqrt{\dfrac{2x + 1}{2x - 1}}$

(g) $m(x) = \ln \dfrac{(x - 1)^{\frac{2}{5}}}{x + 1}$ **(h)** $y = x^{\frac{1}{\ln x}}$

17. Find the equation of the tangent to the curve $y = \ln (2x + 1)$ at the point where $x = 0$.

7.4 Differentiating Other Logarithmic and Exponential Functions

18. Differentiate.

(a) $y = \log_3 x$ **(b)** $y = \log_{10} (x^3 - 5x + 8)$

(c) $f(t) = \log_{10} \dfrac{-t}{\sqrt{t + 1}}$ **(d)** $H(x) = 300(5)^{3x - 1}$

(e) $q(x) = 1.9^x + x^{1.9}$ **(f)** $y = 14^{2x + 1}$

(g) $G(x) = (3)^{4^x}$ **(h)** $y = -5x^2 \log_6 x$

19. Find the equation of the tangent to the curve $y = \log_3 x$ at point $(9, 2)$. Graph the function and include any asymptotes. Can the tangent line intersect an asymptote? Explain your answer.

20. **(a)** Nuclear physicist Theo takes a 50-mg sample of radium-226. Help him find a formula for the mass of radium-226 that remains after t years. The half-life of radium-226 is 1590 years.

(b) Explain to Theo how he could find the mass after 1000 years, to the nearest milligram.

(c) When will the mass decrease to 10 mg?

(d) What is the rate of decay at the point where the mass is 10 mg?

7.5 Sketching Graphs of Exponential and Logarithmic Functions

21. For each function,

    i. discuss the intervals of increase and decrease

    ii. discuss the maximum and minimum values

    iii. discuss concavity

    iv. draw its graph

    (a) $y = e^x + 2$ **(b)** $y = -3e^x - 5$ **(c)** $y = xe^{-3x}$

    (d) $y = x^2 e^{-x^2}$ **(e)** $y = xe^{-\frac{1}{2}x^2}$ **(f)** $y = x^4 e^x$

22. The profit function of a commodity is $P(x) = xe^{-0.5x^2}$, where $x > 0$. Find the maximum value of the function.

23. Discuss $y = 2 \ln (1 - x^2)$ in terms of the following. Then graph the function.

    (a) domain

    (b) intercepts

    (c) asymptotes

    (d) intervals of increase and decrease

    (e) local maximum and minimum values

    (f) concavity

7.6 Models of Exponential Growth

24. Find the derivative of each function.

    (a) $f(w) = 4e^{2w}$ **(b)** $y = 32e^{-3x}$

    (c) $Q(x) = -18e^{-0.4x}$ **(d)** $y = 180e^{1.7t}$

    (e) $P(t) = 2000e^{0.06t}$ **(f)** $A(x) = -1278e^{-23.49x}$

25. A carton of orange juice, which has a temperature of 42°F, is placed in a room where the air temperature is 74°F. How long does the temperature of the juice take to rise to 50°F? Assume that $k = -0.4$ and t represents time in hours.

26. Let r be the annual interest rate. The time it takes for an amount of money to double in size is t. Interest is compounded continuously. Show that $\ln 2 = rt$.

Knowledge and Understanding

27. Differentiate.

(a) $y = (x - 1)e^{2x}$ (b) $y = \log_5 (2x)$ (c) $y = \ln x^2$ (d) $y = \ln (\ln x^2)$

28. Discuss the extrema, the intervals of increase and decrease, and asymptotes for each function. Graph the function. Verify your results with technology.

(a) $y = xe^x + 2$

(b) $y = \dfrac{x}{\ln x}$

29. (a) Graph $y = 5^x$ and its inverse.

(b) Find the equation of the tangent to the graph of $y = 5^x$ at point $(2, 25)$.

(c) Find the equation of the tangent to the graph of the inverse at point $(25, 2)$.

(d) Graph the tangents.

Application

30. Suppose the inflation rate averages 2.5% per year. How much will a new car cost in the year 2018 if the cost of the same type of car in 2001 was $27 000?

31. Suppose that 1500 years ago, one of your ancestors invested $10 at 10%/a, compounded annually. What would be the worth of this investment now?

32. Radioactive tracers are used for medical diagnosis. Dr. Davis has to order iodine-131, with a half-life of eight days, to diagnose a patient who may have thyroid problems. She orders 30 units of iodine-131. The shipment will arrive in two days. How much of the substance, in terms of units, arrives? What is the rate of decay at that point in time?

Thinking, Inquiry, Problem Solving

33. Find the 1000th derivative of $f(x) = e^{-3x}$. (Hint: Look for a pattern!)

34. Is it possible to find the derivative of $y = \ln x$ using another method? If so, how?

35. A radioactive substance has a half-life of 55 days. Find the rate of decay of a 5-g sample of the substance when its mass is 5 g, 50 days later, and 500 days later.

Communication

36. Do any of the graphs of these functions have points of inflection? Explain your answer and graph the functions.

(a) $y = 120e^x$

(b) $y = x^2e^x$

(c) $y = x \ln x$

(d) $y = 3 - 2 \log x$

37. Explain how interest compounded monthly and interest compounded continuously are different.

38. How are the graphs of $y = e^x$, $y = -e^x$, and $y = e^{-x}$ alike? different?

Chapter 7 Performance Task

In several places throughout this chapter, you combined the function $y = e^x$ with other functions. For instance, some questions asked you to graph or analyze $y = x^2e^x$ or $y = x^4e^x$. It is interesting to look at graphs that are of the general form: $y = x^ne^x$ for $n \geq 2$ to see if there are patterns in the graphs and properties of the functions. To determine patterns, start with a few familiar graphs.

1. **(a)** Discuss $f(x) = x^4e^x$ in terms of the following: domain, intercepts, asymptotes, intervals of increase and decrease, local maximum and minimum values, and concavity. Use this information to sketch the graph of f.

    (b) State and verify the local extrema of f.

    (c) State and verify the inflection points of f.

2. **(a)** Discuss $g(x) = x^9e^x$ in terms of the following: domain, intercepts, asymptotes, intervals of increase and decrease, local maximum and minimum values, and concavity. Use this information to sketch the graph of g.

    (b) State and verify the local extrema of g.

    (c) State and verify the inflection points of g.

3. You may want to use graphing technology to examine other values of n in $y = x^ne^x$ to look for patterns.

4. Consider the function $h(x) = x^ne^x$, $n \geq 2$. For each question below you will need to think about when n is even and when n is odd.

    (a) How many extrema will $h(x)$ have? Justify your answer mathematically.

    (b) Determine the number of inflection points of $h(x)$. Justify your answer mathematically.

    (c) Sketch $h(x) = x^ne^x$, $n \geq 2$ when n is even.

    (d) Sketch $h(x) = x^ne^x$, $n \geq 2$ when n is odd.

5. Do your conclusions from question 4 hold true when $n = 1$? Explain.

6. What values of n will produce an inflection point at $x = -20$?

Chapter 7 Review Test

RATES OF CHANGE IN EXPONENTIAL AND LOGARITHMIC FUNCTION MODELS

1. **Knowledge and Understanding:** Differentiate.

   (a) $y = \ln 4x$　　　　　　　　(b) $y = \log_4 (x - 2)$

   (c) $y = 100(1.05)^x$　　　　　(d) $y = xe^{3x}$

2. Find the equation of the tangent to the curve $y = e^{2x-1}$ at the point where $x = 2$.

3. **Communication:** Explain the significance of the room temperature in Newton's Law of Cooling.

4. A radioactive substance decays exponentially over time. The mass of a sample of the substance that remains after t years is given by $P = 100(e)^{-0.18t}$, where P is expressed as a percent.

   (a) Determine the half-life of the substance.

   (b) How fast is the substance decaying at the point where the half-life is reached?

5. **Application:** The value of a major purchase, such as a car, depreciates each year because the item gets older. The value of a car is given by $V(t) = 27\,000(e)^{-0.05t}$, where $V(t)$ is the value of the purchase in dollars after t years.

   (a) What was the purchase price of the car?

   (b) How much did the value depreciate during its third year (from $t = 2$ to $t = 3$)?

   (c) What is the instantaneous rate of change (in dollars per year) of the value at five years ($t = 5$)?

6. For $f(x) = x^2 e^x$, find the intervals of increase. Graph the function.

7. **Thinking, Inquiry, Problem Solving:** The data in the table shows the population of a school over 10 years. Create algebraic and graphical models for this data. Determine whether the rate of change of population is increasing or decreasing. Justify your answer.

Year	Number of Students
1990	580
1991	650
1992	700
1993	775
1994	850
1995	945
1996	1025
1997	1150
1998	1250
1999	1375

Cumulative Review Test 3

DIFFERENTIAL CALCULUS: COMPOSITE, EXPONENTIAL, AND LOGARITHMIC FUNCTIONS

1. Consider the graph of $y = f(x)$.
   Let $g(x) = 2x + 1$, $h(x) = -x + 3$, and $k(x) = (h \circ f \circ g)(x)$.

   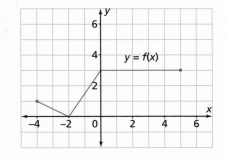

   (a) Evaluate.

        i. $k(2)$ **ii.** $k(-0.5)$

        iii. $k(-1.5)$ **iv.** $k(0)$

        v. $k(-2.5)$ **vi.** $k(3)$

   (b) Graph $y = k(x)$.

   (c) Explain how to derive the graph of $y = k(x)$ by transforming the graph of $y = f(x)$.

2. Determine $f'(2)$ if $f(x) = 4x^2 + \dfrac{3}{x + 1}$.

3. Let $y = \sqrt{2x + \sqrt{2x + \sqrt{2x + 1}}}$. Determine $\dfrac{dy}{dx}$ for $x = 0$.

4. Two posts, one 4 m high and the other 6 m high, stand 10 m apart. They are to be stayed by two wires, attached to a single stake in the ground. The wires go from the stake to the tops of the posts. Where should the stake be placed to use the least amount of wire?

5. Let $\dfrac{2x + 3y}{x - y} = 5$.

   (a) Determine $\dfrac{dy}{dx}$.

   (b) Determine $\dfrac{dy}{dx}$ in a different way. Show that the two results are the same.

6. The length and width of a rectangle are expressed in terms of a variable p, which starts at 0 and increases by 2 units per second. The width is defined by $w = 16p - p^2$ and the length by $l = 2p + 1$. Both length and width are in centimetres.

   (a) Determine the rate at which the area is changing at 3 s.

   (b) Determine the time when the rectangle achieves its maximum area.

   (c) Graph the area of the rectangle versus time.

   (d) Determine the time when the area is increasing at the greatest rate.

7. You may have noticed that the air pressure in an airplane varies. The atmospheric pressure, y, varies with the altitude, x, above the Earth in kilometres. For altitudes up to 10 km, the pressure in millimetres of mercury is given by $y = 760e^{-0.125x}$. What is the atmospheric pressure

   (a) 5 km above the Earth?

   (b) 2 km above the Earth?

   (c) 10 km above the Earth?

8. Explain why $\lim\limits_{h \to 0} \dfrac{e^h - 1}{h} = 1$ using a graph. Explain the steps for proving that the derivative of $y = e^x$ is $\dfrac{dy}{dx} = e^x$.

9. Find the derivative of each of the following.

   (a) $y = (6)^{3x - 8}$

   (b) $f(x) = (-4)(e^{5x + 1})$

   (c) $g(x) = \ln(2x + 7)^4$

   (d) $y = \log_5 (x^3 - x^2)^5$

10. $3500 is invested at 8%/a, compounded monthly.

    (a) Determine an equation for A, the amount of the investment after t years.

    (b) How much is the investment worth after five years? What is the rate of increase, $\dfrac{dA}{dt}$, of the money's value at that point?

    (c) What is the investment worth after 10 years? What is the rate of increase, $\dfrac{dA}{dt}$, of the money's value at that point?

11. Discuss $y = x(2)^{-x}$ in terms of its domain, intercepts, asymptotes, intervals of increase and decrease, local maximum and minimum values, and concavity. Then graph the function.

12. Newton's Law of Cooling states that the cooling rate of any object is proportional to the temperature difference between the object and its surroundings. Germaine is cooking a Thanksgiving dinner. She wants the roast turkey to cool to a certain temperature just in time for her guests' arrival. She takes the turkey out of a 350°F oven and places it on the dinner table in a room where the temperature is 21°C. After 5 min, the turkey is 320°F.

    (a) What is the temperature of the turkey 15 min after Germaine takes it out of the oven?

    (b) How long does it take for the turkey to cool down to 21°C?

    (*Hint*: Remember to convert!)

Explorations Appendix

EXPLORATION Investigating Factors of Polynomial Functions

PURPOSE

In this exploration, you will look for patterns when dividing with polynomial functions. You will use these patterns to help predict the remainder.

EQUIPMENT

- scientific calculator or graphing calculator

PROCEDURE

What is the relation between a binomial divisor and the remainder?

1. (a) Let $P(x) = x^2 + 6x - 3$.

    (b) Evaluate $P(2)$.

    (c) Divide $P(x)$ by $(x - 2)$. Use either long division or synthetic division.

    (d) What is the relation between $x = 2$ and the divisor $x - 2$?

    (e) Compare the remainder from (c) with $P(2)$. What do you notice?

2. (a) Let $P(x) = 4x^2 - 8x + 2$.

    (b) Evaluate $P(-1)$.

    (c) Use either long division or synthetic division to divide $P(x)$ by $(x + 1)$.

    (d) What relation exists between $x = -1$ and the divisor $x + 1$?

    (e) Compare the remainder from (c) with $P(-1)$. What do you notice?

3. (a) Let $P(x) = -2x^3 + 3x^2 - 9x - 5$.

    (b) Evaluate $P(4)$.

    (c) Use either long or synthetic division to divide $P(x)$ by $(x - 4)$.

    (d) What relation exists between $x = 4$ and the divisor $x - 4$?

    (e) Compare the remainder from (c) with $P(4)$. What do you notice?

4. (a) Let $P(x) = 6x^4 - 2x^3 + 4x^2 - 5x + 1$. Predict the remainder if $P(x)$ is divided by $x + 3$.

    (b) Use either long division or synthetic division to verify your prediction.

DEVELOPING A NOTION OF THE REMAINDER THEOREM

1. Suppose you must divide any polynomial
   $P(x) = a_n x^n + a_{n-1} x^{n-1} + \ldots + a_2 x^2 + a_1 x + a_0$ by a binomial $x - k$.
   How can you determine the remainder without actually dividing?

2. (a) Let $P(x) = 8x^3 - 4x^2 + 6x - 10$.

   (b) Evaluate $P\left(\frac{1}{2}\right)$.

   (c) Use either long division or synthetic division to divide $P(x)$ by $(2x - 1)$.

   (d) What is the relationship between $x = \frac{1}{2}$ and the divisor $2x - 1$?

   (e) Compare the remainder from (c) with $P\left(\frac{1}{2}\right)$. What do you notice?

3. Suppose you divide any polynomial $P(x) = a_n x^n + a_{n-1} x^{n-1} + \ldots + a_2 x^2 + a_1 x + a_0$ by a binomial $jx - k$. How can you determine the remainder without actually dividing?

DEVELOPING A NOTION OF THE FACTOR THEOREM

1. When you divide a polynomial by a binomial, what must be the remainder if the binomial is a factor of the polynomial?

2. (a) Predict the remainder if $x^2 - 7x - 18$ is divided by $x + 2$.

   (b) Use long division or synthetic division to check your prediction.

   (c) Is $x + 2$ a factor of $x^2 - 7x - 18$? Explain your answer.

3. Determine which binomials are factors of $x^3 - x^2 - 14x + 24$ without dividing.

   (a) $x + 2$ (b) $x + 1$ (c) $x - 3$ (d) $x - 2$

4. Let a polynomial be $P(x) = a_n x^n + a_{n-1} x^{n-1} + \ldots + a_2 x^2 + a_1 x + a_0$ and a binomial be $x - k$. How can you determine if the binomial is a factor of $P(x)$?

5. Suggest a method for deciding whether a binomial is a factor of polynomial $P(x)$ or not.

6. Determine at least one binomial factor for each polynomial.

   (a) $P(x) = x^3 - 4x^2 + x + 6$ (b) $P(x) = 3x^3 + 4x^2 - 5x - 2$

EXPLORATION Modelling Real Data with Polynomial Functions and Solving Polynomial Equations

PURPOSE

In 1999, about 6 665 000 females were part of the Canadian labour force. These women represented about 59% of all the women of a certain age who could work. The table shows data for other years. The data could be modelled with a polynomial function.

Year	1981	1982	1983	1985	1990	1992	1995	1999
Years Since 1980	1	2	3	5	10	12	15	19
Number of Females Working (%)	53	52	54	55	58	57	56	59

Source: Statistics Canada

In this exploration, you will use a graphing calculator to graph the data, find the best polynomial model for this data, and solve the polynomial equation for a specific situation.

EQUIPMENT

- TI-83 Plus calculator

PROCEDURE

1. Press [STAT] [1] to edit the lists. Clear any other data from the lists. Enter the years since 1980 into **L1** and the corresponding percent values into **L2**.

2. Create a scatter plot by defining a stat plot. Press [2nd] [Y=] [1] [ENTER]. Check that the screen on the graphing calculator looks like the one shown.

3. To see the graph, press [ZOOM] [9].

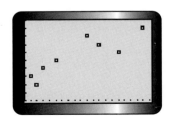

4. There are four possible polynomial models for the curve of best fit. The model could be linear, quadratic, cubic, or quartic. The points in the scatter plot do not seem to fit either a linear model or a quadratic model. Try a cubic model. Press [STAT] and select **CALC** ([▶]). Then select **6:CubicReg** (press [6] or scroll down).

5. Enter **L1** and **L2**. Press [2nd] [1], [2nd] [2], [VARS]. Select **Y-VARS**, then press 1. Press 1 again (or press [ENTER]) to store the equation of the cubic polynomial in **Y1** of the equation editor. Press [ENTER] to display the results.

(To see **R²**, the coefficient of determination, select **DiagnosticOn** from the **CATALOG** menu. Press [2nd] [0] and scroll down until you see **DiagnosticOn**. Then press [ENTER] twice. See the Technology Appendix.)

6. To display the curve of the cubic polynomial, press [GRAPH]. The coefficients **a**, **b**, **c**, and **d** define the general cubic equation $y = ax^3 + bx^2 + cx + d$. **R²** tells how well the model fits the data. The closer to 1, the better the fit.

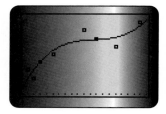

7. Graph **Y3** = 58 on the same axes.

ANALYSIS

1. How well does the cubic polynomial model the data?

2. What is the restricted domain for this model?

3. Suggest a different polynomial model that might fit the data better. Explain your choice.

4. Determine the quartic polynomial that models the data. To do this, repeat steps 4 to 6 in the procedure. For step 4, choose **7:QuartReg**. For step 5, store the quartic polynomial in **Y2** of the equation editor by pressing [2nd] [1] [,] [2nd] [2] [,] [VARS], selecting **Y-VARS**, and then pressing [1] [2]. Press [ENTER] to display the results. What is the value of **R²**? Press [GRAPH] to see the curves of both the cubic function and the quartic polynomial function.

5. Which function is the better model? Justify your choice.

6. Determine when 58% of females are working.

7. Write the equation that represents the points of intersection of the line $y = 58$ with the cubic function. Do the same with the quartic function.

The table shows how much land was planted in peas in Canada.

Year	1997	1998	1999	2000	2001
Land Planted with Peas (thousands of hectares)	848.5	1084.5	851.3	1240.2	1460.9

Source: Statistics Canada

1. Using graphing technology, make a scatter plot of the data.

2. Find a cubic model and a quartic model of the data. Which model fits the data better? Justify your decision.

3. Comment on the shape of the GRAPH for each model over an unrestricted domain.

4. State the restricted domain for each model. Explain why the domain is restricted.

5. If there were no restrictions on the domain, when would 2 000 000 ha of land be planted with peas?

3 EXPLORATION Turning Curves into Straight Lines

PURPOSE

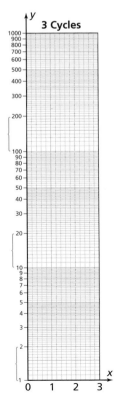

For many applications, you will want to change an exponential curve into a straight line, because

- a straight line is easier to draw
- you can interpolate and extrapolate more easily using a linear relation
- you can see intercepts and the slope more easily
- you can directly relate the intercepts and the slope to the growth factors

In this exploration, you will graph an exponential function on semilogarithmic paper.

USING SEMILOGARITHMIC GRAPH PAPER

In the diagram, you can see that the vertical axis of the semilogarithmic graph paper has a logarithmic scale. The vertical axis is commonly based on powers of 10.

Notice that the distance between 10^0 and 10^1 is the same as the distance between 10^1 and 10^2 and the distance between 10^2 and 10^3.

- semilogarithmic graph paper
- pencil and ruler

1. Set up and label two different grids, as shown.

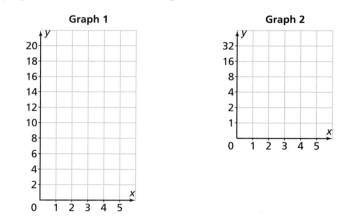

2. On each grid, graph $y = 2^x$.

3. Compare the graphs. What is different and what is the same?

4. Describe the scale of the y-axis in the second graph.

The graph paper in the second graph is semilogarithmic, because only one scale is logarithmic.

USING SEMILOGARITHMIC GRAPH PAPER

Debbie deposits some money into a savings account. The table shows the growth of this money over a number of years. She makes no other deposits or withdrawals.

t (years)	5	10	15	20
Amount ($)	8400	14 100	23 700	39 700

1. How much did Debbie initially deposit into the account?

2. How much will be in the account after 25 years?

Solution

1. First plot the points on semilog graph paper. Draw the line of best fit.

Notice that the line crosses the y-axis at about 5000. So $y = 5000$ if $x = 0$.

In the general exponential growth function $y = c(a)^x$, c represents the initial amount. In this case, $c = 5000$.

Therefore, Debbie deposited $5000 into the account.

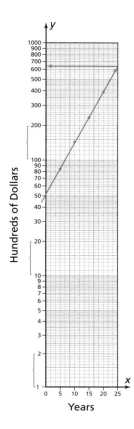

Hundreds of Dollars

Years

2. Choose a point on the line to help to determine a, the growth factor. Point $(5, 8400)$ appears to be on the line. Substitute this point into $y = 5000(a)^x$.

$$y = 5000(a)^x \qquad \text{Substitute x = 5 and y = 7400.}$$
$$8400 = 5000(a)^5 \qquad \text{Divide by 5000.}$$
$$\frac{8400}{5000} = a^5 \qquad \text{Take the fifth root of each side.}$$
$$\left(\frac{8400}{5000}\right)^{\frac{1}{5}} = a \qquad \text{Evaluate.}$$
$$a \doteq 1.11 \qquad \text{Evaluate.}$$

So the estimated equation is $y = 5000(1.11)^x$.

Now use the equation to find the amount of the deposit after 25 years.

$$y = 5000(1.11)^x$$
$$y = 5000(1.11)^{25}$$
$$y \doteq 69\ 297.32$$

Therefore, the investment will be worth about $67 900.32 after 25 years.

You could also estimate the amount after 25 years from the graph.

FURTHER YOUR ANALYSIS

1. Plot points $P(2, 60)$ and $Q(12, 240)$ on semilog graph paper.
   Find the equation of the exponential function that includes these points.

2. After a dog is sprayed with flea spray, the fleas disappear at an exponential rate. These observations are made:

Time Elapsed (min)	10	20	25
Number of Fleas	105	36	22

Graph this data on semilog paper. Then, using the graph, estimate
(a) the number of fleas that were on the dog just before the dog is sprayed
(b) the time at which less than 1 flea is left

4 EXPLORATION · Investigating Rates of Change in Body Temperature

PURPOSE

In this exploration, you will use a temperature sensor to measure your body temperature for two minutes. Then you will allow the temperature sensor to return to room temperature. By analyzing the data, you will improve your understanding of the difference between **average** and **instantaneous** rates of change.

EQUIPMENT

- TI-83 Plus calculator
- TI CBL (Calculator-Based Laboratory)
- temperature sensor
- CBL/CBR application
- unit-to-unit link cable

PROCEDURE

1. Find a suitable place, such as a table or a desk, to set up your equipment. Choose a location that will permit you to hold the temperature sensor tightly between both hands for two minutes.

2. Turn the calculator ⬚ON⬚, press ⬚APPS⬚, and then execute the CBL/CBR application. When the first screen appears, press ⬚ENTER⬚ and then choose **2:DATA LOGGER**, which appears on the next screen. Ensure that you do the following:

   - Choose **PROBE:Temp** for the temperature sensor.
   - For **#SAMPLES**, enter 36 (12 samples each minute for 3 min).
   - For **INTRVL(SEC)**, enter 5 (1 sample every 5 s).
   - Choose °F for the temperature **UNITS**. (This scale produces a better graph than the Celsius scale.)
   - Choose **RealTme** for **PLOT** to plot the graph as the data are collected.
   - Choose **On** for **DIRECTNS**.

3. Scroll down to **GO...** and press ⬚ENTER⬚.

4. Follow the directions on the next few screens.

   (a) Use the unit-to-unit link cable to link the CBL and the TI-83 Plus. Then press ⬚ENTER⬚.

   (b) Plug the temperature probe into the CH 1 port of the CBL and press ⬚ENTER⬚.

temperature
sensor

(c) Turn the CBL on and press ENTER.

(d) The calculator will check the link connection. If a **LINK ERROR** occurs, follow the directions on the screen.

(e) When you are ready to start, grasp the temperature sensor with both hands as shown in the diagram. Another student should press ENTER to begin the data collection process.

5. After exactly two minutes, release the temperature sensor and allow it to rest on the desk for one additional minute.

6. Observe the graph that has been plotted. You can use the TRACE key to see more points in the graph.

7. Press ENTER followed by 2nd MODE and choose **4:QUIT** to exit the CBL Application.

8. To examine the data collected in a table, press STAT and choose **1:EDIT**. Scroll up to highlight **L1**, press 2nd STAT, and choose **TTEMP**. Then press ENTER twice. The data for time in seconds will be displayed in **L1**. Scroll up to highlight **L2**, press 2nd STAT, choose the name **TEMP**, and then press ENTER twice. The data for temperature in degrees Farenheit will be displayed in **L2**. Press GRAPH to display the graph of temperature versus time.

ANALYSIS

1. At what time was the temperature the highest? the lowest?

2. What does the highest temperature correspond to? the lowest temperature?

3. Are there any times when the temperature remained fairly constant? Why would the temperature remain fairly constant?

4. (a) At what times was the temperature increasing? decreasing?

   (b) Determine the average rate of temperature change over an interval of time when the temperature

   i. increased   **ii.** decreased   **iii.** remained fairly constant

   (c) Make a conjecture about the significance of the sign ($+$ or $-$) of a rate of change and the behaviour of the graph.

5. When did the greatest rate of change occur? When was the temperature rising most rapidly? When was the temperature falling most rapidly?

6. Determine the average rate of change in temperature between

   (a) 25 s and 50 s   **(b)** 25 s and 45 s   **(c)** 25 s and 40 s

   (d) 25 s and 35 s   **(e)** 25 s and 30 s

7. Using the average rates of change you calculated for step 6, predict the rate at which the temperature is changing at exactly 25 s. Explain how you arrived at your estimate.

1. How could you improve your estimate? Suggest how you could modify the experiment so that the data would give a better estimate of the rate of temperature change at exactly 25 s.

2. Conduct the experiment again using your suggested changes and determine a new estimate for the rate of temperature change at exactly 25 s.

5 EXPLORATION Investigating Limiting Values of Functions

PURPOSE

In this exploration, you will use the TI-83 Plus calculator to investigate limits of a function and how they relate to the function's graph and table.

EQUIPMENT

- TI-83 Plus calculator

PROCEDURE 1   EXAMINING THE LIMIT OF A POLYNOMIAL FUNCTION

1. In the equation editor, ensure that all functions have been cleared. Then enter the function $y = x^4 + 2x^3 - 13x^2 - 14x + 24$. Press WINDOW and set **Xmin=-10, Xmax=10, Xscl=1, Ymin=-30, Ymax=30, Yscl=1, Xres=1**.

2. Press GRAPH to display the graph.

3. Investigate $\lim\limits_{x \to 1} (x^4 + 2x^3 - 13x^2 - 14x + 24)$.

$y = x^4 + 2x^3 - 13x^2 - 14x + 24$

   (a) *Approaching x = 1 from the right*
   Press TRACE and position the cursor near the point where $x = 2$. Use ◄ to scroll toward $x = 1$. Observe the coordinates of the points on the graph as you scroll. Determine the value that y approaches as x approaches 1.

   (b) *Approaching x = 1 from the left*
   Position the cursor near the point where $x = 0$. Use ► to scroll toward $x = 1$. Observe the coordinates as you scroll. Determine the value that y approaches as x approaches 1.

   (c) From your results, can you accurately predict
   $$\lim\limits_{x \to 1} (x^4 + 2x^3 - 13x^2 - 14x + 24)?$$

4. Refine your prediction by examining a table for the function.

  (a) *Approaching $x = 1$ from the right*

  i. Press 2nd WINDOW to view **TABLE SETUP**, then set **TblStart=2** and **ΔTbl=−0.1**. Press 2nd GRAPH. Use ▲ and ▼ to examine the values of y (**Y1**) as x decreases toward 1.

  ii. Repeat the steps in (i), but set **TblStart=1.1** and **ΔTbl=−0.01**. Press 2nd GRAPH. Examine the values of y as x approaches 1.

  iii. Repeat the steps in (i), but set **TblStart=1.01** and **ΔTbl=−0.001**. Press 2nd GRAPH. Examine the values of y as x approaches 1.

  (b) *Approaching $x = 1$ from the left*

  i. As before, press 2nd WINDOW to view **TABLE SETUP**. Set **TblStart=0** and **ΔTbl=0.1**. Press 2nd GRAPH. Use ▲ and ▼ to examine the values of y as x increases toward 1.

  ii. Repeat, setting **TblStart=0.9** and **ΔTbl=0.01**.

  iii. Repeat, setting **TblStart=0.99** and **ΔTbl=0.001**.

ANALYSIS 1

1. What can you conclude about the value of
$$\lim_{x \to 1} (x^4 + 2x^3 - 13x^2 - 14x + 24)?$$

2. In the tables, what y-value does the calculator always display for $x = 1$?

3. Explain how your answer to step 2 relates to the limit value you found for step 1.

4. In this procedure, you changed the **TblStart** and **ΔTbl** settings to create three different tables. Explain why those particular settings were chosen.

5. What settings would you use to examine the limit in each case to create a fourth table for extending the procedure?

  (a) approaching from the right

  (b) approaching from the left

PROCEDURE 2 **EXAMINING THE LIMIT OF A RECIPROCAL FUNCTION**

1. In the equation editor, ensure that all functions have been cleared. Then enter the function $y = \frac{1}{x}$. Press WINDOW and set **Xmin=−3**, **Xmax=3**, **Xscl=1**, **Ymin=−5**, **Ymax=5**, **Yscl=1**, **Xres=1**.

2. Press GRAPH to display the graph.

3. Investigate $\lim_{x \to 0} \frac{1}{x}$, using TRACE to see the coordinates of points on both sides of $x = 0$. Describe what you observe.

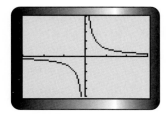

$y = \frac{1}{x}$

4. Refine your prediction using a table.

    (a) *Approaching x = 0 from the right*

        i. Start by setting **TblStart=1** and **ΔTbl=−0.1** on the **TABLE SETUP** screen. Use ▲ and ▼ to examine the values of y as x decreases toward 0.

        ii. Repeat, setting **TblStart=0.1** and **ΔTbl=−0.01**.

        iii. Repeat, setting **TblStart=0.01** and **ΔTbl=−0.001**.

    (b) *Approaching x = 0 from the left*

        i. Start by setting **TblStart=−1** and **ΔTbl=0.1**. Use ▲ and ▼ to examine the values of y as x increases toward 0.

        ii. Repeat, setting **TblStart=−0.1** and **ΔTbl=0.01**.

        iii. Repeat, setting **TblStart=−0.01** and **ΔTbl=0.001**.

ANALYSIS 2

1. What can you conclude about the value of $\lim\limits_{x \to 0} \dfrac{1}{x}$?

2. In the tables, what y-value does the calculator always display for $x = 0$?

3. Why does this occur?

FURTHER YOUR ANALYSIS

Investigate each limit, using the graphing calculator to create graphs and tables.

(a) $\lim\limits_{x \to 3} (x^3 + 2x^2 - 5x - 4)$

(b) $\lim\limits_{x \to 3} \dfrac{1}{x - 3}$

(c) $\lim\limits_{x \to -2} [-5(x + 2)^2 + 4]$

(d) $\lim\limits_{x \to -4} \dfrac{3}{4 + x}$

---

6 EXPLORATION Investigating the Behaviour of the Derivative of Polynomial Functions

PURPOSE

In this activity, you will sketch the graph of several polynomial functions and predict the behaviour of the derivative by examining tangent lines at various points along the curve. Then you will verify your findings using graphing technology.

EQUIPMENT

- graph paper
- TI-83 Plus calculator

PROCEDURE

1. Factor the polynomial function $f(x) = 6x - x^2$ and determine the zeros.

2. Determine several other points on the graph by completing the table.

x	−2	−1	0	1	2	3	4	5	6	7	8
$f(x)$											

3. Using the zeros and the table, draw an accurate graph of the function.

4. On your graph, draw the approximate tangent line at each plotted point.

ANALYSIS

1. Moving from left to right, for what values of x does the function increase? decrease?

2. **(a)** Use your graph to approximate the slope of each tangent line to two decimal places. Copy and complete the table.

x	−2	−1	0	1	2	3	4	5	6	7	8
Slope of Tangent											

(b) Check the accuracy of your slope approximations using graphing technology.

   i. Enter the function into **Y1** of the equation editor and press ZOOM 8 to graph the function using an integer scale.

   ii. Move the cursor to the origin and press ENTER.

   iii. Using TRACE, move the cursor to $(-2, -16)$.

   iv. Press 2nd PRGM 5 and ENTER to draw the tangent line.

   v. The equation of the tangent line is given in the form $y = mx + b$. Compare the calculator slope to your prediction and adjust the value in your table, if necessary.

   vi. Press TRACE, move the cursor to $(-1, -7)$, and repeat steps iv and v.

   vii. Repeat vi for each x-value in the table.

3. **(a)** Examine the slopes of the tangent lines in the interval where the function is increasing. What do you notice?

   (b) What can you conclude about the slope of all tangent lines when a function is increasing?

4. **(a)** Examine the slopes of the tangent lines in the interval where the function is decreasing. What do you notice?

   (b) What can you conclude about the slope of all tangent lines when a function is decreasing?

5. (a) What is the absolute maximum value of this function? Verify your prediction by completing the square or using graphing technology.

   (b) What is the slope of the tangent line at the maximum value?

   (c) What can you conclude about the slope of the tangent line at a maximum point?

6. (a) Differentiate the original function.

   (b) Clear all tangent lines by pressing [2nd] [PRGM] [1].

   (c) Enter the derivative into **Y2** of the equation editor and graph by pressing [ZOOM] [6].

7. (a) Where is the derivative positive? negative? zero? How does this information relate to the original function $f(x)$?

   (b) How do these intervals compare with the intervals that you found for the slopes of all lines tangent to $f(x)$?

FURTHER YOUR ANALYSIS

1. Repeat all the steps of the procedure and analysis above for the function $f(x) = x^2 - 4x$.

2. Are your conclusions about the behaviour of the derivative any different for this function? Explain.

3. Generalize the results of this activity by explaining how the derivative of a function behaves

   (a) when the function is increasing

   (b) when the function is decreasing

   (c) at a maximum value

   (d) at a minimum value

EXPLORATION Investigating the Behaviour of the Second Derivative of Polynomial Functions

PURPOSE

You have seen that polynomial functions can increase and decrease over different intervals on the domain. These changes in the values of a function result in graphs that appear to have "hills" and "valleys." Any function that contains a hill is said to be "concave down" on that interval, while a valley is described as "concave up." The point where a curve changes from concave down to concave up or vice versa is called a **point of inflection**.

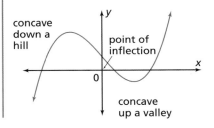

In this activity you will sketch the graph of a polynomial function and examine the behaviour of the second derivative of the function. Then you will relate your findings back to the shape of the original function.

EQUIPMENT

• TI-83 Plus calculator

PROCEDURE 1

1. Enter $f(x) = x^2$ into Y1 in the equation editor. Press $\boxed{\text{ZOOM}}$ $\boxed{6}$ to graph the function. Describe the shape of the graph. Use the differentiation rules to determine $f'(x)$ and enter this function into **Y2** in the equation editor. Press $\boxed{\text{GRAPH}}$. Is $f'(x)$ increasing or decreasing? Predict if $f''(x)$ will be positive or negative. To check your prediction, find $f''(x)$ algebraically. Enter it into **Y3** and press $\boxed{\text{GRAPH}}$.

2. Clear all functions from the equation editor and repeat step 1 for each of the following functions. (After you have examined a function and both the first and second derivatives, clear the equation editor before moving on to the next.)

   (a) $f(x) = x^2 - 4x + 5$ **(b)** $f(x) = 2x^2 + 3x + 4$

   (c) $f(x) = 4x^2 - 6x - 3$ **(d)** $f(x) = 6x^2 + 10x - 5$

ANALYSIS 1

1. What common shape do all of the above functions have? What do you notice about the behaviour of the first derivative of these functions? What do you notice about the sign of the second derivative of these functions?

PROCEDURE 2

1. Enter $f(x) = -x^2$ into Y1 in the equation editor. Press ZOOM 6 to GRAPH the function. Describe the shape of the graph. Find $f'(x)$ and enter this function into Y2 in the equation editor. Press GRAPH. Is $f'(x)$ increasing or decreasing? Predict whether $f''(x)$ will be positive or negative. To check your prediction, find $f''(x)$ algebraically. Enter it into **Y3**. Press GRAPH.

2. Repeat step 1 for each function.

   (a) $f(x) = -x^2 - 3x + 2$ **(b)** $f(x) = -2x^2 + 4x + 5$

   (c) $f(x) = -5x^2 - x - 1$ **(d)** $f(x) = -0.5x^2$

ANALYSIS 2

1. What common shape do all of the above functions have? What do you notice about the behaviour of the first derivative of these functions? What do you notice about the sign of the second derivative of these functions?

FURTHER YOUR ANALYSIS

1. Clear the equation editor, then enter the function $f(x) = x^3 - 6x$ into Y1. Graph by pressing ZOOM 6

   (a) Predict where the function is concave up and concave down.

   (b) Predict where the first derivative is increasing or decreasing.

   (c) Predict where the second derivative is positive or negative

   (d) Find $f'(x)$ and $f''(x)$. Enter $f'(x)$ into Y2 and $f''(x)$ into Y3, and graph them to check your predictions.

2. **(a)** At what value of x does the graph change from concave down to concave up?

   (b) What is the slope of the tangent line to the first derivative at this value?

   (c) For any polynomial function, what must the second derivative equal at the point where the function changes concavity?

3. Generalize the results of this activity by copying and completing the table.

	Concave Upward		Concave Downward		Point of Inflection	
Shape of $f(x)$						
Sign of $f'(x)$						
Sign of $f''(x)$						

EXPLORATION Investigating Rational Functions Using a Graphing Calculator

PURPOSE

Adding, subtracting, or multiplying two polynomial functions yields another polynomial function. Dividing two polynomial functions results in a function that is *not* a polynomial. The quotient is called a **rational function**. You are already familiar with the properties of the reciprocal function $f(x) = \frac{1}{x}$, which is the simplest rational function. In this exploration, you will investigate the special features of the graphs of rational functions. Do the graphs of all rational function have the same features?

EQUIPMENT

• TI-83 Plus calculator

PROCEDURE

1. Using a graphing calculator, set the window ($\boxed{\text{WINDOW}}$) for *x*-values from -4.7 to 4.7 and for *y*-values from -5 to 5. Enter the rational function $f(x) = \frac{x-2}{x+1}$ into **Y1** of the equation editor. Obtain the graph. Graph the function in your notebook. Indicate the zeros, any vertical asymptote(s), any horizontal asymptote(s), or any other line that the graph approaches, for example, an oblique asymptote. Write the equations of the asymptotes if you know them. (Hint: Use $\boxed{\text{TRACE}}$ to investigate zeros and asymptotes.)

2. Repeat question 1 for each rational function. Be sure to clear each function before graphing a new one.

   (a) $f(x) = \frac{2x+1}{x-1}$ **(b)** $f(x) = \frac{1}{x^2}$ **(c)** $f(x) = \frac{(2x-1)}{x^2}$

   (d) $f(x) = \frac{7}{(x+3)(x-1)}$ **(e)** $f(x) = \frac{x}{x^2-9}$ **(f)** $f(x) = \frac{x^2-2x-3}{x^2+x-6}$

   (g) $f(x) = \frac{9}{x^2+3}$ **(h)** $f(x) = \frac{x^2-1}{x}$ **(i)** $f(x) = \frac{(x-1)(2x+5)}{3x+5}$

ANALYSIS

1. Compare all your sketches. Does each graph have at least one vertical asymptote? Is it possible to tell if the graph will have a vertical asymptote from the function's equation? Explain your answer.

2. Does each graph have at least one horizontal asymptote? Is it possible to tell if the graph will have a horizontal asymptote from the function's equation? Explain your answer.

3. Do all rational functions have zeros? How do you determine zeros from the function's equation?

4. The graphs of the functions in (h) and (i) have oblique asymptotes. What makes these functions different from the other functions? Rewrite the function in (h) by separating the function equation into two fractions and then sinplifying each fraction. Explain how you can get the equation of the oblique asymptote from this new form of the equation.

5. The new form of equation for the function in (h) has a linear part and a rational part. Enter the linear part as a second equation into your calculator. Graph the original function and the linear equation on the same set of axes. What do you notice? What is the equation of the oblique asymptote?

---

9 EXPLORATION Unreduced Rational Functions: Another Look at the $\frac{0}{0}$ Case

PURPOSE

You have learned from section 5.2 that a function should be simplified before solving a limit by substitution. Sometimes substituting into an unreduced rational fraction can result in the indeterminate case, $\frac{0}{0}$. In this exploration, you will examine the special feature of the graph of an unreduced rational function.

EQUIPMENT

• TI-83 Plus calculator

PROCEDURE

1. Using a graphing calculator, set the window for x- and y-values from -5 to 5. Enter $f(x) = x - 2$ into **Y1** and $g(x) = \frac{2x^2 - 7x + 6}{2x - 3}$ into **Y2**.

   Display the graphs of both functions in the same window. Describe what you see. What does this tell you about the two functions?

2. Clear the graph of $f(x) = x - 2$ and regraph. Do you see any change in the graph? Take a closer look at part of the graph by changing the window settings to the ones shown here. Press GRAPH.

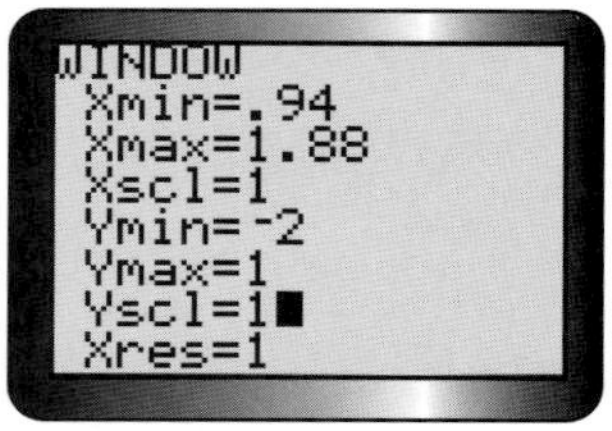

   ```
   WINDOW
   Xmin=.94
   Xmax=1.88
   Xscl=1
   Ymin=-2
   Ymax=1
   Yscl=1■
   Xres=1
   ```

Trace along the curve slowly from left to right. Having set the window correctly, you should see that the x-value displayed increases by 0.01 each time you press ▶. What happens to the graph when you reach the point where $x = 1.5$? What y-value is displayed? Where is the trace cursor? What does your answer tell about $g(x)$ at that point? Continue tracing the graph. Has the cursor returned?

3. Factor the numerator of $g(x)$. Explain why the graphs of $f(x)$ and $g(x)$ look the same. Explain why the graph of $g(x)$ has a hole in it at the point where $x = 1.5$. What is the domain of $f(x)$? of $g(x)$?

4. How many zeros does $g(x)$ have? Does this surprise you? Explain your answer.

ANALYSIS

1. Describe the graph of $h(x) = \dfrac{2x^2 + x - 1}{x + 1}$ without graphing. Factor the numerator first. Verify your answer with a graphing calculator. State the domain and range and any zeros of $h(x)$.

2. By first factoring the denominator, describe the graph of $f(x) = \dfrac{x - 3}{x^2 - 3x}$, without graphing. Verify your answer with a graphing calculator. State the domain and range and any zeros of $f(x)$.

3. In Example 3 of section 5.2, the graph of $f(x) = \dfrac{x^3 + 1}{x + 1}$ did not appear to have a hole in it. By using different window settings, show that there is a hole in the graph. At what point does the hole occur?

FURTHER YOUR ANALYSIS

1. For each rational function, describe the graph without graphing. State the domain and the zeros. At what point do the holes, if any, occur? Then verify your answers using a graphing calculator.

   (a) $f(x) = \dfrac{x^2 - 2x - 15}{x + 3}$

   (b) $g(x) = \dfrac{x + 1}{x^2 - 4x - 5}$

   (c) $f(x) = \dfrac{x^3 - 27}{x - 3}$

   (d) $m(x) = \dfrac{x^5 - 1}{x^2 - 1}$

2. Create a function with

   (a) a zero at $x = 1$ and a hole at $x = 2.5$

   (b) zeros at $x = -4$ and $x = 2$ and a hole at $x = -1$

   (c) a vertical asymptote with equation $x = 3$ and a hole at $x = 0$

3. Verify the functions you created for question 2 using a graphing calculator.

EXPLORATION Local Linearity in Rational and Other Functions

PURPOSE

In chapter 2, you learned that a function is differentiable at a number a in the domain of the function if $f'(a)$ exists. For $f'(a)$ to exist, then $\lim\limits_{h \to 0} \dfrac{f(a + h) - f(a)}{h}$ must exist, and the slopes of the secant lines approach a single value. The graph of a function that is differentiable at a point resembles the tangent line at that point. In this case, the function is "locally linear." In this exploration, you will use a [ZOOM] instruction on a graphing calculator to investigate the local linearity of some functions.

EQUIPMENT

- TI-83 Plus calculator

PROCEDURE

1. Use a graphing calculator to graph $f(x) = \dfrac{x + 1}{x - 3}$ for x-values from -9.4 to 9.4 and y-values from -6.2 to 6.2. Press [TRACE] and scroll left or right until you reach point $(2, -3)$. Now zoom in ([ZOOM] 2 [ENTER]) three times. The graph should be linear. Look at the window settings to see changes in them. Investigate other points on the graph of $f(x)$. Remember to reset the window settings to the original values before you begin to zoom in. Does the graph always become linear after zooming in three times?

ANALYSIS

1. Graph $g(x) = \dfrac{4x}{x^2 + 1}$. Determine whether the graph is locally linear at **(a)** $(0, 0)$ and **(b)** $(1, 2)$. For each point, how many times did you zoom in before the graph became linear? What were the window settings for the last time you zoomed in for each point? Explain the results.

2. Investigate whether $h(x) = |x|$ is locally linear at point $(0, 0)$. Enter the function **Y1** of the equation editor by pressing [Y=] [MATH] [▶] [1] [X,T,Θ,n] [)] [GRAPH].

3. With the same <u>window settings</u> in step 1 of the procedure, enter $|x| + 2$ into **Y1** and enter $\sqrt{x^2 + 0.0001} + 1.99$ into **Y2**. Display the graphs. What do you notice? Trace to point $(0, 2)$ and zoom in a few times. Now what do you notice? What can you say about the differentiability of each function at $(0, 2)$? Explain.

Investigate the local linearity of each function.

1. $f(x) = \dfrac{x^3 - 27}{x - 3}$ at $x = 3$ **2.** $f(x) = \sqrt{3 - x}$ at $x = 3$

3. $f(x) = \begin{cases} 1 & \text{if } x < 1 \\ (x - 1)^2 + 1 & \text{if } x \geq 1 \end{cases}$ at $x = 1$

4. $f(x) = \begin{cases} 3 - x^2 & \text{if } x \leq 2 \\ -1 & \text{if } x > 2 \end{cases}$ at $x = 2$

5. $f(x) = |x - 4|$ at $x = 4$ **6.** $f(x) = (2x - 5)^{\frac{2}{3}}$ at $x = 2.5$

---

11 EXPLORATION Investigating the Relationship between Functions

PURPOSE

In this exploration, you will examine the relationships among three variables in a problem involving a radar gun.

Sometimes people wonder about the accuracy of radar guns used to catch speeding drivers. Suppose the operator is not very close to the road. In this case, the radar gun measures the speed of the car at an angle, instead of straight on. In this activity, you will do an experiment that models this situation.

EQUIPMENT

- TI-83 Plus calculator
- TI CBR (Calculator-Based Ranger)
- measuring tape or metre stick
- masking tape

PROCEDURE

1. Lay a strip of masking tape on the floor to represent a straight road.

2. Locate a point 1 m from the "road" and mark the spot with masking tape. This point represents the radar gun.

3. Set up the CBR at one end of the road. Have someone walk (or move a large solid object) along the road toward the CBR at a constant speed. The independent variable in this case is the elapsed time in seconds. The dependent variable is the distance from the CBR, in metres.

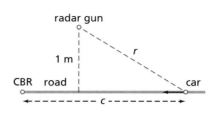

To enter the data using the graphing calculator, press STAT and select **1:Edit**. Enter the values for the elapsed time in **L1**. ENTER the corresponding values for distance into **L2**. Choose at least 10 pairs of values. Round all values to the nearest tenth. Use a good range of values.

4. As the "car" moves along the road, measure the distance from the car to the CBR, c, and from the car to the radar gun, r, with the measuring tape at different points as the car passes by. You should include some of the same c-values that you collected in step 3. Record your data in a table. Use the distance to the CBR as the independent variable, c, and the distance to the radar gun, r, as the dependent variable.

ANALYSIS

In addition to the variables c and r defined above, let t be the time in seconds since the CBR was started.

1. **(a)** Before looking at the data, predict the graph of r versus c and sketch it.
   (b) Graph the relationship between r and c. Draw a smooth curve through the points.
   (c) Compare your prediction with the actual graph. Explain any differences.
   (d) What does the slope of the tangent at any point on this graph represent?

2. **(a)** Using the data collected from the CBR, graph c versus t by hand.
   (b) What should this graph look like if the speed of the car was constant?
   (c) What does the slope of the tangent at any point on this graph represent?

3. **(a)** Use the stat list editor (STAT **1:Edit**) to find the value of c when $t = 2.0$ (or close to 2.0).
   (b) Use this c-value to determine the value of r after 2.0 s.
   (c) Compare these two distances. Explain.
   (d) Create a table for r versus t. Graph r versus t on the same set of axes that you used for graphing c versus t in step 2(a).
   (e) What does the slope of the tangent at any point on the graph of r versus t represent?
   (f) Compare the slopes of the tangents to both graphs at $t = 2.0$. Interpret the slopes in terms of the speed measured by the radar gun and the actual speed of the car.
   (g) When is the radar gun's reading closest to the actual speed of the car? Explain.

1. The graph of distance versus time for a car travelling along a straight road is shown.

   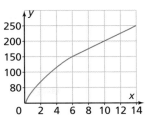

   (a) Describe the motion of the car.

   (b) Graph the distance as measured by the radar gun versus time. Assume the car passes the radar gun after 8 s.

2. A police officer is standing 2 m from the side of a straight road. A car is travelling at a constant speed of 30 m/s along the road on the same side by which the officer is standing. Let t be the elapsed time since the radar gun was pointed at the car (in seconds), c be the distance the car has travelled (in metres) during that time, and r be the distance from the car to the radar gun at any time t. Determine formulas for

   (a) c in terms of t (b) r in terms of c (c) r in terms of t

---

12 EXPLORATION Using Technology to Investigate Composite Functions

PURPOSE

In this activity, you will experiment with different combinations of functions to better understand the effect of operations on the graphs of functions.

EQUIPMENT

- TI-83 Plus calculator

PROCEDURE

EXPERIMENTING WITH FUNCTION OPERATIONS

Press **Zoom**, and then select **6:ZStandard** to set up the graphing window on the calculator. In each activity, clear any old equations from the equation editor before entering new ones. You may have to adjust the window to view a graph properly.

1. (a) Enter **Y1=$\sqrt{\ }$ (X)**, **Y2=0.2X²−X−1**, and **Y3=1/X** and graph them on the same axes.

   (b) Different expressions for **Y4** are given. Do the following for each one.

      • Enter and graph **Y4**. To enter **Y1**, **Y2**, and **Y3** press $\boxed{\text{VARS}}$. Then select **Y-VARS** and **1:Function…**. Press $\boxed{\text{ENTER}}$ and select the correct variable.

- Describe in writing how each expression of **Y4** affects the graphs of **Y1**, **Y2**, and **Y3**.
- Write the expression for **Y4** in function notation.

   i. Y4=3Y1   ii. Y4=−2Y1
   iii. Y4=5Y2   iv. Y4=Y3+3
   v. Y4=Y2−5   vi. Y4=Y1+Y2
   vii. Y4=5Y1+Y3   viii. Y4=Y1−3Y2+5

2. **(a)** Enter **Y1=2X+3**, **Y2=X−2**, and **Y3=0.2X²−X−1** and graph them on the same axes.

   (b) Different expressions for **Y4** are given. Do the following for each one.
   - Enter and graph **Y4**.
   - Describe in writing how each expression of **Y4** affects the graphs of **Y1**, **Y2**, and **Y3**.
   - Write the expression for **Y4** in function notation.

   ii. Y4=3Y2   ii. Y4=X*Y2
   iii. Y4=Y1*Y2   iv. Y4=Y1*Y3
   v. Y4=3/Y2   vi. Y4=3/Y1
   vii. Y4=Y1/Y2   viii. Y4=Y1/Y3

3. **(a)** Enter **Y1= 2X+3** and **Y2= X−2** and graph them on the same axes.

   (b) Different expressions for **Y3** are given. Do the following for each one.
   - Enter and graph **Y3**.
   - Describe in writing how each expression of **Y3** affects the graphs of **Y1** and **Y2**.
   - Write the expression for **Y3** in function notation.

   i. Y3=Y2^2   ii. Y3=Y2^3
   iii. Y3=Y2^(−1)   iv. Y3=Y2^(1/2)
   v. Y3=Y2^(−1/2)   vi. Y3=Y1+ Y2^2
   vii. Y3=1+2X+ Y2^2   viii. Y3=(1+2X+ Y2)^2

4. **(a)** Enter **Y1=2X+3**, **Y2=0.2X²−X−1**, and **Y3=√ (X)** into the equation editor and graph.

   (b) Different expressions for **Y4** are given In this case, each expression is the composition of two functions. Do the following for each one.
   - Enter and graph **Y4**.
   - Describe in writing how each expression of **Y4** affects the graphs of **Y1**, **Y2**, and **Y3**.

   (c) Can you find an expression for **Y4** without using the **Y** variables?

   i. Y4=Y1(Y2(X))   ii. Y4=Y2(Y1(X))
   iii. Y4=Y1(Y3(X))   iv. Y4=Y3 (Y1(X))
   v. Y4=Y2(Y3 (X))   vi. Y4=Y3(Y2(X))
   vii. Y4=Y2(Y2(X))   viii. Y4=Y3 (Y3 (X))

5. (a) Enter **Y1=X+3**, **Y2=X²**, **Y3=√(X)**, and **Y4=2X−5** into the equation editor and graph.

(b) Each graph represents some combination of **Y1**, **Y2**, **Y3**, and **Y4**. Enter expressions into **Y5** using **Y1**, **Y2**, **Y3**, and **Y4** to produce each graph.

i.   ii.

iii.   iv.

v.   vi.

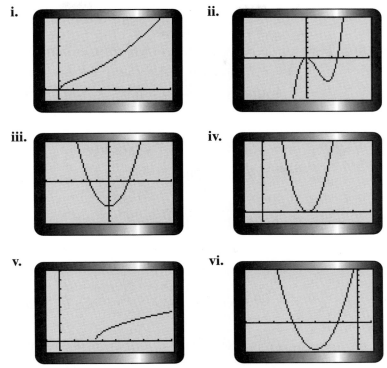

ANALYSIS

1. What type of function results when you
   (a) add a linear and quadratic function?
   (b) multiply a quadratic function by a linear function?
   (c) multiply a quadratic function by another quadratic?
   (d) take the composite of a linear function followed by a quadratic function?
   (e) take the composite of a quadratic function followed by another quadratic function?

13 EXPLORATION Investigating Related Rate Models

PURPOSE

When water drains from a funnel into a graduated cylinder, several things change. In this exploration, you will investigate the relations among several variables for one function.

EQUIPMENT

- large, conical funnel
- ruler
- graduated cylinder
- water
- stopwatch
- TI-83 Plus calculator

PROCEDURE

1. Measure and record the height of the cone. Estimate the location of the apex if necessary. Also measure and record the radius of the opening at the top of the funnel.

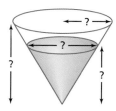

2. Plug the opening at the bottom and fill the funnel completely with water.

3. Allow the water to drain from the funnel and into the graduated cylinder for 5 s and then quickly plug the opening again. (Start over again and use a shorter time interval if the water drains out too quickly.)

4. Measure the vertical distance from the apex of the cone to the top of the surface of the water remaining in the funnel. Measure the diameter of the top surface of the water and record the radius. Record the volume of water in the graduated cylinder.

5. Repeat steps 3 and 4 until the funnel is empty. Use the same time interval each time you do step 3.

ANALYSIS

1. (a) Enter the values for time (**L1**), height (**L2**), radius (**L3**), and volume (**L4**) using the stat list editor of the TI-83 Plus.

   (b) What was the volume of water in the funnel before you began?

   (c) Calculate the volume of water remaining in the funnel at each time. Enter the values into **L5**.

Let t be the elapsed time in seconds, h be the height of the water's surface in centimetres, r be the radius of the water's surface in centimetres, V be the volume of water in the funnel in cubic centimetres, and A be the area of the water's surface in square centimetres.

2. **(a)** Graph the data for height versus radius.
   (b) What type of relation is height versus radius? Explain your choice.
   (c) Use regression to find the curve of best fit for this relation.
   (d) What is the domain of this relation?
   (e) Could you have determined this relation without measuring r and h every 5 s?
   (f) Determine $\frac{dh}{dr}$. What does $\frac{dh}{dr}$ represent in the context of this problem?

3. **(a)** Graph the data for height versus time.
   (b) What type of relation is height versus time? Explain.
   (c) Use regression to find the curve of best fit for this relation. What is the domain?
   (d) Determine $\frac{dh}{dt}$.
   (e) Describe the rate of change of height over time.

4. **(a)** Graph the data for radius versus time.
   (b) What type of relation is radius versus time? Explain your choice.
   (c) Use the relations you found in question 2 and 3 to determine $\frac{dr}{dt}$.
   (d) Use regression to find the curve of best fit between r and t. What is the domain?
   (e) Determine $\frac{dr}{dt}$ using the equation you found in (d).
   (f) Why might the two expressions you found for $\frac{dr}{dt}$ be different?
   (g) Describe the rate of change of the radius over time.

5. **(a)** Graph the data for volume versus time.
   (b) What type of relation is volume versus time? Explain.
   (c) Determine $\frac{dV}{dt}$ using the formula for the volume of a cone and the relations you found in questions 2 to 4. Could you determine $\frac{dV}{dt}$ in a different way?
   (d) Use regression to find the curve of best fit between V and t.
   (e) Determine $\frac{dV}{dt}$ using the equation you found in (d).
   (f) Why might the two expressions you found for $\frac{dV}{dt}$ be different?
   (g) Describe the rate of change of the volume over time.

1. **(a)** Write a formula for the area of the top surface of the water as a function of r.

    (b) Use this formula to determine $\dfrac{dA}{dt}$.

    (c) Graph the data for area versus time. Use regression to find the curve of best fit for the data. Use this equation to find another expression for $\dfrac{dA}{dt}$. Compare the two results.

---

14 EXPLORATION Introducing *e*

....

PURPOSE

In this exploration, you will look at a new number that has many useful properties.

PROCEDURE

1. You will begin with a graph of $y = a^x$, where $a > 1$, for $a = 2, 3, 5, 10$. First copy and complete the table.

x	$y = 2^x$	$y = 3^x$	$y = 5^x$	$y = 10^x$
-2				
-1				
0				
1				
2				
3				

2. Now graph these four functions on the same set of axes by hand or with graphing technology.

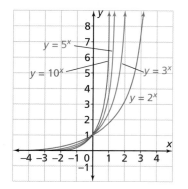

1. Using a graph or table, find each limit.

   (a) $\lim_{x \to \infty} a^x$ **(b)** $\lim_{x \to -\infty} a^x$ **(c)** $\lim_{x \to 0} a^x$

2. Consider the slope of the tangent line to each graph in the diagram at point $(0, 1)$. For instance, is the slope of the tangent to the curve $y = 2^x$ greater than or less than 1? Are the slopes of the tangents to the curves $y = 5^x$ or $y = 3^x$ greater than or less than 1?

3. Estimate a value for a so that the slope of the tangent at $(0, 1)$ is 1. This value is between two integers. What are these two integers?

4. Draw the graph of $y = a^x$ for the value of a you chose.

5. You probably graphed $y = e^x$ in question 4. e is a special number. The function $y = e^x$ is called the **natural exponential function**.

6. Use your calculator to find the value of e. (Let $x = 1$.) Compare this value with your estimate.

7. Using your graph of $y = e^x$, determine each limit.

   (a) $\lim_{x \to \infty} e^x$ **(b)** $\lim_{x \to -\infty} e^x$ **(c)** $\lim_{x \to 0} e^x$

15 EXPLORATION Newton's Law of Cooling

PURPOSE

As soon as a cup of hot coffee is poured, it begins to cool. Would the graph of time versus temperature be linear or nonlinear? What type of function models this situation better?

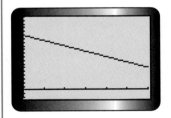 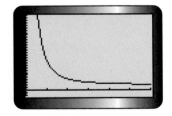

In this exploration, you will collect data and create a model of the cooling temperature of a cup of coffee.

EQUIPMENT

- TI-83 Plus calculator
- TI CBL (Calculator-Based Laboratory)
- temperature sensor
- CBL/CBR application
- unit-to-unit link cable
- cup of warm, but not scalding, liquid

1. Fill a cup with very warm, but not scalding, liquid. Place the cup on a flat surface, close to the CBL and calculator.

2. Turn the calculator ON, press APPS, and execute the CBL/CBR application. When the first screen appears, press ENTER and then choose **2:DATALOGGER**, which appears on the next screen. Be sure to do the following:
   • Choose **PROBE:Temp** for the temperature sensor.
   • For **#SAMPLES**, enter 30 (2 samples each minute for 15 min).
   • For **INTRVL(SEC)**, enter 30 (1 sample every 30 s)
   • Choose °C for the temperature units.
   • Choose **RealTme** for **PLOT** to plot the graph as the data are collected.
   • Choose **On** for **DIRECTNS**.

3. Scroll down to **GO…** and press ENTER.

4. Follow the directions on the next few screens.
   (a) Use the unit–to–unit link cable to link the CBL and the TI-83 Plus, then press ENTER.
   (b) Plug the temperature probe into CH 1 port of the CBL and press ENTER.
   (c) Turn the CBL on and press ENTER.
   (d) The calculator will check the link connection. If a **LINK ERROR** occurs, follow the directions on the screen.

5. Once you are satisfied with the placement of your equipment, use the temperature probe to record the room temperature. Press ENTER to collect the data.

6. After 30 s, the room temperature is displayed. Record this value, then immediately place the temperature sensor into the hot liquid. Use the calculator and CBL to collect data for the next 14 min and 30 s.

1. Observe the shape of the graph that is plotted. Will the temperature ever reach 0°C? What is the lowest recorded temperature?

2. What kind of function models the collected data?

3. Can you find an algebraic model to fit the data?

1. Press ENTER followed by 2nd MODE and choose **4:QUIT** to exit the CBL Application.

2. To examine the collected data in a table, press STAT and choose **1:EDIT.** Scroll up to highlight **L1**, then press 2nd STAT and choose the name **TTEMP**. Press ENTER twice. The TIME data will be displayed in **L1**. Scroll up to highlight **L2**, then press 2nd STAT and choose the name **TEMP**. Press ENTER twice. The TEMPERATURE data will be displayed in **L2**.

3. Enter the value for room temperature in **L3**. Calculate the difference between the temperature of the liquid, **L2**, and room temperature, **L3**, by scrolling over and up to highlight **L4**. Then enter "=L2–L3", followed by [ENTER].

4. Delete the first entry in each of the four lists, **L1** to **L4**. (This action eliminates the initial room temperature reading.)

5. Create a scatter plot using **L1** and **L4**.

6. Find the curve of best fit by performing an exponential regression using **L1** and **L4**. Refer to the **Technology Appendix** if necessary.

7. The exponential algebraic model is of the form $y = c(a)^x$. Can you change the base of your equation to e? In other words, can you create an equation in the form $y = c(e)^{kx}$? Explain.

8. The values in **L4** are the differences between the temperature of the liquid and the temperature of the air in the room. So, $y = T - S$, where T is the temperature of the liquid and S is the temperature of the surrounding air. Your algebraic model should now resemble Newton's Law of Cooling. After a long time, the temperature of the liquid will eventually reach room temperature. This law states that the rate at which a warm body cools is almost proportional to the temperature difference between the temperature of the warm object and the temperature of its surroundings.

$$T = (T_0 - S)e^{kt} + S \qquad \text{where } S \text{ is the surrounding temperature}$$

T_0 is the initial temperature of the object

k is a constant

T is the final temperature

9. Rewrite your algebraic model in the form $T = (T_0 - S)e^{kt} + S$.

Technology Appendix:
Using the TI-83 Plus Graphing Calculator

Preparing the Calculator

Before you graph any relation, be sure to clear any information left on the calculator from the last time it was used. You should always do the following:

1. **Clear all data in the lists.**
   Press $\boxed{\text{2nd}}$ $\boxed{+}$ $\boxed{4}$ $\boxed{\text{ENTER}}$.

2. **Turn off all stat plots.**
   Press $\boxed{\text{2nd}}$ $\boxed{\text{Y=}}$ $\boxed{4}$ $\boxed{\text{ENTER}}$.

3. **Clear all equations in the equation editor.**
   Press $\boxed{\text{Y=}}$, then press $\boxed{\text{CLEAR}}$ for each equation.

4. **Set the window so that the axes range from –10 to 10.**
   Press $\boxed{\text{ZOOM}}$ $\boxed{6}$. Press $\boxed{\text{WINDOW}}$ to verify.

Entering and Graphing Relations

Enter the equation of the relation into the equation editor. The calculator will display the graph.

1. **Graph.**
   To graph $y = 2x + 8$, press $\boxed{\text{Y=}}$ $\boxed{2}$ $\boxed{\text{X,T,Θ,n}}$ $\boxed{+}$ $\boxed{8}$ $\boxed{\text{GRAPH}}$. The graph will be displayed as shown.

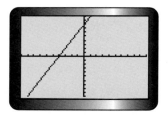

2. **Enter all linear equations in the form $y = mx + b$.**
   If m or b is a fraction, enter it between brackets. For example, enter $2x + 3y = 7$ in the form $y = -\frac{2}{3}x + \frac{7}{3}$ as shown.

3. **Press $\boxed{\text{GRAPH}}$ to view the graph.**

Tracing on the Graph

Press $\boxed{\text{TRACE}}$ to find the coordinates of any point on a graph. Use the left and right arrow keys to cursor along the graph. Press $\boxed{\text{ZOOM}}$ $\boxed{8}$ $\boxed{\text{ENTER}}$ $\boxed{\text{TRACE}}$ to trace using integer intervals.

Viewing the Graph in Better Detail

To see a closer view of a particular area of a graph, cursor over to that point and press $\boxed{\text{ZOOM}}$ $\boxed{2}$ $\boxed{\text{ENTER}}$. To see a broader view of the graph, press $\boxed{\text{ZOOM}}$ $\boxed{3}$ $\boxed{\text{ENTER}}$.

Sometimes when you enter an equation and press $\boxed{\text{GRAPH}}$, the graph does not appear in the viewing window at all or appears, incorrectly, as a vertical or horizontal line. This happens when the viewing window is too small or too big. In this case, use **ZoomFit**. Press $\boxed{\text{ZOOM}}$ $\boxed{0}$. You may still have to zoom in or out.

Using the Split Screen

To see a graph and the equation editor at the same time, press $\boxed{\text{MODE}}$ and cursor to **Horiz.** Press $\boxed{\text{ENTER}}$ to select this, then press $\boxed{\text{2nd}}$ $\boxed{\text{MODE}}$ to return to the home screen.

Enter $y = x^2$ in **Y1** of the equation editor, then press $\boxed{\text{GRAPH}}$.

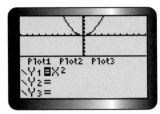

To see a graph and a table at the same time, press $\boxed{\text{MODE}}$ and cursor to **G-T** (Graph-Table). Press $\boxed{\text{ENTER}}$ to select this, then press $\boxed{\text{GRAPH}}$.

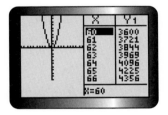

Using the Table Feature

It is possible to view the table with different increments. For example, to see the table start at $x = 0$ and increase in increments of 0.5, press $\boxed{\text{2nd}}$ $\boxed{\text{WINDOW}}$ and adjust the settings as shown.

Press $\boxed{\text{GRAPH}}$.

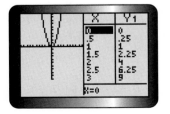

Finding the Point of Intersection

The TI-83 Plus can draw several graphs at the same time. This feature lets you graph simple linear equations and find their point of intersection. For example, find the point where $y = 5x + 4$ and $y = -2x + 18$ intersect as follows.

1. **Enter both equations into the equation editor.**

2. **Press $\boxed{\text{GRAPH}}$.**
   The point of intersection is out of view.

3. **Use the intersect command.**
   Press $\boxed{\text{2nd}}$ $\boxed{\text{TRACE}}$ $\boxed{5}$.

4. **The calculator will ask you to verify the two curves and enter a guess (optional) for the point of intersection.**
   Press $\boxed{\text{ENTER}}$ after each screen appears.

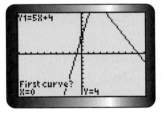

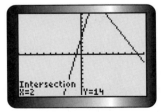

The point of intersection is exactly $(2, 14)$.

Finding the Zeros of a Relation

To find the zeros of a relation, use the **zero** command.

1. **Start by entering** $y = -(x + 3)(x - 5)$ **in the equation editor, then press** GRAPH ZOOM 6.

2. **Access the** zero **command.**
    Press 2nd TRACE 2.

3. **Use the left and right arrow keys to cursor along the curve to any point to the left of the zero.**
    Press ENTER to set the left bound.

4. **Cursor along the curve to any point to the right of the zero.**
    Press ENTER to set the right bound.

5. **Press** ENTER **again to display the coordinates of the zero (the** x**-intercept).**

6. **Repeat to find the second zero.**

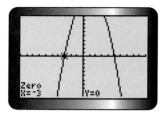

Finding the Maximum or Minimum Values of a Relation

The optimal value can be found using the **minimum** command or the **maximum** command.

1. **Enter** $y = -2x^2 - 12x + 30.$
    Graph it and adjust the window as shown. This graph opens downward, so it has a maximum.

    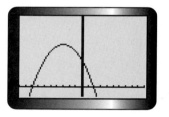

2. **Use the** maximum **command.**
    Press 2nd TRACE 4. For parabolas that open upward, press 2nd TRACE 3 to use the minimum command.

3. **Use the left and right arrow keys to cursor along the curve to any point to the left of the maximum value.**
    Press ENTER to set the left bound.

    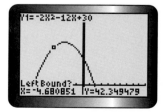

4. **Cursor along the curve to any point right of the maximum value.**
   Press [ENTER] to set the right bound.

5. **Press [ENTER] again to display the coordinates of the optimal value.**

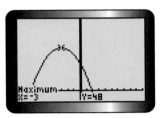

Scatter Plots and Lines and Curves of Best Fit

The coach of a soccer team wants to know if there is a relationship between the number of shots his team takes during a game and the number of goals they score. He collected this data from the last few games.

Shots	11	20	24	28	27	33	17	38
Goals	1	2	0	3	2	3	1	4

1. **Enter the data into lists.**
   Press [STAT] [ENTER]. Cursor over to the first position in **L1** and enter the values for shots. Press [ENTER] after each value. Enter the goals in **L2**.

2. **Turn on the stat plots.**
   To create a scatter plot, press [2nd] [Y=] [1] [ENTER]. Turn on Plot 1 by making sure the cursor is over **On**, the **Type** is set to the graph type you prefer, and **L1** and **L2** appear after **Xlist** and **Ylist**.

3. **Display the graph.**
   Press [ZOOM] [9] to activate **9:ZoomStat**.

Finding the Line of Best Fit Using Linear Regression

For linear data, a line of best fit can be determined.

4. **Draw the linear regression line.**
   Superimpose a line of best fit on the scatter plot by pressing [STAT] and moving the cursor to **CALC** and pressing [4]. This activates the linear regression function.

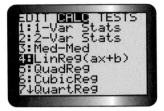

5. **Enter the data to be analyzed.**
   Enter each list, separated by a comma. Press [2nd] [1] [,] [2nd] [2] [,] [VARS]. Scroll over to **Y-VARS**. Press [1] twice. This action stores the equation of the line of best fit into **Y1** of the equation editor.

6. **Display the results of the analysis.**
   Press [ENTER].

7. **Plot the line.**
   Press [GRAPH].

8. **Analyze the results.**
   The letter a is the slope of the line and the letter b is the y-intercept. The letter r is the correlation coefficient and is used to determine how well the model fits the data. The value r^2 is the percentage of data represented by the model.

   In this case, the equation is about $y = 0.11x - 0.84$.

Note: If r is not displayed, turn on the diagnostics function. Press [2nd] [0] and scroll down to **DiagnosticOn**. Press [ENTER] twice. Repeat steps 4 to 6.

Finding the Curve of Best Fit Using Other Regressions

This table gives the height of a baseball above the ground, from the time it was hit to the time it touched the ground.

Time (s)	0	1	2	3	4	5	6
Height (m)	2	27	42	48	43	29	5

Create a scatter plot of the data. (See steps 1 to 3 in the first column of the previous page.) The data is clearly nonlinear. Use a curve of best fit to model the data.

To find the equation of the curve of best fit you could use **quadratic regression**, **cubic regression**, **quartic regression**, or **exponential regression**.

1. **Press [STAT] and scroll over to CALC.**
   Decide on which type of polynomial to use to model the data. Press [5] to enable **QuadReg**, [6] to enable **CubicReg**, [7] to enable **QuartReg**, and [0] to enable **ExpReg**.

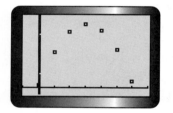

2. **Enter the data to be analyzed.**
   Enter each list, separated by a comma. Press [2nd] [1] [,] [2nd] [2] [,] [VARS]. Scroll over to **Y-VARS**. Press [1] twice. This action stores the equation of the curve of best fit into **Y1** of the equation editor.

3. **Display the results of the analysis.**
   Press [ENTER].

4. **Plot the curve.**
   Press [GRAPH].

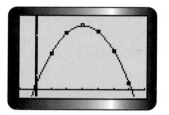

5. **Analyze the results.**
   In the case of quadratic, cubic, and quartic regression, the coefficients a, b, c, d, and e define the general polynomial equation $y = ax^n + bx^{n-1} + cx^{n-2} + dx^{n-3} + e$ for the curve of best fit, where $n \in 2$, 3, and 4. For exponential regression the coefficients a and b define the general exponential equation $y = ab^x$. R^2 is the percentage of the data represented by the model. For this relation, quadratic regression was used and the equation is about $y = -4.90x^2 + 29.93x + 1.98$.

Graphing the Inverse of a Function

Enter the equation of a function into **Y1** of the equation editor. For example, use $y = x^2$. Use the inverse operation in the **DRAW** menu. Press [2nd] [PRGM] [8]. To enter the expression **Y1**, press [VARS]. Scroll over to **Y-VARS**. Press [1] twice. Press [ENTER].

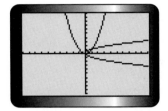

OPERATIONS SPECIFIC TO CALCULUS

Drawing Tangent Lines

Enter $V(t) = \frac{1}{9}(120 - t)^2$ into **Y1** of the equation editor. Adjust the window and display the graph. Use the **Tangent** command in the **Draw** menu to draw a tangent line at a point and estimate its slope. Press [2nd] [PRGM]. Choose **5:Tangent(** .

Scroll to $x = 60$ or enter 60 for the x-coordinate. Press [ENTER]. The tangent line is drawn and its equation is displayed.

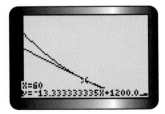

Press [2nd] [PRGM] [1] to clear the drawn tangent lines. The function will be regraphed without the tangent lines.

Graphing the First and Second Derivatives of a Function

Enter a function such as $y = x^2$ into **Y1** of the equation editor. Press [ENTER]. To graph the derivative, use the **nDeriv** operation. Press [MATH] [8].

To enter the expression **Y1**, press [VARS]. Scroll over to **Y-VARS**. Press [1] twice. Press [(] [X,T,Θ,n] [)] [,] [X,T,Θ,n] [,] [X,T,Θ,n] [)] to enter the expression, variable name, and general value of X.

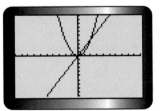

Press [GRAPH]. The original function is graphed first and the derivative is graphed next. **nDeriv(** approximates the derivative.

To graph the second derivative, enter **nDeriv(Y2(X), X, X)** into **Y3**. (See the above procedure.) Remember to select **Y2** from the **Function** menu.

You can deselect a function to be graphed. Position the cursor over the equal sign of the desired function in the equation editor. Press [ENTER]. Only the functions whose equal signs are shaded will be graphed when [GRAPH] is pressed.

Trigonometry Appendix

TR.1   The Trigonometric Functions

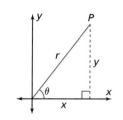

The primary trigonometric functions for point $P(x, y)$ as shown in the diagram are

$$\left.\begin{array}{l} \sin \theta = \dfrac{y}{r} \\[2mm] \cos \theta = \dfrac{x}{r} \end{array}\right\} \quad \text{where } r = \sqrt{x^2 + y^2} \qquad \tan \theta = \dfrac{y}{x}, x \neq 0$$

A point $P(x, y)$ on a circle of radius r, rotated through angle θ, can be expressed as the ordered pair $(r \cos \theta, r \sin \theta)$. Rotating $P(x, y)$ on the unit circle, where $r = 1$, through angle θ produces this graph of $y = \sin \theta$ and $y = \cos \theta$. Both curves represent sinusoidal functions. Each function has a period of 2π, an amplitude of 1, a maximum value of 1, and a minimum value of -1. Recall that 2π radians equals one revolution.

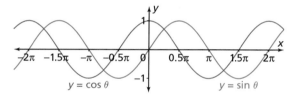

Graph of $y = \sin \theta$ and $y = \cos \theta$

The reciprocals of the trigonometric functions are also functions. The function $f(\theta) = \dfrac{1}{\sin \theta}$ is called the **cosecant function**, which is defined by $\csc \theta = \dfrac{r}{y}$.

Since $\sin \theta = 0$ when $\theta = 0, \pi, 2\pi, \ldots$ and $\csc \theta$ is undefined, the graph of $y = \csc \theta$ approaches but does not cross the vertical lines $\theta = 0, \theta = \pi,$ $\theta = 2\pi, \ldots$. These lines are then vertical asymptotes. When $\theta = \dfrac{\pi}{2}, \dfrac{5\pi}{2}, \ldots$ and $\theta = -\dfrac{3\pi}{2}, -\dfrac{7\pi}{2}, \ldots$, $\sin \theta = 1$ and $\csc \theta = 1$. When $\theta = \dfrac{3\pi}{2}, \dfrac{7\pi}{2}, \ldots$ and $\theta = -\dfrac{\pi}{2}, -\dfrac{5\pi}{2}, \ldots$, $\sin \theta = -1$ and $\csc \theta = -1$. Since $|\sin \theta| \leq 1$, then $|\csc \theta| \geq 1$. The sign of $\csc \theta$ is the same as the sign of $\sin \theta$. When $|\sin \theta|$ approaches 0, $|\csc \theta|$ approaches ∞.

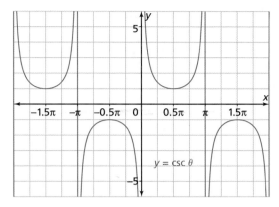

Graph of y = csc θ

Here is the graph of $y = \csc \theta$.

Like the sine function, $y = \csc \theta$ is periodic, and the period is 2π. The cosecant function is defined by $\csc \theta = \dfrac{r}{y} = \dfrac{1}{\sin \theta}$ for all θ, except where $\sin \theta = 0$.

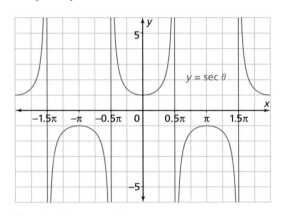

Graph of y = sec θ

Apply the same analysis to the reciprocal of the cosine function, which is called the **secant function**, sec θ. The graph of this function is shown. Like the cosine function, $y = \sec \theta$ is periodic, and the period is 2π. The secant function is defined by $\sec \theta = \dfrac{r}{x} = \dfrac{1}{\cos \theta}$ for all θ, except where $\cos \theta = 0$.

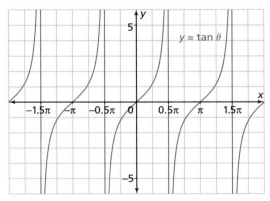

Graph of y = tan θ

The tangent function, tan θ, can also be obtained from the unit circle. The tangent function is periodic with a period of π. The tangent function is defined by $\tan \theta = \dfrac{y}{x} = \dfrac{\sin \theta}{\cos \theta}$ for all θ, except where $\cos \theta = 0$. The graph of this function is also shown.

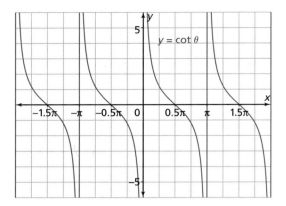

Graph of $y = \cot \theta$

The reciprocal of the tangent function is the cotangent function, $\cot \theta$. This function is also periodic, and the period is π. The cotangent function is defined by

$$\cot \theta = \frac{x}{y} = \frac{\cos \theta}{\sin \theta} \text{ for all } \theta, \text{ except where } \sin \theta = 0.$$

Summary

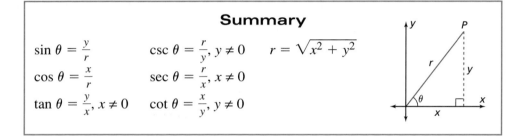

$$\sin \theta = \frac{y}{r} \qquad \csc \theta = \frac{r}{y}, y \neq 0 \qquad r = \sqrt{x^2 + y^2}$$

$$\cos \theta = \frac{x}{r} \qquad \sec \theta = \frac{r}{x}, x \neq 0$$

$$\tan \theta = \frac{y}{x}, x \neq 0 \qquad \cot \theta = \frac{x}{y}, y \neq 0$$

You should already know the trigonometric identities in the box. In all cases, the function is not defined where the denominator is 0.

$$\sin^2 \theta + \cos^2 \theta = 1 \qquad \tan \theta = \frac{\sin \theta}{\cos \theta}$$

$$\sec \theta = \frac{1}{\cos \theta} \qquad \cot \theta = \frac{1}{\tan \theta} \text{ or } \cot \theta = \frac{\cos \theta}{\sin \theta}$$

$$\csc \theta = \frac{1}{\sin \theta} \qquad \tan \theta = \frac{1}{\cot \theta}$$

Example 1

Prove the identity.

(a) $\tan^2 x + 1 = \sec^2 x$

(b) $\cot^2 x + 1 = \csc^2 x$

Solution

(a) $\sin^2 x + \cos^2 x = 1$
Divide both sides by $\cos^2 x$.

$$\left(\frac{\sin^2 x}{\cos^2 x}\right) + 1 = \frac{1}{\cos^2 x}$$

$$\left(\frac{\sin x}{\cos x}\right)^2 + 1 = \left(\frac{1}{\cos x}\right)^2$$

$$\tan^2 x + 1 = \sec^2 x$$

(b) $\sin^2 x + \cos^2 x = 1$
Divide both sides by $\sin^2 x$.

$$1 + \left(\frac{\cos^2 x}{\sin^2 x}\right) = \frac{1}{\sin^2 x}$$

$$\left(\frac{\cos x}{\sin x}\right)^2 + 1 = \left(\frac{1}{\sin x}\right)^2$$

$$\cot^2 x + 1 = \csc^2 x$$

Example 2

Prove the identity.

(a) $\csc x - \sin x = (\cos x)(\cot x)$ **(b)** $\tan \theta + \cot \theta = (\tan \theta)(\csc^2 \theta)$

Solution

(a) Left side: Right side:

$$\csc x - \sin x = \frac{1}{\sin x} - \sin x \qquad\qquad (\cos x)(\cot x) = \cos x \left(\frac{\cos x}{\sin x} \right)$$

$$= \frac{1 - \sin^2 x}{\sin x} \qquad\qquad\qquad\qquad = \frac{\cos^2 x}{\sin x}$$

$$= \frac{\cos^2 x}{\sin x}$$

left side $=$ right side, so $\csc x - \sin x = (\cos x)(\cot x)$

(b) $\tan \theta + \cot \theta = \dfrac{1}{\cot \theta} + \cot \theta$

$$= \frac{1 + \cot^2 \theta}{\cot \theta}$$

$$= \frac{\csc^2 \theta}{\cot \theta}$$

$$= (\tan \theta)(\csc^2 \theta)$$

TR.1 Exercises

1. Use a calculator to evaluate the following, to four decimal places.
   (a) $\sec (-2.8)$ **(b)** $\csc (1.6)$ **(c)** $\tan (0.94)$ **(d)** $\cot (-6.3)$

2. Explain why there is no real solution for each equation.
   (a) $\sin x = 2$ **(b)** $\cos x = -1.25$ **(c)** $\sec x = 0.5$ **(d)** $\csc x = -0.1$

3. Given $\cos \theta = \dfrac{24}{25}$ and $0 < \theta < \dfrac{\pi}{2}$, evaluate
   (a) $\sin \theta$ **(b)** $\sec \theta$ **(c)** $\csc \theta$ **(d)** $\tan \theta$

4. Given $\sin x = \dfrac{4}{5}$ and $0 < x < \dfrac{\pi}{2}$, evaluate
   (a) $\cos x$ **(b)** $\tan x$ **(c)** $\sec x$
   (d) $\csc x$ **(e)** $\cot x$

5. Given $\tan a = 2$, show that $\sin a = \dfrac{2}{\sqrt{5}}$ and $\cos a = \dfrac{1}{\sqrt{5}}$ when $0 < a < \dfrac{\pi}{2}$.

6. Given $\cos t = \dfrac{5}{13}$ and $0 < t < \dfrac{\pi}{2}$, find $\sec t$, $\csc t$, and $\tan t$.

7. Graph, showing two complete periods.
   (a) $y = -\sin x$ **(b)** $y = -2 \sin \left(x + \dfrac{\pi}{2} \right)$
   (c) $y = 3 \sin 2x$ **(d)** $y = 3 \sin (2x + \pi)$

8. Graph.

    (a) $y = \sec x$ **(b)** $y = \sec 2x$

    (c) $y = \tan x - 1$ **(d)** $y = \tan 2x$

9. Prove each identity.

    (a) $(\sin x)(\sec x) = \tan x$

    (b) $\cos^2 x - \sin^2 x = 1 - 2 \sin^2 x$

    (c) $\sec x - \cos x = (\sin x)(\tan x)$

    (d) $\dfrac{1 - \sin t}{\cos t} = \dfrac{\cos t}{1 + \sin t}$

    (e) $\dfrac{\sec \theta - 1}{1 - \cos \theta} = \sec \theta$

    (f) $\dfrac{1 + \tan x}{\sin x} - \sec x = \csc x$

    (g) $\tan \theta + \cot \theta = \dfrac{1}{\cos \theta \sin \theta}$

    (h) $\dfrac{\sin t - \cos t}{\cos t} + \dfrac{\sin t + \cos t}{\sin t} = (\sec t)(\csc t)$

    (i) $\dfrac{1 + \tan^2 x}{1 + \cot^2 x} = \dfrac{1 - \cos^2 x}{\cos^2 x}$

    (j) $\tan x + \cot x = (\sec^2 x)(\cot x)$

    (k) $\dfrac{1}{1 + \sec x} + \dfrac{1}{1 - \sec x} = -2 \cot^2 x$

    (l) $\dfrac{1 - (\sin^2 t)(\cos^2 t)}{\cos^4 t} = \tan^4 t + \tan^2 t + 1$

10. Graph $y = \sin x$ and $y = -\dfrac{x}{3} + 1$ on the same set of axes. Find an approximate solution to $3 \sin x = 3 - x$, where $-\dfrac{\pi}{2} < x < \dfrac{3\pi}{2}$.

TR.2 Trigonometric Sum and Difference Formulas

In general, $\cos (a + b) \neq \cos a + \cos b$. For example, if $a = b = \dfrac{\pi}{4}$, then $\cos (a + b) = \cos \dfrac{\pi}{2}$, which equals 0, but $\cos a + \cos b = 2 \cos \dfrac{\pi}{4}$, which equals $\sqrt{2}$.

But you can establish a relation between $\cos (a + b)$, $\cos a$, $\cos b$, $\sin a$, and $\sin b$.

First find a formula for $\cos (a - b)$.

Consider points $Q(\cos a, \sin a)$ and $P(\cos b, \sin b)$ on the unit circle (diagram I). Rotate the circle so that P maps onto $A(1, 0)$ (diagram II).

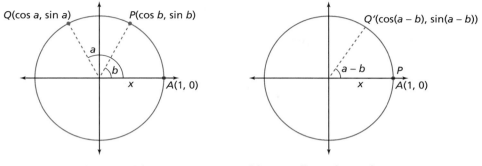

Diagram I, angles *a* and *b*　　　　　**Diagram II, angle *a* − *b***

Since the angle between P and Q is $(a - b)$, the image of Q under the rotation becomes point $Q'(\cos(a - b), \sin(a - b))$. The linear distance PQ equals the linear distance AQ'. By the distance formula,

$$PQ = \sqrt{(\cos a - \cos b)^2 + (\sin a - \sin b)^2} \text{ and}$$

$$AQ' = \sqrt{[\cos (a - b) - 1]^2 + [\sin (a - b) - 0]^2}.$$

Since $PQ = AQ'$, $(PQ)^2 = (AQ')^2$. Therefore,

$$\cos^2 a - 2(\cos a)(\cos b) + \cos^2 b + \sin^2 a - 2(\sin a)(\sin b) + \sin^2 b$$
$$= \cos^2 (a - b) - 2 \cos (a - b) + 1 + \sin^2 (a - b)$$

Rearrange the terms and use the identity $\cos^2 \theta + \sin^2 \theta = 1$ for all θ.

$$(\cos^2 a + \sin^2 a) + (\cos^2 b + \sin^2 b) - 2[(\cos a)(\cos b) + (\sin a)(\sin b)]$$
$$= [\cos^2 (a - b) + \sin^2 (a - b)] - 2 \cos (a - b) + 1$$

$$1 + 1 - 2[(\cos a)(\cos b) + (\sin a)(\sin b)] = 1 - 2 \cos (a - b) + 1$$

$$-2[(\cos a)(\cos b) + (\sin a)(\sin b)] = -2 \cos (a - b)$$

$$\cos (a - b) = (\cos a)(\cos b) + (\sin a)(\sin b)$$

Use this result to derive a formula for $\cos (a + b)$. Recall that $\cos (-\theta) = \cos \theta$ and $\sin (-\theta) = -\sin \theta$. Rewrite $a + b$ as $a - (-b)$.

$$\cos (a + b) = \cos [a - (-b)]$$
$$= (\cos a)[\cos (-b)] + (\sin a)[\sin (-b)]$$
$$= (\cos a)(\cos b) + (\sin a)(-\sin b)$$
$$= (\cos a)(\cos b) - (\sin a)(\sin b)$$

$$\cos (a + b) = (\cos a)(\cos b) - (\sin a)(\sin b)$$

Find the corresponding formulas for $\sin (a + b)$ and $\sin (a - b)$ using $\cos \left(\dfrac{\pi}{2} - \theta \right) = \sin \theta$ and $\sin \left(\dfrac{\pi}{2} - \theta \right) = \cos \theta$.

$$\sin (a + b) = \cos \left[\frac{\pi}{2} - (a + b) \right]$$
$$= \cos \left[\left(\frac{\pi}{2} - a \right) - b \right]$$
$$= \cos \left(\frac{\pi}{2} - a \right)(\cos b) + \sin \left(\frac{\pi}{2} - a \right)(\sin b)$$

$$\sin (a + b) = (\sin a)(\cos b) + (\cos a)(\sin b)$$

Substituting $(-b)$ for b in the formula for $\sin (a + b)$ gives

$$\sin (a - b) = \sin [a + (-b)]$$
$$= (\sin a)[\cos (-b)] + (\cos a)[\sin (-b)]$$
$$= (\sin a)(\cos b) + (\cos a)(-\sin b)$$

$$\sin (a - b) = (\sin a)(\cos b) - (\cos a)(\sin b)$$

To derive a formula for $\tan (a + b)$, begin with $\tan \theta = \frac{\sin \theta}{\cos \theta}$.

$$\tan (a + b) = \frac{\sin (a + b)}{\cos (a + b)}$$
$$= \frac{(\sin a)(\cos b) + (\cos a)(\sin b)}{(\cos a)(\cos b) - (\sin a)(\sin b)}$$

Divide the numerator and denominator by $(\cos a)(\cos b)$ and simplify. So

$$\tan (a + b) = \frac{\tan a + \tan b}{1 - (\tan a)(\tan b)}$$

To derive a formula for $\tan (a - b)$, write $\tan [a + (-b)]$ and use the formula above, noting that $\tan (-b) = -\tan b$.

Use the trigonometric sum formulas to derive formulas for $\sin 2a$, $\cos 2a$, and $\tan 2a$.

$$\tan (a - b) = \tan [a + (-b)] = \frac{\tan a - \tan b}{1 + (\tan a)(\tan b)}$$

$$\sin 2a = \sin (a + a)$$
$$= (\sin a)(\cos a) + (\sin a)(\cos a)$$
$$= 2(\sin a)(\cos a)$$

$$\cos 2a = \cos (a + a)$$
$$= (\cos a)(\cos a) - (\sin a)(\sin a)$$
$$= \cos^2 a - \sin^2 a$$

or

$$\cos 2a = \cos^2 a - \sin^2 a$$
$$= \cos^2 a - (1 - \cos^2 a)$$
$$= 2\cos^2 a - 1$$

or

$$\cos 2a = \cos^2 a - \sin^2 a$$
$$= (1 - \sin^2 a) - \sin^2 a$$
$$= 1 - 2\sin^2 a$$

$$\tan 2a = \tan(a + a)$$
$$= \frac{\tan a + \tan a}{1 - \tan^2 a}$$
$$= \frac{2\tan a}{1 - \tan^2 a}$$

Summary

Sum and Difference Formulas

$$\cos(x + y) = (\cos x)(\cos y) - (\sin x)(\sin y)$$
$$\cos(x - y) = (\cos x)(\cos y) + (\sin x)(\sin y)$$
$$\sin(x + y) = (\sin x)(\cos y) + (\cos x)(\sin y)$$
$$\sin(x - y) = (\sin x)(\cos y) - (\cos x)(\sin y)$$
$$\tan(x + y) = \frac{\tan x + \tan y}{1 - (\tan x)(\tan y)}$$
$$\tan(x - y) = \frac{\tan x - \tan y}{1 + (\tan x)(\tan y)}$$

Double Angle Formulas

$$\sin 2x = 2(\sin x)(\cos x)$$
$$\cos 2x = \cos^2 x - \sin^2 x$$
$$= 2\cos^2 x - 1$$
$$= 1 - 2\sin^2 x$$
$$\tan 2x = \frac{2\tan x}{1 - \tan^2 x}$$

Example 1

Prove $\cos(x + \pi) = -\cos x$.

Solution

$$\cos(x + \pi) = (\cos x)(\cos \pi) - (\sin x)(\sin \pi)$$
$$= (\cos x)(-1) - (\sin x)(0)$$
$$= -\cos x$$

Example 2

Prove $\dfrac{\sin 2x}{1 + \cos 2x} = \tan x$.

Solution

$$\dfrac{\sin 2x}{1 + \cos 2x} = \dfrac{2(\sin x)(\cos x)}{1 + \cos^2 x - \sin^2 x}$$

$$= \dfrac{2(\sin x)(\cos x)}{\sin^2 x + \cos^2 x + \cos^2 x - \sin^2 x}$$

$$= \dfrac{2(\sin x)(\cos x)}{2 \cos^2 x}$$

$$= \dfrac{\sin x}{\cos x}$$

$$= \tan x$$

TR.2 Exercises

1. Simplify.

   (a) $\cos 2x \cos x - \sin 2x \sin x$
   (b) $\cos 2x \cos 3x + \sin 2x \sin 3x$
   (c) $\sin 3x \cos 4x - \cos 3x \sin 4x$
   (d) $\sin\left(\dfrac{\pi}{4} + x\right) - \cos\left(\dfrac{\pi}{4} + x\right)$
   (e) $\cos 5G \sin G + \cos G \sin 5G$
   (f) $\cos 3\theta \cos 5\theta - \sin 3\theta \sin 5\theta$

2. Simplify.

   (a) $2 \cos^2\left(\dfrac{\pi}{6}\right) - 1$
   (b) $2 \sin\left(\dfrac{x}{4}\right) \cos\left(\dfrac{x}{4}\right)$
   (c) $1 - 2 \sin^2\left(\dfrac{\pi}{12}\right)$
   (d) $\cos^2 8x - \sin^2 8x$
   (e) $1 - 2 \sin^2\left(\dfrac{x}{4}\right)$
   (f) $\dfrac{2 \tan\left(\dfrac{x}{6}\right)}{1 - \tan^2\left(\dfrac{x}{6}\right)}$

3. Given $\sin x = \dfrac{4}{5}$ and $\sin y = -\dfrac{12}{13}$, $0 < x < \dfrac{\pi}{2}$, $\dfrac{3\pi}{2} < y < 2\pi$, evaluate

   (a) $\cos (x + y)$
   (b) $\sin (x + y)$
   (c) $\cos (x - y)$
   (d) $\sin (x - y)$
   (e) $\tan (x + y)$
   (f) $\tan (x - y)$

4. Use the formula for $\sin (x + y)$ to prove that $\sin\left(x + \dfrac{\pi}{2}\right) = \cos x$.

5. Prove.

   (a) $\cos\left(-\dfrac{\pi}{2} - x\right) + \cos\left(-\dfrac{\pi}{2} + x\right) = 0$
   (b) $\sin (\pi + x) + \sin (\pi - x) = 0$

6. Given $\sin x = \dfrac{3}{5}$ and $0 < x < \dfrac{\pi}{2}$, find $\sin 2x$ and $\cos 2x$.

7. Simplify $\dfrac{\sin (f + g) + \sin (f - g)}{\cos (f + g) + \cos (f - g)}$.

8. Given $\sin x = \dfrac{5}{13}$ and $0 < x < \dfrac{\pi}{2}$, find $\sin 2x$.

9. Given $\cos x = -\dfrac{4}{5}$ and $\pi < x < \dfrac{3\pi}{2}$, find $\tan 2x$.

10. Prove each identity.

(a) $\dfrac{\cos 2x + 1}{\sin 2x} = \cot x$

(b) $\dfrac{\sin 2x}{1 - \cos 2x} = \cot x$

(c) $(\sin x + \cos x)^2 = 1 + \sin 2x$

(d) $\cos^4 \theta - \sin^4 \theta = \cos 2\theta$

(e) $\cot \theta - \tan \theta = 2 \cot 2\theta$

(f) $\cot \theta + \tan \theta = 2 \csc 2\theta$

(g) $\dfrac{1 + \tan x}{1 - \tan x} = \tan \left(x + \dfrac{\pi}{4} \right)$

(h) $\csc 2x + \cot 2x = \cot x$

(i) $\dfrac{2 \tan x}{1 + \tan^2 x} = \sin 2x$

(j) $\sec 2t = \dfrac{\csc t}{\csc t - 2 \sin t}$

(k) $\sec 2\theta = \dfrac{1}{2}(\sec \theta)(\csc \theta)$

(l) $\sec t = \dfrac{\sin 2t}{\sin t} - \dfrac{\cos 2t}{\cos t}$

(m) $\sin \left(\dfrac{\pi}{4} + x \right) + \sin \left(\dfrac{\pi}{4} - x \right) = \sqrt{2} \cos x$

(n) $\sin \left(\dfrac{\pi}{2} - x \right) \cot \left(\dfrac{\pi}{2} + x \right) = -\sin x$

TR.3 Derivatives of Trigonometric Functions

To find the derivatives of the primary trigonometric functions, you need two basic limits, which are

$$\lim_{x \to 0} \frac{\sin x}{x} = 1 \text{ and } \lim_{x \to 0} \frac{\cos x - 1}{x} = 0, \text{ where } x \text{ is in radians}$$

The proof of these limits is omitted here, but you can verify them by graphing the functions on a graphing calculator.

To find $\dfrac{d}{dx}(\sin x)$, use the sum formula for the sine function and the two limits above.

First evaluate $\dfrac{\Delta y}{\Delta x}$, where $y = \sin x$.

$$\frac{\Delta y}{\Delta x} = \frac{\sin (x + \Delta x) - \sin x}{\Delta x}$$

$$= \frac{(\sin x)(\cos \Delta x) + (\cos x)(\sin \Delta x) - \sin x}{\Delta x}$$

$$= \frac{(\sin x)(\cos \Delta x - 1) + (\cos x)(\sin \Delta x)}{\Delta x}$$

$$= \frac{(\sin x)(\cos \Delta x - 1)}{\Delta x} + \frac{(\cos x)(\sin \Delta x)}{\Delta x}$$

Next take the limit to find the derivative.

$$\frac{d}{dx}(\sin x) = \lim_{x \to 0} \frac{\Delta y}{\Delta x}$$

$$= (\sin x) \lim_{x \to 0} \frac{\cos \Delta x - 1}{\Delta x} + (\cos x) \lim_{x \to 0} \frac{\sin \Delta x}{\Delta x}$$

$$= (\sin x)(0) + (\cos x)(1)$$

$$= \cos x$$

To find the derivative of $\cos x$, recall that $\cos x = \sin\left(\frac{\pi}{2} - x\right)$ and $\cos\left(\frac{\pi}{2} - x\right)$.

$$\frac{d}{dx}(\cos x) = \frac{d}{dx}\left[\sin\left(\frac{\pi}{2} - x\right)\right]$$

$$= \frac{d}{dx}\left[\sin\left(\frac{\pi}{2} - x\right)\right] \cdot \frac{d}{dx}\left(\frac{\pi}{2} - x\right)$$

$$= \cos\left(\frac{\pi}{2} - x\right)(-1)$$

$$= -\sin x$$

$$\frac{d}{dx}(\sin x) = \cos x \quad \text{and} \quad \frac{d}{dx}(\cos x) = -\sin x$$

Example 1

Find $\frac{dy}{dx}$ for $y = \tan x$.

Solution

Recall that $\tan x = \frac{\sin x}{\cos x}$.

$$\frac{d}{dx}(\tan x) = \frac{d}{dx}\left(\frac{\sin x}{\cos x}\right)$$

$$= \frac{(\cos x)\frac{d}{dx}(\sin x) - (\sin x)\frac{d}{dx}(\cos x)}{\cos^2 x}$$

$$= \frac{(\cos x)(\cos x) - (\sin x)(-\sin x)}{\cos^2 x}$$

$$= \frac{\cos^2 x + \sin^2 x}{\cos^2 x}$$

$$= \frac{1}{\cos^2 x}$$

$$= \sec^2 x$$

Example 2

Find $\frac{dy}{dx}$ for $y = \sin(1 + x^3)$.

Solution

$$\frac{d}{dx}[\sin(1 + x^3)] = \frac{d}{dx}[\sin(1 + x^3)] \cdot \frac{d}{dx}(1 + x^3)$$

$$= \cos(1 + x^3) \cdot (3x^2)$$

$$= 3x^2 \cos(1 + x^3)$$

You will differentiate the other trigonometric functions in the exercises.

The derivatives of the other trigonometric functions are summarized in the box.

Summary

$$\frac{d}{dx}(\sin x) = \cos x \qquad\qquad \frac{d}{dx}(\cos x) = -\sin x$$

$$\frac{d}{dx}(\tan x) = \sec^2 x \qquad\qquad \frac{d}{dx}(\csc x) = -(\csc x)(\cot x)$$

$$\frac{d}{dx}(\sec x) = (\sec x)(\tan x) \qquad\qquad \frac{d}{dx}(\cot x) = -\csc^2 x$$

TR.3 Exercises

1. Find y'.

    (a) $y = \sin 2x$ **(b)** $y = x^2 \sin x$ **(c)** $y = \sin\left(\dfrac{\pi}{2} - x\right)$

    (d) $y = \cos x \sin x$ **(e)** $y = \cos^2 x$ **(f)** $y = \cos x \sin^2 x$

    (g) $y = \dfrac{\cos x}{x}$ **(h)** $y = \dfrac{\cos x}{2 + \sin x}$

2. Find $f'(x)$.

    (a) $f(x) = \cot x$ **(b)** $f(x) = \sec x$ **(c)** $f(x) = \csc x$

3. Find $\dfrac{dy}{dx}$.

    (a) $y = \csc x \cot x$ **(b)** $y = \tan x \sin x$ **(c)** $y = x \cos \dfrac{1}{x}$

    (d) $y = \sin \sqrt{1 + x^3}$ **(e)** $y = \sin^2 x \tan^2 x$ **(f)** $y = \dfrac{\cos x}{1 + \sin^2 x}$

    (g) $y = \csc^2 x$ **(h)** $y = \sqrt{\pi + \cos x}$ **(i)** $y = x^2 \sin^3 x$

4. Find the slope of the tangent to the curve $y = \cos 2x$ at point $\left(\dfrac{\pi}{6}, \dfrac{1}{2}\right)$.

5. An object moves along a line so that in t seconds its position is $s = \dfrac{\sin t}{3 + \cos 2t}$, where s is the displacement in metres. Find the object's velocity at $t = \dfrac{\pi}{4}$.

6. A particle moves along a line so that at time t its position is $s = 4 \sin 4t$.

    (a) When does the particle change direction?

    (b) What is the particle's maximum velocity?

    (c) What is the particle's minimum distance from the origin? maximum distance?

7. **(a)** Graph $f(x) = \cos x + \sin x$.

    (b) Find the coordinates of the point where the tangent to the curve $f(x)$, where $0 \le x \le \pi$, is horizontal.

8. Evaluate.

(a) $\displaystyle\lim_{x \to 0} \frac{\sin 3x}{x}$ (b) $\displaystyle\lim_{x \to 0} \frac{\tan x}{x}$ (c) $\displaystyle\lim_{x \to 0} x \csc x$ (d) $\displaystyle\lim_{x \to 0} \frac{\cos x - 1}{2x}$

9. Find $f''(x)$.

(a) $f(x) = \cos^2 x$ (b) $f(x) = \cos x \cot x$

10. Find $\dfrac{dy}{dx}$ by implicit differentiation.

(a) $x \sin 2y = y \cos 2x$ (b) $x \cos 2y = y \sin 2x$

(c) $x + \tan 2xy = 0$ (d) $y^2 = \sin^4 x + \cos^4 x$

TR.4   Applications Involving Rates of Change

You will often use trigonometric expressions to solve problems involving the rate of change of an angle or the rate of turning.

Example 1

Two rods are 10 cm and 15 cm long, respectively. These rods are hinged together at one end. The other ends are joined by an elastic band. Steve pulls the ends joined by an elastic band apart, forming a triangle. The angle between the two rods where they are hinged together increases at a rate of 1°/h. At what rate is the area of the triangle increasing when the angle between the rods is 45°?

Solution

Let the angle between the rods be r. The area of the triangle is

$$A = \frac{1}{2}(15h)$$
$$= \frac{15}{2}(10 \sin r)$$
$$= 75 \sin r$$

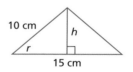

You want to find $\dfrac{dA}{dt}$, given $\dfrac{dr}{dt} = 1$, in degrees per hour.

$$\frac{dA}{dt} = \frac{d}{dt}(75 \sin r)$$
$$= 75 \frac{d}{dr}(\sin r)\frac{dr}{dt}$$

To find the derivative of the sine, the angle r must be in radians, so $\dfrac{dr}{dt} = \dfrac{\pi}{180}$, in radians per hour. Therefore,

$$\frac{dA}{dt} = 75\frac{d}{dr}(\sin r)\left(\frac{\pi}{180}\right)$$
$$= \frac{75\pi}{180} \cos r$$

When $r = \dfrac{\pi}{4}$, $\dfrac{dA}{dt} = \dfrac{75\pi}{180} \cos \dfrac{\pi}{4}$, or about 0.93.

The area of the triangle is increasing at a rate of 0.93 cm²/h when $r = \dfrac{\pi}{4}$, or 45°.

Example 2

A Ferris wheel 60 m in diameter turns at a uniform rate of 2 revolutions per minute. What is the maximum rate at which the height of a chair on the wheel changes?

Solution

From the diagram, the height is

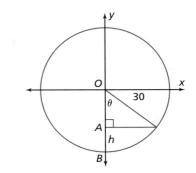

$$h = OB - OA$$
$$= 30 - 30 \cos \theta$$

$$\frac{d\theta}{dt} = 2 \text{ r/min} = 4 \pi \text{ rad/min}$$

$$\frac{dh}{dt} = \frac{d}{dt}(30 - 30 \cos \theta)$$
$$= \frac{d\theta}{dt}(30 - 30 \cos \theta)\frac{d\theta}{dt}$$
$$= (30 \sin \theta)(4\pi)$$
$$= 120\pi \sin \theta$$

The maximum value of $\sin \theta$ occurs when $\theta = \dfrac{\pi}{2}$ and $\sin \theta = 1$. Therefore, the maximum rate of change in height is 120π m/min.

Example 3

An airplane is flying due west at an altitude of 3000 m and at a speed of 200 m/s. A searchlight is pointed at the airplane turns so that it follows the airplane. What is the rate of turning of the searchlight when the airplane is 2000 m due east of the searchlight?

Solution

Let the position of the searchlight be $(0, 0)$ and the position of the airplane be $(x, 3000)$. You know that $\dfrac{dx}{dt} = -200$ m/s and you want to find $\dfrac{d\theta}{dt}$ when $x = 2000$.

From the diagram, $\cot \theta = \dfrac{x}{3000}$ or $x = 3000 \cot \theta$. Therefore,

$$\frac{dx}{dt} = 3000\frac{d}{d\theta}(\cot \theta)\frac{d\theta}{dt}$$

Substituting and simplifying,

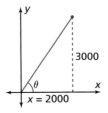

$$-200 = 3000(-\csc^2 \theta)\frac{d\theta}{dt}$$

$$\frac{d\theta}{dt} = \frac{200}{3000}\csc^2 \theta \quad \text{or} \quad \frac{d\theta}{dt} = \frac{1}{15}\sin^2 \theta$$

For $x = 2000$, $\sin \theta = \dfrac{3}{\sqrt{13}}$ and $\dfrac{d\theta}{dt} \doteq 0.0046$.

The searchlight is turning at about 0.046 rad/s or 2.6°/s.

TR.4 Exercises

1. Given $y = 4 \sin \theta$, find $\dfrac{d\theta}{dt}$ when $\dfrac{dy}{dt} = 5$ and $\theta = \dfrac{\pi}{3}$.

2. Given $y = 500 \tan \theta$, find $\dfrac{d\theta}{dt}$ when $\dfrac{dy}{dt} = 25$ and $\theta = \dfrac{\pi}{4}$.

3. Two sides of an isosceles triangle, each 25 cm long, are being moved away from each other so that the angle between them is increasing at the rate of 6°/min. What is the rate of increase of the area of the triangle when the angle between the two sides is 60°?

4. Andrea stands 200 m from a rocket that is fired directly up in a fireworks display. At what rate is Andrea lifting her head, to watch the rocket going up, at the instant the rocket reaches a height of 150 m and is travelling at a rate of 10 m/s?

5. Suppose that the sun is going down at a rate of 15°/h. How fast is the shadow of a 25-m flagpole lengthening when the angle of elevation of the sun is $\dfrac{\pi}{3}$ rad?

6. A 10-m ladder is leaning against a wall. The foot of the ladder is sliding away from the wall at a rate of 10 cm/s. What is the rate of change of the acute angle made by the ladder and the floor when the foot of the ladder is 4 m from the wall?

7. A balloon is released 200 m from an observer. The balloon rises vertically at 50 m/min. At what rate is the angle of elevation of the observer's line of sight increasing after 6 min?

8. A kite is 27 m above the ground with 45 m of string let out. As more string is let out, the kite moves horizontally at 3 km/h directly away from the child who is flying it. Assuming the string is straight, find the rate at which the angle between the string and the horizontal is changing.

9. A searchlight on a ship 1 km from shore casts a spot of light on the shore-line. The searchlight is rotating at a rate of 1 rpm. How fast is the spot on the shore moving at the point nearest the searchlight? How fast is it moving when the spot is 250 m farther down the shore?

10. Seth stands on a wharf that is 5 m above the water and pulls in a rope that is attached to a small boat at the rate of 0.5 m/s. How fast is the angle between the rope and the surface of the water changing when there is 10 m of rope between Seth and the boat?

TR.5 Optimization Using Trigonometric Functions

You can often use the trigonometric functions to solve maximum and minimum problems.

Example 1

Find the largest rectangle, by area, that can be inscribed within the ellipse $\frac{x^2}{4^2} + \frac{y^2}{3^2} = 1$.

Solution

Consider the inscribed and circumscribed circles. The radii of these circles are 3 and 4, respectively. Define an auxiliary angle θ, where $0 \le \theta \le \frac{\pi}{2}$, relative to a point (x, y) on the ellipse. Then $x = 4 \cos \theta$ and $y = 3 \sin \theta$.

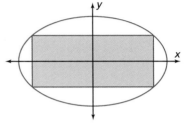

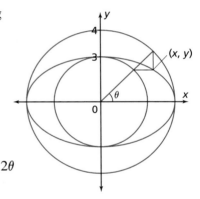

To show that these equations define the ellipse, first recall that $\cos^2 \theta + \sin^2 \theta = 1$. Substituting for $\cos \theta$ and $\sin \theta$ gives $\frac{x^2}{4^2} + \frac{y^2}{3^2} = 1$. Therefore, (x, y) lies on the ellipse for any θ.

Let A represent the area of the inscribed rectangle with (x, y) at one corner. Then $A = 4xy$. Since $\sin 2\theta = 2 \sin \theta \cos \theta$,

$$A = 4xy \qquad\qquad \frac{dA}{d\theta} = 48 \cos 2\theta$$
$$= 4(4 \cos \theta)(3 \sin \theta)$$
$$= 24 \sin 2\theta$$

To maximize the area, solve $\frac{dA}{d\theta} = 0$.

$$48 \cos 2\theta = 0$$
$$\cos 2\theta = 0$$

$$2\theta = -\frac{\pi}{2} \quad \text{or } 2\theta = \frac{\pi}{2}$$

$$\theta = \frac{\pi}{4} \quad \text{since } 0 \le \theta \le \frac{\pi}{2}$$

Therefore,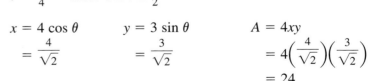

$$x = 4 \cos \theta \qquad y = 3 \sin \theta \qquad A = 4xy$$
$$= \frac{4}{\sqrt{2}} \qquad\qquad = \frac{3}{\sqrt{2}} \qquad\qquad = 4\left(\frac{4}{\sqrt{2}}\right)\left(\frac{3}{\sqrt{2}}\right)$$
$$= 24$$

Use the second derivative to verify that an area of 24 square units is a maximum.

$$\frac{d^2A}{d^2\theta} = -96 \sin 2\theta$$
$$= -96 \sin \frac{\pi}{2}$$
$$= -96$$

Since the second derivative is negative, 24 square units is a maximum area. Therefore, the largest possible area for a rectangle inscribed in this ellipse is 24 square units.

Example 2

A storage shed, 3 m high and 2 m from front to back, is located beside a high vertical wall.

(a) Find the length of the shortest ladder that can reach from the ground, over the shed, to the wall above.

(b) Find the angle that this ladder makes with the ground.

Solution

As shown in the diagram, let θ be the angle between the ladder and the ground, and let the total length of the ladder be $l = l_1 + l_2$, where l_1 is the length from the ground to the corner of the shed and l_2 is the length from the corner to the wall.

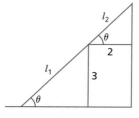

$$\sin \theta = \frac{3}{l_1} \qquad\qquad \cos \theta = \frac{2}{l_2}$$

$$l_1 = \frac{3}{\sin \theta} \qquad\qquad l_2 = \frac{2}{\cos \theta} \qquad\qquad l = l_1 + l_2$$
$$= 3 \csc \theta \qquad\qquad\quad = 2 \sec \theta \qquad\qquad\quad = 3 \csc \theta + 2 \sec \theta$$

$$\frac{dl}{d\theta} = -3 \csc \theta \cot \theta + 2 \sec \theta \tan \theta$$
$$= -\frac{3 \cos \theta}{\sin^2 \theta} + \frac{2 \sin \theta}{\cos^2 \theta}$$

To find a minimum, solve $\frac{dt}{d\theta} = 0$.

$$\frac{3 \cos \theta}{\sin^2 \theta} = \frac{2 \sin \theta}{\cos^2 \theta}$$
$$3 \cos^3 \theta = 2 \sin^3 \theta$$
$$\left(\frac{\sin \theta}{\cos \theta}\right)^3 = \frac{3}{2}$$
$$\tan \theta = \sqrt[3]{\frac{3}{2}}$$
$$\theta = \tan^{-1} \sqrt[3]{\frac{3}{2}}$$
$$= 48.86°$$

Use the second derivative to verify.

$$\frac{d^2l}{d^2\theta} = 3 \csc \theta + 6 \cot^2 \theta + 2 \sec \theta + 4 \tan^2 \theta \sec \theta$$

At $\theta = 48.86°$, $\frac{d^2 l}{d^2 \theta} \doteq 21.07$. The second derivative is positive, so the value of the function at $\theta \doteq 48.86°$ is a minimum.

At $\theta = 48.86°$, $l = 3 \csc 48.86° + 2 \sec 48.86° \doteq 7.02$.

The shortest ladder is about 7.02 m long and makes an angle of about 48.9° with the ground.

TR.5 Exercises

1. List the values of θ for which each function is a minimum.
   (a) $\cos \theta$ (b) $\sin \theta$

2. Which of these functions have maximum values?
   (a) $\sec \theta$ (b) $\tan \theta$ (c) $\csc \theta$ (d) $\cot \theta$

3. Use the Pythagorean identities to find an equation of each curve in the xy-plane. Name the curve.
   (a) $x = 5 \cos \theta$, $y = 3 \sin \theta$ (b) $x = 2 \cos \theta$, $y = -4 \sin \theta$
   (c) $x = 3 \sec \theta$, $y = 4 \tan \theta$

4. (a) For $-2\pi < \theta < 2\pi$, find all maximum and minimum values of the given function.
   (b) State the intervals where $f(\theta)$ is increasing and where it is decreasing.
   (c) Sketch the curve.
      i. $f(\theta) = \sin \theta + \cos \theta$ ii. $f(\theta) = \sin \theta - \cos \theta$
      iii. $f(\theta) = 3 \sin \theta + 4 \cos \theta$ iv. $f(\theta) = \sec \theta + 3 \tan \theta$

5. Find the rectangle of greatest area that can be inscribed in the circle $x^2 + y^2 = 36$.

6. Find the rectangle of greatest area that can be inscribed in the ellipse $\frac{x^2}{15^2} + \frac{y^2}{8^2} = 1$.

7. A tool shed 250 cm high and 100 cm deep is built against a wall. Find the shortest ladder that can reach from the ground, over the shed, to the wall behind.

8. A 3-m wide corridor makes a right angle turn as shown on the left. Find the longest rod that can be carried horizontally around this corner.

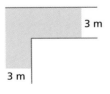

3 m

3 m

9. Find the length of the longest rod that can be carried around the corner in question 8 if the corridor is 3 m high and the rod does not have to be carried horizontally. Hint: How should the third dimension be utilized?

10. A billboard is 6 m high and its base is 10 m above eye level. How far away from the plane of the sign should you stand to make the sign subtend the greatest possible angle at your eye?

Trigonometry Summary

ANGLE MEASUREMENT

π radians $= 180°$

$1° = \dfrac{\pi}{180}$ rad $\qquad$ 1 rad $= \dfrac{180°}{\pi}$

$s = r\theta$ $\quad$ (θ in radians)

RIGHT ANGLE TRIGONOMETRY

$\sin \theta = \dfrac{\text{opp}}{\text{hyp}} \qquad \csc \theta = \dfrac{\text{hyp}}{\text{opp}}$

$\cos \theta = \dfrac{\text{adj}}{\text{hyp}} \qquad \sec \theta = \dfrac{\text{hyp}}{\text{adj}}$

$\tan \theta = \dfrac{\text{opp}}{\text{adj}} \qquad \cot \theta = \dfrac{\text{adj}}{\text{opp}}$

TRIGONOMETRIC FUNCTIONS

$\sin \theta = \dfrac{y}{r} \qquad \csc \theta = \dfrac{r}{y}$

$\cos \theta = \dfrac{x}{r} \qquad \sec \theta = \dfrac{r}{x}$

$\tan \theta = \dfrac{y}{x} \qquad \cot \theta = \dfrac{x}{y}$

GRAPHS OF THE TRIGONOMETRIC FUNCTIONS

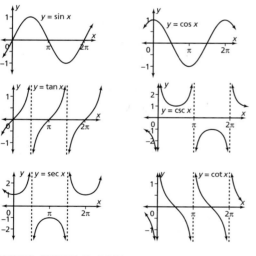

THE SINE LAW

$\dfrac{\sin A}{a} = \dfrac{\sin B}{b} = \dfrac{\sin C}{c}$

THE COSINE LAW

$a^2 = b^2 + c^2 - 2bc \cos A$

$b^2 = a^2 + c^2 - 2ac \cos B$

$c^2 = a^2 + b^2 - 2ab \cos C$

TRIGONOMETRIC FUNCTIONS OF IMPORTANT ANGLES

θ	radians	$\sin \theta$	$\cos \theta$	$\tan \theta$
0°	0	0	1	0
30°	$\dfrac{\pi}{6}$	$\dfrac{1}{2}$	$\dfrac{\sqrt{3}}{2}$	$\dfrac{1}{\sqrt{3}}$
45°	$\dfrac{\pi}{4}$	$\dfrac{1}{\sqrt{2}}$	$\dfrac{1}{\sqrt{2}}$	1
60°	$\dfrac{\pi}{3}$	$\dfrac{\sqrt{3}}{2}$	$\dfrac{1}{2}$	$\sqrt{3}$
90°	$\dfrac{\pi}{2}$	1	0	–

FUNDAMENTAL IDENTITIES

$\csc \theta = \dfrac{1}{\sin \theta} \qquad \sec \theta = \dfrac{1}{\cos \theta}$

$\tan \theta = \dfrac{\sin \theta}{\cos \theta} \qquad \cot \theta = \dfrac{\cos \theta}{\sin \theta}$

$\cot \theta = \dfrac{1}{\tan \theta} \qquad \sin^2 \theta + \cos^2 \theta = 1$

$1 + \tan^2 \theta = \sec^2 \theta \qquad 1 + \cot^2 \theta = \csc^2 \theta$

$\sin (-\theta) = -\sin \theta \qquad \cos (-\theta) = \cos \theta$

$\tan (-\theta) = -\tan \theta \qquad \sin \left(\dfrac{\pi}{2} - \theta \right) = \cos \theta$

$\cos \left(\dfrac{\pi}{2} - \theta \right) = \sin \theta \qquad \tan \left(\dfrac{\pi}{2} - \theta \right) = \cot \theta$

ADDITION AND SUBTRACTION FORMULAS

$\sin (x + y) = \sin x \cos y + \cos x \sin y$

$\sin (x - y) = \sin x \cos y - \cos x \sin y$

$\cos (x + y) = \cos x \cos y - \sin x \sin y$

$\cos (x - y) = \cos x \cos y + \sin x \sin y$

$\tan (x + y) = \dfrac{\tan x + \tan y}{1 - \tan x \tan y}$

$\tan (x - y) = \dfrac{\tan x - \tan y}{1 + \tan x \tan y}$

DOUBLE-ANGLE FORMULAS

$\sin 2x = 2 \sin x \cos x \qquad \cos 2x = \cos^2 x - \sin^2 x$

$\tan 2x = \dfrac{2 \tan x}{1 - \tan^2 x} \qquad\quad = 2 \cos^2 x - 1$

$\qquad\qquad\qquad\qquad\qquad = 1 - 2 \sin^2 x$

HALF-ANGLE FORMULAS

$\sin^2 x = \dfrac{1 - \cos 2x}{2} \qquad \cos^2 x = \dfrac{1 + \cos 2x}{2}$

Glossary

absolute maximum: the largest value of a function on a closed interval.

absolute minimum: the smallest value of a function on a closed interval.

absolute value: the value of a number without regard to its sign. For $a \in \mathbf{R}$, $|a| = a$ if $a \neq 0$ and $|a| = -a$ if $a < 0$.

acceleration: the rate of change of velocity with respect to time; the second derivative of displacement with respect to time.

asymptote: a line to which a graph of a curve becomes arbitrarily close as $|x|$ or $|y|$ increases without bound.

average cost function: a rational function that equals the average cost per unit, based on the number of units produced: $AC(x) = \dfrac{C(x)}{(x)}$.

average profit function: a rational function that equals the average profit per unit, based on the number of units sold: $AP(x) = \dfrac{P(x)}{x}$.

average rate of change: for a function $f(x)$, the average rate of change over the interval (x_1, x_2) is $\dfrac{f(x_2) - f(x_2)}{x_2 - x_1}$. On a graph, this is the slope of the corresponding secant line.

break-even point: the volume of production or sales where profit equals zero, or total revenue equals total cost.

business model: if $P(x)$, $R(x)$, and $C(x)$ represent the total profit, revenue, and cost, respectively, associated with producing or selling x units, then $P(x) = R(x) - C(x)$.

calculus: a branch of mathematics (also called analysis) that deals with derivatives or instantaneous rates of change and other related topics.

common logarithm: a logarithm with base 10. $\log x = \log_{10} x$.

complex number: a number in the form $a + bi$, where a and b are real numbers and $i^2 = -1$.

composite function: a function that results when one function is applied to the output of another function. $(f \circ g)(x) = f(g(x))$.

concavity: if the graph of a function is cupped upward (i.e., it opens upward), it is said to be **concave up**. If it is cupped downward, it is **concave down**. The graph of f is concave up [down] on an interval if f' is increasing [decreasing] on the interval, or if f'' is positive [negative] on the interval.

continuous compounding: When interest is compounded continuously, the current amount is $A = P(e)^{in}$, where P is the initial principal, i is the interest rate per compounding period, and n is the number of periods.

continuous function: a function whose graph is a smooth curve without any holes or breaks. Function $f(x)$ is **continuous at a** if $\lim\limits_{x \to a} f(x) = f(a)$. It is **continuous** if it is continuous at a for all a in the domain.

critical number: for a function $f(x)$, any number c such that $(c, f(c))$ is a critical point.

critical point: for a function $f(x)$, any point at which $f'(x)$ is zero or does not exist.

cubic function: a polynomial function of degree 3.

cusp: a spike on a curve where the slopes of the secant lines approach ∞ from one side and $-\infty$ from the other.

decomposition: any process to determine the component functions that make up a composite function.

decreasing function: a function $f(x)$ whose value decreases as x increases.

degree of a polynomial: the highest exponent of the variable.

demand function: a function $p(x)$ that relates the number of items sold, x, to the price, p.

derivative at a point: for function $f(x)$ at point $(a, f(a))$, the derivative is $f'(a) = \lim\limits_{h \to 0} \dfrac{f(a + h) - f(a)}{h}$, if it exists.

derivative function: for a function $f(x)$, the derivative function is $f'(x) = \lim\limits_{h \to 0} \dfrac{f(x + h) - f(x)}{h}$, for all x for which the limit exists.

differentiable: a function f is differentiable at a if $f'(a)$ exists. It is differentiable on an interval if it is differentiable at every point in the interval.

differentiation: the process of finding the derivative.

discontinuity: a point where a function is not continuous.

discontinuous function: a function that is not continuous.

e: an irrational real constant, equal to approximately 2.718. The number has several important properties, such as $\dfrac{d}{dx}e^x = e^x$. See the Fundamental Limit of Calculus.

end behaviour: a description of the values of $f(x)$ as $x \to \infty$ or $x \to -\infty$.

end-behaviour model: a simple function that approximates the end behaviour of another function. Function $g(x)$ is an end-behaviour model for $p(x)$ if and only if $\lim\limits_{x \to \infty} \dfrac{p(x)}{g(x)} = 1$ or $\lim\limits_{x \to -\infty} \dfrac{p(x)}{g(x)} = 1$.

exponential function: a function of the form $f(x) = c(a^x)$.

exponential growth: a situation modelled by $y = c(a^x)$, where a is the growth rate and c is the initial value.

extreme point: a point that is either a maximum or a minimum.

factor theorem: for a polynomial function $P(x)$, $(jx - k)$ is a factor of P if and only if $P\left(\dfrac{k}{j}\right) = 0$.

first derivative test: a test to determine if a critical point is a local maximum, a local minimum, or neither. If $f'(x)$ changes from negative to positive at $x = c$, then $f(c)$ is a local minimum. If $f'(x)$ changes from positive to negative at $x = c$, $f(c)$ is a local maximum. If $f'(x)$ does not change sign at $x = c$, $f(c)$ is not an extreme point.

fundamental limit of calculus: $e = \lim\limits_{x \to \infty} \left(1 + \dfrac{1}{x}\right)^x$.

i: an imaginary number such that $i^2 = -1$.

implicit differentiation: finding a derivative by differentiating both sides of an implicit relation and solving the resulting equation for the derivative.

implicit relation: a relation between variables that is not stated as an explicit formula. For example, $y = x^2$ is an explicit relation; $x^2 + y^2 = 4$ is an implicit relation.

inadmissible: a solution to an equation that does not make sense in the context of the problem being modelled.

increasing function: a function $f(x)$ whose value increases as x increases.

indeterminate form: an expression that is not precisely determined, for example, a limit that evaluates to $\frac{0}{0}$ or $\frac{\infty}{\infty}$.

infinity: an unbounded number greater than every real number, denoted by ∞. The real number line extends toward $-\infty$ in one direction and toward ∞ in the other.

infinite limit: if the values of a function $f(x)$ increase [decrease] without bound as x approaches a then $\lim_{x \to a} f(x) = \infty \,[\, \lim_{x \to a} f(x) = -\infty \,]$.

inflection point: a point on a graph where the concavity changes from concave up to concave down, or vice versa.

instantaneous rate of change: the rate of change of a function at a point $(a, f(a))$. Equals the slope of the tangent at the point or $\lim_{x \to a} \dfrac{f(x) - f(a)}{x - a}$.

inverse function: for function $y = f(x)$, the inverse function $f^{-1}(x)$ is such that $x = f^{-1}(y)$. To find the equation of the inverse function, interchange the dependent and independent variables.

jump discontinuity: a discontinuity where the one-sided limits exist but are not equal.

Leibniz notation: the derivative of $y = f(x)$ with respect to x expressed as $\dfrac{dy}{dx}$ or $\dfrac{d}{dx} f(x)$.

limit: for a function $f(x)$, $\lim_{x \to a} f(x) = L$ means that as x gets closer and closer to a, the value of $f(x)$ gets closer and closer to L. For continuous functions, $\lim_{x \to a} f(x) = f(a)$, but for other functions the limit may not exist, or it may not equal $f(a)$. The left-hand and right-hand limits, $\lim_{x \to a^-} f(x)$ and $\lim_{x \to a^+} f(x)$, may not be equal.

limit at infinity: $\lim_{x \to \infty} f(x) = L$ or $\lim_{x \to -\infty} f(x) = L$ means that the function approaches a finite value, L, as x approaches either ∞ or $-\infty$.

local maximum: a function value that is greater than or equal to all other function values in its neighbourhood.

local minimum: a function value that is less than or equal to all other function values in its neighbourhood.

logarithmic function: for $a > 0$ and $a \neq 1$, $y = \log_a x$ if and only if $x = a^y$.

logarithm laws:

products: $\log_a mn = \log_a m + \log_a n$

quotients: $\log_a \frac{m}{n} = \log_a m - \log_a n,\ n \neq 0$

powers: $\log_a m^p = p \log_a m$

equality: $\log_a m = \log_a n \Leftrightarrow m = n,\ a \in \mathbf{R},\ a > 0$

marginal rates: marginal profit, revenue, or cost is the rate of change of profit, revenue, or cost with respect to the number of units produced or sold, e.g., $\dfrac{dP}{dx}$, where P is the profit function and x is the number of units sold.

natural logarithm: a logarithm with base e. The expressions $y = \log_e x$, $y = \ln x$, and $e^y = x$ are equivalent.

optimization problem: a real-world problem where you must find the maximum or minimum value of a variable.

piecewise function: a function with different definitions, depending on the value of the independent variable.

polynomial in one variable: an expression of the form $a_n x^n + a_{n-1} x^{n-1} + \ldots + a_1 x + a_0$, where a_i are real numbers, $a_n \neq 0$, and n is a natural number.

polynomial function: a function whose equation is defined by a polynomial in one variable.

polynomial inequality: an inequality where the expression is a polynomial, e.g., $x^2 - 25 > 0$.

quadratic formula: the solutions of $ax^2 + bx + c = 0$ are given by $x = \dfrac{-b \pm \sqrt{b^2 - 4ac}}{2a}$.

quartic function: a polynomial function of degree 4.

quotient law for limits: if all limits exist and are real, then the limit of a rational function equals the limit of the numerator function divided by the limit of the denominator function (which must not be 0).

rational function: a function that can be expressed as $f(x) = \dfrac{p(x)}{q(x)}$, where $p(x)$ and $q(x)$ are polynomial functions, $q(x) \neq 0$.

rational zero test: for a polynomial in standard form with integer coefficients, every rational zero is of the form $\dfrac{p}{q}$, where p is a factor of the constant term and q is a factor of the leading coefficient.

related rates: a situation where two variables both vary with respect to time and there is a known relation between them.

remainder theorem: if a polynomial function $f(x)$ is divided by $(jx - k)$, then the remainder is equal to $f\!\left(\dfrac{k}{j}\right)$.

removable discontinuity: a discontinuity that can be removed by redefining the function at the point of discontinuity to make it continuous.

restricted domain: a domain that is defined to be some subset of $\mathbf{R}$, for example, $\{x \in \mathbf{R} \mid x \geq 0\}$.

root: a value of the variable that makes an equation true.

secant: a line that passes through two points on the graph of a relation.

second derivative: the derivative of the derivative of a function.

second derivative test: a test that uses the second derivative to decide whether a critical point is a local minimum or maximum. If $f''(c) > 0$, $f(c)$ is a minimum. If $f''(c) < 0$, $f(c)$ is a maximum. If $f''(c) = 0$, the test fails.

speed: the magnitude of velocity, ignoring direction.

synthetic division: a shortcut method of doing long division of a polynomial by a divisor of the form $(x - k)$.

tangent: a line that touches the graph of a relation. See *instantaneous rate of change*.

turning point: a point where a function changes from increasing to decreasing or vice versa; either a local maximum or a local minimum.

velocity: rate of change of position with respect to time.

zero of a function: a point where a function has a value of zero.

Answers

Note: *D.N.E.* stands for *does not exist.*

Chapter 1

Getting Ready, page 4

1. **(a)** 11 **(b)** 120 **(c)** -17 **(d)** 64
2. **(a)** $3 - 2i$ **(b)** $-1 + 3i$ **(c)** 4 **(d)** $-16i$
3. **(a)** $x^2 - 4x - 12$ **(b)** $-8x^2 + 14x + 15$
   (c) $11x^2 + x$ **(d)** $-x^2 + x + 7$
4. **(a)** $(x - 6)(x - 2)$ **(b)** $(2x - 1)(x + 3)$
   (c) $(3x + 1)(2x + 5)$ **(d)** $(2x + 1)(3x + 4)$
   (e) $(2x - 5)(2x + 5)$ **(f)** $(x + 1)(2x - 5)$
5. **(a)** $x = -4$ or $x = 2$ **(b)** $x = \frac{5}{2}$ or $x = -\frac{8}{3}$
   (c) $x = -1$ or $x = 6$ **(d)** $x = \frac{1}{2}$ or $x = -\frac{5}{3}$
   (e) $x = -\frac{2}{3}$ or $x = 5$ **(f)** $x = \frac{3}{2}$ or $x = -\frac{5}{4}$
6. **(a)** $x = 0.94$ or $x = -0.83$ **(b)** $x = 0.86$ or $x = -0.88$
   (c) $x = -0.91$ or $x = 1.41$
7. **(a)** $x^2 + 1$ **(b)** $4x^2 + 9$
   (c) $x^2 - 4x + 5$ **(d)** $21 - 20i$
8. **(a)** $x = 2i$ or $x = -2i$ **(b)** $x = 1 + 2\sqrt{3}i$ or $x = 1 - 2\sqrt{3}i$
   (c) $x = 3 + \sqrt{5}i$ or $x = 3 - \sqrt{5}i$
9. **(a)** $x < 4$;

   -2 -1 0 1 2 3 4 5 6

   (b) $-2 \leq x < 2$;

   -3 -2 -1 0 1 2 3 4 5

   (c) $-6 \leq x \leq 6$;

   -7 -6 -5 -4 -3 -2 -1 0 1 2 3 4 5 6 7

10. **(a)**

    (graph)

    (b) $f(x) > 7$ **(c)** $2 \leq x \leq 4$

11.

    (graph)

    The graph is a parabola opening downward.
    The x and y intercepts give reference points
    for curve sketching. The maximum value
    occurs half way between x-intercepts.

12. **(a)** Once the ball is hit, it stays in air for 1.30 seconds.
    (b) When the ball is hit, after 0.61 seconds it reaches its maximum
    height.
    (c) The maximum height is 2.34 m.
13. The y-intercept is 3 and the x-intercepts are -3 and 2.
    $f(x) = -\frac{1}{2}(x + 3)(x - 2)$
14. **(a)** Since -4 and 3 are the zeros of the function, the function can be:
    $f(x) = a(x + 4)(x - 3)$ where $a \in \mathbf{R}$.
    (b) $f(x) = -2(x + 4)(x - 3)$

15. **(a)**

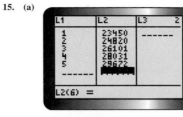

linear pattern

(b) $y = 85.071\ 428\ 57x^2 + 1055.071\ 429x + 22\ 313.8$

(c)

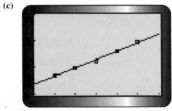

(d) 31 706 800

16. **(a)**

(b) $y = -4.9x^2 + 15.0x + 21.0$

(c)

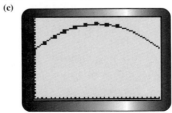

(d) The rockets will hit the ground when t is about 4.11 seconds.

1.1 Exercises, page 14

1. **(a)** $x^3 - 3x^2 - 13x + 15$ **(b)** $6x^3 + 13x^2 + 4x - 3$
  (c) $3x^3 - 21x + 18$ **(d)** $20x^2 - 85x - 75$
  (e) $6x^4 - 7x^3 - 36x^2 + 7x + 6$ **(f)** $-24x^3 + 24x^2 + 90x - 108$

2. **(a)** degree: 3; type of function: cubic
  (b) degree: 3; type of function: cubic
  (c) degree: 3; type of function: cubic
  (d) degree: 2; type of function: quadratic
  (e) degree: 4; type of function: quartic
  (f) degree: 3; type of function: cubic

3. **(a)** $-2, 3$ **(b)** $\frac{5}{3}, -\frac{7}{2}$ **(c)** $4, -3.5$
  (d) $\frac{9}{2}, -\frac{4}{3}, \frac{1}{4}$ **(e)** $\frac{6}{5}, -\frac{4}{3}, \frac{5}{2}$ **(f)** $-3, 3, \frac{5}{2}, \frac{4}{3}$

4. 134 cm^3

5. $9.0 \times 10^{-16} \text{ m}^3$

6. **(a)**
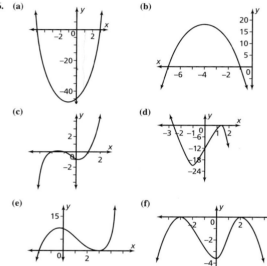
(b)

(c)

(d)

(e)

(f)

7. **(a)** straight line **(b)** U-shaped **(c)** S-shaped
  (d) S-shaped **(e)** U-shaped **(f)** straight line

9. **(a)** intervals of increase: $x < -2, x > 1$; interval of decrease:
  $-2 < x < 1$; turning points: $(-2, 4)$ and $(1, -8)$;
  local maximum value: 4, local minimum value: -8
  (b) interval of increase: $-2 < x < 1$; intervals of decrease:
  $x < -2, x > 1$; turning points: $(-2, -4)$ and $(1, 8)$;
  local maximum value: 8, local minimum value: -4
  (c) intervals of increase: $x < -2.25, -0.25 < x < 1.75$; intervals of
  decrease: $-2.25 < x < -0.25, x > 1.75$; turning points: $(-2.25, 2.5)$,
  $(-0.25, -1)$ and $(1.75, 0.5)$; local maximum value: 2.5, local minimum value: -1
  (d) intervals of increase: $-2 < x < -0.5, x > 1$; intervals of decrease:
  $x < -2, -0.5 < x < 1$; turning points: $(-2, 0), (-0.5, 2.5)$ and
  $(1, 0)$; local maximum value: 2.5, local minimum value: 0

10. **(a)** interval of increase: $x < 0.5$; interval of decrease: $x > 0.5$;
  local maximum value: $(0.5, 24.5)$; no local minimum
  (b) interval of increase: $x > -0.375$; interval of decrease: $x < -0.375$;
  no local maximum; local minimum: $(-0.375, -18.375)$
  (c) intervals of increase: $x < -4.517, x > 0.517$; interval of decrease:
  $-4.517 < x < 0.517$; local maximum: $(-4.517, 3.75)$;
  local minimum: $(0.517, -123.75)$

(d) interval of increase: $-0.215 < x < 1.549$; intervals of decrease:
  $x < -0.215, x > 1.549$; local maximum: $(1.549, 0.316)$;
  local minimum: $(-0.215, -1.056)$
(e) interval of increase: $x < 5$; interval of decrease: $x > 5$; local maximum: $(5, 0)$; no local minimum
(f) intervals of increase: $x < -\frac{1}{3}, x > 3$; interval of decrease:
  $-\frac{1}{3} < x < 3$; local maximum: $(-\frac{1}{3}, 27.778)$; local minimum: $(3, 0)$

11. **(a)** $f(x) = 2(x - 6)(x + 4)$
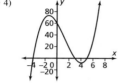

(b) $f(x) = (x - 3)(x - 5)(x + 4)$
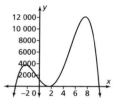

(c) $f(x) = -2(2x - 3)(x + 4)(3x - 5)(x - 10)$
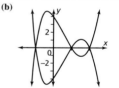

12. **(a)** By knowing the number of zeros, we know the number of times the
  curve is going to intersect or touch the x-axis.
  (b)
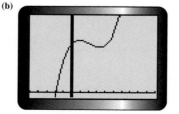

13. The x-intercepts will be correct, but the vertical magnitudes will not be
  specified exactly.

14. **(a)** $f(x) = (x + 2)(x + 1)(x - 1)$ **(b)** $f(x) = -(x + 2)(x - 1)^2$

15. **(a)** $f(x) = -0.4(x + 2)(x + 4)(x - 1)$
  (b) $f(x) = \frac{8}{9}(x + 2)(x + 1)(x - 1)^2$

16. $f(x) = -6(x + 3)(x + 5)$

17. $f(x) = 2(x + 2)(x - 3)(x - 4)$

18. **(a)** $0 \le x \le 4$; 0 represents 1995 and 4 represents 1999 since the
  function is only applied to the period between 1995 and 1999.
  (b)

  shape: S-shaped; turning points: $(3.35, 1178.07)$ and
  $(0.94, 1363.79)$; interval of increase: $x < 0.94, x > 3.35$; interval of
  decrease: $0.94 < x < 3.35$

(c) $1.118\ 847 \times 10^{18}$ J

(d) $5.623\ 235 \times 10^{19}$ J

19. (a)

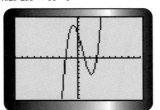

(b) intervals of increase: $x < -0.79$, $x > 2.12$; interval of decrease: $-0.79 < x < 2.12$

(c) 2.12 and -0.79

(d) local maximum: $(-0.79, 8.21)$; local minimum: $(2.12, -4.06)$

20. (a) Advertising cost outside the domain implies that sales may not follow the function $S(x)$ anymore. Budget from \$500 000 to \$3 500 000.

(b)

(c) The maximum sales is \$76 562 500. It occurs when the advertising campaign is \$3 500 000. After this point, the sales drop.

(d) If the model follows the function even when $x > 350$, then when \$6 000 000 is spent on the advertising campaign, sales would be \$0.

21. $k = 3$

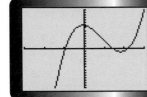

The zeros are $-1, \frac{5}{3}, 2$; $f(x) = (3x - 5)(x - 2)(x + 1)$

22. Examples will vary.

(a) $f(x) = k(x - a)(x - b)$ where $a, b, k \in \mathbf{R}$ and $k > 0$

(b) $f(x) = k(x - a)(x - b)(x - c)$ where $a, b, c, k \in \mathbf{R}$ and $k > 0$

(c) $f(x) = -k(x - a)^2(x - b)$ or $f(x) = -k(x - a)(x - b)^2$ where $a, b, k \in \mathbf{R}$ and $k > 0$

(d) $f(x) = k(x - a)$ where $a, k \in \mathbf{R}$ and $k > 0$

23. (a) $x^2 - 4x + 5$ **(b)** $x^4 - 10x^3 + 50x^2 - 130x + 169 = 0$

1.2 Exercises, page 23

1. (a) cubic; negative; $x \to -\infty, y \to +\infty$; $x \to +\infty, y \to -\infty$; has turning points

(b) quartic; negative; $x \to -\infty, y \to -\infty$; $x \to +\infty, y \to -\infty$; has turning points

(c) quartic; positive; $x \to -\infty, y \to +\infty$; $x \to +\infty, y \to +\infty$; has turning points

(d) cubic; positive; $x \to -\infty, y \to -\infty$; $x \to +\infty, y \to +\infty$; has turning points

2. For odd degree function, two cases exist: $x \to -\infty, y \to +\infty$; $x \to +\infty, y \to -\infty$ or $x \to -\infty, y \to -\infty$; $x \to +\infty, y \to +\infty$. Therefore, it can only have a local maximum or local minimum but no absolute maximum or absolute minimum in the graph of the function. For even degree function, two cases exist: $x \to -\infty, y \to -\infty$; $x \to +\infty, y \to -\infty$ or $x \to -\infty, y \to +\infty$; $x \to +\infty, y \to +\infty$. Therefore, it can either have an absolute maximum or absolute minimum in the graph of the function.

3. determine the finite difference in a set of values until a constant difference is obtained; the number of times the finite differences are executed is the degree of the function.

4. (a) linear **(b)** quadratic **(c)** cubic **(d)** quartic

5. (a) $x \to -\infty, y \to +\infty$; $x \to +\infty, y \to +\infty$

(b) $x \to -\infty, y \to +\infty$; $x \to +\infty, y \to -\infty$

(c) $x \to -\infty, y \to -\infty$; $x \to +\infty, y \to +\infty$

(d) $x \to -\infty, y \to -\infty$; $x \to +\infty, y \to -\infty$

(e) $x \to -\infty, y \to +\infty$; $x \to +\infty, y \to +\infty$

(f) $x \to -\infty, y \to +\infty$; $x \to +\infty, y \to -\infty$

7. (a) $x \to -\infty, y \to -\infty$; $x \to +\infty, y \to -\infty$

(b) $-6, -2, 2$ and 4

(c) $f(x) = -3x^4 - 6x^3 + 84x^2 + 24x - 288$; maximum number of turning points: 3

(d)

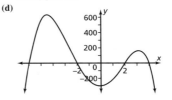

9. (a) $x \to -\infty, y \to +\infty$; $x \to +\infty, y \to +\infty$; $-5, -3$ and 2; $f(x) = 2x^4 + 8x^3 - 26x^2 - 56x + 120$; 3;

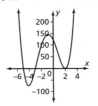

(b) $x \to -\infty, y \to +\infty$; $x \to +\infty, y \to -\infty$; $-3, -1$ and 2; $f(x) = -0.2x^5 - 0.6x^4 + 1.8x^3 + 4.6x^2 - 4.8x - 7.2$; 4;

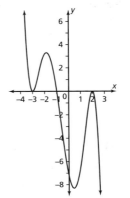

(c) $x \to -\infty, y \to -\infty; x \to +\infty, y \to +\infty; -4, -3, 1, 2$ and 3;

$f(x) = x^7 + 2x^6 - 24x^5 - 26x^4 + 203x^3 + 24x^2 - 612x + 432$;

6;

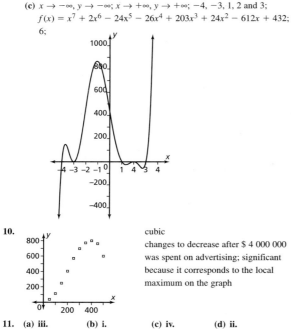

10.

cubic

changes to decrease after $ 4 000 000 was spent on advertising; significant because it corresponds to the local maximum on the graph

11. (a) iii.   (b) i.   (c) iv.   (d) ii.

12. (a)   (b)

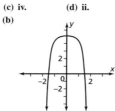

(c)

(d)

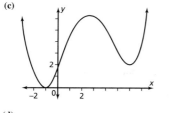

(e)

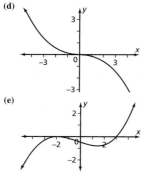

13. (a)

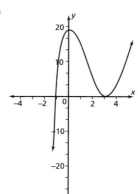

(c) original equation will change
from $f(x) = 2(x - 3)^2(x + 1)$ to
$f(x) = 2(x - 3)(x + 1)^2$

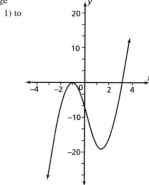

14. (a) -12 (b) 18

15. (a) 6 (b) -21.6

16.

Degree of $f(x)$	Sign of leading coefficient of $f(x)$	End behaviour of $f(x)$ as $x \to +\infty$	End behaviour of $f(x)$ as $x \to -\infty$,
Odd	positive	$y \to +\infty$	$y \to -\infty$
Even	negative	$y \to -\infty$	$y \to -\infty$
Odd	negative	$y \to -\infty$	$y \to +\infty$
Even	positive	$y \to +\infty$	$y \to +\infty$

17. $a_n n!$

18. -1

19. Answers will vary.

1.3 Exercises, page 34

1. (a) $\{(-4, 6), (-2, 5), (1, 5), (4, 10)\}$

(b) $\{(-4, 2), (-2, 3), (1, 1), (4, 2)\}$

(c) $\{(-4, -2), (-2, -3), (1, -1), (4, -2)\}$

(d) $\{(-4, 8), (-2, 4), (1, 6), (4, 24)\}$

2. (a)   (b)

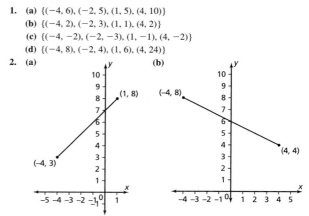

3. (a)

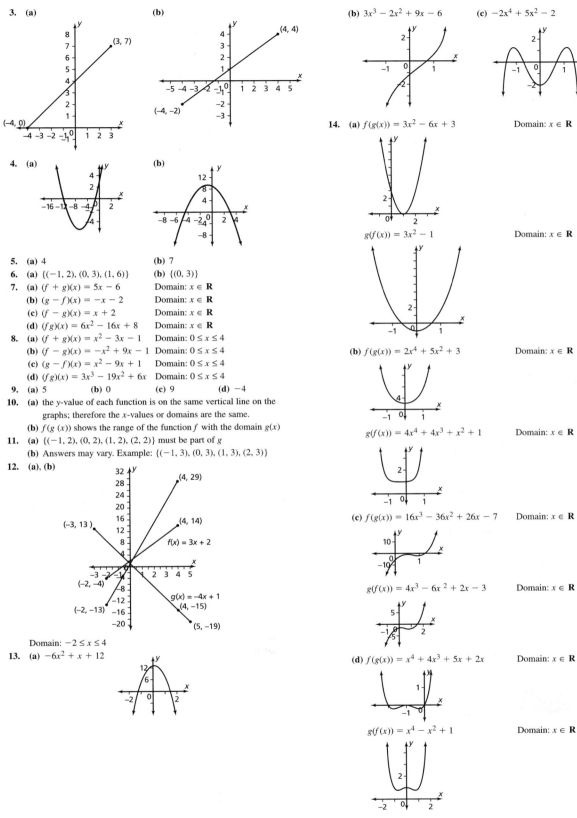

(b) $3x^3 - 2x^2 + 9x - 6$ **(c)** $-2x^4 + 5x^2 - 2$

4. (a)   **(b)**

14. (a) $f(g(x)) = 3x^2 - 6x + 3$ Domain: $x \in \mathbf{R}$

$g(f(x)) = 3x^2 - 1$ Domain: $x \in \mathbf{R}$

5. (a) 4   **(b)** 7

6. (a) $\{(-1, 2), (0, 3), (1, 6)\}$ **(b)** $\{(0, 3)\}$

7. (a) $(f + g)(x) = 5x - 6$ Domain: $x \in \mathbf{R}$
    (b) $(g - f)(x) = -x - 2$ Domain: $x \in \mathbf{R}$
    (c) $(f - g)(x) = x + 2$ Domain: $x \in \mathbf{R}$
    (d) $(fg)(x) = 6x^2 - 16x + 8$ Domain: $x \in \mathbf{R}$

8. (a) $(f + g)(x) = x^2 - 3x - 1$ Domain: $0 \le x \le 4$
    (b) $(f - g)(x) = -x^2 + 9x - 1$ Domain: $0 \le x \le 4$
    (c) $(g - f)(x) = x^2 - 9x + 1$ Domain: $0 \le x \le 4$
    (d) $(fg)(x) = 3x^3 - 19x^2 + 6x$ Domain: $0 \le x \le 4$

(b) $f(g(x)) = 2x^4 + 5x^2 + 3$ Domain: $x \in \mathbf{R}$

9. (a) 5   **(b)** 0   **(c)** 9   **(d)** −4

10. (a) the y-value of each function is on the same vertical line on the graphs; therefore the x-values or domains are the same.
    (b) $f(g(x))$ shows the range of the function f with the domain $g(x)$

$g(f(x)) = 4x^4 + 4x^3 + x^2 + 1$ Domain: $x \in \mathbf{R}$

11. (a) $\{(-1, 2), (0, 2), (1, 2), (2, 2)\}$ must be part of g
    (b) Answers may vary. Example: $\{(-1, 3), (0, 3), (1, 3), (2, 3)\}$

12. (a), (b)

(c) $f(g(x)) = 16x^3 - 36x^2 + 26x - 7$ Domain: $x \in \mathbf{R}$

$g(f(x)) = 4x^3 - 6x^2 + 2x - 3$ Domain: $x \in \mathbf{R}$

Domain: $-2 \le x \le 4$

13. (a) $-6x^2 + x + 12$

(d) $f(g(x)) = x^4 + 4x^3 + 5x + 2x$ Domain: $x \in \mathbf{R}$

$g(f(x)) = x^4 - x^2 + 1$ Domain: $x \in \mathbf{R}$

15. (a)

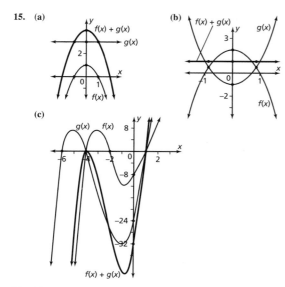

(b)

(c)

17. (a)

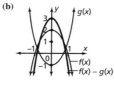

(b)

(c)

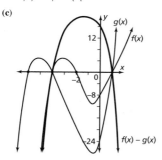

18. (a) $C(x) = 9.45x + 52\ 000$ **(b)** $S(x) = 15.80x$
(c) $P(x) = 6.35x - 52\ 000$
19. (a) $S_R(t) = 24.39t$ **(b)** $S_N(t) = 0.58t$
(c) $S_W(t) = 0.39t$ **(d)** $S_{NW}(t) = 25.36t$ **(e)** \$317.00
20. (a) $A(r) = \pi r^2$ **(b)** $r(C) = \dfrac{C}{2\pi}$
(c) $A(r(C)) = \dfrac{1}{4}\left(\dfrac{C^2}{\pi}\right)$ **(d)** Area $= 1.03$ m^2
21. (a) $S(A) = 200A$ **(b)** $P(S) = 0.15S$ **(c)** $A = 0.2$ m^2
22. (a) $B(T(t)) = 183.75t^2 + 70t + 525$
(b) 1043 bacteria   **(c)** 1.74 hours
23. (a) shop 2   **(b)** $T(t) = t^3 - 1.6t^2 + 1200$ **(c)** \$1.47 million
(d) close shop 1 before costs exceed sales or develop a new marketing strategy
24. $f(x) = 3x^2 + 2x + 5$; $g(x) = 2x^2 - 4x - 2$
25. (a) $C(k) = 27k - 14$ **(b)**

1.4 Exercises, page 42

1. (a) $2x^5 - x^4 - 5x^3 + x^2 + 3x + 5$
(b) $-2x^4 - 2x^3 + 3x^2 + 5x - 3$
(c) $-5x^4 + 3x^3 + 2$ **(d)** $4x^6 + 3x^2 - 2x - 3$
(e) $3x^7 - 4x^2 - 4$ **(f)** $x^4 + 1$
2. (a) $x^2 - 2x - 5$ **(b)** $x^2 - 4x - 4$
(c) $x^2 - 6x - 9$ **(d)** $x^3 + x^2 - 9x - 9$
(e) $x^3 - x^2 + x - 1$ **(f)** $x^3 - 1$
3. (a) 20   **(b)** $x - 22$ **(c)** 0   **(d)** $2x^2 + 2$
4. (a) $x^2 + 3x + 2$ Remainder: $\dfrac{0}{x-3}$
(b) $2x^2 - 5x - 12$ Remainder: $\dfrac{7}{x-1}$
(c) $6x^3 - 5x^2 - 19x + 10$ Remainder: $\dfrac{-2}{x+3}$
(d) $x^2 + 2x - 8$ Remainder: $\dfrac{-4}{2x-3}$
(e) $6x^3 - 31x^2 + 45x - 18$ Remainder: 0
(f) $3x^2 - 1$ Remainder: 0
5. (a) $x^4 - x^3 + x^2 - x + 1$
6. Answers will vary.
7. Answers will vary.
8. (a) yes   **(b)** yes   **(c)** no
(d) no   **(e)** no   **(f)** no
9. (a) 4   **(b)** -11 **(c)** $-3x^2 + 3x + 1$
(d) 10   **(e)** 0   **(f)** $-5x + 10$
10. $p = 10$
11. $p = 2$
12. $(x + 1)$ units
13. $(x + 5)$ units
14. (a) $4x^3 + 12x^2 + x - 23$
15. $(2x + 5)$ cm
16. yes

1.5 Exercises, page 50

2. (a) -1 **(b)** -5 **(c)** 0
(d) -34 **(e)** 30   **(f)** 0
3. (a) yes   **(b)** no   **(c)** yes   **(d)** no
4. $(2x - 5)$
5. (a) $(x + 3)(x - 2)(x - 4)$ **(b)** $(2x + 3)(2x + 5)(x - 1)$
(c) $x(x + 6)(x - 2)(x + 4)$ **(d)** $(x + 5)(x + 2)(4x - 9)(x - 3)$
(e) $x(x + 1)(x + 2)(x - 5)(x - 3)$
(f) $(x + 4)^2(x - 3)^2$
6. (a) $(x + 6)(x + 5)(x - 2)$ **(b)** $(x + 2)(x + 1)(x - 3)$
(c) $(x + 2)(x + 1)(x - 1)(x - 2)$
(d) $(x + 8)(x + 1)(x - 2)(x - 4)$
(e) $(x - 1)(x^2 + 1)$ **(f)** $(x - 1)(x^2 + 1)^2$
7. Use the factors of the constant term, the leading coefficient and the rational zero test and evaluate using the factor theorem.
8. (a) yes; other zeros: -3 and 2   **(b)** no
(c) yes; other zeros: -1 and -3
(d) yes; other zeros: -3, -1 and 0.5
(e) yes; other zero: 1   **(f)** no
9. (a) $(2x + 5)(3x - 2)(x - 1)$ **(b)** $(3x + 7)(x - 1)(3x - 5)$
(c) $(x - 2)^2(3x - 2)(2x + 3)$
(d) $(5x - 1)(x - 2)(2x + 3)(x + 2)$
(e) $(2x + 3)(2x + 1)(2x - 1)$ **(f)** $(2x + 1)(3x - 1)(5x - 1)$
10. (a) (i) $(x - 1)(x^2 + x + 1)$ **(ii)** $(x - 3)(x^2 + 3x + 9)$
(iii) $(x - 5)(x^2 + 5x + 25)$ **(iv)** $(2x - 3)(4x^2 + 6x + 9)$
(b) $(a - b)(a^2 + ab + b^2)$
(c) $(4x - 3)(16x^2 + 12x + 9)$
11. (a) (i) $(x + 1)(x^2 - x + 1)$ **(ii)** $(x + 2)(x^2 - 2x + 4)$
(iii) $(x + 4)(x^2 - 4x + 16)$ **(iv)** $(2x + 5)(4x^2 - 10x + 25)$

(b) $(a + b)(a^2 - ab + b^2)$ **(c)** $(5x + 4)(25x^2 - 20x + 16)$

12. **(a)** $(x - 4)(x^2 + 4x + 16)$ **(b)** $(y + 3)(y^2 - 3y + 9)$
  (c) $(4x + 1)(16x^2 - 4x + 1)$ **(d)** $(5x^2 - 3)(25x^4 + 15x^2 + 9)$
  (e) $8(x^3 + 3)(x^6 - 3x^3 + 9)$ **(f)** $(8 - 3x^4)(64 + 24x^4 + 9x^8)$
  (g) $(x^2 + 11)(x^4 - 11x^2 + 121)$
  (h) $(7x^5 - 2)(49x^{10} + 14x^5 + 4)$

13. **(a)** $(x + 1)(2x^2 + 1)$ **(b)** $(x + 2)(3x^2 - 1)$
  (c) $(2x + 3)(4x^2 + 1)$ **(d)** $(2x + 1)(5x^2 - 2)$
  (e) $x(3x - 1)(2x^3 - 3)$ **(f)** $(2x + 3)(3x^5 - 2)$

14.

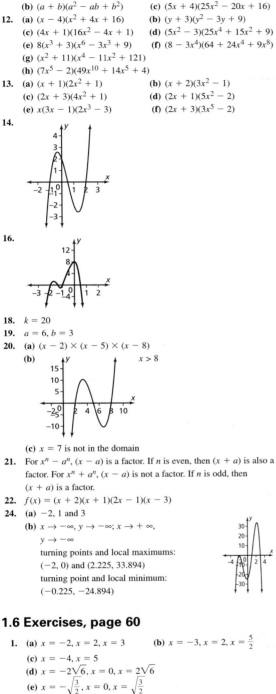

16.

18. $k = 20$
19. $a = 6, b = 3$
20. **(a)** $(x - 2) \times (x - 5) \times (x - 8)$
  (b) $x > 8$

  (c) $x = 7$ is not in the domain
21. For $x^n - a^n$, $(x - a)$ is a factor. If n is even, then $(x + a)$ is also a
  factor. For $x^n + a^n$, $(x - a)$ is not a factor. If n is odd, then
  $(x + a)$ is a factor.
22. $f(x) = (x + 2)(x + 1)(2x - 1)(x - 3)$
24. **(a)** $-2, 1$ and 3
  (b) $x \to -\infty, y \to -\infty; x \to +\infty,$
    $y \to -\infty$
    turning points and local maximums:
    $(-2, 0)$ and $(2.225, 33.894)$
    turning point and local minimum:
    $(-0.225, -24.894)$

1.6 Exercises, page 60

1. **(a)** $x = -2, x = 2, x = 3$ **(b)** $x = -3, x = 2, x = \frac{5}{2}$
  (c) $x = -4, x = 5$
  (d) $x = -2\sqrt{6}, x = 0, x = 2\sqrt{6}$
  (e) $x = -\sqrt{\frac{3}{2}}, x = 0, x = \sqrt{\frac{3}{2}}$
  (f) $x = -\frac{1}{3}, x = \frac{1}{3}, x = -\frac{i}{3}, x = \frac{i}{3}$
2. **(a)** $x = -3, x = 5, x = 6$
  (b) $x = -5, x = -3, x = -2, x = 1$
  (c) $x = -1, x = \frac{1}{2}, x = 3$ **(d)** $x = -2, x = -1, x = \frac{3}{2}$
  (e) $x = -4, x = \frac{1}{2}, x = 2, x = \frac{5}{2}$
  (f) $x = \frac{1}{2}, x = \frac{3}{2}, x = \frac{5}{3}$

3. **(a)** $x = -3, x = 1, x = 2$
  (b) $x = -2, x = -1.24, x = 1, x = 7.24$
  (c) $x = -2, x = 1$ **(d)** $x = -3, x = 0, x = 2$
  (e) $x = -0.86, x = 1.8, x = 2.33$
  (f) $x = -2.71, x = -0.16$
4. $x = -3, x = -\frac{5}{3}, x = \frac{5}{3}, x = 3$
6. **(a)** $4i$ **(b)** $-6i$ **(c)** $2 + 3i$
  (d) $5 - 7i$ **(e)** $-3 - 2i$ **(f)** $-5 + 4i$
7. $4 \times 3 \times 1$ cm
8. **(a)** $x = 1, x = -4i, x = 4i$
  (b) $x = -1, x = 2 - i, x = 2 + i$
  (c) $x = -3, x = 4, x = -3i, x = 3i,$
  (d) $x = 1, x = -\frac{1}{2}i, x = \frac{1}{2}i$
  (e) $x = 1, x = -1, x = 1 - i, x = 1 + i$
  (f) $x = -2 - 3i, x = -2 + 3i, x = -i, x = +i$
9. **(a)** $-5, 2, 3$ **(b)** $-\frac{5}{3}, \frac{1}{2}, 7$
  (c) $0, 3, 5$ **(d)** $-2, 1, 3$
  (e) no real roots   **(f)** $-2, 0, \frac{1}{2}$
10. $x = -1.73$ and $x = 1.41$
11. **(a)** 8 is in the domain; 20 is not in the domain
  (b) set C equal to 15 and solve for t
  (c) 1992
12. $f(x) = a(x^4 - 8x^3 + 27x^2 - 38x + 26), \{a \mid a \neq 0, a \in \mathbf{R}\}$
13. **(a)** $f(x) = a(x^4 - x^3 - 28x^2 - 20x + 48)$ where $a \neq 0, a \in \mathbf{R}$;
    degree: 4
  (b) $f(x) = -2x^4 + 2x^3 + 56x^2 + 40x - 96$
14. $f(x) = \frac{1}{2}(x - 2)(x - 4)(x + 5)$
15. $f(x) = -3(x - 2)(x^2 - 2x + 5)$;
  end behaviour: $x \to -\infty, y \to +\infty$ and
  $x \to \infty, y \to -\infty$; y-intercept: is $(0, 30)$

17. **(b)** $V = x(25 - 1.5x)(30 - 2x), 0 \leq x \leq 15$
  (c) $x = 5.26$ cm
  (d) $x = 1.78$ cm or $x = 9.79$ cm
18. $x^2 + 5x - 84 = 0$ or $x^2 + 19x + 84 = 0$
19. **(a)** 96
  (b) $0°C$ or $372°C$
  (c) $200°C$ or $211°C$
20. **(a)**

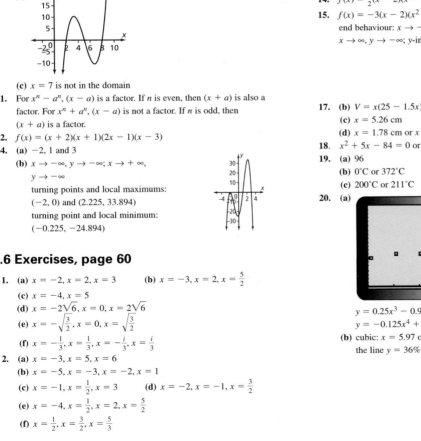

  $y = 0.25x^3 - 0.928\ 57x^2 + 1.464\ 29x + 7.042\ 86$;
  $y = -0.125x^4 + 1.25x^3 - 3.375x^2 + 3.25x + 7$
  (b) cubic: $x = 5.97$ or in the year 2011; quartic: model never intersects
    the line $y = 36\%$

(c)

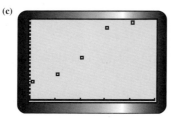

(d) models are not accurate outside the domain $0 \le x \le 4$

21. (a) $f(x) = x^3 - 3x^2 - x + 3$ **(b)** $x = 12$

22. (a) $0 \le t \le 5$

(b) better to use graphing technology since the coefficients are not integers

(c) $t = 0.45$ s, $t = 3.33$ s

23. (a) $x = -1.98$ or $x = 2.25$ or $x = 4.10$ or $x = 7.58$. The population was 400 000 in the years 1951, 1972, 1981, and 1999.

(b) $x = -3.4$ or $x = 9.2$. This implies that in 1944 and 2007, there are no people living in collective dwellings.

(c) $y = -1304.1768x^3 + 19\ 685.9037x^2 - 79\ 936.5040x + 495\ 608.7727$

(d)

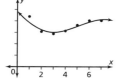

(e) $x = -1.98$ or $x = 2.25$ or $x = 4.10$ or $x = 7.58$; these match the answers in part (a)

(f) quartic function

1.7 Exercises, page 72

1. (a) 22   **(b)** -35 **(c)** 18
  (d) 11   **(e)** -2 **(f)** -2

2. (a) $|x| > 3$ **(b)** $|x| \le 8$ **(c)** $|x| \ge 1$ **(d)** $|x| \ne 5$

3. (a)

(b)

(c)   **(d)**

4. (a) $|x| \le 3$ **(b)** $|x| > 2$ **(c)** $|x| \ge 2$ **(d)** $|x| < 4$

5. (a) $-1 < x < 1$ **(b)** $-\frac{1}{4} \le x \le \frac{1}{2}$

  (c) $-4 < x < -\frac{1}{2}$ or $x > 3$ **(d)** $x \le 1$ or $2 \le x \le 3$

  (e) $x < -5$ or $-4 < x < \frac{3}{2}$ or $x > 2$

  (f) $-3 < x < \frac{1}{2}$ or $\frac{4}{3} < x < 2$

7. (a) $x < -2.59$ **(b)** $x < -1.05$ or $2.11 < x < 4.94$
  (c) $x < -2.61$ or $x > 1.19$ **(d)** $x > 3.26$
  (e) $x < -1.10$ or $0.48 < x < 3.32$ **(f)** $0.80 < x < 2.92$

8. (a) $x \le -1$ or $x \ge 7$ **(b)** $-3 \le x \le 0$ or $x \ge 3$
  (c) $-5 < x < 4$ **(d)** $x < -3$ or $-2 < x < 1$
  (e) $-2 < x < 1$ or $x > 3$ **(f)** $-2 < x < -1$ or $1 < x < 2$

10. (a)

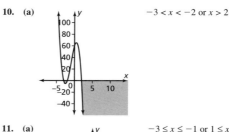

$-3 < x < -2$ or $x > 2$

11. (a)

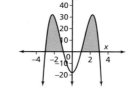

$-3 \le x \le -1$ or $1 \le x \le 3$

12. never negative, $x \in \mathbf{R}$

14. negative everywhere except when $x = \frac{1}{2}$, $x = -\frac{1}{3}$

  $x = \frac{1}{2}$, $x = -\frac{1}{3}$

16. Answers will vary.

17. $0 < x < 1.19$ or $2.77 < x < 3.84$ or from January 1993 to February 1994 and from September 1995 to October 1996

18. (a) $-3.30 \le x \le 0.30$ or $x \ge 2.00$
  (b) $x \le -4.65$ or $0.65 \le x \le 1.00$ or $x > 2.00$

19. $x > 8.73$ or starting from August 1992

20. $x < -2 - \sqrt{6}$, $-2 < x < -2 + \sqrt{6}$, $x > 3$

21. Answers will vary. Example: $f(x) = (x - 2)(-x^2 + x - 2)$

22. $f(x) = -3(x + 2)(x - 1)(x - 3)^2$

23. (a) 500 000 or 900 000 games
  (b) profit: when selling between 500 000 to 900 000 games; lose money: when it sells less than 500 000 games or more than 900 000 games

24. (a) $f(x) = x^3 + 11x^2 + 18x$
  (b) look for its x-intercepts, determine when $f(x) > 0$
  (c) $-9 < x < -2$ or $x > 0$

25. (a) $a = -2$ **(b)** $x = 6$ or $x = -14$
  (c) $-3 < x < 7$ **(d)** $x > 3$ or $x < -9$
  (e) $|x - 5| \le 15$

26. $x < -3.20$, $-1.71 < x < 0.91$, and $x > 3$

Chapter 1 Review, page 75

11. (a) $f(x) = 6x^3 + 17x^2 - 31x - 12$; degree: 3
  (b) $f(x) = 4x^4 - 8x^3 - 11x^2 + 33x - 18$; degree: 4
  (c) $f(x) = 24x^4 - 172x^3 + 390x^2 - 225x - 125$; degree: 4
  (d) $f(x) = x^4 + x^3 - 13x^2 + 6x - 9$; degree: 4

12. $f(x) = -2(x + 2)(x + 1)(x - 4)$

13. (a) $f(x) = (x + 3)(x + 1)(x - 1)(x - 3)$
  (b) increasing: $-2.2 < x < 0$, $x > 2.2$; decreasing: $x < -2.2$, $0 < x < 2.2$

14. (a) 10   **(b)** -12 **(c)** 12

15. (a) end behaviour: $x \to -\infty$, $y \to +\infty$ and $x \to +\infty$, $y \to -\infty$; zeros: $-2, 1, 3$
  (b) end behaviour: $x \to -\infty$, $y \to +\infty$ and $x \to +\infty$, $y \to +\infty$; zeros: $-3, 2$
  (c) end behaviour: $x \to -\infty$, $y \to -\infty$ and $x \to +\infty$, $y \to +\infty$; zeros: -2
  (d) end behaviour: $x \to -\infty$, $y \to -\infty$ and $x \to +\infty$, $y \to -\infty$; zeros: $0, -\frac{7}{5}$

16. (a) turning points: $(-1, 30)$ and $(3, -6)$; intervals of increase: $x < -1, x > 3$; interval of decrease: $-1 < x < 3$

(b) turning points: $(-2.25, -12.5)$, $(0.5, 14)$ and $(3.25, -12.5)$; intervals of increase: $-2.25 < x < 0.5, x > 3.25$; intervals of decrease: $x < -2.25, 0.5 < x < 3.25$

17. (a) $\{(1, 7), (4, 15)\}$　**(b)** $\{(1, -1), (4, -1)\}$
(c) $\{(1, 12), (4, 56)\}$　**(d)** $\{(1, 7)\}$　**(e)** $\{(5, 9)\}$

18. (a)

(b)

(c)

(d)

(e)

19. (a) 1　**(b)** 1
(c) $x^3 - 9x^2 + 26x - 23$　**(d)** $x^3 - 3x^2 + 2x - 1$
20. (a) length $= 200 + 50t$　**(b)** width $= 100 + 40t$
(c) area $= 20\,000 + 13\,000t + 2000t^2$
(d) $252\,000$ m^2
21. (a) quotient: $2x^2 + x - 3$; remainder: -1
(b) quotient: $3x^2 + 7x + 3$; remainder: -3
(c) quotient: $2x^3 + x^2 - 18x - 9$; remainder: 0
(d) quotient: $2x^2 - 5$; remainder: 6
22. $6x^4 + 11x^3 - 84x^2 + 61x + 39$
23. $p = 1$
24. (a) -8　**(b)** -5
25. $2x + 3$ is a factor
26. (a) $(x - 2)(x - 5)(x + 3)$
(b) $(x - 3)(x - 2)(x + 1)(x + 4)$
(c) $(x - 2)(x + 1)(x + 2)(x - 3)$
(d) $(2x - 1)(2x + 5)(3x + 1)$
(e) $x(3x^4 + 1)(2x + 1)$
(f) $x(2x^2 - 1)(x - 5)$
27. (a) $x = -1$ or $x = 1$ or $x = -2$
(b) $x = -4$ or $x = -2$ or $x = -\frac{1}{2}$ or $x = 1$
28. (a) $x = -4.19$ or $x = 1.19$ or $x = 2.00$
(b) $x = -5.16$ or $x = -1.00$ or $x = 1.16$
(c) $x = -1.00, x = 2.00, x = 0.82, x = -1.82$
(d) $x = -3.00, x = -2.00, x = 2.00, x = 3.00$

29. $f(x) = -(x - 1)^2(x^2 - 4x + 13)$
30. (a) $-1 < x < 3, x > 4$　**(b)** $2 < x < 3$
(c) $x \geq 2$　**(d)** no solution
31. (a) $x < -3, -1 < x < 2$　**(b)** $-4 < x < -2, 1 < x < 3$
(c) $x < -1$　**(d)** no solution
32. (a) $|x| < 2$　**(b)** $|x| \leq 5$
(c) $|x| > 3$
33. (a) not a factor　**(b)** is a factor
(c) is a factor　**(d)** is a factor
(e) not a factor　**(f)** is a factor
34. (a) $2x^2 + 3x - 2$　**(b)** $x^3 + 5x^2 - 2x - 24$
(c) quotient: $x^5 - 2x^4 + 4x^3 - 12x^2 + 27x - 54$; remainder: 96
(d) $x^2 + 2x - 8$
35. (a) $x = 3$ or $x = -1$ or $x = -2$
(b) $x = 1$ or $x = -\frac{2}{3}$ or $x = \frac{1}{2}$　**(c)** $x = \frac{3}{4}$
(d) $x = -3$ or $x = \frac{1}{\sqrt{2}}$ or $\frac{\sqrt{2}}{2}$ or $x = -\frac{1}{\sqrt{2}}$ or $-\frac{\sqrt{2}}{2}$
(e) $x = -\frac{3}{2}$ or $x = -1$ or $x = 1$ or $x = 2$
(f) $x = 1, -\sqrt{2}, \sqrt{2}$
36. (a) if x_1, x_2 and x_3 are the intercepts, then
$f(x) = a(x - x_1)(x - x_2)(x - x_3)$, $a \in \mathbf{R}$; use the given point $(x, f(x))$ to evaluate a by substituting in the equation
$f(x) = a\,(x - x_1)(x - x_2)(x - x_3)$
(b) $f(x) = -2(x + 1)(x - 3)(x - 4)$
37. end behaviour: $x \to -\infty, y \to -\infty$ and $x \to +\infty, y \to +\infty$; x-intercepts: $-4, -2$ and 2; interval of increase: $x < -3$ or $x > 0.5$; interval of decrease: $-3 < x < 0.5$; turning points: $(-3, 5)$ and $(0.5, -17)$: local maximum: $(-3, 5)$; local minimum: $(0.5, -17)$; intervals when function greater than 0: $-4 < x < 2$, $x > 2$; intervals when function less than 0: $x < -4, -2 < x < 2$
38.

40. (a) when $t = \frac{5}{3}$ s
(b) when $t = 0.87$ s and $t = 2.62$ s
(c) when 0.56 s $< t < 3.11$ s
41.

$p(x) = -1.2x^3 + 28.2x^2 + 193.0x + 2555.3$; $0 \leq x \leq 10$; 1963: $3\,195\,002$; 1983: $4\,665\,665$; 2040: $8\,033\,525$; population in 2040 appears reasonable
42. $k = 20$; other roots: 2.76 and 0.24
43. $f(x) = m\,(x + 4)(x + 2)(x - 3)^2$ where $m \in \mathbf{R}$

44. $f(x) = x^4 - 6x^3 + 26x^2 - 46x + 65$

Chapter 1 Review Test, page 80

1. **(a)** $f(x) = a_n x^n + a_{n-1} x^{n-1} + \ldots + a_2 x^2 + a_1 x + a_0$; degree: n; leading coefficient: a_n
   (b) $n - 1$ **(c)** n **(d)** degree ≥ 1
   (e) degree: even with no real roots; leading coefficient < 0
2. **(a)** find the range, y-intercept, zeros, the degree, the leading coefficient from the equation; use this information to determine the end behaviour
   (b)
   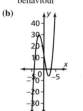
3. yes
4. **(a)** $(2x + 3)(x - 1)(x - 2)$ **(b)** $(2x - 3)(4x^2 + 6x + 9)$
   (c) $(x - 2)(4x^2 + 3)$
5. **(a)** $x = -1$ or $x = 1$ or $x = -4$ or $x = \frac{1}{2}$
   (b) $-2.5 < x < 1$ and $x > 1$
6. **(a)** $x^3 - 7x + 6$ **(b)** $x^4 - 4x^3 + 8x^2 - 16x + 16$
7. **(a)** males: $f(x) = 0.176x^3 - 4.052x^2 + 16.97x + 72.365$; females: $f(x) = 0.022x^3 - 0.64x^2 + 9.01x + 14.369$; in 1983, about 89.3 males per 100 000; in 1983, about 26.5 females per 100 000
   (b) when $x = 6.96$ or about 2010
8. the length of one side of the square must be between 0.11 cm and 13.560 cm
9. $f(x) = 3x^4 + 14x^3 - 11x^2 - 70x + 24$

Chapter 2

Getting Ready, page 84

1. **(a)** $\left(\frac{1}{3}\right)^4$ **(b)** $\left(\frac{1}{7}\right)^2$ **(c)** $\left(\frac{1}{a}\right)^8$ **(d)** $\left(\frac{1}{x}\right)^5$
2. **(a)** 256 **(b)** 243 **(c)** -512 **(d)** -16
   (e) $-\frac{1}{36}$ **(f)** 371.4228 **(g)** $-\frac{1}{32}$ **(h)** 1
   (i) $\frac{4}{9}$ **(j)** $\frac{64}{27}$ **(k)** $\frac{161}{405}$ **(l)** $\frac{13}{16}$
3. **(a)** 2 **(b)** -2 **(c)** 0.25 **(d)** 0.17
   (e) 1.41 **(f)** 0.94 **(g)** 0.12 **(h)** 0.29
4. **(a)** 2^{11} **(b)** 2^9 **(c)** 2^{4-m} **(d)** 2^{3n}
5. **(a)** 9 **(b)** $\frac{257}{4}$ **(c)** $\frac{9}{10}$ **(d)** $\frac{1}{20}$
   (e) $\frac{9}{4}$ **(f)** $\frac{1}{625}$
6. **(a)** -1 **(b)** $\frac{4}{9}$
7. **(a)** x^2y **(b)** $a^{18}b^{10}$ **(c)** $(cd)^6$ **(d)** $\frac{x^{18}}{y^2}$
8. **(a)**

x	y
-1	0.5
0	1
1	2
2	4
3	8
4	16
5	32

(b)

x	y
-1	$\frac{1}{3}$
0	1
1	3
2	9
3	27
4	81
5	243

(c)

x	y
-2	4
-1	2
0	1
1	0.5
2	0.25

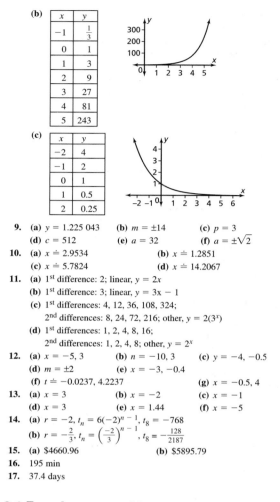

9. **(a)** $y = 1.225\ 043$ **(b)** $m = \pm 14$ **(c)** $p = 3$
   (d) $c = 512$ **(e)** $a = 32$ **(f)** $a = \pm\sqrt{2}$
10. **(a)** $x \doteq 2.9534$ **(b)** $x \doteq 1.2851$
    (c) $x \doteq 5.7824$ **(d)** $x \doteq 14.2067$
11. **(a)** 1st difference: 2; linear, $y = 2x$
    (b) 1st difference: 3; linear, $y = 3x - 1$
    (c) 1st differences: 4, 12, 36, 108, 324; 2nd differences: 8, 24, 72, 216; other, $y = 2(3^x)$
    (d) 1st differences: 1, 2, 4, 8, 16; 2nd differences: 1, 2, 4, 8; other, $y = 2^x$
12. **(a)** $x = -5, 3$ **(b)** $n = -10, 3$ **(c)** $y = -4, -0.5$
    (d) $m = \pm 2$ **(e)** $x = -3, -0.4$
    (f) $t \doteq -0.0237, 4.2237$ **(g)** $x = -0.5, 4$
13. **(a)** $x = 3$ **(b)** $x = -2$ **(c)** $x = -1$
    (d) $x = 3$ **(e)** $x = 1.44$ **(f)** $x = -5$
14. **(a)** $r = -2$, $t_n = 6(-2)^{n-1}$, $t_8 = -768$
    (b) $r = -\frac{2}{3}$, $t_n = \left(\frac{-2}{3}\right)^{n-1}$, $t_8 = -\frac{128}{2187}$
15. **(a)** \$4660.96 **(b)** \$5895.79
16. 195 min
17. 37.4 days

2.1 Exercises, page 92

1. **(a)** 162.0000 **(b)** 5766.5039 **(c)** 0.0977 **(d)** 0.0095
2. **(a)** 1.14 **(b)** 0.94 **(c)** 1.10 **(d)** 0.91
3. **(a)** 3.00 **(b)** 2.92 **(c)** 1.45 **(d)** 0.45
4. **(a)** 300 **(b)** 153 600 **(c)** 1200
   (d) $150(2)^t$ **(e)** 2 457 600 **(f)** 1.611×10^{11}
5. **(a)** \$10 400 **(b)** \$20 800 **(c)** \$41 600
   (d) \$29 415.64 **(e)** \$58 831.28 **(f)** \$93 388.84
6. **(a)** inflation rate: 6% **(b)** deflation rate: 2%
   (c) inflation rate: 1.2% **(d)** deflation rate: 5.8%
7. **(a)** Initial value: 1200; growth rate: 200%
   (b) Initial value: 1; growth rate: 300%
   (c) Initial value: 100; growth rate: 104.8%
   (d) Initial value: 50; growth rate: 500%
8. 0.1845 m
9. **(a)** 5 years: \$1924.68; 10 years: \$2894.06
   (b) \$1280 **(c)** 8.5 % **(d)** \$376.11
10. 21 474 836 480

11. linear equation: y is y-coordinate, m is slope, x is x-coordinate; b is y-int; exponential equation: y is y-coordinate, c is initial value (y-int), a is the growth/decay rate, x is x-coordinate; b and c are similar—they show initial value of function when $x = 0$, m and a are similar—they show how the function increases or decreases as $x \to +\infty$ and $x \to -\infty$, difference of the functions is $y = mx + b$ is linear and $y = c(a)^x$ is a curve

12. $10 197.40

13. 15^{180}

14. 1648

15. 39 628

16. $2980.23

17. For $y = c(a)^x$, $0 < a < 1$ when the rate of change is neg. Examples: deflation, decay, depreciation, decrease in population; $a > 1$ when the rate of change is pos. Examples: growth, inflation, increase in population, bank deposit, loan, investment

18. (a) 0.96   (b) $y = 55(0.96)^t$
    (c) no; after the coffee reaches the room temperature, the temperature will reach equilibrium

19. 72.9%, between 6 and 7 copies

20. 23.5 years

2.2 Exercises, page 103

1. graphs are all in the general form $y = a^x$. When $a > 1$, graphs are similar in that as $x \to -\infty$, $y \to 0$, and as $x \to +\infty$, $y \to +\infty$. When $0 < a < 1$, graphs are similar in that as $x \to -\infty$, $y \to +\infty$, and as $x \to +\infty$, $y \to 0$

2. (a)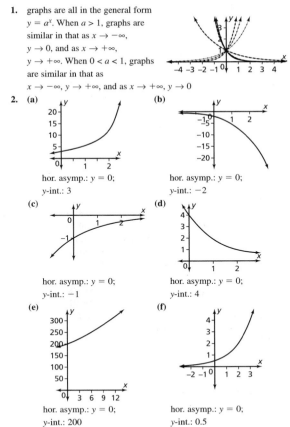

   (a) hor. asymp.: $y = 0$; y-int.: 3
   (b) hor. asymp.: $y = 0$; y-int.: -2
   (c) hor. asymp.: $y = 0$; y-int.: -1
   (d) hor. asymp.: $y = 0$; y-int.: 4
   (e) hor. asymp.: $y = 0$; y-int.: 200
   (f) hor. asymp.: $y = 0$; y-int.: 0.5

3. (a)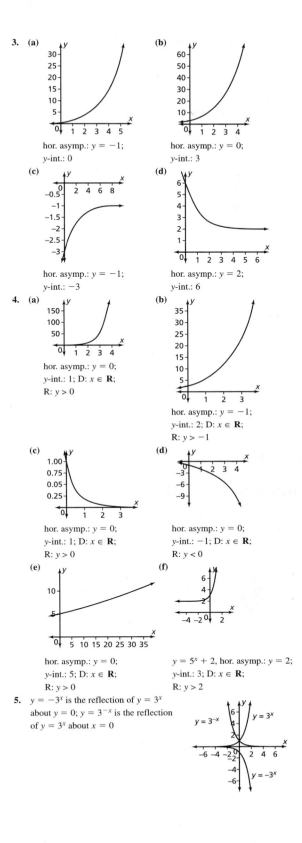

   (a) hor. asymp.: $y = -1$; y-int.: 0
   (b) hor. asymp.: $y = 0$; y-int.: 3
   (c) hor. asymp.: $y = -1$; y-int.: -3
   (d) hor. asymp.: $y = 2$; y-int.: 6

4. (a) hor. asymp.: $y = 0$; y-int.: 1; D: $x \in \mathbf{R}$; R: $y > 0$
   (b) hor. asymp.: $y = -1$; y-int.: 2; D: $x \in \mathbf{R}$; R: $y > -1$
   (c) hor. asymp.: $y = 0$; y-int.: 1; D: $x \in \mathbf{R}$; R: $y > 0$
   (d) hor. asymp.: $y = 0$; y-int.: -1; D: $x \in \mathbf{R}$; R: $y < 0$
   (e) hor. asymp.: $y = 0$; y-int.: 5; D: $x \in \mathbf{R}$; R: $y > 0$
   (f) $y = 5^x + 2$, hor. asymp.: $y = 2$; y-int.: 3; D: $x \in \mathbf{R}$; R: $y > 2$

5. $y = -3^x$ is the reflection of $y = 3^x$ about $y = 0$; $y = 3^{-x}$ is the reflection of $y = 3^x$ about $x = 0$

6. *y*-int.: 500; represents initial value of investment

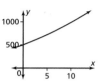

7. graph of $y = 10^x$
 (a) 3.16 **(b)** 15.85 **(c)** 0.50
 (d) 2.15 **(e)** 6.32 **(f)** 1.78

8. $y = 2^x + 3$ is a vert. translation (3 units up) of $y = 2^x$; $y = 2^x - 1$ is a vert. translation (1 unit down) of $y = 2^x$; $y = 5(2^x)$ is a vert. stretch by a factor of 5 of $y = 2^x$

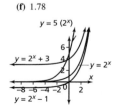

9. **(a)** III; factor is larger than 1 and initial value is pos.
 (b) I; factor is larger than 1 and initial value is neg.
 (c) IV; factor is smaller than 1 and initial value is pos.
 (d) II; factor is smaller than 1 and initial value is neg.

10. According to the graph, after 1 year the time required is 2.70 h and after 5 years the time required is 0.23 h; not a good model—not realistic that a 5-h job can be done in 14 min 5 years later.

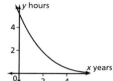

11.

	Function	$x \to +\infty$	$x \to -\infty$	$x \to 0$
(a)	$y = 2^x$	$y \to +\infty$	$y \to 0$	$y \to 1$
(b)	$y = (0.1)^x$	$y \to 0$	$y \to +\infty$	$y \to 1$
(c)	$y = (1.02)^x$	$y \to +\infty$	$y \to 0$	$y \to 1$
(d)	$y = 3^{x+1}$	$y \to +\infty$	$y \to 0$	$y \to 3$

12. **(a) i.** 45 mg **ii.** 33.75 mg **iii.** 18.98 mg
 (b)

Time (h)	0	1	2	3	4	5
Amount of Caffeine (mg)	60	45	33.75	25.31	18.98	14.24

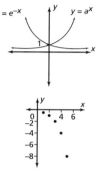

 (c) $y = 60(0.75)^t$ where y is amount of the caffeine left in mg and t is time in hours
 (d) 14.23 h

13. Equations will vary. Both graphs have same *y*-int. (1), but the factors are different. One is a vertical reflection of the other about the *y*-axis.

14. $y = \left(-\frac{1}{2}\right)(2)^{n-1}$, $n \geq 1$; it is an example of exponential equation with $-\frac{1}{2}$ as the initial value and 2 as the factor

15. **(a)** $V = 5000(1.10)^t$
 (b) 7.3 years

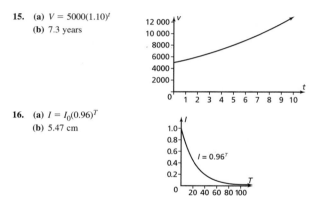

16. **(a)** $I = I_0(0.96)^T$
 (b) 5.47 cm

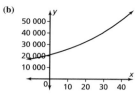

17. For $y = a^x$, if $0 < a < 1$ the end behaviour is, as $x \to -\infty$, $y \to +\infty$ and $x \to +\infty$, $y \to 0$; if $a > 1$ the end behaviour is, as $x \to -\infty$, $y \to 0$ and $x \to +\infty$, $y \to +\infty$

18. Example:

x	-2	-1	0	1	2	3
y	1.1875	1.75	4	13	49	193
First Difference	0.5625	2.25	9	36	144
Second Difference	1.6875	6.75	27	108

 (a) geometric sequence with common ratio 4
 (b) geometric sequence with common ratio 4

19. **(a)** $x = -\frac{1}{2}$ **(b)** $x = -3$ **(c)** $x = 1$

20. **(a)** X and Y1 correspond to B, X and Y2 correspond to A
 (b) graph A **(c)** graph A: 8; graph B: 5

2.3 Exercises, page 110

1. A
2. **(a)** 2480 **(b)** 9920 **(c)** 62 988
 (d) 40 632 320 **(e)** 1.745×10^{17} **(f)** 3.219×10^{36}
3. **(a)** 1.25 kg **(b)** 1.77 kg
 (c) 0.74 kg **(d)** 2.97 kg
4. **(a)**

Time (years)	0	1	2	3	4	5	6
Population	23 000	23 460	23 929	24 408	24 896	25 394	25 902

 (b)

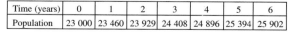

 (c) $P = (23\,000)(1.02)^t$ where t is time in years and P is the population
 (d) 28 037 **(e)** 13.42 years **(f)** 30 910
5. **(a)** 1.024 **(b)** $P = (35\,000)(1.02)^t$ **(c)** 44 years
6. **(a)** 1.5 h
 (b) $P = (3000)(2)^{\frac{t}{1.5}}$ where t is time and P is population
 (c) 120 952 bacteria **(d)** 4762 bacteria
7. 2.18 mg
8. 6.66 years
9. **(a)** $N = (1)\left(\frac{1}{2}\right)^{\frac{t}{2.5 \times 10^5}}$ where N is mass in grams and t is time in years
 (b) 0.99 g

10. similarities: have the form $y = c(a)^x$; better to have several forms because these forms specialize on the particular field such as compound interest, growth, decay and geometric sequences

11. 72.42%

12. (a) \$183.54   (b) 7.86 years

13. (a) \$295 245   (b) 9.96 years

14. 0.966

15. 0.880

16. 6%/a

17. growth: $a > 1$; decay: $0 < a < 1$

18. 12.39%

19. (a) 1750 to 1800: 28.57%; 1800 to 1850: 31.11%; 1850 to 1900: 35.59%; 1900 to 1950: 56.25%

    (b) $P = (7 \times 10^8)(1.3788)^t$ where t is the number of 50-year periods since 1750 and P is the population

    (c) no; adjust by using the population value of 2000 as a point to derive the formula

20. 2 036 579

2.4 Exercises, page 117

1.

Exponential Form	Logarithmic Form
$8 = 2^3$	$3 = \log_2 8$
$16 = 2^4$	$4 = \log_2 16$
$1000 = 10^3$	$3 = \log 1000$
$2^{\frac{1}{2}} = \sqrt{2}$	$\frac{1}{2} = \log_2 \sqrt{2}$
$2^{-3} = \frac{1}{8}$	$-3 = \log_2 \frac{1}{8}$
$25^{-\frac{1}{2}} = \frac{1}{5}$	$-\frac{1}{2} = \log_{25} \frac{1}{5}$

2. (a) $5^2 = 25$ (b) $2^4 = 16$ (c) $3^3 = 27$

    (d) $2^{-1} = 0.5$ (e) $4^{\frac{1}{2}} = 2$ (f) $7^0 = 1$

3. (a) $3 = \log_2 8$ (b) $\frac{1}{2} = \log_9 3$ (c) $4 = \log_{10} 10\ 000$

    (d) $-2 = \log_3 \frac{1}{9}$ (e) $\frac{1}{3} = \log_{125} 5$ (f) $-\frac{1}{2} = \log_4 \frac{1}{2}$

4. (a) 3   (b) $\frac{1}{2}$ (c) 1

    (d) 0   (e) $\frac{1}{2}$ (f) 3

    (g) 1   (h) 7   (i) -1

5. (a) Original: $y = 4^x$: D: $x \in \mathbf{R}$; R: $y > 0$; asymp.: $y = 0$; Inverse: $y = \log_4 x$: D: $x > 0$; R: $y \in \mathbf{R}$; asymp.: $x = 0$

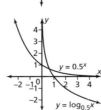

    (b) Original: $y = \log_5 x$: D: $x > 0$; R: $y \in \mathbf{R}$; asymp.: $x = 0$; Inverse: $y = 5^x$: D: $x \in \mathbf{R}$; R: $y > 0$; asymp.: $y = 0$

    (c) Original: $y = (0.5)^x$: D: $x \in \mathbf{R}$; R: $y > 0$; asymp.: $y = 0$; Inverse: $y = \log_{0.5} x$: D: $x > 0$; R: $y \in \mathbf{R}$; asymp.: $x = 0$

(d) Original: $y = \log_7 x$: D: $x > 0$; R: $y \in \mathbf{R}$; asymp.: $x = 0$; Inverse: $y = 7^x$: D: $x \in \mathbf{R}$; R: $y > 0$; asymp.: $y = 0$

(e) Original: $y = 10^x$: D: $x \in \mathbf{R}$; R: $y > 0$; asymp.: $y = 0$; Inverse: $y = \log_{10} x$: D: $x > 0$; R: $y \in \mathbf{R}$; asymp.: $x = 0$

(f) Original: $y = \log_4 x$: D: $x > 0$; R: $y \in \mathbf{R}$; asymp.: $x = 0$; Inverse: $y = 4^x$: D: $x \in \mathbf{R}$; R: $y > 0$; asymp.: $y = 0$

6. $y = 3 \log_5 x$ is vertically stretched version of $y = \log_5 x$ and $y = 3 \log_5 x + 4$ is vertically translated version of $y = 3 \log_5 x$.

7. (a) $x = 2.00$ (b) $x = 100.00$ (c) $x = -2.00$

    (d) $x = 6309.57$ (e) $x = -3.00$ (f) $x = 316.23$

8. (a) $a > 1$: $f(x)$ passes through (1, 0). D: $x > 0$; R: $y \in \mathbf{R}$; asymp.: $x = 0$; $x \to 0$, $y \to -\infty$ and $x \to +\infty$, $y \to +\infty$. $0 < a < 1$: $f(x)$ passes through (1, 0). D: $x > 0$; R: $y \in \mathbf{R}$; asymp.: $x = 0$; $x \to 0$, $y \to +\infty$ and $x \to +\infty$, $y \to -\infty$.

    (b) logarithm must result in a unique exponent; if the base is 1, any exponent works

9. (a) D: $x > -6$; R: $y \in \mathbf{R}$ (b) D: $x > 0$; R: $y \in \mathbf{R}$

    (c) D: $x > 0$; R: $y \in \mathbf{R}$ (d) D: $x > 0$; R: $y \in \mathbf{R}$

    (e) D: $x > -2$; R: $y \in \mathbf{R}$ (f) D: $x > 0$; R: $y \in \mathbf{R}$

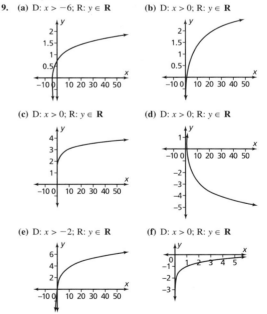

10. The graphs are reflections of one another on the line $y = x$. The domain and range are switched, and x's are switched for y's for the domain, range, and asymptote.

11. $t = \log_3 N - 1$; 3 h 12 min

12. (a)

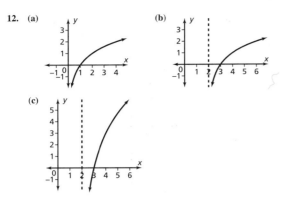

(b)

(c)

First $y = \log_2 x$ is horizontally translated 2 units to the right making the equation $y = \log_2(x - 2)$. Then the equation is vertically sketched by a factor of 3, finalizing the equation $y = 3 \log_2(x - 2)$.

14. true

15. i. d   ii. e   iii. c   iv. a   v. b

Graph	Equation	x-int.	y-int.	End behaviour as $x \to +\infty$	End behaviour as $x \to -\infty$
i	$y = (0.5)^x$	None	$(0, 1)$	$y \to 0$	$y \to +\infty$
ii	$y = -\log_2 x$	$(1, 0)$	None	$y \to -\infty$	Not applicable
iii	$y = 4^x$	None	$(0, 1)$	$y \to +\infty$	$y \to 0$
iv	$y = \log_4 x$	$(1, 0)$	None	$y \to +\infty$	Not applicable
v	$y = -(2)^x$	None	$(0, -1)$	$y \to -\infty$	$y \to 0$

16. (a) inverse functions of one another
(b) $a > 0$ and $x = a^y > 0$

17. (a) $f^{-1}(x) = \log_3 x$ **(b)** $(f^{-1} \circ f)(x), (f \circ f^{-1})(x) = x$

18. (a) $y = x^3$ **(b)** $y = \log_2\left(\frac{x}{3}\right)$

(c) $y = \log_{0.5} x - 2$ **(d)** $y = 2^{\frac{x-2}{3}} + 3$

19. (a) $y = 100(2)^{\frac{x}{0.32}}$
(b)   **(c)**

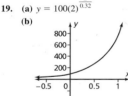

(d) $y = 0.32 \log_2\left(\frac{x}{100}\right)$ **(e)** 0.69 hours

20. (a)

Amount of Sodium 24 (mg)(x)	100	50	25	12.5	6.25
Number of hours (y)	0	15	30	45	60

(b)   **(c)** $y = -15 \log_2 0.01x$

21. (a) Original: $y = 3 \log(x + 1)$: D $= x > -6$;
R $= y \in \mathbf{R}$; asymp.: $x = -6$;

Inverse: $y = 10^{\frac{x}{3}} - 6$: D $= x \in \mathbf{R}$;
R $= y > -6$; asymp.: $y = -6$

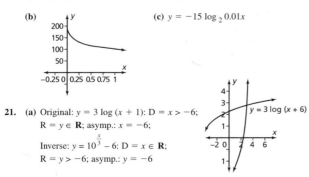

$y = 3 \log(x + 6)$

(b) Original: $y = -2 \log_5 3x$: D $= x > 0$; $y = -2 \log_5 3x$
R $= y \in \mathbf{R}$; asymp.: $x = 0$;

Inverse: $y = \left(\frac{1}{3}\right)\left(\frac{1}{5}\right)^{\frac{x}{2}}$: D $= x \in \mathbf{R}$;
R $= y > 0$; asymp.: $y = 0$

(c) Original: $y = 2 + 3 \log x$: D $= x > 0$;
R $= y \in \mathbf{R}$; asymp.: $x = 0$; Inverse:
$y = 10^{\frac{x-2}{3}}$: D $= x \in \mathbf{R}$; R $= y > 0$;
asymp.: $y = 0$

$y = 10^{\frac{x-2}{3}}$
$y = 2 + 3 \log x$

(d) Original: $y = 20(8)^x$: D $= x \in \mathbf{R}$;
R $= y > 0$; asymp.: $y = 0$; Inverse:
$y = \log_8\left(\frac{x}{20}\right)$: D $= x > 0$; R $= y \in \mathbf{R}$;
asymp.: $x = 0$

$y = 20(8)^x$

(e) Original: $y = 2(3)^{x+2}$: D $= x \in \mathbf{R}$;
R $= y > 0$; asymp.: $y = 0$;
Inverse: $y = \log_3\left(\frac{x}{18}\right) - 2$:
D $= x > 0$; R $= y \in \mathbf{R}$; asymp.: $x = 0$

$y = 2(3)^{x+2}$

(f) Original: $y = -5^x - 3$: D $= x \in \mathbf{R}$;
R $= y < -3$; asymp.: $y = -3$;
Inverse: $y = \log_5[-(x + 3)]$:
D $= x < -3$; R $= y \in \mathbf{R}$; asymp.: $x = -3$

2.5 Exercises, page 125

1. (a) 4   **(b)** 4   **(c)** 2
(d) 2   **(e)** 3   **(f)** 5

2. (a) $\log_2 14 + \log_2 9$ **(b)** $\log_5 735 - \log_5 40$
(c) $\frac{1}{2} \log_7 25$ **(d)** $\log_6 9 + \log_6 8 + \log_6 7$
(e) $4 \log_3 15$ **(f)** $\log_4 81 - \log_4 30$

3. (a) 2   **(b)** 1   **(c)** 9   **(d)** 1
(e) 2   **(f)** 2   **(g)** 2   **(h)** 20

4. (a) $\frac{2}{3}$ **(b)** $\frac{3}{4}$ **(c)** $\frac{2}{3}$
(d) $\frac{3}{2}$ **(e)** $\frac{2}{3}$ **(f)** -2

5. (a) $\frac{2}{3}$ **(b)** $\frac{5}{3}$ **(c)** 4
(d) $\frac{3}{5}$ **(e)** 2   **(f)** -3

6. (a) $\log_5 56$ **(b)** $\log_3 2$ **(c)** $\log_2 45$
(d) $\log_3 4$ **(e)** $\log_4 3\sqrt{2}$ **(f)** $\log 16$

7. $\frac{41}{4}$

8. (a) $x + y$ **(b)** $y - x$ **(c)** $3x$

9. (a) $x = 50$ **(b)** $x = 6$ **(c)** $x = 60$ **(d)** $x = 432$ **(e)** $x = 384$

10. (a) $\log_2 xyz$ **(b)** $\log_5 \frac{uw}{v}$ **(c)** $\log_6 \frac{a}{bc}$
(d) $\log_2 xy$ **(e)** $\log_3 3x^2$ **(f)** $\log_4 \frac{x^5}{y}$

11. 0.3

12. $w = y\sqrt{x}$

13. $\log_a MN = \log_a M + \log_a N$ $a^M a^N = a^{M+N}$
$\log_a \frac{M}{N} = \log_a M - \log_a N$ $\frac{a^M}{a^N} = a^{M-N}$
$\log_a M^N = N \log_a M$ $(a^M)^N = a^{MN}$

14. **(a)** 4.82 **(b)** 0.80 **(c)** 3.82
(d) 1.35 **(e)** 1.69 **(f)** 3.49

15. 10 log 3

16. **(a)** 10 dB **(b)** 60 dB **(c)** 90 dB **(d)** 120 dB

17. Answers will vary. Example:
$\log_6 8 + \log_6 9 + \log_6 3 = \log_6 (8)(9)(3) = \log_6 216 = 3$

18. **(a)**

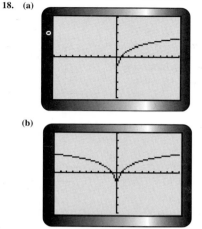

(b)

graphs have different domain; In $y = \log x + \log 2x$, $x > 0$,
so x cannot be neg. In $y = \log 2x^2$, $x \neq 0$, so x can be neg.

19. Answers will vary. Example: $y = \log 3 + \log x = \log 3x$

20. Answers will vary. Examples:
Addition: $y = \log 6 + \log 3 = \log (6)(3) = \log 18$;
Subtraction: $y = \log 18 - \log 3 = \log \left(\frac{18}{3}\right) = \log 6$;
Power: $y = \log 8 = \log 2^3 = 3 \log 2$

2.6 Exercises, page 132

1. **(a)** $x = \pm 6.00$ **(b)** $x = \pm 2.71$ **(c)** $x = 4.27$
(d) $x = 2.54$ **(e)** $x = \pm 2.64$ **(f)** $x = 2.15$

2. **(a)** $x = 2.63$ **(b)** $x = 2.58$ **(c)** $x = 3.17$
(d) $x = 3.20$ **(e)** $x = 35.00$ **(f)** $x = 3.39$

3. **(a)** $x = 2.49$ **(b)** $x = 0.06$ **(c)** $x = 8.33$
(d) $x = -1.50$ **(e)** $x = 0.04$ **(f)** $x = 0.73$

4. **(a)** $x = 4.85$ **(b)** $x = 1.05$ **(c)** $x = 0.01$
(d) $x = 1.03$ **(e)** $x = 3.09$ **(f)** $x = 1.67$

5. 28.22 years

6. **(a)** $x = 2.0$ **(b)** $x = 7.6$ **(c)** $x = 1.5$
(d) $x = 14.0$ **(e)** $x = 44.3$ **(f)** $x = 1.3$

7. 3761.5 years

8. 4.52 days

9. 10.1 years

10. 1.15 min

11. 10 questions

12. 6 years

13. graph and find value of x when $y = 5^x = 90$; take log of both sides and solve for x; guess and check

14. **(a)**

Number of Bounces	0	1	2	3	4	5
Height (m)	6.00	3.60	2.16	1.30	0.78	0.47

(b)

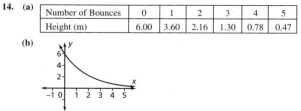

(c) $h = 6(0.6)^n$ where h is height in metres and n is number of bounces
(d) 0.013 m **(e)** between the 6th and 7th bounce

15. 45 days

16. **(a)**

Thickness (mm)	Intensity
0	100.00%
1	95.00%
2	90.25%
3	85.74%
4	81.45%
5	77.38%
6	73.51%
7	69.83%
8	66.34%
9	63.02%
10	59.87%

(b) $I = (0.95)^S$ where S is thickness and I is intensity
(c) about 9.96 mm

17. power law

18. **(a)** 112 mg **(b)** 25 h after 11:00 p.m.

19. **(a)** $x = -1.60$ **(b)** $x = -4.86$ **(c)** $x = -0.42$

20. 0.161

2.7 Exercises, page 140

1. **(a)** linear **(b)** logarithmic **(c)** logarithmic **(d)** linear

2. similarities: scales have a large range of intensity, are measured logarithmically; differences: Richter scale ranges from 1 to 12 while decibel scale ranges from 0 to 130, the formulae of the scales are different

3. **(a)** 10^4 times **(b)** 10^6 times **(c)** 10^3 times

4. **(a)** $10^{1.5}$ times **(b)** $10^{0.5}$ times **(c)** 10^3 times

5. **(a)** 3.49 **(b)** 4.35 **(c)** 3.52 **(d)** 2.30

6. $10^{2.5}$ times

7. $10^{0.9}$ times

8. **(a)** 0.01 mol/L **(b)** 1.58×10^{-4} mol/L **(c)** 2.51×10^{-6} mol/L

9. **(a)** 0.01 mol/L **(b)** 7.94×10^{-5} mol/L
(c) 2.51×10^{-7} mol/L **(d)** 1.58×10^{-8} mol/L
(e) 3.16×10^{-9} mol/L **(f)** 1.26×10^{-12} mol/L

10. **(a)** 7 **(b)** more acidic; it is to the left of distilled water on pH scale

11. 19.95 times

12. **(a)** 2.85 **(b)** 5.97×10^{24} ergs

13. smaller numbers are easier to understand and manage; Example: measurement of sound intensity

14. **(a)** frequency of C‴ is double of the frequency of C″; frequency of C″ is double of the frequency of C′
(b) 2112 Hz **(c)** 132 Hz

15. it is incorrect to compare the scale directly, should compare the intensity given by 10^M where M is the scale; scale 8 earthquake is 10^4 times more intense than the scale 4 earthquake, not $\frac{8}{4} = 2$ times

16. **(a)** range is too large to manage (58 to 10^{17})
(b) Answers will vary. Example: "log" all numbers so the range would be from log 58 (= 1.76) to log 10^{17} (= 17)

(c) adjustment is not needed

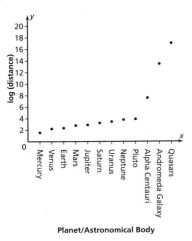

Planet/Astronomical Body

2.8 Exercises, page 146

1. (a) $x = 5$ **(b)** $x = \frac{1}{25}$ **(c)** $x = \sqrt{3}$
   (d) $x = 9$ **(e)** $x = \sqrt[3]{81} \doteq 4.33$ **(f)** $x = 2$

2. (a) $x = -3$ **(b)** $x = 64$ **(c)** $x = 2$ or $x = -2$
   (d) $x = 8$ **(e)** $x = \frac{1}{16}$ **(f)** $x = 4$

3. (a) $x = 8$ **(b)** $x = 21$ **(c)** $x = 8$ **(d)** $x = 2$
   (e) $x = \frac{1}{3}$ **(f)** $x = 25$ **(g)** $x = 3$ **(f)** $x = 100$

4. (a) $x = -0.3$ **(b)** $x = 8.0$ **(c)** $x = 2.0$ **(d)** $x = 1.7$

5. (a) 2.46   **(b)** 7.71   **(c)** 2.53
   (d) −1.18   **(e)** 2.40   **(f)** 2.16

6. (a) $x = \frac{8}{3}$ **(b)** $x = 5$ **(c)** $x = \frac{25}{6}$
   (d) $x = 50$ **(e)** $x = 3$ **(f)** $x = 8.1$

7. (a) $x > 2$ **(b)** $x = 3$

8. (a) $x = 5$ **(b)** $x = 6$ **(c)** $x = 3$ or $x = 6$

9. (a) since $\log_b m = \log_b n$, $m = n$
   (b) quotient and power properties
   (c) product property

10. (a) 3.16×10^{-8} W/m²   **(b)** 1.58×10^{-4} W/m²

11. 201.4 μ

12. $x = 2.89$ and $x = -1.39$

13. 2.90 m

14. $x = 4$

15. x and a must be pos. and $y \in \mathbf{R}$ since $a^y = x$

16. (a) $x = 0.80$ **(b)** $x = 2.15$ **(c)** $x = 3.16$ **(d)** $x = 0.33$

17. $x = 2 + 2\sqrt{2}$

18. (a) $x = 3$ **(b)** $x = 16$

19. (a) $x = \dfrac{-1 + \sqrt{333}}{2}$ **(b)** $x = 2$

20. (a) 6   **(b)** 4   **(c)** $\log_2 3$

2.9 Exercises, page 152

1. (a) $A = 4000(1.05)^t$ where t is time in years and A is amount of money
   (b) $6515.58   **(c)** 5%

2. (a) $y = 100.34(1.25)^x$ where x is speed in m/s and y is oxygen consumption
   (b) 100.34 units
   (c) 16.5 m/s

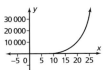

3. Answers will vary. Sinusoidal model: the value oscillates back and forth

4. (a) $A = 40.80(0.7474)^t$ where A is amount of caffeine in mg and t is time in hours
   (b) 8.96 h
   (c) 2.38 h

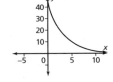

5. (a) $y = 850.64(1.15)^x$ where y is number of bacteria and x is time in hours
   (b) 4.96 h

6. (a)

   (b) yes; from the graph, the data decreases exponentially

   (c) $y = 29.36(0.7192)^x$ where x is toss number and y is number of dice remaining

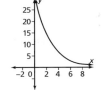

7. (a) 1.4, 1.4, 1.4, 1.3, 1.3, 1.3, 1.3, 1.4
   (b) $S = 4.847(1.35)^{\frac{T}{5}}$ **(c)** $y = 5.06(1.06)^x$
   (d) 11.9°C

8. (a) $y = 0.0017(1.7698)^x$ **(b)** 76.98%

9. (a)

$m = 2.05d^{4.04}$

   (b) power graph is better because it follows trend better

10. For $y = ca^x$; y: dependent variable; x: independent variable; c: initial value; a: factor; increasing if $a > 1$, decreasing if $0 < a < 1$, constant if $a = 1$

11. (a)

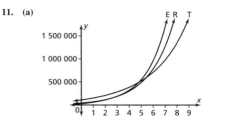

(b) average price for Edmonton is going to exceed that of Regina, which is going to exceed that of Toronto

(c) Edmonton 11.6%
Regina 10.0%
Toronto 6.6%

12. (a) revenue of the compact disc grows exponentially from 1991 to 1996

(b) $y = 219.04(1.3397)^x$ where y is revenue in millions and x is time ($x = 0$ implies 1990–91)

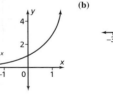

(c) model is appropriate since the value approximately matches that of the revenue shown by Statistics Canada

(d) 76 billions

(e) Answers will vary.

(f) Answers will vary; the product can be popular music/rock, equation: $y = 359.74(1.1498)^x$; this model fits the points

13. (a) $P = 30.75(1.008418)^t$ where t is time in years and P is population

(b) growth rate of Canada is less than the growth rate of Ontario and Alberta

Chapter 2 Review, page 158

11. (a) 800 **(b)** 204 800 **(c)** $200(2)^n$

12. (a) $200 129 **(b)** $273 890 **(c)** $125 000(1.04)^n$

13. 11 518

14. (a) they are reflections about y-axis

(b) they are reflections about x-axis

15. (a)

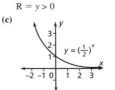

hor. asymp.: $y = 0$;
y-int.: 1; D $= x \in \mathbf{R}$;
R $= y > 0$

(b)

hor. asymp.: $y = 0$;
y-int.: −1; D $= x \in \mathbf{R}$;
R $= y < 0$

(c)

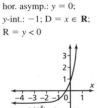

hor. asymp.: $y = 0$;
y-int.: 1; D $= x \in \mathbf{R}$;
R $= y > 0$

(d)

hor. asymp.: $y = -1$;
y-int.: 1; D $= x \in \mathbf{R}$;
R $= y > -1$

(e)

hor. asymp.: $y = 1$;
y-int.: −2; D $= x \in \mathbf{R}$;
R $= y < 1$

(f)

hor. asymp.: $y = 2$;
y-int.: −2; D $= x \in \mathbf{R}$;
R $= y < 2$

(g)

hor. asymp.: $y = 0$;
y-int.: 6; D $= x \in \mathbf{R}$;
R $= y > 0$

(h)

hor. asymp.: $y = 0$;
y-int.: 10; D $= x \in \mathbf{R}$;
R $= y > 0$

(i)

hor. asymp.: $y = -1$;
y-int.: 24; D $= x \in \mathbf{R}$; R $= y > -1$

16. $y = 3^x \rightarrow y = -3^x$: reflection about x-axis;
$y = 3^x \rightarrow y = \left(\frac{1}{3}\right)^x$: reflection about y-axis;
$y = 3^x \rightarrow y = 3^x + 2$: vert. translation up;
$y = 3^x \rightarrow y = 3^x - 1$: vert. translation down;
$y = 3^x \rightarrow y = 5(3^x)$: vert. stretch

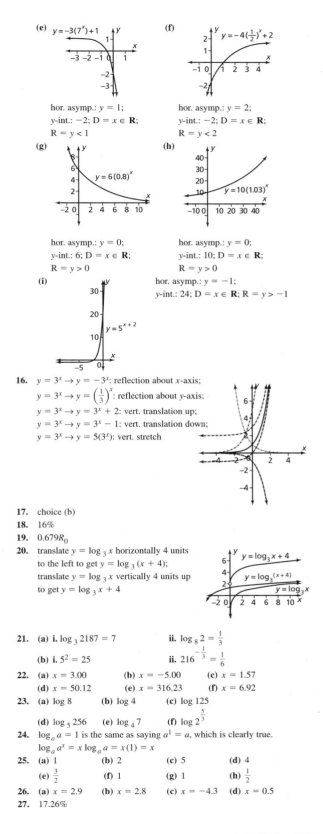

17. choice (b)

18. 16%

19. $0.679R_0$

20. translate $y = \log_3 x$ horizontally 4 units to the left to get $y = \log_3 (x + 4)$;
translate $y = \log_3 x$ vertically 4 units up to get $y = \log_3 x + 4$

21. (a) i. $\log_3 2187 = 7$ **ii.** $\log_8 2 = \frac{1}{3}$

(b) i. $5^2 = 25$ **ii.** $216^{-\frac{1}{3}} = \frac{1}{6}$

22. (a) $x = 3.00$ **(b)** $x = -5.00$ **(c)** $x = 1.57$
(d) $x = 50.12$ **(e)** $x = 316.23$ **(f)** $x = 6.92$

23. (a) $\log 8$ **(b)** $\log 4$ **(c)** $\log 125$
(d) $\log_5 256$ **(e)** $\log_4 7$ **(f)** $\log 2^{\frac{5}{3}}$

24. $\log_a a = 1$ is the same as saying $a^1 = a$, which is clearly true.
$\log_a a^x = x \log_a a = x(1) = x$

25. (a) 1 **(b)** 2 **(c)** 5 **(d)** 4
(e) $\frac{3}{2}$ **(f)** 1 **(g)** 1 **(h)** $\frac{1}{2}$

26. (a) $x = 2.9$ **(b)** $x = 2.8$ **(c)** $x = -4.3$ **(d)** $x = 0.5$

27. 17.26%

28. 3580 years

29. 15 849 times

30. river water, 794 times

31. 1 258 925 times

32. (a) $x = 2$ (b) $x = 49$
(c) $x = 3$ or $x = -3$ (d) $x = -4$

33. (a) $x = 30$ (b) $x = \frac{2}{3}$
(c) $x = 6$ (d) $x = 6$ or $x = 3$

34. $\frac{18}{5}$

35. (a) 6.1%   (b) $3268.19

36. (a) $N = 49.79(0.6905)^t$ where t is time in hours and N is amount of caffeine
(b) after 7 h
(c) 1.87 h

37. (a) $I = 109.8(0.951)^m$, where m is depth under water in metres and I is light intensity as a percentage
(b) 10%: 47.7 m; 0%: never

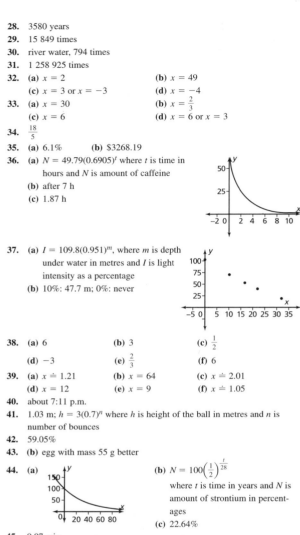

38. (a) 6   (b) 3   (c) $\frac{1}{2}$
(d) -3 (e) $\frac{2}{3}$ (f) 6

39. (a) $x \doteq 1.21$ (b) $x = 64$ (c) $x \doteq 2.01$
(d) $x = 12$ (e) $x = 9$ (f) $x \doteq 1.05$

40. about 7:11 p.m.

41. 1.03 m; $h = 3(0.7)^n$ where h is height of the ball in metres and n is number of bounces

42. 59.05%

43. (b) egg with mass 55 g better

44. (a)
(b) $N = 100\left(\frac{1}{2}\right)^{\frac{t}{28}}$
where t is time in years and N is amount of strontium in percentages
(c) 22.64%

45. 9.97 min

46. (a) i. 9.4 billion
ii. 19.8 billion
iii. 7.74 billion

(b) similarities: same general form, all pass through (5, 0), shape of graphs; differences: concavity of graphs because they have different factors

47. Half life: $y = c\left(\frac{1}{2}\right)^{\frac{t}{h}}$ where $a = \frac{1}{2}$, $x = \frac{t}{h}$ and h is the half-life;
doubling period: $y = c(2)^{\frac{t}{h}}$ where $a = 2$, $x = \frac{t}{h}$ and h is the doubling period

48. linear: $y = ax + b$; exponential: $y = ca^x$; if intervals between successive y-values are constant, use linear model; if intervals between successive y-values are continuously getting larger or smaller, use exponential model

49. stretch $y = \log_2 x$ by factor of 4 to get $y = 4 \log_2 x$; reflect $y = 4 \log_2 x$ in x-axis and vertically shift by factor of -4 to get $y = -4 \log_2 x - 4$

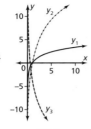

Chapter 2 Review Test, page 164

1. $a < 1$; end behaviour: $x \to -\infty$, $y \to +\infty$ and $x \to +\infty$, $y \to 0$

2. (a) $\frac{6}{5}$ (b) -3 (c) 4

3. (a) $x = 81.00$ (b) $x = 0.33$
(c) $x = 3.27$ (d) $x = 4.00$

4. similarities: reflected image of one another on the y-axis; differences: end-behaviour

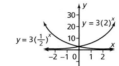

5. (a) 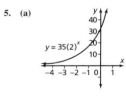 (b)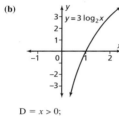

D $= x \in \mathbf{R}$; R $= y > 0$; asymp.: $y = 0$
D $= x > 0$; R $= y \in \mathbf{R}$; asymp.: $x = 0$

6. 5.95 years

7. $N = 35(2)^{\frac{t}{45}}$ where N is mass in mg and t is time in minutes

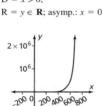

8. (a) A: $N_A = 35(2)^{\frac{t}{3}}$, 26%/h; B: $N_B = 85(3)^{\frac{t}{4}}$ s, 32%/h
(b) 20.35 h before the experiment starts

Cumulative Review Test 1, page 165

1. (a) increasing: $x < -0.5$, $x > 3$; decreasing: $-0.5 < x < 3$
(b) increasing: $-2 < x < 0.5$, $x > 3.2$; decreasing: $x < -2$, $0.5 < x < 3.2$

2.

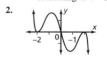

3. (a) $x^2 - 2x + 1$ (b) $x^2 + 2x + 1 + \frac{x}{x^2 - 2x + 1}$

4. (a) S-shaped   (b) W-shaped

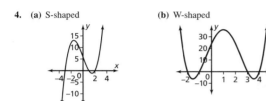

5. $k = 39$

6. male 69.81, female 76.58; female expected to live longer; from 67.52 to 74.87 − increased by 7.35 years; born in 1962 or 1992

7.

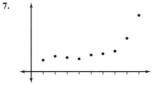

$P(x) = 6.54x^3 − 59.10x^2 + 160.69x + 297.10$

in 1500; between 1531 and 1849

8. 59 min

9.

x	y	First Differences	Second Differences
−2	$−\frac{22}{25}$	$\frac{8}{25}$	$\frac{32}{25}$
−1	$−\frac{3}{5}$	$\frac{8}{5}$	$\frac{32}{5}$
0	1	8	32
1	9	40	
2	49		

patterns: first and second differences form geometric series

10. (a) $x = −3, −1, 1, 4$ (b) $−3 \le x \le 0.5, x \ge 5$
     (c) $x = 1.11$ (d) $x = 2.83$

11. $y = a^x$: y-int: 1, x-int: none; asymp.: $y = 0$; $D = x \in \mathbf{R}$; $R = y > 0$;
     $y = \log_a x$: y-int: none, x-int: 1; asymp.: $x = 0$; $D = x > 0$; $R = y \in \mathbf{R}$

12. 5

13. 48 days

14. 39.81 times

15. The properties are different. The domain, range, and restrictions differ.

Chapter 3

Getting Ready, page 170

1. (a) 3   (b) −1   (c) −1   (d) $\frac{2}{3}$

2. (a) $3x − y − 6 = 0$ (b) $2x + 3y − 18 = 0$
   (c) $x − y + 5 = 0$ (d) $4x − y − 2 = 0$
   (e) $x − 5y − 9 = 0$

3. (a) $−15x^2 + 6x + 6$ (b) $−14x^2 + 44x$
   (c) $x^2 − 4x − 12$ (d) $3x^2 + 2x − 8$
   (e) $−4x^2 − 56x − 196$ (f) $6x^2 + 17xy + 12y^2$
   (g) $−70x^2 + 55x + 75$ (h) $−6x^3 + 10x^2 − 2x − 2$

4. (a) $(x + 2)(x + 3)$ (b) $(a − 3)^2$ (c) $(c − 3)(c + 5)$
   (d) $(d + 6)(d − 3)$ (e) $(x − 8)(x − 2)$ (f) $(m − 7)(m + 2)$
   (g) $(c − 7)(c − 8)$ (h) $(x + 8)(x − 6)$ (i) $(a + 9)(a − 4)$

5. (a) $2(s + 3)(s − 1)$ (b) $3(v + 5)(v − 2)$
   (c) $(3x + 1)(x + 2)$ (d) $(3b + 2)(2b + 3)$
   (e) $(d + 4)(d − 4)$ (f) $(3 − a)(3 + a)$
   (g) $(5x + 2)(5x − 2)$ (h) $(z + 4)^2$ (i) $(2c − 5)^2$

6. (a) $x = 2.00$ (b) $c = −2.00$
   (c) $x = −2.00$ (d) $x = 11.00$

   (e) $x = 8.00$ or $−4.00$ (f) $x = −5.00$ or $−7.00$
   (g) $x \doteq 3.58$ or 0.42 (h) $c \doteq 0.59$ or $−3.93$
   (i) $x = 1.00, 4.00,$ or $−1.00$ (j) $x = −2.00, −1.00,$ or $−5.00$

7. (a) $−17$ (b) 10   (c) $\frac{53}{8}$ (d) 7.68

8. (a)   (b)   (c)   (d)

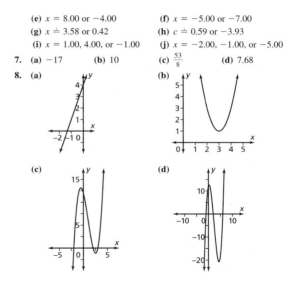

9. (a) $x > 4$ (b) $x \ge −3$ (c) $−3 < x < 3$
   (d) $x \le 3$ or $x \ge 8$ (e) $−5 < x < −3$ (f) $x < −7$ or $x > 8$

10. (a) $y = −x^2 + 9$ (b) $y = x^3 − 5x^2 + 2x + 8$
   (c) $y = x^4 − 7x^3 + x^2 + 27x + 18$

11. 1st differences: 30.1, 20.3, 10.5, 0.7, −9.1, −18.9, −28.7
   2nd differences: all $−9.8$
   2nd differences are constant, therefore a quadratic relationship
   algebraic model: $y = −4.9x^2 + 35x + 0.5$

3.1 Exercises, page 178

1. (a) 5   (b) 4   (c) 3
   (d) 2.5   (e) 2.1   (f) 2.01

2. 2

3. (a)

Interval	$\Delta f(x)$	Δx	Average rate of change $\frac{\Delta f(x)}{\Delta x}$
$2 \le x \le 3$	25	1	25
$2 \le x \le 2.5$	11.25	0.5	22.5
$2 \le x \le 2.1$	2.05	0.1	20.5
$2 \le x \le 2.01$	0.2005	0.01	20.05

   estimated rate of change: 20

(b)

Interval	$\Delta f(x)$	Δx	Average rate of change $\frac{\Delta f(x)}{\Delta x}$
$1 \le x \le 2$	15	1	15
$1.5 \le x \le 2$	8.75	0.5	17.5
$1.9 \le x \le 2$	1.95	0.1	19.5
$1.99 \le x \le 2$	0.1995	0.01	19.95

   estimated rate of change: 20
   (c) both 20, although (a) approaches from the right (b) from the left

4. (a) i. 107   ii. 71   iii. 56   iv. 45.44   v. 43.24   vi. 43.024
   (b) 43; instantaneous rate of change of $g(x)$ at (2, 23).

5. (a) 10.003   (b) 0.002   (c) 16.007   (d) −108

6. (a)

Interval	Δd	Δt	Average rate of change $\frac{\Delta d}{\Delta t}$
$3 \le t \le 4$	34.3	1	34.3
$3 \le t \le 3.5$	15.925	0.5	31.85
$3 \le t \le 3.1$	2.989	0.1	29.89
$3 \le t \le 3.01$	0.294 49	0.01	29.45

   (b) 29.4 m/s   (c) velocity

7. (a) 61 cm³/cm   (b) 75 cm³/cm

8. (a) -30 m/s   (b) 120 m   (c) -35 m/s

    (d) (a): rate of change of height averaged over the interval from 1 to 4 s;
(b): limiting value of the sequence of average rates of change as the
interval between the x-coordinates of the points (1, 170) and (4, 80)
is continuously decreased to zero; (c): height of the pebble above
the ground at $t = 3$ s

9. (a) 230 people/year   (b) 6000 people   (c) 290 people/year

    (d) (a): rate of change of population averaged over the interval from 5 to
15 (years after 1990); (b): limiting value of the sequence of average
rates of change as the interval between the x-coordinates of the
points (5, 3700) and (15, 6000) is continuously decreased to 0;
(c): population of a town in 2005 (15 years after 1990)

10. (a) -9.8 m/s   (b) -9.8 m/s

11. (a)

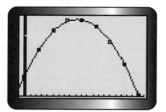

$h(t) = -4.9t^2 + 9.1t + 1.5$

    (b) 6.7 m/s   (c) -3.2 m/s   (d) 4.2 m/s; -5.6 m/s

    (e) due to the change in the ball's direction of motion—neg. sign at
1.5 s indicates the ball is falling toward the ground

12. $251.50 fee/revenue

13. -14.0 m/s

14. (a) skydiver's falling velocity; m/s   (b) 19.6 m/s

15. (a)

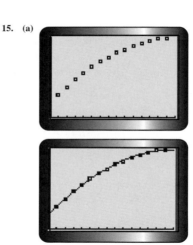

    (b) 42°F/min

    (c) instantaneous rates of change become smaller at each interval

16. (a)

$y = -1.58x^2 + 48.27x + 76.79$

    (b) Answers may vary.

Interval	$\Delta f(x)$	Δx	Average rate of change $\frac{\Delta f(x)}{\Delta x}$
$5 \leq x \leq 6$	30.89	1	30.89
$5 \leq x \leq 5.5$	15.84	0.5	31.68
$5 \leq x \leq 5.1$	3.23	0.1	32.30
$5 \leq x \leq 5.01$	0.32	0.01	32.00

    instantaneous rate of change $= 32°$F/min

17. (a) find $f(b)$ and $f(a)$; average rate of change $= \frac{f(b) - f(a)}{b - a}$

    (b) calculate average rates of change over several intervals in the
domain (with a value closer and closer to c); find the number that
the average rates of change approach as the difference between c and
the other value decreases to zero

18. (a) 100π cm²/cm   (b) 240π cm²/cm

19. (a) $\frac{112}{3}\pi$ cm³/cm   (b) 64π cm³/cm

20. 36 cm²/cm

21. 160π cm²/cm

3.2 Exercises, page 190

1. (a) 1   (b) 3   (c) -2 (d) 3

2. $y = 4x - 20$

3. $y = \frac{1}{2}x - 4$

4. (a) 4   (b) -12

5. 8.25

6. (a)
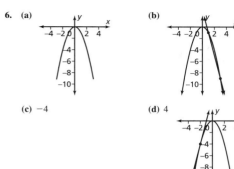

(c) −4   **(d)** 4

7. (a) 92 km/h
(b) 95.5 km/h
(c) speed

8. Approaching from the left:

Q	P	Δx	Δy	Slope of Secant PQ
$(-2, 6)$	$(-1, 1)$	-1	5	-5
$(-1.5, 3.25)$	$(-1, 1)$	-0.5	2.25	-4.5
$(-1.1, 1.41)$	$(-1, 1)$	-0.1	0.41	-4.1
$(-1.01, 1.0401)$	$(-1, 1)$	-0.01	0.0401	-4.01
$(-1.001, 1.004\ 001)$	$(-1, 1)$	-0.001	0.004 001	-4.001

Approaching from the right:

Q	P	Δx	Δy	Slope of Secant PQ
$(0, -2)$	$(-1, 1)$	1	3	-3
$(-0.5, -0.75)$	$(-1, 1)$	0.5	-1.75	-3.5
$(-0.9, 0.61)$	$(-1, 1)$	0.1	-0.39	-3.9
$(-0.99, 0.9601)$	$(-1, 1)$	0.01	-0.0399	-3.99
$(-0.999, 0.99\ 601)$	$(-1, 1)$	0.001	$-0.003\ 999$	-3.999

$-4.001 <$ slope of tangent < -3.999
$\therefore$ slope of tangent at $(-1, 1) = -4$

9. 12
10. (a) slope $= 16$; $y = 16x - 17$ **(b)** slope $= 0$; $y = 5$
(c) slope $= 0$; $y = -5$ **(d)** slope $= 2$; $y = 2x + 10$
11. (a) $1 + x + x^2, x \neq 1$
(b) i.

x	2	1.5	1.1	1.01	1.001
m_{TS}	7	4.75	3.31	3.0301	3.003 001

ii.

x	0	0.5	0.9	0.99	0.999
m_{TS}	1	1.75	2.71	2.9701	2.997 001

(c) 3   **(d)** $y = 3x - 4$
12. (a) $1 - x$ **(b)** -1
13. 12
14. (a) $x^2 + 2x + 4, x \neq 2$ **(b)** 12
15. $y = 3x - 8$
16. $y = -3x + 8$
17. Answers will vary. Example: the process is time-consuming
18. 0.9 m/day
19. Answers will vary.
20. $x + 10y - 51 = 0$
21. $y = -11x + 24$
22. 80π cm^2/cm

3.3 Exercises, page 202

1. (a) i. 3   **ii.** 3   **iii.** 3
  (b) i. -1 **ii.** 3   **iii.** does not exist
2. (a) 15   **(b)** 2   **(c)** 3   **(d)** -5
3. Answers will vary. Examples:
(a)
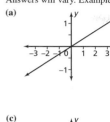
(b)
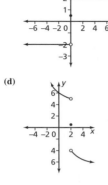

(c)

(d)

4. (a) 19   **(b)** 3
(c) does not exist (left and right hands limits differ)
(d) 15   **(e)** 18   **(f)** -7 **(g)** -6
(h) 219   **(i)** $\frac{1}{8}$ **(j)** $-\frac{1}{5}$
5. (a) 3   **(b)** $+\infty$ **(c)** does not exist
(d) 4   **(e)** 30   **(f)** 2
7. (a) -22 **(b)** -5 **(c)** 40
(d) 203   **(e)** 0   **(f)** 1674
8. 4
9. (a) i.
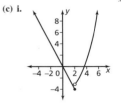

ii. always continuous
(b) i.

ii. discontinuous at $x = 1$ ($\lim_{x \to 1^-} f(x) = -1$, $\lim_{x \to 1^+} f(x) = 1$)
(c) i.

ii. discontinuous at $x = 2$ ($\lim_{x \to 2^-} f(x) = -4$, $\lim_{x \to 2^+} f(x) = -3$)

(d) i.

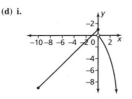

ii. discontinuous at $x = 0$ ($\lim\limits_{x \to 0^-} f(x) = 1$, $\lim\limits_{x \to 0^+} f(x) = 0$)

10. Answers will vary. Examples:
  (a) amount of gas used by a car with respect to the distance it travels
  (b) a library charging 2¢ for the first day for an overdue item and 5¢ for each day that follows up to a max. of 25¢

11. (a)

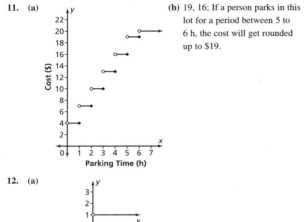

Parking Time (h)

  (b) 19, 16; If a person parks in this lot for a period between 5 to 6 h, the cost will get rounded up to $19.

12. (a)

(b) i. -1 **ii.** 1   **iii.** does not exist
(c) no; $\lim\limits_{x \to 0} f(x)$ does not exist ($\lim\limits_{x \to 0^-} f(x) \neq \lim\limits_{x \to 0^+} f(x)$).
13. $a = -1, b = 3$
14. yes; reasons will vary. Example: when the limit of a function $f(x)$ at $x = a$, where a is a point on the curve, exists and is equal to $f(a)$, then there are no holes or breaks on the curve
15. Answers will vary. Examples:
  (a) The amount of newly learned material remembered versus the number of days: A person rapidly forgetting newly learned materials on the first few days following acquisition, then gradually leveling off to a threshold on the days that follow.
  (b) The population of a species of bacteria versus time: The population declines to almost zero as winter approaches; however, following a brief period of cessation of growth, as spring comes, the population increases again (the population can never reach zero).
  (c) The progressive tax system (the percentage of tax on a person's income versus the income earned): A person pays a certain percentage of tax on income if his or her income is within a certain range.

16.

17. (a)

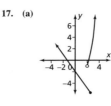

  (b) discontinuous; $\lim\limits_{x \to 2^+} f(x)$ does not exist ($\lim\limits_{x \to 2^-} f(x) = 4$ and $\lim\limits_{x \to 2^+} f(x) = -1$).

18. (a) 2   **(b)** 4
  (c) discontinuous because there is a hole on the curve—the limit at $x = 3$ exists but it does not equal $f(3)$

19. (a)

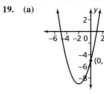

  (b) $x + 4$
  (c) 4; slope of the tangent at $x = 0$

21. Answers will vary. Examples:
  (a) A graph of elevation above sea level versus distance travelled: A person walking on a hill falls into a hole, then climbs back up.
  (b) Library overdue fine system: A library charging 2¢ for the first day for an overdue item and 5¢ for each day that follows up to a maximum of 25¢.
  (c) In physics, the strength of the potential gravitational energy of an object versus its distance from the earth. When the distance is 0, the energy is $-\infty$; when the distance is ∞, the energy is 0.

22. (a) 0   **(b)** does not exist   **(c)** does not exist
23. (a) 1   **(b)** 1   **(c)** does not exist

3.4 Exercises, page 213

1. (a) $5a + 5h - 2$; $5h$
  (b) $a^2 + 2ah + h^2 + 3a + 3h - 1$; $2ah + h^2 + 3h$
  (c) $a^3 + 3a^2h + 3ah^2 + h^3 - 4a - 4h + 1$; $3a^2h + 3ah^2 + h^3 - 4h$
  (d) $a^2 + 2ah + h^2 + a + h - 6$; $2ah + h^2 + h$
  (e) $-7a - 7h + 4$; $-7h$
  (f) $4 - 2a - 2h - a^2 - 2ah - h^2$; $-2h - 2ah - h^2$
2. (a) 4   **(b)** -3 **(c)** 2
  (d) 4   **(e)** -2 **(f)** $\frac{1}{2}$
3. (a) $4x + 4$ **(b)** -5 **(c)** $-16x - 3$
  (d) $18x^2 - 7$ **(e)** $-20x$ **(f)** $3x^2 + 2x + 1$
4. (a) $2x$ **(b)** $-10x + 6$ **(c)** $6x^2$
  (d) $-6x - 7$ **(e)** 5   **(f)** $15x^2 - 12x + 3$
5. (a) $x^2 - 6x + 5$ **(b)** 0   **(c)** $y = -4$
6. $2x + 8$
7. (a) $y = 9x - 19$ **(b)** $y = -8x - 15$ **(c)** $y = -4x - 8$
  (d) $y = 2x - 2$ **(e)** $y = -4$ **(f)** $y = 7x - 1$
8. (a) $y = -2x + 2$ **(b)**

9. (a) $A(3, -2)$, $B(5, 6)$ **(b)** $y = 4x - 14$
  (c) $y = 2x - 8$ **(d)** $y = 6x - 24$

10. $f(3) = 4, f'(3) = 9$; $f(3)$ is the y-coordinate of the point where $x = 3$. $f'(3)$ is the slope of the tangent of $f(x)$ at $x = 3$

11. **i.** $f'(a)$, or $\lim\limits_{h \to 0} \dfrac{f(a + h) - f(a)}{h}$, does not exist
    ii. slope of the tangent of the graph of $f(x)$ is undefined at $x = a$

12. **(a)** 575 km/h   **(b)** $y = 14.286x^2 + 507.143x - 121.429$
    (c) 592.859 km/h

13. **(a)** $\dfrac{500}{9}$ L   **(b)** $-\dfrac{200}{27}$ L/min   **(c)** $-\dfrac{200}{27}$ L/min

14. 50 raccoons/month

15. **(a)** $\dfrac{1900}{3}\pi$ cm³/cm   **(b)** 256π cm³/cm

16. $(0, 0)$

17. 1162.25 thousands of dollars/year since 1982

18. **(a)** -1.6 m/s
    (b) rate of change in the height of the ball with respect to time when $t = 2$

19. 9

20. $(3, -8)$

21. $\left(\dfrac{4}{3}, -\dfrac{1}{27}\right)$ and $(1, 0)$

22. $y = -2x - 1$ and $y = 6x - 9$

3.5 Exercises, page 222

1. **(a)** $6x$ **(b)** $6x$

2. **(a)** $4x^3$ **(b)** 0 **(c)** 1 **(d)** $3x^3$ **(e)** $\dfrac{1}{4}x^{-\frac{1}{2}}$
    (f) $-15x^{-4}$ **(g)** $-6x^{-3}$ **(h)** $-\dfrac{3}{2}x^{-\frac{3}{2}}$ **(i)** $-\dfrac{5}{4}x^{-\frac{5}{4}}$ **(j)** $-\dfrac{3}{2}x^{-\frac{1}{2}}$

3. **(a)** 0 **(b)** 5 **(c)** $12x^2$ **(d)** $324x^3$ **(e)** $\dfrac{5}{3}x^{\frac{2}{3}}$
    (f) $-\dfrac{1}{3}x^{-\frac{4}{3}}$ **(g)** $8x^{-3}$ **(h)** $x^{\frac{1}{2}}$ **(i)** $\dfrac{5}{2}x^{\frac{3}{2}}$ **(j)** $-9.8x$

4. **(a)**   **(b)**

(c)   **(d)**

5. **(a)** $-10x^{-3}$ **(b)** $3x^{-\frac{1}{2}}$ **(c)** 0 **(d)** $-20x^{-6}$
    (e) 0 **(f)** $-18x^2$ **(g)** $-36x^5$ **(h)** $-0.375x^{-1.5}$
    (i) $-42x^{-7}$ **(j)** $2\pi x^8$

6. $\dfrac{5}{4}$

7. $y = 2x - \dfrac{5}{3}$

8. $y = 3x - 1$ and $y = 3x + 1$

9. 4.5

10. The student needs to find $f'(2)$, the slope of the tangent to the graph of $f(x)$ at $x = 2$. By substituting $x = 2$ before differentiating the function, he found the slope of the tangent to the constant function, $y = 32$.

11. **(a)** 34.3 m/s   **(b)** 39.2 m/s   **(c)** 54.2 m/s

12. **(a)** 75 m   **(b)** 30 m/s   **(c)** 60 m/s   **(d)** 14 s

13. $C'(t) = -\dfrac{100}{t^2}$; $-4, -0.04, -0.01$ (rates of change of percentage with respect to time at 5, 50 and 100 min)

15. **(a)** $x = 0$ **(b)** $x = 0$ **(c)** $x = 0$ **(d)** no

16. $y = 12x - 16$ and $y = 3x + 2$

17. $(2 + 2\sqrt{2}, -24 - 16\sqrt{2})$ and $(2 - 2\sqrt{2}, -24 + 16\sqrt{2})$

18. 8.3 m

19. $y = 8x - 4$ or $y = 24x - 36$

20. $\left(-\dfrac{1}{2}, -\dfrac{3}{16}\right)$

21. **(b)** $4\pi r^2$; the surface area of a sphere

3.6 Exercises, page 229

1. **(a)** $6x + 2$

2. **(a)** $8x + 5$ **(b)** $3x^2 - 10x + 2$
    (c) 3 **(d)** $8x^{-3} + 5$
    (e) 8 **(f)** $6x + 2$
    (g) $-\dfrac{12}{x^5} + \dfrac{2}{x^2}$ **(h)** $24x^3 - 9x^2 + 18x - 5$

3. **(a)** 3 **(b)** -11 **(c)** -24
    (d) -6 **(e)** 6 **(f)** -24

4. **(a)** $y = -x - 9$ **(b)**

5. Answers will vary. Examples: Sum rule: The sum of differentiable functions is also differentiable and its derivative is equal to the sum of their derivatives; Difference rule: The difference between differentiable functions is also differentiable and its derivative is equal to the difference between their derivatives.

6. $20x^3 - 24x^2 + 6x - 6$

7. **(a)** $y = -5x$ **(b)** $y = -7x - 3$
    (c) $y = -3x + 1$ **(d)** $8x + 4y - 3 = 0$

9. **(a)** $y = x - 5$ **(b)** $y = -3x - 6$
    (c) $y = 19x$ **(d)** $y = 561x - 1269$

10. $y = -14x$ and $y = 6x$

11. **(a)** 20 000 L   **(b)** -2000 L/min   **(c)** after 1 min
    (d) -6000 L/min   **(e)** 4.5 min   **(f)** -4472 L/min

12. **(a)** when no items are sold, the firm is losing money (neg. profit). The firm has a start-up cost of $9600. To earn a profit, it needs to generate more than $9600.
    (b) $845/item, $-$875/item, $196/item
    (c) $2625, $6325, $9016   **(d)** $12 < x < 40$

13. **(a)** 500; 320   **(b)** 0; -12
    (c) $B(0)$ = blood sugar level with no insulin
        $B(30)$ = blood sugar level with 30 mg of insulin
        $B'(0)$ = rate of change in blood sugar level with no insulin
        $B'(30)$ = rate of change in blood sugar level with 30 mg insulin
    (d) -20; 0; $B'(50)$: patient's blood sugar level is decreasing at 20 units/mg of insulin 1 h after 50 mg of insulin is injected; $B(50)$: patient's blood sugar level is zero 1 h after 50 mg of insulin is injected. Values are illogical because a person's blood sugar level can never reach zero and continue to decrease (neg. blood sugar level).

14. (a) i. $\left(\frac{1}{5}, \frac{1}{5}\right)$ ii. $\left(-\frac{1}{4}, -\frac{13}{4}\right)$ iii. $\left(\frac{1}{3}, \frac{103}{27}\right)$ and $(5, -47)$

(b) At these points, the slope of the tangent to the curve is zero (the rate of change of the value of the function with respect to the domain is zero).

15. $a = -4$, $b = 32$, $c = 0$

16. (a) 100 (b) 1200 (c) 370 bacteria per hour

17. (a) 2.857 87 cups/day (b) 0.210 845 cups/day per day

18. (a) -188

(b) slope of tangent to $f(x)$ at $x = 3$; rate of change in value of $f(x)$ with respect to x at $x = 3$

20. $(-2, -21)$ and $(-2, 6)$. Points may vary.

3.7 Exercises, page 241

1. (a) 2 forward (b) 4

2.

Displacement [$f(t)$]	Velocity [$f'(t)$]	Time [t]
kilometres	kilometres per hour	hour
metres	metres per second	second
metres	metres per minute	minute
centimetres	centimetres per second	second

3. (a) $v(t) = 2t - 4$; 10 m; 6 m/s
(b) $v(t) = 3$; 22 m; 3 m/s
(c) $v(t) = 0$; 12 m; 0 m/s
(d) $v(t) = 3t^2 - 4t + 4$; 94 m; 59 m/s

4. (a) 9.1 m (b) 9 m/s
(c) 7 m/s; 4 m/s; 0 m/s; -2 m/s (d) 49.1 m; 49.6 m; 49.1 m
(e) after 18 s (f)

```
      y
   40
   30
   20
   10
  -5  0    5 10 15 20  x
   -2
```

5. (a) 16 m/s (b) 200 m (c) -42.8 m/s
(d) 8.2 s (e) -64.6 m/s

6. 154.3 m

7. (a)

```
   y
40 000
30 000
20 000
10 000
  0   20   40   x
```

(b) 22 000 people

(c) 150 people/year (d) 864 people/year (e) yes, in 1988

8. (a) -150 fish/year; 90 fish/year; -60 fish/year
(b) 75 fish/year (c) between 2005 and 2006

9. (a) 40 m (b) 12 m/s; 36 m/s (c) 2 s or 3 s
(d) advancing: $0 \le t < 2$ and $t > 3$; retreating: $2 < t < 3$
(e) 57 m

10. (a) 136 cm (b)

```
   0  20  36 38 40  56    90      148
  cm  cm  cm cm cm  cm    cm       cm
```

11. (a) $-3t^3 + 29.9t^2 - 88.7t + 77.9$
(b) 78 (c) $2.235 < t < 4.409$
(d) 9.7 m/s (e) -2 m/s

12. (a) $h(t) = 0.25t^2 - 3.75t + 9$ (b) -3.75 m/s
(c) -1 m/s (d) 3.75 m/s
(e) 4.5 m below moving down; at hill's height moving up; 5.5 m above moving up

13. (a) between 1990 and 1991 (b) increasing

14. (a) farthest: 1 and 3 (curved path); shortest: 2 (Pythagoras)
(b) fastest: 1 (large slope of tangent); slowest: 2 (small slope of tangent)
(c) fastest: 3 (large slope of tangent); slowest: 1 (small slope of tangent)
(d)

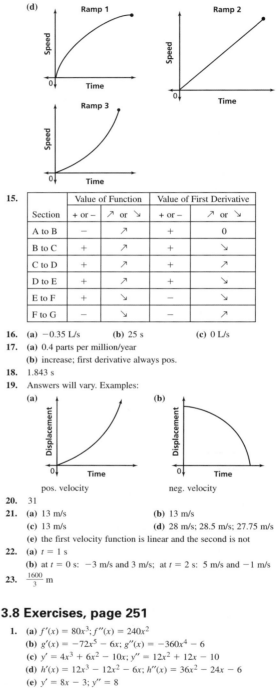

15.

Section	Value of Function + or −	Value of Function ↗ or ↘	Value of First Derivative + or −	Value of First Derivative ↗ or ↘
A to B	−	↗	+	0
B to C	+	↗	+	↘
C to D	+	↗	+	↗
D to E	+	↗	+	↘
E to F	+	↘	−	↘
F to G	−	↘	−	↗

16. (a) -0.35 L/s (b) 25 s (c) 0 L/s

17. (a) 0.4 parts per million/year
(b) increase; first derivative always pos.

18. 1.843 s

19. Answers will vary. Examples:
(a)

```
Displacement
           |
           | Time
0
```
pos. velocity

(b)

```
Displacement
           |
           | Time
0
```
neg. velocity

20. 31

21. (a) 13 m/s (b) 13 m/s
(c) 13 m/s (d) 28 m/s; 28.5 m/s; 27.75 m/s
(e) the first velocity function is linear and the second is not

22. (a) $t = 1$ s
(b) at $t = 0$ s: -3 m/s and 3 m/s; at $t = 2$ s: 5 m/s and -1 m/s

23. $\frac{1600}{3}$ m

3.8 Exercises, page 251

1. (a) $f'(x) = 80x^3$; $f''(x) = 240x^2$
(b) $g'(x) = -72x^5 - 6x$; $g''(x) = -360x^4 - 6$
(c) $y' = 4x^3 + 6x^2 - 10x$; $y'' = 12x^2 + 12x - 10$
(d) $h'(x) = 12x^3 - 12x^2 - 6x$; $h''(x) = 36x^2 - 24x - 6$
(e) $y' = 8x - 3$; $y'' = 8$
(f) $y' = 5$; $y'' = 0$
(g) $f'(x) = 0$; $f''(x) = 0$
(h) $y' = -12x^{-4} + 6x^2$; $y'' = 48x^{-5} + 12x$

2. (a) 105 (b) 3 (c) -6 (d) -78
(e) 3 (f) 1448 (g) $-\frac{202}{27}$ (h) $-\frac{185}{16}$

3. (a) -6 **(b)** $48x^2$

(c) $60x^2 - 12x + 14$ **(d)** $-12x + 16$

(e) -26 **(f)** 0 **(g)** 0 **(h)** $30x^{-4} + 6x$

4. $-84x^2 - 12x + 10$

5. (a) $s''(t) = 12$ **(b)** $s(t) = s(0) - 5$ **(c)** $s'(t) = 5$

(d) $s(t) \times s'(t) < 0$ **(e)** $s'(t) \times s''(t) < 0$

6. (a) $s'(3) = -57$; $s''(3) = -44$; accelerating

(b) $s'(2) = 6$; $s''(2) = -24$; decelerating

(c) $s'(2) = -14.6$; $s''(2) = -9.8$; accelerating

(d) $s'(5) = -29$; $s''(5) = -9.8$; accelerating

7. (a) 108 m   **(b)** -45 m/s   **(c)** -18 m/s^2

8. (a) 6 m/s   **(b)** 0.6 s   **(c)** 1.5 s

(d) -8.7 m/s   **(e)** -9.8 m/s^2, 9.8 m/s^2

9. (a) 0 m/s; 10 m/s^2

(b) $t = \frac{1}{3}$ or 2; before $t = \frac{1}{3}$: moving away from origin;

after $t = \frac{1}{3}$: moving toward origin; before $t = 2$: moving away from;

after $t = 2$: moving toward origin

(c) $t = 1.2$; moving at constant velocity

10. -1.7 m/s^2

11. (a)

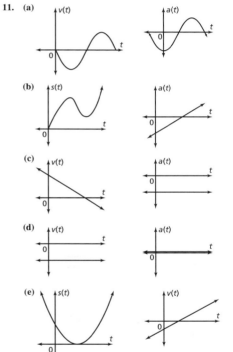

(b)

(c)

(d)

(e)

12. (a) 189 m/s   **(b)** 27 s   **(c)** 2916 m   **(d)** -6.2 m/s^2

13. (a) (Assume that right is pos.) Object starts to the right of the origin and moves away from it (velocity is pos. and decreasing and acceleration is neg. and constant); stops, turns around and moves in other direction (velocity increases to certain point, then decreases, all the while being neg.; acceleration increasing from neg. to pos.); the object then stops and turns around again, speeds up away from the origin (velocity is pos. and increasing; acceleration is pos. and constant).

(b) Starts to the right of origin, moves toward it while gradually coming to a stop (velocity is neg. but increasing to zero); object then turns around and moves away from the origin, with speed gradually increasing (velocity is now pos. and increasing); acceleration is pos. and constant throughout.

14. (a)

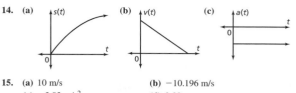

(b)   **(c)**

15. (a) 10 m/s   **(b)** -10.196 m/s

(c) -3.92 m/s^2 **(d)** 2.09 s

16. (a) $s'(t) = 3t^2 - 18t + 24$; $s''(t) = 6t - 18$

(b) upward: $t < 2$ and $t > 4$; downward $2 < t < 4$ **(c)** 44 m

(d)

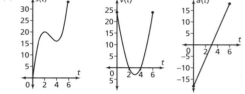

(e) speeding up: $2 < t < 3$ and $t > 4$;

slowing down: $0 < t < 2$ and $3 < t < 4$

17. f: cubic; f': parabola; f'': straight line; As you differentiate using the power rule, the degree of the derivative is always one less than that of the original function.

18. (a) -1 m/s^2 **(b)** -1 m/s^2

(c) (a) is slope of the secant of the derivative function over interval $0 \le t \le 5$; (b) is slope of the tangent of the derivative function at $t = 2.5$.

(d) yes

19. -0.965 m/s^2

20. $\left(\frac{2}{3}, -\frac{20}{3} \right)$

Chapter 3 Review, page 256

11. (a) i. 18 **ii.** 13.5 **iii.** 10.62 **iv.** 10.0602 **v.** $10.006\ 002$

vi. $10.000\ 600\ 02$

(b) 10; rate of change of $f(x)$ at $x = 1$

12. 22

13. (a) 2.4 s   **(b)** -4.074 m/s

14. (a) 6 **(b)** $y = 6x - 6$ **(c)**

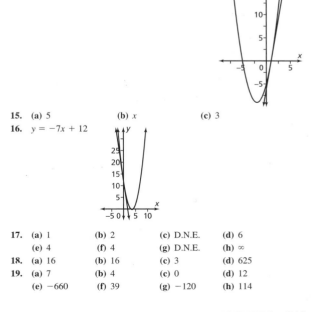

15. (a) 5 **(b)** x **(c)** 3

16. $y = -7x + 12$

17. (a) 1 **(b)** 2 **(c)** D.N.E.   **(d)** 6

(e) 4 **(f)** 4 **(g)** D.N.E.   **(h)** ∞

18. (a) 16 **(b)** 16 **(c)** 3 **(d)** 625

19. (a) 7 **(b)** 4 **(c)** 0 **(d)** 12

(e) -660 **(f)** 39 **(g)** -120 **(h)** 114

20. (a) $4x$ **(b)** $-2x + 3$ **(c)** $12x^2 - 3$
(d) $-8x - 8$ **(e)** 6 **(f)** $18x^2 + 2x + 2$

21. (a) $y = 2x + 1$ **(b)** $y = 4x - 8$ **(c)** $y = 4x + 1$
(d) $y = -5x + 11$ **(e)** $y = x - 1$ **(f)** $y = 38x + 53$

22. (a) $(0, -1)$ **(b)**

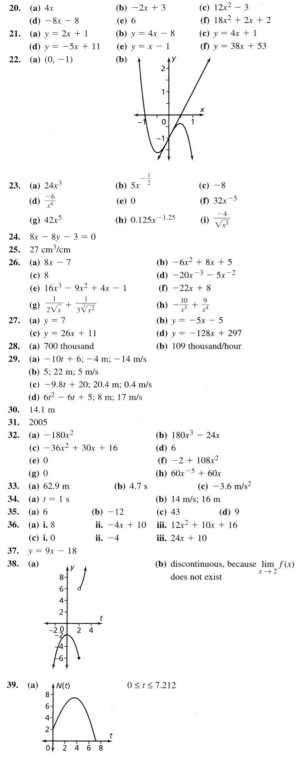

23. (a) $24x^3$ **(b)** $5x^{-\frac{1}{2}}$ **(c)** -8
(d) $\frac{-6}{x^4}$ **(e)** 0 **(f)** $32x^{-5}$
(g) $42x^5$ **(h)** $0.125x^{-1.25}$ **(i)** $\frac{-4}{\sqrt{x^3}}$

24. $8x - 8y - 3 = 0$

25. 27 cm³/cm

26. (a) $8x - 7$ **(b)** $-6x^2 + 8x + 5$
(c) 8 **(d)** $-20x^{-3} - 5x^{-2}$
(e) $16x^3 - 9x^2 + 4x - 1$ **(f)** $-22x + 8$
(g) $\frac{1}{2\sqrt{x}} + \frac{1}{3\sqrt[3]{x^2}}$ **(h)** $-\frac{10}{x^3} + \frac{9}{x^4}$

27. (a) $y = 7$ **(b)** $y = -5x - 5$
(c) $y = 26x + 11$ **(d)** $y = -128x + 297$

28. (a) 700 thousand **(b)** 109 thousand/hour

29. (a) $-10t + 6$; -4 m; -14 m/s
(b) 5; 22 m; 5 m/s
(c) $-9.8t + 20$; 20.4 m; 0.4 m/s
(d) $6t^2 - 6t + 5$; 8 m; 17 m/s

30. 14.1 m

31. 2005

32. (a) $-180x^2$ **(b)** $180x^3 - 24x$
(c) $-36x^2 + 30x + 16$ **(d)** 6
(e) 0 **(f)** $-2 + 108x^2$
(g) 0 **(h)** $60x^{-5} + 60x$

33. (a) 62.9 m **(b)** 4.7 s **(c)** -3.6 m/s²

34. (a) $t = 1$ s **(b)** 14 m/s; 16 m

35. (a) 6 **(b)** -12 **(c)** 43 **(d)** 9

36. (a) i. 8 **ii.** $-4x + 10$ **iii.** $12x^2 + 10x + 16$
(c) i. 0 **ii.** -4 **iii.** $24x + 10$

37. $y = 9x - 18$

38. (a)

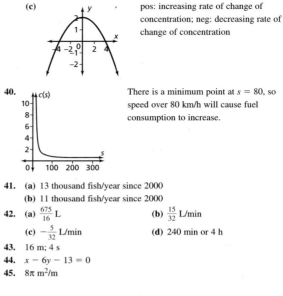

(b) discontinuous, because $\lim_{x \to 2} f(x)$ does not exist

39. (a)

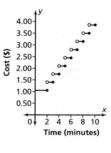

$0 \le t \le 7.212$

(b) increases to a certain level then decreases to zero

(c)

pos: increasing rate of change of concentration; neg: decreasing rate of change of concentration

40.

There is a minimum point at $s = 80$, so speed over 80 km/h will cause fuel consumption to increase.

41. (a) 13 thousand fish/year since 2000
(b) 11 thousand fish/year since 2000

42. (a) $\frac{675}{16}$ L **(b)** $\frac{15}{32}$ L/min
(c) $-\frac{5}{32}$ L/min **(d)** 240 min or 4 h

43. 16 m; 4 s

44. $x - 6y - 13 = 0$

45. 8π m²/m

Chapter 3 Review Test, page 262

1. (a) average rate of change in the amount of waste taken to the landfill between 1995 and 2000
(b) instantaneous rate of change in the amount of waste taken to the landfill in 1994

2. (a) $8x + 6$ **(c)** 8

3. (a) -6 **(b)** $+\infty$

4. (a) $14x - 9$; 14 **(b)** $-15x^2 + 4x - 8$; $-30x + 4$

5. rate increases to $(0.5, 60.25)$, then decreases to end of shift

6. $y = 4x + 5$

7. $y = -4x + 4$ and $y = -4x - 4$

8. (a) 0.5 m **(b)** 35 m/s **(c)** 3.57 s
(d) accelerating: $t > 3.57$ s, decelerating: 0 s $< t < 3.57$ s
(e) 7.2 s

9. discontinuous because there are breaks in the graph

Chapter 4

Getting Ready, page 266

1. (a) $4x^2(2x - 1)$ **(b)** $(x + 2)(x - 8)$
(c) $(x + 5)^2$ **(d)** $(x - 3)(x^2 + 3x + 9)$
(e) $(x + 2)(x^2 - 2x + 4)$ **(f)** $(x + 3)(x - 3)(3x + 5)$
(g) $(2x - 1)(2x + 1)(x + 2)$ **(h)** $(2x - 3)(x - 2)(5x + 1)$

2. (a) $x = -3$ **(b)** $x = -2$
(c) $x = 4.25$ **(d)** $x = -2$ or $x = 4$
(e) $x = -3$ or $x = 5$ **(f)** $x = \frac{1}{2}$ or $x = -\frac{5}{3}$
(g) $x = 4$ or $x = 7$ **(h)** $x = 9$ or $x = -6$

(i) $x = \frac{3}{2}$ or $x = -\frac{4}{3}$ **(j)** $x \doteq 3.22$ or $x \doteq -0.62$

(k) $x = -1$ or $x = 1.75$ **(l)** $x \doteq 1.93$ or $x \doteq -0.43$

3. (a) $x = 3, x = -5$ or $x = 7$ **(b)** $x = -\frac{1}{3}, x = \frac{5}{2}$ or $x = -2$

(c) $x = -1, x = 2$ or $x = 6$ **(d)** $x = 6, x \doteq 2.87$ or $x \doteq -0.87$

(e) $x = 6$ **(f)** $x = 6$ or $x = -6$

(g) $x = -0.5$ or $x = 0.5$ **(h)** $x \doteq 3.91$

4. (a) $x < -5$ or $x > 4$ **(b)** $-\frac{1}{2} < x < 3$

(c) $x < -5$ or $x > 7$ **(d)** $-\frac{7}{2} < x < \frac{5}{3}$

(e) $-3 < x < 1$ or $x > 6$ **(f)** $x < -2$ or $-\frac{3}{2} < x < \frac{1}{5}$

5. (a) $\frac{d}{dx}x^n = nx^{n-1}$, $n \neq 0$ where n is the coefficient; power is decreased by one; Example: $\frac{d}{dx}x^8 = 8x^7$

(b) $\frac{d}{dx}c = 0$ where c is a constant; derivative is zero;

Example, $\frac{d}{dx}(10) = 0$

(c) $\frac{d}{dx}[f(x) + g(x)] = \frac{d}{dx}[f(x)] + \frac{d}{dx}[g(x)]$; derivative of the sum of $f(x)$ and $g(x)$ is the sum of the derivative of $f(x)$ and derivative of $g(x)$; examples will vary.

(d) $\frac{d}{dx}[f(x) - g(x)] = \frac{d}{dx}[f(x)] - \frac{d}{dx}[g(x)]$; derivative of the difference of $f(x)$ and $g(x)$ is the difference of the derivative of $f(x)$ and derivative of $g(x)$; examples will vary.

6. (a) 0 **(b)** 4

(c) $-10x - 3$ **(d)** $21x^2 + 12x - 9$

(e) $20x^3 - 18x$ **(f)** $-6x^{-3} + 4$

(g) $-5x^{-2} - 7$ **(h)** $8x^3 + 36x^5 + 9$

(i) $3x^{-4} + 2x - 6$ **(j)** $18x + 30$

7. (a) 0 **(b)** 0

(c) -10 **(d)** $42x + 12$

(e) $60x^2 - 18$ **(f)** $18x^{-4}$

(g) $10x^{-3}$ **(h)** $24x^2 + 180x^4$

(i) $-12x^{-5} + 2$ **(j)** 18

8. (a) 2 **(b)** -1 **(c)** 47

(d) -114 **(e)** 1 **(f)** 426

9. (a) $x \to -\infty; y \to +\infty; x \to +\infty; y \to +\infty$

(b) $x \to -\infty; y \to +\infty; x \to +\infty; y \to -\infty$

(c) $x \to -\infty; y \to -\infty; x \to +\infty; y \to -\infty$

(d) $x \to -\infty; y \to -\infty; x \to +\infty; y \to +\infty$

10. (a)   **(b)**

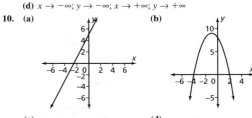

(c)   **(d)**

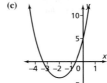
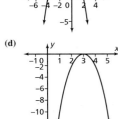

(e)   **(f)**

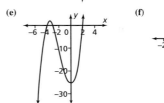

11. (a) increasing: $x > 5$; decreasing: $x < 5$; turning point: $(5, 1)$ local min.

(b) increasing: $x < -2, x > 0$; decreasing: $-2 < x < 0$; turning points: $(-2, 5)$ local max., $(0, 1)$ local min.

12. (a) increasing: $x > 1.5$; decreasing: $x < 1.5$; turning point: $(1.5, -5.75)$ local min.

(b) increasing: $x > 2.87, x < 0.46$; decreasing: $0.46 < x < 2.87$; turning points: $(2.87, -8.06)$ local min., $(0.46, -1.12)$ local min.

(c) increasing: $x > 1.5$; decreasing: $x < 1.5$; turning point: $(1.5, -1.69)$ local min.

(d) increasing: $-0.17 < x < 0.89$; decreasing: $x < -0.17, x > 0.89$; turning points: $(-0.17, -0.08)$ local min.; $(0.89, 2.15)$ local max.

13. (a) $x = 0.555$ or $x = -1.543$ **(b)** $x = 1.544$

(c) $x < -1.774$ or $-0.743 < x < 1.517$

(d) $x < -2.236$ or $x > 2.236$

14. $f'(0) = -2$

15. (a) $7x - y - 3 = 0$ **(b)** $9x - y + 15 = 0$

(c) $75x + y - 112 = 0$ **(d)** $5x + y - 6 = 0$

4.1 Exercises, page 273

1. (a) increasing: $x > 4$; decreasing: $x < 4$

(b) increasing: $x < -2$; decreasing: $x > -2$

(c) increasing: $x < -2; x > 2$; decreasing: $-2 < x < 2$

(d) increasing: $x < -1.8, 0 < x < 1.8$; decreasing: $-1.8 < x < 0, x > 1.8$

2. (a) no; $f'(x)$ cannot be neg.; f is an increasing function so slope of f is pos. for all x

(b) no; $f'(x)$ cannot be pos.; f is a decreasing function so slope of f is neg. for all x

3. A: neg.; B: pos.; C: neg.; D: pos.

4. (a) $x > -2$ **(b)** $x > 4$

(c) $x < -2$ or $x > 5$ **(d)** $-\frac{2}{3} < x < 4$

(e) $x < -9$ or $x > 9$ **(f)** $x < 4$ or $x > 6$

(g) $-5 < x < 6$ **(h)** $x < -0.75$ or $x > 0.5$

(i) $-2.5 < x < 4$ **(j)** $x < -\frac{1}{3}$ or $x > 4$

5. (a) $2; x \in \mathbf{R}; x \in \mathbf{R}$ **(b)** -4; no solution; no solution

(c) $2x; x > 0; x > 0$ **(d)** $-4x; x < 0; x < 0$

(e) $8x + 8; x > -1; x > -1$ **(f)** $-10x - 20; x < -2; x < -2$

6. (a) $-3; x \in \mathbf{R}; x \in \mathbf{R}$ **(b)** 5; no solution; no solution

(c) $6x; x < 0; x < 0$ **(d)** $-6x; x > 0; x > 0$

(e) $6x + 12; x < -2; x < -2$ **(f)** $-8x - 32; x > -4; x > -4$

7. (a) increasing: $x \in \mathbf{R}$; decreasing: none

(b) increasing: none; decreasing: $x \in \mathbf{R}$

(c) increasing: none; decreasing: none

(d) increasing: $x > -2$; decreasing: $x < -2$

(e) increasing: $x < 0$; decreasing: $x > 0$

(f) increasing: $x < 1$; decreasing: $x > 1$

(g) increasing: $x < -2, x > 2$; decreasing: $-2 < x < 2$

(h) increasing: $x < -3, x > 3$; decreasing: $-3 < x < 3$

(i) increasing: $-1 < x < 1$; decreasing: $x < -1, x > 1$

(j) increasing: $x < 0, x > 0$; decreasing: none

8. (a) increasing: $x > 0$; decreasing: $x < 0$

(b) increasing: $x < -1$; decreasing: $x > -1$

(c) increasing: $-1 < x < 0, x > 1$; decreasing: $x < -1, 0 < x < 1$

(d) increasing: $-2 < x < 0, x > 1$; decreasing: $x < -2, 0 < x < 1$

(e) increasing: $x < -2, 0 < x < 2$; decreasing: $-2 < x < 0, x > 2$

(f) increasing: $x > 0$; decreasing: $x < 0$

9. increasing: $x < -1, x > 2$; decreasing: $-1 < x < 2$

10. (a) 20 s

11. increasing: $-1 < x < 0, x > 1$; decreasing: $x < -1, 0 < x < 1$

12. (a) increasing: $t < 1.07$ s; decreasing: $t > 1.07$ s

(b) increasing: never; decreasing: $t \geq 0$

13. increasing: $0 \leq x \leq 24\ 400$; decreasing: $24\ 400 < x \leq 35\ 000$

14.

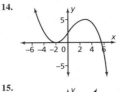

15.

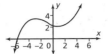

17. no

18. $f(x) = 0.0121x^2 - 0.1307x + 3.1334$; increasing $x > 5.40$;
decreasing $x < 5.40$

20. decreases: $x < 2$; increases: $x > 2$

21. (a) $a > 0$; $3ac > b^2$, $d \in \mathbf{R}$
(b) $a < 0$; $3ac > b^2$, $d \in \mathbf{R}$

4.2 Exercises, page 283

1. (a) iii.   (b) iv.   (c) i.   (d) ii.

2. (a)   (b)

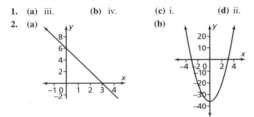

3. (b) absolute max.: 40; absolute min.: 0

4. (a) $x = 0$ (b) absolute max.: 5; absolute min.: -11

5. (a) 0   (b) -3 (c) 4
(d) ± 3 (e) $0, \pm\sqrt{2}$ (f) $\pm 1, \pm 2$

6. (a) abs. max.: 6; abs. min.: 2   (b) abs. max.: 16; abs. min.: -4
(c) abs. max.: -1; abs. min.: -37 (d) abs. max.: 575; abs. min.: -1
(e) abs. max.: 21; abs. min.: 1   (f) abs. max.: 23; abs. min.: -13
(g) abs. max.: 100; abs. min.: -156 (h) abs. max.: 25; abs. min.: 0
(i) abs. max.: 14; abs. min.: -21 (j) abs. max.: 98; abs. min.: -27

7. absolute max.: 20; absolute min.: -7

8. critical numbers: $-5, 3$;
max.: 175; min.: -81

9. critical numbers: $0, \pm 3$;
local max.: 0; local min.: -81

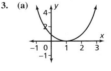

10. 30°C

11. no critical points: $b^2 - 3ac < 0$; Example: $x^3 + 3x^2 + 4x + 1$
one critical point: $b^2 - 3ac = 0$; Example: $x^3 + 3x^2 + 3x + 1$
two critical points: $b^2 - 3ac > 0$; Example: $x^3 + 3x^2 + x + 1$

12. (a)

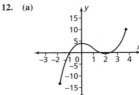

(b) $\{x \mid -2 \leq x \leq 4, x \in \mathbf{R}\}$
(c) increasing: $-2 \leq x < 0$, $2 < x \leq 4$;
decreasing: $0 < x < 2$

13. absolute max.: 42; absolute min.: 10

14. $p = -2, q = 6$; absolute and local min. since $f(x)$ is a quadratic that
opens upward, $f(0) = 6, f(2) = 6$

15. (a) $k < 0$ (b) $k = 0$ (c) $k > 0$

16. $a = -1, b = 3, c = 0, d = 0$

17. absolute max.: consider all local max. and end points—the one with the
highest value is the absolute max.
absolute min.: consider all local min. and end points—the one with the
smallest value is the absolute min.

18. (a) 1

19. (a) yes, when $k \leq 0$
(b) no; either 1 or 3 but not 2

20. absolute max.: 1; absolute min.: -1

4.3 Exercises, page 292

1. (a) $f(x)$: quartic function; $f'(x)$: cubic function
(b) $f(x)$: cubic function; $f'(x)$: quadratic function is.

2. (a)   (b)

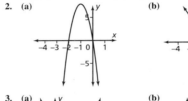

3. (a)   (b)

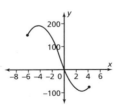

4. $f' > 0$ over beginning of interval,
then $f' < 0$ over rest of interval;
f has one local max

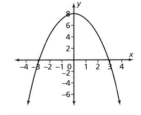

5. $x < -2, -2 < x < 1, 1 < x < 4$ and $x > 4$

6. (a) $x = -3$ at $(-3, 11)$; max.: 11; min.: none
(b) $x = 1$ at $(1, 5)$, $x = 2$ at $(2, 4)$; max.: 5; min.: 4
(c) $x = -3$ at $(-3, 45)$, $x = 3$ at $(3, -63)$; max.: 45; min.: -63
(d) $x = -1$ at $(-1, 9)$, $x = 0$ at $(0, 10)$ and $x = 1$ at $(1, 9)$;
max.: 10; min.: 9
(e) $x = 0$ at $(0, 2)$, $x = 1$ at $(1, 1)$; max.: none; min.: 1
(f) $x = -0.25$ at $(-0.25, -0.0469)$, $x = 0$ at $(0, 0)$ and $x = 1$ at
$(1, -2)$; max.: 0; min.: -0.0469 and -2
(g) $x = 0$ at $(0, 0)$, $x = -1.5$ at $(-1.5, -1.6875)$;
max.: none; min.: -1.6875
(h) $x = 0$ at $(0, 0)$, $x = 2$ at $(2, 16)$; max.: 16; min.: 0

7. **(a)** $x = 2$; increasing: $x > 2$;
decreasing: $x < 2$; min.: $(2, 1)$

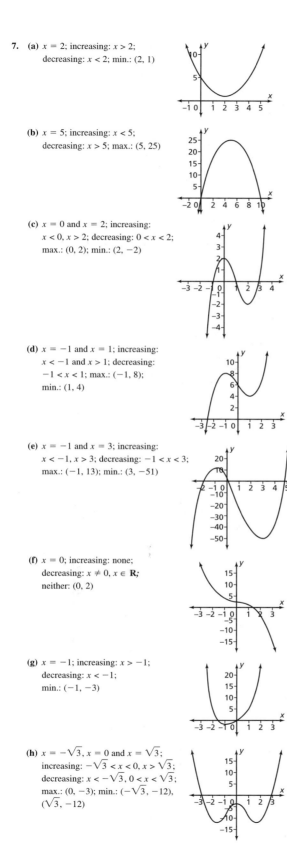

(b) $x = 5$; increasing: $x < 5$;
decreasing: $x > 5$; max.: $(5, 25)$

(c) $x = 0$ and $x = 2$; increasing:
$x < 0, x > 2$; decreasing: $0 < x < 2$;
max.: $(0, 2)$; min.: $(2, -2)$

(d) $x = -1$ and $x = 1$; increasing:
$x < -1$ and $x > 1$; decreasing:
$-1 < x < 1$; max.: $(-1, 8)$;
min.: $(1, 4)$

(e) $x = -1$ and $x = 3$; increasing:
$x < -1, x > 3$; decreasing: $-1 < x < 3$;
max.: $(-1, 13)$; min.: $(3, -51)$

(f) $x = 0$; increasing: none;
decreasing: $x \neq 0, x \in \mathbf{R}$;
neither: $(0, 2)$

(g) $x = -1$; increasing: $x > -1$;
decreasing: $x < -1$;
min.: $(-1, -3)$

(h) $x = -\sqrt{3}, x = 0$ and $x = \sqrt{3}$;
increasing: $-\sqrt{3} < x < 0, x > \sqrt{3}$;
decreasing: $x < -\sqrt{3}, 0 < x < \sqrt{3}$;
max.: $(0, -3)$; min.: $(-\sqrt{3}, -12)$,
$(\sqrt{3}, -12)$

8. critical number: $x = 2$ at $(2, -44)$; increasing: $x > 2$; decreasing: $x < 2$;
local min.: $(2, -44)$; local max.: none

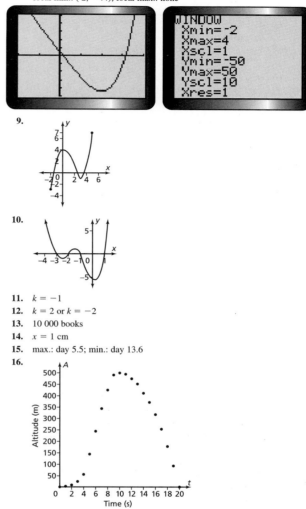

9.

10.

11. $k = -1$
12. $k = 2$ or $k = -2$
13. 10 000 books
14. $x = 1$ cm
15. max.: day 5.5; min.: day 13.6
16.

17. no; Example: $y = x^3$ — critical point is at $x = 0$, which is neither a local
min. nor a local max.
18. 15 m $\times$ 15 m
19. $(0.25, -2.625)$
20. \$5/bushel
21. max. slope: none; min. slope: $-\dfrac{17}{3}$

4.4 Exercises, page 300

1. **(a)** $(x)(3x^2) + (1)(x^3)$
(b) $(4x)(x^2 - 2x) + (2x^2)(2x - 2)$
(c) $(3 - 2x^3)(4) + (-6x^2)(5 + 4x)$
(d) $(6x + 4)(2x^2 - 9) + (3x^2 + 4x - 6)(4x)$
(e) $(16x^3 - 16x)(4x^4 - 8x^2) + (16x^3 - 16x)(4x^4 - 8x^2)$
(f) $(4x^3 - 2x^2 + 8x)(-2x - 5) + (12x^2 - 4x + 8)(-x^2 - 5x + 3)$

2. $F'(x) = [b(x)][c'(x)] + [b'(x)][c(x)]$

3. **(a)** $105x^6 - 120x^5 + 150x^4 - 140x^3$
(b) $105x^6 - 120x^5 + 150x^4 - 140x^3$
(c) same

4. (a) $-60x^3 + 33x^2 + 130x - 21$
(b) $-60x^3 + 33x^2 + 130x - 21$
(c) same

5. (a) $25x^4 + 87x^2 - 42$ (b) $18t^2 + 32t - 7$
(c) $36x^3 - 108x^2 + 72x$ (d) $7x^6 - 27x^2$
(e) $-70x^{-3} + 25x^{-6}$ (f) $\frac{9}{2}\sqrt{z^7} - 3\sqrt{z}$
(g) $25t^2 + 6t - 6t^{\frac{1}{2}}$ (h) $-\frac{5}{3}z^{-\frac{8}{3}} - \frac{4}{3}z^{-\frac{7}{3}} - 8z^{-3}$

6. $54x^5 - 60x^4 + 40x^3 - 30x^2 + 10x - 2$

7.

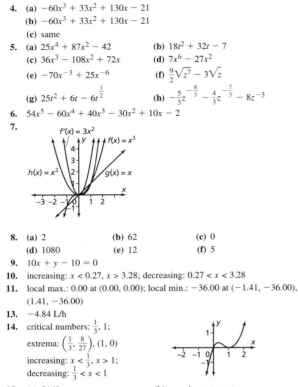

8. (a) 2   (b) 62   (c) 0
(d) 1080   (e) 12   (f) 5

9. $10x + y - 10 = 0$

10. increasing: $x < 0.27, x > 3.28$; decreasing: $0.27 < x < 3.28$

11. local max.: 0.00 at $(0.00, 0.00)$; local min.: -36.00 at $(-1.41, -36.00)$, $(1.41, -36.00)$

13. -4.84 L/h

14. critical numbers: $\frac{1}{3}$, 1;
extrema: $\left(\frac{1}{3}, \frac{8}{27}\right)$, $(1, 0)$
increasing: $x < \frac{1}{3}$, $x > 1$;
decreasing: $\frac{1}{3} < x < 1$

15. (a) \$140   (b) yes, 4 empty seats

18. (a) $(0, 0)$, $(2\sqrt{2}, -64)$, $(-2\sqrt{2}, -64)$ (b) critical points

20. $x - 4y - 13 = 0$, $2x - 8y - 3\sqrt{5} - 19 = 0$, $2x - 8y + 3\sqrt{5} - 19 = 0$

4.5 Exercises, page 309

1. 35 and 35
2. 50 and 50
3. -11 and 11
4. 95 and 95
5. 110 cm × 110 cm
6. 8 m × 8 m
7. 125 m × 166.67 m
8. 450 m²
9. 16.04 m (front) × 29.93 m (side)
10. 35.726 cm × 75.726 cm × 12.137 cm
11. 6 m × 6 m × 4 m
12. 12.1 cm × 18.2 cm × 18.2 cm
13. draw a diagram, figure out the dimension, figure out the volume V, find the derivative of V, set it equal to 0, solve for x, show V is a maximum at this x
14. 1024π cm³
15. radius: 4.3 cm; height: 8.6 cm
16. radius: 3.84 cm; height: 7.67 cm. For an actual can, $r \doteq 4$ cm and $h \doteq 12$ cm. Reasons given for this may vary.
17. 2.74 m × 3.65 m × 3.65 m
18. 250 000 cm³
19. 3723.37 cm³
20. \$50
21. \$100
22. \$81.25
23. \$800

24. 12 m²
25. 17.92 m²
26. 42 m for the square and 33 m for the circle
27. list the relationship between variables given, set up the equation to be minimized/maximized, substitute the first equation found into the second equation found so that the equation has only one unique variable, find the derivative of the equation, set it equal to zero, solve for the variable to find the critical points, show that the critical points are a maximum, minimum, or neither
28. $2\sqrt{3}$ m²
29. 1396 cm³
30. radius: 8.16 cm; height: 11.55 cm

4.6 Exercises, page 319

1. (a) revenue: $-x^2 + 60x$; profit: $-x^2 + 35x - 150$; average cost: $150x^{-1} + 25$
(b) revenue: $-0.6x^3 + 5000x$; profit: $-0.6x^3 + 2500x - 4500$; average cost: $4500x^{-1} + 2500$
(c) revenue: $-0.025x^2 + 50x$; profit: $-0.055x^2 + 80x - 3000$; average cost: $3000x^{-1} - 30 + 0.03x$
(d) revenue: $-0.75x^2 + 155x$; profit: $-0.8x^2 + 200x - 5350$; average cost: $5350x^{-1} - 45 + 0.05x$

2. (a) $C'(x) = 25$; $R'(x) = 60 - 2x$; $P'(x) = -2x + 35$
(b) $C'(x) = 2500$; $R'(x) = -1.8x^2 + 5000$; $P'(x) = -1.8x^2 + 2500$
(c) $C'(x) = 0.06x - 30$; $R'(x) = -0.05x + 50$; $P'(x) = -0.11x + 80$
(d) $C'(x) = 0.1x - 45$; $R'(x) = -1.5x + 155$; $P'(x) = -1.6x + 200$

3. (a) demand: $p = \frac{3500 - x}{100}$; $0 \le x \le 3500$
(b) $p = \frac{3800 - x}{100}$; $0 \le x \le 3800$
(c) $p = \frac{2100 - x}{100}$; $0 \le x \le 2100$

4. (a) revenue: $\frac{3500x - x^2}{100}$; $R'(x) = \frac{3500 - 2x}{100}$
(b) revenue: $\frac{3800x - x^2}{300}$; $R'(x) = \frac{3800 - 2x}{300}$
(c) revenue: $\frac{2100x - x^2}{120}$; $R'(x) = \frac{2100 - 2x}{120}$

5. (a) \$2.8/L/day   (b) 2236 L/day
6. (a) \$300/pizza/month   (b) 4500 pizzas/month
7. (a) \$500/pair of shoes/month   (b) 1100 pairs of shoes/month
8. (a) $R(x) = 600\,000x - 3000x^2$
(b) $P(x) = -4000x^2 + 400\,000x - 8\,000\,000$
(c) \$400 000   (d) \$8000/1000 organizers
(e) max. profit: \$2 000 000; sales: 50 000 units of organizers
9. (a) 22 361 units   (b) 22 045 units
10. 19 704 units
11. selling x items: company earned the max. amount of profit; selling $(x + 1)$ items: profit begins to decrease
12. 775 units
13. 30
14. (a) $x \doteq 3.21$ or $x \doteq 46.79$ (b) \$975
15. \$1100 or \$1125
16. \$70 000
17. (a) 135 units   (b) 100 units
18. (a) \$160   (b) 15.79%
19. To maximize profit, the company should sell 3000 units. Therefore, the company should adjust their production capacity from 2500 to 3000.
20. 132 units
21. \$25

4.7 Exercises, page 329

1. (a) $f(x)$: parabola; $f'(x)$: slanted line with pos. slope; $f''(x)$: hor. line
(b) $f(x)$: 3 turning points; $f'(x)$: 2 turning points; $f''(x)$: 1 turning point

2. (a)

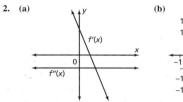

(b)

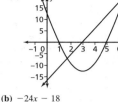

3. (a) 12   **(b)** $-24x - 18$
(c) $60x^2 - 14$ **(d)** $240x^4 + 48x^2 - 6$
(e) 12   **(f)** $48x$

4. (a)

	Intervals		
	$x < -2$	$-2 < x < 4$	$x > 4$
$3(x - 4)$	$-$	$-$	$+$
$(x + 2)$	$-$	$+$	$+$
$f''(x)$	$+$	$-$	$+$
$f(x)$	concave up	concave down	concave up

inflection points at $x = 2, 4$

(b)

	Intervals			
	$x < -\frac{1}{2}$	$-\frac{1}{2} < x < 3$	$3 < x < 5$	$x > 5$
$-(2x + 1)$	$+$	$-$	$-$	$-$
$(x - 3)$	$-$	$-$	$+$	$+$
$(x - 5)$	$-$	$-$	$-$	$+$
$f''(x)$	$+$	$-$	$+$	$-$
$f(x)$	concave up	concave down	concave up	concave down

inflection points at $x = -\frac{1}{2}, 3, 5$

5. (a) pos.: $x < A, C < x < D, x = D, D < x < E, x > G$;
    neg.: $A < x < B, x = B, B < x < C, E < x < F, x = F, F < x < G$;
    zero: $x = A, x = C, x = E, x = G$
(b) pos.: $B < x < C, x = C, C < x < D, F < x < G, x = G, x > G$;
    neg.: $x < A, x = A, A < x < B, D < x < E, x = E$,
    $E < x < F$; zero: $x = B, x = D, x = F$

6. inflection point: $(0, 5)$

7. (a) inflection point: none; concave down: $x \in \mathbf{R}$; concave up: none
(b) inflection point: none; concave down: none; concave up: $x \in \mathbf{R}$
(c) inflection point: none; concave down: none; concave up: $x \in \mathbf{R}$
(d) inflection point: $(1, -5)$ and $(-1, -5)$;
    concave down: $-1 < x < 1$; concave up: $x < -1, x > 1$
(e) inflection point: $(1, -13)$ and $(-3, -189)$;
    concave down: $-3 < x < 1$; concave up: $x < -3, x > 1$
(f) inflection point: $(0, 10)$ and $(3, -71)$;
    concave down: $0 < x < 3$; concave up: $x < 0, x > 3$

8. (a) concave up: $x \in \mathbf{R}$; concave
    down: none; increasing:
    $x > -3$; decreasing: $x < -3$;
    min.: $(-3, -19)$; max.: none;
    point of inflection: none

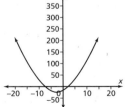

(b) concave up: $x < 1$; concave
    down: $x > 1$; increasing:
    $0 < x < 2$; decreasing: $x < 0$,
    $x > 2$; min.: $(0, 0)$; max.: $(2, 4)$;
    point of inflection: $(1, 2)$

(c) concave up: $x > 0$; concave
    down: $x < 0$; increasing:
    $x < -1, x > 1$; decreasing:
    $-1 < x < 1$; min.: $(1, -6)$;
    max.: $(-1, -2)$; point of
    inflection: $(0, -4)$

(d) concave up: $x > 2$; concave
    down: $x < 2$; increasing: $x \neq 2$,
    $x \in \mathbf{R}$; decreasing: none; min.:
    none; max.: none; point of
    inflection: $(2, 0)$

(e) concave up: $x \in \mathbf{R}$; concave
    down: none; increasing:
    $x > 1$; decreasing: $x < 1$;
    min.: $(1, -4)$; max.: none;
    point of inflection: none

(f) concave up: $x > 0$; concave
    down: $x < 0$; increasing:
    $x < -3, x > 3$; decreasing:
    $-3 < x < 3$; min.: $(3, -15)$;
    max.: $(-3, 21)$; point of
    inflection: $(0, 3)$

(g) concave up: $x < -\frac{2}{\sqrt{3}}$,
    $x > \frac{2}{\sqrt{3}}$; concave down:
    $-\frac{2}{\sqrt{3}} < x < \frac{2}{\sqrt{3}}$;
    increasing: $-2 < x < 0$ and
    $x > 2$; decreasing: $x < -2$ and
    $0 < x < 2$; min.: $(-2, -4)$ and $(2, -4)$; max.: $(0, 0)$;
    points of inflection: $\left(\frac{2}{\sqrt{3}}, -\frac{20}{9}\right)$ and $\left(-\frac{2}{\sqrt{3}}, -\frac{20}{9}\right)$

(h) concave up: $x < -4, x > 1$; concave down: $-4 < x < 1$; increasing:
    $-6.381 < x < 0$,
    $x > 1.881$; decreasing:
    $x < -6.381, 0 < x < 1.881$;
    min.: $(1.881, -6.466)$ and
    $(-6.381, -852.222)$;
    max.: $(0, 26)$; points of inflec-
    tion: $(1, 9)$ and $(-4, -486)$

(i) concave up: $x < 2, x > 4$;
    concave down: $2 < x < 4$;
    increasing: $1 < x < 4, x > 4$;
    decreasing: $x < 1$; min.:
    $(1, -27)$; max.: none;
    points of inflection:
    $(2, -16)$ and $(4, 0)$

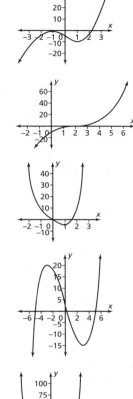

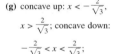

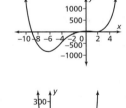

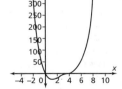

10. concave up: $x < 1, x > 3$; concave down: $1 < x < 3$;
    points of inflection: $(1, 0)$ and $(3, -16)$

11. (a)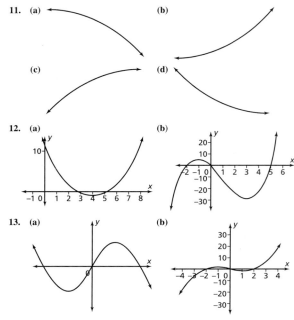

(b)

(c)

(d)

12. (a)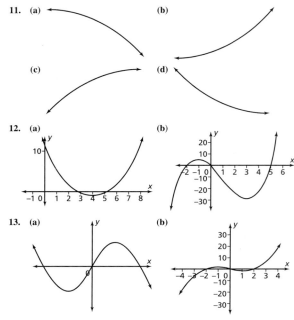

(b)

13. (a)

(b)

14. no

15. (a) max.: 16 at (3, 16); min.: none
    (b) max.: none; min.: -16.25 at $(-2.5, -16.25)$
    (c) max.: $6\sqrt{3}$ at $(-\sqrt{3}, 6\sqrt{3})$; min.: $-6\sqrt{3}$ at $(\sqrt{3}, -6\sqrt{3})$;
      neither: (0, 0)
    (d) max.: 4 at (2, 4); min.: 0 at (0, 0)
    (e) max.: none; min.: 0 at (0, 0)
    (f) max.: 1 at (1, 1); min.: 0 at (0, 0) and (2, 0)

16. 4000 units

17. no inflection points for $n = 1$, $n = 2$, and $n = 4$; an inflection point at $(c, 0)$ for $n = 3$; it appears that inflection points for $f(x)$ could only occur if n is odd and greater than one.

18. no; concavity does not change at max. or min. point.

19. $k = 12$ or $k = -12$

Chapter 4 Review, page 334

11. (a) increasing: $x > 2$; decreasing: $x < 2$
    (b) increasing: $x < 0$, $x > 2$; decreasing: $0 < x < 2$
    (c) increasing: $x > 0.6$; decreasing: $x < 0.6$
    (d) increasing: $-\sqrt{10} < x < 0$, $x > \sqrt{10}$;
      decreasing: $x < -\sqrt{10}$, $0 < x < \sqrt{10}$
    (e) increasing: $x < -\sqrt{5}$, $-1 < x < 1$, $x > \sqrt{5}$;
      decreasing: $-\sqrt{5} < x < -1$, $1 < x < \sqrt{5}$
    (f) increasing: $-0.5 < x < 0$, $x > 5$; decreasing: $x < -0.5$, $0 < x < 5$

12. (a) increasing: $0 < t < 0.97$ s; decreasing: $t > 0.97$ s
    (b) always decreasing

13. increasing: $t > 2.5198$ h; decreasing: $t < 2.5198$ h

14. (a) max.: $f(7) = 41$; min.: $f(1) = 5$
    (b) max.: $f(3) = 36$; min.: $f(-3) = -18$
    (c) max.: $f(5) = 67$; min.: $f(-5) = -63$
    (d) max.: $f(4) = 2752$; min.: $f(-2) = -56$
    (e) max.: $f(-1) = 7$; min.: $f(2) = -20$
    (f) max.: $f(0) = 0$; min.: $f(-3) = f(3) = -81$

15. (a) $0 < t \leq 4.3$ **(b)** $t = 2.14$ s   **(c)** 22.95 m

16. $108x + y + 4 = 0$

17.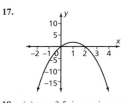

18. (a) $x = 3.5$; increasing: $x > 3.5$;
    decreasing: $x < 3.5$; max.: none;
    min.: $(3.5, -30.25)$

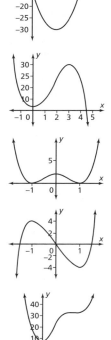

    (b) $x = 0$ and $x = 3$; increasing:
    $0 < x < 3$; decreasing: $x < 0$, $x > 3$;
    max.: (3, 30); min.: (0, 3)

    (c) $x = -1$, $x = 0$ and $x = 1$;
    increasing: $-1 < x < 0$, $x > 1$;
    decreasing: $x < -1$, $0 < x < 1$;
    max.: (0, 2); min.: $(-1, 0)$, (1, 0)

    (d) $x = -1$, $x = 1$; increasing: $x < -1$,
    $x > 1$; decreasing: $-1 < x < 1$;
    max.: $(-1, 4)$; min.: $(1, -4)$

    (e) $x = 0$, $x = 3$; increasing:
    $0 < x < 3$, $x > 3$; decreasing:
    $x < 0$; max.: none; min.: (0, 6);
    neither: (3, 33)

    (f) $x = 0$, $x = \frac{4}{3}$; increasing:
    $x < 0$, $x > \frac{4}{3}$; decreasing: $0 < x < \frac{4}{3}$;
    max.: (0, 0); min.: $\left(\frac{4}{3}, -\frac{256}{81}\right)$

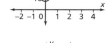

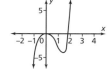

19. 80

20. (a) $48x^3 - 81x^2 + 40x - 45$ **(b)** $-36t^2 - 50t + 39$
    (c) $100x^3 - 90x^2 + 18x$ **(d)** $96x^7 + 42x^6 - 108x^5$
    (e) $-32x^{-3} + 40x^{-6}$ **(f)** $7z^{2.5} - 5$

21. $76x - y - 28 = 0$

22. $x = -0.61$, $x = 0.88$
    decreasing: $-0.60 < x < 0.88$;
    increasing: $x < -0.60$, $x > 0.88$

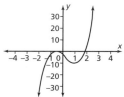

23. 45 000 m²; 150 m $\times$ 300 m

24. 6.26 m $\times$ 6.26 m $\times$ 5.32 m

25. $850/month

26. (a) $9/L/day   (b) 2828 L/day

27. (a) $R(x) = 5000x - 10x^2$
    (b) $P(x) = -9.95x^2 + 5200x - 8000$
    (c) $92 020
    (d) $4603/1000 magazines
    (e) $671 396.98; 261 300 magazines

28. (a) 85 units   (b) 60 units

29. (a) concave up: $x > 1$; concave down: $x < 1$; inflection point: $(1, -47)$
    (b) concave up: $x > 1.5$; concave down: $x < 1.5$; inflection point: $(1.5, 24.5)$
    (c) concave up: $x < -3, x > 3$; concave down: $-3 < x < 3$; inflection point: $(3, -155)$ and $(-3, -155)$
    (d) concave up: $x < -\sqrt{2}, x > \sqrt{2}$; concave down: $-\sqrt{2} < x < \sqrt{2}$; inflection point: $(-\sqrt{2}, -20)$ and $(\sqrt{2}, -20)$

30. (a) increasing: $x > -3$; decreasing: $x < -3$; concave up: $x \in \mathbf{R}$; max.: none; min.: $(-3, -10)$; point of inflection: none
    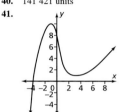

    (b) increasing: $x < -1, x > 2$; decreasing $-1 < x < 2$; concave up: $x > 0.5$; concave down: $x < 0.5$; max.: $(-1, 10)$; min.: $(2, -17)$; point of inflection: $(0.5, -3.5)$
    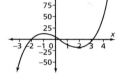

    (c) increasing: $x < -2, x > 3$; decreasing $-2 < x < 3$; concave up: $x > 0.5$; concave down: $x < 0.5$; max.: $(-2, 44)$; min.: $(3, -81)$; point of inflection: $(0.5, -18.5)$
    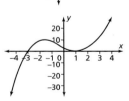

    (d) increasing: $x > 2$; decreasing $x < 2$; concave up: $x \in \mathbf{R}$; max.: none; min.: $(2, -48)$; point of inflection: none

    (e) increasing: $x < -1.67, x > 1$; decreasing $-1.67 < x < 1$; concave up: $x > -0.33$; concave down: $x < -0.33$; max.: $(-1.67, 9.48)$; min.: $(1, 0)$; point of inflection: $(-0.33, 4.74)$

    (f) increasing: $x \in \mathbf{R}$; decreasing: none; concave up: $-0.71 < x < 0, x > 0.71$; concave down: $x < -0.71$, $0 < x < 0.71$; max.: none; min.: none; point of inflection: $(0.71. 41.19)$, $(-0.71, -41.19)$, $(0, 0)$

32. (a) increasing: $-2 < x < -1, x > 0$; decreasing: $x < -2, -1 < x < 0$
    (b) max. value: 2 at $(-1, 2)$; min. value: 1 at $(0, 1)$ and $(-2, 1)$

33. (a) concave down: $x < -2$; concave up: $x > -2$; inflection point: $(-2, -5)$

34. 40 units

35. $f(c)$ might give a point of inflection instead. Example: $x = 0$ for the function x^3

36. from $3 \leq x \leq 10$ the function is decreasing; if x_1 and x_2 are on the interval, and $x_1 < x_2$, then $f(x_1) > f(x_2)$. Since $3 < 6$ then $f(3) > f(6)$.

37. (a)   (b)
    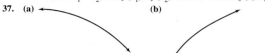

38. 0 cm/s

39. radius: 10.84 cm; height: 5.42 cm

40. 141 421 units

41.
    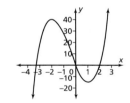

43. garden: 22.25 m × 22.25 m; patio: 12.25 m × 12.25 m

Chapter 4 Review Test, page 340

1. $x = 0, \pm 2$, increasing: $-2 < x < 0, x > 2$; decreasing: $x < -2, 0 < x < 2$

2. absolute max.: 24.5 at $(3, 24.5)$; absolute min.: -7 at $(-4, -7)$; local max.: 17.054 at $(-2.107, 17.054)$; local min.: 0.446 at $(1.107, 0.446)$

3. 50 calculators

4. x-int.: 1.864, -0.082, -3.282; y-int: -2; min.: $(1, -16)$; max.: $(-2, 38)$; concave down: $x < -0.5$; concave up: $x > -0.5$; point of inflection: $(-0.5, 11)$
   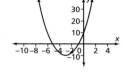

5. $6

6. (a) $25x^4 - 69x^2 - 42$ (b) $32x^3 - 90x^2 + 6x + 58$

7. (a) square: 112 cm; circle: 88 cm
   (b) square: 0 cm; circle: 200 cm

8. $48x - y - 28 = 0$ and $46x - y - 23 = 0$

9. because it is either concave up or concave down throughout the domain

10. radius: 3.99 cm; height: 19.96 cm

Chapter 5

Getting Ready, page 344

1. (a) $5x^2 - 2x - 2$ (b) $x^3 - 4x^2 + 3x - 3$
   (c) $-x^2 - 2x$ (d) $-2x^6 + 6x^5 - x^4 - 3x^3 + 4x^2$

2. (a) $(x + 8)(x - 3)$ (b) $(2x + 1)(x - 4)$
   (c) $(3x - 4)(x + 3)$ (d) $(x - 3)(x^2 + 3x + 9)$
   (e) $(2x + 5)(4x^2 - 10x + 25)$
   (f) $\left(\frac{1}{9}x^2 + 1\right)\left(\frac{1}{3}x + 1\right)\left(\frac{1}{3}x - 1\right)$
   (g) $(x - 1)(x - 3)(x + 2)$
   (h) $(x - 1)(2x - 3)(x + 4)$

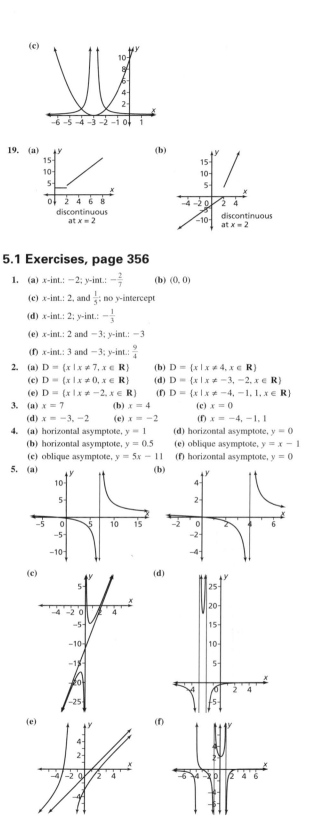

(i) $(x - 1)(x + 1)(2x - 3)(x + 5)$

(j) $2(x - \sqrt{2})(x + \sqrt{2})(x + 3)$

3. **(a)** $P(x) = -x^2 + 12x - 28; x = 6 \pm 2\sqrt{2}; 6$

    (b) $P(x) = -2x^2 + 18x - 45; \frac{13}{2} \pm \frac{\sqrt{79}}{2}; 6.5$

    (c) $P(x) = -3x^2 + 18x - 18; x = 3 + \sqrt{3}; 3$

4. **(a)** $\frac{1}{3}, x \neq 0, 4$ **(b)** $\frac{x + 4}{3}, x \neq 5$

    (c) $\frac{x - 3}{x + 3}, x \neq 4, -3$ **(d)** $\frac{x + 3}{x - 3}, x \neq \frac{1}{2}, 3$

    (e) $(x + 1)(x - 3), x \neq -\frac{1}{2}$ **(f)** $\frac{x + 1}{3x^2 + 8x + 6}, x \neq 2$

5. **(a)** $x + 1, x \neq 0, \pm 1$ **(b)** $\frac{1}{x(x - 1)}, x \neq 0, 1, 2$

    (c) $\frac{2}{x - 3}, x \neq \pm 3$ **(d)** $\frac{2x - 11}{(x - 5)(x - 2)(x + 5)}, x \neq 2, \pm 5$

    (e) $\frac{1}{3x(3x + h)}, x \neq 0, -\frac{h}{3}, h \neq 0$

    (f) $\frac{x^2 + 3x + 20}{2(x + 4)^2}, x \neq -4$

6. **(a)** $-\frac{3}{2}$ **(b)** $\frac{1}{3}$ **(c)** $\frac{3}{2}$ or 3   **(d)** -0.6

7. f is undefined at $x = 0$ and $x = 4$

    (a) -5 **(b)** 0 **(c)** $39\ 999$

    (d) $-2.000\ 025\ 001$ **(e)** $-1.999\ 975\ 001$ **(f)** -3

8. **(a)** $x = \pm 6$ **(b)** $x = -\frac{2}{5}$ or $\frac{3}{2}$

    (c) $x = 0$ or $-\frac{2}{3}$ **(d)** $x = \pm 3, -1$

9. **(a)** $x \in \mathbf{R}$ **(b)** $x \in \mathbf{R}$ **(c)** $\{x \mid x \neq -1, x \in \mathbf{R}\}$

10. **(a)** $x - \frac{16}{x}$ **(b)** $3x + 4 - \frac{5}{x}$ **(c)** $x^2 + 2x - \frac{8}{x^2}$

11. **(a)** $y = 7$ **(b)** $y = 5$ **(c)** $y = -3$

12. **(a)** $x = 2$ **(b)** $x = -4$ **(c)** $x = 5$

13. **(a)** $x = 3$ **(b)** $x = \frac{5}{4}$

    (c) $x = -1$ **(d)** $x = 3$

14. 25

15. 8

16. y-coordinates of points on $f(x)$ are reciprocals of those of $g(x)$

17. **(a)** $y = \frac{1}{2x}; x = 0$ **(b)** $y = \frac{1}{x - 4}; x = 4$

    (c) $y = \frac{1}{(x - 3)^2}; x = 3$

18. **(a)**   **(b)**

19. **(a)**   **(b)**

discontinuous at $x = 2$ discontinuous at $x = 2$

5.1 Exercises, page 356

1. **(a)** x-int.: -2; y-int.: $-\frac{2}{7}$ **(b)** $(0, 0)$

    (c) x-int.: 2, and $\frac{1}{5}$; no y-intercept

    (d) x-int.: 2; y-int.: $-\frac{1}{3}$

    (e) x-int.: 2 and -3; y-int.: -3

    (f) x-int.: 3 and -3; y-int.: $\frac{9}{4}$

2. **(a)** $D = \{x \mid x \neq 7, x \in \mathbf{R}\}$ **(b)** $D = \{x \mid x \neq 4, x \in \mathbf{R}\}$

    (c) $D = \{x \mid x \neq 0, x \in \mathbf{R}\}$ **(d)** $D = \{x \mid x \neq -3, -2, x \in \mathbf{R}\}$

    (e) $D = \{x \mid x \neq -2, x \in \mathbf{R}\}$ **(f)** $D = \{x \mid x \neq -4, -1, 1, x \in \mathbf{R}\}$

3. **(a)** $x = 7$ **(b)** $x = 4$ **(c)** $x = 0$

    (d) $x = -3, -2$ **(e)** $x = -2$ **(f)** $x = -4, -1, 1$

4. **(a)** horizontal asymptote, $y = 1$ **(d)** horizontal asymptote, $y = 0$

    (b) horizontal asymptote, $y = 0.5$ **(e)** oblique asymptote, $y = x - 1$

    (c) oblique asymptote, $y = 5x - 11$ **(f)** horizontal asymptote, $y = 0$

5. **(a)**   **(b)**

    (c)   **(d)**

    (e)   **(f)**

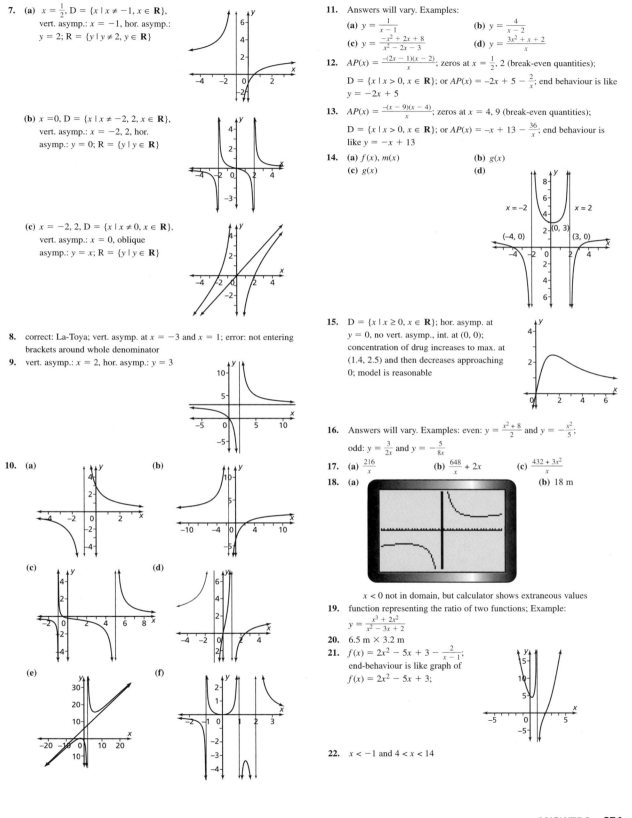

7. (a) $x = \frac{1}{2}$, $D = \{x \mid x \neq -1, x \in \mathbf{R}\}$, vert. asymp.: $x = -1$, hor. asymp.: $y = 2$; $R = \{y \mid y \neq 2, y \in \mathbf{R}\}$

(b) $x = 0$, $D = \{x \mid x \neq -2, 2, x \in \mathbf{R}\}$, vert. asymp.: $x = -2, 2$, hor. asymp.: $y = 0$; $R = \{y \mid y \in \mathbf{R}\}$

(c) $x = -2, 2$, $D = \{x \mid x \neq 0, x \in \mathbf{R}\}$, vert. asymp.: $x = 0$, oblique asymp.: $y = x$; $R = \{y \mid y \in \mathbf{R}\}$

8. correct: La-Toya; vert. asymp. at $x = -3$ and $x = 1$; error: not entering brackets around whole denominator

9. vert. asymp.: $x = 2$, hor. asymp.: $y = 3$

10. (a) **(b)** **(c)** **(d)** **(e)** **(f)**

11. Answers will vary. Examples:

(a) $y = \dfrac{1}{x - 1}$ **(b)** $y = \dfrac{4}{x - 2}$

(c) $y = \dfrac{-x^2 + 2x + 8}{x^2 - 2x - 3}$ **(d)** $y = \dfrac{3x^2 + x + 2}{x}$

12. $AP(x) = \dfrac{-(2x - 1)(x - 2)}{x}$; zeros at $x = \frac{1}{2}$, 2 (break-even quantities); $D = \{x \mid x > 0, x \in \mathbf{R}\}$; or $AP(x) = -2x + 5 - \frac{2}{x}$; end behaviour is like $y = -2x + 5$

13. $AP(x) = \dfrac{-(x - 9)(x - 4)}{x}$; zeros at $x = 4$, 9 (break-even quantities); $D = \{x \mid x > 0, x \in \mathbf{R}\}$; or $AP(x) = -x + 13 - \frac{36}{x}$; end behaviour is like $y = -x + 13$

14. (a) $f(x)$, $m(x)$ **(b)** $g(x)$
(c) $g(x)$ **(d)**

15. $D = \{x \mid x \geq 0, x \in \mathbf{R}\}$; hor. asymp. at $y = 0$, no vert. asymp., int. at $(0, 0)$; concentration of drug increases to max. at $(1.4, 2.5)$ and then decreases approaching 0; model is reasonable

16. Answers will vary. Examples: even: $y = \dfrac{x^2 + 8}{2}$ and $y = -\dfrac{x^2}{5}$; odd: $y = \dfrac{3}{2x}$ and $y = -\dfrac{5}{8x}$

17. (a) $\dfrac{216}{x}$ **(b)** $\dfrac{648}{x} + 2x$ **(c)** $\dfrac{432 + 3x^2}{x}$

18. (a) **(b)** 18 m

$x < 0$ not in domain, but calculator shows extraneous values

19. function representing the ratio of two functions; Example: $y = \dfrac{x^3 + 2x^2}{x^2 - 3x + 2}$

20. 6.5 m $\times$ 3.2 m

21. $f(x) = 2x^2 - 5x + 3 - \dfrac{2}{x - 1}$; end-behaviour is like graph of $f(x) = 2x^2 - 5x + 3$;

22. $x < -1$ and $4 < x < 14$

5.2 Exercises, page 367

1. (a) $\frac{4}{3}$ **(b)** -2 **(c)** $\frac{5}{2}$
  (d) $\frac{33}{10}$ **(e)** 0 **(f)** $\frac{3}{5}$

3. does not exist; $\lim\limits_{x \to 3^-} f(x) = -\infty$ and $\lim\limits_{x \to 3^+} f(x) = \infty$

4. does not exist; $\lim\limits_{x \to 3^-} g(x) = \infty$ and $\lim\limits_{x \to 3^+} g(x) = \infty$

5. (a) ∞ **(b)** $-\infty$ **(c)** ∞
  (d) $-\infty$ **(e)** ∞ **(f)** $-\infty$

6. (a) undefined   **(b)** indeterminate
  (c) indeterminate   **(d)** cannot substitute infinity

7. (a) 0.25   **(b)** 2   **(c)** 3   **(d)** -3
  (e) $\frac{1}{3}$ **(f)** 12   **(g)** $-\frac{3}{5}$ **(h)** $-\frac{1}{25}$
  (i) 8   **(j)** 0   **(k)** $\frac{1}{2}$ **(l)** 27

8. (a) asymp.: $x = -2$; $\lim\limits_{x \to -2^-} f(x) = \infty$, $\lim\limits_{x \to -2^+} f(x) = -\infty$
  (b) asymp.: $x = -3, 3$; $\lim\limits_{x \to -3^-} f(x) = -\infty$, $\lim\limits_{x \to -3^+} f(x) = \infty$,
    $\lim\limits_{x \to 3^-} f(x) = \infty$, $\lim\limits_{x \to 3^+} f(x) = -\infty$
  (c) asymp.: $x = -3$; $\lim\limits_{x \to -3^-} f(x) = -\infty$, $\lim\limits_{x \to -3^+} f(x) = \infty$
  (d) asymp.: $x = -\frac{2}{3}, 5$; $\lim\limits_{x \to -\frac{2}{3}^-} f(x) = \infty$, $\lim\limits_{x \to -\frac{2}{3}^+} f(x) = -\infty$,
    $\lim\limits_{x \to 5^-} f(x) = \infty$, $\lim\limits_{x \to 5^+} f(x) = -\infty$

9. graph function, take limit as $x \to \infty$ by finding an end-behavior model, take limit as $x \to \infty$ by dividing numerator and denominator by highest power of x in denominator

10. (a) $\frac{5}{4}$ **(b)** $\frac{4}{3}$ **(c)** -3 **(d)** 0
  (e) ∞ **(f)** 1   **(g)** 1   **(h)** ∞

11. Vitaly did not simplify to reduce the denominator.

12. (a) -1 **(b)** does not exist; $f(3)$ does not exist
  (c) -5 **(d)** $\frac{3}{5}$

13. (a) vert. asymp.: $x = -5$; $\lim\limits_{x \to -5^-} f(x) = \infty$, $\lim\limits_{x \to -5^+} f(x) = -\infty$;
    hor. asymp.: $y = 3$
  (b) vert. asymp.: $x = 1$; $\lim\limits_{x \to 1^-} g(x) = \infty$, $\lim\limits_{x \to 1^+} g(x) = \infty$;
    hor. asymp.: $y = 1$
  (c) vert. asymp.: $x = -2$; $\lim\limits_{x \to -2^-} h(x) = -\infty$, $\lim\limits_{x \to -2^+} h(x) = \infty$;
    hor. asymp.: $y = 1$
  (d) vert. asymp.: $x = 2$; $\lim\limits_{x \to 2^-} m(x) = -\infty$, $\lim\limits_{x \to 2^+} m(x) = \infty$;
    hor. asymp.: none

14. (a) no   **(b)** yes

15. (a) \$9080   **(b)** \$4085.56
  (c) car's value approaches \$90   **(d)** \$90

17. (a) $y = 0$ **(b)** $y = 4$

18. can say $\lim\limits_{x \to a} (f(x) \times g(x)) \neq \lim\limits_{x \to a} f(x) \times \lim\limits_{x \to a} g(x)$

19. fails for $\lim\limits_{x \to a} \frac{p(x)}{q(x)}$ when $q(a) = 0$; Examples will vary.
    $f(x) = \lim\limits_{x \to 1} \frac{x^2 - 2}{x - 1}$

20. $7.99 \leq f(x) \leq 8.01$

21. (a) $x = 3$ **(b)** $2.99 \leq x \leq 3.01$
  (c) $2.999\,000\,5 \leq x \leq 3.001\,000\,5$

22. limit is in indeterminant form $\left(\frac{0}{0}\right)$ so may or may not exist; Examples will vary.

5.3 Exercises, page 375

1. (a) condition 2   **(b)** condition 3
  (c) conditions 1 and 2

2. (a) $x = -3$, conditions 1 and 2
  (b) $x = -1$, condition 2; $x = 5$, conditions 1 and 2
  (c) $x = 1$, 1, conditions 1 and 2

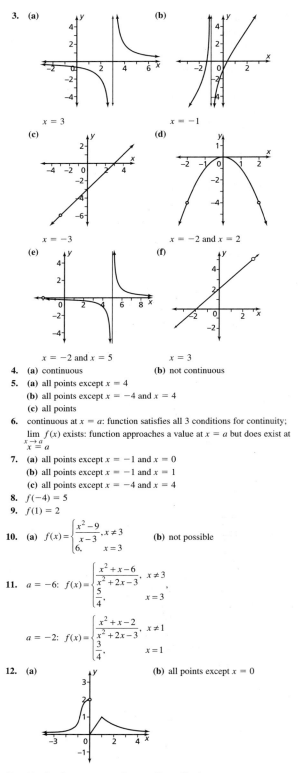

3. (a) $x = 3$ **(b)** $x = -1$
  (c) $x = -3$ **(d)** $x = -2$ and $x = 2$
  (e) $x = -2$ and $x = 5$ **(f)** $x = 3$

4. (a) continuous   **(b)** not continuous

5. (a) all points except $x = 4$
  (b) all points except $x = -4$ and $x = 4$
  (c) all points

6. continuous at $x = a$: function satisfies all 3 conditions for continuity; $\lim\limits_{x \to a} f(x)$ exists: function approaches a value at $x = a$ but does exist at $x = a$

7. (a) all points except $x = -1$ and $x = 0$
  (b) all points except $x = -1$ and $x = 1$
  (c) all points except $x = -4$ and $x = 4$

8. $f(-4) = 5$

9. $f(1) = 2$

10. (a) $f(x) = \begin{cases} \dfrac{x^2 - 9}{x - 3}, & x \neq 3 \\ 6, & x = 3 \end{cases}$ **(b)** not possible

11. $a = -6$: $f(x) = \begin{cases} \dfrac{x^2 + x - 6}{x^2 + 2x - 3}, & x \neq 3 \\ \dfrac{5}{4}, & x = 3 \end{cases}$,
    $a = -2$: $f(x) = \begin{cases} \dfrac{x^2 + x - 2}{x^2 + 2x - 3}, & x \neq 1 \\ \dfrac{3}{4}, & x = 1 \end{cases}$

12. (a)   **(b)** all points except $x = 0$

13. (a) all points except $x = 0$ **(b)** at all points
  (c) all points except $x = 2$ **(d)** all points except $x = 1$

(e) all points except $x = -1$ and $x = 5$

(f) at all points

(g) all points except $x = -1$

14. Answers will vary. Example: $f(x) = \begin{cases} \dfrac{x^2 + x - 2}{x + 2}, & x \le 3 \\ x + 2, & x > 3 \end{cases}$

15. functions in 13(b) and 13(f); satisfy all 3 conditions of continuity

16. $A = 4$

17. $\lim\limits_{x \to a} f(x)$ exists, $f(a)$ exists, $\lim\limits_{x \to a} f(x) = f(a)$; Examples will vary.

18. $A = B - 3$ and either $B > 1$ and $A > -2$ or $B < 1$ and $A < -2$

19. statement is true; Examples will vary.

5.4 Exercises, page 383

1. **(a)** $\dfrac{3}{(3 - x)^2}$ **(b)** $\dfrac{3}{(1 + x)^2}$ **(c)** $\dfrac{3x^2 + 2}{x^2}$

2. **(a)** $\dfrac{6}{(x + 3)^2}$ **(b)** $\dfrac{6x^5 - 72x^3}{(x^2 - 6)^2}$

   (c) $\dfrac{x^4 + 2x^3 + 5x^2 - 2}{(x^2 + x + 1)^2}$ **(d)** $\dfrac{2x^2 + 20x + 30}{x^2(x + 3)^2}$

   (e) $\dfrac{3x^2 - 2x^3}{(1 - x)^2}$ **(f)** $\dfrac{bc - ad}{(cx - d)^2}$

   (g) $\dfrac{2x^2 + 6x + 2}{(2x + 3)^2}$ **(h)** $\dfrac{15x^4 + 40x^3 - 9}{(x + 2)^2}$

   (i) $\dfrac{2x^4 - 2}{x^3}$ **(j)** $\dfrac{-5x^2 + 2x - 3}{x^2(x - 3)^2}$

4. **(a)** $\dfrac{-x - 11}{(x + 1)^3}$ **(b)** $\dfrac{10x^3 - 45x^2}{2(x - 3)^2}$

   (c) $\dfrac{x^2 - 4x + 10}{(x - 2)^2}$ **(d)** $\dfrac{-9x^2 + 90x - 17}{(3x + 1)^2(3x - 2)^2}$

5. $\dfrac{3x^4 + 2}{x^2}$

6. $y = 3x - 2$

7. **(a)** $y = \dfrac{3}{4}x + \dfrac{25}{4}$ **(b)** $y = -\dfrac{3}{4}x - \dfrac{5}{4}$

8. **(a)** $\left(1, \dfrac{5}{2}\right)$ and $\left(-1, -\dfrac{5}{2}\right)$ **(b)** $\left(2, \dfrac{1}{2}\right)$ and $\left(-2, \dfrac{3}{2}\right)$

9. **(a)** position: 1, velocity: $\dfrac{1}{6}$, acceleration: $-\dfrac{1}{18}$, speed: $\dfrac{1}{6}$

   (b) position: $\dfrac{8}{3}$, velocity: $\dfrac{4}{9}$, acceleration: $\dfrac{10}{27}$, speed: $\dfrac{4}{9}$

10. yes, when $t = 0.24$ s

11. $t = 2.83$

12. $c'(t) = \dfrac{250}{(25 + t)^2}$

13. $t = 1.87$ h

14. $p'(t) = \dfrac{25}{(t + 1)^2}$

15. $\dfrac{dy}{dx} = \dfrac{6x}{(2x^2 + 1)^2}$, positive for $x > 0$

16. $\dfrac{dy}{dx} = \dfrac{v\frac{du}{dx} - u\frac{dv}{dx}}{v^2}$

17. **(a)** 1 cm **(b)** $t = 1$ s **(c)** 0.25 cm/s

    (d) no; radius will never reach 2 cm ($y = 2$ is horizontal asymptote of the graph)

18. $P'(t) = -\dfrac{390}{(3t + 2)^2}$ is rate of change of population. $P''(t) = \dfrac{2340}{(3t + 2)^3}$ is how the rate of change of population is changing. Examples will vary. As years pass, rate of change is increasing.

19. $y = -\dfrac{x}{2}$ and $y = -\dfrac{x}{18}$

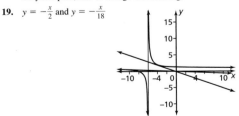

20. Examples will vary. Rule: If $f(x) = ax + b$ and $y = \dfrac{1}{f(x)}$, then $y' = \dfrac{-a}{(ax + b)^2}$.

5.5 Exercises, page 391

1. **(a)** $\lim\limits_{h \to 0^-} \dfrac{f(2 + h) - f(2)}{h} \ne \lim\limits_{h \to 0^+} \dfrac{f(2 + h) - f(2)}{h}$

   (b) corner at $x = 2$, so $\lim\limits_{h \to 0^-} \dfrac{f(2 + h) - f(2)}{h} \ne \lim\limits_{h \to 0^+} \dfrac{f(2 + h) - f(2)}{h}$

   (c) vertical tangent at $(2, 1)$, so slope is undefined

2. **(a)** **i.** all points except $x = 0$; **ii.** nowhere; **iii.** $x = 0$

   (b) **i.** all points except $x = 0$ and $x = 3$; **ii.** $x = 3$; **iii.** $x = 0$

   (c) **i.** all points except $x = 1$; **ii.** $x = 1$; **iii.** nowhere

3. **(a)** discontinuity **(b)** corner **(c)** vertical tangent

   (d) cusp **(e)** discontinuity **(f)** vertical tangent

4. **(a)** not defined (vertical asymptote)

   (b) not defined (vertical asymptote)

   (c) cusp **(d)** corner **(e)** not defined (vertical asymptote)

   (f) restricted domain **(g)** vertical asymptote

   (h) discontinuity

5. **(c)** cusp at $(2, 0)$ but is differentiable at $x = 1$

6. **(a)** all points except $x = -1$ and $x = 4$

   (b) all points except $x = 2$ **(c)** all points except $x = 1$

7. **(a)** $x = 0.25$ and $x = 0$ **(b)** $x = -3$ and $x = 3$

   (c) $1 < x < 6$

8. left and right hand limit of $\dfrac{f(x + h) - f(x)}{h}$ would be different

9. **(a)** not defined at $x = 1$ (vertical asymptote)

   (b)

   (c) $f(x)$: 100 000 000; $g(x)$: 0 **(d)** Answers will vary.

10. no

12. discontinuity or restricted domain, graph has corner or cusp, graph has vertical tangent; Examples will vary.

13. **(a)** $a = 4 + 2b$ **(b)** $a = -8, b = -6$

14. **(a)** $6b = 2a + 5$ **(b)** $a = \dfrac{11}{4}, b = \dfrac{7}{4}$

15. converse is not true. Counterexamples will vary.

Exercise 5.6, page 401

1. 1.5, min.

2. 6 cm $\times$ 6 cm

3. 3.16 m $\times$ 6.33 m

4. 8 m $\times$ 12 m; 48 m

5. 17.3 m $\times$ 34.6 m

6. 25 m $\times$ 40 m

7. 60 m $\times$ 80 m

8. 50 m $\times$ 75 m

9. 4 m $\times$ 8 m

10. 20 km/h

11. 11.3 cm $\times$ 17.0 cm

12. 8.5 cm $\times$ 14.1 cm

13. 5 cm $\times$ 10 cm $\times$ 10 cm

14. 2.38 m $\times$ 2.38 m $\times$ 2.65 m

15. 14.94 cm $\times$ 14.94 cm $\times$ 22.40 cm

16. 0.585 m $\times$ 1.170 m $\times$ 0.438 m

17. radius 2.75 m, height 21.05 m

18. radius 0.66 m, height 1.54 m

19. **(a)** 0.60 m $\times$ 1.29 m $\times$ 1.32 m

    (b) 0.50 m $\times$ 1.41 m $\times$ 1.41 m

20. if optimization problems are done correctly they can save people time, money, and material; applications of these problems are endless. Example: soup manufacturer trying to make the biggest can possible out of a fixed amount of material

21. 84.4 km/h

22. 30 lamps, 50 lamps

23. 5.53 tonnes

24. 5 people, $294

25. Example questions will vary. To solve an optimal value problem: read problem and identify what needs to be maximized/minimized; draw a diagram, assign variable names, and note relationships between variables; create an algebraic model; note the domain and graph if possible; find where the derivative is zero or does not exist, use the 1st or 2nd derivative test to determine if a max. or min. point was found,. if graph is not available, evaluate function at endpoints for extreme values; interpret solution

26. optimal speed for several distances is 90 km/h; length of trip does not affect optimal speed

27. radius 0.542, height 1.08

28. $\sqrt{\dfrac{a}{b}}$

30. $\dfrac{x^3}{(s-x)^3} = \dfrac{a}{b}$

5.7 Exercises, page 414

1. (a) $D = \{x \mid x \neq 0, x \in \mathbf{R}\}$; x-int.: 1
   (b) $D = \{x \mid x \in \mathbf{R}\}$; x- and y-int.: 0
   (c) $D = \{x \mid x \neq 2, x \in \mathbf{R}\}$; x- and y-int.: 0
   (d) $D = \{x \mid x \neq 5, x \in \mathbf{R}\}$; x-int..: 2 and 8; y-int.: $-\dfrac{16}{15}$

2. (a) vert. asymp.: $x = 0$; hor. asymp.: $y = 0$
   (b) vert. asymp.: none; hor. asymp.: $y = 0$
   (c) vert. asymp.: $x = 2$; hor. asymp.: $y = 1$
   (d) vert. asymp.: $x = 5$; oblique: $y = \dfrac{x}{3} - \dfrac{5}{3}$

3. (a) $f'(x) = \dfrac{-x+2}{x^3}$; critical value: 2
   (b) $f'(x) = \dfrac{-2(x-1)(x+1)}{(x^2+1)^2}$; critical values: -1 and 1
   (c) $f'(x) = \dfrac{-2}{(x-2)^2}$; critical values: none
   (d) $f'(x) = \dfrac{x^2 - 10x + 34}{3(x-5)^2}$; critical values: none

4. (a) increasing: $0 < x < 2$; decreasing: $x < 0$ and $x > 2$
   (b) increasing: $-1 < x < 1$; decreasing: $x < -1$ and $x > 1$
   (c) decreasing: $x < 2$ and $x > 2$
   (d) increasing: $x < 5$ and $x > 5$

5. (a) $f''(x) = \dfrac{2(x-3)}{x^4}$; concave up: $x > 3$; concave down: $x < 0$ and $0 < x < 3$
   (b) $f''(x) = \dfrac{4x(x^2-3)}{(x^2+1)^3}$; concave up: $-1.732 < x < 0$ and $x > 1.732$; concave down: $x < -1.732$ and $0 < x < 1.732$
   (c) $f''(x) = \dfrac{4}{(x-2)^3}$; concave up: $x > 2$; concave down: $x < 2$
   (d) $f''(x) = \dfrac{-6}{(x-5)^3}$; concave up: $x > 5$; concave down: $x < 5$

6. (a) local min.: none; local max.: $\left(2, \dfrac{1}{4}\right)$; point of inflection: $\left(3, \dfrac{2}{9}\right)$
   (b) local max.: $\left(\sqrt{2}, \dfrac{\sqrt{2}}{2}\right)$; local min.: $\left(-\sqrt{2}, -\dfrac{\sqrt{2}}{2}\right)$; points of inflection: $\left(-\sqrt{3}, -\dfrac{\sqrt{3}}{2}\right)$, $(0, 0)$, and $\left(\sqrt{3}, \dfrac{\sqrt{3}}{2}\right)$
   (c) local max.: none; local min.: none; points of inflection: none
   (d) local max.: none; local min.: none; point of inflection: none

7. (a) 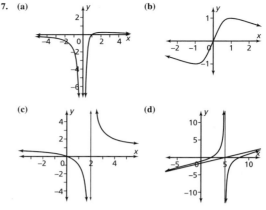 (b)
   (c) (d)

8. (a) no symmetry
   (b) since $f(-x) = -f(x)$, graph has symmetry about origin
   (c) no symmetry
   (d) no symmetry
   if $f(-x) = -f(x)$, graph has symmetry about origin;
   if $f(-x) = f(x)$, graph has symmetry about y-axis

9. (b)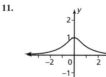

10. $D = \{x \mid x \neq 0, x \in \mathbf{R}\}$; x-int.: 1; vert. asymp.: $x = 0$; hor. asymp.: $y = 0$; increasing: $0 < x < 2$; decreasing: $x < 0$ and $x > 2$; concave up: $x > 3$; concave down: $x < 0$ and $0 < x < 3$; max.: $x = 2$; point of inflection: (3, 0.889)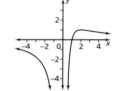

11.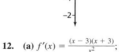

12. (a) $f'(x) = \dfrac{(x-3)(x+3)}{x^2}$; $f''(x) = \dfrac{18}{x^3}$
   (b) $f'(x) = \dfrac{-x^2 + 3}{x^4}$; $f''(x) = \dfrac{2(x^2 - 6)}{x^5}$

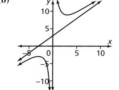
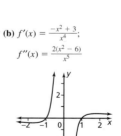

(c) $f'(x) = \dfrac{-(x+2)}{(x-2)^3}$;

$f''(x) = \dfrac{2(x+4)}{(x-2)^4}$

(d) $f'(x) = \dfrac{-2(x-2)}{(x^2-4x)^2}$;

$f''(x) = \dfrac{6x^2 - 24x + 32}{(x^2-4x)^3}$

13. begins to decrease when $t = 1.58$; c increases to $t = 1.58$, then slowly decreases approaching zero

(e) $f'(x) = \dfrac{1}{(x+2)^2}$;

$f''(x) = \dfrac{-2}{(x+2)^3}$

(f) $f'(x) = \dfrac{(x^2-1)(x^2+1)}{x^4}$;

$f''(x) = \dfrac{4}{x^5}$

14. **(a)** **(b)** at $t = 1.826$ s

(c) at $t = 1.826$ **(d)**

15. **(a)** approximately 2250 frogs

(b) when $t = 2.887$

(g) $f'(x) = \dfrac{x(x-2)}{(x-1)^2}$;

$f''(x) = \dfrac{2}{(x-1)^3}$

(h) $f'(x) = \dfrac{-6}{(4x-3)^2}$;

$f''(x) = \dfrac{48}{(4x-3)^3}$

16. 1732 items are sold;

17. **(a)** **(b)**

(i) $f'(x) = \dfrac{4x}{(x^2+1)^2}$;

$f''(x) = \dfrac{4(1-3x^2)}{(x^2+1)^3}$

(j) $f'(x) = \dfrac{9}{(x+3)^2}$;

$f''(x) = \dfrac{-18}{(x+3)^3}$

18. **(a)** f': f'':

(k) $f'(x) = \dfrac{-x^2+2}{(x^2+2)^2}$;

$f''(x) = \dfrac{2x(x^2-6)}{(x^2+2)^3}$

(l) $f''(x) = \dfrac{x^2+2x-1}{(x+1)^2}$;

$f''(x) = \dfrac{4}{(x+1)^3}$

(b) f': f'':

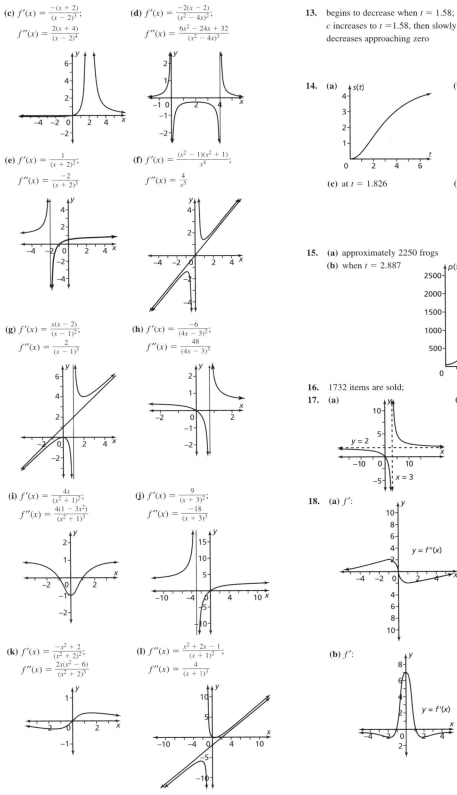
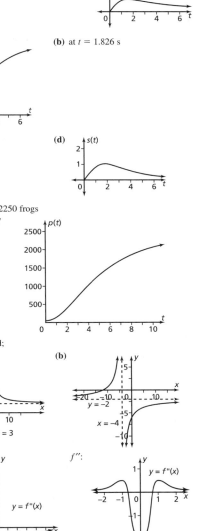
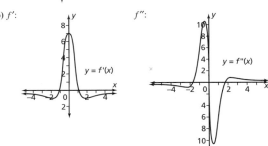

19. (a)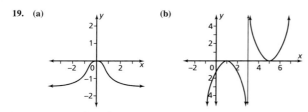
(b)

(c)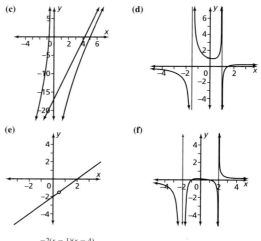
(d)

(e)
(f)

20. (a) A: f, C: f', B: f''; when derivative is taken, degree of denominator increases by 1

(b) F: f, E: f', D: f''; when derivative is taken, degree of denominator increases by 1

21. (a) true; if $f'(3) = 0$, graph changes from pos. to neg. or neg. to pos. in which case a local max. or local min. exists at $x = 3$

(b) false; graph could have oblique asymptote if highest degree of x in numerator is exactly one greater than highest degree of x in denominator

(c) true; if $f'(2) = 0$, concavity at $x = 2$ changes from concave up to concave down or concave down to concave up. This makes $x = 2$ a point of inflection.

22. Analysis will vary slightly.

23. $a = 1$; $b = 2$

24. disagree; counterexample is question 20

25. $f(x) = \dfrac{x-1}{x}$

26. $f(x) = \dfrac{4}{1+x^2}$

27. (a)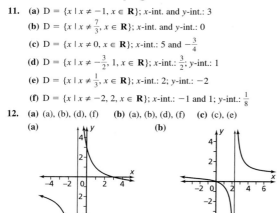

Chapter 5 Review, page 419

11. (a) D $= \{x \mid x \neq -1, x \in \mathbf{R}\}$; x-int. and y-int.: 3

(b) D $= \{x \mid x \neq \frac{7}{3}, x \in \mathbf{R}\}$; x-int. and y-int.: 0

(c) D $= \{x \mid x \neq 0, x \in \mathbf{R}\}$; x-int.: 5 and $-\frac{3}{4}$

(d) D $= \{x \mid x \neq -\frac{3}{2}, 1, x \in \mathbf{R}\}$; x-int.: $\frac{3}{2}$; y-int.: 1

(e) D $= \{x \mid x \neq \frac{1}{3}, x \in \mathbf{R}\}$; x-int.: 2; y-int.: -2

(f) D $= \{x \mid x \neq -2, 2, x \in \mathbf{R}\}$; x-int.: -1 and 1; y-int.: $\frac{1}{8}$

12. (a) (a), (b), (d), (f) **(b)** (a), (b), (d), (f) **(c)** (c), (e)

(a)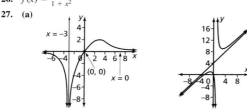
(b)

13. $AP(x) = \dfrac{-2(x-1)(x-4)}{x}$: easy to see what break-even quantities are; $AP(x) = -2x + 10 - \dfrac{8}{x}$: easy to tell what curve will look like in long run.; curve will act as line $AP(x) = -2x + 10$ as it approaches infinity; break-even points: $x = 1$, $x = 4$

14. (a) $-\frac{1}{2}$ **(b)** does not exist; vert. asymp. at $x = 2$
(c) -11 **(d)** 2

15. (a) vert. asymp.: $x = -\frac{1}{2}$; $x \to -\frac{1}{2}^-$, $f(x) \to \infty$; $x \to -\frac{1}{2}^+$, $f(x) \to -\infty$; hor. asymp.: $y = \frac{1}{2}$

(b) vert. asymp.: $x = -2$; $x \to -2^-$, $g(x) \to \infty$; $x \to -2^+$, $g(x) \to \infty$; hor. asymp.: $y = 1$

(c) vert. asymp.: $x = -3$; $x \to -3^-$, $h(x) \to \infty$; $x \to -3^+$, $h(x) \to -\infty$; hor. asymp.: $y = -1$

(d) vert. asymp.: $x = -4$; $x \to -4^-$, $m(x) \to -\infty$; $x \to -4^+$, $g(x) \to \infty$; hor. asymp.: none

16. (a) $-\frac{2}{3}$ **(b)** $\frac{1}{6}$ **(c)** -3 **(d)** 0
(e) ∞ **(f)** 1 **(g)** 1 **(h)** ∞

17. (a) $x = 5$, conditions 1 & 2 **(b)** none
(c) $x = 6$, conditions 1 & 2, $x = 2$, condition 2
(d) none

18. (a) discontinuous **(b)** continuous

19. (a) $\begin{cases} \dfrac{x^2-4}{x+2}, x \neq -2 \\ -4, x = -2 \end{cases}$ **(b)** $\begin{cases} \dfrac{x^2+x-12}{x-3}, x \neq 3 \\ 7, x = 3 \end{cases}$

20. (a) $f'(x) = -\dfrac{5}{(x-1)^2}$ **(b)** $f'(x) = \dfrac{2x^2(x-3)(x+3)}{(x^2-3)^2}$

(c) $f'(x) = \dfrac{2x^4 + 2x^3 - x^2 + 1}{(2x^2 + x - 1)^2}$ **(d)** $f'(x) = \dfrac{5x^2 + 4x + 8}{3(x^2 + 4x)^2}$

(e) $f'(x) = \dfrac{x^3(8 - 3x)}{(2-x)^2}$ **(f)** $f'(x) = -\dfrac{ad + bc}{(cx - d)^2}$

(g) $f'(x) = \dfrac{3x^2 + 2x + 12}{(3x + 1)^2}$ **(h)** $f'(x) = \dfrac{8x^5 - 20x^4 - 3}{(x-2)^2}$

(i) $f'(x) = \dfrac{-x^4 - 3}{x^4}$ **(j)** $f'(x) = \dfrac{-x^2 + 6x - 15}{x^2(x-5)^2}$

21. (a) $s(2) = 1$, $v(2) = \frac{1}{3}$, $a(2) = -\frac{1}{9}$
(b) $s(1) = 4$, $v(1) = 1$, $a(1) = 1$

22. $S(x) = \dfrac{0.3x^2 + 27\,000}{(x + 45\,000)^2}$

23. (a) vert. asymp. at $x = 2$; not defined there
(b) corner at $x = 2$, not defined there
(c) cusp at $x = 2$

24. (a) discontinuity, hole **(b)** corner
(c) discontinuity, vertical asymptote **(d)** cusp
(e) discontinuity, restricted domain **(f)** vertical tangent

25. (a) not differentiable, not defined
  (b) not differentiable, not defined
  (c) differentiable   (d) not differentiable, corner
26. 47.4 cm × 79.1 cm
27. radius 2.55 cm; height 19.58 cm
28. (a) $\sqrt{1.2}$ m × $\sqrt{1.2}$ m × 0.75 m; 5.69 m³
  (b) $\sqrt{1.8}$ m × $\sqrt{1.8}$ m × 0.5 m; 6.28 m³
29. D = $\{x \mid x \neq 1, c \in \mathbf{R}\}$; x-int. and y-int.: 0;
  vert. asymp.: $x = 1$; $x \to 1^-$, $f(x) \to \infty$;
  $x \to 1^+$, $f(x) \to \infty$; hor. asymp.: $y = 0$;
  decreasing: $x < -1$, $x > 1$; increasing:
  $-1 < x < 1$; local min: $(-1, -1.25)$;
  concave down: $x < -2$; concave up:
  $-2 < x < 1$, $x > 1$; point of inflection:
  $(-2, -1.11)$

30. (a) $f'(x) = \dfrac{2x^2 - 3}{x^4}$;
  $f''(x) = \dfrac{-4(x^2 - 3)}{x^5}$

  (b) $f'(x) = \dfrac{(x + 3)}{(x - 3)^3}$;
  $f''(x) = \dfrac{2(x + 6)}{(x - 3)^4}$

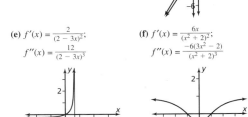

  (c) $f'(x) = \dfrac{1}{(x + 3)^2}$;
  $f''(x) = -\dfrac{2}{(x + 3)^3}$

  (d) $f'(x) = \dfrac{2x^4 - 3}{x^4}$;
  $f''(x) = \dfrac{12}{x^5}$

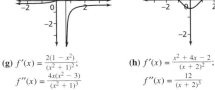

  (e) $f'(x) = \dfrac{2}{(2 - 3x)^2}$;
  $f''(x) = \dfrac{12}{(2 - 3x)^3}$

  (f) $f'(x) = \dfrac{6x}{(x^2 + 2)^2}$;
  $f''(x) = \dfrac{-6(3x^2 - 2)}{(x^2 + 2)^3}$

  (g) $f'(x) = \dfrac{2(1 - x^2)}{(x^2 + 1)^2}$;
  $f''(x) = \dfrac{4x(x^2 - 3)}{(x^2 + 1)^3}$

  (h) $f'(x) = \dfrac{x^2 + 4x - 2}{(x + 2)^2}$;
  $f''(x) = \dfrac{12}{(x + 2)^3}$

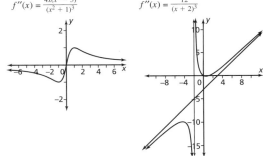

31. C: f, B: f'; A: f''; as derivative is taken, degree of denominator increases by one
32. (a) -1 (b) limit does not exist
  (c) 2   (d) $-\dfrac{2}{7}$
33. $y = -\dfrac{14}{5}x - \dfrac{9}{5}$
34. (b)

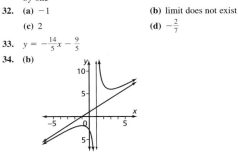

35. (a) $f(x)$, $r(x)$ (b) $h(x)$ (c) $h(x)$
  $f(x)$: vert. asymp.: $x = 7$, $x = -2$; $x \to -2^-$, $f(x) \to -\infty$;
  $x \to -2^+$, $f(x) \to \infty$; $x \to 7^-$, $f(x) \to \infty$; $x \to 7^+$, $f(x) \to -\infty$;
  hor. asymp.: $y = 0$
  $g(x)$: vert. asymp.: $x = 3$; $x \to 3^-$, $g(x) \to -\infty$; $x \to 3^+$,
  $g(x) \to -\infty$; $h(x)$: oblique asymp.: $y = x$
  $r(x)$: vert. asymp.: $x = -4$, $x = 4$; $x \to -4^-$, $r(x) \to \infty$; $x \to -4^+$,
  $r(x) \to -\infty$; $x \to 4^-$, $rf(x) \to -\infty$; $x \to 4^+$, $rf(x) \to \infty$; $r(x)$ has a
  hor. asymp. at $x = 1$
36. $c'(t) = \dfrac{7(1 - 2t^2)}{(2t^2 + 1)^2}$; $c''(t) = \dfrac{28(2t^3 - 3)}{(2t^2 + 1)^3}$; $c'(t)$: rate of change of
  concentration of drug in bloodstream t h after taken orally; $c''(t)$: how
  rate of change of concentration of drug in bloodstream is changing
37. Explanations will vary.

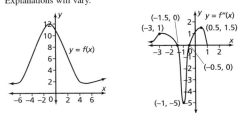

38. $A = -35$: $f(x) = \begin{cases} \dfrac{x^2 + 2x - 35}{x^2 - 4x - 5}, x \neq 5 \\ 2, x = 5 \end{cases}$;

  $A = 1$: $f(x) = \begin{cases} \dfrac{x^2 + 2x + 1}{x^2 - 4x - 5}, x \neq -1 \\ 0, x = -1 \end{cases}$
39. 1.39 g/L/min, 1.80 g/L/min; assume tank has infinite capacity
40. 0.529 m × 0.715 m × 1.323 m
41. no; Examples will vary.
42. yes; $a = 1$, $b = 8$, $c = 2\sqrt{2}$ or 2.8

Chapter 5 Review Test, page 426

1. (a) p has oblique asymp.:   (b)
  $y = 0.75x$; q has hor.
  asymp.: $y = 0$, and
  vert. asymp., $x = -1$
  and $x = 3$ r has a
  hor. asymp., $y = 1$, and
  vert. asymp., $x = \pm 1$; s has
  vert. asymp. at $x = 2$

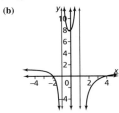

2. (a) 2   (b) does not exist, vertical asymptote at $x = 4$
  (c) $\dfrac{5}{2}$ (d) $-\dfrac{2}{5}$

3. **(a)** none   **(b)** discontinuous at $x = 7$, vertical asymptote

4. **(a)** increasing, $P'(t) \geq 0$ **(b)** 969 people per year
   (c) no; $P(t) = 50$ has negative solution

5. $y = x;\ y = -\frac{5}{27}x + \frac{32}{27}$

6. **(a)** $x = \frac{1}{2}$: vert. asymp.
   (b) $x = -1$: not defined; $x = 1$: vert. asymp.

7. radius 1.5 m, height 0.707 m

8. $D = \{x\,|\, x \neq 0, x \in \mathbf{R}\}$; x-int.: -2;
y-int.: 8; vert. asymp.: $x = 0$;
$x \to 0^-, f(x) \to -\infty;\ x \to 0^+,$
$f(x) \to \infty$; hor. asymp.: none;
increasing: $x > 1.59$;
decreasing: $x < 0$,
$0 < x < 1.59$, local min.: $(1.59,$
$7.56)$; concave up: $x < -2, x > 0$;
concave down: $-2 < x < 0$;
inflection point: $(-2, 0)$

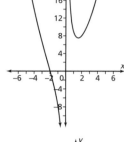

9. if $f'(x) > 0$, then $f(x)$ is increasing;
if $f'(x) < 0$, then $f(x)$ is decreasing;
for a stationary point, $f'(x) = 0$;
changes from neg. to pos. are local min.
points; slope gives concavity

Cumulative Review 2, page 427

1. **(a)** $y' = 12x;\ x = 0$; increasing $x > 0$, decreasing $x < 0$
   (b) $y' = -10x + 20;\ x = 2$; increasing $x < 2$, decreasing $x > 2$
   (c) $y' = 12x + 16;\ x = -\frac{4}{3}$; increasing $x > -\frac{4}{3}$; decreasing $x < -\frac{4}{3}$
   (d) $y' = 6x^2 - 24;\ x = \pm 2$; increasing $x < -2, x > 2$;
decreasing $-2 < x < 2$
   (e) $y' = -8x^3 + 8x;\ x = 0, \pm 1$; increasing $x < -1, 0 < x < 1$;
decreasing $-1 < x < 0, x > 1$
   (f) $y' = 2x^3 + x^2 - 13x + 6;\ x = \frac{1}{2}, 2, -3$; increasing $-3 < x < \frac{1}{2}$,
$x > 2$; decreasing $x < -3, \frac{1}{2} < x < 2$

2. $y = -3x + 1$

3. **(a)** 21   **(b)** 18   **(c)** -16
   (d) -217 **(e)** -136 **(f)** 28 144

4. 12.6; rate of change of the height of the arrow with respect to time at
3 s; 2.8 m/s

5. 19.6 m/s; 19.6 m/s; 53.7 m/s

6. \$26 billion/year

7. 10 m; 13 m/s, 28 m/s; never; advancing: $t \geq 0$; retreating: never; 218.3

8. decelerating; velocity is pos. and acceleration is neg.

9. 17.54 cm

10. \$40, yes; 100 empty seats

11. \$200 000

12. **(a)** $f'(x) = \frac{2}{(1-x)^2}$ **(b)** $f'(x) = \frac{4}{(x+3)^2}$ **(c)** $f'(x) = \frac{2x^2 + 1}{3x^2}$

13. $D = \{t\,|\, t \neq -2, t \in \mathbf{R}\,\}$;
int.: $(-254.8, 0), (0, 21\,150)$;
vert. asymp.: $t = -2$;
hor. asymp.: $V(t) = 166$;
worth \$166 in the long run

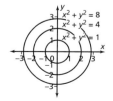

14. **(a)** $m(x) = \frac{1}{3x}, y = 0$ **(b)** $m(x) = 3, y = 3$

15. Answers will vary. Example: $f(x) = \begin{cases} \dfrac{x^2 - 3x - 4}{x - 4}, & x > -1 \\ x - 4, & x \leq -1 \end{cases}$

16. $f(x) = \begin{cases} \dfrac{1}{x}, & \text{if } x < 1 \\ x, & \text{if } x \geq 1 \end{cases}$: left- and right-sided limits of derivative are not same;

$f(x) = \begin{cases} \dfrac{1}{x}, & \text{if } x < 1 \\ 2 - x, & \text{if } x \geq 1 \end{cases}$: left- and right-sided limits of derivative are same

17. 64 chairs/week; 50 chairs/week

18. $x \doteq 2.4495$; $R(x)$ has point of inflection here.

Chapter 6

Getting Ready, page 432

1. **(a)** $m = 2.25$ **(b)** $m = 3$ **(c)** $m = 2$
   Line (b); magnitude of slope is greatest

2. **(a)** $f^{-1}(x) = \{(-9, 0), (-7, 2), (3, 1), (4, -1), (5, -2)\}$;
D of f: $x \in \{-2, -1, 0, 1, 2\}$; R of f: $y \in \{-9, -7, 3, 4, 5\}$;
D of f^{-1}: $x \in \{-9, -7, 3, 4, 5\}$; R of f^{-1}: $y \in \{-2, -1, 0, 1, 2\}$;
D of f = R of f^{-1}; R of f = D of f^{-1}
   (b)

x	10	5	2	1	2
$g^{-1}(x)$	-3	-2	-1	0	1

   D of f: $x \in \{-3, -2, -1, 0, 1\}$; R of f: $y \in \{1, 2, 5, 10\}$;
D of f^{-1}: $x \in \{1, 2, 5, 10\}$; R of f^{-1}: $y \in \{-3, -2, -1, 0, 1\}$;
D of f = R of f^{-1}; R of f = D of f^{-1}
   (c) D of f: $x \in \{1, 3, 4, 7\}$; R of f: $y \in \{0, 2, 5\}$;
D of f^{-1}: $x \in \{0, 2, 5\}$; R of f^{-1}: $y \in \{1, 3, 4, 7\}$;
D of f = R of f^{-1}; R of f = D of f^{-1}

3. **(a)** $D = x \in \mathbf{R}$; $R = y \in \mathbf{R}$ **(b)** $D = x \in \mathbf{R}$; $R = \{y\,|\, y \geq 2, y \in \mathbf{R}\}$
   (c) $D = \{x\,|\, x \geq 0, x \in \mathbf{R}\}$; $R = \{y\,|\, y \geq 0, y \in \mathbf{R}\}$
   (d) $D = x \in \mathbf{R}$; $R = \{y\,|\, y \geq -68.918, y \in \mathbf{R}\}$
   (e) $D = s \in \mathbf{R}$; $R = \{y\,|\, y \geq 0.147, y \in \mathbf{R}\}$
   (f) $D = \{x\,|\, x \neq 0.906, x \in \mathbf{R}\}$; $R = y \in \mathbf{R}$
   (g) $D = \{t\,|\, t \neq 1, t \in \mathbf{R}\}$; $R = \{y\,|\, y \geq -0.406, y \in \mathbf{R}\}$
   (h) $D = \{u\,|\, u \geq 2 \text{ or } u < -6, u \in \mathbf{R}\}$; $R = \{y\,|\, y \geq 0, y \neq 1, y \in \mathbf{R}\}$
   (i) $D = a \in \mathbf{R}$; $R = \{y\,|\, y \geq 0, y \in \mathbf{R}\}$

4. **(a)** $f^{-1}(x) = \frac{x + 3}{2}$ **(b)** $g^{-1}(x) = \frac{3 \pm \sqrt{41 - 16x}}{8}$
   (c) $h^{-1}(x) = \frac{x^2 - 9}{9}, x \geq 0$ **(d)** $k^{-1}(x) = 4x - 1$
   (e) $q^{-1}(x) = (-1 - x)^{\frac{1}{3}}$ **(f)** $r^{-1}(x) = \pm\sqrt{x^2 + 16}, x \geq 0$

5. **(a)** they all have the same   **(b)** they all have the same
   centre, $(0, 0)$, but with   centre, $(0, 0)$, but with
   radii 2, $2\sqrt{2}$, and   different minor and
   1 respectively   major axes

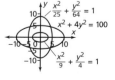

6. **(a)** $f'(x) = 0$ **(b)** $f^{-1}(x) = \frac{1}{2\sqrt{x}}$
   (c) $f'(x) = 4$ **(d)** $f'(x) = 23x^{22}$

(e) $f'(x) = 4x$ **(f)** $f'(x) = -12x^3 - 3$

(g) $f'(x) = \frac{4x^{\frac{1}{3}}}{3}$ **(h)** $f'(x) = 35x^6 + 18x^5 - 8x^3 + 5$

(i) $f'(x) = \frac{x-1}{3}$ **(j)** $f'(x) = 2x + \frac{2}{x^2}$

(k) $f'(x) = 9x^2 - 2x + 9$ **(l)** $f'(x) = \frac{-x^2 - 2x + 2}{(x^2 + 2)^2}$

(m) $f'(x) = (\sqrt{x} + 2)(6x^5 - 12x^2 + 7) + \left(\frac{1}{2\sqrt{x}}\right)(x^6 - 4x^3 + 7x - 3)$

(n) $f'(x) = (\sqrt[3]{x} + 3)\left(\frac{-1}{x^2}\right) + \left(\frac{1}{3\sqrt[3]{x^2}}\right)\left(\frac{1}{x} - 6\right)$

(o) $f'(x) = \frac{0.3x^2}{(10 - 0.1x^3)^2}$

7. (a) increasing: $x < 0,\ 0 < x < 12$; decreasing: $x > 12$

(b) critical points: $(0, -5)$, $(12, 6907)$; points of inflection: $(0, -5)$, $(8, 4091)$

(c) concave up: $0 < x < 8$;   **(d)**
concave down: $x < 0,\ x > 8$

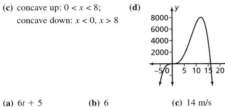

8. (a) $6t + 5$ **(b)** 6   **(c)** 14 m/s

9. (a) $y = -1056x + 1841$ **(b)** $y = -3x + 10$

(c) $y = \frac{17}{4}a - 2$ **(d)** $y = \frac{243}{3721}x - \frac{5022}{3721}$

6.1 Exercises, page 439

1. (a) i. 3   **ii.** 7   **iii.** 11   **iv.** 15   **v.** does not exist   **vi.** 3   **vii.** 7
viii. does not exist

(b) $\{-0.5, 0, 0.5, 1\}$ **(c)**

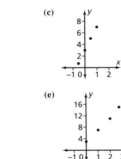

(d) $\{0, 1, 2, 3\}$ **(e)**

2. (a) i. $14 - 6x$ **ii.** 14   **iii.** 20   **iv.** 2   **v.** $7 - 6x$ **vi.** 7   **vii.** 13   **viii.** -5

(b) impossible, no solution

3. (a) $\{(1, 3), (2, 1)\}$ **(b)** $\{(1, 7), (2, 5), (3, 2)\}$

(c) $\{(1, 1), (2, 2), (3, 3), (4, 4)\}$ **(d)** $\{(1, 1), (3, 3), (4, 4)\}$

4. (a) i. $(x + 2)^2$ **ii.** $x^2 + 2$ **(b)** $x = -\frac{1}{2}$

6. (a) $5 - 3\sqrt{5}$ **(b)** $\sqrt{x^2 - 3x}$ **(c)** $\{x \mid x \ge 3 \text{ or } x \le 0, x \in \mathbf{R}\}$

7. (a) Answers can vary. Example: $g(x) = x^2 + 6, f(x) = \sqrt{x}$

(b) Answers can vary. Example: $g(x) = 5x - 8, f(x) = x^6$

(c) Answers can vary. Example: $g(x) = 6x + 7, f(x) = 2^x$

(d) Answers can vary. Example: $g(x) = x^3 - 7x + 2, f(x) = \frac{1}{x}$

(e) Answers can vary. Example: $g(x) = 10x + 5, f(x) = \sin^2 x$

(f) Answers can vary. Example: $g(x) = (x + 4)^2, f(x) = \sqrt[3]{x}$

8.

Point on f	Point on g	Point on $f \circ g$
$(4, 1)$	$(3, 4)$	$(3, 1)$
$(1, 5)$	$(2, 1)$	$(2, 5)$
$(0, -1)$	$(1, 0)$	$(1, -1)$
$(-1, 5)$	$(0, -1)$	$(0, 5)$
$(3, 3)$	$(-1, 3)$	$(-1, 3)$

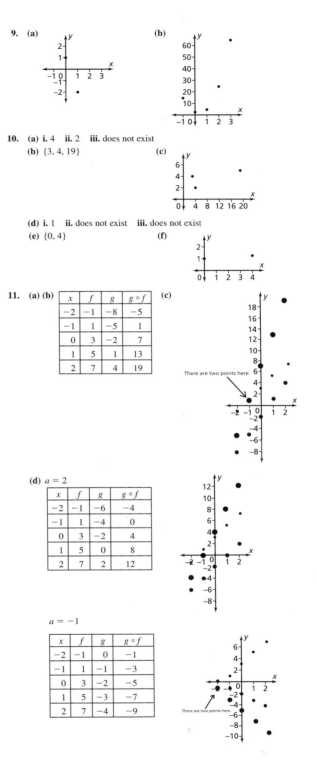

9. (a)   **(b)**

10. (a) i. 4   **ii.** 2   **iii.** does not exist

(b) $\{3, 4, 19\}$ **(c)**

(d) i. 1   **ii.** does not exist   **iii.** does not exist

(e) $\{0, 4\}$ **(f)**

11. (a) (b)   **(c)**

x	f	g	$g \circ f$
-2	-1	-8	-5
-1	1	-5	1
0	3	-2	7
1	5	1	13
2	7	4	19

(d) $a = 2$

x	f	g	$g \circ f$
-2	-1	-6	-4
-1	1	-4	0
0	3	-2	4
1	5	0	8
2	7	2	12

$a = -1$

x	f	g	$g \circ f$
-2	-1	0	-1
-1	1	-1	-3
0	3	-2	-5
1	5	-3	-7
2	7	-4	-9

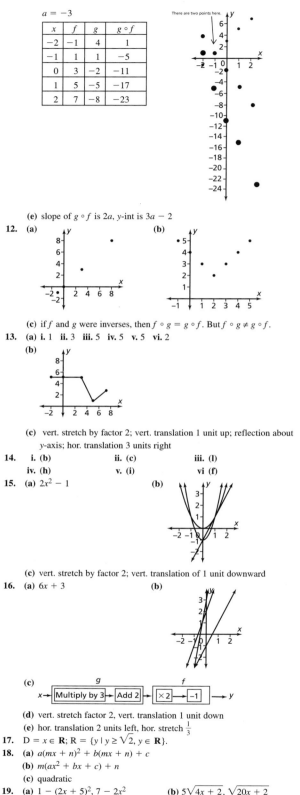

$a = -3$

x	f	g	$g \circ f$
-2	-1	4	1
-1	1	1	-5
0	3	-2	-11
1	5	-5	-17
2	7	-8	-23

(e) slope of $g \circ f$ is $2a$, y-int is $3a - 2$

12. (a) (b)

(c) if f and g were inverses, then $f \circ g = g \circ f$. But $f \circ g \neq g \circ f$.

13. (a) i. 1 ii. 3 iii. 5 iv. 5 v. 5 vi. 2
(b)

(c) vert. stretch by factor 2; vert. translation 1 unit up; reflection about y-axis; hor. translation 3 units right

14. i. (b) ii. (c) iii. (l)
iv. (h) v. (i) vi (f)

15. (a) $2x^2 - 1$ (b)

(c) vert. stretch by factor 2; vert. translation of 1 unit downward

16. (a) $6x + 3$ (b)

(c) $x \rightarrow$ [Multiply by 3] $\rightarrow$ [Add 2] $\xrightarrow{g}$ [×2] $\rightarrow$ [−1] $\xrightarrow{f} y$

(d) vert. stretch factor 2, vert. translation 1 unit down
(e) hor. translation 2 units left, hor. stretch $\frac{1}{3}$

17. $D = x \in \mathbf{R}$; $R = \{y \mid y \geq \sqrt{2}, y \in \mathbf{R}\}$.

18. (a) $a(mx + n)^2 + b(mx + n) + c$
(b) $m(ax^2 + bx + c) + n$
(c) quadratic

19. (a) $1 - (2x + 5)^2$, $7 - 2x^2$ (b) $5\sqrt{4x + 2}$, $\sqrt{20x + 2}$

(c) $\sqrt{(x^2 + 2)^2 - 2}$, x^2 (d) $\frac{1 + x^2}{x^2}$, $\frac{1}{x^2 + 1}$

(e) x, x (f) $\sin(x^2 + 2)$, $\sin^2 x + 2$

(g) $2x + 3x^{\frac{1}{2}} - 2$, $(2x^2 + 3x - 2)^{\frac{1}{2}}$

(h) $\frac{2x^2 - 1}{5x^2}$, $\left(\frac{2x - 1}{5x}\right)^2$

20. (a) $x - 6$ (b) $x - 9$ (c) $x - 12$ (d) $x - 3n$

21. $g(x) = x + 2$ or $g(x) = 1 - x$

23. (a)

(b) first differences are not constant
(c) $h(t) = -4.286t^2 - 0.371t + 3.017$
(d) yes; $R^2 \doteq 0.999$
(f) not really; -0.895; there
is a fairly strong
negative correlation, but
graph suggests a curve

(h) yes; -0.999; since data
has almost perfect nega-
tive correlation, points
fit straight line very well

(i) $h(t) = -4.286(t + 0.045)^2 + 3.026$ ($g(t) = t + 0.043$,
$f(t) = -4.286t^2 + 3.026$)

24. (a) $n(100) = 65$; $n(180) = 9$ (b) $c(8) = 80.2$; $c(48) = 85$
(c) \$82.05 (d) \$37.95 (e) \$1138.50
(f) $c[n(p)] = 0.002\left[\frac{5(360 - p)}{p - 80} + 2\right]^2 + 80$
(g) total profit $= n(p)[p - c(n(p))]$
(h)

6.2 Exercises, page 453

1. (a) $12(3x + 5)^3$ (b) $-3(2 - x)^2$
2. (a) $\frac{24}{(5 + 3x)^5}$ (b) $\frac{18}{(1 - 2x)^4}$
3. (a) $\frac{3}{2\sqrt{3x + 15}}$ (b) 3 if $x > \frac{1}{3}$, -3 if $x < \frac{1}{3}$
4. (a) $-\frac{8x - 1}{2(4x^2 - x)^{\frac{3}{2}}}$ (b) $-\frac{20}{3(2x - 5)^{\frac{5}{3}}}$

5. $(3u^2 + 6)(8x^3 + 6x)$

6. (a) $192(x - 2)^2$ (b) $(40x + 10)(4x^2 + 2x - 3)^4$

(c) $-\dfrac{6}{(12 - 6x)^{\frac{4}{5}}}$ (d) $\dfrac{3x^2 - 8x + 6}{2\sqrt{x^3 - 4x^2 + 6x}}$

(e) $\dfrac{2x - 2}{3(x^2 - 2x)^{\frac{2}{3}}}$ (f) $3x\sqrt{x^2 - 1}$

(g) $\dfrac{-4(4x + 7)}{(2x^2 + 7x - 6)^5}$ (h) $\dfrac{2}{(5 - x)^3}$

(i) $\dfrac{60(2 + x^2)}{(6x + x^3)^6}$ (j) $\dfrac{-21x^2 + 2x}{2(7x^3 - x^2)^{\frac{3}{2}}}$

(k) $\dfrac{-(24x^3 - 2)}{(6x^4 - 2x)^{\frac{6}{5}}}$ (l) $\dfrac{3(2 + \sqrt{x})^2}{2\sqrt{x}}$

7. -6

8. $f'(0)$ undefined

9. $-4; 35$

10. $-\dfrac{2}{x^2}\left(\dfrac{1}{x} - 3\right)$

11. -32

12. $x < -1$

13. $\dfrac{1}{30}$

14. (a) $v(t) = \frac{2}{3}(t^2 + t)^{-\frac{1}{3}}(2t + 1); a(t) = \frac{2}{9}(t^2 + t)^{-\frac{4}{3}}(2t^2 + 2t - 1)$

(b) 1.931 m/s   (c) 2.360 m/s

(d) undefined   (e) 0.141 m/s²

15. (a) -0.5 m/s   (b) 0 m/s

(c)

16. $f'(x) = \dfrac{2}{(\sqrt{x^2 + 1})^3}, f''(x) = \dfrac{-6x}{(\sqrt{x^2 + 1})^5}$

17. As time goes by, the object travels towards, but never reaches, a point $\frac{5}{2}$ units to the right of the origin. Initially, its velocity is 5, but gradually decreases toward zero while remaining positive over time. Its acceleration also gradually decreases toward zero.

18. $(2, 0), (-2, 0), \left(\dfrac{2}{\sqrt{5}}, \dfrac{4096}{125}\right), \left(-\dfrac{2}{\sqrt{5}}, \dfrac{4096}{125}\right)$

19. $2x(x^2 - 1)(3x^2 + 7)$

20.

21. (a) $x \in \mathbf{R}$ (b) $\left\{x \mid x \neq \frac{3}{2}, x \in \mathbf{R}\right\}$

22. $-\sqrt{3} < x < 0$ and $x > \sqrt{3}$

23.

24. b^{10}

25. $a = 2.3^{-\frac{5}{3}}, b = 3^{-\frac{2}{3}}, c = 9$

6.3 Exercises, page 462

1. (a) $2s$ (b) $-\dfrac{2}{u^2}$ (c) -1 (d) $\dfrac{8}{9}$

2.

3. (a) $g(x) = f(h(x))$, where $h(x) = x^2 - 3x$ (b) $-\dfrac{2x - 3}{(x^2 - 3x)^2}$

4. (a) $f(x) = u + 5u^{-1}$, where $u = 2x - 3$; $g(x) = \sqrt{u} + 5u$, where $u = 2x - 3$

(b) $2[1 - 5(2x - 3)^{-2}]$

5. (a) $g(x) = h(f(x))$, where $f(x) = 2x - 3, h(x) = \sqrt{x} + 5x$

(b) $\dfrac{1}{\sqrt{2x - 3}} + 10$

6. (a) $6(2x - 5)^2(3x^2 + 4)^4(13x^2 - 25x + 4)$

(b) $\dfrac{8x(4x^2 + 2x - 3)^4}{52x^2 + 16x - 9}$

(c) $2(5 + x)(4 - 7x^3)^5(-70x^3 - 315x^2 + 4)$

(d) $\dfrac{6(-9x + 7)}{(3x + 5)^5}$ (e) $\dfrac{2(2x - 5)^2(4x^2 + 48x + 5)}{(x + 8)^3}$

(f) $\dfrac{-3x^3(7x - 16)}{4(x - 2)^{\frac{3}{2}}}$ (g) $\dfrac{8(2x + 5)^3(x + 3)(x + 2)}{(6 - x^2)^5}$

(h) $-9(4x + x^2)^{-10}(4 + 2x)$

(i) $2(3x + 2)^{-\frac{1}{2}}(2x - x^3)^{-3}[-33x^3 - 24x^2 + 18x + 16]$

(j) $\dfrac{-2x}{(x^2 + 1)^{\frac{1}{2}}(x^2 - 1)^{\frac{3}{2}}}$

(k) $5[2x + (3x^2 - 5x)^3]^4[2 + 3(3x^2 - 5x)^2(6x - 5)]$

(l) $\dfrac{2 + \frac{3}{2}\sqrt{x}}{2\sqrt{2x + x^{\frac{3}{2}}}}$

7. (a) $\dfrac{1}{2\sqrt{x}(\sqrt{x} + 1)^2}$ (b) $\dfrac{5}{2(2x + 1)^{\frac{1}{2}}(x + 3)^{\frac{3}{2}}}$

8. $3\left\{1 - \dfrac{6x + 11}{[x - 3(x + 2)^2]^2}\right\}$

9. $-2 - 5[t^{-2} - (3t + 5)^4]^4[-2t^{-3} - 12(3t + 5)^3]$

11. $-\dfrac{4}{3}$

12. $-2\{1 - [2x - 5(x - 2)^3]^{-2}[2 - 15(x - 2)^2]\}$

13. $\dfrac{3(3x - 1)}{\sqrt{(3x - 1)^2 - 1}}$

14. $y = 1472x - 2816$

15. $x < -1$ and $x > 1$

16. $(2, 0), \left(\dfrac{13}{2}, \dfrac{1}{6\sqrt{2}}\right)$

17. $(4, 4)$

18. $16; -280$

19. 0

21. (a) $g(x) = f \circ f \circ f \circ f(x)$

(b) $g'(x) = (f'(f(f(f(x)))))(f'(f(f(x))))(f'(f(x)))(f'(x)) =$
$[1 + (1 + (1 + (1 + x)^{-1})^{-1})^{-1}]^{-2}$
$[1 + (1 + (1 + x)^{-1})^{-1}]^{-2}[1 + (1 + x)^{-1}]^{-2}[1 + x]^{-2}$

22. greatest: 0.309 m and 29.691 m; weakest: 15 m

23. $a = 2$

6.4 Exercises, page 471

1. $\left(-\frac{48}{37}, \frac{8}{37}\right)$

2. $\left[\left(\frac{4}{3}\right)^{\frac{1}{3}}, \left(\frac{4}{3}\right)^{\frac{2}{3}}\right]$

3. $(-1, 0)$

4. 0.707 km

5. 0.171 km

6. **(a)** $(1, 1)$ **(b)** $(0, 0)$

7. 1.7381 km

8. 1.02 h; 192.06 km

9. 2:23.25

10. Example: A north-south highway intersects an east-west highway at a point P. A vehicle crosses P at 12 a.m., travelling west at a constant speed of 100 km/h. At the same instant, another vehicle is 10 km north of P, travelling south at 80 km/h. Find the time when the two vehicles are closest to each other and the distance between them at that time.

11. 1.15 km $\left(\text{or } \frac{2}{\sqrt{3}} \text{ km}\right)$ down the coast

12. He should drive off road directly to the point on the road 20 km west of Gulch City, then drive east the rest of the way.

13. 115.5 km down the coast

14. lay 92.4 m of cable below water and 153.8 m along the shoreline

15. lay 807.9 m of pipe along the road and 560 m of pipe elsewhere

16. $4\sqrt{2} \times 3\sqrt{2}$

17. no; take the derivative of an equation representing what needs to be found with respect to the variable one needs to optimize and solve for that variable by setting the derivative equal to 0

18. 5.67 km down the shoreline

20. 5.12 km from Ancaster; 7.68 km from Dundas

6.5 Exercises, page 478

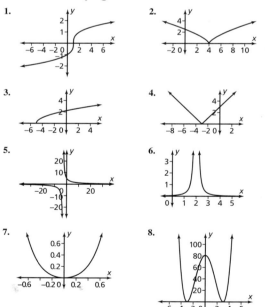

6.6 Exercises, page 483

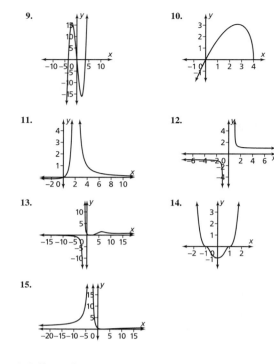

1. **(a)** $3x^2$ **(b)** $20x^3$ **(c)** $\frac{dy}{dx}$ **(d)** $3y^2\frac{dy}{dx}$ **(e)** $30y^5\frac{dy}{dx}$

2. **(a)** $y + x\frac{dy}{dx}$ **(b)** $8x^3y + 2x^4\frac{dy}{dx}$
   (c) $2xy^2 + 2x^2y\frac{dy}{dx}$ **(d)** $10xy^3 + 15x^2y^2\frac{dy}{dx}$
   (e) $-8x^3y^6 - 12x^4y^5\frac{dy}{dx}$

3. $-\frac{7}{2}$

5. **(a)** $\frac{-x}{y}$ **(b)** $\frac{x}{y}$ **(c)** $-\frac{x^2}{y^2}$ **(d)** $-\sqrt{\frac{y}{x}}$
   (e) $-\left[\frac{2x-y}{2y-x}\right]$ **(f)** $-\left[\frac{y^2+2xy}{x^2+2xy}\right]$
   (g) $\frac{1-2xy^3}{1+3x^2y^2}$ **(h)** $\frac{8xy-3(x^2+y^2)}{6xy-4x^2}$

6. **(a)** 4 **(b)** $-\frac{1}{2}$ **(c)** $-\frac{8}{3}$
   (d) $-\frac{5}{7}$ **(e)** $-\frac{27}{11}$ **(f)** 0

7. $y = -4x + 1.5$

8. $\frac{3}{4}$

9. $-\frac{1}{8}$

11. 10:01:12 a.m.

13. -3.30 units/s

14. $\frac{dy}{dx} = \pm\frac{x}{\sqrt{16-x^2}}$ or $\frac{dy}{dx} = \frac{-x}{y}$; preferred method will vary

15. $\frac{27}{20}$

16. $4\sqrt{x+y} - 1$

17. $\frac{4}{(x+y)^2} - 1$

18. **(a)** $0, \frac{1}{3}$ **(b)**

662 ANSWERS

19. $\frac{3-x}{2y+6}$

20. (a) $\frac{dP}{dV} = -\frac{k}{V^2}$

   (b) if volume is large, rate of change of pressure is closer to 0; but as volume increases, pressure decreases.

21. $-\frac{x+y}{x}$

23. $\sqrt{2}a \times \sqrt{2}b$

6.7 Exercises, page 492

1. (a) $\frac{2}{\sqrt{3}}$ (b) $4\sqrt{30}$

2. (a) 3   (b) -5

3. (a) $-\frac{4}{5}$ (b) $\frac{25}{2}$

4. (a) does not exist   (b) does not exist

5. y at $x = 2$ and $\frac{dx}{dt}$ at $x = 2$

6. $-\frac{3}{2}$

7. (a) $-\frac{3x}{2y}$ (b) a value of x and the value of y at that value of x

8. 10 units/s [up]

9. -10

10. (a) $\frac{dA}{dt} = 2\pi r\left(\frac{dr}{dt}\right)$ (b) $\frac{dV}{dt} = 4\pi r^2\left(\frac{dr}{dt}\right)$

   (c) $\frac{dA}{dt} = 8\pi r\left(\frac{dr}{dt}\right)$ (d) $x\left(\frac{dx}{dt}\right) + y\left(\frac{dy}{dt}\right) = r\left(\frac{dr}{dt}\right)$

   (e) $\frac{dV}{dt} = \pi\left[r^2\left(\frac{dh}{dt}\right) + 2rh\left(\frac{dr}{dt}\right)\right]$

   (f) $\frac{dA}{dt} = 2\pi\left[(2r + h)\left(\frac{dr}{dt}\right) + r\left(\frac{dh}{dt}\right)\right]$

11. 10π m²/s

12. 800π cm³/s

13. 2π cm³/s

14. 0.0955 cm/s

15. At first, balloon will accelerate very slowly; as it shrinks, air resistance will decrease and balloon will accelerate more quickly.

16. 2529.65 m²/h

17. (a)   (b)

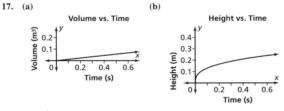

   (c) $\frac{1}{40\pi h^2}$

   (d) As height increases with respect to time, the slope of the graph of height vs. time decreases and approaches 0.

   Hence, $\lim\limits_{t \to \infty} \frac{dh}{dt} = \lim\limits_{h \to \infty} \frac{1}{40\pi h^2} = 0$.

   (e) 0.000 605 m/s

18. (a) $-\left(\frac{0.4}{2h+1}\right)$ m²/s, where $h =$ depth of water   (b) $\doteq 0.018$ m/s

19. (a) $-3.2l$ (b) $3.2l(2l - w)$

   (c) -1024 cm³/s   (d) $25.6(t - 10)(3t - 7)$

   (e)

20. (a) P moves along the line $x + 2y = 10$

   (b) 5 units/s   (c) -2.5 units/s   (d) $(8.05, 0.975)$

   (e) 0.0559 units   (f) 5.59 units/s

   (g) determine the speed using the x-speed, y-speed, and the Pythagorean theorem

21. (a) $y = -2\,785.714x^2 + 11\,133\,185.71x - 1.112\,346 \times 10^{10}$

   (b) $y = 0.001\,48x + 26.781$

   (c) $-4.123x^2 + 16\,477.115x + 16\,462\,694.02$

   (d) $-8.246x + 16\,477.115$

   (e) Answers will vary.

22. (a) 67 glasses, to nearest glass

   (b) yes, for all t; $c(t)$ rises to its max. in the summer, when lemonade is in higher demand, and it decreases to its min. in the winter, when lemonade is in less demand

23. 0.433 m/s

24. 3.073 m/s

25. (a) $\frac{-15\,000 + 13\,600t}{\sqrt{(-250 + 60t)^2 + (100t)^2}}$ km/h

   (b) 214.4 km

26. 16.464 km along the shoreline from his destination

27. 0.986 m/s

28. 2.652 m from the edge of the pool

29. Identify all quantities and draw a labelled sketch; Write an equation with the variables whose rates of change are given or to be determined; Differentiate with respect to time using the chain rule; substitute and solve.

30. $\frac{1}{3\pi}$ cm/s

31. 60 cm

Chapter 6 Review, page 497

13. Answers will vary. Example: $f(x) = x + 2$, $g(x) = x - 1$, $f \circ g(x) = x + 1$ with domain $\{1, 3, 4\}$

14. (a) x or $-x + 2$ (b) x

   (c) f and g are inverses of each other

15. $D = \{x \neq -5, x \neq 2, x \in \mathbf{R}\}$

16. (a) $f'(x) = 5(4x^2 + 3x)^4(8x + 3)$

   (b) $g'(x) = \frac{20x - 5}{2\sqrt{10x^2 - 5x}}$ (c) $h'(x) = \frac{21(12x^2 - 12x)}{(4x^3 - 6x^2)^4}$

   (d) $y' = -\frac{2}{3(x + 5)^{\frac{5}{3}}}$

17. 2

18. increasing: $x < 0$; decreasing: $x > 0$

19. (a) $f'(x) = (6x^2 - 5x)^4(2x - 1)^3(168x^2 - 150x + 25)$

   (b) $g'(x) = \frac{9x^3(7x - 2)}{\sqrt{3x^3 - x^2}}$

   (c) $h'(x) = \frac{(2x + 5)(-56x^3 - 132x^2 + 180x)}{(4x^3 - 6x^2)^4}$

   (d) $y' = \frac{5(3x^2 - 5)^4(3x^2 - 6x + 5)}{(x - 1)^6}$

20. $\frac{dP}{dt} = 0.5[2t + 5(t^2 - 5t)^3]^{-0.5}[2 + 15(t^2 - 5t)^2(2t - 5)]$

21. min.: $(0.655, -11.131)$; max.: $(-0.655, 11.131)$

22. $(1, 1)$

23. 9 min 41 s, 23.681 km

24. 5.24 m from the closest point of the conduit to the house (toward the direction of the main cable line)

25. $f'(x) = 3(x - 1)^2$,

   $f''(x) = 6(x - 1)$

26. $f'(x) = \dfrac{64 - 16x}{(x + 4)^3}$,

$f''(x) = \dfrac{32x - 256}{(x + 4)^4}$

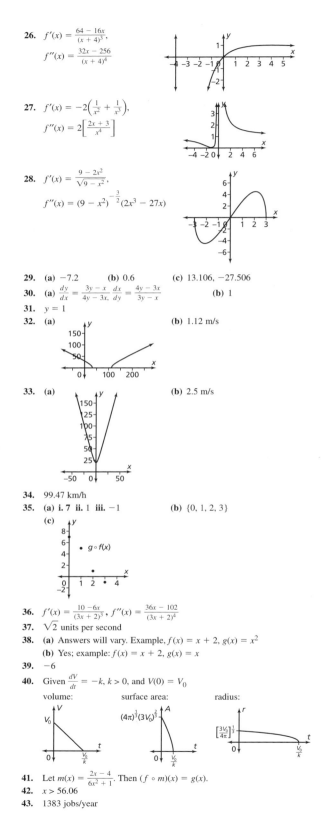

27. $f'(x) = -2\left(\dfrac{1}{x^2} + \dfrac{1}{x^3}\right)$,

$f''(x) = 2\left[\dfrac{2x + 3}{x^4}\right]$

28. $f'(x) = \dfrac{9 - 2x^2}{\sqrt{9 - x^2}}$,

$f''(x) = (9 - x^2)^{-\frac{3}{2}}(2x^3 - 27x)$

29. (a) -7.2 (b) 0.6 (c) $13.106, -27.506$

30. (a) $\dfrac{dy}{dx} = \dfrac{3y - x}{4y - 3x}, \dfrac{dx}{dy} = \dfrac{4y - 3x}{3y - x}$ (b) 1

31. $y = 1$

32. (a)   (b) 1.12 m/s

33. (a)   (b) 2.5 m/s

34. 99.47 km/h

35. (a) i. 7 ii. 1 iii. -1 (b) $\{0, 1, 2, 3\}$

(c)

36. $f'(x) = \dfrac{10 - 6x}{(3x + 2)^3}$, $f''(x) = \dfrac{36x - 102}{(3x + 2)^4}$

37. $\sqrt{2}$ units per second

38. (a) Answers will vary. Example, $f(x) = x + 2, g(x) = x^2$

(b) Yes; example: $f(x) = x + 2, g(x) = x$

39. -6

40. Given $\dfrac{dV}{dt} = -k, k > 0$, and $V(0) = V_0$

volume: surface area: radius:

41. Let $m(x) = \dfrac{2x - 4}{6x^2 + 1}$. Then $(f \circ m)(x) = g(x)$.

42. $x > 56.06$

43. 1383 jobs/year

44. 0

45. (a)   (b) $x = -\dfrac{1}{3}$, 1, 2.6, 5, 6.6

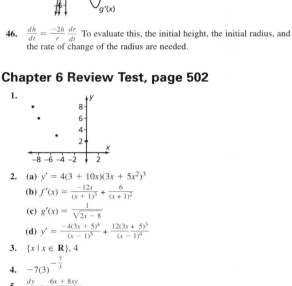

46. $\dfrac{dh}{dt} = \dfrac{-2h}{r}\dfrac{dr}{dt}$ To evaluate this, the initial height, the initial radius, and the rate of change of the radius are needed.

Chapter 6 Review Test, page 502

1.

2. (a) $y' = 4(3 + 10x)(3x + 5x^2)^3$

(b) $f'(x) = \dfrac{-12x}{(x + 1)^3} + \dfrac{6}{(x + 1)^2}$

(c) $g'(x) = \dfrac{1}{\sqrt{2x - 8}}$

(d) $y' = \dfrac{-4(3x + 5)^4}{(x - 1)^5} + \dfrac{12(3x + 5)^3}{(x - 1)^4}$

3. $\{x \mid x \in \mathbf{R}\}$, 4

4. $-7(3)^{-\frac{7}{3}}$

5. $\dfrac{dy}{dx} = \dfrac{6x + 8xy}{15y^2 - 4x^2}$

6. (a) $\dfrac{dy}{dt} = 3\sqrt{\dfrac{y}{x}}$

(b)

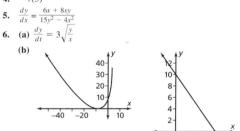

(c) graph of y versus t has the derivatives which is the graph $\dfrac{dy}{dt}$

7. 6.25×10^{-4} m/h

8. 0.0477 m/min; 0.2285 m/min

Chapter 7

Getting Ready, page 506

1. (a) $2^6 = 64$ (b) $5^0 = 1$ (c) $3^3 = 27$

(d) $a^y = x$ (e) $2^{-3} = \dfrac{1}{8}$ (f) $10^2 = 100$

2. (a) $\log_{10} 10\,000 = 4$ (b) $\log_3 \dfrac{1}{9} = -2$

(c) $\log_2 8 = 3$ (d) $\log_{10} 0.001 = -3$

(e) $\log_a y = x$ (f) $\log_{\sqrt{81}} 9 = \dfrac{1}{2}$

3. (a) 2 (b) 3 (c) $\dfrac{1}{2}$ (d) 0

(e) -1 (f) $\dfrac{3}{2}$ (g) 3 (h) 4

4. (a) $D = x \in \mathbf{R}$; $R = y > 0$ **(b)** $D = x \in \mathbf{R}$; $R = y < 0$

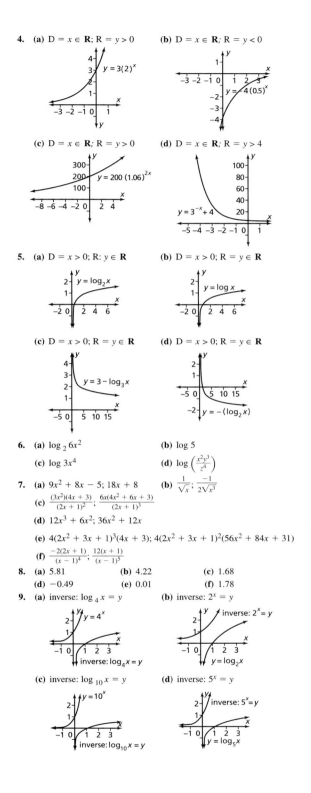

$y = 3(2)^x$

$y = -4(0.5)^x$

(c) $D = x \in \mathbf{R}$; $R = y > 0$ **(d)** $D = x \in \mathbf{R}$; $R = y > 4$

$y = 200\,(1.06)^{2x}$

$y = 3^{-x} + 4$

5. (a) $D = x > 0$; R: $y \in \mathbf{R}$ **(b)** $D = x > 0$; $R = y \in \mathbf{R}$

$y = \log_2 x$

$y = \log x$

(c) $D = x > 0$; $R = y \in \mathbf{R}$ **(d)** $D = x > 0$; $R = y \in \mathbf{R}$

$y = 3 - \log_3 x$

$y = -(\log_2 x)$

6. (a) $\log_2 6x^2$ **(b)** $\log 5$

(c) $\log 3x^4$ **(d)** $\log\left(\frac{x^2 y^3}{z^4}\right)$

7. (a) $9x^2 + 8x - 5$; $18x + 8$ **(b)** $\frac{1}{\sqrt{x}}$; $\frac{-1}{2\sqrt{x^3}}$

(c) $\frac{(3x^2)(4x + 3)}{(2x + 1)^2}$; $\frac{6x(4x^2 + 6x + 3)}{(2x + 1)^3}$

(d) $12x^3 + 6x^2$; $36x^2 + 12x$

(e) $4(2x^2 + 3x + 1)^3(4x + 3)$; $4(2x^2 + 3x + 1)^2(56x^2 + 84x + 31)$

(f) $\frac{-2(2x + 1)}{(x - 1)^4}$; $\frac{12(x + 1)}{(x - 1)^5}$

8. (a) 5.81   **(b)** 4.22   **(c)** 1.68

(d) -0.49 **(e)** 0.01   **(f)** 1.78

9. (a) inverse: $\log_4 x = y$ **(b)** inverse: $2^x = y$

$y = 4^x$ inverse: $\log_4 x = y$

inverse: $2^x = y$ $y = \log_2 x$

(c) inverse: $\log_{10} x = y$ **(d)** inverse: $5^x = y$

$y = 10^x$ inverse: $\log_{10} x = y$

inverse: $5^x = y$ $y = \log_5 x$

(e) inverse: $\log_{0.5} x = y$ **(f)** inverse: $10^x = y$

$y = (0.5)^x$

inverse: $\log_{0.5} x = y$

$y = 10^x$ $y = \log x$

10. (a) $x = 3.66$ **(b)** $x = 7$

(c) $x = 2.32$ **(d)** $x = 1.15$

(e) $x = 14\,348\,907$ **(f)** $x = 3$ or $x = 6$

(g) $x = 12$ or $x = -12$ **(h)** $x = 4.29$

11. 6.96 g

12. 2.82 years

13. middle of 2001

14. (a) $F'(x) = f'(x) \cdot g(x) + f(x) \cdot g'(x)$

(b) $F'(x) = \frac{f'(x) \cdot g(x) - f(x) \cdot g'(x)}{[g(x)]^2}$

(c) $F'(x) = f'(g(x)) \cdot g'(x)$

(d) $F'(x) = cf'(x)$

15. (a) i. $D = x \in \mathbf{R}$ **ii.** x-int.: 0, -1.5; y-int.: 0

iii. none **iv.** increasing: $x < -1$, $x > 0$;
decreasing: $-1 < x < 0$ **v.** local min.:
$(0, 0)$; local max.: $(-1, 1)$ **vi.** concave
down: $x < -0.5$; concave up: $x > -0.5$

(b) i. $D = x \neq -4$, $x \in \mathbf{R}$ **ii.** x-int.: 0; y-int.: 0

iii. $x = -4$ and $y = x - 4$
iv. increasing: $x < -8$, $x > 0$;
decreasing: $-8 < x < -4$, $-4 < x < 0$
v. local max.: $(-8, -16)$; local min.:
$(0, 0)$ **vi.** concave down: $x < -4$;
concave up: $x > -4$

$x = -4$

(c) i. $D = x \geq 2$ **ii.** x-int.: 2 **iii.** none
iv. increasing: $x \geq 2$ **v.** none
vi. concave down: $x \geq 2$

(d) i. $D = x \in \mathbf{R}$ **ii.** x-int.: 0; y-int.: 0

iii. $y = 0$ **iv.** increasing: $-1 < x < 1$;
decreasing: $x < -1$, $x > 1$
v. local min.: $(-1, -0.5)$; local max.:
$(1, 0.5)$ **vi.** concave down: $x < -\sqrt{3}$,
$0 < x < \sqrt{3}$; concave up:
$-\sqrt{3} < x < 0$, $x > \sqrt{3}$

7.1 Exercises, page 512

1. $332.01

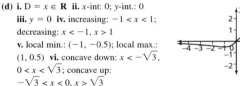

$y = e^{-x}$ $y = 2e^x + 1$

$y = e^x$

$y = 3 - e^x$

2. (a) reflection about x-axis.

(b) vertical stretch by 2 and vertical translation of 1 unit up.

(c) reflection about x-axis and vertical translation of 3 units up.

3. (a) $e^6 > \pi^4 + \pi^5$ **(b)** $e^\pi > \pi^e$

4. (a) $D = x \in \mathbf{R}; R = y > -1$ (b) $D = x \in \mathbf{R}; R = y > 0$

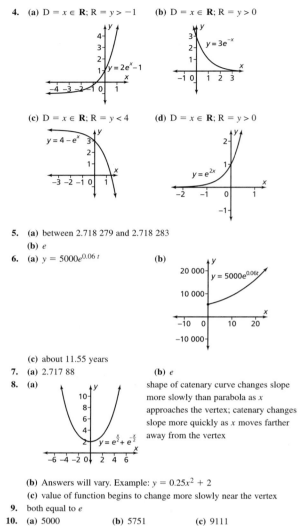

(c) $D = x \in \mathbf{R}; R = y < 4$ (d) $D = x \in \mathbf{R}; R = y > 0$

5. (a) between 2.718 279 and 2.718 283
  (b) e
6. (a) $y = 5000e^{0.06\,t}$ (b)

(c) about 11.55 years
7. (a) 2.717 88 (b) e
8. (a)

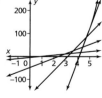 shape of catenary curve changes slope more slowly than parabola as x approaches the vertex; catenary changes slope more quickly as x moves farther away from the vertex

(b) Answers will vary. Example: $y = 0.25x^2 + 2$
(c) value of function begins to change more slowly near the vertex
9. both equal to e
10. (a) 5000 (b) 5751 (c) 9111
11. between 2.08 and 2.21 depending on age
12. (a) 4 terms: $2.\dot{6}$; 5 terms: $2.708\dot{3}$; 6 terms: $2.71\dot{6}$; 7 terms: $2.718\,0\dot{5}$
  (b) expression in (a) is a particular case derived from the general form. The value of x is 1.
13. x-int: none; y-int: $(0, 1)$; end behaviour: $x \to -\infty$ $y \to 0$; $x \to +\infty$ $y \to +\infty$; D: $x \in \mathbf{R}$; R: $y > 0$; increasing and concave up: $x \in \mathbf{R}$; local min: none; local max: none; absolute min: none; absolute max: none
14. (a)

(b)

x	y	Estimated Slope of Tangent at (x, y)
0	1	1
1	e	e
2	e^2	e^2
3	e^3	e^3
4	e^4	e^4
5	e^5	e^5

7.2 Exercises, page 519

1. (a) $2e^{2x}$ (b) e^{x+2} (c) $2e^x$
  (d) $-e^x$ (e) e^x (f) $-2e^{-x}$
  (g) $2 + 3e^x$ (h) $3e^{2+3x}$ (i) $35e^{5x}$
2. (a) $3e^3$ (b) $-2e$ (c) $-2e^{-2}$ (d) 4
3. (a) $2xe^x + 2e^x$ (b) xe^x (c) 0
  (d) $x^4e^x + 4x^3e^x$ (e) $\dfrac{xe^x - e^x}{x^2}$ (f) $x^2e^x + 2xe^x$
  (g) $\dfrac{2x(2-x)}{e^x}$ (h) $e^{-2x}(1 - 2x)$ (i) $\dfrac{(e^x)(x+1)}{(x+2)^2}$
4. $-30e^{-0.3x}$; -15%/year
5. $y = -ex$

6. (a) $D = x \geq 0; R = y \geq 1; f'(x) = \dfrac{e^{\frac{1}{2}}}{2\sqrt{x}}$; increasing: $x > 0$; decreasing: none

(b) $D = x \in \mathbf{R}; R = y > 0; f'(x) = -2e^{-2x}$; increasing: none; decreasing: $x \in \mathbf{R}$

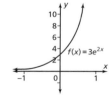

(c) $D = x \in \mathbf{R}; R = y > 0; f'(x) = 6e^{2x}$; increasing: $x \in \mathbf{R}$; decreasing: none

(d) $D = x \in \mathbf{R}; R = y \geq 2$; $f'(x) = e^x(1 - e^{-2x})$; increasing: $x > 0$; decreasing: $x < 0$

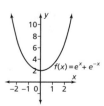

7.

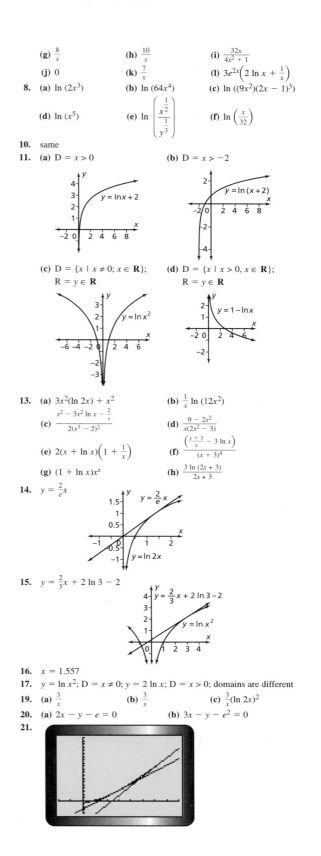

$x - ey + 2e - 2 = 0$

$y = 2 - e^{-x}$

8. $x > -1$; where f is increasing

9. $x + y - 2 = 0$

10. no; example: $f(x) = Ce^x$, $C \in \mathbf{R}$

11. increasing: $0 < x < 2$;
decreasing: $x < 0$, $x > 2$

$y = x^2 e^{-x}$

12.

Exponential Curve	Point	Slope at Point
$y = e^x$	$(0, 1)$	1
$y = e^x$	$(3, e^3)$	e^3
$y = e^{2x}$	$(0, 1)$	2
$y = e^{x+2}$	$(1, e^3)$	e^3

13. (a) $y' = -3e^x$; $y'' = -3e^x$
   (b) $y' = e^{2x} + 2xe^{2x}$; $y'' = 4e^{2x} + 4xe^{2x}$
   (c) $y' = e^x(3 - x)$; $y'' = e^x(2 - x)$

14. (a) $(2 + 3e^{-x})^2(-9e^{-x})$ (b) $e x e^{-1}$
   (c) $e^{e^x + x}$ (d) $-25(1 - e^{5x})^4(e^{5x})$

15. separate into two parts using product rule, apply chain rule

16. (a) $\left(-1, -\dfrac{1}{e}\right)$ (b) $\left(-1, \dfrac{1}{e}\right)$ (c) $(1, 2e)$ and $\left(-3, -\dfrac{6}{e^3}\right)$

17. $\dfrac{dy}{dx} = \dfrac{1 + ye^{xy}}{1 - xe^{xy}}$

18. (a) $x = 0$: $x - y + 1 = 0$; $x = 1$: $ex - y = 0$;
   at $x = 2$: $e^2x - y - e^2 = 0$; $x = 3$: $e^3x - y - 2e^3 = 0$
   (b) For $Ax + By + C = 0$,
   the A's form the sequence $e^0, e^1, e^2, e^3, \dots$
   the B's form the sequence $-1, -1, -1, -1, \dots$
   the C's form the sequence $1e^0, 0e^1, -1e^2, -2e^3, \dots$
   (c) $e^a x - y - (a - 1)e^a = 0$

7.3 Exercises, page 526

1. (a) 1.609   (b) 2.773
   (c) 1.242   (d) 1.386
   (e) 5.332   (f) 0.609

2. (a) $\dfrac{1}{x}$ (b) $\dfrac{1}{x + 2}$ (c) $\dfrac{3}{x}$ (d) $\dfrac{1}{2x}$
   (e) $\dfrac{4}{x}$ (f) $\dfrac{2}{2x - 5}$ (g) $\dfrac{5}{x}$ (h) $\dfrac{5}{x}$
   (i) $\dfrac{6}{x}$ (j) $\dfrac{-2}{x}$ (k) $\dfrac{6x^2}{2x^3 + 1}$ (l) $\dfrac{6(2x + 3)}{x^2 + 3x}$

3. (a) $\ln 2 \doteq 0.693$, $\ln 3 \doteq 1.099$, $\ln 6 \doteq 1.792$; $\ln 2 + \ln 3 = \ln 6$;
   sum property of logarithms
   (b) $\ln 20 \doteq 2.996$, $\ln 5 \doteq 1.609$, $\ln 4 \doteq 1.386$; $\ln 20 - \ln 5 = \ln 4$;
   difference property of logarithms
   (c) $\ln 3 \doteq 1.099$, $\ln 3^5 \doteq 5.493$; $5 \ln 3 = \ln 3^5$;
   power law of logarithms

4. (a) $\ln 24$ (b) $\ln 40$ (c) $\ln 8$
   (d) $\ln 279\ 841$ (e) $\ln 27$ (f) $\ln 36$

6. (a) $x = 2.773$ (b) $x = 8.389$ or -6.389
   (c) $x = 2.414$ (d) $x = 7.389$

7. (a) $\dfrac{1}{2x\sqrt{\ln x}}$ (b) $\dfrac{1 - 3\ln x}{x^4}$ (c) 3
   (d) $\dfrac{2}{x}$ (e) $x^3 + 4x^3 \ln x$ (f) $\dfrac{-\ln 3}{x(\ln 2x)^2}$

(g) $\dfrac{8}{x}$ (h) $\dfrac{10}{x}$ (i) $\dfrac{32x}{4x^2 + 1}$
(j) 0 (k) $\dfrac{7}{x}$ (l) $3e^{2x}\left(2\ln x + \dfrac{1}{x}\right)$

8. (a) $\ln (2x^3)$ (b) $\ln (64x^4)$ (c) $\ln ((9x^2)(2x - 1)^3)$
   (d) $\ln (x^5)$ (e) $\ln\left(\dfrac{x^{\frac{1}{2}}}{y^{\frac{1}{3}}}\right)$ (f) $\ln\left(\dfrac{x}{32}\right)$

10. same

11. (a) $D = x > 0$ (b) $D = x > -2$

$y = \ln x + 2$ $y = \ln (x + 2)$

   (c) $D = \{x \mid x \neq 0; x \in \mathbf{R}\}$;   (d) $D = \{x \mid x > 0, x \in \mathbf{R}\}$;
   $R = y \in \mathbf{R}$ $R = y \in \mathbf{R}$

$y = \ln x^2$ $y = 1 - \ln x$

13. (a) $3x^2(\ln 2x) + x^2$ (b) $\dfrac{1}{x}\ln (12x^2)$
   (c) $\dfrac{x^2 - 3x^2 \ln x - \frac{2}{x}}{2(x^3 - 2)^2}$ (d) $\dfrac{9 - 2x^2}{x(2x^2 - 3)}$
   (e) $2(x + \ln x)\left(1 + \dfrac{1}{x}\right)$ (f) $\dfrac{\left(\frac{x + 3}{x} - 3\ln x\right)}{(x + 3)^4}$
   (g) $(1 + \ln x)x^x$ (h) $\dfrac{3\ln (2x + 3)}{2x + 3}$

14. $y = \dfrac{2}{e}x$

$y = \dfrac{2}{e}x$ $y = \ln 2x$

15. $y = \dfrac{2}{3}x + 2\ln 3 - 2$

$y = \dfrac{2}{3}x + 2\ln 3 - 2$ $y = \ln x^2$

16. $x = 1.557$

17. $y = \ln x^2$; $D = x \neq 0$; $y = 2\ln x$; $D = x > 0$; domains are different

19. (a) $\dfrac{3}{x}$ (b) $\dfrac{3}{x}$ (c) $\dfrac{3}{x}(\ln 2x)^2$

20. (a) $2x - y - e = 0$ (b) $3x - y - e^2 = 0$

21.

22. (a) $-\dfrac{1}{x^2}$ (b) $-\dfrac{4}{x^2}$

23. (a)

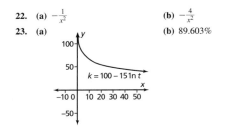

$k = 100 - 15\ln t$

(c) 62.726% (d) 14.443%

(e) $t = 6$, $K' = -2.5$; $t = 12$, $K' = -1.25$; $t = 24$, $K' = -0.625$; increasing

24. $\dfrac{2}{x} + 1$; $\dfrac{2}{x} + 1$; same

25. tangents are inverses of each other and are parallel to $y = x$

26. (a) $\left(\dfrac{-x-1}{x}\right)\left(\dfrac{y}{1+y}\right)$ (b) $-2y$

(c) -1 (d) $\left(1 - \dfrac{1}{x}\right)y$

27. (a) Answers may vary.

x	y (to the nearest tenth of a centimetre)
53	0.0
60	0.8
70	1.7
80	2.6
100	4.1
120	5.3
104	6.3
160	7.2

(b) Answers may vary: $m \doteq -25.99$; $n \doteq 6.54$;
$y = -25.99 + 6.54\ln x$; correct to within about ±0.1 cm

(c) $y' = \dfrac{6.54}{x}$; $\dfrac{6.54}{x} \times 10^4$ cm/Hz; decreasing

28. (a) $\dfrac{1}{x\ln x}$

(b) $f(x)$: D = $\{x > 1, x \in \mathbf{R}\}$; R = $y \in \mathbf{R}$;
$f'(x)$: D = $\{0 < x < 1, x > 1, x \in \mathbf{R}\}$; R = $y < -e$, $y > 0$

7.4 Exercises, page 534

1. (a) $5^x \ln 5$ (b) $(0.47)^x \ln 0.47$

(c) $(52)^{2x}(\ln 52)(2)$ (d) $5(2^x)(\ln 2)$

(e) $4e^x$ (f) $-6(10^{3x})\ln 10$

2. (a) $\dfrac{1}{x\ln 2}$ (b) $\dfrac{1}{x\ln 3}$ (c) $\dfrac{2}{x\ln 4}$

(d) $\dfrac{-3}{x\ln 7}$ (e) $\dfrac{-1}{x\ln 10}$ (f) $\dfrac{3}{x\ln 6}$

3. (a) $\dfrac{1}{(x+2)(\ln 3)}$ (b) $(2^{4x+4})(\ln 2)$

(c) $\dfrac{1}{x\ln 8}$ (d) $\dfrac{-6}{(2x+3)\ln 3}$

(e) $(3200)(2^x)(\ln 2)$ (f) $(32\,768)(\ln 64)(2^{6x})$

(g) $\dfrac{-2}{(5-2x)(\ln 10)}$ (h) $-3(10)^{2\,-\,3x}(\ln 10)$

(i) $\dfrac{1}{(x+3)(\ln 8)}$ (j) $100(1.02)^x(\ln 1.02)$

4. (a) \$ 2114.81 (b) $1200(1.12)^t$

(c) $1200(1.12)^t(\ln 1.12)$ (d) \$ 239.67/year

5. (a) $x^5(5^x)(\ln 5) + 5x^4 5^x$ (b) $\dfrac{(2x+1)}{(x^2+x+1)(\ln 7)}$

(c) $\dfrac{3^x}{x\ln 3} + 3^x\ln x$ (d) $\dfrac{2^{4x}(4x\ln 2 - 3)}{x^4}$

(e) $(1 + \ln x)\dfrac{1}{\ln 2}$ (f) $(0.64)(10)^{0.2x}(\ln 10)$

(g) $2^x\left(\dfrac{1}{x}\right) + 2^x(\ln 2)(\ln x)$ (h) $x(3x)^{x^2}\left(\dfrac{1}{x} + x + 2x\ln 3x\right)$

(i) $3^{\ln x}(\ln 3)\left(\dfrac{1}{x}\right)$ (j) $\left[\dfrac{1}{5^{2x}\ln(5)}\right]\left[\dfrac{4}{x} - 2\ln(5)\ln(3x^4)\right]$

6. (a) $5000(1.08)^t$ (b) $5000(1.08)^t(\ln 1.08)$

(c) \$830.77/year (d) \$874.50/year

7. $(24\ln 2)x - y + 24 - 72\ln 2 = 0$

8. $(10\ln 10)x - y + 10 - 10\ln 10 = 0$%/year

9. (a) $t = 3.802$ years (b) -9.12%/year

10. (a) D of $f(x)$: $x \neq 2.5$; $f'(x) = \dfrac{-2}{(5 - 2x)(\ln 10)}$; D of $f'(x)$: $x < 2.5$

(b) D of $f(x)$: $x \in \mathbf{R}$; $f'(x) = 200(1.02)^{4x}(\ln 1.02)$; D of $f'(x)$: $x \in \mathbf{R}$

(c) D of $f(x)$: $x \neq 2$, $x \neq -2$; $f'(x) = \dfrac{2x}{(x^2 - 4)(\ln 3)}$;
D of $f'(x)$: $x > 2$, $x < -2$

(d) D of $f(x)$: $x \in \mathbf{R}$; $f'(x) = \ln 3$; D of $f'(x)$: $x \in \mathbf{R}$

11. tangent: $(\ln 10 + 1)x - (\ln 10)y - 10 = 0$

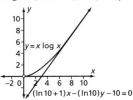

$y = x\log x$

$(\ln 10 + 1)x - (\ln 10)y - 10 = 0$

12. (a) $(9\ln 3)x - y + 9 - 18\ln 3 = 0$

(b) $x - (9\ln 3)y + (18\ln 3) - 9 = 0$

(c)

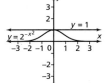

13. (a) $1000(1.06)^t(\ln 1.06)$

(b) $A'(2) = \$65.47$/year; $A'(5) = \$77.98$/year; $A'(10) = \$104.35$/year

(c) no (d) $\dfrac{A'(t)}{A(t)} = \ln 1.06 \doteq 0.058\,27$

(e) ratio of $\dfrac{A'(t)}{A(t)}$ is constant

14. tangent: $y = 1$

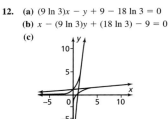

$y = 2^{-x^2}$ $y = 1$

16. k will always cancel out because k is constant

17. slope of $y = 3^x$ at $(0, 1)$ > slope of $y = \log_3 x$ at $(1, 0)$

7.5 Exercises, page 541

1. (a) D = $x \in \mathbf{R}$; R = $y \in \mathbf{R}$ (b) D = $x > 0$; R = $y \geq 1$

(c) D = $x \in \mathbf{R}$; R = $y > 0$ (d) D = $x > 0$; R = $y \in \mathbf{R}$

2. (a) increasing: $x \in \mathbf{R}$; (b) increasing: $x > 1$;
decreasing: none decreasing: $0 < x < 1$

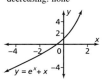

$y = e^x + x$

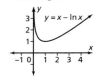

$y = x - \ln x$

(c) increasing: $x \in \mathbf{R}$;
decreasing: none

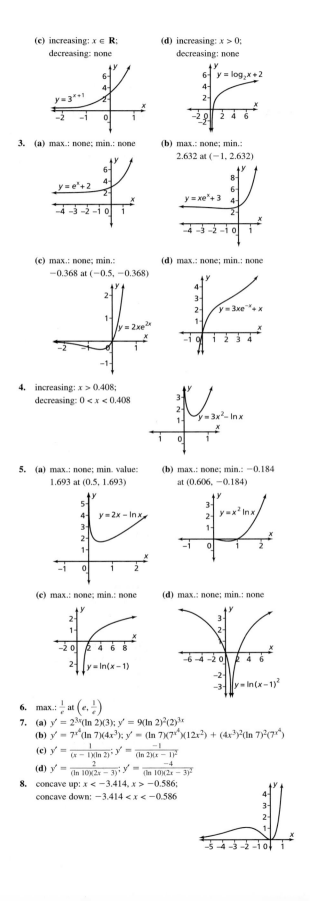

(d) increasing: $x > 0$;
decreasing: none

$y = \log_2 x + 2$

3. (a) max.: none; min.: none

$y = e^x + 2$

(b) max.: none; min.:
2.632 at $(-1, 2.632)$

$y = xe^x + 3$

(c) max.: none; min.:
-0.368 at $(-0.5, -0.368)$

$y = 2xe^{2x}$

(d) max.: none; min.: none

$y = 3xe^{-x} + x$

4. increasing: $x > 0.408$;
decreasing: $0 < x < 0.408$

$y = 3x^2 - \ln x$

5. (a) max.: none; min. value:
1.693 at $(0.5, 1.693)$

$y = 2x - \ln x$

(b) max.: none; min.: -0.184
at $(0.606, -0.184)$

$y = x^2 \ln x$

(c) max.: none; min.: none

$y = \ln(x - 1)$

(d) max.: none; min.: none

$y = \ln(x - 1)^2$

6. max.: $\frac{1}{e}$ at $\left(e, \frac{1}{e}\right)$

7. (a) $y' = 2^{3x}(\ln 2)(3)$; $y'' = 9(\ln 2)^2(2)^{3x}$

(b) $y' = 7^{x^4}(\ln 7)(4x^3)$; $y'' = (\ln 7)(7^{x^4})(12x^2) + (4x^3)^2(\ln 7)^2(7^{x^4})$

(c) $y' = \frac{1}{(x-1)(\ln 2)}$; $y'' = \frac{-1}{(\ln 2)(x-1)^2}$

(d) $y' = \frac{2}{(\ln 10)(2x-3)}$; $y'' = \frac{-4}{(\ln 10)(2x-3)^2}$

8. concave up: $x < -3.414$, $x > -0.586$;
concave down: $-3.414 < x < -0.586$

10. (a) $D = |x| < \sqrt{2}$; y-int.: ln 2; x-int.:
$+1$; asymptote: $x = \pm\sqrt{2}$; increasing:
$-\sqrt{2} < x < 0$; decreasing: $0 < x < \sqrt{2}$;
local max.: $(0, \ln 2)$; concave down:
$-\sqrt{2} < x < \sqrt{2}$

(b) $D = x \in \mathbf{R}$; y-int.: 0; x-int.: 0;
asymptote: $y = 0$; increasing: $x < -2$;
$x > 0$, decreasing; $-2 < x < 0$;
local max.: $\left(-2, \frac{4}{e^2}\right)$; local min.:
$(0, 0)$; concave up: $x < -\sqrt{2} - 2$,
$x > \sqrt{2} - 2$; concave down:
$-\sqrt{2} - 2 < x < \sqrt{2} - 2$

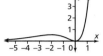

(c) $D = x \neq 0$; no intercepts; asymptotes:
$x = 0$, $y = 1$; decreasing:
$x > 1$; no max. or min.;
concave up: $-0.5 < x < 0$, $x > 0$;
concave down: $x < -0.5$

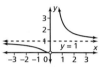

$y = 1$

11. max.: none; min.: -0.0183 at $(-4, -0.0183)$

12. (a)

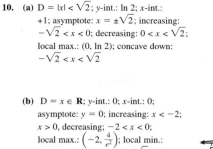

$d = 200t(2)^{-t}$

(b) increasing: $t > 2.89$; decreasing: $t < 2.89$
(c) $200°$/s
(d) when the degree between the door frame and the door is zero

14. (b) $y = \ln(e^x - e^{-2})$
15. decreasing for all $t > 0$

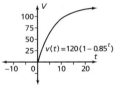

$v(t) = 120(1 - 0.85^t)$

16. $D = x > 0$; no intercepts;
asymptote.: $x = 0$; increasing: $x > 1$;
decreasing: $0 < x < 1$; local max.:
none; local min.: $(1, 1)$;
concave up: $x > 0$

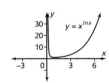

$y = x^{\ln x}$

7.6 Exercises, page 549

1. (a) $35e^x$ **(b)** $50e^{2x}$ **(c)** $-3e^{-0.2x}$
(d) $490e^{1.4x}$ **(e)** $1620e^{1.08x}$ **(f)** $-30e^{-0.15x}$

2. (a) $240e^{3.0973t}$ **(b)** 1.79×10^8 bacteria/h

3. rate of change is proportional to y which in this case is $0.02y$;
all examples of form $y = Ce^{0.02t}$, where $c \in \mathbf{R}$ and t is the variable

4. \$6793.28

5. yes

6. $58°$C

7. 79.39 min

9. (a) $v(t) = (49.8675)(0.8006)^t$ **(b)** $t = 20$ s
(c) $v = 10.5$ km/h   **(d)** 50 km/h   **(e)** decreasing at all times

10. (a) 4440   **(b)** $P(t) = 4500(1.02)^t - 7500(1.02^{t+1} - 1)$
(c) $P'(t) = 4500(1.02)^t \ln 1.02 - 7500(1.02)^{t+1} \ln 1.02$

Chapter 7 Review, page 551

9. (a)
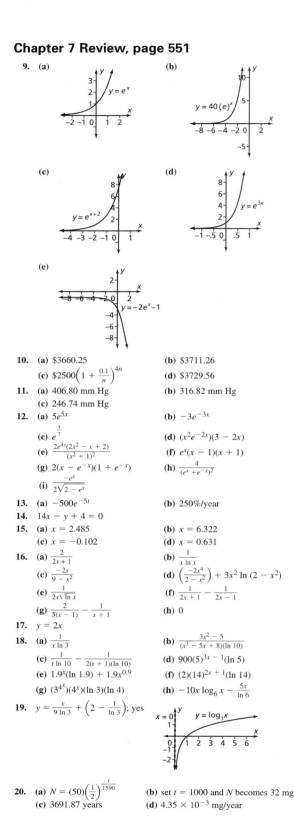

y = e^x graph

(b)

$y = 40\,(e)^x$ graph

(c)

$y = e^{x+2}$ graph

(d)

$y = e^{3x}$ graph

(e)

$y = -2e^x - 1$ graph

10. (a) \$3660.25 **(b)** \$3711.26
(c) $\$2500\left(1 + \dfrac{0.1}{n}\right)^{4n}$ **(d)** \$3729.56

11. (a) 406.80 mm Hg **(b)** 316.82 mm Hg
(c) 246.74 mm Hg

12. (a) $5e^{5x}$ **(b)** $-3e^{-3x}$
(c) $e^{\frac{x}{7}}$ **(d)** $(x^2 e^{-2x})(3 - 2x)$
(e) $\dfrac{2e^{4x}(2x^2 - x + 2)}{(x^2 + 1)^2}$ **(f)** $e^x(x - 1)(x + 1)$
(g) $2(x - e^{-x})(1 + e^{-x})$ **(h)** $\dfrac{4}{(e^x + e^{-x})^2}$
(i) $\dfrac{-e^x}{2\sqrt{2 - e^x}}$

13. (a) $-500e^{-5t}$ **(b)** 250%/year
14. $14x - y + 4 = 0$
15. (a) $x = 2.485$ **(b)** $x = 6.322$
(c) $x = -0.102$ **(d)** $x = 0.631$
16. (a) $\dfrac{2}{2x + 1}$ **(b)** $\dfrac{1}{x \ln x}$
(c) $\dfrac{-2x}{9 - x^2}$ **(d)** $\left(\dfrac{-2x^4}{2 - x^2}\right) + 3x^2 \ln(2 - x^2)$
(e) $\dfrac{1}{2x\sqrt{\ln x}}$ **(f)** $\dfrac{1}{2x + 1} - \dfrac{1}{2x - 1}$
(g) $\dfrac{2}{5(x - 1)} - \dfrac{1}{x + 1}$ **(h)** 0
17. $y = 2x$
18. (a) $\dfrac{1}{x \ln 3}$ **(b)** $\dfrac{3x^2 - 5}{(x^3 - 5x + 8)(\ln 10)}$
(c) $\dfrac{1}{t \ln 10} - \dfrac{1}{2(t + 1)(\ln 10)}$ **(d)** $900(5)^{3x - 1}(\ln 5)$
(e) $1.9^x(\ln 1.9) + 1.9x^{0.9}$ **(f)** $(2)(14)^{2x + 1}(\ln 14)$
(g) $(3^{4^x})(4^x)(\ln 3)(\ln 4)$ **(h)** $-10x \log_6 x - \dfrac{5x}{\ln 6}$
19. $y = \dfrac{x}{9 \ln 3} + \left(2 - \dfrac{1}{\ln 3}\right)$; yes

$y = \log_3 x$ graph, $x = 0$

20. (a) $N = (50)\left(\dfrac{1}{2}\right)^{\frac{t}{1590}}$ **(b)** set $t = 1000$ and N becomes 32 mg
(c) 3691.87 years **(d)** 4.35×10^{-3} mg/year

21. (a) increasing: $x \in \mathbf{R}$; decreasing: none; max.: none; min.: none; concave up: $x \in \mathbf{R}$; concave down: none

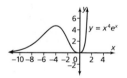

$y = e^x + 2$ graph

(b) increasing: none; decreasing: $x \in \mathbf{R}$; max.: none; min.: none; concave up: none; concave down: $x \in \mathbf{R}$

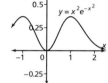

$y = -3e^x - 5$ graph

(c) increasing: $x < \dfrac{1}{3}$; decreasing: $x > \dfrac{1}{3}$; max.: $\left(\dfrac{1}{3}, \dfrac{1}{3e}\right)$; min.: none; concave up: $x > \dfrac{2}{3}$; concave down: $x < \dfrac{2}{3}$

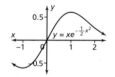

$y = xe^{-3x}$ graph

(d) increasing: $x < -1$, $0 < x < 1$; decreasing: $-1 < x < 0$, $x > 1$; max.: $\left(-1, \dfrac{1}{e}\right)$, $\left(1, \dfrac{1}{e}\right)$; min.: (0, 0); concave up: $x < -1.510$, $-0.468 < x < 0.468$; $x > 1.510$; concave down: $-1.510 < x < -0.468$, $0.468 < x < 0.510$

$y = x^2 e^{-x^2}$ graph

(e) increasing: $-1 < x < 1$; decreasing: $x < -1$, $x > 1$; max.: $\left(1, \dfrac{1}{\sqrt{e}}\right)$; min.: $\left(-1, -\dfrac{1}{\sqrt{e}}\right)$; concave up: $-\sqrt{3} < x < 0$, $x > \sqrt{3}$; concave down: $x < -\sqrt{3}$, $0 < x < \sqrt{3}$

$y = xe^{-\frac{1}{2}x^2}$ graph

(f) increasing: $x < -4$, $x > 0$; decreasing: $-4 < x < 0$; max.: $\left(-4, \dfrac{256}{e^4}\right)$; min.: (0, 0); concave up: $x < -6$, $-2 < x < 0$; $x > 0$; concave down: $-6 < x < -2$

$y = x^4 e^x$ graph

22. $x = \dfrac{1}{\sqrt{e}}$

23.

$y = 2 \ln(1 - x^2)$ graph

(a) $D = -1 < x < 1$ **(b)** int.: (0, 0)
(c) asymp.: $x = -1$ and $x = 1$
(d) increasing: $-1 < x < 0$; decreasing: $0 < x < 1$
(e) local max.: (0, 0); local min.: none
(f) concave up: none; concave down: $-1 < x < 1$

24. (a) $8e^{2w}$ **(b)** $-96e^{-3x}$ **(c)** $7.2e^{-0.4x}$
(d) $306e^{1.7t}$ **(e)** $120e^{0.06t}$ **(f)** $30\,020.22e^{-23.49x}$
25. 0.719 h
27. (a) $e^{2x}(2x - 1)$ **(b)** $\dfrac{1}{x(\ln 5)}$

(c) $\frac{2}{x}$ (d) $\frac{1}{x \ln |x|}$

28. (a) max.: none; min.: $2 - \frac{1}{e}$ at

$\left(-1, 2 - \frac{1}{e}\right)$; increasing: $x > -1$;

decreasing: $x < -1$; asymp.: $y = 2$

(b) max.: none; min.: e at (e, e);

increasing: $x > e$; decreasing:

$0 < x < 1, 1 < x < e$; asymp.: $x = 1$

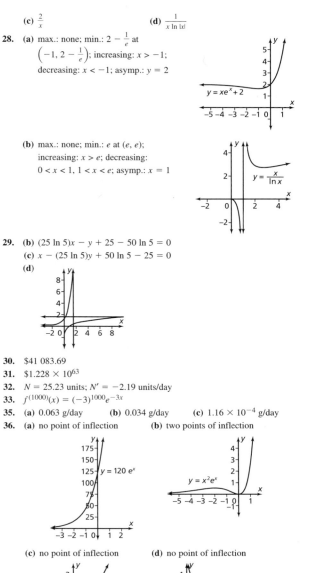

29. (b) $(25 \ln 5)x - y + 25 - 50 \ln 5 = 0$

(c) $x - (25 \ln 5)y + 50 \ln 5 - 25 = 0$

(d)

30. \$41 083.69

31. \$1.228 × 10^{63}

32. $N = 25.23$ units; $N' = -2.19$ units/day

33. $f^{(1000)}(x) = (-3)^{1000}e^{-3x}$

35. (a) 0.063 g/day   (b) 0.034 g/day   (c) 1.16 × 10^{-4} g/day

36. (a) no point of inflection   (b) two points of inflection

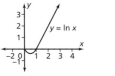

(c) no point of inflection   (d) no point of inflection

37. Compound continuously grows faster than compound monthly and their formulae are different. The formula for compounded monthly is

$A = N\left(1 + \frac{i}{12}\right)^{12t}$ and for compounded continuously is $A = Ne^{it}$.

38. $y = -e^x$ is a reflection of $y = e^x$ about the x-axis.

$y = e^{-x}$ is a reflection of $y = e^x$ about the y-axis.

Chapter Review 7 Test, page 556

1. (a) $\frac{1}{x}$ (b) $\frac{1}{(x-2)(\ln 4)}$

(c) $100(1.05)^x(\ln 1.05)$ (d) $3xe^{3x} + e^{3x}$

2. $2e^3x - y - 3e^3 = 0$

3. as time approaches infinity, temperature of object approaches room temperature

4. (a) 3.85 years   (b) 9%/year

5. (a) \$27 000   (b) \$1191.49   (c) \$1051.38/year

6. increasing: $x < -2, x > 0$;

decreasing: $-2 < x < 0$

7. $y = (580)e^{0.09t}$ where t is time since 1990

in years and y is number of students;

rate of change in population is increasing

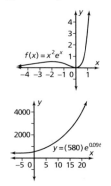

Cumulative Review 3 Test, page 557

1. (a) **i.** 0 **ii.** 0 **iii.** 3 **iv.** 0 **v.** 2 **vi.** does not exist

(b)

(c) reflect about the x-axis, translate horizontally 0.5 units to the left, and translate vertically 3 units up

2. $\frac{47}{3}$

3. $\frac{7}{4}$

4. 4 m away from the 4 m post

5. (a) $\frac{3}{8}$

6. (a) 344 m²/s   (b) 5.29 s

(c)   (d) 2.58 s

7. (a) 406.80 mmHg   (b) 591.89 mmHg   (c) 217.74 mmHg

8. express $\frac{de^x}{dx}$ as a limit, use the exponent

laws to factor out a limit—independent

term, use $\lim\limits_{h \to 0} \frac{e^h - 1}{h} = 1$

9. (a) $y' = 3\,(6^{3x-8}) \ln 6$ (b) $f'(x) = -20e^{5x+1}$

(c) $g'(x) = \frac{8}{2x+7}$ (d) $y' = \frac{5(3x-2)}{x(x-1)\ln 5}$

10. (a) $3500\left(\frac{12.08}{12}\right)^{12t}$

(b) investment: \$5214.46; rate of increase: \$415.77/year

(c) investment: \$7768.74; rate of increase: \$619.44/year

11. D: $x \in \mathbf{R}$; int.: $(0, 0)$; asymp.: $y = 0$;

increasing: $x < \frac{1}{\ln 2}$; decreasing: $x > \frac{1}{\ln 2}$;

local max.: $\left(\frac{1}{\ln 2}, \frac{1}{e \ln 2}\right)$; local min.: none;

concave up: $x > \frac{2}{\ln 2}$; concave down: $x < \frac{2}{\ln 2}$

12. **(a)** 131.4°C

(b) in theory, never; in fact, about 221 min

TR.1 Exercises, page 599

1. **(a)** -1.0613 **(b)** 1.0004 **(c)** 1.3692 **(d)** -59.4662

2. **(a)** $-1 \leq \sin x \leq 1$ **(b)** $-1 \leq \cos x \leq 1$
(c) $-1 \leq \cos x \leq 1$ **(d)** $-1 \leq \sin x \leq 1$

3. **(a)** $\sin \theta = \frac{7}{25}$ **(b)** $\sec \theta = \frac{25}{24}$
(c) $\csc \theta = \frac{25}{7}$ **(d)** $\tan \theta = \frac{7}{24}$

4. **(a)** $\cos x = \frac{3}{5}$ **(b)** $\tan x = \frac{4}{3}$
(c) $\sec x = \frac{5}{3}$ **(d)** $\csc x = \frac{5}{4}$
(e) $\cot x = \frac{3}{4}$

6. $\sec t = \frac{13}{5}$, $\csc t = \frac{13}{12}$, $\tan t = \frac{12}{5}$

7. **(a)**

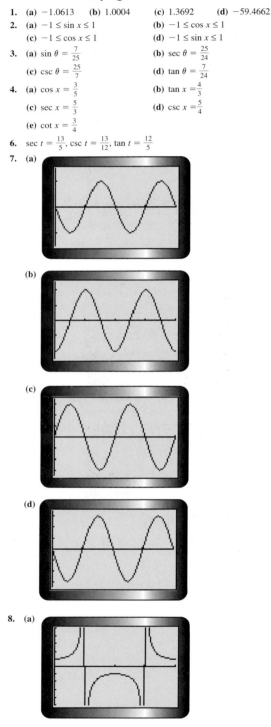

(b)

(c)

(d)

8. **(a)**

(b)

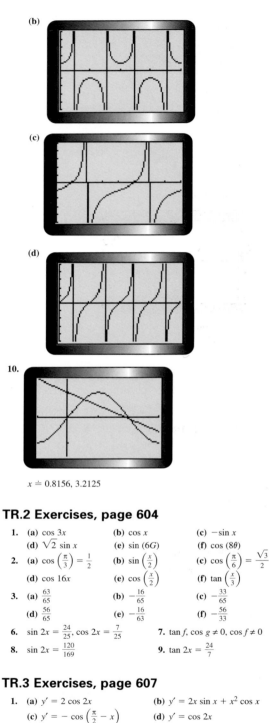

(c)

(d)

10.

$x \doteq 0.8156, 3.2125$

TR.2 Exercises, page 604

1. **(a)** $\cos 3x$ **(b)** $\cos x$ **(c)** $-\sin x$
(d) $\sqrt{2} \sin x$ **(e)** $\sin (6G)$ **(f)** $\cos (8\theta)$

2. **(a)** $\cos \left(\frac{\pi}{3}\right) = \frac{1}{2}$ **(b)** $\sin \left(\frac{x}{2}\right)$ **(c)** $\cos \left(\frac{\pi}{6}\right) = \frac{\sqrt{3}}{2}$
(d) $\cos 16x$ **(e)** $\cos \left(\frac{x}{2}\right)$ **(f)** $\tan \left(\frac{x}{3}\right)$

3. **(a)** $\frac{63}{65}$ **(b)** $-\frac{16}{65}$ **(c)** $-\frac{33}{65}$
(d) $\frac{56}{65}$ **(e)** $-\frac{16}{63}$ **(f)** $-\frac{56}{33}$

6. $\sin 2x = \frac{24}{25}$, $\cos 2x = \frac{7}{25}$ **7.** $\tan f$, $\cos g \neq 0$, $\cos f \neq 0$

8. $\sin 2x = \frac{120}{169}$ **9.** $\tan 2x = \frac{24}{7}$

TR.3 Exercises, page 607

1. **(a)** $y' = 2 \cos 2x$ **(b)** $y' = 2x \sin x + x^2 \cos x$
(c) $y' = -\cos \left(\frac{\pi}{2} - x\right)$ **(d)** $y' = \cos 2x$
(e) $y' = -2 \cos x \sin x$ **(f)** $y' = 2 \cos^2 x \sin x - \sin^3 x$
(g) $y' = -\frac{x \sin x + \cos x}{x^2}$ **(h)** $y' = -\frac{2 \sin x + 1}{(2 + \sin x)^2}$

2. **(a)** $f'(x) = -\csc^2 x$ **(b)** $f'(x) = \sec x \tan x$
(c) $f'(x) = -\cot x \csc x$

3. **(a)** $\frac{dy}{dx} = -\csc x \cot^2 x - \csc^3 x$ **(b)** $\frac{dy}{dx} = \sec^2 x \sin x + \sin x$

(c) $\frac{dy}{dx} = \cos\left(\frac{1}{x}\right) + \frac{1}{x}\sin\left(\frac{1}{x}\right)$ **(d)** $\frac{dy}{dx} = \frac{3x^2\cos(\sqrt{1+x^3})}{2\sqrt{1+x^3}}$

(e) $\frac{dy}{dx} = 2\sin^2 x\tan x + 2\tan^3 x$

(f) $\frac{dy}{dx} = -\frac{\sin^3 x + 2\cos^2 x\sin x + \sin x}{(1+\sin^2 x)^2}$

(g) $\frac{dy}{dx} = -2\csc^2 x\cot x$ **(h)** $\frac{dy}{dx} = -\frac{\sin x}{2\sqrt{\pi + \cos x}}$

(i) $\frac{dy}{dx} = 2x\sin^3 x + 3x^2\cos x\sin^2 x$

4. $-\sqrt{3}$

5. $\frac{5\sqrt{2}}{18}$ m/s

6. (a) $t = \frac{\pi}{8} + \frac{\pi k}{2}$, $t = \frac{3\pi}{8} + \frac{\pi k}{2}$ where $k \in \mathbf{I}$

(b) 16 units/s

(c) minimum distance: 0 , maximum distance: 4 units

7. (a) 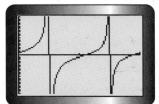 **(b)** $\left(\frac{\pi}{4}, \sqrt{2}\right)$

8. (a) 3 **(b)** 1 **(c)** 1 **(d)** 0

9. (a) $f''(x) = -2\cos(2x)$

(b) $f''(x) = 2\csc x + 2\cot^2 x\csc x - \cos x\cot x$

10. (a) $\frac{dy}{dx} = \frac{\sin(2y) + 2y\sin(2x)}{\cos(2x) - 2x\cos(2y)}$ **(b)** $\frac{dy}{dx} = \frac{\cos(2y) - 2y\cos(2x)}{\sin(2x) + 2x\sin(2y)}$

(c) $\frac{dy}{dx} = -\frac{1 + 2y\sec^2(2xy)}{2x\sec^2(2xy)}$ **(d)** $\frac{dy}{dx} = \frac{-2(\sin^3 x\cos x + \cos^3 x\sin y)}{y}$

TR.4 Exercises, page 609

1. $\frac{d\theta}{dt} = \frac{5}{2}$ **2.** $\frac{d\theta}{dt} = \frac{1}{40}$

3. $\frac{dA}{dt} = 16.4$ cm^2/min **4.** $\frac{d\theta}{dt} = \frac{4}{125}$ rad/s

5. 8.73 m/h **6.** $\frac{d\theta}{dt} \doteq -0.011$ rad/s

7. $\frac{d\theta}{dt} = \frac{1}{13}$ rad/min **8.** $\frac{d\theta}{dt} = -\frac{1}{90}$ rad/s

9. 104.7 m/s, 111.3 m/s **10.** $\frac{d\theta}{dt} = \frac{\sqrt{3}}{60}$ m/s

TR.5 Exercises, page 613

1. (a) $\theta = \pi + 2\pi k$ where $k \in \mathbf{I}$ **(b)** $\theta = \frac{3\pi}{2} + 2\pi k$ where $k \in \mathbf{I}$

2. (a) maximum at $\theta = \pi + 2\pi k$ where $k \in \mathbf{I}$

(b) no maximum value

(c) maximum at $\theta = \frac{3\pi}{2} + 2\pi k$ where $k \in \mathbf{I}$

(d) no maximum value

3. (a) $\frac{x^2}{25} + \frac{y^2}{9} = 1$, ellipse **(b)** $\frac{x^2}{4} + \frac{y^2}{16} = 1$, ellipse

(c) $\frac{x^2}{9} - \frac{y^2}{16} = 1$, hyperbola

4. i) (a) maximum value: $\sqrt{2}$, minimum value: $-\sqrt{2}$

(b) over $0 \le \theta \le 2\pi$, increasing: $0 < \theta < \frac{\pi}{4}$ and $\frac{5\pi}{4} < \theta < 2\pi$;

decreasing: $\frac{\pi}{4} < \theta < \frac{5\pi}{4}$

(c)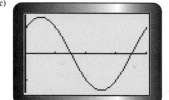

4. ii) (a) maximum value: $\sqrt{2}$, minimum value: $-\sqrt{2}$

(b) over $0 \le \theta \le 2\pi$, increasing: $0 < \theta < \frac{3\pi}{4}$ and $\frac{7\pi}{4} < \theta < 2\pi$;

decreasing: $\frac{3\pi}{4} < \theta < \frac{7\pi}{4}$

(c)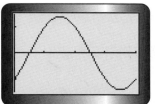

4. iii) (a) maximum value: 5, minimum value: -5

(b) over $0 \le \theta \le 2\pi$, with $\varphi = \tan^{-1}\left(\frac{3}{4}\right) \doteq 0.6435$;

increasing: $0 < \theta < \varphi$ and $\pi + \varphi < \theta < 2\pi$;

decreasing: $\varphi < \theta < \pi + \varphi$

(c)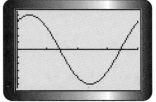

4. iv) (a) maximum value: $+\infty$, minimum value: $-\infty$

(b) Over $0 \le \theta \le 2\pi$, increasing: everywhere except $\theta = \frac{\pi}{2}, \frac{3\pi}{2}$

(c)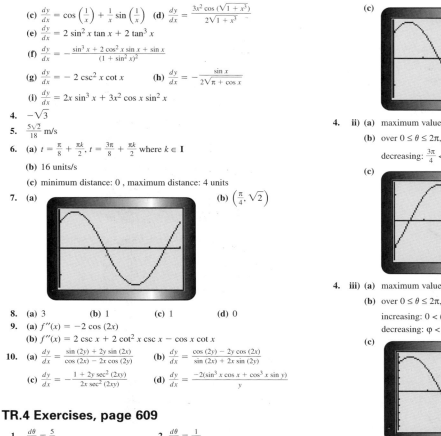

5. area = 72, rectangle: $(-3\sqrt{2}, 3\sqrt{2})$, $(3\sqrt{2}, 3\sqrt{2})$, $(3\sqrt{2}, -3\sqrt{2})$, $(-3\sqrt{2}, -3\sqrt{2})$

6. area = 240, rectangle: $\left(-\frac{a}{\sqrt{2}}, \frac{b}{\sqrt{2}}\right)$, $\left(\frac{a}{\sqrt{2}}, -\frac{b}{\sqrt{2}}\right)$, $\left(-\frac{a}{\sqrt{2}}, -\frac{b}{\sqrt{2}}\right)$, $\left(-\frac{a}{\sqrt{2}}, \frac{b}{\sqrt{2}}\right)$

7. length $= \dfrac{50\left(1 + 2.5^{\frac{2}{3}}\right)^{\frac{1}{2}}\left(5 + 2(2.5)^{\frac{1}{3}}\right)}{2.5^{\frac{1}{3}}}$

8. length $= 6\sqrt{2}$ m

9. length $= 9$ m

10. distance $= 4\sqrt{10}$ m

Index

Absolute extrema, finding, 280
Absolute maximum and minimum, 277, 278, 282, 287
Absolute value, 67
Acceleration due to gravity, 249, 251
Adding and subtracting functions, 28–29, 31
Asymptote(s), 98
    finding the equations of, 348–350, 354
    horizontal, 348, 355
    oblique, 353, 354, 355
    vertical, 347, 355
Average cost function, 317, 366
Average profit function, 346, 352, 360
Average rate of change, 172–173, 177, 237, 240

Basic business model, 313
Break-even point, 314
Break-even quantities, 353

Calculus, 183
Chain rule, 449, 453
Common logarithm, 116
Composite function, 31–32, 434, 439
Composition of functions, 31, 434
    of discrete relations, 436
    domain and range, 435
    of a function and its inverse, 436, 438
    and rates of change, 447–448
Concavity, 322
    test for, 323, 329
Constant law (limit), 200
Constant multiple rule (derivative), 220, 222
Constant multiplier law (limit), 200
Constant rule (derivative), 217, 222
Continuous compound interest, 511
Continuous function, 197, 200
Continuity (of rational functions), 374
    and differentiability, 390
Critical number, 279, 414
Critical point, 279
Cubic function, 7, 10, 12, 14

Decomposition of a function, 437–438
Decay rate, 91
Decreasing function, 8–9, 268, 273
Degree, 7, 14
Demand function, 313
Derivative, 207, 250
    of composite functions, 449, 453, 517, 524, 532, 533
    of a composite function involving a power function, 450

of a constant function, 217, 222
determining from first principles, 210
of the difference of two functions, 227, 229
of exponential function, 515–516, 532
as a function, 209
of a function multiplied by a constant, 220, 222
higher, 247, 250, 380–381
of an inverse function, 482
of logarithmic function, 523, 530–531
notation, 207
of any polynomial function, 227, 229
of a power function, 218–219, 222
of a product, 297
of a quotient, 379–380, 383
as a rate of change, 209
as a slope of a tangent, 209
of the sum of two functions, 226, 229
Determining the derivative from first principles, 210
Determining the equation of a function from its graph, 12
Difference of cubes, 51
Difference function, 29
Difference rule (derivative), 227, 229
Differentiability of a function, 210–211, 213, 387–388
    and continuity, 390
Differentiation
    implicit, 479–480
    rules, 458
Discontinuous function, 198, 371–373
Discrete data, 176
Division statement, 39
Double root, 69
Doubling period, 107

e (the number), 508–509
End behaviour, 19–21, 353
    model(s), 364, 369
Even function, 357
Exponential decay, 91
Exponential function, 96
    behaviour, 98–99
    doubling period, 107
    graphs of, 97, 100, 103
    half-life, 107
    various forms of, 107
Exponential growth, 87–88, 544–545
Exponent laws, 121
Extremum, 282

Factor theorem, 46–48, 50
First derivative test
    for absolute extrema, 287, 292
    for local extrema, 287, 291
    using to graph functions, 288–289
Function(s)
    absolute maximum of, 277, 278, 287
    absolute minimum of, 277, 278, 287
    adding, 28
    average profit, 346
    composite, 31–32, 434, 439
    continuous, 197–198
    continuity (of rational functions), 374
    cubic, 7, 10, 12, 14
    decomposition of, 437–438
    decreasing, 8–9, 268, 273
    degree, 14, 20
    demand, 313
    derivative of, 207
    difference, 29
    differentiability of, 387–388
    discontinuous, 198, 371–373
    domain, restricted, 10
    end behaviour and model(s), 19–21, 96, 353, 364, 366
    even, 357
    exponential, 96
    identity, 438
    increasing, 8–9, 268, 272
    leading coefficient, 7, 20
    limit, 185, 194, 195
    linear, 7, 10, 11, 14
    local maximum of, 9, 277, 287
    local minimum of, 9, 277, 287
    logarithmic, 114–115
    maximum value of, 282
    minimum value of, 282
    multiplying, 30
    natural logarithmic, 522
    quadratic, 7, 10, 12, 14
    quartic, 7
    rational, 346, 355
    second derivative, 247
    subtracting, 28, 29
    zeros, 10, 13, 14, 21, 66
Fundamental Limit of Calculus, 508, 511

Graph(s)
    of functions, 14, 23
Graphing
    composite functions, 473–477
    a derivative given graph of function, 281–282

exponential and logarithmic functions, 537–541
the first and second derivatives of a function, 328, 412
a function from the graph of its derivative, 291, 413
rational functions, 351–352, 405–410
Growth rate, 88–90

Half-life, 107
Horizontal motion, 236–237, 241

Identity function, 438
Implicit
differentiation, 479–480
relation, 479
Inadmissible solution, 55
Increasing and decreasing functions, test for, 269
Increasing function, 8–9, 268, 272
Indeterminate form, 362–364, 366
Infinity, symbols for, 19
Instantaneous rate of change, 174–177, 178, 187, 190, 238, 240
Intercepts, 29
Intervals of increase and decrease, 269

Jump discontinuity, 373

Leading coefficient, 7, 20
Left-hand limit, 195
Limit(s), 185, 194
and average cost function, 365–366
basic, 199
constant law, 200
constant multiplier law, 200
indeterminate form, 362–364, 366
infinite, 361–362
left-hand, 195
one-sided, 195
of polynomial functions, 200
quotient law, 365
of rational functions, 360–362
right-hand, 195
sum/difference law, 200
that fail to exist, 196
two-sided, 195
Limiting value, 190

Linear function, 7, 10, 11, 14
Local maximum and minimum, 9, 277, 287
Logarithm(s)
common, 116, 129
equivalent, 124
evaluating (logs without base 10), 131, 525
laws of, 121–123
natural, 522
Logarithmic function, 114–115
Logarithmic scale, 83, 135
Logistic equation, 547–548

Marginal profit, revenue, and cost, 314–315
Marginal rate, 313
Multiplying functions, 30–31
Natural logarithm, 522
Natural logarithm function, 522
Newton's Law of Cooling, 546–547, 548

One-sided limits, 195
Optimization problems, solving, 303–309, 395–400, 465–467, 469–470

pH scale, 139
Piecewise function, 195
Point of inflection, 323–324, 329
Point of tangency, 183
Polynomial, 6, 7
degree, 7
equation, 54
factoring, 50
function, 7
leading coefficient, 7
roots, 55–56, 60
standard form, 7
Polynomial function, 7
derivative, 227, 229
limits of, 200
Power rule (derivative), 218, 222
general power rule, 219, 222
Product rule (derivatives), 297

Quadratic formula, 68
Quadratic function, 7, 10, 12, 14
Quartic function, 7
Quotient law (limits), 365

Quotient rule (derivatives), 379, 383

Rate(s) of change
average, 172–173, 237, 240
and composition of functions, 447–448
instantaneous, 174–177, 178, 187, 190, 238, 240
marginal rate, 313
Rational function, 346, 355
Rational zero test, 48
Related rates, 486
solving related rate problems, 486–491
Remainder theorem, 45–46, 50
Restricted domain, 10
Richter magnitude scale, 135–137
Right-hand limit, 195

Secant, 184, 190
slope of, 186
Second derivative function, 247, 380–381
Second derivative test, 326–327, 329
Slope, 183
as limiting value, 190
of a secant, 186
of a tangent line, 183, 186
Sound intensity, 137–138
Speed, 234
Standard form, 7
Sum of cubes, 51
Sum/difference law (derivative), 200
Sum rule (derivative), 226, 229
Synthetic division, 40–42

Tangent line, 183, 190, 192
finding the equation of, 298
slope, 183, 186
Tangent problem, 183
Test for increasing and decreasing functions, 269
Tetrahedron, 3
Turning point, 9, 20
Two-sided limit, 195

Velocity, 234, 250
Vertical motion, 234–235, 241

Zeros, 10, 13, 14, 21, 66

Technology Index

Graphing technology, 9, 58, 69, 101, 189, 239, 290, 304, 306, 308, 309, 346, 398, 412, 465, 508, 538
approximating the slope of a tangent line, 184
Calculate menu, 347, 353

creating a table using Lists, 22, 240
cubic regression, 239
exponential regression, 149–150
identifying the x-intercepts, 65–66

numerical derivative function, nDeriv(, 382
quadratic regression, 290
quartic regression, 176
solving a polynomial inequality, 66
ZoomFit, 58

Photo Credits

COVER Joao Paulo/Getty Images/The Image Bank

Chapter 1 Page 1 CORBIS RF/MAGMA; Page 2 PhotoDisc; Page 3 © Owen Franken/CORBIS/MAGMA; Page 18 © Chris Hellier/CORBIS/MAGMA; Page 37 MARY EVANS PICTURE LIBRARY

Chapter 2 Page 81 PhotoDisc; Page 82 PhotoDisc; Page 83 CORBIS RF/MAGMA; Page 120 © Bettmann/CORBIS/MAGMA; Page 134 © Bettmann/CORBIS/MAGMA; Page 163 Environment Canada, © Her Majesty the Queen in Right of Canada, represented by the Minister of Public Works and Government Services Canada, 1999

Chapter 3 Page 167 © James A. Sugar/CORBIS/MAGMA; Page 168 © Duomo/CORBIS/MAGMA; Page 169 Jorg Greuel/Getty Images/The Image Bank; Page 193 © Bettmann/CORBIS/MAGMA; Page 224 © CORBIS/MAGMA; Page 245 © Bettmann/CORBIS/MAGMA

Chapter 4 Page 263 PhotoDisc; Page 264 PhotoDisc; Page 265 SuperStock; Page 295 © Bettmann/CORBIS/MAGMA

Chapter 5 Page 341 PhotoDisc; Page 342 PhotoDisc; Page 343 Dave Starrett; Page 386 © Bettmann/CORBIS/MAGMA; Page 404 © Bettmann/CORBIS/MAGMA

Chapter 6 Page 429 CP Picture Archive; Page 430 © Buddy Mays/CORBIS/MAGMA; Page 431 PhotoDisc; Page 485 © Bettmann/CORBIS/MAGMA; Page 496 MARY EVANS PICTURE LIBRARY

Chapter 7 Page 503 © Roger Ressmeyer/CORBIS/MAGMA, Page 504 © Bettmann/CORBIS/MAGMA; Page 505 SuperStock; Page 511 © Bettmann/CORBIS/MAGMA

Explorations Appendix Page 579 Winnipeg Sun/Brian Donogh/CP Picture Archive

ALGEBRAIC FORMULAS

ARITHMETIC OPERATIONS

$$a(b + c) = ab + ac \qquad \frac{a}{b} + \frac{c}{d} = \frac{ad + bc}{bd}, \, b, \, d \neq 0$$

$$\frac{a + c}{b} = \frac{a}{b} + \frac{c}{b}, \, b \neq 0 \qquad \frac{\frac{a}{b}}{\frac{c}{d}} = \frac{a}{b} \times \frac{d}{c} = \frac{ad}{bc}, \, b, \, c, \, d \neq 0$$

NUMBER SYSTEMS

Natural Numbers $\quad \mathbf{N} = \{1, 2, 3, 4, ...\}$
Whole Numbers $\quad \mathbf{W} = \{0, 1, 2, 3, ...\}$
Integers $\quad \mathbf{I} = \{... -3, -2, -1, 0, 1, 2, 3, ...\}$
Rational Numbers $\quad \mathbf{Q} = \left\{\frac{a}{b} \mid a, b \in \mathbf{I}, b \neq 0\right\}$
Irrational Numbers $\quad \tilde{Q} = \{\text{any number that is not rational}\}$
Real Numbers $\quad \mathbf{R} = \mathbf{Q} \cup \tilde{Q}$
Complex Numbers $\quad \mathbf{C} = \{a + bi \mid a, b \in \mathbf{R} \text{ and } i^2 = -1\}$

EXPONENTS AND RADICALS

$$x^0 = 1, x \neq 0$$

$$x^m x^n = x^{m+n} \qquad \qquad \frac{x^m}{x^n} = x^{m-n}, x \neq 0$$

$$(x^m)^n = x^{mn} \qquad \qquad x^{-n} = \frac{1}{x^n}, x \neq 0$$

$$(xy)^n = x^n y^n \qquad \qquad \left(\frac{x}{y}\right)^n = \frac{x^n}{y^n}, y \neq 0$$

$$x^{\frac{1}{n}} = \sqrt[n]{x}, n \neq 0 \qquad \qquad x^{\frac{m}{n}} = \sqrt[n]{x^m} = (\sqrt[n]{x})^m, n \neq 0$$

If n is odd, then $\sqrt[n]{x}$ is the nth root of x.

If n is even and $x \geq 0$, then $\sqrt[n]{x}$ is the non-negative nth root of x.

If n is even and $x < 0$, then $\sqrt[n]{x}$ is not a real number.

$$\sqrt[n]{xy} = \sqrt[n]{x}\sqrt[n]{y} \qquad \qquad \sqrt[n]{\frac{x}{y}} = \frac{\sqrt[n]{x}}{\sqrt[n]{y}}, y \neq 0$$

FACTORING SPECIAL POLYNOMIALS

$$x^2 - y^2 = (x + y)(x - y)$$
$$x^3 + y^3 = (x + y)(x^2 - xy + y^2)$$
$$x^3 - y^3 = (x - y)(x^2 + xy + y^2)$$

BINOMIAL THEOREM

$$(x + y)^2 = x^2 + 2xy + y^2 \qquad (x - y)^2 = x^2 - 2xy + y^2$$
$$(x + y)^3 = x^3 + 3x^2y + 3xy^2 + y^3$$
$$(x - y)^3 = x^3 - 3x^2y + 3xy^2 - y^3$$
$$(x + y)^n = x^n + nx^{n-1}y + \frac{n(n-1)}{2}x^{n-2}y^2$$
$$+ \, ... + \binom{n}{k}x^{n-k}y^k + ... + nxy^{n-1} + y^n$$

where $\binom{n}{k} = \frac{n(n-1)...(n-k+1)}{1 \cdot 2 \cdot 3 \cdot ... \cdot k}$

QUADRATIC FORMULA

If $ax^2 + bx + c = 0$, then $x = \frac{-b \pm \sqrt{b^2 - 4ac}}{2a}$, $a \neq 0$ and a, b, c are real numbers.

INEQUALITIES AND ABSOLUTE VALUE

For all real numbers a, b, and c:
 If $a < b$ and $b < c$, then $a < c$.
 If $a < b$, then $a + c < b + c$. (addition property)
 If $a < b$, then $a - c < b - c$. (subtraction property)
 If $a < b$ and $c > 0$, then $ca < cb$. (multiplication property)
 If $a < b$ and $c < 0$, then $ca > cb$. (multiplication property)
 If $a < b$ and $c > 0$, then $\frac{a}{c} < \frac{b}{c}$. (division property)
 If $a < b$ and $c < 0$, then $\frac{a}{c} > \frac{b}{c}$. (division property)
 If $a > 0$, then
  $|x| = a$ means $x = a$ or $x = -a$
  $|x| < a$ means $-a < x < a$
  $|x| > a$ means $x > a$ or $x < -a$

$ax + b$

GEOMETRIC FORMULAS

Some formulas for area, A, circumference, C, volume, V, and surface area, SA.

Right Triangle (Pythagorean Theorem)
$$a^2 + b^2 = c^2$$

Triangle $\quad A = \frac{1}{2}bh$

$$= \frac{1}{2}ab \sin \theta$$

$$= \sqrt{s(s - a)(s - b)(s - c)}; \, s = \frac{1}{2}(a + b + c)$$

Circle
$$A = \pi r^2$$
$$C = 2\pi r$$

Sector of Circle
$$A = \frac{1}{2}r^2\theta$$
$$s = r\theta \, (\theta \text{ in radians})$$

Rectangular Prism
$$V = lwh$$
$$SA = 2(lw + wh + lh)$$

Sphere
$$V = \frac{4}{3}\pi r^3$$
$$SA = 4\pi r^2$$

Cylinder
$$V = \pi r^2 h$$
$$SA = 2\pi r(r + h)$$